An Introduction to Genetic Analysis

An Introduction to Genetic Analysis

THIRD EDITION

- **David T. Suzuki**
  University of British Columbia

- **Anthony J. F. Griffiths**
  University of British Columbia

- **Jeffrey H. Miller**
  University of California, Los Angeles

- **Richard C. Lewontin**
  Harvard University

W. H. Freeman and Company / New York

Library of Congress Cataloging-in-Publication Data

Main entry under title:
An Introduction to genetic analysis.
    Rev. ed. of: An introduction to genetic analysis/
David T. Suzuki. 2nd ed. c1981.
    Bibliography: p.
    Includes index.
    1. Genetics. 2. Genetics—Methodology. I. Suzuki,
David T., 1936-   . II. Suzuki, David T., 1936-
Introduction to genetic analysis.
QH430.I62 1985   575.1   85-12978
ISBN 0-7167-1705-0
ISBN 0-7167-1721-2 (international student ed.)

Printed in the United States of America
    3 4 5 6 7 8 9 0 KP 4 3 2 1 0 8 9 8 7

Contents

Preface

■ The great power of modern genetics and its position of prominence in biological research have grown from a blend of classical and molecular techniques. Each analytical approach has its unique strengths. Classical genetics is unparalleled in its ability to explore uncharted biological terrain; molecular genetics is equally unparalleled in its ability to unravel cellular mechanisms. It would be unthinkable to teach one without the other. By giving both due prominence in this book, we have attempted to present a balanced view of genetics as practiced today.

The partnership of classical and molecular genetics has always presented a teaching problem: the order and manner in which the two partners should be introduced to the student. A common solution is to introduce both classical and molecular sides of each genetic principle concurrently. This approach makes use of the wisdom of hindsight — the teacher or writer addresses the student from the lofty vantage point of current understanding of the diverse parts of genetics and how they interrelate. We have chosen a different approach. It seems to us that students begin much as biologists did at the turn of the century, asking general questions about the laws governing inheritance. Thus the first half of the book is a more or less historical treatment of classical eukaryotic genetics, modified somewhat by the need to organize the material under specific genetic concepts. Some molecular information is provided where necessary, but this aspect is not emphasized. Armed with classical principles, the students can proceed to the second half of the book, which integrates molecular techniques and information into the classical framework. Progression from the general perspective to the specific seems to be a natural one, and makes sense not only in research but in teaching about research.

Geneticists today can be divided into two broad groups: those concerned with the mechanisms of heredity and those using techniques of genetics to probe other fundamental biological processes or phenomena. Both of these approaches are emphasized and recur as themes throughout the text. However, as the title of this book suggests, the main theme is genetic analysis. This emphasis reflects our belief that the best way to understand genetics is by understanding how genetic inferences are made. In any science, findings are important in themselves, but equally important are the modes of inference and the techniques of analysis, because these are the keys to future exploration. Quantitative analysis is particularly important. Many of the abstract ideas in genetics, from independent assortment to the existence of repetitive DNA, have been based on the analysis of quantitative data. The problems at the end of each chapter provide the student with the opportunity to apply these analytical methods to experimental situations. The problems are arranged in order of the presentation of topics in the chapter and in order of increasing difficulty. Particularly challenging problems are marked with an asterisk. These problem sets constitute an essential aspect of teaching, because the act of working a problem effectively simulates the modus operandi of genetic analysis. Yet despite this emphasis on quantitative analysis, the only mathematics required for understanding the text and working the problems is arithmetic and basic algebra.

This edition, the third, has been revised extensively. We made changes partly because we ourselves saw the need to update and improve pedagogy and partly because of the suggestions of users and reviewers. In the past 10 years, the balance between classical and molecular genetics has changed considerably, so that molecular genetics is emphasized more in this edition than in the previous ones, in recognition of its increasing application in all areas of the life sciences.

Chapter 1 is a new chapter formed of the introduction and the first chapter of the second edition. This chapter provides an overview of genetics and places it in its biological context. Chapter 3 contains a treatment of mitosis and meiosis more extensive than that in the second edition, with the inclusion of the famous McLeish and Snoad photographic series from Lily. Chapter 6 is now entitled "Linkage II" to emphasize that it is a specialized extension of the basic linkage analysis in Chapter 5, "Linkage I." The former chapter on chromosome mutation has been split into two smaller chapters, one on changes in chromosome structure (Chapter 8) and one on changes in chromosome number (Chapter 9). The chapter on DNA structure (10) has been moved forward in the book to introduce the concept of DNA earlier. To accommodate this change, the chapter on bacteria and phage recombination (13) now appears later.

The central part of the book (roughly, molecular genetics) received a great deal of attention in the present revision as we attempted to find the best way of introducing the molecular material into the classical framework established in the first part of the book. These chapters have been revised by our new coauthor, Jeffrey Miller. Major changes have been made in the chapters on the nature of the gene (11) and on manipulation of DNA (14). A former chapter on mechanisms of genetic change has been split into three smaller and more manageable chapters focusing on gene mutation (15), recombination (16), and transposable genetic elements (17), each of which now is an essential component of modern genetics. Chapter 18 is a completely new chapter, consisting of the classic studies on genetic control mechanisms in prokaryotes. Chapter 19 is an equivalent chapter for eukaryotes and is an extensively revised version of the second-edition chapter on the structure and function of chromosomes. Chapter 15 (gene mutation) and 19 (eukaryotic control mechanisms) have been almost completely rewritten.

Several special features aid the student. Throughout the text, key concepts are summarized in Messages. These provide convenient stopping points from which readers may orient themselves within each chapter and may be used as a convenient way of reviewing the material. A summary at the end of each chapter also provides a means of reviewing the important concepts. Key terms are set in boldface type, and most are defined in the Glossary at the end of the book. Further Readings and Answers to Selected Problems for each chapter also are in a section at the end of the book.

Many new and challenging additions have been made to the problem sets, and some old problems have been removed to make room for them. In addition there are many new illustrations, a large number of which are derived from *Scientific American* illustrations.

This book has been radically redesigned. Of the new design features we are particularly pleased with the addition of a second color, which greatly improves the clarity of the figures and enhances the general appearance of the book.

A Solutions Manual and a completely revised Instructor's Manual, both by Kathleen Diamond of the University of California at Los Angeles are available from the publisher. Furthermore, a slide set with an explanatory booklet is available that colorfully illustrates many of the genetic principles set out in the book.

We would like to offer our special thanks to Barry Ganetzky, University of Wisconsin, Madison, whose exhaustive and thought provoking reviews were enormously helpful to us.

We also extend our thanks to the following reviewers, whose insights and suggestions were most helpful to us throughout the revision process: Janice B. Spofford, University of Chicago; T. M. Rizki, University of Michigan; James Courtright, Marquette University; John Roth, University of Utah; Jacqueline L. Hoffman, Washington University; Peter Wejksnora, University of Wisconsin, Milwaukee; Jerry Feldman, University of California, Santa Cruz; H. James Price, Texas A & M University; J. Kenneth Shull, Jr., Loyola University; Sheldon Ladd, Colorado State University; Edward Klekowski, University of Massachusetts, Amherst; John C. Lucchesi, University of North Carolina, Chapel Hill; R. H. Richardson, University of Texas, Austin; Carol Robacker, Texas Technical University; and Matthew J. Temple, Georgetown University Hospital.

We hope this book will stimulate the reader to do some first-hand experimental genetics, whether as a professional scientist, student, or amateur plant or animal breeder. Failing this, we hope to impart some lasting impression of the precision, elegance, and power of genetic analysis.

David T. Suzuki
Anthony J. F. Griffiths
Jeffrey H. Miller
Richard C. Lewontin

CHAPTER 1

Genetics and the Organism

■ Why study genetics? The answers to this question constitute the major part of this book, but at the outset a summary answer can be given. Although a relatively young discipline, genetics has assumed a position of central importance in biology. In addition to this powerful unifying role, genetics has gained a position of great importance in human affairs. The findings of genetic research have had considerable impact not only in the applied areas of biology, medicine, and agriculture but also in such areas as philosophy, law, and religion. It is a rare newspaper, nowadays, that does not address some aspect of genetics.

The Scope of Genetics

Why has genetics become so important? To answer this question we must first define genetics. **Genetics** is *the study of genes through their variation.* A **gene** is the basic functional unit of heredity, which is composed of a section of a long, threadlike biological molecule called **deoxyribose nucleic acid,** best known by its abbreviation **DNA.** In the nuclei of higher organisms are found the **chromosomes,** each a very long, single, continuous DNA molecule containing thousands of unique functional units, the genes, as part of its length. Each of the trillions of cells in a human being has 46 chromosomes, in two equivalent sets of 23. Each of the 23 in a set is unique and is matched only by its equivalent partner in the other set. An average human chromosome contains about a 50-millimeter length of DNA, and, therefore, one total chromosome set of 23 is the equivalent of about one meter of DNA.

Geneticists study all aspects of genes. The study of the modes of gene transmission from generation to generation is broadly called **transmission genetics,** the study of gene structure and function is called **molecular genetics,** and the study of gene behavior in populations is called **population genetics.** These three form the major subdivisions of the field of genetics, although, as with all categories invented by humans, the subdivision is to a certain extent arbitrary and there is considerable overlap. It is the knowledge of how genes act and how they are transmitted down through the generations that has unified biology; previously, specific sets of biological phenomena had each been relegated to separate disciplines. An understanding of how genes act is now an essential prerequisite for such biological fields of study as development, cytology, physiology, and morphology. An understanding of gene transmission is a fundamental aspect of areas such as ecology, evolution, and taxonomy. Further unification has resulted from the discovery that the basic chemistry of gene structure and function is very similar across the entire spectrum of life on the earth. These points may seem trite to those who have grown up in the light of current knowledge, but it is important to realize that our modern view of biology and its interrelated parts is a relatively recent phenomenon. Not so long ago, biology was fragmented into many camps that rarely communicated with each other. Today, however, every biologist must be a bit of a geneticist, because the findings and techniques of genetics are being applied and used in all fields. Genetics, in fact, provides the modern paradigm for all of biology.

Message   Genetics has provided a unifying thread for the previously disparate fields of biology.

What have been some of the success stories of genetics within basic biology? For just about any feature of biological structure or function—such as size, shape, number of parts, color, pattern, behavioral pattern, or biochemical function—that has been looked at in experimental organisms, genes have been found to be involved. Determining the location of these genes on their respective chromosomes is relatively easy. It has been found that the major way in which genes exert their effect is through controlling the myriad chemical reactions that go on inside cells, and thousands of specific genes have each been associated with a specific chemical reaction. The control of gene action (how genes are "turned on" and "turned off") has been intensely studied in some organisms, and the mechanism in these cases is well understood. Many different genes have been isolated in the test tube, and their particular chemical structures determined. Such studies have provided important clues about how genes perform their functions. A gene can be removed from one organism and introduced into another, either for the convenience of propagating large amounts of the gene for later study or to examine its effects in another biological system. Genes can be modified at will to study the effects of these changes on biological processes; such changes can involve a large part of the genes, or very localized regions of interest to the experimenter. Most genes have been found to reside rather stably at specific chromosomal locations, but other pieces of DNA have been found to be capable of sudden relocation to new areas. Last but not least, most of these findings have tremendous relevance for evolutionary processes, which of course are concerned with changes in the structure and function of the gene set.

Clearly, the advances in genetics have been truly astounding, particularly over the last three decades. Many recent accomplishments—such as the isolation and characterization of individual genes, which researchers in the 1950s believed could never happen in their lifetimes—have already come to be regarded as routine procedures in current work in genetics.

This chapter presents an overview of the subject of genetics, by way of an orientation to the rest of the book. We shall deal first with generalities about genes, their inheritance, and the ways in which they interact with the environment. Then we shall discover the unique ways in which geneticists identify specific genes, and examine the use of these techniques in studying biological phenomena. Finally, we shall consider some of the ways in which genetics has interacted with human society.

Gene Transmission

Genetics embraces two contradictory aspects of nature: offspring resemble their parents, yet they are not identical to their parents. The offspring of lions are lions and never lambs, yet no two lions are identical, even if they come from the same litter. We have no trouble recognizing the differences between sisters, for example, and even "identical" twins are recognized as distinctive individuals by their parents and close friends. But we also can notice subtle similarities between parents and children. As we shall see, **heredity** (the similarity of offspring to parents) and **variation** (the difference between parents and offspring, and between the offspring themselves) turn out to be two aspects of the same fundamental mechanism.

When humans began domesticating plants and animals (around 10,000 years ago), they necessarily became involved with both heredity and variation, because they had to choose the organisms with advantageous characteristics from among those at their disposal and then seek to propagate these traits in future generations. References to sound breeding practices in Egyptian tomb inscriptions and in the Bible convince us that conscious concern with genetic phenomena is at least as old as civilization. The farmers and shepherds involved with such concerns could quite deservedly have claimed to be called geneticists. But the formal study of genetics, as a coherent and unified theory of heredity and variation, is little more than a century old.

Modern genetics as a set of principles and analytic rules began with the work of an Augustinian monk, Gregor Mendel, who worked in a monastery in the middle of the nineteenth century in what is now Brno in Czechoslovakia. Mendel was taken into the monastery by its director, Abbot Knapp, with the express purpose of trying to discover a firm mathematical and physical foundation underlying the practice of plant breeding. Knapp and others in Brno were interested in fruit breeding. They believed that recent advances in mathematics in the physical sciences could be a model for building a science of variation. Mendel was recommended to Knapp as a good scholar of mathematics and physics, although a rather mediocre student of biology!

Mendel's methods, which he developed in the monastery garden, are the ones still used today (in an extended form), and they form an integral part of genetic analysis. (Mendel's work is considered in detail in Chapter 2.) Mendel realized that both the similarities and the differences among parents and their offspring can be explained by a mechanical transmission of discrete hereditary units, which we now call genes, from parent to offspring. We now know that in all organisms—whether bacteria, fungi, animals, or plants—there is a regular passage of hereditary information from parent to offspring by means of the genes. The regularities we observe in heredity and variation are a consequence of the regularities of the mechanical lanes of transmission and activity of these genes.

Recall that each gene is a portion of a DNA molecule. In more than one sense, then, DNA is truly the thread of life: not only is a DNA molecule itself a threadlike string of genes, but the DNA handed down from parent to offspring represents a narrow connecting thread between the generations. When we say that a woman has her mother's hair or a man has his father's nose, what we really mean is that the parent has handed on, in egg or sperm, the instructions necessary to direct the synthesis of that specific feature.

Out of these basic considerations emerge two vastly powerful and unique properties of DNA that make it the fundamental molecule of life. The first of these is its ability to serve as a model for the production of replicas of itself, termed replication. This property is the key to transmission and forms the basis of transmission genetics. A parental organism transmits a replica of its DNA to the progenitor cell of an individual of the next generation. As this progenitor cell goes through its rounds of division to produce a multicellular organism, each division is accompanied by the production of identical replicas of the DNA of the progenitor cell, which are apportioned into each new cell. Thus, replication is the mechanism through which life persists across the generations in a stable fashion.

The second property of DNA that makes it a fundamental molecule of life is its ability to act as a carrier of information. For example, embodied into the one meter of DNA that constitutes a human chromosome set is the information needed to build a specimen of *Homo sapiens*. The word information means "that which is necessary to give form"; this is precisely what the DNA of the genes does. The information is "written" into the sequence of DNA in the form of a molecular code.

Gene and Organism

Precisely how does information become form? At the level of molecules, the answer to this question embraces much of what was defined previously as molecular genetics. Basically, the phenomena and structures of life are produced by an interaction of DNA with the inanimate world, the nonliving environment. The universe naturally tends to disarray; order tends spontaneously to disorder; complex and orderly objects become piles of dust; the reverse does not occur unaided. Yet DNA causes an eddy in this river of chaos; through its interaction with the disorderly components of the universe, the most orderly system that we know about is born: the phenomenon of life. One of the unexpected discoveries arising from the study of DNA function

Figure 1-1. The genes of a moss direct environmental components to be shaped into a moss, whereas the genes of a tree cause a tree to be constructed from the same components. (From Grant Heilman.)

is that the mechanism of converting information into form is virtually identical across all groups of organisms on this planet. We humans share a common genetic chemistry with the entire variety of life forms on the earth—a staggering spectrum, including some 286,000 species of flowering plants, 500,000 species of fungi, and 750,000 species of insects.

A general view of the interaction of DNA with the environment is a necessary prelude to the detailed analyses that are found in the chapters ahead. We must put the gene and the environment into perspective, in order to provide a framework on which the details of genetic analysis can be hung.

It is a characteristic of living organisms that they mobilize the components of the world around themselves and convert these components into their own living material, or into artifacts that are extensions of themselves. An acorn becomes an oak tree, using in the process only water, oxygen, carbon dioxide, some inorganic materials from the soil, and light energy.

The seed of an oak tree develops into an oak, while the spore of a moss develops into a moss, although both are growing side by side in the same forest (Figure 1-1). The two plants that result from these developmental processes

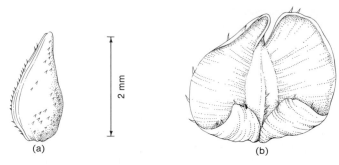

Figure 1-2. The fruits of two different forms of *Plectritis congesta*, the sea blush. (a) Wingless fruits. (b) Winged fruits. Any one plant has either all wingless or all winged fruits, and only the fruits are different. The striking difference in appearance is determined by a simple genetic difference.

resemble their parents and differ from each other, even though they have access to the same narrow range of inorganic materials from the environment. The specifications for building living protoplasm from the environmental materials are passed in the form of genes from parent to offspring through the physical materials of the fertilized egg. As a consequence of the information in the genes, the seed of the oak develops into an oak, and the moss spore becomes a moss.

What is true for the oak and moss is also true within species. Consider plants of the species *Plectritis congesta*, the sea blush. Two forms of this species are found wherever the plants grow in nature: one form has winged fruits, and the other has wingless fruits (Figure 1-2). These plants will self-pollinate, and we can observe the offspring that result from such "selfs" when these are grown in a greenhouse under uniform conditions. It is commonly observed that the progeny of a winged-fruited plant are all winged-fruited, and the progeny from a wingless-fruited plant all have wingless fruits. Since all the progeny were grown in an identical environment, we can safely conclude that the difference between the original plants must result from the different genes they carry.

The *Plectritis* example involves inherited forms that both can be considered perfectly normal. Yet the determinative power of genes is equally well demonstrated when a gene becomes abnormal. The human inherited disease sickle-cell anemia provides a good example. In this case, careful study has revealed the chain of events whereby the gene has impact upon the organism, from the submicroscopic molecular level, through the microscopic level, to the macroscopic anatomical level. The underlying cause of the disease is a variation in hemoglobin, the oxygen-transporting protein molecule found in red blood cells. Normal people have a type of hemoglobin called hemoglobin A, the information for which is encoded in a single unique type of gene. A minute chemical change at the molecular level in the DNA of this gene results in the production of a slightly changed hemoglobin, termed hemoglobin S. In people possessing only hemoglobin S, the ultimate effect of this small change is severe ill health and usually death. The gene works its effect on the organism through a complex "cascade effect," as summarized in Figure 1-3.

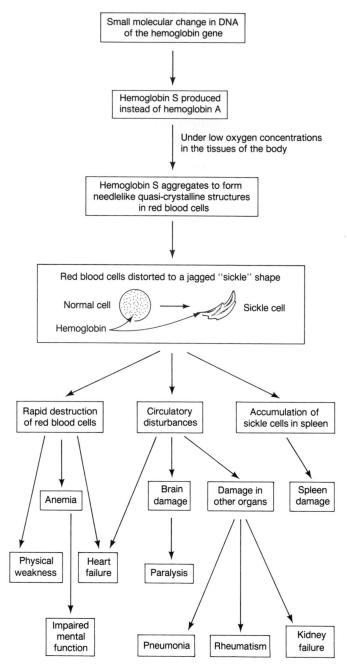

Figure 1-3. Chain of events resulting in sickle-cell anemia in humans.

Observations like these lead to a model of the interaction of genes and environment like that shown in Figure 1-4. In this view, the genes act as a set of instructions for turning more or less undifferentiated environmental materials into a specific organism, much as blueprints specify what form of house is to be built from basic materials. The same bricks, mortar, wood, and nails can be made into an A-frame or a flat-roofed house, according to different plans. Such a model implies that the genes are really the dominant elements in the determination of organisms; the environment simply supplies the undifferentiated raw materials.

But now consider two monozygotic ("identical") twins,

the product of a single fertilized egg that divided and produced two complete individuals with identical genes. Suppose that the twins are born in England but separated at birth and taken to different countries. If one is raised in China by Chinese-speaking foster parents, she will speak perfect Chinese, while her sister raised in Budapest will speak fluent Hungarian. Each will absorb the cultural values and customs of her environment. Although the twins begin life with identical genetic properties, the different cultural environments in which they live produce differences between the sisters (and differences from their parents). Obviously, the difference in this case is due to the environment, and genetic effects are of little importance.

This example suggests the model of Figure 1-5, which is the opposite of that shown in Figure 1-4. Here the genes impinge on the system, giving certain general signals for development, but the environment determines the actual course of change. Imagine a set of specifications for a house that simply calls for "a floor that will support 30 pounds per square foot" or "walls with an insulation factor of 15"; the actual appearance and nature of the structure would be determined by the available building materials.

Our different types of examples—of purely genetic effect versus that of the environment—lead to two very different models. Given a pair of seeds and a uniform growth environment, we would be unable to predict future growth patterns solely from a knowledge of the environment. In any environment we can imagine, if growth occurs at all, the acorn will become an oak and the spore will become a moss. On the other hand, considering the twins, no information about the set of genes they inherit could possibly enable us to predict their ultimate languages and cultures. Two individuals that are *genetically different* may develop differently in the *same environment,* but two *genetically identical* individuals may develop differently in *different environments.*

In general, of course, we deal with organisms that differ in both genes and environment. If we wish to understand and predict the outcome of the development of a living organism, we must first know the genetic constitution that it inherits from its parents. Then we must know the *historical sequence* of environments to which the developing organism is exposed. We emphasize the historical sequence of environments rather than simply the general environment. Every organism has a developmental history from birth to death. What an organism will become in the next moment depends critically both on the environment it encounters during that moment and on its present state. It makes a difference to an organism not only what environments it encounters but in what sequence it encounters them. A fruit fly *(Drosophila)* develops normally at 20°C. If the temperature is briefly raised to 37°C early in the pupal stage of development, the adult fly will be missing part of the normal vein pattern on its wings. However, if this "temperature shock" is administered just 24 hours later, the fly develops normally.

Considering the general nature of interactions between gene and environment, we see that there is no reason to prefer either of the asymmetrical models of Figures 1-4 and 1-5. Instead, we can create a more general model (Figure 1-6). Genes and environment are seen here as symmetrical factors whose states jointly determine (by some rules of development) the actual organism.

Message   The developmental transformation of an organism from one stage of its life to another is a result of the unique interaction of its genes and its environment at each moment of its life history. Organisms are determined neither by their genes nor by their environment; rather, they are the consequence of the interaction of genes *and* environment.

Genotype and Phenotype

In studying the reaction whereby genes and environment produce an organism, geneticists have developed some useful terms, which are introduced in this section.

A typical organism resembles its parents more than it resembles unrelated individuals. Thus we often speak as if the individual characteristics themselves are inherited: "He gets his brains from his mother," or "She inherited diabetes from her father." Yet our discussion in the preceding section shows that such statements are invalid. "His brains" and "her diabetes" develop through long sequences of events in the life histories of the affected persons, and both genes and environment play roles in those sequences. In the biological sense, individuals inherit only the molecular structures of the fertilized eggs from which they develop. Individuals inherit their *genes,* not the end products of their individual developmental histories.

To prevent such confusion between genes (which are inherited) and developmental outcomes (which are not),

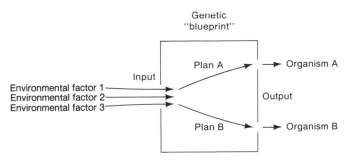

Figure 1-4. A model of determination that emphasizes the role of genes.

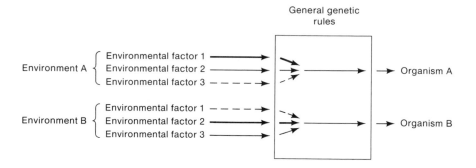

Figure 1-5. A model of determination that emphasizes the role of the environment.

geneticists make a fundamental distinction between the genotype and the phenotype of an organism. Organisms belong to the same **genotype** if they have the same set of genes. Organisms belong to the same **phenotype** if they resemble each other in some manifest way.

Strictly speaking, the genotype describes the complete set of genes inherited by an individual, and the phenotype describes *all* aspects of the individual's morphology, physiology, behavior, and ecological relationships. In this sense, no two individuals that have ever lived belong to the same phenotype, because there is always some difference (however slight) between them in morphology or physiology. Moreover, except for individuals produced from another by asexual reproduction, any two organisms differ at least a little in genotype. In practice, we use the terms genotype and phenotype in a more restricted sense. We deal with some partial phenotype description (say, eye color) and with some subset of the genotype (say, the genes that influence eye pigmentation).

Message   When geneticists use the terms phenotype and genotype, they generally mean "partial phenotype" and "partial genotype" with respect to some defined set of traits and genes.

Note one very important difference between genotype and phenotype: the genotype is essentially a fixed character of the organism; it remains constant throughout life and is unchanged by environmental effects. Most phenotypes change continually throughout the life of the individual; the direction of that change is a function of the sequence of environments that the individual experiences. Fixity of genotype does not imply fixity of phenotype.

The Norm of Reaction

How can we quantify the relation between the genotype, the environment, and the phenotype? For a particular genotype, we could prepare a table showing the phenotype that would result from that genotype for development in each possible environment. Such a tabulation of environment-phenotype relationships for a given genotype is called the **norm of reaction** of the genotype. In practice, of course, we can make such a tabulation only for a partial genotype, a partial phenotype, and some particular aspects of the environment. For example, we might specify the eye size of a fruit fly that would result from development at various constant temperatures for several different partial genotypes.

Figure 1-7 represents just such norms of reaction for three partial genotypes in the fruit fly *Drosophila melanogaster*. The graph is a convenient summary of more extensive tabulated data. The size of the fly eye is measured by counting its individual facets, or cells. The vertical axis of the graph shows the number of facets (on a logarithmic scale); the horizontal axis shows the constant temperature at which the flies develop.

Three norms of reaction are shown on the graph. Flies of the *wild-type* genotype (characteristic of flies in natural populations) show somewhat smaller eyes at higher temperatures of development. Flies of the abnormal *ultra-bar* genotype have smaller eyes than *wild-type* flies at any particular temperature of development. Higher temperatures also have a stronger effect upon eye size in the *ultra-bar* flies (the *ultra-bar* line slopes more steeply). Any fly of the other abnormal genotype, *infra-bar,* also has smaller eyes than any *wild-type* fly, but higher temperatures have the opposite effect on flies of this genotype. *Infra-bar* flies raised at a higher temperature tend to have larger eyes than those

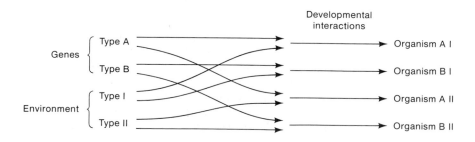

Figure 1-6. A more realistic model of determination that emphasizes the interaction of genes and environment.

raised at lower temperatures. These norms of reaction indicate that the relationship between genotype and phenotype is complex rather than simple.

Message   A single genotype can produce many different phenotypes, depending on the environment. A single phenotype may be produced by various different genotypes, depending on the environment.

If we know that a fruit fly has the *wild-type* genotype, this information alone does not tell us whether its eye has 800 or 1000 facets. On the other hand, the knowledge that a fruit fly's eye has 170 facets does not tell us whether its genotype is *ultra-bar* or *infra-bar*. We cannot even make a general statement about the effect of temperature on eye size in *Drosophila*, because the effect is opposite in two different genotypes. We see from Figure 1-7 that some genotypes do differ unambiguously in phenotype, no matter what the environment: any *wild-type* fly has larger eyes than any *ultra-bar* or *infra-bar* fly. But other genotypes overlap in phenotypic expression: the eyes of *ultra-bar* flies may be larger or smaller than those of *infra-bar* flies, depending on the temperatures at which the individuals developed.

To obtain a norm of reaction like those in Figure 1-7, we must allow different individuals of identical genotype to

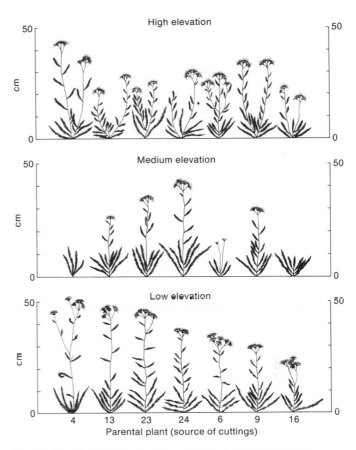

Figure 1-8. Norms of reaction to elevation for seven different *Achillea* plants (seven different genotypes). A cutting from each plant was grown at low, medium, and high elevations. (Carnegie Institution of Washington.)

develop in many different environments. To carry out such an experiment, we must be able to obtain or produce many zygotes with identical genotypes. For example, to test a human genotype in 10 environments, we would have to obtain identical decuplets and raise each individual in a different milieu. Obviously, that is possible neither biologically nor socially. At the present time, we do not know the norm of reaction of any human genotype for any character in any set of environments. Nor is it clear how we can ever acquire such information without unacceptable manipulation of human individuals.

For a few experimental organisms, special genetic methods make it possible to replicate genotypes and thus determine norms of reaction. Such studies are particularly easy in plants that can be propagated vegetatively — that is, by cuttings. The pieces cut from a single plant all have the same genotype, so all offspring produced in this way have identical genotypes. Figure 1-8 shows the results of a study using such vegetative offspring of the plant *Achillea*. Many plants were collected, and three cuttings were taken from each plant. One cutting was planted at low elevation (30 meters above sea level), one at medium elevation (1400 meters), and one at high elevation (3050 meters). Figure 1-8 shows the mature individuals that developed from cuttings of seven collected (parental) plants; the three plants of

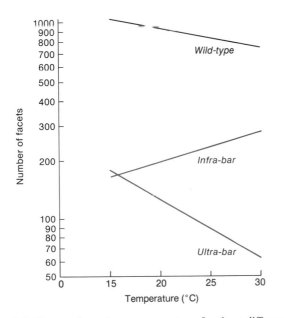

Figure 1-7. Norms of reaction to temperature for three different eye-size genotypes of *Drosophila melanogaster: wild-type, infra-bar,* and *ultra-bar.* Eye size is measured by the number of facets in the eye. The term "bar" comes from the eye shape produced by fewer facets.

identical genotype are aligned vertically in the figure for comparison.

First, we note an average effect of environment: in general, the plants grew poorly at the medium elevation. This is not true for every genotype, however; the cutting of plant 24 grew best at the medium elevation. Second, we note that no genotype is unconditionally superior in growth to all others. Plant 4 showed the best growth at low and high elevations but showed the poorest growth at the medium elevation. Plant 9 showed the second-worst growth at low elevation and the second-best at high elevation. Once again we see the complex relationship between genotype and phenotype. Figure 1-9 graphs the norms of reaction derived from the results shown in Figure 1-8. Each genotype has a different norm of reaction, and the norms cross one another so that we cannot identify either a "best" genotype or a "best" environment for *Achillea* growth.

We have seen two different patterns of reaction norms. The difference between *wild-type* and the abnormal eye-size genotypes in *Drosophila* is such that the corresponding phenotypes show a consistent difference, regardless of the environment. Any fruit fly of *wild-type* genotype has larger eyes than any fruit fly of the abnormal genotypes, so we could (imprecisely) speak of "large-eye" and "small-eye" genotypes. In this case, the differences in phenotype between genotypes is much greater than the variation within a genotype for different environments. In the case of *Achillea*, however, the variation for a single genotype in different environments is so great that the norms of reaction cross one another and form no consistent pattern. In this case, it makes no sense to identify a genotype with a particular phenotype except in terms of response to particular environments.

Developmental Noise

Thus far, we have assumed that the phenotype is uniquely determined by the interaction of a specific genotype and a specific environment. But a closer look shows some further unexplained variation. According to Figure 1-7, a *Drosophila* of *wild-type* genotype raised at 16°C has 1000 facets in each eye. In fact, this is only an average value; individual flies studied under these conditions commonly have 980 or 1020 facets. Perhaps these variations are due to slight fluctuations in the local environment or slight differences in genotypes? However, a typical count may show that a fly has, say, 1017 facets in the left eye and 982 in the right eye. In another fly, the left eye has slightly fewer facets than the right eye. Yet the left and right eyes of the same fly are

genetically identical. Furthermore, under typical experimental conditions, the fly has developed as a larva a few millimeters long burrowing in homogeneous artificial food in a laboratory bottle, and then completed its development as a pupa (also a few millimeters long) glued vertically to the inside of the glass high up off the food surface. Surely, the environment has not differed significantly from one side of the fly to the other! But if the two eyes have experienced the same sequence of environments and are identical genetically, then why is there any phenotypic difference between left and right eyes?

Differences in shape and size are partly dependent on the process of cell division that turns the zygote into the multicellular organism. Cell division, in turn, is sensitive to molecular events within the cell, and these may have a relatively large random component. For example, the vitamin biotin is essential for growth, but its *average* concentration is only one molecule per cell! Obviously, any process that depends on the presence of this molecule will necessarily be subject to fluctuations in rate because of random variations in concentration. But if a cell division is to produce a differentiated eye cell, it must occur within a relatively short developmental period during which the eye is being formed. Thus we would expect random variation in such phenotypic characters as the number of eye cells, the number of hairs, the exact shape of small features, and the variation of neurons in a very complex central nervous system —even when the genotype and the environment are precisely fixed. Even in such structures as the very simple nervous system of nematodes, these random variations do occur.

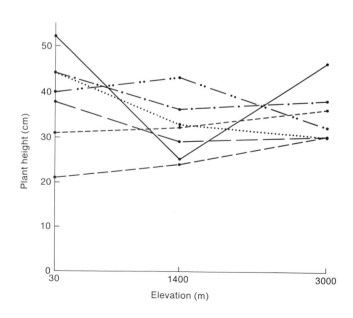

Figure 1-9. Graphic representation of the complete set of results of the type shown in Figure 1-8. Each line represents the norm of reaction of a separate plant. Notice that the norms of reaction cross one another, so that no sharp distinction is apparent.

Message Random events in development lead to an uncontrollable variation in phenotype; this variation is called **developmental noise**. In some characteristics, such as eye cells in *Drosophila*, developmental noise is a major source of the observed variations in phenotype.

Like noise in a verbal communication, developmental noise adds small random variations to the predictable process of development governed by norms of reaction. Adding developmental noise to our model of phenotype development, we obtain something like Figure 1-10. With a given genotype and environment, there is a range of possible outcomes of each developmental step. The development process does contain feedback systems that tend to hold the deviations within certain bounds, so that the range of deviation does not increase indefinitely through the many steps of development. However, this feedback is not perfect. For any given genotype, developing in any given sequence of environments, there remains some uncertainty in the exact phenotype that will result.

Techniques of Genetic Analysis

Our discussion thus far has been based on the wisdom of hindsight. With the wealth of genetic knowledge we now share, we can make generalizations about DNA, genes, phenotypes, and genotypes as though these concepts were self-evident. But obviously this was not always the case; the current wisdom was acquired only after extensive genetic research over the years. Mendel, for example, almost certainly was completely without a conceptual basis for his research at the beginning of his work, but he was able to

piece together his genetic principles from the results of his many experiments. This is true of genetic research in general: we start in the unknown, and then ideas and facts emerge out of experimentation. But how does everyday genetics work? We shall explore the answer to this question in much of the rest of this book, but here let us begin with an overview of the principles of genetic research.

The process of identification of the specific hereditary components of a biological system is called **genetic dissection.** A geneticist is a type of biologist interested in some aspect of the structure or function of organisms. In the same way that an anatomist probes biological structure and function with a scalpel, the geneticist probes biological structure and function armed with genetic variants, usually abnormal. If the geneticist is interested in a biological process X, he or she embarks upon a search for genetic variants affecting X. Each variant identifies a separate component of X. In much the same way that a novice auto mechanic can learn a lot about how an internal combustion engine works by pulling out a spark plug lead, for example, the geneticist "tinkers" with a living system. This approach is tremendously effective in charting the unknown—the invisibility and magnitude of which are often not appreciated by those who have not attempted some kind of research—and represents a truly powerful tool.

Message Genetic dissection is a powerful way of discovering the components of any biological process.

The use and analysis of hereditary variants embodies the primary research tool of the geneticist. This approach is equally powerful from the molecular level, where it can be

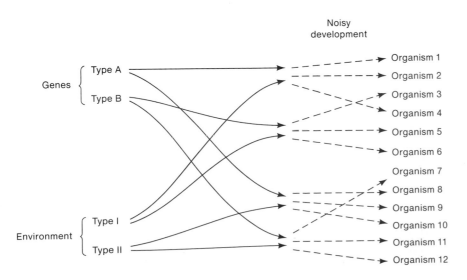

Figure 1-10. A model of phenotypic determination that shows how genes, environment, and developmental noise interact to produce any given phenotype.

used to probe cellular and organismal processes, all the way to the population level, where it can be used to investigate evolutionary processes. The spectrum of variants that has been obtained and studied effectively by geneticists is staggering; as we have seen, there are variants affecting shape, number, biochemical function, and so on. In fact, the general finding has been that variants can be obtained for virtually any biological structure or process of interest to the investigator.

Recall that a set of variants of any given biological character can fall into either of two broad categories: (1) those whose underlying genotypes show nonoverlapping norms of reaction, and (2) those whose underlying genotypes show overlapping norms of reaction. The techniques of genetic analysis are different in each case.

The analysis of genotypes with nonoverlapping norms of reaction has produced most of the phenomenal success of genetics in elucidating the cellular and molecular processes of organisms. The appeal of such systems from the experimenter's viewpoint is that the environment can virtually be ignored, because each genotype produces a discrete, identifiable phenotype. In fact, geneticists have deliberately sought and selected just such variants. Experiments become much easier — in fact, they only become possible — when the phenotype observed is an unambiguous indication of a particular genotype. After all, we cannot observe genotypes; we can visibly distinguish only phenotypes.

The availability of such variants made Mendel's experiments possible. He used genotypes that were established horticultural varieties. For example, in one set of variants, one genotype always produces tall pea plants, and another always produces dwarf plants. Had Mendel chosen variants whose genotypes have overlapping norms of reaction, he would have obtained complex and patternless results like those in the *Achillea* experiments. He could never have identified the simple relationships that became the foundation of genetic understanding. Much of modern molecular genetics is based on research with variants of bacteria that similarly show distinctive characters whose genotypes have nonoverlapping norms of reaction. For instance, modern DNA manipulation technology relies heavily on selection systems based on bacterial genes for drug resistance; the expression of such genes is very clear-cut and reliable.

In this category, the variants tend to be rather drastic. Many such variants could never survive in nature, simply because they are so developmentally extreme. In other cases, such as the winged and wingless fruits of *Plectritis,* the strikingly different forms do appear regularly in natural populations.

Reflecting the importance of discrete variants in developing our present understanding of the genetic basis of life, most of the rest of this book is devoted to analysis of this kind of variation. The story begins with Mendel's research and theories, proceeds through classical genetics, and ends

with the startling discoveries of molecular biology. It must be emphasized that the entire development of this knowledge critically depended on the availability of phenotypes having simple relationships to genotypes. Because our study of genetic analysis necessarily puts so much emphasis on such simple trait differences, you may get the impression that they represent the most common relationship between gene and trait. They do not. Geneticists have to pick and choose among cases of genetic variation to find those with a simple correspondence between genotype and phenotype. For example, among the hundreds of classical mutants of *Drosophila* that have been well enough characterized to place them on specific chromosomes, about half are too variable in their phenotypic expression to be used in further genetic analysis (so-called Rank 4 and Rank 5 mutants). Only a quarter ("Rank 1" mutants) are ideally suited for the purposes of careful genetic analysis. And this count excludes the large number of mutants that were so unreliable that they could not be put on genetic maps in the first place. Even among the most useful mutants, environment and developmental age can be quite important to their expression. The widely used mutation *purple* produces an eye color like the normal ruby color in very young flies, which darkens to a distinguishable difference only with age. The mutation *Curly,* one of the most important tools in genetic analysis in *Drosophila,* results in curled wings at $25°C$, but not at $19°C$, where the flies have normally straight wings.

Whereas simple one-to-one relationships between genotype and phenotype dominate the world of experimental genetics, in the natural world such relationships are quite rare. When norms of reaction for size, shape, color, metabolic rate, reproductive rate, and behavior have been obtained for organisms taken from natural populations, they almost always turn out to be like those of *Achillea.* The relationships of genotype to phenotype in nature are almost always one-to-many rather than one-to-one. This is the underlying cause of the rarity of discrete phenotypic classes in natural populations.

Obviously, the analysis of these one-to-many relationships is far more complex. The researcher is confronted with a bewildering range of phenotypes. Special statistical techniques must be used to disentangle the genetic, environmental, and noise components. Chapter 22 deals with such techniques.

There is another problem that is distinct from the purely analytical difficulties. The major discoveries of genetics were founded on work with discrete norms of reaction. Although these discoveries have revolutionized pure and applied biology, great care must be taken in extrapolating such ideas to systems that are based on complex interaction of gene and environment, especially those found in nature. For example, the difference between yellow-bodied and gray-bodied *Drosophila* in laboratory stocks can be shown to be a simple genetic difference, but it does not follow that skin color in humans obeys similar genetic laws.

In fact, even in *Drosophila,* the various intensities of black pigment in flies from natural populations turn out to be a consequence of the interaction of temperature with a complex genetic system.

Message   In general, the relationship between genotype and phenotype cannot be extrapolated from one species to another or even between phenotypic traits that seem superficially similar within a species. A genetic analysis must be carried out for each particular case.

Our overview of the scope of genetics would not be complete without a discussion of some of the ways in which genetics affects our everyday lives.

Genetics and Human Affairs

Knowledge about hereditary phenomena has been important to humans for a very long time. Civilization itself became possible when nomadic tribes learned to domesticate plants and animals. Long before biology existed as a scientific discipline, people selected grains with higher yields and greater vigor and animals with better fur or meat. They also puzzled about the inheritance of desirable and undesirable traits in the human population. Despite this long-standing concern with heredity and the practice of selective breeding, it was not until the discovery of Mendel's laws that we were able to elucidate the actual basis for inheritance.

As in many areas of science, this new knowledge has produced new challenges as well as solutions to some human problems. For example, early in this century a new wheat strain called Marquis was developed in Canada. This high-quality strain is resistant to disease; furthermore, it matures two weeks earlier than other commercially used strains—a very important factor where the growing season is short. At the time of its introduction, the use of Marquis wheat opened up millions of square miles of fertile soil to cultivation in such northern countries as Canada, Sweden, and the U.S.S.R. Table 1-1 shows how geneticists have bred a wide range of desirable characteristics into another commercial crop, rice. In addition to improving crop varieties, geneticists have learned to alter the genetic systems of insects to reduce their fertility. This technique is providing an important new weapon in the age-old struggle to keep insects out of human crops and habitations.

Such successes in recent years led to the concept of the "Green Revolution" as the scientific answer to the problem of human hunger. Using sophisticated breeding techniques based on new knowledge about genes, geneticists created high-yield varieties of dwarf wheat (Figure 1-11) and rice (Figure 1-12). Extensive planting of these crops around the world did provide new food supplies, but new problems quickly became apparent. These specialized crops require extensive cultivation and costly fertilizers. Figure 1-12 is a norm-of-reaction curve, a classic example of the variable interaction of genotype with environment. The use of the new high-yield varieties produced a wide range of social and economic problems in the impoverished countries where they were most needed. Furthermore, the spread of monoculture (the extensive reliance on a single plant variety) left vast areas at the mercy of some newly introduced or newly evolved form of pathogen—say, a plant disease or an insect pest. With the huge population of humans on earth, our dependence on high-yield varieties of crop plants and domestic animals is becoming increasingly obvious. In a very real sense, the stability of human society depends on the ability of geneticists to juggle the inherited traits that shape life forms, keeping the crops a jump ahead

■ **TABLE 1-1.** Development of pest-resistant strains of rice

Strain	Year developed	Diseases					Insects		
		Blast fungus	Bacterial blight	Leaf-streak virus	Grassy stunt virus	Tungro virus	Green leaf-hopper	Brown hopper	Stem borer
IR 8	1966	MR	S	S	S	S	R	S	MS
IR 5	1967	S	S	MS	S	S	R	S	S
IR 20	1969	MR	R	MR	S	R	R	S	MS
IR 22	1969	S	R	MS	S	S	S	S	S
IR 24	1971	S	S	MR	S	MR	R	S	S
IR 26	1973	MR	R	MR	MR	R	R	R	MR

NOTE: The entries describe each strain's susceptibility or resistance to each pest as follows: S = susceptible; MS = moderately susceptible; MR = moderately resistant; R = resistant. (From *Research Highlights,* I.R.R.I, 1973, p. 11.)

Figure 1-11. A specially bred strain of dwarf wheat *(right)* resists crop damage far better than the normal strain *(left)*. (Courtesy of The Rockefeller Foundation.)

of the destructive parasites and predators (Figure 1-13).

In recent years, advances in biotechnology have led to the creation of special genetically engineered strains of bacteria and fungi that carry specific genes from unrelated organisms such as humans. The microbes produce such useful compounds as insulin, human growth hormone, and the antiviral (and possibly anticancer) agent interferon.

But the most exciting and frightening application of genetic knowledge is to the human species itself. Genetic discoveries have had major effects on medicine. We can now diagnose hereditary disease before or soon after birth, and in some cases we can provide secondary treatments. Using family pedigrees, a genetic counselor can give prospective parents the information they need to make intelligent decisions about the risks of genetic disease in their offspring. Such refined techniques as amniocentesis and fetoscopy provide information about possible genetic disease at early stages of pregnancy. A battery of postnatal chemical tests can detect problems in the newborn infant, so that some corrective techniques can be applied immediately to alleviate the effects of many genetic diseases.

Our new ability to recognize genetic disease poses an important moral dilemma. An estimated 5 percent of our population survives with severe physical or mental genetic defects. This percentage probably will increase with extended exposure to various environmental factors—and, paradoxically, with improved medical technology. As geneticist Theodosius Dobzhansky has remarked,

If we enable the weak and the deformed to live and propagate their kind, we face the prospect of a genetic twilight. But if we let them die or suffer when we can save or help them, we face the certainty of a moral twilight.

Of those patients admitted to pediatric hospitals in North America, 30 percent are estimated to have diseases that can

be traced to genetic causes. The financial burden to society is already significant. Are we prepared to shoulder this genetic burden? How much money are we willing to spend to keep the genetically handicapped alive and to enable them to lead as normal a life as possible?

Many other significant issues are raised by the potential applications of genetic knowledge to human beings. Obviously, the human brain is subject to the same rules of genetic determination as the rest of the body. Does this

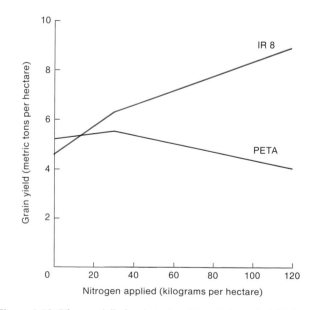

Figure 1-12. The specially bred strain of dwarf rice called IR 8 owes part of its success to its remarkable response to the application of fertilizer. The strain PETA is an older, nondwarf strain showing a more typical response. (From Peter R. Jennings, "The Amplification of Agricultural Production." Copyright © 1976 by Scientific American, Inc. All rights reserved.)

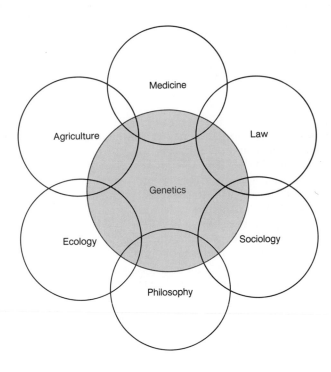

Figure 1-13. The findings of genetics have powerful impacts on many interacting areas of human endeavor.

mean that our thoughts and behavior are extensively determined by inherited predispositions? Or can we view the mind as a clean slate at birth, written upon only by individual experience? The nature of inborn constraints on thought and personality — the implications for present sociological problems — have fascinated many geneticists and other scientists. Such books as *African Genesis, The Territorial Imperative, On Aggression,* and other popular titles on sociobiology have stimulated widespread public interest. A bitter debate has raged about the differences in intelligence among various racial and social groups. Of course, this topic is not new. It was debated by Lycurgus in Sparta against Plato in Athens, and dreams of producing a pure race of superior humans have motivated many important figures in history. As the problem of human overpopulation becomes obvious to almost everyone, there is increased talk of legislated sterilization and the planned selection of human offspring. There is very serious talk, even among geneticists, about the ability of the human race to take control of its own evolution. Others are frightened by the possibilities for disastrous error or unpleasant sociological consequences.

The sophisticated technology of molecular genetics has given us a wide range of new techniques for shaping our genetic makeup. Even more bizarre procedures loom in the near future. We have moved beyond conventional breeding techniques to the ability to make chemical and molecular modifications in the genetic apparatus. While some scientists emphasize the promised benefits of such research,

others raise disturbing questions about possible dangers. Could there be an accidental release from some laboratory of an artificial pathogen that has never existed on this planet before? Such worries have led to calls for a complete moratorium on such research — or at least for legislation that requires ruthlessly efficient containment facilities. A number of popular books warn us of a *Genetic Fix,* a *Biological Time Bomb,* the *Genetic Revolution,* a *Fabricated Man,* and the *Biocrats.* Knowledge of genetic mechanisms has made us aware of other new dangers as well. Some geneticists fear that increased exposure to chemical food additives and to the vast array of chemicals in other commercial products may be changing the human genetic makeup in a very undesirable and haphazard way. This type of random genetic change can also be caused by such environmental agents as fallout from nuclear weapons, radioactive contamination from nuclear reactors, and radiation from various X-ray machines. These agents may be contributing to inherited disease, but they almost certainly are contributing to the incidence of cancer, a genetic disease of the somatic ("body") cells.

The study of genetics is relevant not only to the biologist but to any thinking member of today's complex technological society. A working knowledge of the principles of genetics is essential for making informed decisions on many scientific, political, and personal levels. Such a working knowledge can come only through an understanding of the way that genetic inferences are made — that is, from an understanding of genetic analysis, the subject of this book.

CHAPTER 2

Mendelian Analysis

■ The gene is the focal point of the discipline of modern genetics. In all lines of genetic research, it is the gene that provides the common unifying thread to a great diversity of experimentation. Geneticists are concerned with the transmission of genes from generation to generation, with the nature of genes, with the variation in genes, and with the ways that genes function to dictate the features that constitute any given species.

In this chapter we trace the birth of the gene as a concept. We shall see that genetics is, in one sense, an abstract science: most of its entities began as hypothetical constructs in the minds of geneticists and were later identified in physical form if the reasoning was sound.

The concept of the gene (but not the word) was first set forth in 1865 by Gregor Mendel. Until then, little progress had been made in understanding heredity. The prevailing notion was that the spermatozoon and egg contain a sampling of essences from the various parts of the parental body; at conception, these essences are somehow blended to form the pattern for the new individual. This idea of **blending inheritance** evolved to account for the fact that offspring typically show some characteristics similar to those of both parents. However, attempts to expand and improve this theory never led to much progress.

As a result of his research with pea plants, Mendel proposed instead a theory of **particulate inheritance.** A genetic determinant of a specific character is passed on from one generation to the next as a unit, without any blending of the units. This model explained many observations that could not be explained by blending inheritance. It also proved a very fruitful framework for further progress in understanding the mechanism of heredity.

For many reasons, the importance of Mendel's ideas was not recognized until about 1900 (after his death). His report was then rediscovered by three scientists after each independently had reached the same conclusions. Historically, then, Mendel's work was irrelevant to the development of ideas about heredity. However, his achievement is important, and his analysis provides a good example of basic genetic reasoning, so we now examine Mendel's work.

Mendel's Experiments

Mendel's studies provide an outstanding example of good scientific technique. He chose research material well suited to study of the problem at hand, designed his experiments carefully, collected large amounts of data, and used mathematical analysis to show that the results were consistent with his explanatory hypothesis. The predictions of the hypothesis were then tested in a new round of experimentation. (Some historians of science believe that Mendel may have "fudged" his data to fit his hypothesis, but we shall accept his reports at face value in our discussion here.)

Mendel studied the garden pea (*Pisum sativum*) for two

main reasons. First, peas were available through a seed merchant in a wide array of distinct shapes and colors that are very easily identified and analyzed. Second, peas left to themselves will **self** (self-pollinate) because the male parts (anthers) and female parts (ovaries) of the flower—which produce the pollen and the eggs, respectively—are enclosed in a petal box, or keel (Figure 2-1). The gardener or experimenter can **cross** (cross-pollinate) any two plants at will. The anthers from one plant are clipped off to prevent selfing; pollen from the other plant is then transferred to the receptive area with a paintbrush or on transported anthers (Figure 2-2). Thus the experimenter can readily choose to self or to cross the pea plants.

Other practical reasons for Mendel's choice of peas were that they are cheap and easy to obtain, take up little space, have a relatively short generation time, and produce many offspring. These considerations are typical of those involved in the choice of organism for any piece of genetic research. This is a crucial decision and is nearly always based upon not only scientific criteria but also a good measure of expediency.

Plants Differing in One Character

First, Mendel chose several characters to study. It is important to clarify the meaning of character in this sense. Here, a **character** is a specific property of an organism; geneticists use this term as a synonym for characteristic or trait.

For each of the characters he chose, Mendel obtained lines of plants, which he grew for two years to make sure they were pure lines. A **pure line** is a population that breeds true for the particular character being studied; that is, all offspring produced by selfing or crossing within the population show the same form for this character. By ensuring pure lines in his research material, Mendel made a clever beginning: he had established a basis of identifiable con-

Figure 2-2. One technique of artificial cross-pollination, demonstrated with *Mimulus guttatus,* the yellow monkey flower. Anthers from the male parent are applied to the stigma of an emasculated flower, which acts as the female parent.

stant behavior, so that any changes observed following deliberate manipulation in his research would be scientifically meaningful; in effect, he had set up a control experiment.

Two of the lines Mendel grew proved to breed true for the character of flower color. One line bred true for purple flowers, and the other for white flowers. Any plant in the purple-flowered line—when selfed, or when crossed with others from the same line—produced seeds that all grew into plants with purple flowers. When these plants in turn were selfed or crossed within the line, their progeny also had purple flowers, and so on. The white-flowered line similarly produced only white flowers through all generations. Mendel obtained seven pairs of pure lines for seven characters, with each pair differing in respect to only one character (Figure 2-3).

Each pair of Mendel's plant lines can be said to show a **character difference,** a contrasting difference between two lines of organisms (or between two organisms) with respect to one particular character. The differing lines (or individuals) represent different forms that the character may take: they can be called character forms, character variants, or phenotypes. The useful term phenotype (derived from Greek) literally means "the form that is shown." The term is extensively used in genetics, and we use it in this discussion, even though such words as gene and phenotype were not coined or used by Mendel. We shall describe Mendel's results and hypotheses in terms of more modern genetic language.

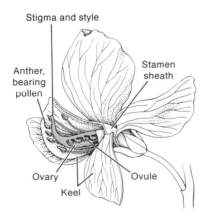

Figure 2-1. Cutaway view of reproductive parts of a pea flower. (After J. B. Hill, H. W. Popp, and A. R. Grove, Jr., *Botany,* McGraw-Hill, 1967.)

Figure 2-3 shows seven characters, each represented by two contrasting phenotypes. Contrasting phenotypes for a particular character are the starting point for any genetic analysis, by Mendel or by the modern geneticist. Of course, the definition of characters is somewhat arbitrary; there are many different ways to "split up" an organism into characters. For example, consider the following different ways of stating the same character and character difference.

Character	Phenotypes
Flower color	Red versus white
Flower redness	Presence versus absence
Flower whiteness	Absence versus presence

In many cases, the description chosen is a matter of convenience (or chance). Fortunately, the choice of definition does not alter the final conclusions of the analysis, except in the names used.

We turn now to some of Mendel's specific experimental results. In our discussion, we shall follow his analysis of the lines breeding true for flower color.

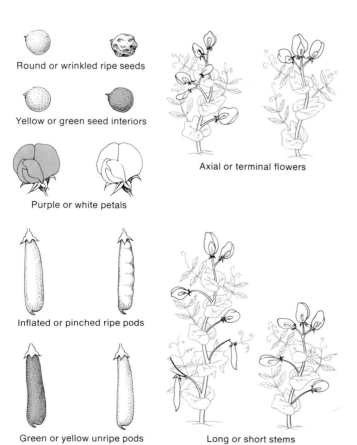

Round or wrinkled ripe seeds

Yellow or green seed interiors

Purple or white petals

Inflated or pinched ripe pods

Green or yellow unripe pods

Axial or terminal flowers

Long or short stems

In one of his early experiments, Mendel used pollen from a white-flowered plant to pollinate a purple-flowered plant. These plants from the pure lines are called the **parental generation** (P). All the plants resulting from this cross had purple flowers (Figure 2-4). This progeny generation is called the **first filial generation** (F_1). (The subsequent generations in such an experiment are called F_2, F_3, and so on.)

Mendel also made a **reciprocal cross.** In most plants, any cross can be made in two ways, depending on which phenotype is used as male (♂) or female (♀). For example, the two crosses

phenotype A ♀ × phenotype B ♂

phenotype B ♀ × phenotype A ♂

are reciprocal crosses. Mendel's reciprocal cross, in which a white flower was pollinated by a purple-flowered plant, produced the same result in the F_1 (Figure 2-5). Mendel concluded that it makes no difference which way the cross is made. If one parent is purple-flowered and the other white-flowered, all plants in the F_1 are purple-flowered. The purple flower color in the F_1 generation is identical to that in the purple-flowered parental plants. In this case, the inheritance obviously is not a simple blending of purple and white colors to produce some intermediate color. To maintain a theory of blending inheritance, we would have to assume that the purple color is somehow "stronger" than the white color, completely overwhelming any trace of the white phenotype in the blend.

Next, Mendel selfed the F_1 plants, allowing the pollen of each flower to fall on the stigma within its petal box. He obtained 929 pea seeds from this selfing (the F_2 individuals) and planted them. Interestingly, some of the resulting plants were white-flowered; the white phenotype had reappeared! Mendel then did something that, more than anything else, marks the birth of modern genetics: he *counted* the numbers of plants with each phenotype. This procedure seems obvious to modern biologists after another century of quantitative scientific research, but it had seldom if ever been used in genetic studies before Mendel's work. There were 705 purple-flowered plants and 224 white-flowered plants. Mendel observed that the ratio of 705 : 224 is almost a 3 : 1 ratio (in fact, it is 3.1 : 1).

Mendel repeated this breeding procedure for six other pairs of pea character differences. He found the same 3 : 1 ratio in the F_2 generation for each pair (Table 2-1). By this time, he was undoubtedly beginning to believe in the significance of the 3 : 1 ratio and seeking an explanation. The white phenotype is completely absent in the F_1 generation,

Figure 2-3. The seven character differences studied by Mendel. (After S. Singer and H. Hilgard, *The Biology of People.* Copyright © 1978, W. H. Freeman and Co.)

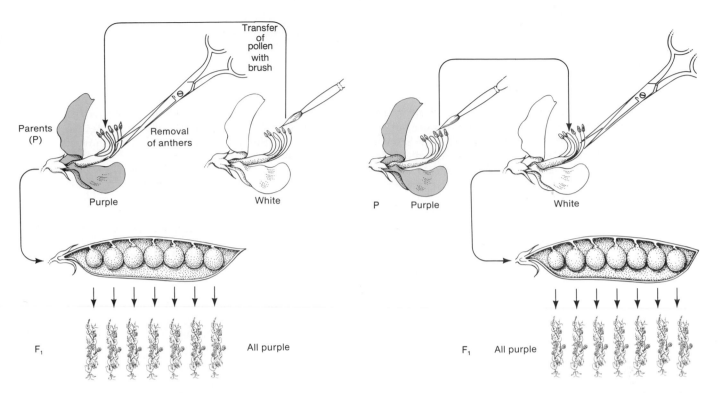

Figure 2-4. Mendel's cross of purple-flowered ♀ × white-flowered ♂.

Figure 2-5. Mendel's cross of white-flowered ♀ × purple-flowered ♂.

but it reappears (in its full original form) in one-fourth of the F_2 plants. It is very difficult to devise an explanation of this result in terms of blending inheritance. Even though the F_1 flowers are purple, the plants still must carry the *potential* to produce progeny with white flowers.

Mendel inferred that the F_1 plants receive from their parents the ability to produce both the purple phenotype and the white phenotype, and that these abilities are retained and passed on to future generations rather than blended. Why is the white phenotype not expressed in the F_1 plants? Mendel invented the terms **dominant** and **recessive** to describe this phenomenon without explaining the mechanism. In modern terms, the purple phenotype is dominant to the white phenotype, and the white phenotype is recessive to the purple. Thus, the phenotype of the F_1 provides the operational definition of dominance.

Mendel made another important observation when he

individually selfed the F_2 plants. In this case, he was working with the character of seed color. Because this character can be observed without growing plants from the peas, much larger numbers of individuals can be counted. (In this species, the color of the seed is characteristic of the offspring—the seed itself—rather than of the parent plant.) Mendel used two pure lines of plants with yellow and green seeds, respectively. In a cross between one plant from each line, he observed that all of the F_1 peas were yellow. Symbolically,

$$P \qquad \text{yellow} \times \text{green}$$
$$\downarrow$$
$$F_1 \qquad \text{all yellow}$$

Therefore, in this character, yellow is dominant and green is recessive.

■ **TABLE 2-1.** Results of all Mendel's crosses in which parents differed for one character

Parent phenotypes	F_1	F_2	F_2 ratio
1. Round × wrinkled seeds	All round	5474 round; 1850 wrinkled	2.96 : 1
2. Yellow × green seeds	All yellow	6022 yellow; 2001 green	3.01 : 1
3. Purple × white petals	All purple	705 purple; 224 white	3.15 : 1
4. Inflated × pinched pods	All inflated	882 inflated; 299 pinched	2.95 : 1
5. Green × yellow pods	All green	428 green; 152 yellow	2.82 : 1
6. Axial × terminal flowers	All axial	651 axial; 207 terminal	3.14 : 1
7. Long × short stems	All long	787 long; 277 short	2.84 : 1

Mendel grew F₁ plants from these yellow F₁ peas and selfed the plants. Of the resulting F₂ peas, 3/4 were yellow and 1/4 were green—the 3:1 ratio again (see the second line of Table 2-1). He then grew plants from 519 of the yellow F₂ peas and selfed each of these F₂ plants. When the peas appeared (the F₃ generation), he found that 166 of the plants had only yellow peas. The remaining 353 plants bore both yellow and green peas on the same plant. Counting all the peas from these plants, he again obtained a 3:1 ratio of yellow to green peas. The green F₂ peas all proved to be pure-breeding green peas; that is, selfing produced only green peas in the F₃ generation.

In summary, all of the F₂ green peas were pure-breeding greens like one of the parents. Of the F₂ yellows, about 2/3 were like the F₁ yellows (producing yellow and green seeds in a 3:1 ratio when selfed), and the remaining 1/3 were like the pure-breeding yellow parent. Thus, the study of the F₃ generation revealed that the apparent 3:1 ratio in the F₂ generation could be more accurately described as a 1:2:1 ratio.

Phenotypic ratio	Genotypic ratio
3/4 yellow	1/4 pure-breeding yellow
	2/4 "impure" yellow
1/4 green ⟶	1/4 pure-breeding green

Further studies showed that these 1:2:1 ratios existed in all of the apparent 3:1 ratios that Mendel had observed. Thus the problem really was to explain the 1:2:1 ratio.

Mendel's explanation was a classic example of a model or hypothesis derived from observation, a model that was well suited for testing by further experimentation. Mendel deduced the following explanation.

1. There are hereditary determinants of a particulate nature. (He saw no blending of phenotypes, so he was forced to this particulate notion.) We now call these determinants genes.

2. Each adult pea plant has two genes—a **gene pair**—in each cell for each character studied. The reasoning here was obvious: the F₁ plants, for example, must have had one gene responsible for the dominant phenotype, called the **dominant gene,** and one gene for the recessive phenotype, which showed up only in later generations, called the **recessive gene.**

3. The members of each gene pair segregate (separate) equally into the gametes. In animals the gametes are readily identifiable as eggs and sperms. Plants produce eggs and sperms too, but these forms are less easily identified as such.

4. Consequently, each gamete carries only one member of each gene pair.

5. The union of gametes, to form the first cell (or zygote) of a new progeny individual, is random and occurs irrespective of which member of a gene pair is carried.

These points can be illustrated diagrammatically for a general case, using A to represent a dominant gene, and a the recessive gene (as Mendel did), much as a mathematician uses symbols to represent abstract entities of various kinds. This is shown in Figure 2-6, which illustrates how these five points explain the 1:2:1 ratio.

The whole model made beautiful sense of the data. However, many beautiful models have been knocked down under test: Mendel's next job was to test it. He did this by taking (for example) an F₁ yellow and crossing it with a green. A 1:1 ratio of yellow to green seeds could be predicted in the next generation. If we use Y to stand for the

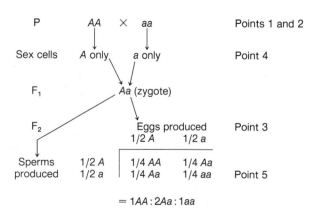

Figure 2-6. Symbolic representation of the P, F₁, and F₂ generations in Mendel's system involving a character difference determined by one gene difference. The five points are those listed in the text.

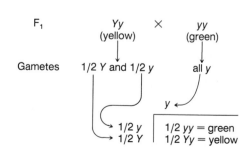

Predicted progeny ratio is 1 yellow : 1 green.

Figure 2-7. Predicted consequences of crossing an F₁ yellow with any green.

dominant gene causing yellow seeds and y to stand for the recessive gene causing green seeds, we can diagram Mendel's predictions as in Figure 2-7. In this experiment, he obtained 58 yellow and 52 green seeds, a very close approximation to the predicted $1:1$ ratio, and confirming the equal segregation of Y and y in the F_1 individual. This concept of **equal segregation** has been given formal recognition as Mendel's first law.

Mendel's First Law The two members of a gene pair segregate (separate) from each other into the gametes, so that one-half of the gametes carry one member of the pair and the other one-half of the gametes carry the other member of the gene pair.

Now we need to introduce some more terms. The individuals represented by Aa are called **heterozygotes,** or sometimes, **hybrids,** whereas those in pure lines are called **homozygotes.** Thus, an AA plant is said to be homozygous for the dominant gene, sometimes called **homozygous dominant;** an aa plant is homozygous for the recessive gene, or **homozygous recessive.** As we saw in Chapter 1, the designated genetic constitution with respect to the character or characters under study is called the genotype. Thus, YY and Yy, for example, are different genotypes even though the seeds of both types are of the same phenotype (that is, yellow). You can see that in such a situation the phenotype can be thought of simply as the outward manifestation of the underlying genotype.

Note that the expressions dominant and recessive have been used in conjunction with both the phenotype *and* the gene. This is accepted usage. The dominant phenotype is established in analysis by the appearance of the F_1. Obviously, however, a phenotype (which is merely a description) cannot really exert dominance. Mendel showed that the dominance of one phenotype over another is in fact due to the dominance of one member of a gene pair over the other.

Let's pause to let the significance of this work sink in. What Mendel had done was to develop an analytical scheme for the identification of major genes regulating any biological character or function. Starting with two different phenotypes (purple and white) of one character (petal color), he was able to show that the difference was caused by differences centering on one gene pair. Let's take the two forms of the petal-color character as an example. Modern geneticists would say that Mendel's analysis had identified a major gene for petal color. What does this mean? It means that in these organisms there is a *kind* of gene that has a profound effect on the color of the petals. This gene can exist in different forms: the dominant form of the gene (represented by C) causes purple petals, and the recessive form of the gene (represented by c) causes white petals. The

forms C and c are called **alleles** (or alternative forms) of that gene for petal color. They are given the same letter symbol to show that they are forms of the same kind of gene. One could express this another way by saying that there is a kind of gene, called phonetically a "see" gene, with alleles C and c. Any individual pea plant will always have two "see" genes, forming a gene pair, and the actual members of the gene pair can be either CC, Cc, or cc. Notice that although the members of a gene pair can produce different effects, they obviously both affect the same character.

Students often find the term allele confusing, and the reason is probably that the words allele and gene are used interchangeably in some situations. For example, "dominant gene" and "dominant allele" both refer to the same thing in an interchangeable way. This stems from the fact that the forms (alleles) of any type of gene are of course genes themselves.

The basic route of Mendelian analysis for a single character is summarized in Table 2-2.

Message Genes originally were inferred (and still are today) by observing precise mathematical ratios in the filial generations issuing from two genetically different parental individuals.

Plants Differing in Two Characters

The experiments described thus far dealt with a single gene pair — that is, a **monohybrid** system; we considered the allelic forms of a gene affecting one character. The next obvious question is what happens when a **dihybrid** cross is made, involving genes affecting two different characters. We can use the same symbolism that Mendel used to indicate the genotype of seed color — Y and y — and seed shape — R and r.

A pure-breeding line of $RRyy$ plants, on selfing, produces seeds that are round and green. Another pure-breeding line is $rrYY$; on selfing, this line produces wrinkled yellow seeds (r is a recessive allele of the seed-shape gene and produces a wrinkled seed; see Figure 2-8). When Mendel crossed plants from these two lines, he obtained round yellow F_1 seeds, as expected. The results in the F_2 are complex (Figure 2-9). Mendel performed similar experiments using other pairs of characters in many other dihybrid crosses; in each case, he obtained $9:3:3:1$ ratios. So, he had another phenomenon to explain, some more numbers to turn into an idea.

He first checked to see whether the ratio for each gene pair in the dihybrid cross is the same as that for a monohybrid cross. If you look at only the round and wrinkled phenotypes and add up all the seeds falling into these two classes, the totals are $315 + 108 = 423$ round, and $101 + 32 = 133$ wrinkled. Hence the monohybrid $3:1$ ratio still

■ **TABLE 2-2.** Summary of the modus operandi for establishing simple Mendelian inheritance

Experimental procedure:	1. Choose pure lines showing a character difference (purple versus white flowers). 2. Intercross the lines. 3. Self the F_1 individuals.
Results:	F_1 is all purple; F_2 is 3/4 purple and 1/4 white.
Inferences:	1. The character difference is controlled by a major gene for flower color. 2. The dominant allele of this gene causes purple petals; the recessive allele causes white petals.

Symbolic interpretation:

Character	Phenotypes	Genotypes	Alleles	Gene
		CC (homozygous dominant)		
	Purple (dominant)		C (dominant)	
Flower color		Cc (heterozygous)		Flower-color gene
	White (recessive)		c (recessive)	
		cc (homozygous) recessive)		

Figure 2-8. Round (*R*) and wrinkled (*r*) garden peas. (Grant Heilman.)

prevails. Similarly, the ratio for yellow to green is $(315 + 101):(108 + 32) = 416:140 \cong 3:1$. From this clue, Mendel concluded that the two systems of heredity are independent. He was mathematically astute enough to realize that the $9:3:3:1$ ratio is nothing more than a random combination of two independent $3:1$ ratios.

This is a convenient point to introduce some elementary rules of probability that we will often use throughout this book.

The Rules of Probability

1. *Definition of probability.*

$$\textbf{Probability} = \frac{\text{The number of times an event is expected to happen}}{\substack{\text{The number of opportunities} \\ \text{for it to happen} \\ \text{(or the number of trials)}}}$$

For example, the probability of rolling a four on a die in a single trial is written

$$p(\text{of a four}) = 1/6$$

because the die has six sides. If each side is equally likely to turn up, then the average result should be one four for each six trials.

2. *The product rule.* The probability of two independent

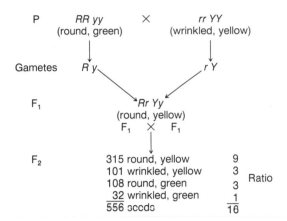

P   RR yy   ×   rr YY
     (round, green)   (wrinkled, yellow)

Gametes   R y   r Y

F₁   Rr Yy
                    (round, yellow)
                    F₁ × F₁

F₂   315 round, yellow   9
          101 wrinkled, yellow   3   Ratio
          108 round, green   3
           32 wrinkled, green   1
          556 seeds   16

Figure 2-9. The F₂ generation resulting from parents differing in two characters.

events occurring simultaneously is the product of each of their respective probabilities. For example, with two dice we have independent objects, and

$$p(\text{of two fours}) = 1/6 \times 1/6 = 1/36$$

3. *The sum rule.* The probability of *either one* of two mutually exclusive events occurring is the sum of their individual probabilities. For example, with two dice,

$$p(\text{of two fours } or \text{ two fives}) = 1/36 + 1/36 = 1/18$$

In the pea example, the F₂ of a dihybrid cross can be predicted if the mechanism for putting R or r into a gamete is *independent* of the mechanism for putting Y or y into a gamete. The frequency of gamete types can be calculated by determining their probabilities according to the rules just given. That is, if you pick a gamete at random, the *probability* of picking a certain type of gamete is the same as the frequency of that type in the population.

We know from Mendel's first law that

$$Y \text{ gametes} = y \text{ gametes} = 1/2$$

$$R \text{ gametes} = r \text{ gametes} = 1/2$$

For an $RrYy$ plant, the probability that a gamete will be R and Y is written $p(RY)$; similarly, $p(Ry)$ denotes the probability that a gamete will be R and y. By the product rule, therefore,

$$p(RY) = 1/2 \times 1/2 = 1/4$$

$$p(Ry) = 1/2 \times 1/2 = 1/4$$

$$p(ry) = 1/2 \times 1/2 = 1/4$$

$$p(rY) = 1/2 \times 1/2 = 1/4$$

Thus we can represent the F₂ generation by a giant grid named (after its inventor) a Punnett square, as shown in Figure 2-10.

The probability of 1/16 shown for each box in the square is derived by further application of the product rule. The assortment of alleles into the male gametes and that into the female gametes are independent events. Thus, for example, the probability (or frequency) of $RRYY$ zygotes (combining an RY male gamete with an RY female gamete) will be $1/4 \times 1/4 = 1/16$. Grouping all the types that will look the same from Figure 2-9, we find the $9:3:3:1$ ratio (now not so mysterious) in all its beauty.

round, yellow	9/16 or 9
round, green	3/16 or 3
wrinkled, yellow	3/16 or 3
wrinkled, green	1/16 or 1

The concept of independence of the two systems (round or wrinkled versus yellow or green) is important. This concept of **independent assortment** has been generalized to give the statement now known as Mendel's second law.

Mendel's Second Law During gamete formation the segregation of one gene pair is independent of other gene pairs.

A note of warning: we shall see later that the phenomenon of gene linkage is an important exception to Mendel's second law.

Note how Mendel's counting led to the discovery of such unexpected regularities as the $9:3:3:1$ ratio, and how a few simple assumptions (such as equal segregation and independent assortment) can explain this ratio that initially seems so baffling. Although it was unappreciated at the time, Mendel's approach was to provide the key to an understanding of genetic mechanisms.

Of course, Mendel went on to test this second law. For example, he crossed an F₁ dihybrid $RrYy$ with a double-homozygous recessive strain $rryy$. Such a cross involving a homozygous recessive is now known as a **testcross.** (We shall see this kind of cross many times later in this book.) For his testcross, Mendel predicted that the dihybrid $RrYy$ should produce the gametic types RY, rY, Ry, and ry in equal frequency — that is, as shown along one edge of the Punnett square, in the frequencies $1/4$, $1/4$, $1/4$, and $1/4$. On the other hand, because it is homozygous, the $rryy$ plant should produce only one gamete type (ry), regardless of equal segregation or independent assortment. Thus the progeny phenotypes should be a direct reflection of the gametic types from the $RrYy$ parent (because the ry contri-

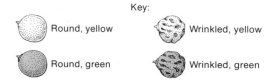

♂ / ♀	R Y 1/4	R y 1/4	r y 1/4	r Y 1/4
R Y 1/4	RR YY 1/16	RR Yy 1/16	Rr Yy 1/16	Rr YY 1/16
R y 1/4	RR Yy 1/16	RR yy 1/16	Rr yy 1/16	Rr Yy 1/16
r y 1/4	Rr Yy 1/16	Rr yy 1/16	rr yy 1/16	rr Yy 1/16
r Y 1/4	Rr YY 1/16	Rr Yy 1/16	rr Yy 1/16	rr YY 1/16

Key:

Round, yellow   Wrinkled, yellow

Round, green   Wrinkled, green

Figure 2-10. Symbolic representation of the genetic and phenotypic constitution of the F_2 generation resulting from parents differing in two characters. (Figure 2-9 shows the P and F_1 generations.)

bution from the *rryy* parent does not alter the phenotype indicated by the other gamete). Mendel predicted a 1:1:1:1 ratio of *RrYy*, *rrYy*, *Rryy*, and *rryy* progeny from this testcross, and his prediction was confirmed. He tested the concept of independent assortment intensively on four different gene pairs and found that it applied to every combination.

Of course, the deduction of equal segregation and independent assortment as abstract concepts that explain the observed facts leads immediately to the question of what structures or forces are responsible for generating them. The idea of equal segregation seems to indicate that both alleles of a pair actually exist in some kind of orderly, paired configuration, from which they can separate cleanly during gamete formation (Figure 2-11). If any other gene pair behaves independently in the same way, then we have independent assortment (Figure 2-12). But this is all speculation at this stage of our discussion, as it was after the rediscovery of Mendel's work. The actual mechanisms are now known, and we shall discuss them later. (We shall see that it is the chromosomal location of genes that is responsible for their equal segregation and independent assortment.)

The key point to appreciate at this stage is that the ground rules for genetic analysis were established by Mendel. His work made it possible to infer the existence and nature of hereditary particles and mechanisms without ever seeing them. All such theories were based on the analy-

sis of phenotype frequencies in controlled crosses; this is the experimental approach still used in much of modern genetics.

Methods for Working Problems

We pause here for a few words on the working of problems. The Punnett square is sure and graphic, but it is unwieldy; it is suited only for illustration, not for efficient calculation.

A branch diagram is useful for solving some problems. For example, the 9:3:3:1 ratio can be derived by drawing a branch diagram and applying the product rule to determine the frequencies. (Note the use of the convention that *R-* represents both *RR* and *Rr*. That is, either allele can occupy the space indicated by the dash.)

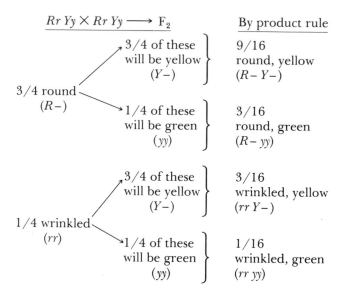

The branch diagram is, of course, a graphic expression of the product rule.

The diagram can be extended to a trihybrid ratio (such as *Aa Bb Cc* × *Aa Bb Cc*) by drawing another set of branches on the end. However, as the number of gene pairs increases, the number of identifiable phenotypes rises startlingly, and the number of genotypes climbs even more steeply, as shown in Table 2-3. With such large class numbers, even the branch method becomes unwieldy.

In such cases, we must resort to devices based directly on the product and sum rules. For example, what proportion of progeny from the cross *Aa Bb Cc Dd Ee Ff* × *Aa Bb Cc Dd Ee Ff* will be *AA bb Cc DD ee Ff*? The answer is easily obtained if the gene pairs all assort independently, thereby allowing use of the product rule. That is, 1/4 of the progeny will be *AA*, 1/4 will be *bb*, 1/2 will be *Cc*, 1/4 will be *DD*, 1/4 will be *ee*, and 1/2 will be *Ff*, so we obtain the answer by multiplying these frequencies:

$p(AA\ bb\ Cc\ DD\ ee\ Ff)$
$$= 1/4 \times 1/4 \times 1/2 \times 1/4 \times 1/4 \times 1/2$$
$$= 1/1024$$

Let us return now to Mendel's work.

When Mendel's results were rediscovered in 1900, his principles were tested in a wide spectrum of eukaryotic organisms (those whose cells contain nuclei). The results of these tests showed that Mendelian genetics (sometimes with extensions that we shall discuss in the next three chapters) is universally applicable. Mendelian ratios (such as $3:1$, $1:1$, $9:3:3:1$, and $1:1:1:1$) were extensively reported (Figure 2-13), suggesting that equal segregation and independent assortment are fundamental hereditary processes found throughout nature. His laws are not merely laws about peas, but laws of the genetics of eukaryotic organisms in general. The experimental approach used by Mendel can be extensively applied in plants. However, in some plants, and in animals, the technique of selfing is impossible. This problem can be circumvented by intercrossing identical genotypes. For example, an F_1 animal resulting from the mating of parents from differing pure lines can be mated to its F_1 siblings (brothers or sisters) and an F_2 produced. The F_1 individuals are genetically identical, so the F_1 cross amounts to a selfing.

Simple Mendelian Genetics in Humans

Other systems present some special problems in the application of Mendelian methodology. One of the most difficult, yet most interesting, is the human species. Obviously, controlled crosses cannot be made, so human geneticists must resort to a scrutiny of established matings in the hope that informative matings have been made by chance. The scrutiny of established matings is called **pedigree analysis.** A member of a family who first comes to the attention of a

TABLE 2-3. Rise in number of genotypic classes as the power of the number of segregating gene pairs

Number of segregating gene pairs	Number of phenotypic classes	Number of genotypic classes
1	2	3
2	4	9
3	8	27
4	16	81
.	.	.
.	.	.
.	.	.
n	2^n	3^n

geneticist is called the **propositus.** Usually the phenotype of the propositus is exceptional in some way—for example, a dwarf. The investigator then traces the history of the character shown to be interesting in the propositus back through the history of the family, and a family tree or pedigree is drawn up using certain standard symbols, given in Figure 2-14. (The terms autosomal and sex-linked in the figure will be explained later; they are included to make the table complete.)

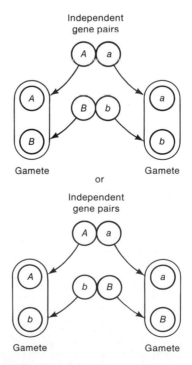

Figure 2-12. Diagrammatic visualization of the segregation of two independent gene pairs into gametes.

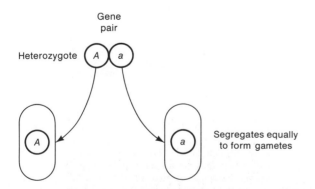

Figure 2-11. Diagrammatic visualization of the equal segregation of one gene pair into gametes.

Figure 2-13. A 9:3:3:1 ratio in the phenotype of kernels of corn. Each kernel represents a progeny individual. The progeny result from a self of an individual of genotype *Aa Bb* where *A* = dark, *a* = light, *B* = smooth, and *b* = wrinkled. Two representative ears of corn are shown.

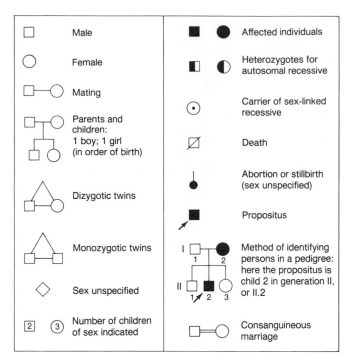

Figure 2-14. Symbols used in human pedigree analysis. (After W. F. Bodmer and L. L. Cavalli-Sforza, *Genetics, Evolution, and Man.* Copyright © 1976, W. H. Freeman and Co.)

Many human diseases and other exceptional conditions are determined by simple Mendelian recessive alleles. There are certain clues in the pedigree that must be sought. Characteristically the condition appears in progeny of unaffected parents. Furthermore, two affected individuals cannot have an unaffected child. Quite often such recessive alleles are revealed by consanguineous matings—for example, cousin marriages. This is particularly true of rare conditions where chance matings of heterozygotes are expected to be extremely rare. It has been estimated, for example, that first-cousin marriages account for about 18 to 24 percent of albino children and 27 to 53 percent of children with Tay-Sachs disease; both are rare recessive conditions. Some other examples of disease-causing recessive alleles in humans are those for cystic fibrosis and phenylketonuria (PKU). A typical pedigree for a rare recessive condition is shown in Figure 2-15. Of course, variants that are not regarded as diseases also may be caused by recessive alleles. These may be rare as in albinism (Figure 2-16) or common as in light eye color (blue or green) in North American populations.

There are also examples of exceptional conditions caused by dominant alleles. (This is in contrast to the situation for such conditions as PKU, where the normal condition is attributable to the dominant allele, and the recessive allele causes PKU.) Once again, there are some simple rules to follow to discern from pedigrees a condition caused by a dominant allele: the condition typically occurs in every generation; unaffected individuals never transmit the condition to their offspring; two affected parents may have unaffected children; and the condition is passed, on average, to one-half of the children of an affected individual. As with

recessive alleles acting in a Mendelian manner, both sexes may be equally affected. Achondroplasia (a kind of dwarfism), Huntington's chorea, and brachydactyly (very short fingers) are examples of exceptional conditions in humans caused by dominant alleles. A typical pedigree of a rare dominant condition is shown in Figure 2-17.

Notice that, in this kind of Mendelian analysis, there is again the notion of identification of genes affecting major

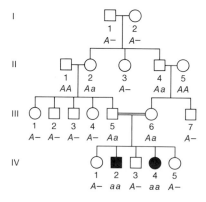

Figure 2-15. Illustrative pedigree, involving an exceptional recessive phenotype determined by the recessive Mendelian allele *a*. Gene symbols normally are not included in pedigree charts, but genotypes are inserted here for reference. Note that individuals II.1 and II.5 marry into the family; they are assumed to be normal because the heritable condition under scrutiny in a pedigree typically is rare. Note also that it is not possible to be certain of the genotype in some individuals with normal phenotype; such individuals are indicated by *A*—.

Figure 2-16. Albinism in an African child. This phenotype is caused by homozygosity for a recessive Mendelian gene. (Courtesy of W. F. Bodmer and L. L. Cavalli-Sforza, *Genetics, Evolution, and Man.* Copyright © 1976, W. H. Freeman and Co.)

biological function, this time in humans. Pedigrees for PKU, for example, demonstrate that there is a kind of gene controlling the character we might call "normal PKU function." The two alleles stand for presence and absence. This identification is an important step toward discovery of the precise way in which the abnormal allele is failing and its possible correction. The medical applications of such genetic analysis obviously are far-reaching. In fact, medical genetics is today a key part of medical training. Simple pedigree analyses have extensive use, not only in such medical research but also in the day-to-day counseling of prospective parents who fear genetic disease in their children.

Simple Mendelian Genetics in Agriculture

As mentioned in Chapter 1, there has been an interest in plant breeding since prehistoric times. The methods used

by Neolithic farmers were probably the same as those used until the discovery of Mendelian genetics. Basically the approach was to select superior phenotypes from seeds or plants derived from natural populations. Particularly desirable were pure lines of favorable phenotype, because these lines produced constant results over generations of planting. Without the knowledge of Mendelian genetics, how is it possible to develop pure lines? It so happens that self-pollinating plants, such as many crop plants, naturally tend to be homozygous, and any heterozygous gene pairs become homozygous over generations of selfing (Figure 2-18). Thus pure lines have developed automatically over the years.

However, these less sophisticated breeding practices suffered from a major problem: the breeder was forced to rely on favorable combinations of genes that occurred in nature. With the advent of Mendelian genetics, it became evident that favorable qualities in different lines could be combined through hybridization and subsequent gene reassortment. This procedure forms the basis of modern plant breeding.

Generation	AA	Aa	aa
0	0	100	0
1	25	50	25
2	37.5	25	37.5
3	43.75	12.5	43.75
4	46.875	6.25	46.875
∞	50	0	50

(a)

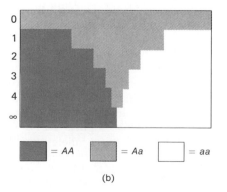

(b)

Figure 2-18. Selfing (and inbreeding in general) produces an increasing proportion of homozygous individuals with time. (a) The relative proportions of the three genotypes are shown through several generations, assuming that all individuals in generation 0 are *Aa*. At each generation, *AA* and *aa* breed true, but *Aa* individuals produce *Aa*, *AA*, and *aa* progeny in a 2 : 1 : 1 ratio. (b) A graphical depiction of the process.

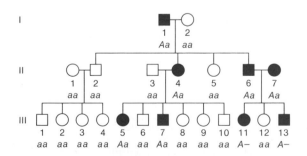

Figure 2-17. Illustrative pedigree involving an exceptional dominant phenotype determined by the dominant Mendelian allele *A*. In this pedigree, most of the genotypes can be deduced.

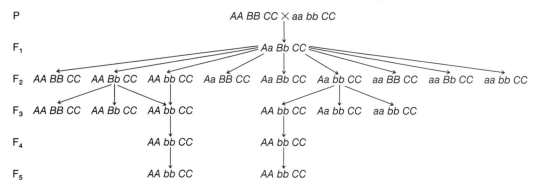

P   AA BB CC × aa bb CC

F₁   Aa Bb CC

F₂   AA BB CC   AA Bb CC   AA bb CC   Aa BB CC   Aa Bb CC   Aa bb CC   aa BB CC   aa Bb CC   aa bb CC

F₃   AA BB CC   AA Bb CC   AA bb CC   AA bb CC   Aa bb CC   aa bb CC

F₄   AA bb CC   AA bb CC

F₅   AA bb CC   AA bb CC

Figure 2-19. The basic technique of plant breeding. A hybrid is generated, and breeding stock is selected in subsequent generations to obtain pure-breeding improved types. For simplicity, we assume here that the parental lines differ in only two genes (*A* and *B*). In this example, the *AA bb CC* genotype is the one desired—that is, tests on the F₂ generation show this to be the most desirable phenotype. A pure-breeding line of this phenotype may be obtained in the F₂. It can also be obtained in the F₃ either from a nonpure parent of similar phenotype *(right)* or from a nonpure parent of different phenotype *(left)*. In typical cases of plant breeding, far larger numbers of genes, individuals, and generations are involved. Furthermore, the breeder usually knows little or nothing about the precise genotypes involved.

For naturally self-pollinating plants, such as rice or wheat, two pure lines (each of different favorable genotype) are hybridized by manual cross-pollination, and hence an F₁ is developed. The F₁ is then allowed to self, and its heterozygous gene pairs assort to produce many different genotypes, some of which represent desirable new combinations of the parental genes. A small proportion of these new genotypes will be pure-breeding already, but if not, several generations of selfing will produce homozygosity of the relevant genes. Figure 2-19 summarizes this method; Figure 2-20 shows an example of the complex series of hybridizations that have taken place in rice.

An example of genetic improvement in a species more familiar to most is the tomato. Anyone who has read a recent seed catalog will be familiar with the abbreviations V, F, and N next to a listed tomato variety. These represent, respectively, resistance to the pathogens *Verticillium, Fusarium,* and nematodes—resistance that has been crossed into the tomatoes, typically from wild forms of tomato. Another familiar phenomenon in tomatoes is determinate as opposed to indeterminate growth pattern. Determinate plants are bushier and more compact, and they do not need as much staking (Figure 2-21). Determinate growth is caused by a recessive allele *sp* (self-pruning), which has been crossed into modern varieties. Another useful allele is *u* (uniform ripening); this allele eliminates the green patch or shoulder around the stem on the ripe fruit.

Such examples could be listed for many pages. The point is that simple Mendelian genetics (as in this chapter) has provided agricultural plant breeding with its rationale and its modern methods. Entire complex genotypes may be constructed from an array of ancestral lines, each showing some desirable feature. When we think of genetic engineer-

ing, we think of the genetic techniques of the 1970s and 1980s, but genetic engineering for plant improvement began long ago.

Mendelian genetics also has provided a formal theoretical basis for animal breeding, enabling a greater efficiency than under traditional practices. More recent techniques such as the use of frozen semen, artificial insemination, frozen embryos, and surrogate mothers in livestock species have enabled breeders to amplify the number of offspring of a specific genotype, a number normally limited by the lifespan of the maternal animal.

The Origin of Variants

Genetic analysis, as we have seen, must start with parental differences. Without variants, no genetic analysis is possible. Where do these variants, this raw material for genetic analysis, come from? This is a question that can be answered in full only in later chapters. Briefly, most of the variants used by Mendel (and by ancestral and modern breeders of plants and animals) arise spontaneously, without the deliberate action of geneticists, in nature or in the breeders' populations. Undoubtedly, some of these variants would be "weeded out" by natural selection, but they may be kept alive through their deliberate nurture by geneticists, either for some specific breeding program or for the elucidation of the basic biological mechanisms of which the different forms are variants.

Genetic Dissection

We have seen that the genetic analysis of variants can identify a gene involved in an important biological process. This is a central aspect of modern genetics; as we saw in Chapter 1, this process is referred to as genetic dissection of biological systems. Mendel was the first genetic surgeon. Using genetic analysis, he was able to identify and distinguish among the several components of the hereditary process in a way as convincing as if he had microdissected those components. The fact that the genes he was using were for pea shape, pea color, and so on was largely irrelevant. Those genes were being used simply as **genetic markers,** which enabled Mendel to trace the hereditary processes of segregation and assortment. A genetic marker is a variant allele that is used to label a biological structure or process throughout the course of an experiment. It is almost as

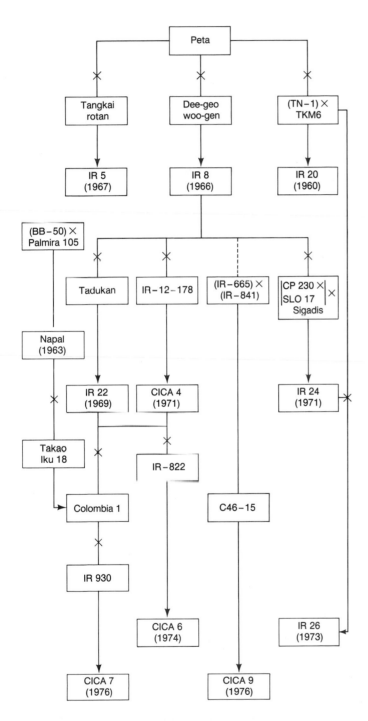

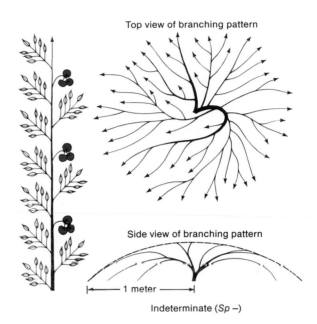

Top view of branching pattern

Side view of branching pattern

|← 1 meter →|

Indeterminate (*Sp*–)

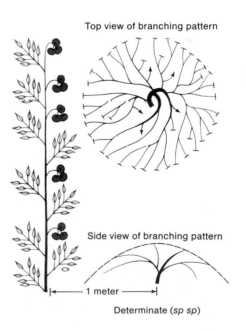

Top view of branching pattern

Side view of branching pattern

|← 1 meter →|

Determinate (*sp sp*)

Figure 2-20. The complex pedigree of modern rice varieties. The progenitor of most modern dwarf types was IR 8, selected from a cross between the vigorous Peta (Indonesian) and the dwarf Dee-geo woo-gen (from Taiwan). Most of the other crosses represent progressive improvement of IR 8. The diagram illustrates the extensive plant breeding that produced modern crop varieties. (From Peter R. Jennings, "The Amplification of Agricultural Production." Copyright © 1976 by Scientific American, Inc. All rights reserved.)

Figure 2-21. Growth characteristics of indeterminate (*Sp*–) and determinate (*sp sp*) tomatoes. Determinate has progressively fewer leaves between inflorescences, and the determinate stems end with a size-arresting inflorescence. Individual stem branches are shown, plus typical branching patterns for mature plants in top and side views. Note the size differences. (Note: the symbol *sp* represents a single gene; many gene symbols involve more than one letter.) (From Charles M. Rick, "The Tomato." Copyright © 1978 by Scientific American, Inc. All rights reserved.)

though Mendel were able to "paint" two alleles different colors and send them through a cross to see how they behaved! Genetic markers are now routinely used in genetics and in all of biology to study all sorts of processes that the marker genes themselves do not directly affect.

Probably without realizing it, Mendel had also invented another aspect of genetic dissection in which the precise genes used *were* important. In this type of analysis, genetic variants are used in such a way that, by studying the variant gene function, we can make inferences about the "normal" operation of the gene and the process it controls. Let's consider the petal-color gene in peas again. This is a major gene affecting an important biological function, which is the color of the petals. Undoubtedly the success or failure of a plant in nature would largely hinge on its having the right kind of petal color, presumably to attract the appropriate pollinator. So Mendel had pinpointed a gene for a process of central importance to the biology of peas, thus opening the way to extensive further study. Genetic dissection is a versatile tool of modern biological research.

Once a gene has been identified, affecting (say) petal color in peas, we have called it a major gene, but what does this really mean? It is major in that it is obviously having a profound effect on the color of the petals. But can we conclude that it is *the* single most important step in the determination of petal color? The answer is no, and the reason may be seen in an analogy. If we were trying to discover how a car engine works, we might investigate this by pulling out various parts and observing the effect on the running of the engine. If a battery cable were disconnected, the engine would stop; we might erroneously conclude that this cable is *the* most important part of the running of the engine. Obviously, other parts are equally necessary, and their removal could also stop or seriously cripple the engine. In a similar way it can be shown (see Chapter 4) that several genes can be identified, all of which have a major and similar effect on petal coloration.

Mendel's work has withstood the test of time and has provided us with the basic groundwork for all modern genetic study. Yet his work went unrecognized and neglected for 35 years following its publication. Why? There are many possible reasons, but here we shall consider just one. Perhaps it was because biological science at that time could not provide evidence for any real physical units within cells that might correspond to Mendel's genetic particles. Chromosomes had certainly not yet been studied, meiosis not yet described, and even the full details of plant life cycles had not been worked out. Without this basic knowledge, it may have seemed that Mendel's ideas were mere numerology.

Message   Mendel's work was the prototypical genetic analysis. As such it is significant for the following reasons.

1.   It showed how it is possible to study some central pro-

cesses of heredity and biology in general through the use of genetic markers.

2.   It showed how the biological functions of genes themselves can be elucidated from the study of variant alleles.

3.   It had far-reaching ramifications in agriculture and medicine.

In the next chapter, we focus on the physical locations of genes in cells and on the consequences of these locations.

Summary

■ Modern genetics is based on the concept of the gene, the fundamental unit of heredity. In his experiments with the garden pea, Mendel was the first to recognize the existence of genes. For example, by crossing a pure line of purple-flowered pea plants with a pure line of white-flowered pea plants and then selfing the F_1 generation, which was entirely purple, Mendel produced an F_2 generation of purple plants and white plants in a $3:1$ ratio. In crosses such as those of pea plants bearing yellow seeds and pea plants bearing green seeds, he discovered that a $1:2:1$ ratio underlies all $3:1$ ratios. From these precise mathematical ratios Mendel concluded that there are hereditary determinants of a particulate nature (now known as genes). In higher plant and animal cells, genes exist in pairs. The forms of a gene are called alleles. Individual alleles can be either dominant or recessive.

In a cross of heterozygous yellow plants with homozygous green plants, a $1:1$ ratio of yellow to green plants was produced. From this ratio Mendel confirmed his so-called first law, which states that two members of a gene pair segregate from each other during gamete formation into equal numbers of gametes. Thus, each gamete carries only one gene for each gene pair. The union of gametes to form a zygote is random and occurs irrespective of which member of a gene pair is carried.

The foregoing conclusions came from Mendel's work with monohybrid crosses. In dihybrid crosses Mendel found $9:3:3:1$ ratios in the F_2, which are really two $3:1$ ratios combined at random. From these ratios Mendel inferred that the two gene pairs studied in a dihybrid cross behave independently. This concept has been stated as Mendel's second law.

Although controlled crosses cannot be made in human beings, Mendelian genetics has great significance for humans. Many diseases and other exceptional conditions in humans are determined by simple Mendelian recessive alleles; other exceptional conditions are caused by dominant alleles. In addition, Mendelian genetics is widely used in modern agriculture. By combining favorable qualities from different lines through hybridization and subsequent gene reassortment, plant and animal geneticists are able to produce new lines of superior phenotype.

Finally, Mendel was responsible for the basic techniques of genetic dissection still in use today. One such technique is the use of genes as genetic markers to trace the hereditary processes of segregation and assortment. The other is the study of genetic variants to discover how genes operate normally.

Problems

1. Holstein cattle normally are black and white. A superb black and white bull, Charlie, was purchased by a farmer for $100,000. The progeny sired by Charlie were all normal in appearance. However, certain pairs of his progeny, when interbred, produced red and white progeny at a frequency of about 25 percent. Charlie was soon removed from the stud lists of the Holstein breeders. Explain precisely why, using symbols.

2. Maple syrup urine disease is a rare inborn error of metabolism. It derives its name from the odor of the urine of affected individuals. If untreated, affected children die soon after birth. The disease tends to recur in the same family, but the parents of the affected individuals are always normal. What does this information suggest about the transmission of the disease: is it dominant or recessive?

3. On a hike into the mountains, you notice a beautiful harebell plant that has white flowers instead of the usual blue. Assuming this effect to be caused by a single gene, outline *precisely* what you would do to find out whether the allele causing white flowers is dominant or recessive to that causing blue.

4. Mother and father both find the taste of a chemical called phenylthiourea very bitter. However, two of their four children find the chemical tasteless. Assuming the inability to taste this chemical to be a monogenic trait, is it dominant or recessive?

5. In humans, the disease galactosemia is inherited as a monogenic recessive trait in a simple Mendelian manner. A woman whose father had galactosemia intends to marry a man whose grandfather was galactosemic. They are worried about having a galactosemic child. What is the probability of this outcome?

6. Huntington's chorea is a rare, fatal disease that usually develops in middle age. It is caused by a dominant allele. A phenotypically normal man in his early twenties learns that his father has developed Huntington's chorea.

   a. What is the probability that he will himself develop the symptoms later on?

   b. What is the probability that his son will develop the symptoms in later life?

7. Achondroplasia is a form of dwarfism inherited as a simple monogenic trait. Two achondroplastic dwarfs marry and have a dwarf child; later they have a second child who is normal.

   a. Is achondroplasia produced by a recessive or a dominant allele?

   b. What are the genotypes of the two parents in this mating?

   c. What is the probability that their next child will be normal? a dwarf?

8. Suppose that a husband and wife are both heterozygous for a recessive gene for albinism. If they have dizygotic (two-egg) twins, what is the probability that both of the twins will have the same phenotype with respect to pigmentation?

9. The plant blue-eyed Mary grows on Vancouver Island and on the lower mainland of British Columbia. Near Nanaimo, one plant was observed in nature that had blotched leaves. This plant, which had not yet flowered, was dug up and taken to a laboratory, where it was allowed to self. Seeds were collected and grown into progeny. One randomly selected (but typical) leaf from each of the progeny is shown:

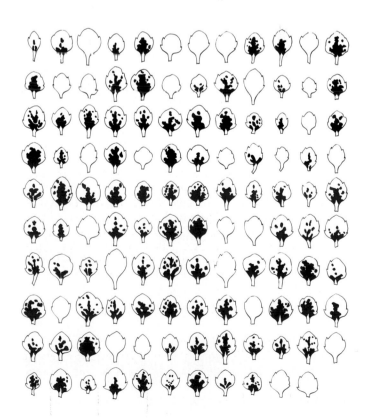

a. Formulate a concise genetic hypothesis to explain these results. Explain all symbols and show all genotypic classes (and the genotype of the original plant).

b. How would you test your hypothesis? Be specific.

10. Some species of plants (called heterostylous) produce two forms that differ in their flowers. The following figure shows two flower forms of the Lompoc fiddleneck *(Amsinckia spectabilis),* a heterostylous species.

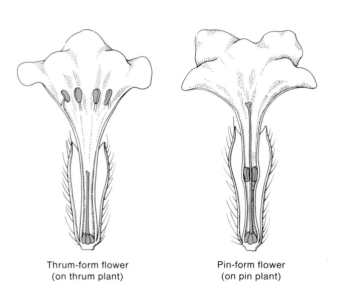

Thrum-form flower
(on thrum plant)

Pin-form flower
(on pin plant)

The following four pollinations are made:

Parents	Progeny
pin plant #1 × pin plant #2	37 pin plants
thrum plant #3 × thrum plant #3	28 thrum plants
thrum plant #3 × pin plant #1	29 thrum plants
thrum plant #4 × pin plant #2	19 pins, 16 thrums

Represent the dominant allele of the heterostyle gene by *H* and the recessive allele by *h.*

a. What are the genotypes of (1) pin plant #1, (2) pin plant #2, (3) thrum plant #3, and (4) thrum plant #4?

b. What proportions of pins and thrums would be expected in the following crosses? (1) Thrum plant #3 × thrum plant #4. (2) Thrum plant #3 × pin plant #2. (3) Thrum plant #4 × thrum plant #4.

(Problem 10 courtesy of F. R. Ganders.)

11. Can it ever be proved that an animal is *not* a carrier of a recessive allele (that is, not a heterozygote for a given gene)? Explain.

12. A green seed is planted in a greenhouse and grows into a plant. When the seeds on this plant are examined, they are all yellow! What must have happened?

13. In nature, individual plants of *Plectritis congesta* bear either winged or wingless fruits, as shown in the figure.

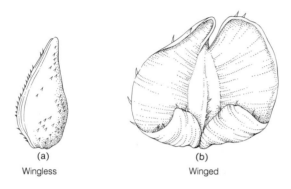

(a)
Wingless

(b)
Winged

Plants were collected from nature before flowering and were crossed or selfed with the results shown in Table 2-4. Interpret these results, and derive the mode of inheritance of these fruit-shaped phenotypes. Use symbols. (NOTE: the progeny marked by asterisks probably have a nongenetic explanation. What do you think it is?)

■ TABLE 2-4.

	Number of progeny plants	
Pollination	Winged	Wingless
Winged (selfed)	91	1*
Winged (selfed)	90	30
Wingless (selfed)	4*	80
Winged × wingless	161	0
Winged × wingless	29	31
Winged × wingless	46	0
Winged × winged	44	0
Winged × winged	24	0

14. The following figure shows four human pedigrees. The black symbols represent an abnormal condition (phenotype) inherited in a simple Mendelian manner.

a. For each pedigree, state whether the abnormal condition is dominant or recessive. Try to state the logic behind your answer.

b. In each pedigree, describe the genotypes of as many individuals as possible.

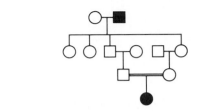

1

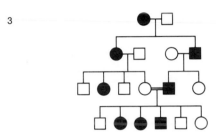

2

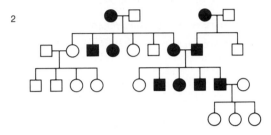

3

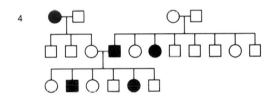

4

respectively. Assume homozygosity unless there is evidence otherwise.

■ TABLE 2-5.

	Number of progeny			
Parental phenotypes	Dark, short	Dark, long	Albino, short	Albino, long
a. Dark, short × dark, short	89	31	29	11
b. Dark, short × dark, long	18	19	0	0
c. Dark, short × albino, short	20	0	21	0
d. Albino, short × albino, short	0	0	28	9
e. Dark, long × dark, long	0	32	0	10
f. Dark, short × dark, short	46	16	0	0
g. Dark, short × dark, long	30	31	9	11

SOURCE: Reprinted by permission of Macmillan Publishing Co., Inc., from *Genetics* by M. Strickberger. Copyright © Monroe W. Strickberger, 1968.

(Problem 18 reprinted with the permission of Macmillan Publishing Co., Inc., from *Genetics* by M. Strickberger. Copyright © Monroe W. Strickberger, 1968.)

19. In tomatoes, two alleles of one gene determine the character difference of purple versus green stems, and two alleles of a separate independent gene determine the character difference of "cut" versus "potato" leaves. Table 2-6 gives the results for five separate matings of tomato plant phenotypes.

■ TABLE 2-6.

		Number of progeny			
Mating	Parental phenotypes	Purple, cut	Purple, potato	Green, cut	Green, potato
1	Purple, cut × green, cut	321	101	310	107
2	Purple, cut × purple, potato	219	207	64	71
3	Purple, cut × green, cut	722	231	0	0
4	Purple, cut × green, potato	404	0	387	0
5	Purple, potato × green, cut	70	91	86	77

SOURCE: A. M. Srb, R. D. Owen, and R. S. Edgar, *General Genetics*, 2d ed. San Francisco: W. H. Freeman and Co., 1965.

a. Determine which alleles are dominant.

b. What are the most probable genotypes for the parents in each cross?

15. When a pea plant of genotype $Aa\,Bb$ produces gametes, what proportion will be $A\,b$? (Assume that the two genes are independent.) Choose the correct answer from the following possible answers: 3/4, 1/2, 9/16, none, or 1/4.

16. When a fruit fly of genotype $Mm\,Nn\,Oo$ is mated to another fly of identical genotypes, what proportion of the progeny flies will be $MM\,nn\,Oo$? (Assume that the three genes are independent.) Choose the correct answer from the following possible answers: 1/2, 1/8, 3/8, 1/32, or 1/64.

17. Suppose that you have two strains of plants; one is $AA\,BB$, the other $aa\,bb$. You cross the two and self the F₁ plants. With respect to these two genes, what is the probability that an F₂ plant will obtain half its alleles from one grandparent and half from the other? What is the probability that it will obtain all its alleles from a single grandparent?

18. In dogs, dark coat color is dominant over albino, and short hair is dominant over long hair. If these effects are caused by two independently assorting genes, write the genotypes of the parents in each of the crosses shown in Table 2-5. Use the symbols C and c for the dark and albino coat-color alleles, and S and s for the short-hair and long-hair alleles,

(Problem 19 from A. M. Srb, R. D. Owen, and R. S. Edgar, *General Genetics,* 2d ed. Copyright © 1965 by W. H. Freeman and Company.)

20. Imagine that, in the mountains of British Columbia, a small group of Sasquatches is discovered. A study of four matings that occur in the group in the course of several years produces the results shown in Table 2-7.

■ TABLE 2-7.

Mating	Parent #1	Parent #2	Progeny
1	Bowlegs, hairy knees	Bowlegs, hairy knees	3/4 bowlegs, hairy knees 1/4 knock-knees, hairy knees
2	Bowlegs, smooth legs	Knock-knees, smooth legs	1/2 bowlegs, smooth legs 1/2 knock-knees, smooth legs
3	Bowlegs, hairy knees	Knock-knees, smooth legs	1/4 bowlegs, smooth legs 1/4 bowlegs, hairy knees 1/4 knock-knees, hairy knees 1/4 knock-knees, smooth legs
4	Bowlegs, hairy knees	Bowlegs, hairy knees	3/4 bowlegs, hairy knees 1/4 bowlegs, smooth legs

a. How many genes are involved in these phenotypes?

b. Which character differences are controlled by which alleles of these genes?

c. Which alleles are dominant or recessive?

d. Only five parents participated in these matings. Give the genotypes of these five individuals.

21. We have dealt mainly with only two pairs of genes, but the same principles hold for more than two at a time. Consider the cross

$$Aa\,Bb\,Cc\,Dd\,Ee \times aa\,Bb\,cc\,Dd\,ee$$

a. What proportion of progeny will *phenotypically* resemble (1) the first parent, (2) the second parent, (3) either parent, and (4) neither parent?

b. What proportion of progeny will *genotypically* resemble (1) the first parent, (2) the second parent, (3) either parent, and (4) neither parent?

*22. Consider two-child families in which the parents have been identified as carriers of an autosomal recessive gene by virtue of having at least one child with the phenotype. When the children of many such two-child families are totaled, what proportion of children in these families will show the phenotype? (NOTE: the answer is not 25 percent.)

23. A man is brachydactylous (very short fingers, rare autosomal dominant) and his wife is not. Both can taste the chemical phenylthiocarbamide (autosomal dominant, polymorphic), but both their mothers could not.

a. Give the genotypes of the couple.

If they have eight children, what is the proability of:

b. All being brachydactylous

c. None being brachydactylous

d. All being tasters

e. All being nontasters

f. All being brachydactylous tasters.

g. None being brachydactylous tasters

h. At least one being a brachydactylous taster

i. The first child being a brachydactylous nontaster

j. The first two children being brachydactylous

k. Having exactly two brachydactylous children

l. The first two children being a brachydactylous taster and a nonbrachydactylous nontaster in any order?

CHAPTER 3

Chromosome Theory of Inheritance

■ The beauty of Mendel's analysis is that data derived from genetic crosses can be interpreted by means of the laws of segregation and independent assortment. Furthermore, it then becomes possible to make predictions about the outcome of later crosses. All this is possible simply by representing abstract hypothetical factors of inheritance (or genes) by symbols — without any concern about their physical nature or their location in a cell. Nevertheless, although the validity of Mendelian principles is verified in many different organisms and genotypes, the next question is obvious: what structure (or structures) within cells corresponds to these hypothetical genes?

A major advance in the development of genetics was the notion that the genes, as characterized by Mendel, were associated with specific cellular structures, the chromosomes. This simple concept has become known as the **chromosome theory** of heredity. Although simple, the idea had profound implications because it united inextricably the disciplines of genetics and cytology and provided a means of correlating the results of breeding experiments with the behavior of structures that could be actually seen under the microscope. This fusion is still an essential part of genetic analysis today and has important applications in medical genetics, agricultural genetics, and evolutionary genetics.

Mitosis and Meiosis

How did the chromosome theory take shape? Evidence gradually accumulated from a variety of sources. One of the first lines of evidence came from the behavior of chromosomes during nuclear division in cells. The observations leading up to the discovery of the two different types of nuclear division, termed *mitosis* and *meiosis,* were as follows. In the interval between Mendel's research and its rediscovery, many biologists were interested in heredity even though they were unaware of Mendel's results, and they approached the problem in a completely different way from his. These investigators were interested in the physical nature of the hereditary material. An obvious place to look was in the gametes because they are the only connecting link between generations. Since egg and sperm differ in size but were believed to contribute equally to the genetic endowment of offspring, the cytoplasm seemed an unlikely seat of the hereditary structures. Nuclei, however, were known to be approximately equal in size in both egg and sperm, so they were considered good candidates for harboring hereditary structures. What was known about the contents of the nuclei? It soon became clear that the most prominent components were the chromosomes, which proved to possess unique properties that set them apart from all other cellular structures. One property that especially intrigued biologists was the constancy of number from cell to cell within an organism, from organism to organism within any one species (but different for different species), and from generation to generation within that species. Two questions, therefore, arose: how is the chromosome number maintained, and why? The first question was answered by observing the behavior of chromosomes during mitosis and meiosis; from those observations arose the postulation of the chromosome theory—that chromosomes are the containing structures for genes.

Mitosis is the nuclear division associated with somatic ("body") cell division. This is the kind of division that produces a number of cells from a single progenitor cell, as for example in the division of a fertilized human egg cell to become a multicellular organism composed of trillions of cells. Each single mitosis is associated with a single cell division to produce two identical daughter cells. **Meiosis** is the name given to the nuclear divisions occurring in cells that are undergoing a special kind of division found only in the sexual cycle. A cell that embarks upon such divisions is called a **meiocyte.** There are two cell divisions of each meiocyte, and two associated meiotic divisions of the nucleus. Hence each original meiocyte produces four cells, which we shall call **products of meiosis.** In humans, meiosis occurs in the gonads, and the products of meiosis are the gametes—sperms (more properly, spermatozoa) and eggs. In flowering plants, meiosis occurs in the anthers and ovaries, and the products of meiosis are **meiospores,** which eventually give rise to gametes. We now turn to the details of these two basic kinds of nuclear division. The following descriptions of the various stages are as general as possible and are applicable to mitosis and meiosis in most organisms in which such divisions occur. Note, however, that the photographic illustrations supplied for each stage (in Figures 3-2 and 3-3) are from one organism (a flowering plant, *Lilium regale*), and a photographic series from any single organism usually *cannot show all* the details of mitosis and meiosis. Hence a parallel series of idealized drawings is also included.

Mitosis

The cell cycle can be divided into several periods: **M, S, G1,** and **G2** (Figure 3-1). Mitosis (M) is usually the shortest period of the cycle, lasting for approximately 5 to 10 percent of the cycle. DNA synthesis occurs in the S period. The G1 and G2 periods stand for the gaps between S and M. Together, G1, S, and G2 constitute **interphase,** the time between mitoses. (Interphase used to be called "resting period"; however, many active cell functions occur in interphase, not the least of which, of course, is DNA synthesis.) The chromosomes are difficult to see during interphase (Figure 3-2a), mainly because they are in an extended state and become intertwined with each other like a tangle of yarn.

The net achievement of mitosis is that each chromosome in the nucleus makes a copy of itself along its length, and then this double structure splits to become two daugh-

ter chromosomes, each going to a different daughter nucleus. The result is two daughter nuclei identical to each other and to the nucleus from which they were derived. The four stages of mitosis are called **prophase, metaphase, anaphase,** and **telophase.** It must be stressed, however, that any nuclear division is a dynamic process on which we impose such arbitrary stages for our own convenience.

Prophase. The onset of mitosis is heralded by the chromosomes becoming more distinct (Figure 3-2b) as they get progressively shorter through a process of contraction or condensation. This condensation is achieved by the chromosome's being thrown into a series of spirals or coils; the coiling produces structures that are more easily moved around (for the same reason, cotton fibers are packaged commercially on spools). As the chromosomes become visible, they take on a double-stranded appearance, each chromosome being composed of two longitudinal halves called **chromatids** (Figure 3-2c). The "sister" chromatids are joined together at a region called the **centromere.** The **nucleoli,** large intranuclear spherical structures, disappear at this stage. The nuclear membrane begins to break down, and the nucleoplasm and cytoplasm become one.

Metaphase. At this stage, the **nuclear spindle** becomes prominent. This is a birdcage-like structure that forms in the nuclear area; it consists of a series of parallel spindle fibers that point to each of two cell poles. The chromosomes move to the equatorial plane of the cell and become attached to spindle fibers at their centromeres (Figure 3-2d).

Anaphase. This stage begins when the pairs of sister chromatids separate, one of a pair to each pole (Figure 3-2e). The separation procedure starts with the centromere, which now appears also to have been divided. As the chromatids move, their two arms appear to trail their centro-

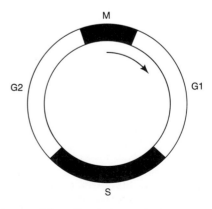

Figure 3-1. Stages of the cell cycle. M = mitosis, S = DNA synthesis, G = gap.

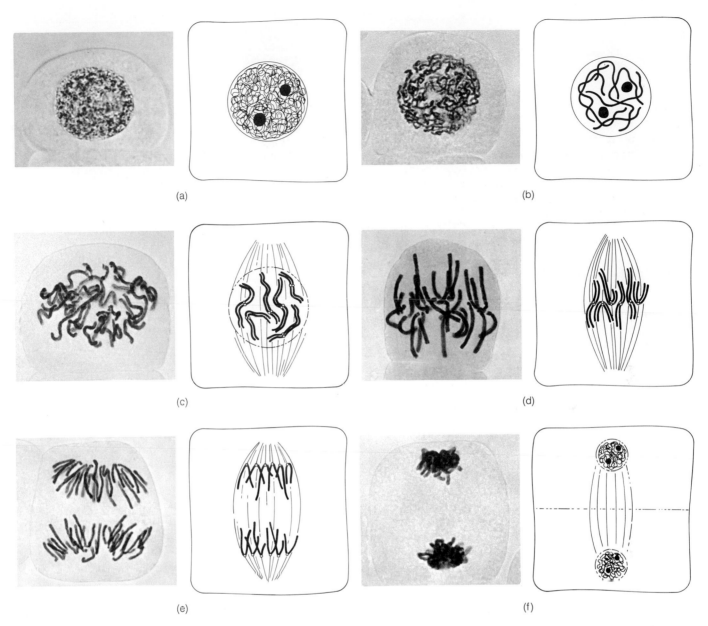

Figure 3-2. Mitosis in root tip cells of *Lilium regale*. (a) Interphase. (b) Early prophase. (c) Late prophase. (d) Metaphase. (e) Anaphase. (f) Telophase. (From J. McLeish and B. Snoad, *Looking at Chromosomes.* Copyright © 1958, St. Martin's, Macmillan.)

mere, and a set of V-shaped structures results, with the points of the V's directed at the poles.

Telophase. Now a nuclear membrane re-forms around each daughter nucleus, the chromosomes uncoil, and the nucleoli reappear, all of which effectively re-forms interphase nuclei (Figure 3-2f). By this time, the spindle has dispersed, and the cytoplasm has been divided into two by a new cell membrane.

In each of the resultant daughter cells, the chromosome complement is identical to that of the original cell. Of course, what were referred to as chromatids now take on the role of full-fledged chromosomes in their own right.

Message Mitosis produces two daughter nuclei that have a chromosomal constitution identical to that of the original nucleus.

Why should organisms devote so much energy to this elaborate mitotic process to ensure exactly equal distribution of chromosomal material, unless the chromosomes played a key role in directing the development of an organism? From this kind of consideration arose the conclusion that chromosomes very probably are crucial in heredity and development.

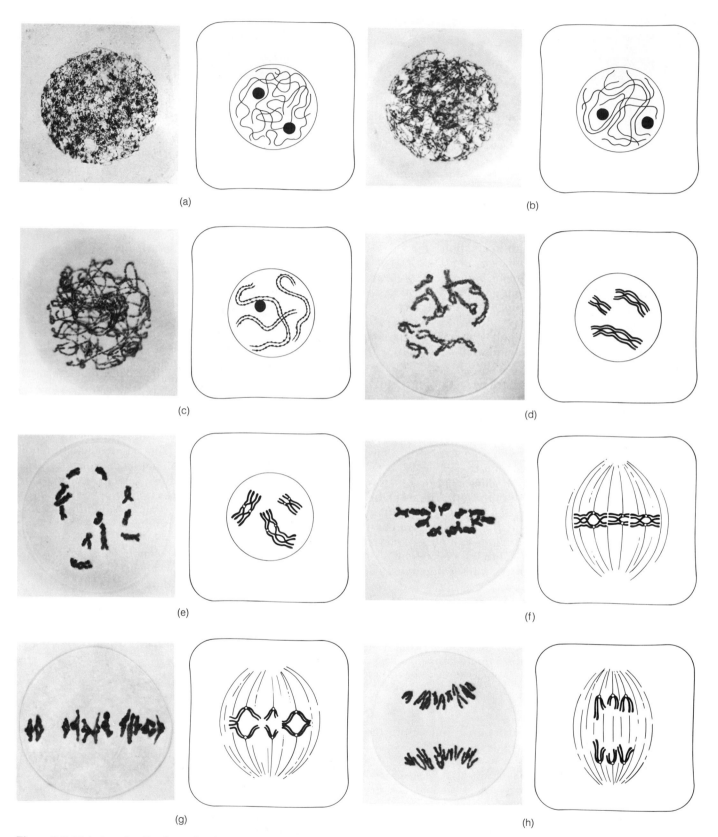

Figure 3-3. Meiosis and pollen formation in *Lilium regale*.
(a) Leptotene. (b) Zygotene. (c) Pachytene. (d) Diplotene. (e) Diakinesis. (f) Metaphase I. (g) Early anaphase I. (h) Later anaphase I. (i) Telophase I. (j) Interphase. (k) Prophase II. (l) Metaphase II. (m) Anaphase II. (n) Telophase II. (o) The tetrad. (p) Young pollen grains. Note: For simplicity, multiple chiasmata are drawn as involving only two chromatids, whereas in reality all four can be involved. (From J. McLeish and B. Snoad, *Looking at Chromosomes.* Copyright © 1958, St. Martin's, Macmillan.)

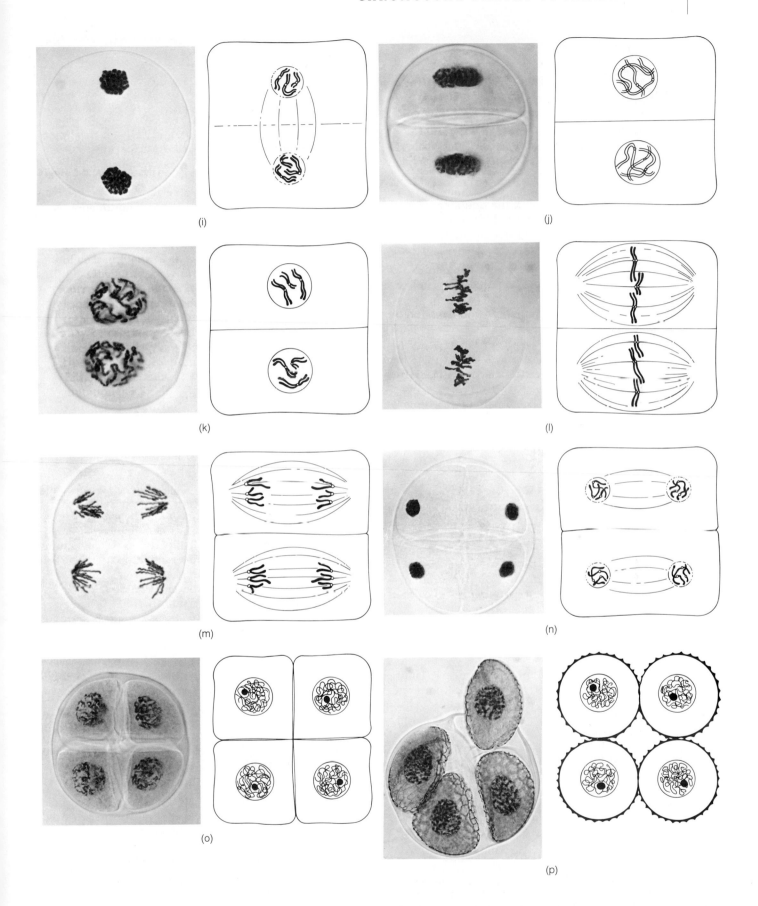

(i)

(j)

(k)

(l)

(m)

(n)

(o)

(p)

Since it was evident that the job of mitosis is to maintain the chromosome number in each nucleus, early investigators noted an apparent conflict in the events of gamete fertilization. They knew that during this process, two nuclei fuse, but that the chromosome number nevertheless remains constant. What prevented the doubling of chromosome number at each generation? This conflict was resolved by the prediction of a special kind of nuclear division that *halved* the chromosome number. This special division, which was eventually discovered in the gamete-producing tissues of plants and animals, was called meiosis.

Meiosis

Meiosis is also preceded by a premeiotic S phase, during which the bulk of DNA synthesis for meiosis occurs. (Some DNA synthesis also occurs during the first prophase of meiosis.) Since meiosis consists of two cell divisions, they are distinguished as meiosis I and meiosis II. The events of meiosis I are quite different from those of meiosis II, and both differ significantly from those of mitosis. Each meiotic division is formally divided into prophase, metaphase, anaphase, and telophase. Of these, the most complex and lengthy is prophase I, which has its own subdivisions: **leptotene, zygotene, pachytene, diplotene,** and **diakinesis.** Once again, try to imagine those processes as dynamic, merging into each other with no clear borders.

Prophase I. LEPTOTENE. The chromosomes become visible at this stage as long, thin threads (Figure 3-3a). No longitudinal doubleness is apparent. The process of chromosome contraction continues in leptotene and throughout the entire prophase. One other feature of leptotene is the development of small areas of thickening, called **chromomeres,** along the chromosome, which give it the appearance of a bead necklace.

ZYGOTENE. This is a time of active pairing (Figure 3-3b) at which it becomes apparent that the chromosome complement of the meiocyte is in fact two complete chromosome sets. Thus, each chromosome has a pairing partner, and the two become progressively paired, or **synapsed,** side by side in zipper fashion. Each pair is called a **homologous pair,** and the two members of a pair are called **homologs.** We see that meiocytes always contain two homologous chromosome sets, or **genomes.** A cell with two homologous genomes is called **diploid.** One genome is said to have a **haploid** chromosome number, usually designated n. Hence diploid cells are $2n$. It should be noted that the occurrence of pairing represents a striking difference from mitosis, in which there is no such process.

What is the mechanism whereby two homologs can pair so precisely along their length? First, how do they find each other in the first place? The probable answer to this is that the ends of the chromosomes, the **telomeres,** are an-

chored in the nuclear membrane, and it is likely that homologous telomeres are close, so that the zippering-up process can begin there. Second, how does the zippering-up work? Although the mechanism involved is not precisely understood, one important factor is an elaborate structure composed of protein and DNA, called a **synaptonemal complex,** that is always found sandwiched between homologs during synapsis (Figure 3-4).

PACHYTENE. This stage is characterized by thick threads representing full synapsis (Figure 3-3c). Thus the number of units in the nucleus is equal to the number n. Nucleoli are often pronounced at this stage. The beadlike thickenings of the chromosomes, called chromomeres, are aligned precisely in the paired homologs, producing a distinctive pattern for each pair.

DIPLOTENE. Here the DNA synthesis that had occurred in the premeiotic S phase becomes manifest as a longitudinal doubleness of each paired homologue (Figure 3-3d). Once again these units, formed by longitudinal division, are called chromatids. Hence, since each member of a homologous pair produces two sister chromatids, the synapsed structure now consists of a bundle of four homologous chromatids. At diplotene the pairing between homologs becomes less tight; in fact, they appear to repel each other, and as they separate slightly, cross-shaped structures called **chiasmata** (singular, **chiasma**) appear between two nonsister chromatids. One or more chiasmata are found on each chromosome pair. Chiasmata are the visible manifestations of events, called **crossovers,** that occurred earlier, probably during zygotene or pachytene, when there is some DNA synthesis. Crossovers represent one major way in which meiosis differs from mitosis (where they occur only rarely). A crossover is a precise breakage-and-reunion event occurring between two nonsister chromatids. Studies performed on abnormal lines of organisms that undergo crossing-over very inefficiently, or not at all, show severe disruption of the orderly events that partition chromosomes into daughter cells at meiosis. Thus, crossing-over obviously plays a key role in determining the behavior of paired homologs, and the occurrence of at least one crossover per pair is usually essential for proper segregation. Crossovers have another interesting role, which is to promote genetic variation by making new gene combinations, as we shall see in Chapter 5.

DIAKINESIS. This stage (Figure 3-3e) does not differ appreciably from diplotene except for further chromosome contraction. By this time, the long filamentous chromosome threads of interphase are replaced by compact units far more maneuverable in the movements of the meiotic division.

Metaphase I. By this time, the nuclear membrane and nucleoli have disappeared, and each pair of homologs takes up

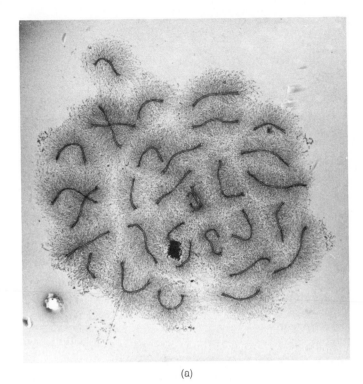

(a)

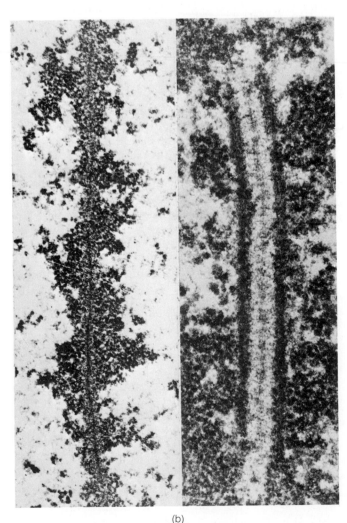

(b)

a position in the equatorial plane (Figure 3-3f). At this stage of meiosis, the centromeres do not divide; such lack of division represents a major difference from mitosis. The two centromeres of a homologous chromosome pair attach to spindle fibers from opposite poles.

Anaphase I.   As in mitosis, anaphase begins when chromosomes move directionally to the poles. The members of one homologous pair move to opposite poles (Figures 3-3g and 3-3h).

Telophase I.   This telophase (Figure 3-3i) and the ensuing "interphase," called **interkinesis** (Figure 3-3j), are variable aspects of meiosis I. In many organisms, these stages do not exist, no nuclear membrane re-forms, and the cells proceed directly to meiosis II. In others, telophase I and the interkinesis are brief in duration; the chromosomes elongate and become diffuse, and the nuclear membrane re-forms. In any case, there is never DNA synthesis at this time, and the genetic state of the chromosomes does not change. The two nuclei that result from meiosis I are effectively haploid. (Here haploidy is best demonstrated by counting centromeres, not chromosomes or chromatids.) The first division is consequently called **reduction division** since it reduces the number by one-half. The second division (at meiosis II) is effectively a mitotic division and resembles mitosis in a haploid cell. It is called **equational division** for this reason.

Prophase II.   This stage is characterized by contracted chromosomes showing the haploid number (Figure 3-3k).

Metaphase II.   The chromosomes arrange themselves on the equatorial plane at this stage (Figure 3-3l). A difference from mitosis is that the chromatids often partly dissociate from each other instead of being closely appressed as in mitosis.

Anaphase II.   Centromeres split and chromatids are pulled to opposite poles by the spindle fibers (Figure 3-3m).

Telophase II.   The nuclei re-form around the chromosomes at the poles (Figure 3-3n).

Figure 3-4. Synaptonemal complexes. (a) In *Hyalophora cecropia*, a silk moth, the normal male chromosome number is 62, giving 31 synaptonemal complexes. In the individual shown here, one chromosome (*center*) is represented three times; such a chromosome is termed trivalent. The DNA is arranged in regular loops around the synaptonemal complex. The black, dense structure is the nucleolus. (b) Regular synaptonemal complex in *Lilium tyrinum*. Note the two lateral elements of the synaptonemal complex and also (*left*) an unpaired chromosome, showing a central core corresponding to one of the lateral elements. (Parts a and b courtesy of Peter Moens.)

The four products of meiosis are shown in Figure 3-3o. Since this series of photographs concerns meiosis in the anthers of a flower, each of the four products of meiosis develops into pollen grains; these are shown in Figure 3-3p. In other organisms, differentiation produces other kinds of structures from the products of meiosis.

In summary, meiosis can be seen to involve one doubling of genetic material (the premeiotic S phase) and two cell divisions. Inevitably this must result in products of meiosis containing half the genetic material of the original meiocyte.

Message Meiosis always occurs in a diploid meiocyte and generally results in four haploid products of meiosis.

A summary of the net events of mitosis and meiosis is shown in Figure 3-5.

The Chromosome Theory of Heredity

The formal statement of the chromosome theory of heredity is usually credited to both Walter Sutton (an American graduate student) and Theodor Boveri (a great German biologist). In 1902, these investigators recognized independently that the behavior of Mendel's genes, during the production of gametes in peas, precisely paralleled the behavior of chromosomes at meiosis: genes are in pairs (so are chromosomes); the members of a gene pair segregate equally into gametes (so do the members of a pair of homologous chromosomes); different gene pairs act independently (so do different chromosome pairs). The similarity is summarized in Figure 3-6.

Message The parallel behavior of genes and chromosomes led to the suggestion that genes are located on chromosomes.

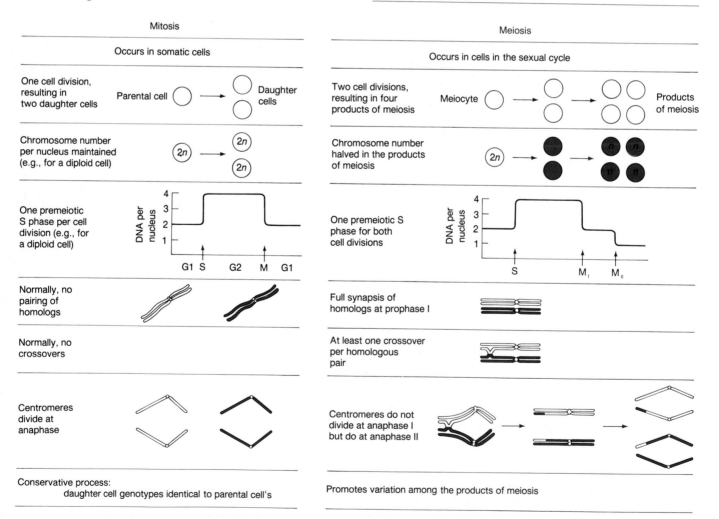

Figure 3-5. Comparison of the main features of mitosis and meiosis.

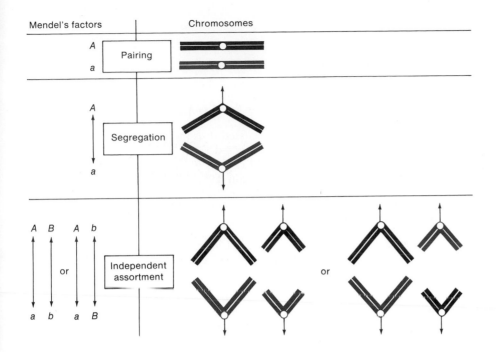

Figure 3-6. Parallels in the behavior of Mendel's hypothetical particles (genes) and chromosomes at meiosis. Black is used to represent one member of a homologous pair and color to represent another.

We saw in Chapter 1 that a major goal of genetics is to explain two apparently conflicting forces of biology: heredity and variation. The two processes of mitosis and meiosis provide a major clue: mitosis is a conservative process, maintaining a genetic status quo, whereas meiosis is a process that generates enormous variation, rather like shuffling the gene pack, through independent assortment and (as we shall see later) through crossing-over.

To modern biology students, the chromosome theory may not seem very earthshaking. However, early in the twentieth century, this hypothesis (which potentially united cytology and the infant field of genetics) was a bombshell. Of course, the first response to such an important hypothesis is to try to pick holes in it. For years after, there was a raging controversy over the validity of what became known as the Sutton-Boveri chromosome theory of heredity.

It is worth considering some of the objections raised to the Sutton-Boveri theory. For example, at the time, chromosomes could not be detected during interphase (between cell divisions). Boveri had to make some very diligent studies of chromosome position before and after interphase in order to argue persuasively that chromosomes retain their physical integrity through interphase, even though they are cytologically invisible at that time. It was also pointed out that in some organisms the chromosomes look alike, so that they might be pairing randomly, whereas Mendel's laws absolutely require segregation of alleles. However, in species where chromosomes do differ in size and shape, it was verified that similar chromosomes do occur in pairs and that the homologs pair and segregate during meiosis.

In 1913, Elinor Carothers found an unusual chromosomal situation in a certain species of grasshopper, a situation that permitted a direct test of whether different chromosome pairs do indeed segregate independently. Studying grasshopper testes, she found one chromosome

pair (that regularly synapses) whose members are nonidentical; this is called a **heteromorphic pair,** and the chromosomes presumably show only partial homology. Furthermore, another chromosome, unrelated to the heteromorphic pair, has no pairing partner at all. Carothers was able to use these unusual chromosomes as visible cytological markers of the behavior of chromosomes during assortment. By looking at anaphase nuclei, she could count the number of times that each dissimilar chromosome of the heteromorphic pair migrated to the same pole as the chromosome with no pairing partner (Figure 3-7). She found that the two patterns of chromosome behavior occur with equal frequency. Although these unusual chromosomes obviously are not typical, the results do suggest that nonhomologous chromosomes assort independently.

Other investigators argued that all chromosomes appear as stringy structures, so that qualitative differences between them cannot be detected. Perhaps all chromo-

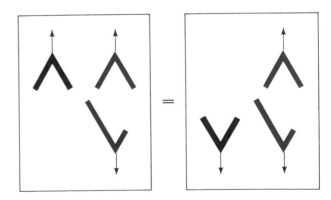

Figure 3-7. The two segregation patterns involving a heteromorphic pair and an unpaired chromosome.

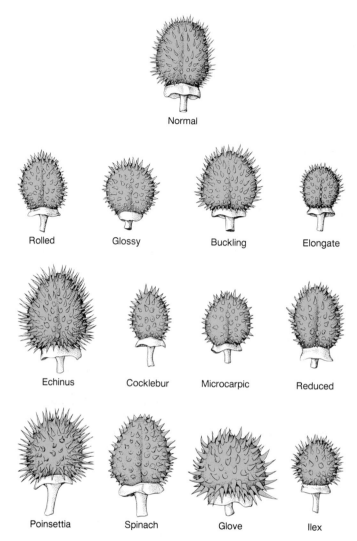

Normal

Rolled   Glossy   Buckling   Elongate

Echinus   Cocklebur   Microcarpic   Reduced

Poinsettia   Spinach   Glove   Ilex

Figure 3-8. Fruits from *Datura* plants, each having one different extra chromosome. Their characteristic appearances show that each chromosome produces a unique effect. (From E. W. Sinnott, L. C. Dunn, and T. Dobzhansky, *Principles of Genetics*, 5th ed., McGraw-Hill Book Co.)

somes are just more or less of the same stuff. It is worth introducing a study out of historical sequence that effectively countered this objection. In 1922 Alfred Blakeslee performed a study on the chromosomes of jimsonweed (*Datura*), which has 12 chromosome pairs. He obtained 12 different strains, each of which had the normal 12 chromosome pairs plus an extra representative of one pair. Blakeslee showed that each strain was phenotypically distinct from the others (Figure 3-8). This result would not be expected if the nonhomologous chromosomes were all alike.

All these results indicated that the behavior of chromosomes closely parallels that of genes. This of course made the Sutton-Boveri theory attractive, but there was as yet no real proof that genes are located on chromosomes. Further observations, however, did provide such proof.

The Discovery of Sex Linkage

In the crosses discussed thus far, it does not matter which sex of parent is selected from which strain under study. That is, reciprocal crosses (such as strain A ♀ × strain B ♂ and strain A ♂ × strain B ♀) yield similar progeny. The first exception to this pattern was discovered in 1906 by L. Doncaster and G. H. Raynor. They were studying wing color in the magpie moth (*Abraxas*), using two different lines — one with light wings, the other with dark. If light-winged females are crossed with dark-winged males, all the progeny have dark wings, thus showing that the allele for light wings is recessive. However, in the reciprocal cross (dark female × light male), all the female progeny have light wings, and all the male progeny have dark wings. Thus, this pair of reciprocal crosses does not give similar results, and in the second cross the wing phenotypes are associated with the sex of the moths. Note that the female progeny of this second cross are phenotypically similar to their fathers, and the males to their mothers. This is sometimes called **crisscross inheritance.** How can we explain these results? Before attempting an explanation, let's consider another example.

William Bateson had been studying the inheritance of feather pattern in chickens. One line had feathers with alternating stripes of dark and light coloring, a phenotype called barred. Another line, nonbarred, had feathers of uniform coloring. In the cross barred male × nonbarred female, all the progeny were barred, thus showing that nonbarred is recessive. However, the reciprocal cross (barred female × nonbarred male) gave barred males and nonbarred females. Again, the result is crisscross inheritance. Can we find an explanation for these similar results with moths and with chickens?

An explanation came from the laboratory of Thomas Hunt Morgan, who in 1909 began studying inheritance in a fruit fly (*Drosophila melanogaster*). Because this organism has played a key role in the study of inheritance, a brief digression about the creature is worthwhile. The life cycle of *Drosophila* is typical of the life cycles of many insects (Figure 3-9).

The flies grow vigorously in the laboratory. In the egg, the early embryonic events lead to the production of a larval stage called the first "instar." Growing rapidly, the larva molts twice, and the third-instar larva then pupates. In the pupa, the larval carcass is replaced by adult structures, and an "imago" (or adult) emerges from the pupal case, ready to mate within 12 to 14 hours. The adult fly is about 2 mm in length, so it takes up very little space. The life cycle is very short (12 days at room temperature) in comparison with that of a human, a mouse, or a corn plant; thus, many generations can be reared in a year. Moreover, the flies are extremely prolific: a single female is capable of laying several hundred eggs. Perhaps the beauty of the animal when observed through a microscope added to its early allure. In

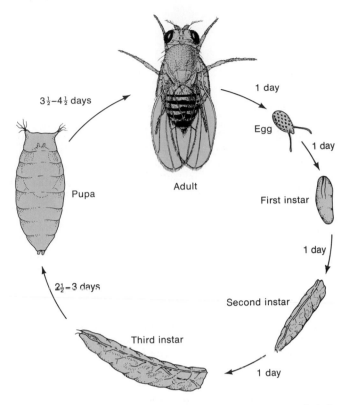

Figure 3-9. Life cycle of *Drosophila melanogaster,* the common fruit fly.

any case, as we shall see, the choice of *Drosophila* was a very fortunate one for geneticists — and especially for Morgan, whose work earned him a Nobel prize in 1934.

The normal eye color of *Drosophila* is bright red. Early in his studies, Morgan discovered a male with completely white eyes. When he crossed this male with red-eyed females, all the F₁ progeny had red eyes, showing that the allele for white is recessive. Crossing the red-eyed F₁ males and females, Morgan obtained a 3:1 ratio of red-eyed to white-eyed flies, but all the white-eyed flies were males. Among the red-eyed flies, the ratio of females to males was 2:1. What was going on?

Morgan gathered further data. When he crossed white-eyed males with red-eyed female progeny of the cross of white males and red females, he obtained red males, red females, white males, and white females in equal numbers. Finally, in a cross of white females and red males (which is the reciprocal of the cross of the original white male with a normal female), all the females were red and all the males were white. This is crisscross inheritance again. However, note that crisscross inheritance was observed in the experiments on chickens and moths when the parental males carried the recessive genes; in the *Drosophila* cross, it is seen when the female parent carries the recessive genes.

Before turning to Morgan's explanation of the *Drosophila* results, we should look at some of the cytological information he was able to use in his interpretations. In 1891, working with males of a species of Hemiptera (the true bugs), H. Henking observed that meiotic nuclei contained 11 pairs of chromosomes and an unpaired element that

moved to one of the poles during the first meiotic division. Henking called this unpaired element an "X body"; he interpreted it as a nucleolus, but later studies showed it to be a chromosome. Similar unpaired elements were later found in other species. In 1905, Edmond Wilson noted that females of *Protenor* (another Hemipteran bug) have seven pairs of chromosomes, whereas males have six pairs and an unpaired chromosome, which Wilson called (by analogy) the X chromosome. The females, in fact, have a pair of X chromosomes.

Also in 1905, Nettie Stevens found that males and females of the beetle *Tenebrio* have the same number of chromosomes, but one of the pairs in males is heteromorphic (of different size). One member of the heteromorphic pair appears identical to the members of a pair in the female; she called this the X chromosome. The other member of the heteromorphic pair is never found in females; she called this the Y chromosome (Figure 3-10). Stevens found a similar situation in *Drosophila melanogaster,* which has four pairs of chromosomes, with one of the pairs being heteromorphic in males. Figure 3-11 summarizes these two basic situations. (You may be wondering about the male grasshoppers studied by Carothers, which had both a heteromorphic pair and an unpaired chromosome. This situation is very unusual, and we needn't worry about it at this point.)

With this background information, Morgan constructed an interpretation of his genetic data. First, it appears that the X and Y chromosomes determine the sex of the fly. *Drosophila* females have four chromosome pairs, whereas males have three normal pairs plus a heteromorphic pair. Thus, meiosis in the female produces eggs that each bear one X chromosome. Although the X and Y chromosomes in males are heteromorphic, they seem to synapse and segregate like homologs (Figure 3-12). Thus, meiosis in the male produces two types of sperm, one type bearing an X chromosome and the other bearing a Y chromosome. According to this explanation, union of an egg with an X-bearing sperm produces an XX (female) zygote, and

Figure 3-10. Segregation of the heteromorphic pair (X and Y) during meiosis in a *Tenebrio* male. The X and Y chromosomes are being pulled to opposite poles during anaphase I. (From A. M. Srb, R. D. Owen, and R. S. Edgar, *General Genetics,* 2d ed. Copyright © 1965, W. H. Freeman and Company.)

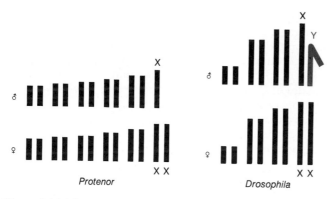

Figure 3-11. Diagrammatic representation of the chromosomal constitutions of males and females in two different insect species.

union with a Y-bearing sperm produces an XY (male) zygote. Furthermore, approximately equal numbers of males and females are expected because of the equal segregation of X and Y.

Morgan next turned to the problem of eye color. Assume that the alleles for red or white eye color are present on the X chromosome, with no counterpart on the Y. Thus, females would have two copies of this gene, whereas males would have only one. This highly unexpected situation proves to fit the data. In the original cross of the white-eyed male with red-eyed females, all F_1 progeny had red eyes, showing that the gene for red eyes is dominant. Therefore, we can represent the two alleles as W (red) and w (white). If we designate the X chromosomes as X^W and X^w to indicate the alleles supposedly carried by them, we can diagram the two reciprocal crosses as shown in Figure 3-13.

As we can see from the figure, the genetic results of the two reciprocal crosses are completely consistent with the known meiotic behavior of the X and Y chromosomes. This experiment strongly supports the notion of chromosomal location of genes; however, it is only a correlation, and it does not constitute a definitive proof of the Sutton-Boveri theory.

Can the same XX and XY chromosome theory be applied to the results of the earlier crosses made with chickens and moths? You will find that it cannot. However, Richard Goldschmidt recognized immediately that these results can be explained with a similar hypothesis, simply assuming that the *males* have pairs of identical chromosomes, whereas the *females* have a heteromorphic pair. To distinguish this situation from the X-Y situation in *Drosophila*, Morgan suggested that the heteromorphic chromosomes in chickens and moths be called W-Z, with males being ZZ and females WZ. Thus, if the genes in the chicken and moth crosses are on the Z chromosome, the crosses can be diagrammed as shown in Figure 3-14.

Again, the interpretation is consistent with the genetic data. In this case, cytological data provided a confirmation of the genetic hypothesis. In 1914, J. Seiler verified that both chromosomes are identical in all pairs in male moths, whereas females have one heteromorphic pair.

Message　The special inheritance pattern of some genes makes it extremely likely that they are borne on the chromosomes associated with sex, which show a parallel pattern of inheritance.

An Aside on Genetic Symbols

In *Drosophila*, a special symbolism for allele designation was introduced defining variant alleles in relation to a "normal" allele. This system is now used by many geneticists, and is especially useful in genetic dissection. For a given *Drosophila* character, the allele that is found most frequently in natural populations (or, alternatively, that found in standard laboratory stocks) is designated as the standard, or **wild-type.** All other alleles are then non-wild-type. The

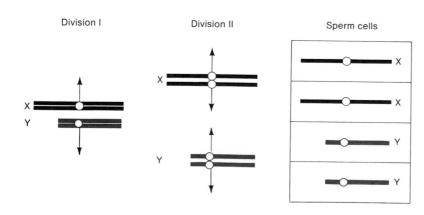

Figure 3-12. Meiotic pairing and the segregation of the X and Y chromosomes into equal numbers of sperms.

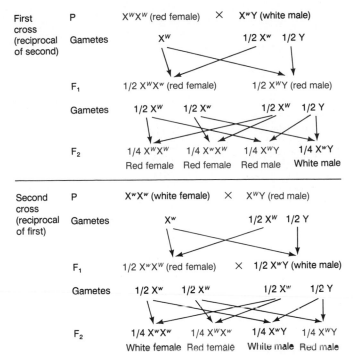

First cross (reciprocal of second)

P	X^wX^w (red female)	$\times$ X^wY (white male)
Gametes	X^w	$1/2\ X^w$ $1/2\ Y$
F₁	$1/2\ X^wX^w$ (red female)	$1/2\ X^wY$ (red male)
Gametes	$1/2\ X^w$ $1/2\ X^w$	$1/2\ X^w$ $1/2\ Y$
F₂	$1/4\ X^wX^w$ $1/4\ X^wX^w$	$1/4\ X^wY$ $1/4\ X^wY$
	Red female Red female	Red male White male

Second cross (reciprocal of first)

P	X^wX^w (white female)	$\times$ X^wY (red male)
Gametes	X^w	$1/2\ X^w$ $1/2\ Y$
F₁	$1/2\ X^wX^w$ (red female)	$\times$ $1/2\ X^wY$ (white male)
Gametes	$1/2\ X^w$ $1/2\ X^w$	$1/2\ X^w$ $1/2\ Y$
F₂	$1/4\ X^wX^w$ $1/4\ X^wX^w$	$1/4\ X^wY$ $1/4\ X^wY$
	White female Red female	White male Red male

Figure 3-13. Explanation of the different results obtained from reciprocal crosses between red-eyed and white-eyed *Drosophila*.

symbolic designation of a gene is provided by the first non-wild allele found. In Morgan's *Drosophila* experiment, this was white eyes, so the non-wild allele is symbolized by w. The wild-type counterpart allele is conventionally represented by a + superscript, so the normal red-eye allele is written w^+.

In the case of polymorphism, several alleles are common in nature, and all could be designated wild-type. Here, appropriate superscripts are used to distinguish alleles. For example, two natural alleles of the alcohol dehydrogenase gene in *Drosophila* are designated Adh^F and Adh^S. (This gene controls the alcohol metabolizing the enzyme alcohol dehydrogenase, and F and S stand for fast and slow movements, respectively, of the enzyme in an electrophoretic gel.)

The wild-type allele is not always dominant over a non-wild-type allele. For the two alleles w and w^+, the use of the lower-case letter indicates that the wild-type is dominant over white (that is, w is recessive to w^+). In another case, the wild-type condition of a fly's wing is straight and flat. A non-wild-type allele causes the wing to be curled. Because this allele is dominant over the wild-type allele, this gene is called Curly, and the non-wild-type allele is written Cy, while the wild-type allele is written Cy^+. Here, note that the capital letter indicates that Cy is dominant over Cy^+. (Also note that multiple letter symbols represent a single gene, not several genes.)

This kind of symbolism is useful because it helps geneticists to focus on the procedure of genetic dissection. The wild-type allele is defined as the normal functioning situation, and non-wild-type alleles (whether recessive or dominant) can be regarded as abnormal. The abnormal alleles then become probes to investigate how the normal situations work, through an examination of the ways in which the normal mechanism can go wrong. Most geneticists interested in using genetics to explore biological processes use this kind of symbolism. You will note that Mendel's convention (*A* and *a*, or *B* and *b*) does not define or emphasize normality. In a pea flower, for example, is purple or white normal? However, the Mendelian symbolism is useful for some purposes; it is used extensively in plant and animal breeding. Table 3-1 summarizes the two systems of symbolism.

Proof of the Chromosome Theory

The correlations between the behavior of genes and the behavior of chromosomes made it very likely that genes were on chromosomes. But this was not a proof of the chromosome theory, and debate continued. The critical proof of the Sutton-Boveri theory came from one of Morgan's students, Calvin Bridges. Since Bridges' experiments involve complex chromosome behavior not fully addressed in

Chickens

First cross (reciprocal of second)	P	Z^BZ^B barred males	$\times$	Z^bW nonbarred females
	F₁	Z^BZ^b barred males		Z^BW barred females
Second cross (reciprocal of first)	P	Z^bZ^b nonbarred males	$\times$	Z^BW barred females
	F₁	Z^BZ^b barred males		Z^bW nonbarred females

Moths

First cross (reciprocal of second)	P	Z^LZ^L dark males	$\times$	Z^lW light females
	F₁	Z^LZ^l dark males		Z^LW dark females
Second cross (reciprocal of first)	P	Z^lZ^l light males	$\times$	Z^LW dark females
	F₁	Z^lZ^L dark males		Z^lW light females

Figure 3-14. Inheritance pattern of genes on the sex chromosomes of two species having the ZW mechanism of sex determination.

■ **TABLE 3-1.** Summary of two systems for assigning symbols to genes

	Recessive variant allele, a		Dominant variant allele, A	
Symbolic system	Symbol for wild-type allele	Symbol for variant allele	Symbol for wild-type allele	Symbol for variant allele
Normal/abnormal	a^+ (or $+^a$ or $+$)	a (or a^-)	A^+ (or $+^A$ or $+$)	A (or A^-)
Mendelian	A	a	a	A

this text until Chapter 8, this section may be omitted for now and returned to later.

We turn now to Bridges' work. Consider a fruit fly cross we have discussed before (now represented in our new symbolism), X^wX^w (white ♀) + $X^{w+}Y$ (red ♂). We know that the progeny are $X^{w+}X^w$ (red ♀♀) and X^wY (white ♂♂). However, Bridges discovered that rare exceptions occur when the cross is made on a large scale. About 1 of every 2000 F_1 progeny is a white-eyed female or a red-eyed male. Because these exceptional progeny resemble their parents of the same sex, the phenotype of females is said to be **matroclinous,** and that of the males is called **patroclinous;** collectively, they are called **primary exceptional progeny.** All the patroclinous males proved to be sterile. However, when Bridges crossed the primary exceptional white-eyed females with normal red-eyed males, 4 percent of the progeny were matroclinous white-eyed females and patroclinous red-eyed males that were fertile. Thus, exceptional offspring were again recovered, but at a higher frequency, and the males were fertile. These exceptional progeny of primary exceptional mothers are called **secondary excep-** **tional offspring** (Figure 3-15). How do we explain the exceptional progeny?

It is obvious that the matroclinous females — which, like all females, have two X chromosomes — must get both of them from their mothers because they are homozygous for w. Similarly, patroclinous males must derive their X chromosomes from their fathers because they carry w^+. Bridges hypothesized that rare mishaps occur during meiosis in the female, whereby the paired X chromosomes fail to separate during either the first or second division. This would result in meiotic nuclei containing either two X chromosomes or no X at all. Such a failure to separate is called nondisjunction; it produces an XX nucleus and a nullo-X nucleus (containing no X). Fertilization of these two types of nuclei will produce four zygotic classes (Figure 3-16). It is important to note that, in these diagrams, the line representing a chromosome is in each case not a single chromosome but a pair of daughter chromatids.

If we assume that the XXX and YO classes die, then the two types of exceptional progeny can be expected to be X^wX^wY (♀) and $X^{w+}O$ (♂) if their chromosomes are examined. Notice that it is implicit in Bridges' model that the sex of *Drosophila* is determined not by the presence or absence of the Y but by the number of X chromosomes. Two X chromosomes produce a female, and one X produces a male, in most situations.

What about the sterility of the primary exceptional males? This is explicable if we assume that the Y chromosome must be present in order to have male fertility.

How can we explain the secondary exceptional offspring? During meiosis in the XXY females, if the two X chromosomes pair and disjoin most of the time, leaving the Y chromosome unpaired, then we should expect equal numbers of X-bearing and XY-bearing eggs. However, we know that the X and Y chromosomes can pair and segregate, because normal males produce equal numbers of X-bearing and Y-bearing sperms. To explain the observed results, we must assume that the Y successfully pairs with an X^w in approximately 16 percent of the pairings in X^wX^wY females, leaving the other X^w free to separate to either pole. One-half (8 percent) of these pairings will result in X^w and X^wY eggs, and the other one-half (8 percent) will result in X^wX^w and Y eggs (Figure 3-17).

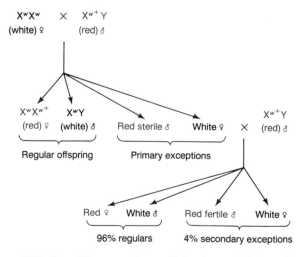

Figure 3-15. *Drosophila* crosses from which primary and secondary exceptional progeny were originally obtained.

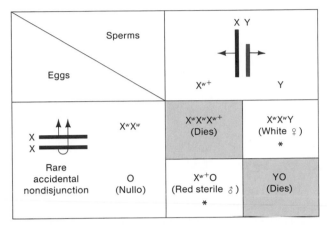

Figure 3-16. Proposed explanation of primary exceptional progeny through nondisjunction of the X chromosomes in the maternal parent.

We can now look at the results of fertilization by equal numbers of X^{w+} and Y sperms (Figure 3-18). We find that one-half of the fertilized X^wX^w and Y eggs will produce $X^wX^wX^{w+}$ and YY zygotes, which we presume die. The other one-half of these fertilized eggs produce the secondary exceptions, X^wX^wY and $X^{w+}Y$. Now we see why the secondary exceptional males are fertile: each of them receives a Y chromosome from the XXY mother.

So far, this is all a model—an intellectual edifice. We have made assumptions about the chromosome location of w and w^+, and we have hypothesized nondisjunction to explain the exceptional progeny. However, if this model is correct, we can now make testable predictions.

1. Cytological study of the primary exceptional progeny (which we have identified through the genetic study) should show that the females are XXY and the males are XO. Bridges confirmed this prediction.

2. Cytological study of the secondary exceptional progeny (which we have identified genetically) should show that the females are XXY and the males are XY. Bridges confirmed this prediction.

3. One-half of the red-eyed daughters of exceptional white-eyed females should be XXY and one-half should be XX. Bridges confirmed this prediction.

4. One-half of the white-eyed sons of exceptional white-eyed females should themselves give exceptional progeny, and all of those that do should be XYY. Bridges confirmed this prediction.

Thus Bridges verified all the testable predictions arising from the assumptions that w and w^+ are indeed on the X chromosome and that an unexplained process of nondisjunction occurs in infrequent cases of meiosis. These confirmations provide unequivocal evidence that genes are associated with chromosomes.

Message   When Bridges used the chromosome theory to predict successfully the outcome of certain genetic analyses, the chromosome location of genes was established beyond reasonable doubt.

Sex Chromosomes in Other Species

Humans and all mammals also show an X-Y sex-determining mechanism, with males XY and females XX. Unlike *Drosophila*, however, it is the presence of the Y that determines maleness in humans. This difference is demonstrated by the sexual phenotypes of the abnormal chromosome types XXY and XO (Table 3-2). However, we postpone a full discussion until a later chapter.

Higher plants show a variety of sexual situations. Some species have both male and female sex organs on the same plant, often combined into the same flower—called **hermaphroditic** species (the rose is an example)—or in sepa-

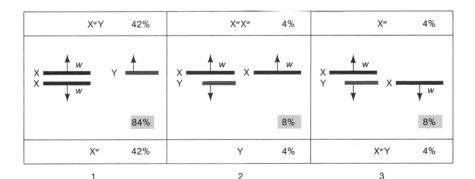

Figure 3-17. Three different segregation patterns in an XXY female fruit fly.

		Sperms	
		X^{w+} (50%)	Y (50%)
Eggs — X–Y pairing (16%)	X^w X^w (4%)	X^w X^w X^{w+} (dies) (2%)	X^w X^w Y (white ♀) (2%)
	Y (4%)	X^{w+} Y (red fertile ♂) (2%)	YY (dies) (2%)
	X^w (4%)	X^{w+} X^w (red ♀) (2%)	X^w Y (white ♂) (2%)
	X^w Y (4%)	X^w X^{w+} Y (red ♀) (2%)	X^w YY (white ♂) (2%)
X–X pairing (84%)	X^w Y (42%)	X^w X^{w+} Y (red ♀) (21%)	X^w YY (white ♂) (21%)
	X^w (42%)	X^w X^{w+} (red ♀) (21%)	X^w Y (white ♂) (21%)

Secondary exceptional progeny phenotype (4%) (4% die) — applies to the top two rows.

"Regular" (expected) progeny phenotypes (92%) — applies to the remaining rows.

Figure 3-18. The proposed origin of secondary exceptional progeny as a result of specific gamete types produced by the XXY parent.

■ **TABLE 3-2.** Chromosomal determination of sex in *Drosophila* and humans

	Sex chromosomes			
Species	XX	XY	XXY	XO
Drosophila	♀	♂	♀	♂
Humans	♀	♂	♂	♀

rate flowers on the same plant — called **monoecious** species (corn is an example). These would be the equivalent of hermaphroditic animals. **Dioecious** species, however, show plants of separate sexes, with male plants bearing flowers containing only anthers, and female plants bearing flowers containing only ovaries (Figure 3-19). Some, but not all, dioecious plants have a heteromorphic pair of chromosomes associated with (and almost certainly determining) the sex of the plant. Of the species with heteromorphic sex chromosomes, a large proportion have an X-Y system. Critical experiments in a few species suggest a *Drosophila*-like system. Table 3-3 lists some examples of dioecious plants with heteromorphic sex-determining chromosomes. Some dioecious plants have no visibly heteromorphic pair of chromosomes; they may still have sex chromosomes, but not visibly distinguishable types. Other dioecious plants have heteromorphic chromosomes that determine sex, but the constitution of the different sexes is much more complex than the simple X-Y system of the *Drosophila* type. We shall not consider these systems.

The sex chromosomes can be tentatively divided into pairing and differential regions (Figure 3-20). These regions are based on studies of meiosis in males. The pairing regions of the X and Y chromosomes are thought to be homologous. The differential region of each chromosome appears to hold genes that have no counterparts on the other kind of sex chromosome. These genes, whether dominant or recessive, show their effects in the male phenotype. Genes in the differential regions are called **hemizygous** ("half-zygous") in the males. Genes in the differential region of the X show an inheritance pattern called **X linkage;** those in the differential region of the Y show **Y linkage.** Genes in the pairing region show what might be called **X-and-Y linkage.** In general, genes on the sex chromosomes show **sex linkage.**

We can introduce some other common terminology here. The sex showing only one kind of sex chromosome (XX ♀ or ZZ ♂) is called the **homogametic** sex; the other (XY ♂ or ZW ♀) is called the **heterogametic** sex. Thus, human and *Drosophila* females (and male birds and moths) are homogametic; that is, they produce only one type of gamete with respect to sex-chromosome constitution. The nonsex chromosomes (what we might call the "regular" chromosomes) are called **autosomes.** Humans have 46 chromosomes per cell: 44 autosomes plus two sex chromosomes. The plant *Melandrium album* has 22 chromosomes per cell: 20 autosomes plus two sex chromosomes.

■ **TABLE 3-3.** Sex-chromosome situations in some dioecious plant species

Species	Chromosome number	Sex-chromosome constitution	
		Female	Male
Cannabis sativa (hemp)	20	XX	XY
Humulus lupulus (hop)	20	XX	XY
Rumex angiocarpus (dock)	14	XX	XY
Melandrium album (campion)	22	XX	XY

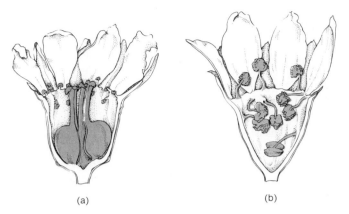

Figure 3-19. Flower forms in *Osmaronia dioica*, a dioecious species. (a) Female flowers. (b) Male flowers.

Genes on the autosomes show the typical kind of inheritance pattern — the type discovered and studied by Mendel. The genes on the different regions of the sex chromosomes show their own typical patterns of inheritance, as follows.

X-Linked Inheritance

We have already seen an example of X-linked inheritance in *Drosophila*: the inheritance pattern of white eye and its wild-type allele. Of course, eye color is not concerned with sex determination, so we see that not all genes on the sex chromosomes are involved with sexual function. The same is true in humans, where many X-linked genes have been discovered through pedigree analysis, of which hardly any could be construed to have any connection to sexual function. Just as we earlier listed rules for detecting autosomal inheritance patterns in humans, we can list clues for detecting X-linked genes in human pedigrees. (We shall soon see that Y-linked genes are very rare in humans, so we can usually ignore them.)

Recessive genes showing X-linked inheritance can be detected in human pedigrees through the following clues.

1. Typically, many more males than females show the recessive phenotype. This is because an affected female can result only when both mother and father bear the gene (for example, $X^A X^a \times X^a Y$), whereas an affected male can result when only the mother carries the gene. If the recessive gene is very rare, almost all observed cases will occur in males.

2. Usually none of the offspring of an affected male will be affected, but all his daughters will carry the gene in masked heterozygous condition, so one-half of their sons will be affected (Figure 3-21).

3. None of the sons of an affected male will inherit the gene, so not only will they be free of the phenotype, but they will not pass the gene along to their offspring.

Some good examples of X-linked recessive genes in humans are those for hemophilia, red-green color blindness, and Duchenne's muscular dystrophy.

Dominant genes showing X-linked inheritance can be detected in human pedigrees through the following clues.

1. The most important clue here is that affected males pass the condition on to all of their daughters but to none of their sons (Figure 3-22).

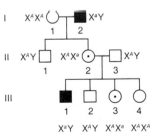

Figure 3-21. Illustrative pedigree showing how X-linked recessives are expressed in males, then carried unexpressed by females in the next generation, to be expressed in their sons. (Note that III.3 and III.4 cannot be distinguished phenotypically.)

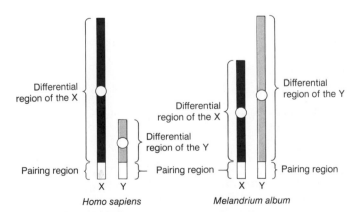

Figure 3-20. Differential and pairing regions of sex chromosomes of humans and of the plant *Melandrium album*. The pairing regions have been located chiefly through cytological examination.

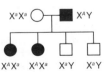

Figure 3-22. Illustrative pedigree showing how X-linked dominants are expressed in all the daughters of affected males.

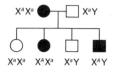

X^A X^a ●—□ X^a Y

○   ●   □   ■
X^a X^a   X^A X^a   X^a Y   X^A Y

Figure 3-23. Illustrative pedigree showing how females affected by an X-linked dominant condition usually are heterozygous and pass the condition to one-half of their progeny.

2. Females, on the other hand, usually pass the condition on to one-half of their sons and daughters (Figure 3-23).

X-linked dominant conditions are relatively rare. One example is hypophosphatemia (vitamin D–resistant rickets).

Y-Linked Inheritance

In humans, genes on the differential region of the Y would be inherited only by males, with transmission from father to son. No examples of such inheritance have been confirmed, although hairy ear rims has been suggested as a likely possibility (Figure 3-24). However, in humans (and in other species with similar sex-determination systems), the presence of the Y and its unique regions determines maleness. Therefore, it seems safe to speculate that "maleness" genes of some kind must exist on the differential region of the Y.

In the fish *Lebistes,* the Y chromosome carries a gene called *maculatus* that determines a pigmented spot at the base of the dorsal fin. This phenotype is passed only from father to son, and females never carry or express the gene, so it seems to be a clear example of Y linkage.

X-and-Y-Linked Inheritance

Are there ways of identifying genes on homologous regions of the sex chromosomes? The existence of homologous regions is itself somewhat in doubt, being in part inferred from pairing association. However, there is a gene pair in *Drosophila* that is inherited in such a way that an X-and-Y location is likely. Curt Stern found that a certain non-wild recessive allele in *Drosophila* causes a phenotype of shorter and more slender bristles; he called it bobbed (b). If a bobbed $X^b X^b$ female is crossed with a wild-type $X^+ Y^+$ male, all the F_1 progeny are wild-type: $X^+ X^b$ ♀♀ and $X^b Y^+$ ♂♂. The same result, of course, would be expected from an autosomal gene pair. However, the X-and-Y linkage is revealed in the F_2:

	Phenotype	Inferred genotype
Males:	wild-type	$X^+ Y^+$ and $X^b Y^+$
Females:	1/2 bobbed	$X^b X^b$
	1/2 wild-type	$X^+ X^b$

The Chromosome Theory in Review

The patterns of inheritance centering on the normal and nondisjunctional behavior of the sex chromosomes provide satisfying confirmation of the chromosome theory of inheritance, which was originally suggested by the parallel behavior of Mendelian genes and autosomal chromosomes. Now we should pause and state clearly the situation for the regular (autosomal) genes, because these are the genes most commonly encountered. Such a summary is best achieved in a diagram; Figure 3-25 illustrates the passage of a hypothetical cell through meiosis. Two gene pairs are shown on two chromosome pairs. The hypothetical cell type has four chromosomes: a pair of homologous long chromosomes and a pair of homologous short ones. (Such size differences between pairs are common.) The genotype of the cell is assumed to be *Aa Bb*.

As the diagram shows, two equally frequent kinds of spindle attachment (4a and 4b) result in two basic kinds of segregation patterns of gene pairs. Meiosis then produces four cells of the genotypes shown from each of these segregation patterns. Because the segregation patterns 4a and 4b are equally common, the meiotic product cells of genotypes *AB, ab, Ab,* and *aB* are produced in equal frequencies. In other words, each of the four genotypes occurs with frequency 1/4. This, of course, is the distribution postulated in Mendel's model and is the one we noted along one edge of the standard Punnett square (see Figure 2-9). We can now understand the exact chromosomal mechanism that produces the Mendelian ratios.

Notice that Mendel's first law (equal segregation) is a direct result of the separation of a pair of homologs (bearing the gene pair under study) into opposite cells at the first division. Notice also that Mendel's second law (independent assortment) results from the independent behavior of separate pairs of homologous chromosomes.

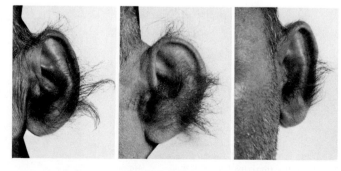

Figure 3-24. Hairy ear rims are thought to be due to a Y-linked gene. (From C. Stern, W. R. Centerwall, and S. S. Sarkar, *The American Journal of Human Genetics* 16(1964):467. By permission of Grune & Stratton, Inc.)

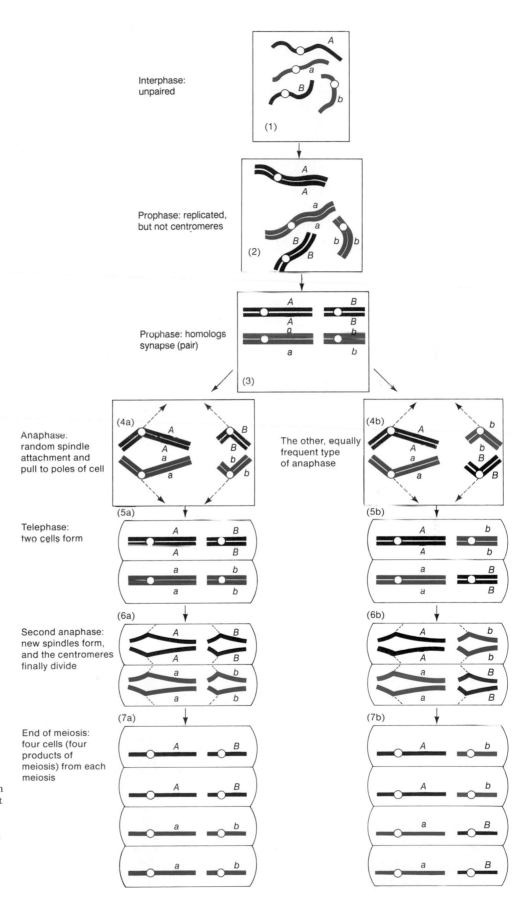

Figure 3-25. The route of two heterozygous gene pairs (on separate chromosome pairs) through meiosis. Steps 1 through 7 represent the various events of meiosis. The a and b series result from the two equally frequent spindle-attachment arrangements in the first meiotic division. In stage 7, note that *A B*, *A b*, *a B*, and *a b* occur with equal frequency.

The chromosome theory was important in many ways. At this point in our discussion, we can stress the importance of the theory in centering attention on the role of the cell genotype in determining the organism phenotype. The phenotype of an organism is determined by the phenotypes of all its individual cells. The cell phenotype, in turn, is determined by the genes (and alleles of those genes) present on the chromosomes of the cell. When we say that an organism is (for example) *AA,* we really mean that each cell of the organism is *AA.* This cell genotype determines how the cell functions, thus controlling the phenotype of the cell and hence the phenotype of the organism.

Message An organism's phenotype is determined by the kinds of genes it has in its cells and by the forms (alleles) of those genes that are present.

Mendelian Genetics and Sexual Cycles

Thus far we have been discussing mainly diploid organisms — organisms with two homologous chromosome sets in each cell. As we have seen, diploid is designated $2n$, where n stands for one chromosome set (for example, the pea cell contains two sets of seven chromosomes, so $2n = 14$). Most of the organisms we encounter in our daily existence are predominantly diploid; these are the so-called higher plants (including flowering plants) and animals (including humans). In fact, evolution seems to have produced a trend toward diploidy (perhaps you can speculate on reasons for this). Nevertheless, a vast proportion (probably the major proportion) of the biomass on the earth is composed of organisms that spend most of their life cycles in a haploid condition, in which each cell has only one set of chromosomes. Important here are the fungi and algae, most of which are predominantly haploid. Bacteria could be considered haploid, but they form a special case because their cells contain no nuclei (they are called prokaryotes),

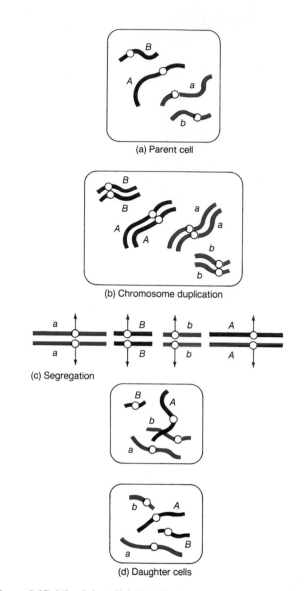

Figure 3-27. Mitosis in a diploid cell of genotype *Aa Bb.*

(a) Parent cell

(b) Chromosome duplication

(c) Segregation

(d) Daughter cells

whereas most other life forms (eukaryotes) do have nuclei. (Bacteria are discussed in Chapter 13.) Also important are organisms that spend part of their life cycles as haploid and another part as diploid. Such organisms are said to show **alternation of generations** (a rather imprecise term; "alternation of $2n$ and n" would be more descriptive). All plants, in fact, show alternation of generations. However, higher forms such as flowering plants have an inconspicuous haploid plant stage that is dependent on the diploid plant, in which it occurs as a specialized structure. Other forms — for example, mosses and ferns — have separate and independent haploid stages.

Do these life cycles show Mendelian genetics? Or is Mendelian inheritance observed only in the higher organisms? The answer is that Mendelian inheritance patterns appear in any organism that has meiosis as part of its cycle, because Mendelian laws are based on the process of meiosis. All the groups of organisms mentioned, except bacteria, utilize meiosis as part of their cycles. We next consider the

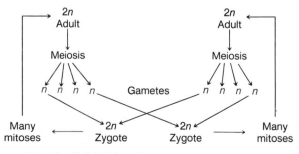

Figure 3-26. The diploid life cycle.

inheritance patterns shown by these less familiar forms, and we compare them to more familiar cycles. This is important because it demonstrates the universality of Mendelian genetics. Furthermore, some of the less familiar organisms have been the subject of extensive genetic research, and a knowledge of their life cycles is essential for their genetic analysis. We describe here three major types of cycle, beginning with the more familiar diploid types.

Diploids

Figure 3-26 summarizes the diploid cycle in skeletal form. This is the cycle shown by most animals (including humans). Meiosis occurs in specialized diploid cells, the meiocytes, which are set aside for the purpose but which are part of the diploid adult organism. The products of meiosis are the gametes (eggs or sperms). Fusion of haploid gametes forms a diploid zygote, which (through mitosis) produces a multicellular organism. Mitosis in a diploid proceeds in the fashion outlined in Figure 3-27.

Haploids

Figure 3-28 shows the basic haploid cycle. Here the "adult" (either multicellular or unicellular) is haploid. How can meiosis possibly occur in a haploid? After all, meiosis involves pairing of two homologous chromosome sets! The answer is that all haploid organisms that undergo meiosis

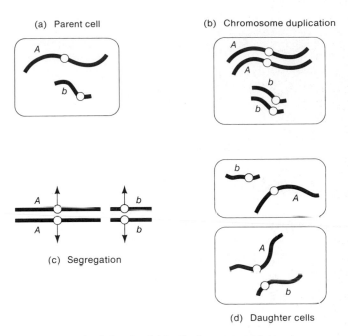

(a) Parent cell (b) Chromosome duplication

(c) Segregation

(d) Daughter cells

Figure 3-29. Mitosis in a haploid cell of genotype $A\,b$.

employ a *transient* diploid stage. In some cases, unicellular haploid adult individuals fuse to form a diploid cell, which then undergoes meiosis. In other cases, specialized (or sometimes representative) haploid cells from different parents fuse to form diploid cells so that meiosis can occur. (These fusing cells are properly called the gametes, so we see that in these cases gametes arise from mitosis.) Meiosis as usual produces haploid products of meiosis, which are called **sexual spores.** The sexual spores in some species become new unicellular adults; in other species, they develop through mitosis into a multicellular haploid individual. In haploids, mitosis proceeds as shown in Figure 3-29, which illustrates a cell arbitrarily designated genotype $A\,b$. Notice that a cross between two adult haploid organisms involves only one meiosis, whereas a cross between two diploid organisms involves a meiosis in each organism. As we shall see, this simplification makes haploids very useful for genetic analysis.

Let's consider a cross in a specific haploid. A convenient organism is the pink bread mold *Neurospora*. This fungus is a multicellular haploid in which the cells are joined end to end to form **hyphae,** or threads of cells. Aerial cells are known as **asexual spores.** These can detach and disperse to form new colonies; alternatively, they can act as male gametes (Figure 3-30). Another specialized cell (which develops inside a knot of hyphae) can be regarded as the female gamete.

What morphological characters can be studied in such an organism? One is the color of the cells. Variants of the

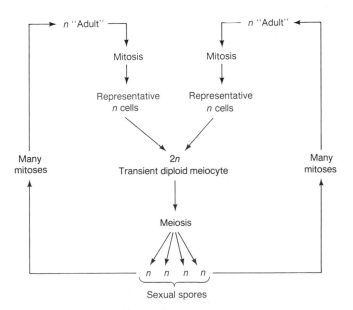

Figure 3-28. The haploid life cycle.

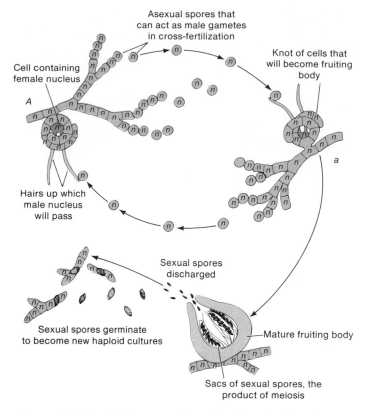

Figure 3-30. Simplified representation of the life cycle of *Neurospora crassa*, the pink bread mold. Self-fertilization is not possible in this species: there are two mating types, determined by the alleles *A* and *a* of one gene. A cross will succeed only if it is *A* × *a*. Male and female nuclei divide mitotically; then fusion occurs to form many diploid nuclei, each of which undergoes meiosis. The sexual spores are the meiotic products.

25 colonial albino cultures

25 fluffy albino cultures

25 colonial pink cultures

In total, one-half of the "progeny" are fluffy and one-half are colonial. Thus these phenotypes are determined by one gene pair that has segregated equally at meiosis. The same is true of the other character: one-half are pink and one-half are albino, so color is determined by a different gene pair. We could represent the four culture types as

$col^+ al^+$ (fluffy pink)

$col\,al$ (colonial albino)

$col^+ al$ (fluffy albino)

$col\,al^+$ (colonial pink)

The 25% : 25% : 25% : 25% ratio is a result of independent assortment, as illustrated in the following branch diagram:

$$1/2\;col^+ \begin{cases} 1/2\;al^+ \longrightarrow col^+\,al^+ \\ 1/2\;al \longrightarrow col^+\,al \end{cases}$$

$$1/2\;col \begin{cases} 1/2\;al \longrightarrow col\,al \\ 1/2\;al^+ \longrightarrow col\,al^+ \end{cases}$$

normal pink color can be found — for example, an albino. Figure 3-31 shows a normal and an albino culture. Another character is the morphological nature of the culture — perhaps fluffy (normal) versus colonial. We can make a cross by allowing the asexual spores to act as male gametes. A culture cannot self in *Neurospora,* because this fungus has two genetically determined mating types, *A* and *a*. Fertile crosses can occur only if strains of different mating types are paired — in this case, *A* × *a*. Crosses are carried out by adding asexual spores of one culture to another. The nucleus of an asexual spore pairs with a female nucleus. This pair undergoes synchronous mitotic division, and, finally, fusions occur to generate transient diploid meiocytes. Then meiosis occurs, and sexual spores, called ascospores, are formed. These ascospores are black and football-shaped; they are shot out of the knot of hyphae, which is now known as a fruiting body. The ascospores can be isolated, each into a culture tube, where each ascospore will grow into a new culture by mitosis (Figure 3-32).

If we cross a fluffy pink culture with a colonial albino culture and isolate and culture 100 ascospores, the resulting cultures (on average) would be

25 fluffy pink cultures

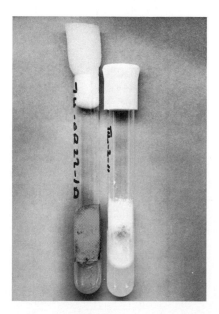

Figure 3-31. A pink wild-type *Neurospora* culture (*left*) and an albino mutant culture (*right*) lacking the reddish carotenid pigment. (Genotypically the cultures are *al⁺* and *al⁻*, respectively.)

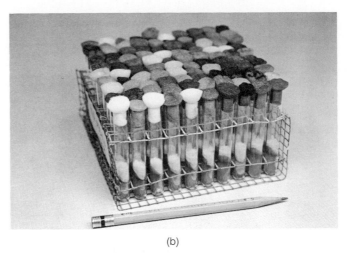

(a)

(b)

Figure 3-32. (a) A *Neurospora* cross made in a petri plate. The many small black spheres are fruiting bodies in which meiosis has occurred, shooting the ascospores (sexual spores) as a fine dust into the condensed moisture on the lid (which has been removed and is sitting on the right side of the plate). (b) A rack of progeny cultures, each resulting from one isolated ascospore.

So we see that, even in such a lowly organism, Mendel's laws are still in operation.

Alternating Haploid/Diploid

In an organism with alternation of generations, there are two stages to the life cycle: one diploid and one haploid. One stage is usually more prominent than the other. For example, what we all recognize as a fern plant is the diploid stage, but the organism does have a small, independent photosynthetic haploid stage that is usually much more difficult to spot on the forest floor. In mosses, the green plant is the haploid stage, and the brownish stalk that grows up out of this plant is a dependent diploid stage that is effectively parasitic on it. In flowering plants, the main green stage is, of course, diploid. The haploid stages of flowering plants are extremely reduced and dependent on the diploid. These haploids are found in the flower. When meiosis occurs in the anther and ovary meiocytes, the haploid products of meiosis are called **spores.** The spores undergo a few mitotic divisions to produce a small multicellular haploid stage, as shown in Figure 3-33. In alternation of generations, the diploid stage is called the **sporophyte,** which means sexual-spore-producing plant, and the haploid stage is called the **gametophyte,** which means gamete-producing plant. The male gametophyte of seed plants is known as a pollen grain. Figure 3-33 shows that in flowering plants, cells of the gametophyte act as egg or sperm in fertilization. In mosses and ferns the sperm cells are highly motile and have to travel from one gametophyte to another in a film of water in order to effect fertilization. The generalized cycle of alternation of generations is shown in Figure 3-34.

Little genetic analysis has been done in plants other than flowering plants, but the potential for study is great, so we shall follow a sample cross in a moss. The character to be studied, of course, can be of the gametophyte or of the sporophyte. Assume that we have a gene pair affecting the

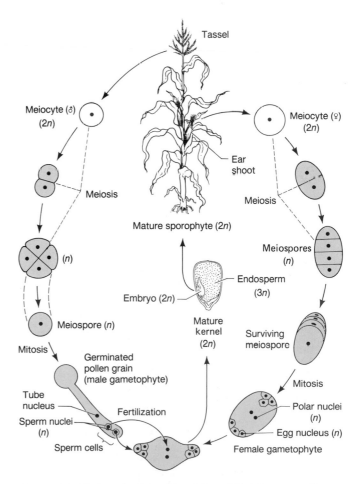

Figure 3-33. The production of the male and female gametophytes of corn.

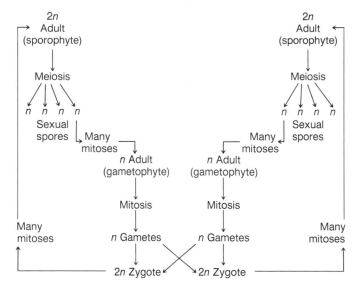

Figure 3-34. The alternation of diploid and haploid stages in the life cycle of plants.

"leaves" of the gametophyte, with w causing wavy edges and w^+ causing smooth edges. Assume a separate gene pair affecting the color of the sporophyte, with r causing reddish coloration and r^+ causing the normal brown coloration. A smooth-leaved gametophyte also bearing an unexpressed allele r is fertilized by transferring onto it male gametes from a wrinkly-leaved gametophyte carrying r^+ (Figure 3-35).

A diploid sporophyte develops, actually on the gametophyte, and it will be brown (because reddish is recessive). The sexual spores produced from this sporophyte will be

$$25\% \; w^+ r^+$$
$$25\% \; w^+ r^-$$
$$25\% \; w^- r^+$$
$$25\% \; w^- r^-$$

Of course, only the leaf character will be identifiable in these gametophytes; the r^+ or r^- designation would have to be determined by appropriate intercrosses. (What proportion of reddish sporophytes is expected if crosses are made at random?)

Once again, Mendel's laws rule the inheritance. It is simply a matter of keeping the ploidy levels (the number of chromosome sets) straight in each part of the cycle, and everything is simple Mendelian ratios.

Message Mendelian laws apply to the products of meiosis in any organism. Their general statement is as follows:

1. At meiosis the members of a gene pair segregate equally into the haploid products of meiosis.

2. At meiosis the segregation of one gene pair is independent of the segregation of gene pairs on other chromosome pairs.

Thus, the theory of chromosomal location of genes perfectly explains inheritance patterns. The chromosome theory of inheritance is no longer in doubt; it forms one of the cornerstones of modern biological theory.

Summary

■ After the rediscovery of Mendelian principles in 1900, scientists set out to discover what structures within cells correspond to Mendel's hypothetical units of heredity, which we now call genes. Recognizing that the behavior of chromosomes during meiosis parallels the behavior of genes, Sutton and Boveri suggested that genes are on chromosomes.

In her experiments with a certain species of grasshopper, Elinor Carothers discovered that nonhomologous chromosomes assort independently. This finding provided further evidence that the behavior of chromosomes closely parallels that of genes. Additional evidence for the validity of the chromosome theory of heredity came from the discovery of crisscross inheritance and the existence of X and Y chromosomes. In his studies of *Drosophila*, Thomas Hunt Morgan showed that the crisscross inheritance of red or

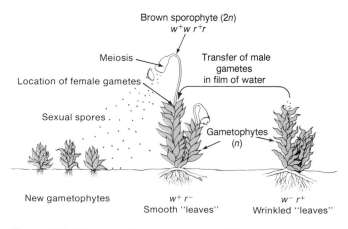

Figure 3-35. Diagrammatic representation of Mendelian genetics in a hypothetical cross in a moss. The w^+ or w alternatives are expressed only in the haploid gametophyte stage, whereas the r^+ or r alternatives are expressed only in the diploid sporophyte stage. In mosses, the diploid stage grows on the haploid stage. Male gametes swim through a water film to get to another plant. There, one male gamete and one female gamete fuse to form a diploid cell that divides at the point of fusion to become the sporophyte.

white eye color is completely consistent with the meiotic behavior of X and Y chromosomes. Finally, Bridges' postulation of nondisjunction (the failure of paired chromosomes to separate) during meiosis enabled him to make testable predictions based on the assumption that the gene for eye color is on the X chromosome and that nondisjunction occurs in infrequent cases of meiosis. The confirmation of these predictions provided unequivocal evidence that genes are on chromosomes.

We now know which chromosomal mechanisms produce Mendelian ratios. Mendel's first law (equal segregation) results from the separation of a pair of homologous chromosomes into opposite cells at the first division. Mendel's second law (independent assortment) is a result of the independent behavior of separate pairs of homologous chromosomes.

Because Mendelian laws are based on meiosis, Mendelian inheritance occurs in any organism with meiosis as a part of its cycle. This includes diploid organisms, haploid organisms, and organisms with alternating haploid and diploid generations.

Problems

1. In a colony of flour beetles, which normally are black, a brown individual is found. In this case, the brown color is due to a dominant allele. Invent a symbol for this gene and its wild-type allele.

2. Human cells normally have 46 chromosomes. For each of the following stages, state the number of chromosomes present in a human cell. a. Metaphase of mitosis b. Metaphase I of meiosis c. Telophase of mitosis d. Telophase I of meiosis e. Telophase II of meiosis (In your answers, count chromatids as chromosomes.)

3. Four of the following events occur in both meiosis and mitosis, but one occurs only in meiosis. Which one? a. Chromatid formation b. Spindle formation c. Chromosome condensation (shortening and thickening) d. Chromosome movement to poles e. Chromosome pairing

4. a. A cell with 10 pairs of chromosomes undergoes mitosis. How many chromosomes does each of the resulting cells have? (1) 2 pairs (2) 5 (3) 20 pairs (4) 20 (5) 10

   b. A cell with 10 pairs of chromosomes undergoes meiosis. How many chromosomes does each of the resulting cells have? (1) 2 pairs (2) 5 (3) 20 pairs (4) 20 (5) 10

5. Suppose that two interesting *rare* cytological abnormalities are discovered in the karyotype of a human male. There is an extra piece (or satellite) on *one* of the chromosomes of pair 4, and there is an abnormal pattern of staining on *one* of the chromosomes of pair 7. Assuming that all the gametes of this male are equally viable, what proportion of his children will have the same visible karyotype as he has? (A karyotype is the total visible chromosome complement.)

6. Suppose that meiosis occurs in the transient diploid stage of the cycle of a haploid organism of chromosome number n. What is the probability that an individual haploid resulting from the meiotic division will have a complete parental set of centromeres (that is, a set all from one parent or all from the other parent)?

7. Assuming the sex chromosomes to be identical, name the proportion of all genes you have in common with the family member: a. Your mother b. Your brother

8. In the plant *Rumex hastatulatus*, females normally have the sex-chromosome constitution XX, and males normally have the sex-chromosome constitution XYY. Draw diagrams to show how meiosis might proceed to produce the gametic types necessary for the maintenance of 1:1 sex ratio of males to females.

9. A wild-type female schmoo who is graceful (G) is mated to a non-wild-type male who is gruesome (g). Their progeny consist solely of graceful males and gruesome females. Interpret these results and give genotypes.

(Problem 9 from E. H. Simon and H. Grossfield, *The Challenge of Genetics*, Addison-Wesley, 1971.)

10. A man with a certain disease marries a normal woman. They have eight children (four boys and four girls); all of the girls have their father's disease, but none of the boys do. What inheritance is suggested? a. Autosomal recessive b. Autosomal dominant c. Y-linked d. X-linked dominant e. X-linked recessive

11. Hypophosphatemia is caused by an X-linked dominant gene in humans. A man with hypophosphatemia marries a normal woman. What proportion of their sons will have hypophosphatemia? a. 1/2 b. 1/4 c. 1/3 d. 1 e. 0

12. A condition known as icthyosis hystrix gravior appeared in a boy in the early eighteenth century. His skin became very thick and formed loose spines that were sloughed off at intervals. When he grew up, this "porcupine man" married and had six sons, all of whom had this condition, and several daughters, who were normal. For four generations, this condition was passed from father to son. From this evidence, what can you postulate about the location of the genes?

13. Duchenne's muscular dystrophy is sex-linked and usually affects only males. Victims of the disease become progressively weaker, starting early in life.

a. What is the probability that a woman whose brother has Duchenne's disease will have an affected child?

b. If your mother's brother (your uncle) had Duchenne's disease, what is the probability that you will receive the gene?

c. If your father's brother had the disease, what is the probability that you will receive the gene?

14. The following pedigree is concerned with an inherited dental abnormality, amelogenesis imperfecta.

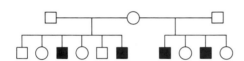

a. What mode of inheritance *best* accounts for the transmission of this trait?

b. Write the genotypes of the individual members according to your hypothesis.

15. A sex-linked recessive gene *c* produces a red-green color blindness in humans. A normal woman whose father was color blind marries a color-blind man.

a. What genotypes are possible for the mother of the color-blind man?

b. What are the chances that the first child from this marriage will be a color-blind boy?

c. Of the girls produced by these parents, what percentage is expected to be color blind?

d. Of all the children (sex unspecified) of these parents, what proportion can be expected to have normal color vision?

16. Male house cats are either black or yellow; females are black, tortoise-shell pattern, or yellow.

a. If these colors are governed by a sex-linked gene, how can these observations be explained?

b. Using appropriate symbols, determine the phenotypes expected in the progeny of a cross between a yellow female and a black male.

c. Repeat part b for the reciprocal of the cross described there.

d. One-half of the females produced by a certain kind of mating are tortoise-shell and one-half are black; one-half of the males are yellow and one-half are black. What colors are the parental males and females in this kind of mating?

e. Another kind of mating produces progeny in the following proportions: 1/4 yellow males, 1/4 yellow fe-

males, 1/4 black males, and 1/4 tortoise-shell females. What colors are the parental males and females in this kind of mating?

17. Mr. Brown is heterozygous for one autosomal gene pair *Bb*, and he carries a recessive X-linked gene *d*. What proportion of his sperms will be *bd*? a. 0 b. 1/2 c. 1/8 d. 1/16 e. 1/4

18. A woman has the rare (hypothetical) disease called quackerlips. She marries a normal man, and all of their sons and none of their daughters are quackerlipped. What is the mode of inheritance of quackerlips? a. Autosomal recessive b. Autosomal dominant c. X-linked recessive d. X-linked dominant

19. What do you think are the advantages and disadvantages for the organism of having genes organized into chromosomes? Why don't genes float free in the nucleus or the cell? (Try to remember to reconsider this question after finishing the book, and see if your answers have changed.)

20. Assume the pedigree presented here to be straightforward, with no complications such as illegitimacy. Trait W, found in individuals represented by the shaded symbols, is rare in the general population. Which of the following patterns of transmission for W are consistent with this pedigree, and which are excluded? a. Autosomal recessive b. Autosomal dominant c. X-linked recessive d. X-linked dominant e. Y-linked

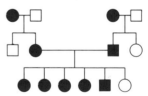

(Problem 20 from A. M. Srb, R. D. Owen, and R. S. Edgar, *General Genetics*, 2d ed. Copyright © 1965 by W. H. Freeman and Company.)

21. In mice, there is a mutant allele that causes a bent tail. From the cross results given in Table 3-4, deduce the mode of inheritance of this trait.

a. Is it recessive or dominant?

b. Is it autosomal or sex-linked?

c. What are the genotypes of parents and progeny in all crosses shown in the table?

■ **TABLE 3-4.**

| Cross | Parents | | Progeny | |
	Female	Male	Female	Male
1	Normal	Bent	All bent	All normal
2	Bent	Normal	1/2 bent, 1/2 normal	1/2 bent, 1/2 normal
3	Bent	Normal	All bent	All bent
4	Normal	Normal	All normal	All normal
5	Bent	Bent	All bent	All bent
6	Bent	Bent	All bent	1/2 bent, 1/2 normal

22. In the following pedigree, a dot represents the occurrence of an extra finger, and a shaded symbol represents the occurrence of an eye disease.

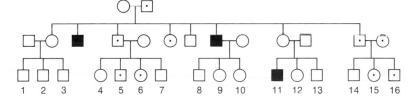

a. What can you tell about the inheritance of an extra finger?

b. What can you tell about the inheritance of the eye disease?

c. What were the genotypes of the original parents?

d. What is the probability that a child of individual 4 will have an extra finger? will have the eye disease?

e. What is the probability that a child of individual 12 will have an extra finger? will have the eye disease?

23. In the ovaries of female mammals (including humans), the first meiotic division produces two cells (as normal), but one cell becomes a small nonfunctional cell called a polar body. Consequently, a second meiotic division occurs in only one of the first-division products. Furthermore, one of the products of the second meiotic division also becomes a polar body. Thus, the net result of one meiosis is one ovum (egg) plus two polar bodies.

a. Diagram this system at the cell level and at the chromosome level.

b. In this system, Mendelian genetics obviously does not operate: the Mendelian ratios observed in mammals are due solely to segregation in the male. Is this statement true or false? Explain your answer.

CHAPTER 4

Extensions to Mendelian Analysis

■ We have seen that Mendel's laws seem to hold across the entire spectrum of eukaryotic organisms — that is, we can identify analogous phenomena that reveal segregation and independent assortment. These laws form a base for predicting the outcome of simple crosses. However, it is only a base; the real world of genes and chromosomes is more complex than is revealed by Mendel's laws, and exceptions and extensions abound. These situations do not invalidate Mendel's laws. Rather, they show that there are more situations than can be explained by segregation and independent assortment of gene pairs and that these situations must be accommodated into the fabric of genetic analysis. This is the challenge we now must meet. Of course, one extension has already been accommodated — sex linkage. This chapter presents a grab bag of other extensions, and the two following chapters discuss two major extensions. We shall see that, rather than creating a hopeless and bewildering situation, these complexities combine to form a precise and unifying set of principles for the genetic analyst. These principles interlock and support each other in a highly satisfying way that has provided great insight into the mechanics of inheritance.

Variations on Dominance Relations

Dominance is a good place to start. Mendel observed (or at least reported) full dominance (and recessiveness) for all the seven gene pairs he studied. He may have been selective in his choice of pea characters to study, because variations on the basic theme crop up quite often in analysis. The problems center on the phenotype of the heterozygote. Some examples will illustrate this.

In four-o'clock plants, when a pure line with red petals is crossed to a pure line with white petals, the F_1 have *not* red petals but pink! If an F_2 is produced, the result is

1/4 red petals	1 C_1C_1
1/2 pink petals	2 C_1C_2
1/4 white petals	1 C_2C_2

The occurrence of an intermediate phenotype in the heterozygote introduces the possibility of **incomplete dominance.** The precise position of the heterozygote on the phenotypic "scale" defines several possibilities, as summarized in Figure 4-1. In practice it is often difficult to determine exactly where on the scale the heterozygote is, however.

The phenotype of the heterozygote is also the key in the phenomenon of **codominance,** in which the heterozygote shows the phenotypes of *both* the homozygotes. In a sense, then, codominance is no dominance at all! A good example is found in the M-N blood-group gene pair in humans. Three blood groups are possible — M, N, and

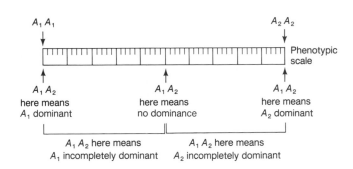

Figure 4-1. Summary of dominance relationships.

MN—and these are determined by the genotypes $L^M L^M$, $L^N L^N$, and $L^M L^N$, respectively. Blood groups actually represent the presence of an immunological antigen on the surface of red blood cells. People of genotype $L^M L^N$ have both antigens. This example shows how the heterozygote can show both phenotypes.

Another interesting example of dominance is found in the human disease sickle-cell anemia. The gene pair concerned affects the oxygen transport molecule hemoglobin, the major constituent of red blood cells. The three genotypes have different phenotypes, as follows:

$Hb^A Hb^A$: Normal. Red blood cells never sickled.

$Hb^S Hb^S$: Severe, often fatal anemia. Red blood cells sickle-shaped.

$Hb^A Hb^S$: No anemia. Red blood cells sickle only under abnormally low oxygen concentrations.

An example of sickle cells is shown in Figure 4-2. In regard to anemia the Hb^A allele is dominant. In regard to blood cell shape there is incomplete dominance. Finally, as we shall now see, in regard to hemoglobin there is codominance! Luckily, the two types of hemoglobin concerned, dictated by the two alleles, have different chemical charges, and this property can be used in a technique called electrophoresis to make a more refined distinction.

In electrophoresis, mixtures of proteins can be separated on the basis of their charges. A small sample of protein (here, hemoglobin from red blood cells) is placed in a small well, cut in a slab of gel. A powerful electric field is applied across this gel, and the hemoglobin moves according to the degree of electrostatic charge. Figure 4-3 is a sketch of a typical electrophoresis apparatus. The gel is actually a supporting web containing electrolyte solution in its spaces; hence the hemoglobin can move easily through the field. After an appropriate time, the gel can be stained for protein, with the results shown in Figure 4-4. The blotches are the stained hemoglobin. We see that homozygous normal people have one type of hemoglobin (A), and

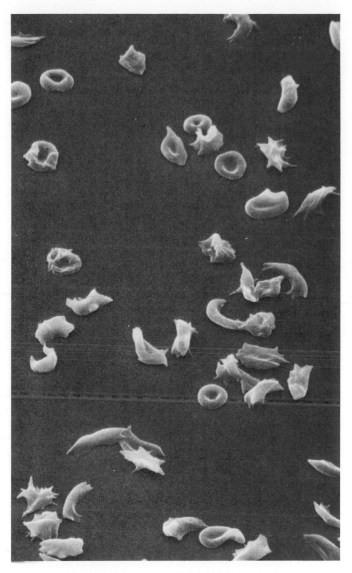

Figure 4-2. Electron micrograph of red blood cells from an individual with sickle-cell anemia. A few rounded cells appear almost normal. (Courtesy of Patricia N. Farnsworth.)

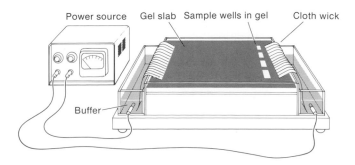

Figure 4-3. Equipment for electrophoresis. Each sample mixture is placed in a well in the gel. The components of the mixture migrate different distances on the gel because of their different electric charges. Several sample mixtures can be tested at the same time (one in each well). The positions of the separated components are later revealed by staining.

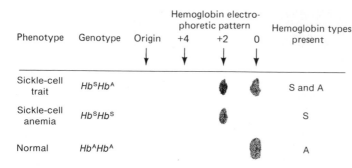

Phenotype	Genotype	Origin	+4	+2	0	Hemoglobin types present
			Hemoglobin electro-phoretic pattern			
Sickle-cell trait	Hb^SHb^A			●	●	S and A
Sickle-cell anemia	Hb^SHb^S			●		S
Normal	Hb^AHb^A				●	A

Figure 4-4. Electrophoresis of hemoglobin from a normal individual, an individual with sickle-cell anemia, and an individual with sickle-cell trait. The smudges show the positions to which the hemoglobins migrate on the starch gel. (After D. L. Rucknagel and R. K. Laros, Jr., "Hemoglobinopathics: Genetics and Implications for Studies of Human Reproduction." *Clinical Obstetrics and Gynecology* 12, 1969, 49–75.)

anemics have another slow-moving type (S). The heterozygotes have both types, A and S.

Sickle-cell anemia illustrates the somewhat arbitrary nature of the terms incomplete dominance and codominance. The type of dominance depends on the phenotypic level at which the observations are being made—organismal, cellular, or molecular.

Message Complete dominance and recessiveness are not essential aspects of Mendel's laws; those laws deal more with the inheritance patterns of genes than with their nature or function.

Multiple Alleles

Early in the history of genetics, it became clear that it is possible to have more than two forms of one kind of gene. Although only two actual alleles of a gene can exist in a diploid cell (and only one in a haploid cell), the total number of possible different allelic forms that might exist in a population of individuals is often quite large. This situation is called **multiple allelism,** and the set of alleles itself is called an **allelic series.** The concept of allelism is a crucial one in genetics, so we consider several examples. The examples themselves serve also to introduce important areas of genetic investigation.

ABO Blood Group in Humans

The human ABO blood-group alleles afford a modest example of multiple allelism. There are four blood types (or phenotypes) in the ABO system, as shown in Table 4-1. The allelic series includes three major alleles, which can be present in any pairwise combination in one individual; thus only two of the three alleles can be present in any one individual. Note that the series include cases of both complete dominance and codominance. In this allelic series, the alleles I^A and I^B each determine a unique form of one type of antigen; the allele i determines a failure to produce either form of that type of antigen.

C Gene in Rabbits

Another example of multiple allelism involves a larger allelic series determining coat color in rabbits. The alleles in this series are C (full color), c^{ch} (chinchilla, a light grayish color), c^h (Himalayan, albino with black extremities), and c (albino). You will have noted the use of a superscript to indicate an allele of a type of gene; this symbolism often is necessary because more than the two symbols C and c are needed to describe multiple alleles. In this series, dominance is in the order of the alleles listed; verify this by careful study of Table 4-2.

Operational Test of Allelism

Now that we have seen two examples of allelic series, it is a good time to pause and consider a question. How do we know that a set of phenotypes is determined by alleles of the same type of gene? In other words, what is the operational test for allelism? For now, the answer is simply the observation of Mendelian single-gene-pair ratios in all combinations crossed. For example, consider three pure-line phenotypes in a hypothetical plant species. Line 1 has round spots on the petals; line 2 has oval spots on the petals; and line 3 has no spots on the petals. Suppose that crosses of the three lines yield the following results:

Cross	F_1	F_2
1×2	all round-spotted	3/4 round, 1/4 oval
1×3	all round-spotted	3/4 round, 1/4 unspotted
2×3	all oval-spotted	3/4 oval, 1/4 unspotted

These results prove that we are dealing with three alleles of a single gene that affects petal spotting. We can choose any symbols we wish. Because we don't know which phenotype is the wild-type, we could follow the rabbit system and use S for the round-spotted allele, s^o for the oval-spotted allele,

---

■ TABLE 4-1. ABO blood groups in humans

Blood phenotype	Genotype
O	ii
A	I^AI^A or I^Ai
B	I^BI^B or I^Bi
AB	I^AI^B

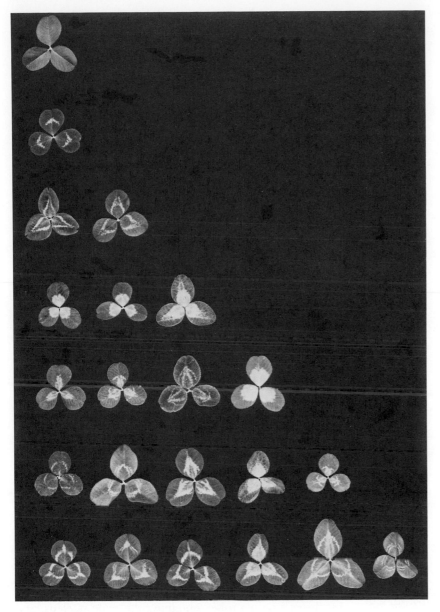

Figure 4-5. Multiple alleles are involved in determining the chevron pattern on the leaves of white clover. The genotype of each plant is shown below. Inspect these data for dominance and codominance. (Courtesy of W. Ellis Davies.)

vv
$V^l V^l$
$V^h V^h$ $\quad$ $V^l V^h$
$V^f V^f$ $\quad$ $V^l V^f$ $\quad$ $V^h V^f$
$V^{ba} V^{ba}$ $\quad$ $V^l V^{ba}$ $\quad$ $V^h V^{ba}$ $\quad$ $V^f V^{ba}$
$V^b V^b$ $\quad$ $V^l V^b$ $\quad$ $V^h V^b$ $\quad$ $V^f V^b$ $\quad$ $V^{ba} V^b$
$V^{by} V^{by}$ $\quad$ $V^l V^{by}$ $\quad$ $V^h V^{by}$ $\quad$ $V^f V^{by}$ $\quad$ $V^{ba} V^{by}$ $\quad$ $V^b V^{by}$

and s for the unspotted allele. Alternatively, we could use S^r for round, S^o for oval, and s for unspotted. The convention provides no firm rules about whether to use capital or small letters, particularly for the alleles in the middle of the series that are dominant to some of their alleles but recessive to others.

■ **TABLE 4-2.** C gene in rabbits

Coat-color phenotype	Genotype
Full color	CC or Cc^{ch} or Cc^h or Cc
Chinchilla	$c^{ch}c^{ch}$ or $c^{ch}c^h$ or $c^{ch}c$
Himalayan	$c^h c^h$ or $c^h c$
Albino	cc

What if crosses between pure-breeding variants affecting one character do not produce single-gene Mendelian ratios? This outcome is covered later in the chapter.

Clover Chevrons

Clover is the common name for plants of the genus *Trifolium*. There are many species—some native to North America and some that grow here as introduced weeds. The red-flowered and white-flowered clovers are familiar to most people. These are *different* species, but each shows considerable variation among individuals in the curious V or "chevron" pattern on the leaves. Much genetic research has been done with white clover; Figure 4-5 shows that the different chevron forms (and the absence of chevrons) constitute an allelic series in this species. Furthermore, several types of dominance relations may be seen in the allele combinations shown in the figure.

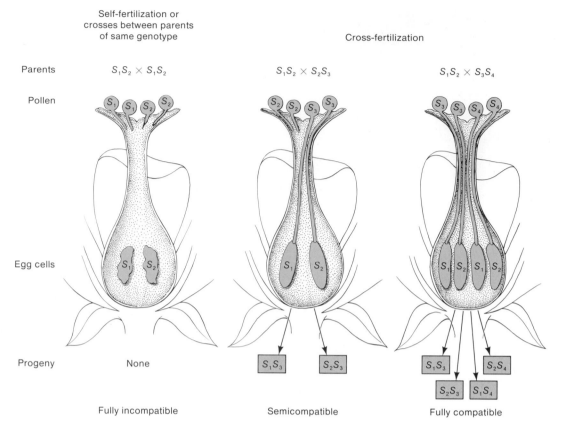

Self-fertilization or crosses between parents of same genotype

Cross-fertilization

Parents: $S_1S_2 \times S_1S_2$ $S_1S_2 \times S_2S_3$ $S_1S_2 \times S_3S_4$

Pollen

Egg cells

Progeny: None S_1S_3 S_2S_3 S_1S_3 S_2S_4 S_2S_3 S_1S_4

Fully incompatible   Semicompatible   Fully compatible

Figure 4-6. Diagram showing how multiple alleles control incompatibility in certain plants. A pollen tube will not grow if the S allele that it contains is present in the female parent. This diagram shows only four multiple alleles, but many plant incompatibility systems use far larger numbers of alleles. Such systems act to promote exchange of genes between plants by making selfing impossible and crosses between near relations very unlikely. (From A. M. Srb, R. D. Owen, and R. S. Edgar, *General Genetics*, 2d ed. Copyright © 1965, W. H. Freeman and Company.)

Incompatibility Alleles in Plants

It has been known for millennia that some plants just will not self-pollinate. A single plant may produce both male and female gametes, but no seeds will ever be produced. The same plants, however, will cross with certain other plants, so obviously they are not sterile. This phenomenon is called **self-incompatibility.** Of course, the pea plants used by Mendel were not self-incompatible, for he was able to self his plants with ease. We now know that incompatibility has a genetic basis and that there are several different genetic systems acting in different self-incompatible species. These systems form very nice examples of multiple allelism.

One of the most common systems is found in many dicot and monocot plants, including sweet cherries, tobacco, petunias, and evening primroses. In each of these species, one gene determines compatibility/incompatibility relations, with many different allelic forms of the gene possible in different plants of any one species. Figure 4-6 shows an example, in which a fully incompatible reaction, a semicompatible reaction, and a fully compatible reaction are all possible.

If a pollen grain bears an S allele that is also present in the maternal parent, then it will not grow; however, if that allele is not in the maternal tissue, then the pollen grain produces a pollen tube containing the male nucleus, and this tube effects fertilization. The number of S alleles in a series in one species can be very large (over 50 in the evening primrose and clover), and cases of more than 100 alleles have been reported in some species.

Tissue Incompatibility in Humans

When an organ or a tissue graft is medically necessary in a human, the success or failure of the graft depends on the genotypes of the host and the donor. If the two are mismatched, rejection of the graft eventually occurs, often accompanied by death of the host (Figure 4-7).

The rejection system is based on two important genes called *HLA-A* and *HLA-B*, which determine the immunological acceptability of the introduced tissue. Each gene has a series of allelic forms. There are eight alleles for *HLA-A*, designated *A1, A2, A3, A9, A10, A11, A28,* and *A29.* By coincidence, there are also eight alleles for *HLA-B*, designated *B5, B7, B8, B12, B13, B14, B18,* and *B27.* (The two

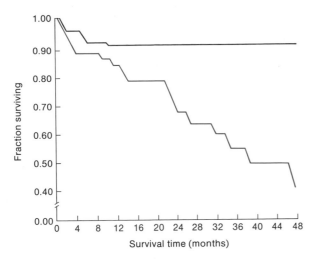

Figure 4-7. The success of kidney transplants in HLA-matched (*black line*) and HLA-mismatched (*colored line*) sibling pairs. HLA refers to genes related to tissue compatibility. (From D. P. Singal et al., *Transplantation* 7:246, copyright © 1965, The Williams & Wilkins Co., Baltimore.)

genes do not show independent assortment, but this need not concern us now. For the moment we shall simply use these allelic series as excellent examples of multiple allelism in humans.)

The HLA type of an individual is determined by testing his or her lymphocytes (white blood cells) with a battery of standard antibodies from donors of known HLA type. In a transplant, the recipient's immune system will recognize the graft as "foreign" and reject it if an allele is present in the donor tissue that is not present in the recipient. In the typing test, this rejection reaction is observed as lymphocyte death. The immune system will not reject tissue that lacks some alleles present in the recipient — it only rejects "strange" alleles. Table 4-3 shows examples.

We might wonder what function these HLA genes normally serve — obviously, tissue transplants have not been a normal aspect of human evolution! One possible answer is that some HLA alleles seem to confer resistance or susceptibility to certain specific diseases (Figure 4-8). Thus these alleles may have played some role in our evolutionary history, in response to some environmental selection pressure. This supposition is supported by the finding that certain ethnic groups and races show a preponderance of specific alleles in their populations. The study of such

alleles is important both in deciphering the history of human evolution and in developing modern medical techniques — not only for transplants, but also for the general study of resistance to disease.

Another very interesting possibility emerging from current research is that the HLA genes may be intimately involved in cancer. Presumably, one of the normal functions of the HLA genes is to recognize cancer cells as a kind of "foreign" agent within the body. The development of cancer cells may be a fairly common event in healthy individuals, with these cells being recognized and destroyed before they cause noticeable damage. A cancerous tumor may be the result of a failure of this detection-and-destruction system at some stage. The HLA genes also play an important role in the normal immune response.

Message A gene can exist in several different states or forms — a situation called multiple allelism. The alleles are said to constitute an allelic series, and the members of a series can show any type of dominance relationship with one another.

As a postscript to this section, it is worth noting that several different "kinds" or "species" of cell-surface anti-

■ **TABLE** 4-3. Success or failure of transplants determined by HLA types

Transplant	Recipient genotype	Donor genotype	Result
1	*A1 A2, B5 B5*	*A1 A1, B5 B7*	Rejected (because of *B7*)
2	*A2 A3, B7 B12*	*A1 A2, B7 B7*	Rejected (because of *A1*)
3	*A1 A2, B7 B5*	*A1 A2, B7 B7*	Accepted
4	*A2 A3, B7 B5*	*A3 A3, B5 B5*	Accepted

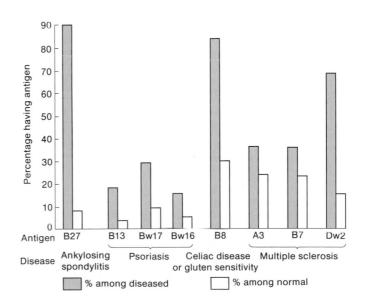

Figure 4-8. Histograms showing effects of specific HLA alleles on predisposition to certain diseases in humans. For example, the allele *B27* is found in 90 percent of individuals with ankylosing spondylitis (a kind of severe rheumatism), but in only 9 percent of normal individuals. Most of the diseases that show such HLA correlations are known to involve the immune system. (From W. F. Bodmer and L. L. Cavalli-Sforza, *Genetics, Evolution, and Man.* Copyright © 1976, W. H. Freeman and Company. Based on data from H. O. McDevitt and W. F. Bodmer, *Lancet* 1:1267, 1974.)

Figure 4-9 A mouse litter from two parents heterozygous for the yellow coat-color allele, which is lethal in a double dose. The larger mice are the parents. Not all progeny are visible.

gens have been discovered. Each of these kinds is, of course, specified by one kind of gene. The different forms one kind of antigen can take are determined by the multiple alleles of the gene concerned.

Lethal Genes

Normal wild-type mice have coats with a rather dark overall pigmentation. In 1904, Lucien Cuenot studied mice having a lighter coat color called yellow. Mating a yellow mouse to a normal mouse from a pure line, Cuenot observed a 1 : 1 ratio of yellow to normal mice in the progeny. This observation suggests that a single gene determines this aspect of coat color and that an allele for yellow is dominant to an allele for normal color. However, the situation became more confusing when he crossed yellow mice with one another. The result was always the same, no matter which yellow mice were used:

$$\text{yellow} \times \text{yellow} \begin{cases} 2/3 \text{ yellow} \\ 1/3 \text{ normal color} \end{cases}$$

Two things are of interest in these results. First, the 2 : 1 ratio is a departure from Mendelian expectations. Second, Cuenot failed to detect (in any generation of breeding) a homozygous yellow mouse.

Cuenot suggested the following explanation for these results. A cross between two heterozygotes would be expected to yield a Mendelian genotype ratio of 1 : 2 : 1. If one of the homozygous classes died before birth, the live births would then show a 2 : 1 ratio of heterozygotes to the surviving homozygotes. In other words, the allele A^Y for yellow is dominant to the normal allele A with respect to its effect on color, and it also acts as a **recessive lethal** allele with respect to a character we could call "survival." Thus a mouse with the homozygous genotype A^YA^Y dies before birth and is not observed among the progeny. All surviving yellow mice must be heterozygous A^YA, so a cross between yellow mice will always yield the following results:

$$A^YA \times A^YA \begin{cases} 1/4 \ AA & \text{normal} \\ 2/4 \ A^YA & \text{yellow} \\ 1/4 \ A^YA^Y & \text{die before birth} \end{cases}$$

The expected Mendelian ratio of 1 : 2 : 1 would be observed among the zygotes, but it is altered to a 2 : 1 ratio of viable progeny because of the lethality of the A^YA^Y genotype. This hypothesis was confirmed by the removal of uteri from pregnant females of the yellow × yellow cross; one-fourth of the embryos were found to be dead. Figure 4-9 shows a typical litter from a cross between yellow mice.

The A^Y allele has effects on two characters: coat color and survival. Such genes known to have more than one distinct phenotypic effect are called **pleiotropic** genes. It is entirely possible that both effects of the A^Y pleiotropic allele are the result of the same basic cause, which promotes yellowness of coat in a single dose and death in a double dose.

Lethal genes are quite common, even in humans. Some lethal effects occur in utero, others much later—in infancy, in childhood, or even in adulthood. Only rarely is a lethal gene associated with a distinguishable heterozygous phenotype, as in yellow mice. One other example you may be familiar with is the tail-less condition in Manx cats. The determining gene is homozygous lethal. Typically, the only detectable effect of a lethal gene is on survival of the individual. In some cases, a specific abnormality can be pinpointed as the cause of death. For example, a recessive lethal gene in rats may have its pleiotropic effects traced to a basic problem in the nature of the rat's cartilage (Figure 4-10).

The lethality of an allele of a gene is often dependent on the environment in which the organism develops. Whereas certain alleles would be lethal in virtually any environment, others are viable in one environment but lethal in another. For example, remember that many of the phenotypes favored and selected by agricultural breeders would almost certainly be wiped out in nature in competition with the normal members of their population. Modern grain varieties provide good examples; it is only the careful nurturing by the farmer that has maintained such phenotypes for our benefit.

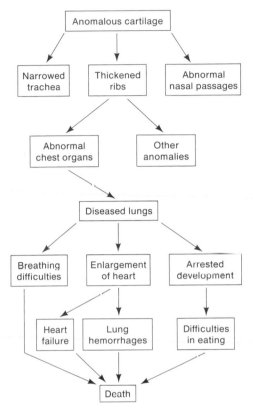

Figure 4-10. Diagram showing how one specific lethal gene causes death in rats. (From I. M. Lerner and W. J. Libby, *Heredity, Evolution, and Society*, 2d ed. Copyright © 1976, W. H. Freeman and Company; after H. Grüneberg.)

In practical genetics, we very commonly encounter situations where perfect expected Mendelian ratios are consistently skewed in one direction by one allele. For example, in the cross $Aa \times aa$, we predict a progeny phenotypic ratio of 50 percent $A-$ and 50 percent aa, but we might consistently observe a ratio such as 55%:45% or 60%:40%. In such a case, the a allele is said to be **subvital**—a kind of partial lethality, expressed in only some individuals. The partial lethality may range from 0 to 100 percent, depending on the rest of the genome and on the environment. We shall return to this topic later.

Several Genes Affecting the Same Character

We saw earlier that, in a genetic dissection, the identification of a major gene affecting a character does not mean that this is the *only* gene affecting that character. An organism is a highly complex machine in which all functions interact to a greater or lesser degree. At the level of genetic determination, the genes likewise can be regarded as interacting. A gene does not act in isolation; its effects depend not only on its own functions but also on the functions of other genes (and on the environment). In many cases, the complex interactions of major genes are detectable through genetic analysis, and we now look at some examples. Typically, the mode of interaction is revealed by **modified Mendelian ratios**.

Coat Color in Mammals

A character that has been extensively studied at the genetic level is coat color in mammals. These studies have revealed a beautiful set of examples of the interplay between different genes in the determination of one character. The best-studied mammal in this regard is the mouse, because of its small size and its short reproductive cycle. However, the genetic determination of coat color in mice has direct parallels in other mammals, and we shall look at some of these as our discussion proceeds. There are at least five interacting major genes involved in determining the coat color of mice: A, B, C, D, and S.

The A Gene. The wild-type allele A produces a phenotype called agouti. Agouti is an overall grayish color with a "brindled" or "mousy" appearance. It is common in many mammals in nature. The effect is produced by a band of yellow on the hair shaft. In the nonagouti phenotype (determined by the allele a), the yellow band is absent, so the coat color appears solid (Figure 4-11).

The lethal yellow A^Y allele is another form of this gene. Another form is a^t, which gives a "black-and-tan" effect involving a cream-colored belly with dark pigmentation

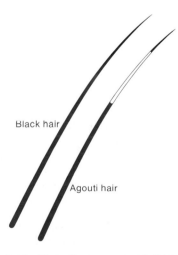

Figure 4-11. Individual hairs from an agouti *(wild-type)* and a black mouse. The yellow band on each hair gives the agouti pattern its "mousy" appearance.

elsewhere. We shall not include these two alleles in the following discussion.

The B Gene.   There are two major alleles of the *B* gene. The allele *B* gives the normal agouti color in combination with *A*, but with *aa* it gives solid black. The genotype *A– bb* gives a color called cinnamon ("mousy" brown), and *aa bb* gives solid brown.

The following sample cross illustrates the inheritance pattern of the *A* and *B* genes.

AA bb (cinnamon) × *aa BB* (black)

or   *AA BB* (agouti) × *aa bb* (brown)

$\downarrow$

F$_1$ all *Aa Bb* (agouti)

$\downarrow$

F$_2$ 9 *A – B –* (agouti)

3 *A – bb* (cinnamon)

3 *aa B –* (black)

1 *aa bb* (brown)

In horses, no *A* agouti gene seems to have survived the generations of breeding, although such a gene does exist in certain wild relatives of the horse. The color we have called brown in mice is called chestnut in horses, and this phenotype also is recessive to black.

The C Gene.   The wild-type allele *C* permits color expression, and the allele *c* prevents color expression. The *cc* constitution is said to be **epistatic** to the other color genes. The word epistatic literally means "standing upon"; the *c* allele in homozygous condition "stands on" (blots out) the expression of other genes concerned with coat color. The *cc* animals, lacking coat color, are called albino. Albinos are common in many mammalian species, but albinos have also been occasionally reported among birds, snakes, and fish. Epistatic genes produce interesting modified ratios, as seen in the following sample cross (where we assume that both parents are *aa*):

BB cc (albino) × *bb CC* (brown)

or   *BB CC* (black) × *bb cc* (albino)

$\downarrow$

F$_1$ all *Bb Cc* (black)

$\downarrow$

F$_2$ 9 *B – C –* (black)   9

3 *bb C –* (brown)   3

3 *B – cc* (albino)
1 *bb cc* (albino)   } 4

A phenotypic ratio of 9 : 3 : 4 is observed. This ratio is the signal for inferring gene interaction of the type called recessive epistasis. In some other organisms, dominant epistasis is observed. (What ratio is produced in dominant epistasis?)

We have already encountered the *c*^{h} (Himalayan) allele in rabbits. It exists also in other mammals, including mice (also called Himalayan) and cats (called Siamese).

It should be pointed out here that the term epistasis is often used in a different way (mainly in population genetics) to describe *any* kind of gene interaction.

The D Gene.   The *D* gene controls the intensity of pigment specified by the other coat-color genes. The genotypes *DD* and *Dd* permit full expression of color in mice, but *dd* "dilutes" the pigment to a milky appearance. Dilute agouti, dilute cinnamon, dilute brown, and dilute black coats all are possible. A gene of this nature is called a **modifier gene.** In the following sample cross, we assume that both parents are *aa CC*.

BB dd (dilute black) × *bb DD* (brown)

or   *BB DD* (black) × *bb dd* (dilute brown)

$\downarrow$

F$_1$ all *Bb Dd* (black)

$\downarrow$

F$_2$ 9 *B – D –* (black)

3 *B – dd* (dilute black)

3 *bb D –* (brown)

1 *bb dd* (dilute brown)

In horses, the *D* allele shows incomplete dominance. Figure 4-12 shows how dilution affects the appearance of chestnut and bay horses.

The S Gene.   The *S* gene controls the presence or absence of spots. The genotype *S –* results in no spots, and *ss* produces a spotting pattern called piebald in both mice and horses. This pattern can be superimposed on any of the coat colors discussed earlier — with the exception of albino, of course.

By this time, the point of the discussion should be obvious. Normal coat appearance in wild mice is produced by a complex set of interacting genes determining pigment type, pigment distribution in the individual hairs, pigment distribution on the animal's body, and the presence or absence of pigment. Similar situations exist for any character in any organism.

Figure 4-13 illustrates some pigment patterns in mice.

Genotype   Phenotype

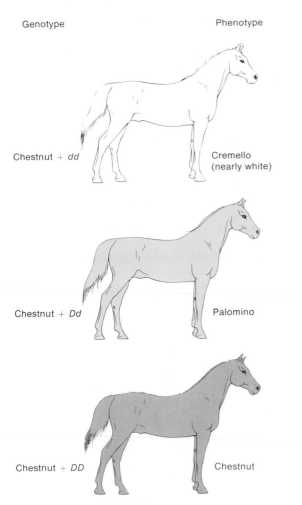

Chestnut + *dd*   Cremello
                         (nearly white)

Chestnut + *Dd*   Palomino

Chestnut + *DD*   Chestnut

Genotype   Phenotype

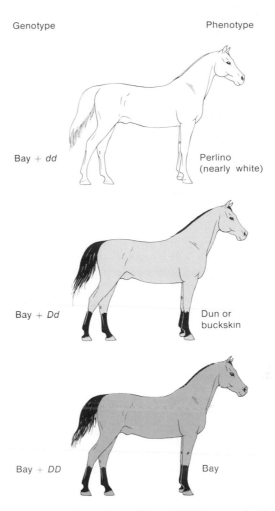

Bay + *dd*   Perlino
                         (nearly white)

Bay + *Dd*   Dun or
                         buckskin

Bay + *DD*   Bay

Figure 4-12. The modifying effect of dilution genes on basic chestnut and bay genotypes in horses. Note the incomplete dominance shown by *D*. (From J. W. Evans et al., *The Horse.* Copyright © 1977, W. H. Freeman and Company.)

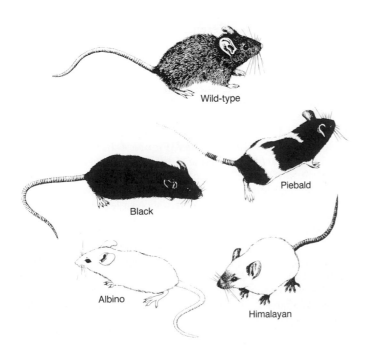

Wild-type

Black

Piebald

Albino

Himalayan

Figure 4-13. Some coat phenotypes in mice.

Examples of Gene Interaction in Other Organisms

Some other kinds of gene interaction are best illustrated in other organisms. Peas provide a good example of one important situation. Two different, independently obtained pure lines of pea plants are both white-petaled. When these lines are crossed, all of the F_1 have purple flowers. The F_2 shows both purple and white plants in a ratio of $9:7$. How can this result be explained? By now, you should immediately suspect that the $9:7$ ratio is a modification of the Mendelian $9:3:3:1$ ratio. The explanation is that two different genes in the pea have similar effects on petal color. Let us represent the alleles of these genes by A, a, B, and b.

white strain 1 $\times$ white strain 2

$AA\,bb \times aa\,BB$

F_1 all $Aa\,Bb$ (purple)

F_2 9 $A-B-$(purple)   9

      3 $A-bb$ (white)

      3 $aa\,B-$(white) $\Big\}$ 7

      1 $aa\,bb$ (white)

Both gene pairs affect petal color. Whiteness can be produced by a recessive allele of either gene pair, but purpleness is a phenotype produced by a combination of the dominant alleles of *both* gene pairs. This phenomenon is called **complementary gene action,** a term that satisfactorily describes how the two dominant alleles are uniting to produce a specific phenotype—in this example, purple pigment. (Note that we might have mistakenly inferred purpleness to be a specific phenotype of one gene pair if we had only one white strain available for our crosses.)

Another important kind of interaction is **suppression** of one gene by another. This interaction is illustrated by the inheritance of the production of a chemical called malvidin in the plant genus *Primula.* Malvidin production is determined by a single dominant gene K. However, the action of this dominant gene may be suppressed by a nonallelic dominant suppressor D. The following pedigree is informative:

$KK\,dd$ (malvidin) $\times$ $kk\,DD$ (no malvidin)

F_1 all $Kk\,Dd$ (no malvidin)

F_2 9 $K-D-$(no malvidin)

      3 $kk\,D-$(no malvidin) $\Bigg\}$ 13

      1 $kk\,dd$ (no malvidin)

      3 $K-dd$ (malvidin)   3

Recessive suppression of both dominant and recessive genes also is known. The suppressor gene may have its own associated phenotype or (as in the malvidin example) have no known phenotypic effect other than the suppression.

Our final example of gene interaction introduces a concept that we shall develop in a later chapter. It concerns the genes that control fruit shape in the plant called shepherd's purse. Two different lines have fruits of different shapes: one is "round," the other "narrow." Are these two phenotypes determined by two alleles of a single gene? A cross between the two lines reveals an F_1 with round fruit; this result is consistent with the hypothesis of a single gene pair. However, the F_2 shows a $15:1$ ratio of round to narrow. Again, this ratio immediately suggests a modification of the $9:3:3:1$ Mendelian ratio, and it can be explained in terms of two **duplicate genes** (Figure 4-14). Apparently, round fruits are produced as a result of the presence of at least one dominant allele of either gene. The two genes appear to be identical in function. (Contrast this $15:1$ ratio with the $9:7$ ratio obtained from complementary genes, where *both* dominant genes are necessary to produce a specific phenotype.)

A summary of the various types of gene interactions producing modified dihybrid Mendelian ratios in diploids is shown in Table 4-4.

Gene interactions also can be detected in haploid organisms. We have already discussed a gene in the fungus *Neurospora* where one allele causes albino asexual spores, as opposed to the normal pinkish-orange color produced by

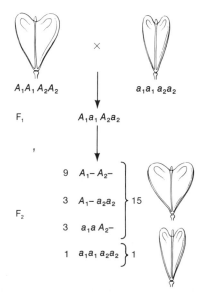

Figure 4-14. Inheritance pattern of duplicate genes controlling fruit shape in shepherd's purse. Either A_1 or A_2 can cause a round fruit.

■ **TABLE 4-4.** Modified dihybrid Mendelean ratios produced by gene interaction

Type of gene interaction	A/B	A/bb	aa/B-	aa/bb
Four distinct phenotypes	9	3	3	1
Complementary gene action	9	7		
Dominant suppression by A of dominant gene B	13		3	
Recessive epistasis by aa of B/b genes	9	3	4	
Dominant epistasis by A of B/b genes	12		3	1
Duplicate genes	15			1

the wild-type allele of the same gene. A cross $al \times al^+$ gives $1/2$ al and $1/2$ al^+ progeny. Another interesting gene, ylo, gives yellow asexual spores, and the cross $ylo \times ylo^+$ gives $1/2$ ylo and $1/2$ ylo^+ progeny. When an al culture is crossed with a ylo culture, the resulting progeny are $1/4$ yellow, $1/4$ wild-type, and $1/2$ albino. How can we explain this result? The answer is a kind of epistasis: al and ylo are forms of separate genes, each of which can affect the normal production of pink pigment. The genotypes in the cross are the following:

Haploid parental cultures $al\,ylo^+$ (albino) $\times$ $al^+\,ylo$ (yellow)

Transient diploid $al^+/al,\ ylo^+/ylo$

    ↓ meiosis

Progeny (cultures from sexual spores)

  $1/4$ $al\,ylo$ (albino) ⎫
  $1/4$ $al\,ylo^+$ (albino) ⎭ $1/2$

  $1/4$ $al^+\,ylo$ (yellow) $1/4$

  $1/4$ $al^+\,ylo^+$ (normal) $1/4$

Message Modified Mendelian ratios reveal that a character is determined by the complex interaction of different genes.

Penetrance and Expressivity

Clearly, genes do not act in isolation. A gene does *not* determine a phenotype by acting alone; it does so only in conjunction with other genes and with the environment. Al-though geneticists do routinely ascribe a particular phenotype to an allele of a gene they have identified, we must remember that this is merely a convenient kind of jargon designed to facilitate genetic analysis. This jargon arises from the ability of geneticists to isolate individual components of a biological process and to study them as part of genetic dissection. Although this logical isolation is an essential aspect of genetics, the message of this chapter is that a gene cannot act by itself.

In the preceding examples, the genetic basis of the dependence of one gene on another has been worked out. In other situations, where the phenotype ascribed to a gene is known to be dependent on other factors but the precise nature of those factors has not been established, the terms *penetrance* or *expressivity* may be very useful in describing the situation.

We have already encountered penetrance in the discussion of lethal alleles. **Penetrance** is defined as the percentage of individuals with a given genotype who exhibit the phenotype associated with that genotype. For example, an organism may be of genotype aa or $A-$ but may not express the phenotype normally associated with its genotype—because of the presence of modifiers, epistatic genes, or suppressors in the rest of the genome or because of a modifying effect of the environment. Penetrance can be used to describe such an effect when the exact cause is not known.

Expressivity, on the other hand, describes the degree or extent to which a given genotype is expressed phenotypically in an individual. Again, the lack of full expression may be due to the rest of the genome or to environmental factors. Figure 4-15 diagrams the distinction between penetrance and expressivity. Obviously, both penetrance and expressivity variation are integral components of the concept of norm of reaction, which was discussed in Chapter 1.

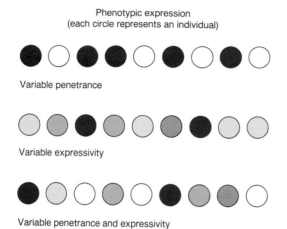

Phenotypic expression
(each circle represents an individual)

Variable penetrance

Variable expressivity

Variable penetrance and expressivity

Figure 4-15. Diagram representing effects of penetrance and expressivity through a hypothetical character "pigment intensity." In each row, all individuals have the same genotype (say, *PP*), giving them the same "potential to produce pigment." However, the effects of the rest of the genome and of the environment may suppress or modify pigment production in each individual.

Human pedigree analysis and predictions in genetic counseling can often be thwarted by the phenomena of penetrance and expressivity. For example, if a disease-causing allele is not fully penetrant (as usually is the case), it is difficult to give a clean genetic bill of health to any individual involved as part of a disease pedigree—for example, individual R in Figure 4-16. On the other hand, pedigree analysis can sometimes identify individuals who do not express but almost certainly have a disease genotype—for example, individual Q in Figure 4-16.

Further examples of variable expressivity are found in Figure 4-17 and in Problem 6 of Chapter 2.

Message The impact of a gene at the phenotype level depends not only on its dominance relations but also on the conditions of the rest of the genome and the condition of the environment.

The exceptions to Mendelian analysis covered in this chapter and following chapters are not the only ones encountered in routine genetic analysis; they are simply among the most common. Each exception—whether, for example, multiple allelism, incomplete dominance, epistasis, or variable expressivity—has its key recognition features at the experimental level. The analyst must be constantly on the lookout for these and any other results that might indicate the uniqueness of any given situation. Such signals often lead to the discovery of new phenomena and to the opening up of new research areas.

Summary

■ Although it has been shown that Mendel's laws apply to all eukaryotic organisms, these laws are only a base for understanding heredity. The real world of genes and chromosomes is much more complex.

In addition to the full dominance that Mendel observed in his experiments, incomplete dominance and codominance may exist. In incomplete dominance, the phenotype of a heterozygote is intermediate between those of the homozygotes. In codominance, the heterozygote shows the phenotypes of both homozygotes.

In his experiments, Mendel reported genes with two forms. It was later discovered that in fact a gene may have more than two forms. This situation is known as multiple allelism. The members of an allelic series may exhibit any type of dominance relationship with the other members. The genes controlling the rejection of incompatible tissues in humans are an example of multiple allelism.

One gene may affect more than one character. Such genes are known as pleiotropic genes. An example is the A^Y allele mice, which affects both coat color and survival.

The identification of a major gene affecting a character does not mean that it is the only gene affecting that character; several genes may be interacting. A good example of gene interaction is the coat color of mice, which is produced by a complex set of interacting genes that determine pigment type, pigment distribution in the hair, pigment distribution on the animal, and the presence or absence of pigment.

Gene interaction often produces modified Mendelian ratios in the F_2. Some kinds of interaction have specific names, such as complementary gene action, epistasis, suppression, and duplicate gene action. Gene interaction occurs in both diploid and haploid organisms.

Two other important extensions to Mendelian analysis are the concepts of penetrance and expressivity. Penetrance is the percentage of individuals of a specific genotype who express the phenotype associated with that genotype. Expressivity refers to the degree of expression, or severity, of a particular genotype at the phenotypic level.

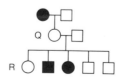

Figure 4-16. Lack of penetrance illustrated by a pedigree for a dominant gene. Individual Q must have the gene (because it was passed on to the progeny), but it was not expressed in the phenotype. An individual such as R cannot be sure that his or her genotype lacks the gene.

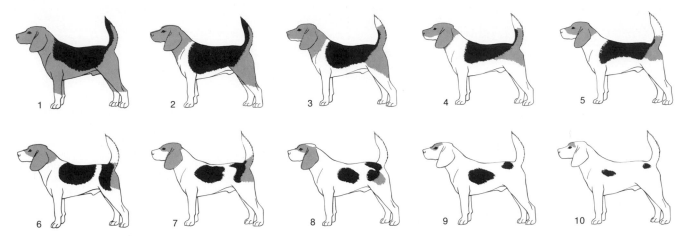

Figure 4-17. Ten grades of piebald spotting in beagles. Each of these dogs has the causative gene S^P; the variation in expressivity is attributed to modifying genes. (Adapted from Clarence C. Little,

The Inheritance of Coat Color in Dogs. Copyright © 1957 by Cornell University. Used by permission of the publisher, Cornell University Press.)

Problems

1. In *Clarkia elegans* plants, the allele for white flowers is recessive to the allele for pink flowers. Pollen from a heterozygous pink flower is placed on the pistil of a white flower. What is the expected ratio of phenotypes in the progeny? a. 1 pink:1 white b. 1 red:2 pink:1 white c. all pink d. 3 pink:1 white e. All white

(Problem 1 courtesy of F. R. Ganders.)

2. "Erminette" fowls have mostly light-colored feathers with an occasional black one, giving a "flecked" appearance. A cross of two erminettes produced a total of 48 progeny consisting of 22 erminettes, 14 blacks, and 12 pure whites. What genetic basis of the erminette pattern is suggested? How would you test your hypothesis?

3. In a moss, a certain protein is studied through electrophoresis. We consider two electrophoretic protein forms (P1 and P2), determined by two alleles, *P1* and *P2*. In this moss, the protein is found in both sporophyte and gametophyte. A gametophyte showing P1 is crossed with a gametophyte showing P2. What protein forms will be detected upon electrophoresis of the sporophyte? When this sporophyte produces spores, what gametophytes will result in what proportions?

4. In the plant incompatibility system described in Figure 4-6, progeny from the cross *S1S3* × *S2S4* are intercrossed in all combinations as males and as females. Name the proportion of the crosses for each of the following possible results: a. Fully fertile b. Fully sterile c. Partially fertile

5. In some compatibility systems in plants, pollen compatibility type is determined by the diploid genotype of the male parent. Often in these systems there is dominance of *S* alleles, not only in the male but also in the female. Assume the dominance series *S1* > *S2* > *S3* > *S4*. Thus, *S1S2* is type 1, *S2S3* is type 2, and so on. Assume that compatibility is possible only between different types. From the cross *S1S2* × *S3S4*, the progeny are intercrossed in all combinations. What will be the proportion of compatible matings? What progeny will be produced from the compatible matings?

6. In the multiple allelic series $C^+ > C^{ch} > C^h$, dominance is from left to right as shown. In a cross of $C^+C^{ch} \times C^{ch}C^h$, what proportion of the progeny will be Himalayan? a. 100 percent b. 3/4 c. 1/2 d. 1/4 e. 0 percent

7. a. The extremities of mammals show lower temperature than the rest of the body. What do you suppose this fact might have to do with the action of Himalayan alleles in mice and other animals?

   b. If a small patch of hair is shaved from the back of a Himalayan mouse and the area is kept covered with an ice pack, what color would you expect the hair to be when it grows back in this area? (1) white; (2) agouti; (3) black; (4) cinnamon, (5) yellow.

8. In a maternity ward, four babies become accidentally mixed up. The ABO types of the four babies are known to be O, A, B, and AB. The ABO types of the four sets of parents are determined. Indicate which baby belongs to each set of parents: a. AB × O b. A × O c. A × AB d. O × O

9. The M, N, and MN blood groups are determined by two alleles, L^M and L^N. The Rh$^+$ (rhesus positive) blood group is caused by a dominant allele R of a different gene. In a court case concerning a paternity dispute, each of two men claimed three children to be his own. The blood groups of the men, the children, and their mother were as follows:

Husband	O	M	Rh$^+$
The wife's lover	AB	MN	Rh$^-$
Wife	A	N	Rh$^+$
Child 1	O	MN	Rh$^+$
Child 2	A	N	Rh$^+$
Child 3	A	MN	Rh$^-$

From this evidence, can the paternity of the children be established?

10. On a fox ranch in Wisconsin, a mutation arose that gave a "platinum" coat color. The platinum color proved very popular with buyers of fox coats, but the breeders could not develop a pure-breeding platinum strain. Every time two platinums were crossed, some normal foxes appeared in the progeny. For example, in repeated matings of the same pair of platinums, a total of 82 platinums and 38 normals was produced. This result was typical of all other such matings. State a *concise* genetic hypothesis to account for these results.

11. Over a period of several years, Hans Nachtsheim investigated an inherited anomaly of the white blood cells of rabbits. This anomaly, termed the Pelger anomaly, in its usual condition involves an arrest of the typical segmentation of the nuclei of certain of the white cells. This anomaly does not appear to seriously inconvenience the rabbits.

    a. When rabbits showing the typical Pelger anomaly were mated with rabbits from a true-breeding normal stock, Nachtsheim counted 217 offspring showing the Pelger anomaly and 237 normal progeny. What appears to be the genetic basis of the Pelger anomaly?

    b. When rabbits with the Pelger anomaly were mated to each other, Nachtsheim found 223 normal progeny, 439 showing the Pelger anomaly, and 39 extremely abnormal progeny. These very abnormal progeny not only had defective white blood cells but also showed severe deformities of the skeletal system; almost all of them died soon after birth. In genetic terms, what do you suppose these extremely defective rabbits represented? Why do you suppose that there were only 39 of them?

    c. What additional experimental evidence might you collect to support or disprove your answers to part b?

    d. About one human in a thousand (in Berlin) shows a Pelger anomaly of white blood cells very similar to that described in rabbits. It is inherited as a simple dominant, but the homozygous type has not been observed in humans. Can you suggest why, if you are permitted an analogy with the condition in rabbits?

    e. Again by analogy with rabbits, what genetic situations might be expected among the children of a man and woman each showing the Pelger anomaly?

    (Problem 11 is from A. M. Srb, R. D. Owen, and R. S. Edgar, *General Genetics*, 2d ed. Copyright © W. H. Freeman and Company, 1965.)

12. You have been given a single virgin *Drosophila* female. You notice that the bristles on her thorax are much shorter than normal. You mate her with a normal male (with long bristles) and obtain the following F_1 progeny: 1/3 short-bristle females, 1/3 long-bristle females, and 1/3 long-bristle males. A cross of the F_1 long-bristle females with their brothers gives only long-bristle F_2. A

cross of short-bristle females with their brothers gives 1/3 short-bristle females, 1/3 long-bristle females, and 1/3 long-bristle males. Explain these data.

13. In *Drosophila*, a dominant allele H reduces the number of body bristles, giving rise to a "hairless" condition. In the homozygous condition H is lethal. An independently assorting dominant allele S has no effect on bristle number except in the presence of H, in which case a single dose of S suppresses the hairless phenotype, thus restoring the hairy condition. However, S also is lethal in the homozygous (SS) condition.

    a. What ratio of hairy to hairless individuals would you find in the live progeny of a cross between two hairy flies both carrying H in the suppressed condition?

    b. If the hairless progeny are backcrossed with a parental fly, what phenotypic ratio is expected in the live progeny?

14. In Labrador retriever dogs, the dominant gene B gives black coat color, whereas b gives brown. On another chromosome the gene E shows dominant epistasis over the B and b genes, resulting in a "golden" coat color, whereas e allows expression of B and b. A breeder wants to determine the genotypes of his three dogs, so he interbreeds them over several years as follows:

	Cross	Progeny
I	dog 1 (golden female) $\times$ dog 2 (golden male)	6/8 golden 1/8 black 1/8 brown
II	dog 1 (golden female) $\times$ dog 3 (black male)	4/8 golden 3/8 black 1/8 brown

    a. What are the genotypes of the three dogs?

    b. Show how the observed progeny ratios were produced.

15. In squash plants, white and yellow are fruit colors, and disk and sphere are fruit shapes. The cross of white, disk $\times$ yellow, sphere produces an F_1 of all white, disk. Selfing the F_1 produces an F_2 of 9/16 white, disk; 3/16 white, sphere; 3/16 yellow, disk; and 1/16 yellow, sphere. Interpret, using symbols of your own choosing.

16. Two albinos marry and have four normal children. How is this possible?

17. In corn, pure lines are obtained that have either sun-red, pink, scarlet, or orange kernels when exposed to sunlight (normal kernels remain yellow in sunlight). Table 4-5 gives the results of some crosses between these lines. Analyze the results of each cross, and provide a unifying hypothesis to account for *all* the results. (Explain all symbols you use.)

■ TABLE 4-5.

Cross	Parental phenotypes	F₁ phenotypes	F₂ phenotypes
1	Sun-red × pink	All sun-red	66 sun-red, 20 pink
2	Orange × sun-red	All sun-red	998 sun-red, 314 orange
3	Orange × pink	All orange	1300 orange, 429 pink
4	Orange × scarlet	All yellow	182 yellow, 80 orange, 58 scarlet

18. Many kinds of wild animals have the agouti coloring pattern, in which each hair has a yellow band around it (see Figure 4-11).

a. In black mice and other black animals, the yellow band is not present, and the hair is all black. This absence of wild agouti pattern is called nonagouti. When mice of a true-breeding agouti line are crossed with nonagoutis, the F₁ is all agouti, and the F₂ has a 3 : 1 ratio of agoutis to nonagoutis. Diagram this cross, letting A = agouti and a = nonagouti. Show the phenotypes and genotypes of the parents, their gametes, the F₁, their gametes, and the F₂.

b. Another inherited color deviation in mice substitutes brown for the black color in the wild-type hair. Such brown-agouti mice are called cinnamons. When wild-type mice are crossed with cinnamons, the F₁ is all wild-type, and the F₂ has a 3 : 1 ratio of wild-type to cinnamon. Diagram this cross as in part a, letting B = wild-type black and b = the brown of the cinnamon.

c. When mice of a true-breeding cinnamon line are crossed with mice of a true-breeding nonagouti (black) line, the F₁ is all wild-type. Use a genetic diagram to explain this result.

d. In the F₂ of the cross in part c, a fourth color called chocolate appears in addition to the parental cinnamon and nonagouti and the wild-type of the F₁. Chocolate mice have a solid, rich-brown color. What is the genetic constitution of the chocolates?

e. Assuming that the $A-a$ and $B-b$ allelic pairs assort independently of each other, what would you expect to be the relative frequencies of the four color types in the F₂ described in part d? Diagram the cross of parts c and d, showing phenotypes and genotypes (including gametes).

f. What phenotypes (and in what proportions) would be observed in the progeny of a backcross of F₁ mice from part c to the cinnamon parent stock? to the nonagouti (black) parent stock? Diagram these backcrosses.

g. Diagram a testcross for the F₁ of part c. What colors would result, and in what proportions?

h. Albino (pink-eyed white) mice are homozygous for the recessive member of an allelic pair $C-c$, which assorts independently of the $A-a$ and $B-b$ pairs. Suppose that you have four different highly inbred (and therefore presumably homozygous) albino lines. You cross each of these lines with a true-breeding wild-type line, and you raise a large F₂ progeny from each cross. What genotypes for the albino lines would you deduce from the F₂ phenotypes shown in Table 4-6?

■ TABLE 4-6.

		Numbers of F₂ progeny			
F₂ of line	Wild-type	Nonagouti (black)	Cinnamon	Chocolate	Albino
1	87	0	32	0	39
2	62	0	0	0	18
3	96	30	0	0	41
4	287	86	92	29	164

(Problem 18 is adapted from A. M. Srb, R. D. Owen, and R. S. Edgar, *General Genetics*, 2d ed. Copyright © W. H. Freeman and Company, 1965.)

19. In rats, yellow coat color is determined by an allele A that is not lethal when homozygous. At a separate gene that assorts independently, the allele R produces a black coat. Together, A and R produce a grayish coat, whereas $aa\ rr$ is white. A gray male is crossed with a yellow female, and the F₁ is 3/8 yellow, 3/8 gray, 1/8 black, and 1/8 white. Deduce the genotypes of the parents.

20. Normal *Drosophila melanogaster* have deep red eyes. You are able to establish two homozygous lines, one having bright scarlet eyes and the other having dark brown eyes. When you cross scarlet-eyed flies with brown-eyed flies, all of the F₁ progeny have deep red eyes. An F₁ × F₁ cross produces the following progeny: 432 red eyes, 158 scarlet eyes, 139 brown eyes, and 52 white eyes. Explain these results, using symbols of your own devising.

21. In the fowl, the genotype $rr\,pp$ gives single comb, $R-P-$ gives walnut comb, $rr\,P-$ gives pea comb, and $R-\,pp$ gives rose comb.

■ TABLE 4-7.

F₂ from cross of part	Wild-type		White-eyed		Scarlet-eyed		Brown-eyed	
	♂	♀	♂	♀	♂	♀	♂	♀
a	44	88	86	11	14	34	16	29
b	88	90	180	175	28	29	24	26

a. What comb types will appear (and in what proportions) in F₁ and in F₂ if single-combed birds are crossed with birds of a true-breeding walnut-combed strain?

b. What are the genotypes of the parents in a walnut-combed × rose-combed mating from which the progeny are 3/8 rose-combed, 3/8 walnut-combed, 1/8 pea-combed, and 1/8 single-combed?

c. What are the genotypes of the parents in a walnut-combed × rose-combed mating from which all the progeny are walnut-combed?

d. How many genotypes will produce a walnut phenotype? Write them out.

22. F₂ phenotypic ratios of 27 : 37 have been observed. What is their genetic basis? (HINT: You may find it useful to consider trihybrids.)

(Problems 21 and 22 are adapted from A. M. Srb, R. D. Owen, and R. S. Edgar, *General Genetics*, 2d ed. Copyright © W. H. Freeman and Company, 1965.)

*23. *Answer the parts of this problem in sequence.* You have two homozygous lines of *Drosophila*, one found in Vancouver (line A) and the other found in Los Angeles (line B). Both lines have bright scarlet eyes, a phenotype quite distinct from the deep red eyes of the wild-type.

a. A cross of line-A males with line-B females produces an F₁ of 200 wild-type males and 198 wild-type females. From this result, what can you say about the inheritance of eye color in the two lines?

b. A cross of line-B males with line-A females produces an F₁ of 197 scarlet-eyed males and 201 wild-type females. What does this result indicate about the inheritance of eye color?

c. When you intercross the F₁ progeny from part a, you obtain the following F₂ progeny: 151 wild-type females, 49 scarlet-eyed females, 126 scarlet-eyed males, and 74 wild-type males. Diagram the genotypes of the parents and of the F₁ offspring. Indicate the expected ratios of F₂ genotypes and phenotypes.

*24. *Answer the parts of this problem in sequence.* In *Drosophila melanogaster*, wild-type eyes are deep red in color. You have obtained two lines of *Drosophila*, line A and line B, in which the eyes are white.

a. A cross of line-A males with line-B females produces an F₁ of 435 wild-type males and 428 wild-type females. What can you conclude about lines A and B?

b. A cross of line-B males with line-A females produces an F₁ of 420 white-eyed males and 405 wild-type females. What can you conclude about lines A and B?

c. Two sets of F₂ progeny are obtained by separately intercrossing the F₁ flies from parts a and b. Two new eye colors appear in the F₂ progeny: bright scarlet and brownish. Table 4-7 summarizes the phenotypes observed in the F₂ generations. Explain these results. Diagram the crosses for all parts of this problem.

25. When true-breeding brown dogs are mated with true-breeding white dogs, all the F₁ pups are white. When F₁ × F₁ crosses are made, the F₂ progeny are 118 white, 32 black, and 10 brown pups. What is the genetic basis for these results?

26. In corn, three dominant alleles called *A*, *C*, and *R* must be present to produce colored seeds. Genotypes *A – C – R –* are colored; all others are colorless. A colored plant is crossed with three tester plants of known genotype. With *aaccRR*, it produces 50 percent colored seeds. With *aaCCrr*, it produces 25 percent colored seeds. With *AAccrr*, it produces 50 percent colored seeds. What is the genotype of the colored plant?

27. In the fungus *Neurospora* (haploid), a mutant gene *td* results in an inability of the fungus to make its own tryptophan, so that growth can occur only if tryptophan is supplied in the medium. The allele *su* assorts independently of *td*; its only known effect is to suppress the td phenotype. Therefore, strains carrying both *td* and *su* do not require tryptophan for growth.

a. If a *td su* strain is crossed with a genotypically wild-type strain, what genotypes are expected in the progeny, and in what proportions?

b. What will be the ratio of tryptophan-dependent to tryptophan-independent progeny in the cross of part a?

28. In horses, assume that there are three color-affecting genes with the following effects: *WW* is lethal, *Ww* is white, and *ww* allows color; *BB* or *Bb* is black, and *bb* is chestnut; *OO* or *Oo* is solid, and *oo* has white spots on color. A white stallion and a white mare, each heterozygous for all these

genes, are mated. What are the expected frequencies of possible phenotypes in the live offspring? What frequencies of phenotypes would be expected if the stallion were *Ww Bb oo*?

29. In mice, a cross is made of *AA BB CC DD SS* × *aa bb cc dd ss*. (These gene symbols are explained in the text of this chapter.) What phenotypes would be produced in the F₂, and in what proportions?

30. Bean anthracnose is a fungus disease affecting beans. Two different bean varieties, A and B, and two different lines of parasitic fungus, α and β, are obtained. Fungus line α produces disease in bean variety A but not in variety B. Fungus line β produces disease in bean variety B but not in variety A. The cross A × B is made and an F₁ and F₂ are obtained. Both generations are treated with a mixture containing fungus from both lines α and β. None of the F₁ show any disease reaction. In the F₂, the ratio of unaffected to diseased plants is 9 : 7.

   a. Interpret these results genetically.

   b. If the two parasite lines were crossed, how would you expect their progeny to react with bean variety A? with B? Make a testable prediction. (For simplicity, assume that the fungus is haploid.)

31. The following pedigree is for a dominant, autosomal gene. How is this pedigree possible, and what can you deduce about the genotype of individual A?

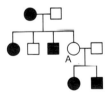

32. Three plants of *Collinsia grandiflora* (blue-eyed Mary) are found in different populations, all having spots on their leaves, as shown in the figure. From the following, select the reason for this variation, and outline the experimental steps that led to your conclusion: a. Different alleles of one gene b. Variable expressivity due to modification by other genes c. Variable expressivity due to environmental effects

33. In foxgloves, the gene *M* causes the production of magenta pigment in the petal, and *m* produces no pigment, resulting in white petals with faint yellowish spots. At an unlinked locus, the gene *D* enhances pigment production, resulting in a dark magenta, whereas *d* does not enhance, resulting in light magenta. At another unlinked locus *W* prevents pigment deposition in all parts of the petals except the spots resulting (in the presence of *M*) in white petals with magenta spots. The allele *w* does not prevent pigment deposition. The four possible phenotypes are summarized in the following diagram.

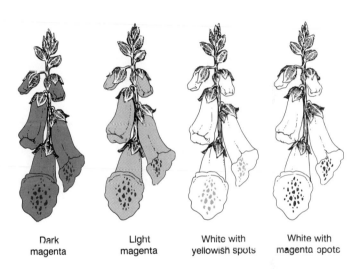

| Dark magenta | Light magenta | White with yellowish spots | White with magenta spots |

Consider the following two crosses.

Cross	Parents		Progeny
I	dark magenta	× white with yellowish spots	1/2 dark magenta 1/2 light magenta
II	white with yellowish spots	× light magenta	1/2 white with magenta spots 1/4 dark magenta 1/4 light magenta

In each case, give the genotypes of parents and progeny with respect to these three gene pairs.

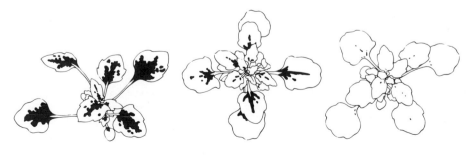

34. A phenotype is the result of the interaction of an individual's genotype and the environment. Monozygotic ("identical") twins represent an interesting genetic phenomenon, and the study of such twins sometimes can shed light on the relative contributions of genotype and environment to phenotype. The following table shows fingerprint patterns from a family whose members included a pair of monozygotic twins ("sibs," or siblings, is a general term for brothers and sisters). Which of the differences within the family do you think can be attributed to environmental variation (or to developmental noise)? Can you find any differences that must be genetic? (NOTE: monozygotic twins begin as the identical daughter cells from the first mitotic division of a zygote.)

(From Giorgio Schreiber, *Journal of Heredity* 9:403, 1930.)

CHAPTER 5

Linkage I: Basic Eukaryotic Chromosome Mapping

■ We have already established the basic principles of segregation and assortment, and we have correlated them with chromosomal behavior during meiosis. Thus, from the cross $Aa\,Bb \times Aa\,Bb$, we expect a $9:3:3:1$ ratio of phenotypes. As we saw in Bridges' study of nondisjunction, exceptions to simple Mendelian expectations can direct the experimenter's attention to new discoveries. Just such an exception involving a dihybrid cross provided the clue to the important concepts discussed in this chapter.

Message   Exceptions to predicted behavior often are the source of important new insights.

The Discovery of Linkage

In the early years of this century, William Bateson and R. C. Punnett were studying inheritance in the sweet pea. They studied two pairs of genes, one affecting flower color (P, purple, and p, red) and the other affecting the shape of pollen grains (L, long, and l, round). They made a dihybrid cross, $PP\,LL$ (purple, long) $\times pp\,ll$ (red, round), and then selfed the F_1 $Pp\,Ll$ heterozygotes to get an F_2. Table 5-1 shows the proportions of each phenotype in the F_2 plants.

The results of this cross are a striking deviation from the expected $9:3:3:1$ ratio. What is going on? This does not look like something that can be explained as a modified Mendelian ratio. Note that two phenotypic classes are larger than expected: the purple, long phenotype and the red, round phenotype. Bateson and Punnett speculated that the size of these two classes is due to an excess of the two gametic types $P\,L$ and $p\,l$. Because these were the original parental gametic types, it occurred to the researchers that there might be a physical **coupling** between dominant genes (P and L) and between the recessive genes (p and l) that had prevented their independent assortment in the F_1. However, they did not know what the nature of this coupling might be.

The explanation of Bateson and Punnett's results had to await the development of *Drosophila* as a genetic tool. After coupling was first described, Thomas Hunt Morgan found a similar deviation from Mendel's second law while studying two autosomal gene pairs in *Drosophila*. One of these gene pairs affects eye color (pr, purple, and pr^+, red), and the other affects wing length (vg, vestigial, and vg^+, normal). Morgan crossed $pr\,pr\,vg\,vg$ flies with $pr^+pr^+\,vg^+vg^+$, and then testcrossed the doubly heterozygous F_1 females: $pr\,pr^+\,vg\,vg^+\,♀ \times pr\,pr\,vg\,vg\,♂$.

The use of the testcross is extremely important. Because one parent (the tester) contributes gametes carrying only recessive alleles, the phenotypes of the offspring represent the gametic contribution of the doubly heterozygous other parent. Hence, the analyst can concentrate on one

■ **TABLE** 5-1. Observed and expected phenotypes in the F₂ from the dihybrid cross

Phenotype	Numbers of individuals observed	Approximate numbers of individuals expected (from 9:3:3:1 ratio)
Purple, long (P– L–)	284	215
Purple, round (P– ll)	21	71
Red, long (pp L–)	21	71
Red, round (pp ll)	55	24
	381	381

meiosis and forget about the other. This is in contrast to the situation in an F₁ self, where there are two sets of meiotic divisions to consider—one for the male parental gametes and one for the female. Morgan's results were as follows, with the F₂ individuals designated in terms of the genes contributed by the F₁ female:

$$pr^+vg^+ \quad 1339$$
$$prvg \quad 1195$$
$$pr^+vg \quad 151$$
$$prvg^+ \quad \underline{154}$$
$$2839$$

Obviously, these numbers are a drastic deviation from the Mendelian prediction of a 1:1:1:1 ratio, and they indicate a coupling of genes. The largest classes are the two gene combinations, pr^+vg^+ and $prvg$, originally introduced by the parental flies. You can see that the testcross makes the situation much clearer. It directly reveals the gene combinations in the gamete population from one sex in the F₁, thus clearly showing the coupling that could only be inferred from Bateson and Punnett's F₁ self. The testcross also reveals something new: there is approximately a 1:1 ratio between the two parental types and also between the two nonparental types.

When each parent in a cross was homozygous for one of the recessive genes, an F₁ testcross produced different results:

$$P \qquad pr^+pr^+vgvg \times prprvg^+vg^+$$

$$\downarrow$$

$$F_1 \qquad pr^+prvg^+vg \,♀ \times prprvgvg \,♂$$

The following progeny were obtained from the testcross:

$$pr^+vg^+ \quad 157$$
$$prvg \quad 146$$
$$pr^+vg \quad 965$$
$$prvg^+ \quad \underline{1067}$$
$$2335$$

Again, the results are not even close to a 1:1:1:1 Mendelian ratio. Now, however, the largest classes are those having one or the other dominant gene, rather than two dominants or two recessives as before. But notice that once again the gene combinations originally contributed to the F₁ by the parental flies provide the most frequent classes in the F₂. In the early work on coupling, Bateson and Punnett coined the term **repulsion** to describe this situation, because it seemed to them that the nonallelic dominant genes were "repelled" from each other—the opposite of the situation in coupling, where the dominant genes seemed to "stick together." How can we explain these two phenomena, coupling and repulsion?

Morgan suggested that in coupling both pairs of genes being studied are located *on the same pair of homologous chromosomes.* Thus, when *pr* and *vg* are introduced from one parent, they are physically located on the same chromosome, whereas *pr⁺* and *vg⁺* are on the homologous chromosome from the other parent (Figure 5-1). This hypothesis also explains repulsion. In that case, one parental chromosome carries *pr* and *vg⁺*, and the other carries *pr⁺* and *vg*. Repulsion, then, is just another case of coupling: in this case, the genes coupled are one dominant and one nonallelic recessive. This hypothesis explains why gene combinations from P remain together, but how do we explain the existence of nonparental combinations?

Morgan suggested that, when homologous chromosomes pair during meiosis, there is occasionally a physical exchange of chromosome parts by a process called crossing-over. Figure 5-2 illustrates this process, which results in a physical exchange of chromosome segments. The original gene arrangement on the two chromosomes is called the **parental** combination. The two new combinations are called **crossover types, exchange products, intrachromosomal recombinants,** or simply **recombinants.**

This hypothesis may seem a bit farfetched. Is there any

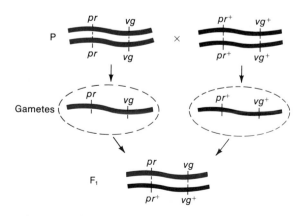

Figure 5-1. Simple inheritance of two gene pairs located on the same chromosome pair.

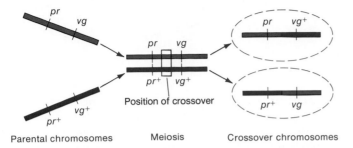

Figure 5-2. Diagrammatic representation of the process of crossing-over during meiosis. Homologous chromosomes exchange parts in the crossover.

cytologically observable process that could account for something like crossing-over? We saw in Chapter 3 that, during meiosis, when duplicated homologous chromosomes are paired with each other, two nonsister chromatids often appear to cross each other, whereas the other two do not. This is diagrammed in Figure 5-3. Recall that the resulting cross-shaped structure is called a chiasma. To Morgan, the appearance of the chiasmata was a perfect visual corroboration of the concept of crossing-over. (Note that they seem to indicate that crossing-over occurs between chromatids, not between unduplicated chromosomes. We shall return to this point later.) For the present, let us accept Morgan's interpretation that chiasmata are the cytological counterparts of crossovers, and leave the proof until Chapter 16. Note that Morgan did not arrive at this interpretation out of nowhere; he was looking for a *physical* explanation for his *genetic* results. His achievement in correlating the results of breeding experiments with cytological phenomena thus serves to emphasize the importance of the chromosome theory as a powerful basis for research.

Message   Chiasmata are the visible manifestations of crossovers.

Data like those just presented, showing coupling and repulsion in testcrosses and in F_1 selfs, are commonly encountered in genetics. Clearly, results of this kind represent a departure from independent assortment. Such exceptions, in fact, constitute a major addition to Mendel's view of the genetic world.

Message   When two gene pairs are located close together on the same chromosome pair, they do not show independent assortment.

The general situation in which gene pairs reside on the same chromosome pair is termed **linkage.** Two gene pairs on the same chromosome pair are said to be linked. It is also proper to refer to linkage of specific alleles: for example, in a *Aa Bb* individual, *A* might be linked to *b*, and *a* would then of necessity be linked to *B*. These terms graphically allude to the existence of a physical entity linking the genes — that

is, the chromosome itself! You may wonder why such genes are referred to as "linked" rather than "coupled"; the answer is that coupling and repulsion have come to indicate two different types of linkage conformation in a double heterozygote, as follows.

coupling conformation $\dfrac{pr \qquad vg}{pr^+ \qquad vg^+}$

repulsion conformation $\dfrac{pr \qquad vg^+}{pr^+ \qquad vg}$

In other words, coupling refers to the linkage of two dominant or two recessive genes, whereas repulsion indicates linkage of one dominant and one recessive gene in a double heterozygote. A double heterozygote can be assigned a coupling or a repulsion conformation only from a consideration of the parental genotypes or by testcrossing.

Recombination

We have already introduced the term recombination. This term is widely used in many areas of practical and theoretical genetics, so it is absolutely necessary to be clear on its meaning at this stage. Recombination can occur in a variety of situations in addition to meiosis, but for the present let us define it in relation to meiosis. To adapt the definition to other situations, we shall simply replace the words meiotic and meiosis with other appropriate terms.

Definition   Meiotic recombination is any meiotic process that generates a haploid product whose genotype is different from the two haploid genotypes that constituted the meiotic diploid. The product of meiosis so generated is called a recombinant.

This definition makes the important point that the detection of recombination is based on a comparison of the *out-*

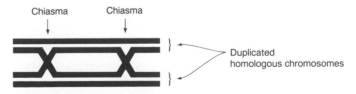

Figure 5-3. Highly diagrammatic representation of chiasmata at meiosis. Each line represents a chromatid of a pair of chromosomes in synapsis during meiosis.

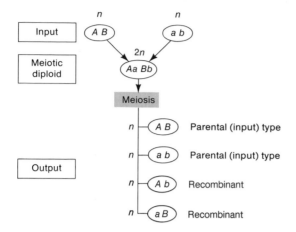

Figure 5-4. Recombination. This diagram shows a meiosis, comparing its input haploid genotypes to its output haploid genotypes.

put (or product) genotypes of meiosis with the *input* genotypes (Figure 5-4). The input genotypes are the two haploid types that combined to make the meiotic diploid—that is, the diploid cell or group of cells whose meiosis we are considering.

The definition of recombination applies to both haploid and diploid life cycles. In haploids, the situation is identical to that shown in Figure 5-4. The phenotypes of the haploid input and output are used to determine genotypes directly, because in this case the input and the output are individuals. In diploid cycles, however, the input and the output are gametes! To detect recombination in a diploid cycle, we must have pure-breeding parents, so that we know their gametic contribution. Furthermore, we cannot detect recombinant output gametes directly: we must testcross the meiotic diploid under study—in this case, an individual—to reveal the recombinants produced by meiosis (Figure 5-5). If a testcross offspring is shown to have been constituted from a recombinant product of meiosis, it too is called a recombinant. Notice again that the testcross allows us to concentrate on *one* meiotic system, avoiding ambiguity. In a self of the F₁ in Figure 5-5, for example, an *AA Bb* offspring (which would demonstrate recombination in F₁) cannot be distinguished from *AA BB* without further extensive crosses.

There are two kinds of recombination, and they produce recombinants by completely different methods. But a recombinant is a recombinant, so how can we decide which type of recombination has occurred in any particular progeny? The answer lies in the *frequency* of recombinants, as we shall soon see. First, though, let us consider the two types of recombination.

Interchromosomal Recombination

Interchromosomal recombination is achieved by Mendelian independent assortment. The two recombinant classes always make up 50 percent of the progeny; that is, there are 25 percent of each recombinant type among the progeny (Figure 5-6). If we observe this frequency, we can infer that the gene pairs under study are assorting independently.

The simplest interpretation of these frequencies is that

the gene pairs are on separate chromosome pairs. However, as has already been hinted, gene pairs that are far apart on the *same* chromosome pair can act virtually independently, producing the same result. We shall see in the next chapter how a large amount of crossing-over effectively unlinks the distantly linked gene pairs.

Intrachromosomal Recombination

The sign of intrachromosomal recombination is a recombinant frequency of less than 50 percent. The physical linkage of parental gene combinations prevents the free assortment of gene pairs (Figure 5-7). We saw an example of this situation in Morgan's data (page 80), where the recombinant frequency was $(151 + 154) \div 2839 = 10.7$ percent. This is obviously much less than the 50 percent we would expect with independent assortment. What is the significance of recombinant frequencies greater than 50 percent? The answer is that such frequencies are *never* observed, as we shall prove in Chapter 6.

Linkage Symbolism

Our symbolism for describing crosses becomes cumbersome with the introduction of linkage. We can show the genetic constitution of each chromosome in the *Drosophila* cross as

$$\frac{pr \qquad vg}{pr^+ \qquad vg^+}$$

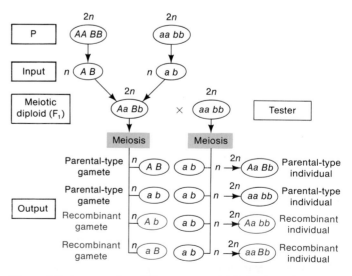

Figure 5-5. An expansion of Figure 5-4 to clarify the process of recombination in diploid organisms. Note that Figure 5-4 is actually a part of this figure. In a diploid meiosis, the recombinant meiotic products are most readily detected by a cross to a recessive tester.

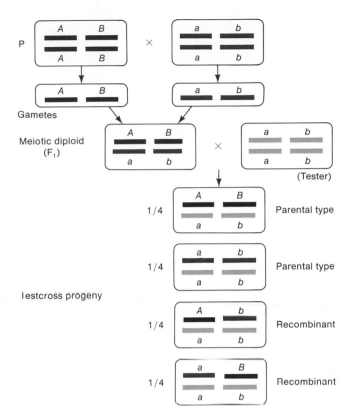

Figure 5-6. Interchromosomal recombination, which always produces a recombinant frequency of 50 percent. This diagram shows a diploid organism, but we can see the haploid situation by removing the part marked P and the testcross.

where each line represents a chromosome, the genes above being on one chromosome and those below on the other. A crossover is represented by $\times$ between the two chromosomes, so that

$$
\begin{array}{cc}
pr & vg \\
\hline
\multicolumn{2}{c}{\times} \\
\hline
pr^+ & vg^+
\end{array}
$$

is the same as

$$
\begin{array}{cc}
pr & vg \\
& \\
pr^+ & vg^+
\end{array}
$$

We can simplify the genotypic designation of linked genes by drawing a single line, with the genes on each side being on the same chromosome; now our symbol is

$$
\begin{array}{cc}
pr & vg \\
\hline
pr^+ & vg^+
\end{array}
$$

But this gives us problems in typing and writing, so let's tip the line to give us $prvg/pr^+vg^+$, still keeping the genes on one chromosome on one side of the line, and those of its

homolog on the other. We always designate linked genes on each side in the same order, so it is always ab/ab, never ab/ba. That being the case, we can indicate the wild-type allele with a plus sign (+), and $prvg/pr^+vg^+$ becomes $prvg/++$. From now on, we'll use this kind of designation unless its use creates an ambiguity.

If we now reconsider the results obtained by Bateson and Punnett, we can easily explain the coupling phenomenon by means of the concept of linkage. Their results are complex because they did not do a testcross. See if you can derive estimated numbers for recombinant and parental types in the gametes.

Linkage of Genes on the X Chromosome

Until now, we have been considering recombination in autosomal genes. If, however, we were to look at sex-linked genes, a testcross would not be necessary. (Don't confuse linkage with sex linkage. Linkage describes the association of genes on the same chromosome, whereas sex linkage

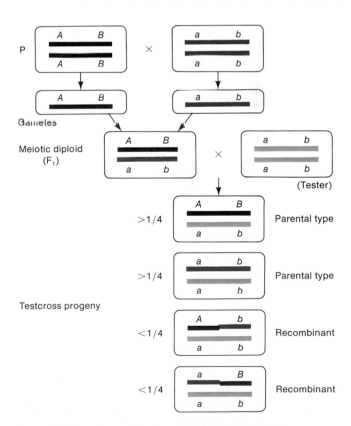

Figure 5-7. Intrachromosomal recombination, which always produces a recombinant frequency equal to or (usually) less than 50 percent. Again, a diploid organism is shown.

describes the association of genes with an X chromosome or other sex-determining chromosome.) Consider what happens when recombination involves the X chromosome. A female, heterozygous for two different sex-linked genes, will produce male progeny hemizygous for those genes, so that the mother's gametic genotype will be the son's phenotype. Let's take an example, using the genes y (yellow body) and y^+ (brown body), and w (white eye) and w^+ (red eye). In the following cross, Y represents the Y chromosome; do not confuse it with the y/y^+ gene.

P $y+/y+ \; ♀ \times +w/Y \; ♂$ (that is, $yw^+/yw^+ \; ♀ \times y^+w/Y \; ♂$)

F_1 $y+/+w \; ♀ \times y+/Y \; ♂$ (that is, $yw^+/y^+w \; ♀ \times yw^+/Y \; ♂$)

The number of F_2 males in each phenotypic class is

$$
\begin{array}{ccr}
y & w & 43 \\
+ & w & 2146 \\
y & + & 2302 \\
+ & + & \underline{22} \\
& & 4513
\end{array}
$$

These classes reflect the products of meiosis in the F_1 female. The system is in effect a testcross, because the F_2 males obtain only a Y chromosome from the F_1 $y+/Y$ males, and thus they have only one allele (obtained from the mother) for each of the genes we are considering. The recombinant frequency in this case is $(43 + 22) \div 4513 = 1.4$ percent.

Linkage Maps

The frequency of recombinants for the *Drosophila* autosomal genes we studied (*pr* and *vg*) was 10.7 percent of the progeny, much greater than that for the linked genes on the X chromosome. Apparently, the amount of crossing-over between linked gene pairs is not constant. Indeed, there is no reason to expect that crossing-over between different linked gene pairs would occur with the same frequency. As Morgan studied more linked genes, he saw that the proportion of recombinant progeny varied considerably, depending on which linked gene pairs were being studied, and he thought that these variations in crossover frequency might somehow reflect the actual distances separating genes on the chromosomes. Morgan assigned the study of this problem to a student, Alfred Sturtevant, who (like Bridges) became one of the great geneticists. Morgan asked Sturtevant, still an undergraduate at the time, to make some sense of the data on crossing-over between different linked genes. In one night, Sturtevant developed a method for describing relationships between genes that is still used today.

For example, consider a testcross from which we obtain the following results:

$$
\left.
\begin{array}{lr}
prvg/prvg & 165 \\
++/prvg & 191
\end{array}
\right\} \text{Parental (noncrossover) types}
$$

$$
\left.
\begin{array}{lr}
pr+/prvg & 23 \\
+vg/prvg & \underline{21}
\end{array}
\right\} \text{Recombinant (crossover) types}
$$
$$
\phantom{\left.\begin{array}{l}+vg/prvg\end{array}\right\}} 400
$$

The progeny in this example represent 400 female gametes, of which 44 (or 11 percent) are recombinant. Sturtevant suggested that we can use this percentage of recombinants as a quantitative index of the linear distance between two gene pairs on a **genetic map,** or **linkage map,** as it is sometimes called.

The basic idea here is quite simple. Imagine two specific gene pairs a certain fixed distance apart (Figure 5-8). Now imagine crossovers occurring randomly along the paired homologs. In some meiotic divisions, a crossover occurs by chance in the chromosomal region between these gene pairs; from these meioses, the recombinants are produced. In other meiotic divisions, no crossover occurs in the intervening region; no recombinants result from these meioses. Sturtevant postulated a rough proportionality: the greater the distance between the linked genes, the greater the chance of a crossover's occurring in the intervening region, and hence the greater the proportion of meioses in which a crossover occurs here. Thus, by measuring the frequency of recombinants, we can obtain a measure of the map distance between the gene pairs.

Message   One **genetic map unit (m.u.)** is the distance between gene pairs for which one product of meiosis out of 100 is recombinant. Put another way, a **recombinant frequency (RF)** of 0.01 (or 1 percent) is defined as 1 m.u. (A map unit is sometimes referred to as a **centimorgan** (cM), in honor of Thomas Hunt Morgan.)

A direct consequence of this relationship is that if genes A and B are separated by five map units, whereas genes A and C are separated by three map units, then B and C should be either eight or two map units apart. Sturtevant found this to be the case. In other words, his analysis strongly suggested the idea that genes are arranged in some linear order.

The place on the map that represents a gene pair is called the **gene locus** (plural, **loci**). The locus of the eye-color gene pair and the locus of the wing-shape gene pair, for example, are 11 map units apart. They are usually diagrammed this way:

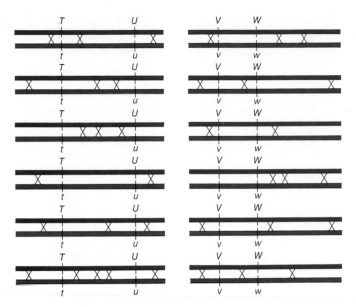

X = Position of crossover

Figure 5-8. Proportionality between chromosomal distance and recombinant frequency. Each line represents a chromosome pair (four chromatids) during meiosis, and the crosses represent the positions of the crossovers that are taking place. On the left, two distant gene pairs (T and U) are shown; on the right (a different chromosome) are two close gene pairs (V and W). Crossovers occur at random along the chromosomes, and there are more of them between T and U than between V and W, so the recombinant frequency for T and U will be higher than that for V and W.

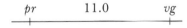

although they could be diagrammed equally well like this:

$$pr^+ \qquad 11.0 \qquad vg^+$$

or like this:

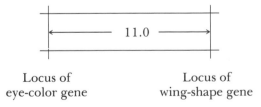

Locus of
eye-color gene

Locus of
wing-shape gene

Usually the locus of this eye-color gene is referred to in shorthand as the "pr locus," after the most famous non-wild allele, but it means the place on the chromosome where any allele of this gene will be found.

Given a genetic distance in map units, we can predict frequencies of progeny in different classes. For example, of the progeny from a testcross of a $pr\,vg/++$ heterozygote,

$5\frac{1}{2}$ percent will be $pr+/pr\,vg$ and $5\frac{1}{2}$ percent will be $+vg/pr\,vg$; of the progeny from a testcross of a $pr+/+vg$ heterozygote, $5\frac{1}{2}$ percent will be $pr\,vg/pr\,vg$ and $5\frac{1}{2}$ percent will be $++/pr\,vg$.

There is a strong implication that the "distance" on a genetic map is a physical distance along a chromosome, and Morgan and Sturtevant certainly intended to imply just that. But we should realize that the genetic map is another example of an entity constructed from a purely genetic analysis. The genetic map could have been derived without even knowing that chromosomes existed. Furthermore, at this point in our discussion, we cannot say whether the "genetic distances" calculated by means of recombinant frequencies in any way reflect actual physical distances on chromosomes, although cytogenetic analysis of *Drosophila* has shown that genetic distances are, in fact, roughly proportional to chromosome distances. Nevertheless, it must be emphasized that the hypothetical structure (the linkage map) was developed with a very real structure (the chromosome) in mind. In other words, the chromosome theory provided the framework for the development of linkage mapping.

Let's follow some examples from *Drosophila*. In our first example, the non-wild-type alleles are sc (scute, or loss of certain thoracic bristles), ec (echinus, or roughened eye surface), and vg (vestigial wing). If we take sc/sc, ec/ec, vg/vg triple-recessive flies and cross these with wild-types, a triple heterozygote $sc/+$, $ec/+$, $vg/+$ is established in the F_1. We can take F_1 females of this genotype and testcross them with sc/sc, ec/ec, vg/vg. (By drawing the genotypes this way, we don't commit ourselves to any particular linkage arrangement at this stage of the analysis.) The progeny, listed as the gametic types from the triple heterozygote, will be as follows. The numbers are invented for the purpose of illustration, but they are based on real linkage values for these particular genes.

sc	ec	vg	235
$+$	$+$	$+$	241
sc	ec	$+$	243
$+$	$+$	vg	233
sc	$+$	vg	12
$+$	ec	$+$	14
sc	$+$	$+$	14
$+$	ec	vg	16
			1008

There is considerable deviation from the $1:1:1:1:1:1:1:1$ ratio we expect for a trihybrid cross of independently assorting genes, so linkage must be involved. The four classes with the largest numbers must consist of those individuals that are not the result of a crossover between linked loci. Which loci are linked? Taking only the four largest classes, we can determine whether sc and ec are linked. (Remember that by sc and ec we really mean the gene sites, or loci, represented by $sc/+$ and $ec/+$.) Ignoring vg then, we get

sc	ec	235
+	+	241
sc	ec	243
+	+	233

There are only two classes, $sc\,ec$ and $++$; so we know they are linked and that these are the two parental classes. What about vg? Let's ask whether ec and vg are linked and ignore sc (because we know it is linked to ec). The data then are

ec	vg	235
+	+	241
ec	+	243
+	vg	233

which is a nearly perfect $1:1:1:1$ ratio, showing that vg is assorting independently of ec (and sc). So we know sc and ec are on one chromosome, and vg assorts independently. We can calculate the genetic distance between sc and ec by looking at the smaller classes, which (if we ignore vg because it is assorting independently) are obviously derived from crossovers.

sc	+	12
+	ec	14
sc	+	14
+	ec	16

The distance between sc and ec is $[(12+14+14+16)/1008] \times 100 = 5.5$ map units, and we can diagram the genetic maps as

```
sc        5.5       ec        vg
+-------------------+         +--+
```

Now let's take another cross, in which the genes are sc, ec, and another non-wild-type, cv (crossveinless, or absence of a crossvein on the wing). We cross flies homozygous for sc, ec, and cv with homozygous wild-type to get triple-heterozygote females, which we then testcross to obtain (again, invented numbers)

sc	ec	cv	417
+	+	+	430
sc	+	+	25
+	ec	cv	29
sc	ec	+	44
+	+	cv	37
+	ec	+	0
sc	+	cv	0
			982

First, do these genes assort independently? We see that there are two classes, $sc\,ec\,cv$ and $+++$, that occur much more often than the others, thereby showing that we are not getting a $1:1:1:1$ ratio of independent assortment of any two pairs. Moreover, they are reciprocal classes (that is, the alleles in one are all different from those in the other); so sc, ec, and cv must have been on one of the homologous chromosomes and $+$, $+$, and $+$ on the other. We now know the three genes are linked; so we can determine how far apart they are. Looking at one pair of loci at a time, let's take sc and ec first (we can cover up the cv and consider only the sc and ec pair of loci).

sc	ec	~~cv~~	417
+	+	~~+~~	430
sc	+	~~+~~	25
+	ec	~~cv~~	29
sc	ec	~~+~~	44
+	+	~~cv~~	37
+	ec	~~+~~	0
sc	+	~~cv~~	0
			982

There are $417+430+44+37=928$ parentals and $25+29=54$ recombinants with respect to these two gene pairs. Therefore, the genetic distance between sc and ec is 5.5 map units $[(54/982) \times 100]$, which is the same distance found earlier for another cross involving these loci. The map can be diagrammed as

```
sc        5.5       ec
+-------------------+
```

Now let's take ec and cv; the data are

~~sc~~	ec	cv	417
~~+~~	+	+	430
~~sc~~	+	+	25
~~+~~	ec	cv	29
~~sc~~	ec	+	44
~~+~~	+	cv	37
~~+~~	ec	+	0
~~sc~~	+	cv	0
			982

There are $417+430+25+29=901$ parentals and $44+37=81$ recombinants. The distance between ec and cv, then, is $(81/982) \times 100 = 8.2$, and the map is

```
ec        8.2       cv
+-------------------+
```

The distance between sc and ec being 5.5 and that between ec and cv being 8.2, we can draw a map as either

```
   ec    5.5    sc    cv
   +------+-----+-----+
        <------ 8.2 ------>
```

or

```
   sc    5.5    ec        8.2        cv
   +------+-------+---------+
```

Now let's see how far *sc* and *cv* are apart, forgetting *ec*:

sc	//	cv	417
+	//	+	430
sc	/	+	25
+	//	cv	29
sc	//	+	44
+	/	cv	37
+	//	+	0
sc	/	cv	0
			982

There are $417 + 430 = 847$ parentals and $25 + 29 + 44 + 37 = 135$ recombinants for a distance of $(135/982) \times 100 = 13.7$ map units. We know then that the map should be drawn as

```
   sc    5.5    ec        8.2        cv
   +------+-------+---------+
        <-------- 13.7 -------->
```

Double Crossovers

Let's turn to another cross in which the genes are *cv* and two more non-wild types, *ct* (cut, or snipped wing edges) and *v* (vermilion, or bright scarlet eye color). A homozygous *cv ct v* fly is crossed with a homozygous wild-type fly to yield a triply heterozygous female, which is then testcrossed to give

cv	ct	v	580
+	+	+	592
cv	+	+	45
+	ct	v	40
cv	ct	+	89
+	+	v	94
cv	+	v	3
+	ct	+	5
			1448

Again we recognize a pretty obvious linkage of all three gene pairs by the absence of Mendelian ratios, the *cv ct v* and +++ classes being the parental chromosomes. Unlike the previous cross, this cross yields six classes of recombinant chromosomes. We can calculate map distances between two

Figure 5-9. Double-crossover chromatids involving two linked gene pairs are normally not detected genetically because recombinant genotypes are not produced.

gene pairs at a time, ignoring the third again. Let's ignore *v* and look at *cv* and *ct*, for which the recombinant classes are *cv*+ and +*ct*; the genetic distance is 6.4 map units, or $[(45 + 40 + 3 + 5)/1448] \times 100$. Doing the same for *ct* and *v* (and ignoring *cv*), we get a distance of 13.2 map units, or $[(89 + 94 + 3 + 5)/1448] \times 100$. Now if we ignore *ct* and look at *cv*+ and +*v* recombinants, we find the distance to be 18.5 map units, or $[(45 + 40 + 89 + 94)/1448] \times 100$. This shows that *cv* and *v* are the farthest apart and that *ct* must be between them. However, if we add the distances between *cv* and *ct* (6.4) and between *ct* and *v* (13.2), we get a value of 19.6, which is larger than the computed value of 18.5. Why? We see that eight of the flies (*cv*+*v* and +*ct*+) were included in calculations for both the *cv*-to-*ct* and the *ct*-to-*v* intervals, but *not* for the calculations for the *cv*-to-*v* interval, even though *two crossovers* had taken place between *cv* and *v* in each of these chromosomes. The reason becomes obvious if we look at a representation of this **double-crossover** event (Figure 5-9).

Although two crossovers have taken place between *cv* and *v*, the genetic result is that *cv* and *v* remain linked in the parental combination. Only when *ct* and its wild-type allele are present can we recognize the double-crossover chromosome. So, in a calculation of the *cv*-to-*v* distance, we should add in *twice* the number of double-recombinant types ($8 \times 2 = 16$). When this is done, the *cv*-to-*v* distance becomes $[(45 + 40 + 89 + 94 + 16)/1448] \times 100 = 19.6$ m.u., which is the same as the combined values.

In almost any crossover study of three linked genes, the double-recombinant classes will be the most rare. Knowing that, we could have determined the gene order (which gene is in the middle) without calculating map distances. We know from the nonrecombinant classes that the parental combination of genes was *cv ct v*/+++. If we do not know the proper gene order, then it could be any of *cv v ct*, *v cv ct*, and *cv ct v*, as shown in Figure 5-10. Of these sequences,

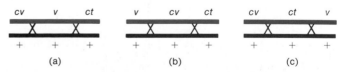

Figure 5-10. Three different gene-pair orders are possible. Each case leads to a different double-recombinant genotype.

only the one shown in part c of the figure would generate the genotypes of the double-crossover classes $cv+v$ and $+ct+$.

Interference

The detection of the double-exchange class allows us to ask another question. Are exchanges occurring in each of two different regions of the same chromosome independently of each other? We know that we get recombinants between cv and ct 6.4 percent of the time and between ct and v 13.2 percent of the time. If a crossover in one of these regions in no way affects the probability of a crossover's occurring in the other region (that is, if they are independent), then the probability that an individual will be produced that is recombinant in both regions at once is the product of the individual recombinant frequencies. If there is independence, then the expected frequency of double-recombinant types is $0.064 \times 0.132 = 0.0084$ (0.84 percent). In a sample of 1448, we would expect $1448 \times 0.0084 = 12$ double crossovers, whereas we actually observed 8. Had we obtained a million progeny, the observed number of doubles would still have been lower than the expected. What does that mean? It means that crossing-over in one region is not independent of crossing-over in the other; in fact, when a crossover does occur in one region, it decreases the likelihood that another will occur in the other region. The effect of a crossover in one region on the likelihood of a crossover in another region is called **interference.** We may quantify this effect by the **coefficient coincidence (c.c.),** which is simply the number of double recombinants observed divided by the number expected.

An **interference value (I)** is calculated by subtracting the c.c. from 1:

$$I = 1 - \text{c.c.} = 1 - \frac{\text{frequency or number of observed doubles}}{\text{frequency or number of expected doubles}}$$

In our example,

$$I = 1 - 8/12 = 0.33 \quad \text{or} \quad 33\%$$

When there are no double crossovers, the c.c. is 0, so I is 1; interference is complete (as in the sc-ec-cv interval in the example on page 87). When there are fewer doubles than expected, the c.c. is less than 1, making I a positive number; there is interference. When the c.c. is 1, $I = 0$; there is no interference. Finally, when there are more doubles than expected, the c.c. is greater than 1, making I a negative number; interference is negative. Figure 5-11 further explores the effects of interference by showing the redistribution of progeny types due to interference, using two adjacent regions each 20 m.u. long. When there is no interference the expected frequency of double recombinants is $0.2 \times 0.2 = 0.04$. For 10 percent interference, the observed number of double recombinants can be calculated from the formula

$$I = 0.1 = 1 - \frac{\text{observed doubles}}{0.04}$$

The frequency of observed doubles comes to 0.036. The difference of 0.004 ($= 0.040 - 0.036$) obviously is the reduction in the double-recombinant class, but at the same time there is a reduction in the nonrecombinant class and an increase in both the single-recombinant classes by the same amount. (Note in the figure that the map distances in I and II remain the same.)

You may have noticed that we always used heterozygous females for testcrosses in our crossover studies in *Drosophila*. When $prvg/++$ males are crossed with $prvg/prvg$ females, only $prvg/++$ and $prvg/prvg$ progeny are recovered. This result shows that crossing-over does not occur in *Drosophila* males. However, this absence of crossing-over in one sex is limited to certain species; it is not the case for males of all species (or for the heterogametic sex). In other organisms, crossing-over can occur in XY males or in WZ females. The reason for this sex difference is that

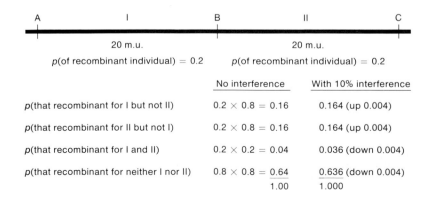

	No interference	With 10% interference
A I B II C		
20 m.u. 20 m.u.		
p(of recombinant individual) = 0.2 p(of recombinant individual) = 0.2		
p(that recombinant for I but not II)	$0.2 \times 0.8 = 0.16$	0.164 (up 0.004)
p(that recombinant for II but not I)	$0.2 \times 0.8 = 0.16$	0.164 (up 0.004)
p(that recombinant for I and II)	$0.2 \times 0.2 = 0.04$	0.036 (down 0.004)
p(that recombinant for neither I nor II)	$0.8 \times 0.8 = 0.64$	0.636 (down 0.004)
	1.00	1.000

Figure 5-11. How to calculate the expected frequencies of nonrecombinant, single-recombinant, and double-recombinant types, with and without interference. The loci A and B are separated by distance I (20 m.u.); loci B and C are separated by distance II (20 m.u.).

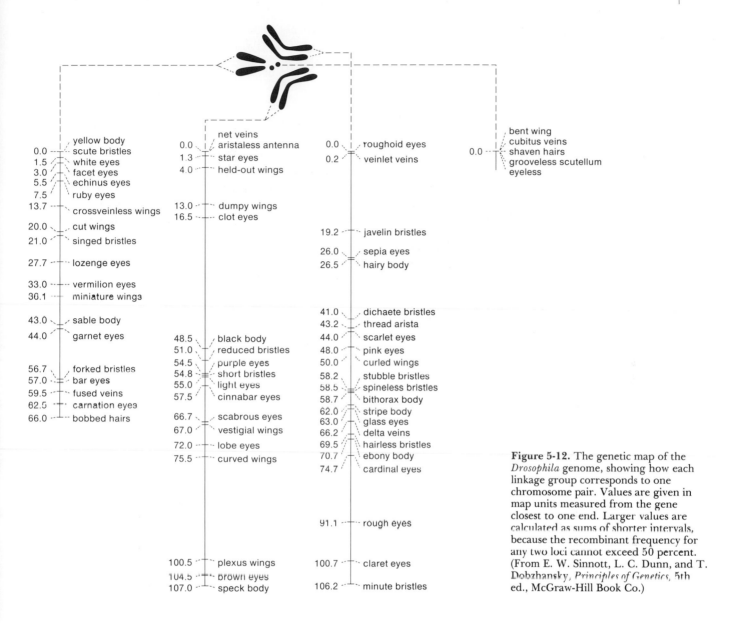

Figure 5-12. The genetic map of the *Drosophila* genome, showing how each linkage group corresponds to one chromosome pair. Values are given in map units measured from the gene closest to one end. Larger values are calculated as sums of shorter intervals, because the recombinant frequency for any two loci cannot exceed 50 percent. (From E. W. Sinnott, L. C. Dunn, and T. Dobzhansky, *Principles of Genetics*, 5th ed., McGraw-Hill Book Co.)

Drosophila males have an unusual prophase I, with no synaptonemal complexes.

Linkage maps are an essential aspect of the experimental genetic study of any organism. They are the prelude to any serious piece of genetic manipulation. Many organisms have had their genes intensively mapped in this way. The resultant maps represent a tremendous amount of basic applied genetic analysis. Figures 5-12 and 5-13 show two examples of linkage maps, from *Drosophila* and from the tomato.

The χ^2 Test

We come now to a subject that emerges naturally at this point in the discussion, a subject that is particularly relevant to the detection of linkage. It has been stated that the functional test for the presence or absence of linkage is based on the relative frequencies of the meiotic product types. If there is no linkage, the four product-cell types AB, ab, Ab, and aB are produced in a $1:1:1:1$ ratio, and this fixes the recombinant frequency at 50 percent. If there is linkage, there is deviation from the $1:1:1:1$ ratio, and two types (the recombinants) are present in a minority (<50 percent). In practical terms, the following question must be answered in any particular case: "Is this a $1:1:1:1$ ratio?" An answer of "yes" indicates absence of linkage, and "no" indicates linkage. "Obvious" departures from the $1:1:1:1$ ratio present no decision problems, but smaller departures are trickier to handle, and they require further analytical approaches.

What is the precise problem here? An example will be helpful. A double heterozygote in coupling conformation produces 500 meiotic products distributed as follows:

AB 140

ab 135

Ab 110

aB 115

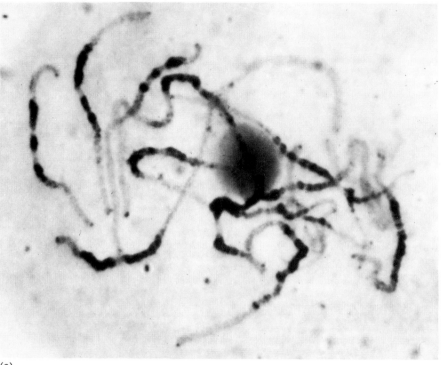

(a)

Figure 5-13. The tomato genome. (a) Photomicrograph of a meiotic pachytene (prophase I) from anthers. (b) Diagram corresponding to part a, identifying the 12 chromosome pairs. Colored centromeres are flanked by densely staining chromosome regions called heterochromatin. Heterochromatin is thought to be genetically inert. (Opposite page, c) Genetic map of the tomato genome. The 12 linkage groups correspond to the 12 chromosome pairs of part b. Centromeres and heterochromatin regions are indicated. (Part a courtesy of Charles M. Rick, Parts b, c from Charles M. Rick, "The Tomato." Copyright © 1978 by Scientific American, Inc. All rights reserved.)

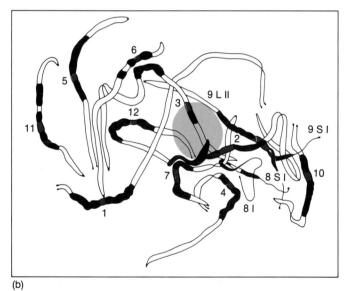

(b)

By the application of the recombinant-frequency test, we find 225 recombinants, or 45 percent. This is admittedly less than 50 percent, but not convincingly so. The skeptic would say, "This is merely a chance deviation from a $1:1:1:1$ ratio! If you repeatedly grabbed samples of 500 marbles from a dark sack containing equal numbers of red, blue, yellow, and green marbles, you would fairly often get a variation this great from the $1:1:1:1$ ratio." What should we decide? The χ^2 test can help in this kind of predicament.

The χ^2 test in general tells how often deviations from expectations will occur purely on the basis of chance. The procedure is as follows.

1. *State a simple hypothesis that gives a precise expectation.* Obviously, in our example, the best hypothesis is "lack of linkage," which gives an expected $1:1:1:1$ ratio. This **null hypothesis** is obviously better than a hypothesis of linkage, which is not precise because (as we have seen) the recombinant frequency can be large or small.

2. *Calculate χ^2.* This value *always* is calculated from actual numbers—never from percentages, fractions, or decimal fractions. In fact, part of the usefulness of the χ^2 test is that it takes sample size into consideration. The sample is composed of several operational classes, with O the observed number in any class and E the expected

(c)

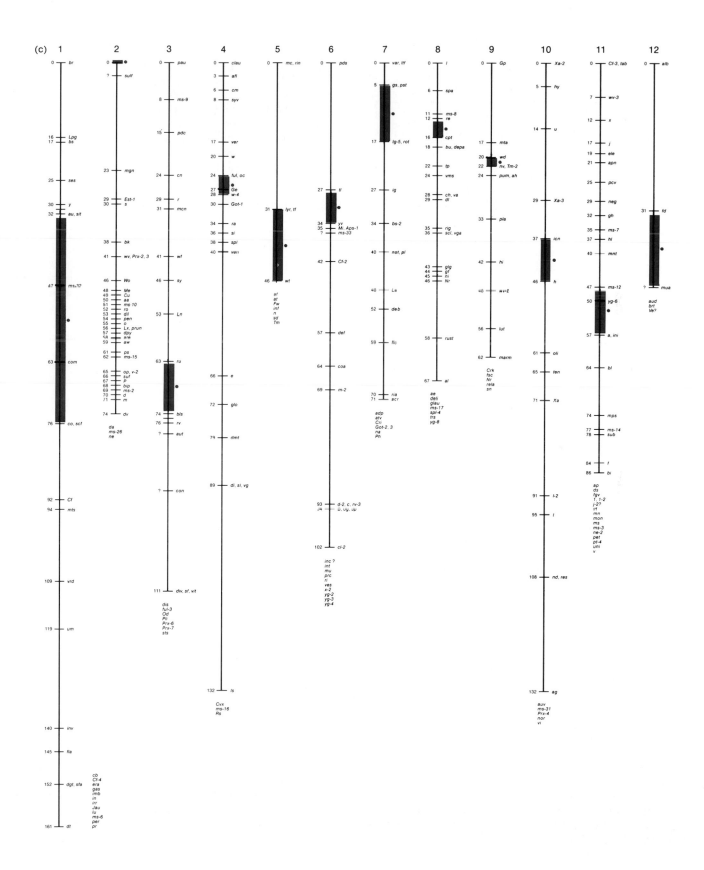

■ **TABLE 5-2.** Calculation of χ^2

Class	O	E	$(O - E)^2$	$\dfrac{(O - E)^2}{E}$
AB	140	125	225	1.8
ab	135	125	100	0.8
Ab	110	125	225	1.8
aB	$\dfrac{115}{500}$	$\dfrac{125}{500}$	100	$\dfrac{0.8}{\chi^2 = 5.2}$

number based on the null hypothesis. The formula for calculating χ^2 is as follows:

$$\chi^2 = \text{total of } \frac{(O - E)^2}{E} \text{ over all classes}$$

In our example, we would set up the calculation as shown in Table 5-2.

3. Using χ^2, calculate the probability p of obtaining the present results if the null hypothesis is correct. Before this can be done, another item must be computed: the number of degrees of freedom (df). In the present context, the number of degrees of freedom can be simply defined as

$$\text{df} = (\text{number of classes} - 1)$$

In our example,

$$\text{df} = (4 - 1) = 3$$

We now turn to the table of χ^2 values (Table 5-3), which will give us our p values if we plug in our computed χ^2 and df values. Looking along the df = 3 line, we find our χ^2 value of 5.2 lies between the p values of 0.5 (50 percent) and 0.1 (10 percent). Hence we can conclude that our p value is just greater than 10 percent (0.1). What this means is that, if our null hypothesis is correct, a deviation *at least* as great as that observed is expected a little more than 10 percent of the time.

4. *Reject or accept the null hypothesis.* How do we know which p value is too low to be acceptable? Scientists in general arbitrarily use the 5 percent level. Any p value less than 5 percent results in rejection of the null hypothesis, and any value greater than 5 percent results in acceptance of the null hypothesis. In the case of acceptance, of course, the null hypothesis is not proved, merely possible. In the case of rejection, the hypothesis is not disproved, merely improbable. Now that we have accepted our null hypothesis of absence of linkage, we must live with it and acknowledge that the skeptic had a point!

In this way, the χ^2 test helps decide between linkage and absence of linkage. In fact, a major use of the χ^2 test in genetics is in the determination of linkage. But there are several other situations in which the χ^2 test is useful, and these will involve testing actual results against simple expectations of a hypothesis.

For example, the test is ideal (as we have seen) for testing deviations from any genetic ratio: $3:1$, $9:3:3:1$, $9:7$, $1:1$, and so on. But there are pitfalls here. Suppose, for example, you believe you have identified a major gene affecting a specific biological function. You testcross a presumed heterozygote $A\,a$ to a homozygous recessive individ-

■ **TABLE 5-3.** Critical values of the χ^2 distribution

df	0.995	0.975	0.9	0.5	0.1	0.05	0.025	0.01	0.005	df
1	.000	.000	0.016	0.455	2.706	3.841	5.024	6.635	7.879	1
2	0.010	0.051	0.211	1.386	4.605	5.991	7.378	9.210	10.597	2
3	0.072	0.216	0.584	2.366	6.251	7.815	9.348	11.345	12.838	3
4	0.207	0.484	1.064	3.357	7.779	9.488	11.143	13.277	14.860	4
5	0.412	0.831	1.610	4.351	9.236	11.070	12.832	15.086	16.750	5
6	0.676	1.237	2.204	5.348	10.645	12.592	14.449	16.812	18.548	6
7	0.989	1.690	2.833	6.346	12.017	14.067	16.013	18.475	20.278	7
8	1.344	2.180	3.490	7.344	13.362	15.507	17.535	20.090	21.955	8
9	1.735	2.700	4.168	8.343	14.684	16.919	19.023	21.666	23.589	9
10	2.156	3.247	4.865	9.342	15.987	18.307	20.483	23.209	25.188	10
11	2.603	3.816	5.578	10.341	17.275	19.675	21.920	24.725	26.757	11
12	3.074	4.404	6.304	11.340	18.549	21.026	23.337	26.217	28.300	12
13	3.565	5.009	7.042	12.340	19.812	22.362	24.736	27.688	29.819	13
14	4.075	5.629	7.790	13.339	21.064	23.685	26.119	29.141	31.319	14
15	4.601	6.262	8.547	14.339	22.307	24.996	27.488	30.578	32.801	15

ual aa, expecting a $1:1$ phenotypic ratio in the progeny. Out of 200 progeny, 116 are Aa and 84 are aa. Here $\chi^2 = (16^2 \div 100) + (16^2 \div 100) = 5.12$ with 1 df. The p value is 2.5 percent, so you reject the null hypothesis that there is a single gene pair segregating. Actually, however, you must recall that the $1:1$ ratio is expected if there is a single pair of alleles *of equal viability* segregating. With the rejection of the null hypothesis, you must now reject *either* the notion of a single allele pair *or* that of their equal viability (or both). The χ^2 test cannot tell you which portion of a compound null hypothesis to reject, so care must be taken to determine all the hidden assumptions in a null hypothesis if error is to be avoided in the application of statistical testing.

Message   The χ^2 test is used to test experimental results against the expectations derived from a null hypothesis. The test generates a p value that is the probability of obtaining a specific deviation at least as great as that observed, assuming that the null hypothesis is correct.

Early Thoughts on the Nature of Crossing-Over

The idea that intrachromosomal recombinants were produced by some kind of exchange of material between homologous chromosomes was a convincing one. But experimentation was necessary to test the idea. One of the first steps was to correlate the occurrence of a genetic recombinant with the occurrence of chromosome exchange. Several investigators approached this problem in the same way. In 1931, Harriet Creighton and Barbara McClintock were studying two loci of chromosome 9 of corn: one affecting seed color (C, colored, and c, colorless) and the other affecting endosperm composition (Wx, waxy, and wx, starchy). Furthermore, the chromosome carrying C and Wx was distinguished from its homolog by the presence of a large, densely staining element (called a knob) on the C end and by a longer piece of chromosome on the Wx end; thus, the heterozygote was

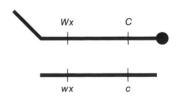

When they separated genetic recombinants from nonrecombinants, Creighton and McClintock found that all the

nonrecombinants retained the parental chromosome arrangements, whereas all the recombinants were

or

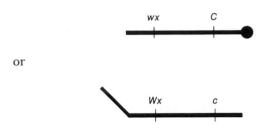

Thus, the correlation between the genetic and cytological events of intrachromosomal recombination was firmly established.

The chiasmata seemed to represent the sites of the exchange process, but the final proof of this did not come until 1978 (see page 357).

But what is the mechanism of chromosome exchange in a crossover event? Is it a breakage and reunion process like splicing sound tapes? Or is it a process that only *appears* to consist of a breakage and a reunion? An idea that favors the latter was proposed in 1928 by John Belling, who studied meiosis in plant chromosomes and observed bumps along the chromosome (the chromomeres), which he thought might correspond to genes (Figure 5-14). Belling visualized the genes as beads strung together with some nongenic linking substance. He reported that, during prophase of meiosis, chromomeres duplicate so that newly made chromomeres are stuck to the originals (Figure 5-15). After duplication, the newly formed chromomeres are fastened together, but, because all the chromomeres are tightly juxtaposed, the linking elements could switch from a newly made chromomere on one homologous chromo-

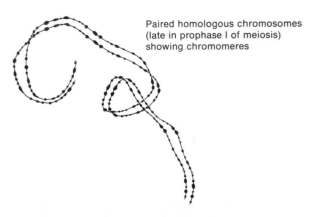

Paired homologous chromosomes (late in prophase I of meiosis) showing chromomeres

Figure 5-14. Diagrammatic representation of the chromomeres that are important in Belling's copy-choice model.

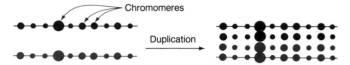

Figure 5-15. Division of the chromomeres according to Belling's model.

some to an adjacent one on the other homolog. This model became known as the **copy-choice model** (or switch model) of crossing-over. You can see how it can generate a crossover chromatid that would seem to have arisen from a physical breakage and the reunion of chromosomes (Figure 5-16). You can also see that it suggests that the event producing recombinant chromosomes can take place only between newly made chromomeres (and hence newly made chromatids), so that any multiple crossover could involve only two chromatids.

Thus, the copy-choice model predicts that, in every meiosis in which multiple crossovers occur (for example, double crossovers and even higher multiples), only two chromatids out of the four would ever be involved. The prediction could be tested if only we had some way of recovering all four products from individual meiotic divisions. Each group of four could then be examined for the presence of multiple recombinants. In any group of four that contains at least one multiple recombinant, there must be two accompanying parental types for the copy-choice model to be possible. Luckily, several haploid organisms are suited to the recovery of all four products of a single meiosis. These organisms are some fungi and some unicellular algae. We consider the full analysis of these groups of four (called *tetrad analysis*) at length in Chapter 6. But we need them right now to answer one specific question: What companion genotypes are found in tetrads containing multiple recombinants? Several types of such tetrads are possible, but one interesting situation (often encountered in tetrad analysis) is illustrated in the following diagram, in which the genes are linked in the order shown:

$$A B C \times a b c$$

$$\downarrow$$

$$\left.\begin{array}{l} A B c \\ A b C \\ a B C \\ a b c \end{array}\right\} \text{The four products of a single meiotic division}$$

Note that a recombination event has occurred between the first two loci (A/a and B/b) *and* between the second two loci (B/b and C/c) in the same meiosis; a double-exchange event has occurred (and one of the two products, $A b C$, is a

double recombinant). *But* more than two chromatids must have been involved; in fact, three *must* have been involved in this case (Figure 5-17). Thus, Belling's suggestion (which would predict that only two chromatids could ever be involved) is most unlikely. (We shall see some *positive* evidence for the model of breakage and reunion in Chapter 16.)

Message The breakage and reunion model of chromosome crossing-over wins by default.

The ability to isolate the four products of meiosis in fungi and algae also clears up another mystery, about whether crossing-over occurs at the two-strand (two-chromosome) stage or at the four-strand (four-chromatid) stage. If it occurs at the two-strand stage (before replication), there can never be more than two different products of a given meiosis. If it occurs at the four-strand stage (after replication), up to four different products of meiosis are possible (Figure 5-18). In fact, four different products of a single meiosis are regularly observed, showing that crossing-over occurs at the four-strand stage of meiosis.

Crossing-over is a remarkably precise process. The synapsis and exchange of chromosomes is such that no segments are lost or gained, and four complete chromosomes emerge in a tetrad. At present, however, the actual mechanisms of crossing-over and interference are still somewhat of an enigma, although several attractive models do exist, and a lot is known about the sorts of chemical reactions that might ensure precision at the molecular level. We shall return to these points in Chapter 16.

Linkage Mapping by Recombination in Humans

Humans, partly because of their relatively large chromosome number and partly because of the lack of suitable pedigrees containing what amount to testcrosses, have revealed very few examples of autosomal linkage through recombination analysis. The X chromosome, however, has been far more amenable to analysis because of hemizygosity in males. Consider the following situation involving the rare recessive genes for defective sugar processing (g)

Figure 5-16. The hooking together of the newly synthesized chromomeres according to Belling's model. Joining usually forms parental combinations, but sometimes a switch can occur.

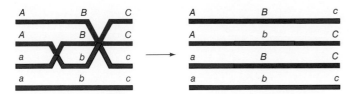

Figure 5-17. One of the several possible types of double-crossover tetrads that are regularly observed, showing how more than two chromatids must be involved. This evidence makes Belling's copy-choice (switch) model very unlikely.

and for color blindness *(c)*. A doubly affected male, *cg*/Y, marries a normal woman (who is almost certainly *C G*/*C G*). The daughters of this mating are coupling-conformation heterozygotes. When they marry, they will almost certainly marry normal men *C G*/Y, and their male children provide an opportunity for the study of the frequency of recombinants (Figure 5-19). Using such pedigrees, the total frequency of recombinants may be estimated. A map based on such techniques is shown in Figure 5-20. Further data on mapping in humans have been provided by less conventional techniques, as we shall see in Chapter 6.

Linkage studies occupy a large proportion of the routine day-to-day activities of geneticists. When a new variant gene is discovered, one of the first questions to be asked concerning it is "Where does it map?" Not only is this knowledge a necessary component in the engineering and maintenance of genetic stocks for research use, but it is also of fundamental importance in the piecing together of an overall view of the architecture of the chromosome — and in fact of the entire genome. The operational key for the detection of linkage is the same in studies from viruses to humans, and that key is the nonindependence of genes in their transmission from generation to generation. Look for this key in discussions of linkage in following chapters.

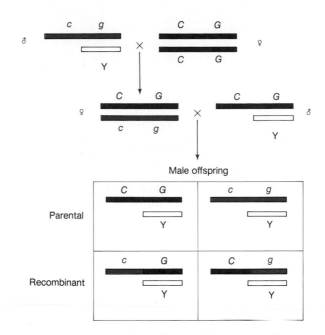

Figure 5-19. The male children of women heterozygous for two X-linked genes can be used to calculate recombinant frequency. Thus, mapping of the X chromosome is possible by studying certain selected pedigrees.

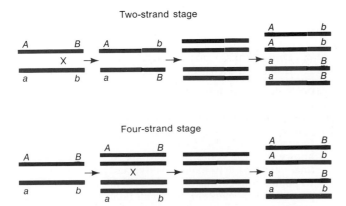

Figure 5-18. Tetrad analysis provides evidence to decide whether crossing-over occurs at the two-strand (two-chromosome) or at the four-strand (four-chromatid) stage of meiosis. Because more than two different products of a single meiosis can be seen in some tetrads, crossing-over cannot occur at the two-strand stage.

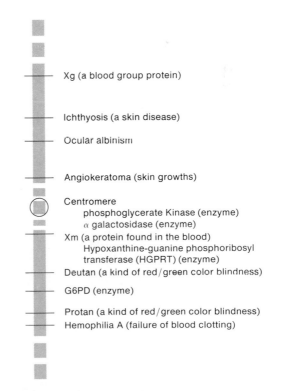

Figure 5-20. A map of the human X chromosome, derived from analysis of recombinant frequencies as indicated in Figure 5-19. (From W. F. Bodmer and L. L. Cavalli-Sforza, *Genetics, Evolution, and Man.* Copyright © 1976 by W. H. Freeman and Co.)

Summary

■ In dihybrid crosses of sweet pea plants, Bateson and Punnett discovered deviations from the $9:3:3:1$ ratio of phenotypes expected in the F_2 generation. The parental gametic types occurred with much greater frequency than the other two classes. Later, in his studies of two different autosomal gene pairs in *Drosophila,* Morgan found a similar deviation from Mendel's law of independent assortment. He postulated that the two gene pairs were located on the same pair of homologous chromosomes. This phenomenon is called linkage.

Linkage explains why the parental gene combinations stay together but not how the nonparental combinations arise. Morgan postulated that during meiosis there may be a physical exchange of chromosome parts by a process called crossing over, or intrachromosomal recombination. Thus there are two types of meiotic recombination. Interchromosomal recombination is achieved by Mendelian independent assortment and results in a recombinant frequency of 50 percent. Intrachromosomal recombination occurs when the physical linkage of the parental gene combinations prevents full assortment of the gene pairs, and the recombinant frequency is less than 50 percent.

As Morgan studied more linked genes, he discovered considerable variation in crossover frequency and wondered if this variation reflected the actual distance between genes. Sturtevant, a student of Morgan's, developed a method of determining the distance between gene pairs on a genetic map based on the percentage of recombinants. A genetic map is another example of a hypothetical entity based on genetic analysis.

Although the basic test for linkage is deviation from the $1:1:1:1$ ratio of progeny types in a testcross, deviation may not be all that obvious. The χ^2 test, which tells how often deviations from expectations will occur purely by chance, can help determine whether linkage exists or not. The χ^2 test has other applications in genetics, in the testing of observed against expected events.

Several theories about how recombinant chromosomes are generated have been set forth. We now know that crossing over is the result of physical breakage and a re-union of chromosomal parts and that it occurs at the four-strand stage of meiosis. The actual mechanism of crossing over, however, remains largely a mystery.

Problems _____

1. A geneticist studying bloops (an exotic organism found only in textbook problems) has been unable to find any examples of linkage. Suggest some explanations for this situation.

2. A strain of *Neurospora* with the genotype *HI* is crossed with a strain with the genotype *hi*. One-half of the progeny are *HI*, and one-half are *hi*. Explain how this is possible.

3. A female animal with genotype *AaBb* is crossed with a double-recessive male *(aa bb)*. Their progeny includes 442 *AaBb*, 458 *aabb*, 46 *Aabb*, and 54 *aaBb*. Explain these results.

4. In a haploid organism, the loci C/c and D/d are linked 8 m.u. apart. In a cross $Cd \times cD$, name the proportion of each of the following progeny classes: a. CD b. cd c. Cd d. Recombinants

5. A fruit fly of genotype BR/br is testcrossed to br/br. In 84 percent of the meioses, no chiasmata occur between the linked gene pairs; in 16 percent of the meioses, one chiasma occurs between them. What proportion of the progeny will be $Bb\,rr$?   a. 50 percent   b. 4 percent   c. 84 percent   d. 25 percent   e. 16 percent

6. An individual heterozygous for four gene pairs *AaBbCcDd* was testcrossed to *aabbccdd*, and 1000 progeny were classified as follows:

$aBCD$	42
$Abcd$	43
$ABCd$	140
$abcD$	145
$aBcD$	6
$AbCd$	9
$ABcd$	305
$abCD$	310

a.   Which gene pairs are linked?

b.   If two pure breeding lines were crossed to produce the heterozygous individual, what were their genotypes?

c.   Draw a linkage map of the linked genes showing their order and their distance apart in map units.

d.   Calculate an interference value if appropriate.

7. In the squirting cucumber, *Echballium elaterium,* there are two separate sexes (it is dioecious) determined not by heteromorphic sex chromosomes but by specific genes. It is known that the genes involved are *M* (male fertility), *m* (male sterility), *F* (female sterility), and *f* (female fertility). In populations of this plant, individuals can be male (approximately 50 percent) or female (approximately 50 percent), but in addition a hermaphrodite type is found, but only at a very low frequency. The hermaphrodite has male and female sex organs on the same plant.

a.   What must be the full genotype of a male plant? (Indicate linkage relations of the genes)

b. What must be the full genotype of a female plant? (Indicate linkage relations of the genes)

c. How does the population maintain an approximately equal proportion of males and females?

d. What is the origin of the rare hermaphrodite?

e. Why are hermaphrodites rare?

*8. There is an autosomal gene N in humans that causes abnormalities in nails and patellae (kneecaps), called the nail-patella syndrome. In marriages of people with the phenotypes [nail-patella syndrome, blood type A] and [normal nail-patella, blood type O], some children are born with the nail-patella syndrome and blood type A. When marriages between such children (unrelated, of course) take place, their children are of the following types:

66% nail-patella syndrome, blood type A

16% normal nail-patella, blood type O

9% normal nail-patella, blood type A

9% nail-patella syndrome, blood type O

Fully analyze these data.

*9. You obtain two lines of *Drosophila*, one having light yellow eyes and the other having bright scarlet eyes. (Remember that wild-type *Drosophila* have deep red eyes.) When you cross a yellow female with a scarlet male, you obtain 251 wild-type females and 248 yellow males in the F_1 generation. When you cross F_1 males and females, you obtain the following F_2 phenotypes: 260 wild-type females, 253 yellow females, 77 wild-type males, 170 yellow males, 183 scarlet males, and 80 brown-eyed males (brown is a new phenotype). Explain these results, using diagrams where possible.

10. In the ovaries of higher plants, a haploid nucleus resulting from meiosis undergoes several mitotic divisions without cell division, forming a multinucleate cell called the female gametophyte. (The male nucleus fuses with just one of these nuclei, which acts as the egg nucleus.) In some conifers, the female gametophyte can be quite large—in fact, large enough to be removed and analyzed electrophoretically. One tree of lodgepole pine *(Pinus contorta)* is heterozygous for fast and slow "electrophoretic alleles" of the enzymes alcohol dehydrogenase (ADH^F/ADH^S) and phosphoglucomutase (PGM^F/PGM^S). A sample of 237 female gametophytes is studied, and the following phenotypes are found: 21 $ADH^F PGM^F$, 19 $ADH^S PGM^S$, 95 $ADH^F PGM^S$, and 102 $ADH^S PGM^F$.

a. Explain these results.

b. Can you think of any other uses in genetics for this female-gametophyte system?

11. Using the data obtained by Bateson and Punnett (Table 5-1), calculate the map distance (in m.u.) separating the color and shape genes. (This will require some trial and error.)

12. You have a homozygous *Drosophila* line carrying the autosomal recessive genes a, b, and c linked in that order. You cross females of this line with males of a homozygous wild-type line. You then cross the F_1 heterozygous males with their heterozygous sisters, and you obtain the following F_2 phenotypes: 1364 $+++$, 365 abc, 87 $ab+$, 84 $++c$, 47 $a++$, 44 $+bc$, 5 $a+c$, and 4 $+b+$.

a. What is the recombinant frequency between a and b? between b and c?

b. What is the coefficient of coincidence?

13. R. A. Emerson crossed two different pure-breeding parental lines of corn and obtained an F_1 that was heterozygous for three recessive genes: an (anther), br (brachytic), and f (fine). He testcrossed the F_1 to a completely homozygous recessive tester and obtained the following progeny phenotypes: 355 anther, 339 brachytic and fine, 88 completely wild-type, 55 anther and brachytic and fine, 21 fine, 17 anther and brachytic, 2 brachytic, and 2 anther and fine.

a. What were the genotypes of the parental lines?

b. Draw a linkage map to illustrate the linkage arrangement of the three genes (include map distances).

c. Calculate the interference value.

14. In corn, the following allelic pairs have been identified in chromosome 3: $+/b$ (plant-color booster versus nonbooster), $+/lg$ (liguled versus liguleless), and $+/v$ (green plant versus virescent). A testcross involving triple recessives and F_1 plants heterozygous for the three gene pairs yields the following progeny phenotypes: 305 $+vlg$, 275 $b++$, 128 $b+lg$, 112 $+v+$, 74 $++lg$, 66 $bv+$, 22 $+++$, and 18 $bvlg$. Give the gene sequence on the chromosome, the map distances between genes, and the coefficient of coincidence.

15. A hemophiliac female rabbit with rickets was mated to a male rabbit that lacked a tail. The F_1 females were all wild-type, and the F_1 males had both rickets and hemophilia. An F_1 self produced the following F_2 progeny:

Phenotype	Male	Female
normal	48	485
tail-less	437	0
rickets	4	16
hemophilia	12	14
hemophilia and rickets	439	485
tail-less and hemophilia	2	0
rickets and tail-less	12	0
hemophilia, tail-less, and rickets	46	0

a. Describe the complete linkage arrangements of tailless, rickets, and hemophilia in rabbits.

b. Does interference exist in this system? If so, calculate.

16. Groodies are useful (but fictional) haploid organisms that are pure genetic tools. A wild-type groody has a fat body, a long tail, and flagella. Non-wild-type lines are known that have thin bodies, or are tail-less, or do not have flagella. Groodies can mate with each other (although they are so shy that we do not know how) and produce recombinants. A wild-type groody is crossed with a thin-bodied groody lacking both tail and flagella. The 1000 baby groodies resulting are classified as shown in the following figure. Assign genotypes, and map the three genes.

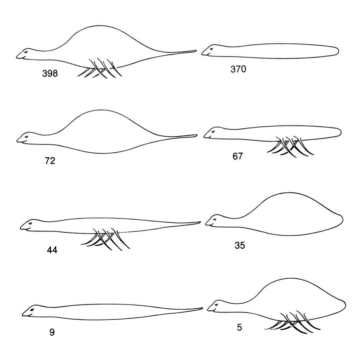

(Problem 16 courtesy of Burton S. Guttman.)

17. Assume that three pairs of alleles are found in *Drosophilia:* $+/x$, $+/y$, and $+/z$. As shown by the symbols, each non-wild allele is recessive to its wild-type allele. A cross between females heterozygous at these three loci and wild-type males yields the following progeny phenotypes: 1010 $+++$ females; 430 $x+z$ males; 441 $+y+$ males; 39 xyz males; 32 $++z$ males; 30 $+++$ males; 27 $xy+$ males; 1 $+yz$ male; and 0 $x++$ males.

a. How were members of the allelic pairs distributed in the members of the appropriate chromosome pair of the heterozygous female parents?

b. What is the sequence of these linked genes in their chromosome?

c. Calculate the map distances between the genes, and the coefficient of coincidence.

d. In what chromosome of *Drosophila* are these genes carried?

*18. You have two homozygous lines of *Drosophila.* Line 1 has bright scarlet eyes and a wild-type thorax. Line 2 has dark brown eyes and a humpy thorax. When you cross virgin females of line 2 with males of line 1, you obtain 232 wild-type males and 225 wild-type females in the F_1 generation. You then cross F_1 males with virgin F_1 females and obtain the following F_2 phenotypes: 283 completely wild-type females; 145 completely wild-type males; 139 wild-thorax, scarlet-eyed males; 78 humpy-thorax, brown-eyed females; 40 humpy-thorax, white-eyed males; 39 humpy-thorax, brown-eyed males; 20 wild-thorax, brown-eyed females; 19 humpy-thorax, wild-eyed females; 11 humpy-thorax, scarlet-eyed males; 10 wild-thorax, white-eyed males; 9 wild-thorax, brown-eyed males; and 8 humpy-thorax, wild-eyed males. Explain these results as fully as possible (using symbols wherever possible).

19. The mother of a family with ten children has blood type Rh^+ and has a very rare condition (elliptocytosis, E) with no adverse clinical effect, in which the red cells are oval rather than round. The father is Rh^- (lacks the Rh^+ antigen) and has normal red cells (symbol: e). The children are 1 Rh^+ e, 4 Rh^+ E, and 5 Rh^- e. Information is available on the mother's parents, who are Rh^+ E and Rh^- e. One of the ten children (who is Rh^+ E) marries someone who is Rh^+ e, and they have an Rh^+ E child.

a. Draw the pedigree of this whole family.

b. Is the pedigree in agreement with the hypothesis that Rh^+ is dominant and Rh^- is recessive?

c. What is the mechanism of transmission of elliptocytosis?

d. Could the genes for E and Rh be on the same chromosome? If so, estimate the map distance between them, and comment on your result.

20. The father of Mr. Spock, first officer of the starship *Enterprise,* came from the planet Vulcan; his mother came from Earth. A Vulcan has pointed ears *(P)*, adrenals absent *(A)*, and a right-sided heart *(R)*. All of these alleles are dominant over normal Earth alleles. These genes are autosomal, and they are linked as shown in this linkage map:

$$P/p \quad \text{15 m.u.} \quad A/a \quad \text{20 m.u.} \quad R/r$$

If Mr. Spock marries an Earth woman and there is no (genetic) interference, what proportion of their children

a. will show Vulcanian appearance for all three characters?

b. will show Earth appearance for all three characters?

c. will have Vulcanian ears and heart but Earth adrenals?

d. will have Vulcanian ears but Earth heart and adrenals?

(Problem 20 is from D. Harrison, *Problems in Genetics,* Addison-Wesley, 1970.)

21. In a certain diploid plant, the three loci A/a, B/b, and C/c are linked as follows:

$$\underset{\substack{20 \text{ m.u.} \qquad 30 \text{ m.u.}}}{\overset{\substack{A/a \qquad\qquad B/b \qquad\qquad C/c}}{\vdash\!\!\!\!\!-\!\!\!\!\!-\!\!\!\!\!-\!\!\!\!\!-\!\!\!\!\!-\!\!\!\!\!-\!\!\!\!\!-\!\!\!\!\!\dashv}}$$

One plant is available to you (call it the parental plant). It has the constitution $A\,b\,c/a\,B\,C$.

a. Assuming no interference, if the plant is selfed, what proportion of the progeny will be of the genotype $a\,b\,c/a\,b\,c$?

b. Again assuming no interference, if the parental plant is crossed with the $a\,b\,c/a\,b\,c$ plant, what genotypic classes will be found in the progeny? What will be their frequencies if there are 1000 progeny?

c. Repeat part b, this time assuming 20 percent interference between the regions.

22. From several crosses of the general type $AA\,BB \times aa\,bb$, the F_1 individuals of type $Aa\,Bb$ were testcrossed to $aa\,bb$. The results are shown in Table 5-4. In each case, use the χ^2 test to decide if there is evidence of linkage.

■ **TABLE 5-4.**

Testcross of F_1 from cross	Number of individuals of genotype			
	$Aa\,Bb$	$aa\,bb$	$Aa\,bb$	$aa\,Bb$
1	310	315	287	288
2	36	38	23	23
3	360	380	230	230
4	74	72	50	44

23. Certain varieties of flax show different resistances to specific races of the fungus called flax rust. For example, the flax variety 77OB is resistant to rust race 24 but susceptible to rust race 22, whereas flax variety Bombay is resistant to rust race 22 and susceptible to rust race 24. When 77OB and Bombay were crossed, the F_1 hybrid was resistant to both rust races. When selfed, it produced an F_2 containing the phenotypic proportions shown in Table 5-5.

■ **TABLE 5-5.**

		Rust race 22	
		Resistant	Susceptible
Rust race 24	Resistant	184	63
	Susceptible	58	15

a. Propose a hypothesis to account for the genetic basis of resistance in flax to these particular rust races. Make a concise statement of the hypothesis, and define any gene symbols you use. Show your proposed genotypes of the 77OB, Bombay, F_1, and F_2 flax plants.

b. Test your hypothesis, using the χ^2 test. Give the expected values, the value of χ^2 (to two decimal places), and the appropriate probability value. Explain exactly what this value is the probability of. Do you accept or reject your hypothesis on the basis of the χ^2 test?

(Problem 23 is adapted from M. Strickberger, *Genetics,* Macmillan, 1968.)

24. In humans the genes for color blindness and hemophilia are both on the X chromosome, with a recombinant frequency of about 10 percent. Linkage of a pathological gene to a relatively harmless one can be used for genetic prognosis. The pedigree below shows some of the people from a more extensive pedigree.

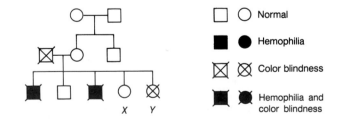

What advice could be given to the women x and y as to the likelihood of their having sons with hemophilia?

(Problem 24 is adapted from J. F. Crow, *Genetics Notes: An Introduction to Genetics,* Burgess Publishing Co., Minneapolis, 1983.)

25. A geneticist mapping the genes A, B, C, D, and E makes two three-point test crosses involving various combinations of these genes.

Series 1			Series 2		
$AABBCCDDEE \times aabbCCddEE$			$AABBCCDDEE \times aaBBccDDee$		
F_1 test-crossed to recessive tester			F_1 test-crossed to recessive tester		
Progeny			Progeny		
ABCDE	316		ABCDE	243	
abCdE	314		aBcDe	237	
ABCdE	31		ABcDe	62	
abCDE	39		aBCDE	58	
AbCdE	130		ABCDe	155	
aBCDE	140		aBcDE	165	
AbCDE	17		aBCDe	46	
aBCdE	13		ABcDE	34	
	1000			1000	

The geneticist also knew that the genes D and E showed independent assortment.

a.   Draw a map of these genes, showing distances in centimorgans wherever possible.

b.   Is there any evidence of chromosome interference?

CHAPTER 6

Linkage II: Special Eukaryotic Chromosome Mapping Techniques

■ This chapter extends the basic treatment of linkage developed in Chapter 5. Three major topics are covered: mapping functions (a more accurate treatment of linkage mapping by recombinant frequency analysis), tetrad analysis, and mitotic genetics. The techniques introduced here are important in many areas of modern genetics, as we shall see in later chapters.

Why should a *second* chapter be devoted to the study of eukaryotic linkage mapping? The simple answer is that the linkage map is such a fundamental tool in the study of heredity that the modern geneticist would be lost without it—much as a novice traveler would be lost without a road map. Consider the following. One of the most basic concerns of genetics is the structure of the genome. This concern could not be addressed without a knowledge of where specific genes are located. Within this area there is a wealth of study, not the least part of which is the interaction of genes with other genes in the same vicinity. There are, for example, control genes that profoundly affect genes adjacent to them on the chromosome. Then there is the issue of gene families and clusters of related and/or controlled genes. All of these areas of study require precise mapping data. A final point: the fantastically complex strains used as an integral part of research in modern biology, both pure and applied, can be synthesized only through an intricate kind of chromosome mechanics that is almost totally dependent on a detailed knowledge of gene linkage.

Mapping Functions

In Chapter 5, we defined the map unit (m.u.) as a recombinant frequency (RF) of 1 percent. We have seen that this definition leads to reasonable estimates of map distances. However, when *larger* locus-to-locus intervals are being examined, the estimate becomes very imprecise, as in the following example:

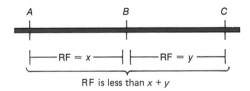

We have seen that we can improve the situation by including the double-recombinant types (twice). However, the point is that map distance (or the "true" distance) between loci is not linearly related to recombinant frequency throughout the range of values possible in mapping experiments. We have the clue provided by double crossovers, but now we must come to grips with the notion that double crossovers are part of a much larger problem of multiple crossovers and their effect on recombinant frequency. It might be pertinent to ask, for example, whether the RF value of x for the A-to-B interval in the example is an accurate reflection of the true distance between the A and B loci. Perhaps some double crossovers occur in this interval alone; we cannot detect them because we have no markers between A and B, but we should account for them if RF is to reflect physical distance at all well. This section describes a mathematical treatment of the problem that does give a way of correcting for multiple exchanges without actually detecting them at the phenotypic level.

Any relationship between one variable entity and another is called a function; the relationship between real map distance and recombination frequency is called the **mapping function.**

Message   The relationship between real map distance and RF is not linear. The mapping function provides a closer approximation to the real relationship.

The Poisson Distribution

To calculate the mapping function, we need a mathematical tool that is widely used in genetic analysis because it describes many genetic phenomena well. It is called the **Poisson distribution.** A distribution is merely a device that describes the frequencies of various classes of samples. The Poisson distribution describes the frequency of classes of samples containing 0, 1, 2, 3, 4, . . . , i events when the average number of events per sample is small in relation to the total number of times that the event could occur. For example, the *possible* number of tadpoles obtainable in a single dip of a net in a pond is quite large, but most dips yield only one or two or none. The number of dead birds on the side of the highway is potentially very large, but in a sample kilometer the number is usually small. Such samplings are described well by the Poisson distribution.

Let's consider a numerical example. We'll randomly distribute 100 one-dollar bills to 100 students in a lecture room, perhaps by scattering them over the class from some vantage point near the ceiling. The average (or mean) number of bills per student is 1.0, but common sense tells us that it is very unlikely that each of the 100 students will capture one bill. We expect a few lucky students to grab three or four bills each, and quite a few should come up with two bills each. However, we would expect most students to get either one bill or none. The Poisson distribution provides a quantitative prediction of the results.

In this example, the event being considered is capture of one bill by a student. We want to divide the students into classes according to the number of events occurring (number of bills captured per student) and find the frequency of each class. Let m represent the mean number of events

(here $m = 1.0$ bill per student). Let i represent the number of events for a particular class (say, $i = 3$ for those students who get three bills each). Let $f(i)$ represent the frequency of the class with i events—that is, the proportion of the 100 students who each capture i bills. The general expression for the Poisson distribution states that

$$f(i) = \frac{e^{-m} m^i}{i!}$$

where e is the base of natural logarithms ($e \cong 2.7$), and ! is the factorial symbol (for example, $3! = 3 \times 2 \times 1 = 6$, and $4! = 4 \times 3 \times 2 \times 1 = 24$; by definition, $0! = 1$). When computing $f(0)$, recall that any number raised to the power of zero is defined as one. Table 6-1 gives values of e^{-m} for m values from 0.000 to 1.000.

In our example, $m = 1.0$. Using Table 6-1, let's compute the frequencies of the classes of students who each capture 0, 1, 2, 3, and 4 bills.

$$f(0) = \frac{e^{-1}\, 1^0}{0!} = \frac{e^{-1}}{1} = 0.368$$

$$f(1) = \frac{e^{-1}\, 1^1}{1!} = \frac{e^{-1}}{1} = 0.368$$

$$f(2) = \frac{e^{-1}\, 1^2}{2!} = \frac{e^{-1}}{2 \times 1} = \frac{e^{-1}}{2} = 0.184$$

$$f(3) = \frac{e^{-1}\, 1^3}{3!} = \frac{e^{-1}}{3 \times 2 \times 1} = \frac{e^{-1}}{6} = 0.061$$

$$f(4) = \frac{e^{-1}\, 1^4}{4!} = \frac{e^{-1}}{4 \times 3 \times 2 \times 1} = \frac{e^{-1}}{24} = 0.015$$

Figure 6-1 shows a histogram of this distribution. We predict that about 37 students will capture no bills, about 37 will capture one bill, about 18 will capture two bills, about 6 will capture three bills, and about 2 will capture four bills. This accounts for all 100 of the students; in fact, you can verify that the Poisson distribution yields $f(5) = 0.003$, in-

Figure 6-1. Poisson distribution for a mean ot 1.0, illustrated in terms of a random distribution of dollar bills to students.

■ **TABLE 6-1.** Values of e^{-m} for m values of 0 to 1

m	e^{-m}	m	e^{-m}	m	e^{-m}	m	e^{-m}
0.000	1.00000	0.250	0.77880	0.500	0.60653	0.750	0.47237
0.010	0.99005	0.260	0.77105	0.510	0.60050	0.760	0.46767
0.020	0.98020	0.270	0.76338	0.520	0.59452	0.770	0.46301
0.030	0.97045	0.280	0.75578	0.530	0.58860	0.780	0.45841
0.040	0.96079	0.290	0.74826	0.540	0.58275	0.790	0.45384
0.050	0.95123	0.300	0.74082	0.550	0.57695	0.800	0.44933
0.060	0.94176	0.310	0.73345	0.560	0.57121	0.810	0.44486
0.070	0.93239	0.320	0.72615	0.570	0.56553	0.820	0.44043
0.080	0.92312	0.330	0.71892	0.580	0.55990	0.830	0.43605
0.090	0.91393	0.340	0.71177	0.590	0.55433	0.840	0.43171
0.100	0.90484	0.350	0.70469	0.600	0.54881	0.850	0.42741
0.110	0.89583	0.360	0.69768	0.610	0.54335	0.860	0.42316
0.120	0.88692	0.370	0.69073	0.620	0.53794	0.870	0.41895
0.130	0.87810	0.380	0.68386	0.630	0.53259	0.880	0.41478
0.140	0.86936	0.390	0.67706	0.640	0.52729	0.890	0.41066
0.150	0.86071	0.400	0.67032	0.650	0.52205	0.900	0.40657
0.160	0.85214	0.410	0.66365	0.660	0.51685	0.910	0.40252
0.170	0.84366	0.420	0.65705	0.670	0.51171	0.920	0.39852
0.180	0.83527	0.430	0.65051	0.680	0.50662	0.930	0.39455
0.190	0.82696	0.440	0.64404	0.690	0.50158	0.940	0.39063
0.200	0.81873	0.450	0.63763	0.700	0.49659	0.950	0.38674
0.210	0.81058	0.460	0.63128	0.710	0.49164	0.960	0.38289
0.220	0.80252	0.470	0.62500	0.720	0.48675	0.970	0.37908
0.230	0.79453	0.480	0.61878	0.730	0.48191	0.980	0.37531
0.240	0.78663	0.490	0.61263	0.740	0.47711	0.990	0.37158
						1.000	0.36788

SOURCE: F. James Rohlf and Robert R. Sokal, *Statistical Tables*, 2d ed. Copyright © 1981 by W. H. Freeman and Co.

dicating the likelihood that no student in this sample of 100 will capture five bills.

Similar distributions may be developed for other m values. Some are shown in Figure 6-2, which uses curves instead of bar histograms.

Derivation of the Mapping Function

The occurrence of crossovers along a chromosome during meiosis also can be described by the Poisson distribution. In any given genetic region, the actual number of crossovers occurring is probably small in relation to the total number of opportunities for such a crossover in that stretch. If we knew the *mean* number of crossovers in the region per meiosis, we could calculate the distribution of meioses with zero, one, two, three, four, and more multiple crossovers. This is unnecessary in the present context because, as we shall see, the only class we are really interested in is the zero class. The reason for this is that we want to correlate real distances with observable RF values, and it turns out that meioses in which there are one, two, three, four, or *any* finite number of crossovers per meiosis all behave similarly in that they produce an RF of 50 percent *among the products of those meioses*, whereas the meiosis with no crossovers pro-

duce an RF of 0 percent. Consequently, the determining force in actual RF values is the ratio of class zero to the rest!

The truth of these statements can be illustrated by considering meioses in which zero, one, and two crossovers occur between nonsister chromatids. (Try the three-cross-

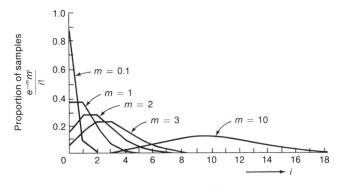

Figure 6-2. Poisson distributions for five different mean values: m is the mean number of events per sample, and i is the actual number of events per sample. (From R. R. Sokal and F. J. Rohlf, *Introduction to Biostatistics*. Copyright © 1973 by W. H. Freeman and Co.)

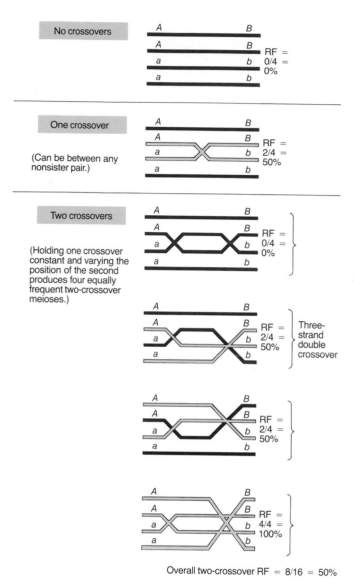

Figure 6-3. Demonstration that the overall RF is 50 percent for meioses in which any nonzero number of crossovers occurs. The color represents a recombinant chromatid.

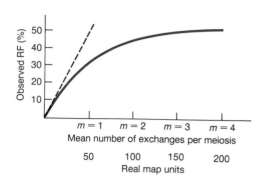

Figure 6-4. The mapping function in graphic form (solid line). The dashed line represents the linear relationship found for small values of m.

sure we can have of *true* genetic distance — the *actual* average number of crossovers in a region.

If we know an RF value, we can calculate m by solving the equation. When we plot the function as a graph, as in Figure 6-4, several interesting points emerge.

1. No matter how far apart two loci are on a chromosome, we never observe an RF value of greater than 50 percent. Consequently, an RF value of 50 percent would leave us in doubt about whether two loci are linked or are on separate chromosomes. Put another way, as m gets larger, e^{-m} gets smaller, and RF approaches $\frac{1}{2}(1 - 0) = \frac{1}{2} \times 1 = 50$ percent. This may be surprising to you: RF values of 100 percent can never be observed, no matter how far apart the loci are!

2. The function is linear for a certain range corresponding to very small m values (genetic distances). Therefore RF is a good measure of distance if the distance is small and no multiple exchanges are likely. In this region, the map unit defined as 1 percent RF has real meaning. Therefore, let's use this region of the curve to define real map units. For small m, such as $m = 0.05$, $e^{-m} = 0.95$, and RF $= \frac{1}{2}(1 - 0.95) = \frac{1}{2}(0.05) = \frac{1}{2} \times m$; for $m = 0.10$, $e^{-m} = 0.90$, and RF $= \frac{1}{2}(1 - 0.90) = \frac{1}{2}(0.10) = \frac{1}{2} \times m$. We see that RF $= m/2$, and this relation defines the dotted line on the graph in Figure 6-4. It allows us to translate m values into real (low-end-of-the-curve-style) map units.

So an m value of 1 is the equivalent of 50 real map units, and we can express the horizontal axis in map units, as indicated on the lower scale. Here we see that two loci separated by 150 real map units show an RF of only 50 percent. For regions of the graph in which the line is not horizontal, we can use the function to convert the RF into map distance simply by drawing a horizontal line to the curve and dropping a perpendicular to the map-unit axis (a process equivalent to using the formula).

Let us consider a specific numerical example of the use of the mapping function. Suppose we get an RF of 27.5 percent. How many real map units does this represent?

$$0.275 = \tfrac{1}{2}(1 - e^{-m})$$

$$0.55 = 1 - e^{-m}$$

over class yourself.) Figure 6-3 tells us that the only way we can get a recombinant product of meiosis is from a meiosis with at least one crossover in the marked region, and then *always* precisely one-half of the products of such meioses will be recombinant. Note that in the figure we consider only crossovers that occur between nonsister chromatids; **sister-chromatid exchange** is thought to be very rare at meiosis. (If it does occur, it can be shown to have no net effect in most meiotic analyses; see Problem 22 for this chapter.)

At last we can derive the mapping function. Recombinants will make up one-half of the products of those meioses in which at least one crossover occurs in the region of interest. The proportion of meioses with at least one crossover is one minus the fraction with zero crossovers. Hence RF $= \frac{1}{2}(1 - e^{-m})$, because the zero-class frequency is $e^{-m}m^0/0! = e^{-m}$. When you think about it, m is the best mea-

therefore,

$$e^{-m} = 1 - 0.55 = 0.45$$

From e^{-m} tables (or by solving the hard way using logarithms), we find that $m = 0.8$, which is 40 real map units. If we had been happy to accept 27.5 percent RF as meaning 27.5 map units, we would have been considerably underestimating the true distance between the loci.

A note to calculator owners: the mapping function may be rearranged as follows:

$$e^{-m} = 1 - 2\,RF$$
$$-m = \ln(1 - 2\,RF)$$
$$m = -\ln(1 - 2\,RF)$$

This form is more convenient for solution by calculator.

Message To get good estimates of mapping distance, put RF values through the mapping function. Alternatively, genes may be mapped through the summation of small genetic intervals in which RF has a linear relationship with map distance.

A corollary of this statement is that for organisms where the chromosomes are already well mapped, such as *Drosophila*, a geneticist usually has little need of a map function to locate newly discovered genes. This is because the map is already divided into small marked regions by the known loci. However, when the process of mapping has just begun in a new organism, or when the available genetic markers are sparsely distributed (as in human maps), the corrections provided by the function are needed.

Tetrad Analysis

We have already hinted (in Chapter 5) at the existence of marvelous organisms in which the four products of a single meiosis are recoverable and testable. The group of four is called a **tetrad**. Tetrad analysis has been possible only in those fungi and single-celled algae in which the products of each meiosis are held together in a kind of bag.

These organisms are all haploid. There are many advantages to using haploids for genetic analysis; a few are listed here.

1. Because the organisms are haploid, there is no complication of dominance. The nuclear genotype is expressed directly in the phenotype.

2. There is only one meiosis to analyze at a time (refer to the discussion of life cycles in Chapter 3), whereas, in diploids, gametes from two different meiotic events fuse to form the zygote. In diploids, the testcross is an attempt to achieve the same end, but the procedure is technically more laborious and sometimes not possible. For example, the products of the cross $+ + \times a\ b$ might be

$$
\begin{array}{ll}
+ + & 45\% \\
a\ b & 45\% \\
a + & 5\% \\
+ b & 5\%
\end{array}
$$

This result permits a direct calculation of RF as 10 percent, so 10 map units separate the *a* and the *b* loci. Note how easy it is to compare product-of-meiosis genotypes with the haploid genotypes that constituted the diploid cells in which meiosis occurred.

3. Because the organisms are small, fast-growing, and inexpensive to culture, it is possible to produce very large numbers of progeny from a cross. Thus, good statistical accuracy is possible; also, very rare events occurring at frequencies as low as 10^{-8} are detectable. Furthermore, useful selective techniques to obtain desirable genotypes are easy to apply.

4. In several well-studied species (such as yeasts and *Neurospora*), the structure and behavior of the chromosomes and gene action are similar to those found in higher organisms. Thus, these simpler forms represent very useful, easily analyzed eukaryotic models.

5. Several haploid types are important in biotechnology. Yeasts and filamentous fungi have long been important industrially, and much selective breeding of these forms has occurred. Now these same forms have become important as hosts for novel DNA types created in the test tube through genetic engineering.

6. Last, but not least, there is the possibility of **tetrad analysis.**

Tetrad analysis itself has proved useful for several reasons.

1. It provides an opportunity to test *directly* some of the assumptions of the chromosome theory of heredity. Our analyses so far have been essentially *random-meiotic-product* analyses. In these studies, individuals are examined and inferences are made about the meioses that produced them. This was the basic approach used by Mendel and by most eukaryotic geneticists since. The following example illustrates this kind of inference. A testcross of *Aa* to *aa* produces a 1 : 1 ratio, from which the equal segregation of *A* and *a* in a single

Example species

Coprinus
lagopus
(mushroom)

Saccharomyces
cerevisiae
(baker's yeast)

and

Chlamydomonas
rheinhardii
(alga)

Aspergillus
nidulans
(green bread mold)

Ascobolus
immersus

Ustilago
hordei
(barley smut)

Neurospora
crassa
(red bread mold)

Tetrads   Octads   Tetrads   Octads

Unordered   Linear

(a)   (b)

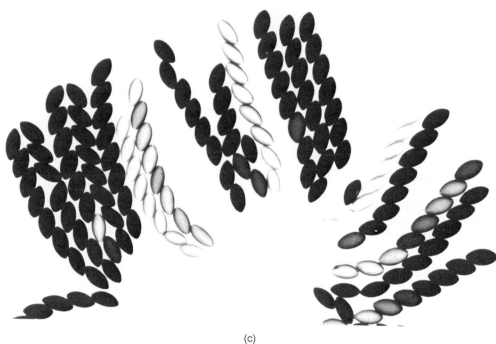

(c)

Figure 6-5. Various forms of tetrads and octads found in different organisms. (a) Unordered. (b) Linear. (c) Normally maturing asci of *Neurospora crassa* (Namboori B. Raju, *European Journal of Cell Biology*, 1980).

meiosis is inferred. The use of tetrads provides a far more direct test of this notion because the direct products of a single meiosis are examined. Furthermore, each meiotic product in the tetrad reinforces inferences about the other three products; the data are interlocking, and they increase the confidence with which we can make judgments on meiotic behavior. In research, this is an extremely useful facility.

2. It makes possible the mapping of centromeres as genetic loci.

3. It permits examination of the distribution of crossovers between the four chromatids, and hence investigation of the possibility of **chromatid interference.**

4. It permits several approaches to studying the mechanism of chromosome exchange (crossing-over). We have already used it to deduce the stage at which crossing-over occurs (four strands) and to rule out Belling's copy-choice hypothesis. But perhaps the most significant use has been in the analysis of gene conversion (see Chapter 16).

5. It provides a unique approach to the study of abnormal chromosome sets (see Chapters 8 and 9).

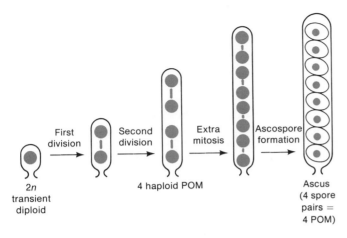

Figure 6-6. A linear meiosis and subsequent mitosis. There is no nuclear passing (change in sequence of nuclei) because there is no spindle overlap. The vertical bars represent spindles; POM = products of meiosis.

Centromere Mapping in Linear Tetrads

Tetrads can take different forms in different organisms. In some species, there are four sexual spores containing the four nuclei, which are the products of meiosis. In other species, there are eight sexual spores: in these cases each of the four meiotic product nuclei undergoes a further mitotic division, producing eight nuclei that are then enclosed in the eight spores. These groups of eight may be called **octads,** but most geneticists also call them tetrads because they represent simply doubled tetrads.

The sexual spores, whether four or eight in number, may be enclosed in two different ways. In some species, the spores are always found in a jumbled arrangement called an **unordered tetrad** (Figure 6-5a). In other species, the spores are arranged in a line, an arrangement called a **linear tetrad** (Figure 6-5b). Species with linear tetrads are particularly interesting because in these species it is possible to map the centromeres easily and include them on a linkage map. A knowledge of the position of the centromere can be extremely useful in a variety of genetic analyses. This ability is particularly useful in study of the lower eukaryotes, whose small chromosomes make cytological identification of centromeres difficult.

How are linear tetrads produced? The linear array of sexual spores is a result of the lack of spindle overlap in the meiotic divisions or in any subsequent mitotic divisions. Because no spindle overlap occurs, the nuclei do not pass each other in the long sac, and a linear array of nuclei (and hence of spores) is produced (Figure 6-6). This particular quirk allows us to map centromeres.

One Locus.   Let's look at a specific cross to see how this works. The species we use is the fungus *Neurospora crassa,* which has a linear octad. In the group of fungi to which *Neurospora* belongs, the spores and the bag surrounding them are together called an **ascus.** The locus under study in this example is the one that controls crossing ability, the so-called **mating-type locus.** There are two alleles, *A* and *a,* each determining a mating type. For a cross to be fertile,

one parent must be *A* and the other *a.* But here we are using these genes merely as genetic markers.

We can cross *A* and *a* cultures by combining them on a medium that promotes the sexual cycle. We can then isolate the octads. From each octad, we can then carefully pick out the eight spores one at a time, in the order found. We can test the culture arising from each spore to see if it is *A* or *a.* Carl Lindegren performed this experiment in the 1930s, obtaining the following results. The bottom of the ascus as written represents the "stalk" where the ascus sac is joined to the rest of the fungal tissue.

	Cross $A \times a$					
Asci	*A*	*a*	*A*	*a*	*A*	*a*
	A	*a*	*A*	*a*	*A*	*a*
	A	*a*	*a*	*A*	*a*	*A*
	A	*a*	*a*	*A*	*a*	*A*
	a	*A*	*A*	*a*	*a*	*A*
	a	*A*	*A*	*a*	*a*	*A*
	a	*A*	*a*	*A*	*A*	*a*
	a	*A*	*a*	*A*	*A*	*a*
Number	126	132	9	11	10	12
			Total = 300			

What do these patterns and their relative proportions mean? The first two types on the left are called **first-division segregation patterns,** or M_I patterns. These asci result from meioses in which there has been no detectable crossover between the mating-type locus and the corresponding centromere locus of that chromosome. Because of this lack of crossover, the two alleles *A* and *a* segregate into separate nuclei at the first meiotic division (M_I) (Figure 6-7). The approximate equality of the first two types (126 ≅ 132) reflects random spindle attachment to the centromeres at the first meiotic division. One pattern is simply an inverted copy of the other.

The four ascus types on the right show **second-division segregation patterns,** or M_{II} patterns. These asci result from meioses in which there *has* been a crossover between the mating-type locus and the centromere locus. As a result of the crossover, *A* and *a* alleles appear in the same nucleus at the end of the first meiotic division, and they do not segregate until the second division (Figure 6-8). The M_{II} pattern in Figure 6-8 is only one of the four observed, so how are the others explained? We must conclude that the attachment of the spindle fibers to the centromere at the second meiotic division must be random. This random attachment produces four patterns, only one of which is shown in Figure 6-8, but all of which must be interpreted as manifestations of the same event: a crossover. The rough equivalence of these classes (9 ≅ 11 ≅ 10 ≅ 12) is a satisfy-

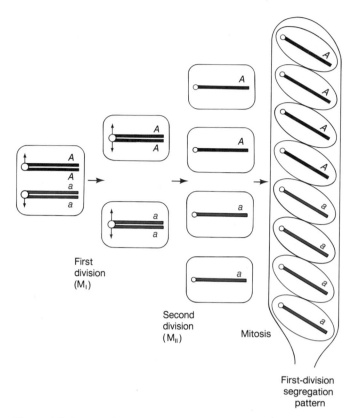

First
division
(M$_I$)

Second
division
(M$_{II}$)

Mitosis

First-division
segregation
pattern

Figure 6-7. Segregation of A and a into separate nuclei at the first meiotic division. The resultant allele pattern in the octad is called a first-division segregation pattern.

ing confirmation of the random spindle-attachment idea. Random spindle attachment is illustrated in Figure 6-9.

Notice in these data that the pairing of spores in the octad reflects the lack of nuclei passing each other in the mitotic division following meiosis. It is obvious that the octad in this species is nothing more than a doubled tetrad, so the asci of *Neurospora* often are informally called tetrads.

We instinctively feel that the relative abundance of M$_I$ versus M$_{II}$ types must reflect the map distance between the centromere locus and the mating-type locus. The total M$_{II}$ pattern frequency is $42/300 = 14$ percent; can we state this simply as a distance of 14 map units (14 m.u.)? The answer is a resounding NO! The reason is an important one: map units are defined as the percentage of *recombinant products of meiosis*. The 14 percent obtained here is the percentage of *meioses* in which a crossover has occurred. One crossover between two loci in a meiosis—in the present case, between a gene locus and a centromere locus—produces only 50 percent recombinant meiotic products in that meiosis (Figure 6-10). Because the recombinant chromatids represent recombinant meiotic products, and because only two of the four products in this kind of meiosis are recombinant, the M$_{II}$ frequency obviously must be halved to obtain a good estimate of the number of map units between the loci. The mating-type locus therefore is 7 m.u. from its centromere.

Message To calculate the distance of a locus from its centromere in map units, simply divide by 2 the percentage of asci showing a second-division segregation pattern for that locus.

In this way, we can locate the centromere on a genetic map with units consistent with other mapping analyses.

Two Loci. In a cross involving linked marker loci (say, $a/+$ and $b/+$), either or both of the gene pairs may show an M$_I$ (or an M$_{II}$) pattern in a tetrad analysis. The combined pattern obtained will depend, of course, on the exact location of the crossover. If the locus order is centromere $-a/+-b/+$, then a crossover between $a/+$ and $b/+$ will produce an M$_{II}$ pattern for $b/+$ and an M$_I$ pattern for $a/+$ (Figure 6-11).

If the relation of several gene loci with respect to the centromere locus (or loci if the genes are unlinked) is unknown, then a linear tetrad analysis can be used to provide this information. We look next at an example of such an analysis.

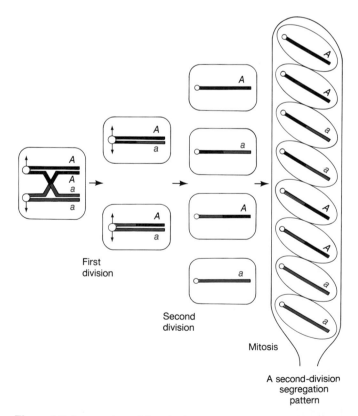

First
division

Second
division

Mitosis

A second-division
segregation
pattern

Figure 6-8. Segregation of A and a into separate nuclei at the second meiotic division because of a crossover. The allele pattern in the octad is called a second-division segregation pattern. (Other second-division patterns are possible.)

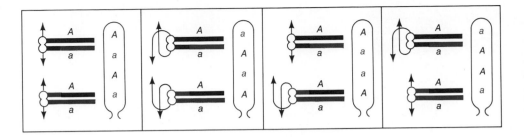

Figure 6-9. Four second-division segregation ascus patterns are equally frequent in linear asci. These are produced by random spindle-to-centromere attachments at the second meiotic division.

The cross is $nic + \times + ad$, in which nic is an allele that causes the fungus to require nicotinic acid in order to grow, and ad is an allele of another gene and confers a requirement for adenine. Normal strains have no medium-supplementation requirements. (Don't worry about these phenotypes for now; they are being used only as genetic markers.) In a cross involving two marker loci, only seven basic linear octad classes are possible (Figure 6-12). The octads are written as tetrads for simplicity, because members of each spore pair are identical. Note also that in arriving at these seven classes, the order of genotypes within the half-ascus has been ignored because it simply reflects random spindle attachment; for example, class 5 contains

+ ad	nic +	+ ad	nic +
nic +	+ ad	nic +	+ ad
+ ad	+ ad	nic +	nic +
nic +	nic +	+ ad	+ ad

All are equivalent asci and may be interconverted by inverting the top two and/or the bottom two genotypes to simulate random spindle attachment.

The asci in Figure 6-12 are labeled to indicate which segregation pattern is shown by each locus. The asci also are labeled according to another classification:

1. **parental ditypes** (PD), in which there are only two genotypes (hence *ditype*) with respect to the marker loci, and both are parental (classes 1 and 5);

2. **nonparental ditypes** (NPD), in which there are only two genotypes, and both are nonparental or recombinant (classes 2 and 6);

3. **tetratype** (T) in which there are four genotypes—two parental and two nonparental (classes 3, 4, and 7).

These classifications are the result of the combinations of M_I and M_{II} segregations, presented in Figure 6-13. Note

that a tetratype can occur only when there is a crossover between at least one locus and its centromere. Now for the calculations.

First, we calculate the distance of each locus from its centromere. For $+/nic$, it is

$$\frac{5 + 90 + 1 + 5}{1000} = \frac{101}{1000} = 10.1\% \ M_{II} = 5.05 \text{ m.u.}$$

For $+/ad$, it is

$$\frac{90 + 90 + 1 + 5}{1000} = \frac{186}{1000} = 18.6\% \ M_{II} = 9.30 \text{ m.u.}$$

However, we still have three linkage possibilities, as shown in Figure 6-14. Most of the asci are $M_I M_I$ parental ditypes (808/1000). Therefore, most genomes are parental, and

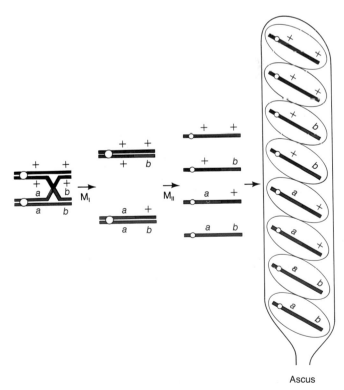

Ascus

Figure 6-11. A first-division segregation pattern for $a/+$ and a second-division segregation pattern for $b/+$ will result from a single crossover with the linkage arrangement shown.

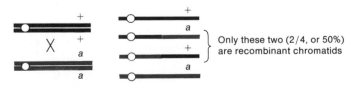

Only these two (2/4, or 50%) are recombinant chromatids

Figure 6-10. Only one-half of the chromatids from a meiosis with a single crossover are recombinant.

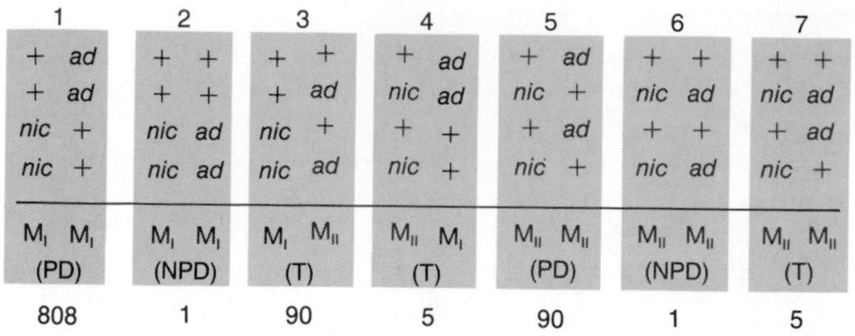

1 2 3 4 5 6 7
+ ad | + + | + + | + ad | + ad | + + | + +
+ ad | + + | + ad | nic ad | nic + | nic ad | nic ad
nic + | nic ad | nic + | + + | + ad | + + | + ad
nic + | nic ad | nic ad | nic + | nic + | nic ad | nic +
M_I M_I (PD) | M_I M_I (NPD) | M_I M_II (T) | M_II M_I (T) | M_II M_II (PD) | M_II M_II (NPD) | M_II M_II (T)
808 1 90 5 90 1 5

Figure 6-12. All the seven possible tetrad types for a cross in which two loci are heterozygous. Some numbers are given as an example, and these are interpreted in the text. The results shown are for a total of 1000 asci. PD = parental ditype (the asci contain only two genotypes, both parental); NPD = nonparental genotype (there are only two genotypes and both are nonparental, or recombinant); and T = tetratype (there are four genotypes, two parental and two nonparental).

independent assortment cannot have occurred; so possibility 1 in the figure can be ruled out.

If we arrange the data in a different way, then possibility 2 also is ruled out as follows:

+/*nic*	+/*ad*	
M_I	M_I	809
M_I	M_{II}	90
M_{II}	M_I	5
M_{II}	M_{II}	96
		1000

Now we can clearly see that a crossover in the centromere-to-*nic* region is almost always (96/101 times) accompanied by a crossover in the centromere-to-*ad* region. We conclude that the *same crossover* simultaneously generates an M_{II} pattern for +/*nic* and for +/*ad*. This is very powerful evidence in favor of possibility 3, with the following crossover producing the observed products:

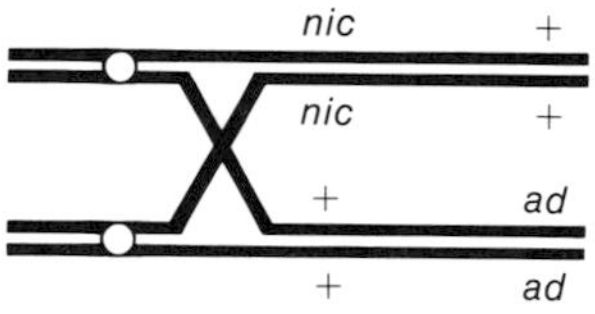

nic +
nic +
+ ad
+ ad

Having ascertained that possibility 3 is correct, we can calculate the recombinant frequency between +/*nic* and +/*ad*. The simple subtraction 9.30 − 5.05 does not give an accurate value for the following reason. We arrived at the figure of 9.30 m.u. by calculating the M_{II} frequency and dividing by 2. In calculating this M_{II} frequency, we now see that we missed quite a few asci containing crossovers between the centromere and the *ad* locus. For example, class 4 was scored as M_I for +/*ad*, but we know now that *two* crossovers occurred in these asci:

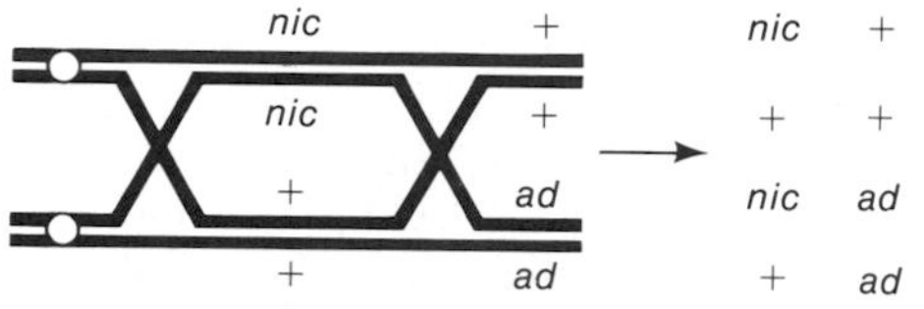

nic +
nic +
+ ad
+ ad
nic +
+ +
nic ad
+ ad

We can better calculate the distance between +/*nic* and +/*ad* by using the formula

$$RF = \frac{NPD + \frac{1}{2}T}{\text{total asci}} \times 100$$

because we know that the NPD asci are full of recombinant genotypes, and the T asci are "half-full" of recombinant genotypes. Therefore,

$$RF = \frac{2 + \frac{1}{2}(100)}{1000} \times 100 = 5.2 \text{ m.u.}$$

Now we can redraw the best map obtainable from these data:

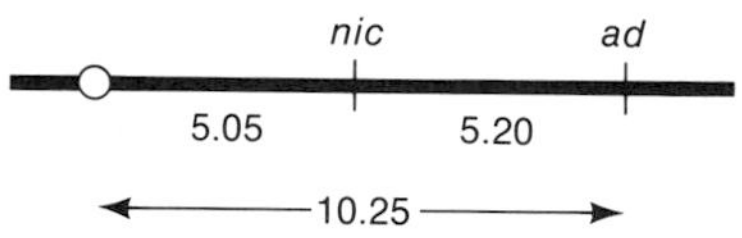

nic
ad
5.05
5.20
10.25

(NOTE: class 6 is a very complex ascus. Draw the crossovers needed to produce it, right now!)

		+/*nic*	
		M_I	M_{II}
+/*ad*	M_I	PD NPD	T only
	M_{II}	T only	T PD NPD

Figure 6-13. Tetratypes can be produced only if there is a second-division segregation for at least one gene.

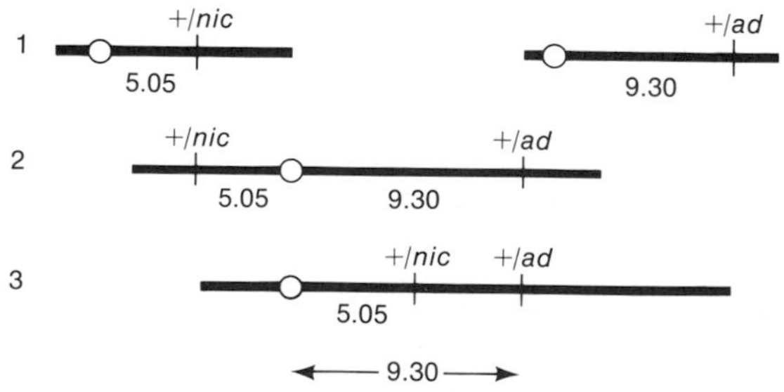

1
+/nic
5.05
+/ad
9.30
2
+/nic
+/ad
5.05
9.30
3
+/nic
+/ad
5.05
9.30

Figure 6-14. The three linkage possibilities for +/*ad* and +/*nic* in the example discussed in the text.

Message   Linear tetrad analysis can be used to map loci in relation to their centromere(s) and to each other.

Analysis of Unordered Tetrads

Because isolation of linear tetrads is a laborious process, unordered tetrads are sometimes used as a less informative but simpler way to study meiotic genetics. The groups of four or eight are recovered clustered together, but not in linear sequence. In *Neurospora*, the fungus shoots the spores out of the ascus sac, and they may be caught as a somewhat scattered group of eight on a collection surface, such as a slide. In many other species, of course, the tetrad is always unordered. Unordered tetrads can be scored only as PD, NPD, or T. Although centromere mapping is not normally possible, useful linkage information is still available. Furthermore, an analysis of unordered tetrads introduces some concepts that are central to a full appreciation of meiotic genetics. Although these specific analyses can be performed only in fungi or algae, the mechanisms revealed (and the analytical thinking involved) are highly relevant and are of direct application to any eukaryotic meiotic system.

Remember that PD asci contain no recombinants, NPD asci are full of recombinants, and T asci have equal numbers of each. Therefore, a T ascus is irrelevant in deciding whether there is linkage, because its class contributes equally to the parental and recombinant genotypes. The critical test for linkage in unordered asci, therefore, is whether NPD is equal to or less than PD.

Message   If the number of PD asci is greater than the number of NPD asci, then the RF must be less than 50 percent, and there must be linkage between the genes.

However, if PD = NPD, then RF = 50 percent, indicating independent assortment, and we cannot say whether the genes are on different chromosomes or are very distantly linked loci. In this dilemma, the T class can be of some use. Let's take an example in which PD = 42, NPD = 48, and T = 10. The χ^2 test (page 89) shows no significant difference between 42 and 48; yet the T frequency clearly shows that the loci are unlinked. Why is this? If they *were* linked they would have to be a very great distance apart to give a 50 percent RF value. We can now ask what T frequency would prevail under such conditions, and then compare it to the observed T frequency.

In a hypothetical cross of $a + \times + b$ in which the a and b loci are linked but very far apart, we can visualize a "maze"

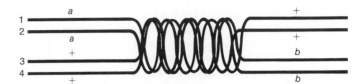

Figure 6-15. When two loci are widely separated on the same chromosome pair, the intervening multiple crossovers effectively unlink the genes concerned. Any of the four genes at one locus can associate at random with any of the four at the other locus.

of crossovers at meiosis something like that shown in Figure 6-15. The following "thought experiment" enables us to determine the PD, NPD, and T frequencies in such a situation.

Let us assume that the $a/+$ locus is close to the centromere so that it always shows an M_I pattern. The large number of crossovers between $a/+$ and $b/+$ effectively uncouples the $b/+$ locus from the centromere. Because of this we can simulate the segregation of b and its $+$ allele by considering the ways of dropping four marbles (two b marbles and two $+$ marbles) into a test tube, as shown in Figure 6-16. Whether the first marble is b or $+$ makes no difference, but in the figure the first is assumed to be $+$. It is the *second* marble that determines the "segregation" pattern of the

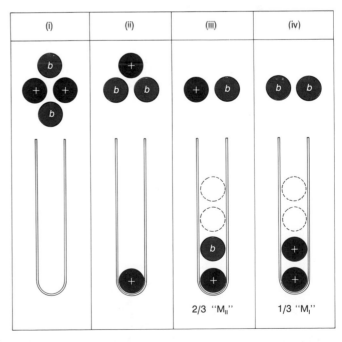

Figure 6-16. Demonstration of the limiting M_I and M_{II} segregation pattern frequencies in linear tetrad analysis. (See text for details.)

marbles in the test tube. There is a 2 out of 3 chance of the second's being b, and a 1 out of 3 chance of its being $+$. The former establishes an M_{II} pattern and the latter an M_I pattern; the order of the last two marbles is irrelevant. Hence, the M_{II} frequency maximum in general is determined to be $\frac{2}{3}$ (66.7 percent). In our example, in combination with the fixed M_I pattern for $a/+$ we see that the M_{II} frequency maximum translates into a tetratype frequency maximum of 66.7 percent. For very distant genes, when both loci show an M_I pattern, equal numbers of PD and NPD asci result, each at a frequency of $(100 - 66.7)/2 = 16.7$ percent. These findings are graphed in Figure 6-17. Note that for linked genes, the only way to produce an NPD ascus is through a four-chromatid double crossover, so this class will be quite small for genes that are tightly linked.

To return to the numerical data where $PD = 42$, $NPD = 48$, and $T = 10$, we see that the tetratype frequency of 10 percent is incompatible with our graph representing linked loci (Figure 6-17), because for linked loci, when $PD = NPD$, the frequency of T *must* be 66.7 percent. Hence the data indicate that the loci concerned are on separate chromosomes.

Now we calculate the equivalent curves for unlinked loci, and we compare these with the ones for linked loci. If loci are unlinked, a tetratype can arise only from an exchange in at least one locus-to-centromere region (see Figure 6-13). The important distance, then, is the combined locus-to-centromere distance. Let's take an example in which two loci on separate chromosomes are very distant from their centromeres. The M_{II} maxima will be 66.7 percent, as shown above. Thus a checkerboard is generated as shown in Figure 6-18, and a set of curves for unlinked loci can be derived as shown in Figure 6-19. Notice that these curves are different from the equivalent ones for linked loci, but only in regions to the left of the flat portions of the curves. If experimental data show $PD = NPD$ and a T frequency of 66.7 percent, then the precise linkage situation cannot be determined without further crosses. These rela-

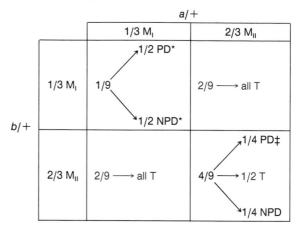

* Because of random spindle attachment.
‡ Because, if you hold one M_{II} pattern constant and draw all four possible M_{II} patterns for the other locus, the following $1:2:1$ ratio for PD : T : NPD is produced:

PD	T	T	NPD
$a +$	$a\ b$	$a +$	$a\ b$
$+ b$	$+ +$	$+ b$	$+ +$
$a +$	$a +$	$a\ b$	$a\ b$
$+ b$	$+ b$	$+ +$	$+ +$

Total $T = 2/9 + 2/9 + 2/9 = 6/9 = 2/3 = 66.7\%$
$PD = 1/9 + 1/18 \qquad = 1/6 = 16.7\%$
$NPD = 1/9 + 1/18 \qquad = 1/6 = 16.7\%$

Figure 6-18. Even for loci that are both distant from their centromeres, tetratype (T) frequency can never exceed 66.7 percent.

tionships are best expressed in terms of the ratio of NPD/T, as follows.

Message   For linked loci, the value of NPD/T lies between 0 and 1/4. For unlinked loci, NPD/T lies between 1/4 and ∞.

At this point, it is worth raising an apparent paradox that is often noticed in this kind of analysis. We have seen that, to convert the M_{II} pattern frequency to map units (in order to derive centromere distances), the simple rule is to divide the M_{II} frequency by 2. Yet we now see that the M_{II} maximum is 66.7 percent, no matter what distance is involved. This value would permit a maximum of 33.3 map units, which seems inconsistent with the maximum of 50 map units known to be possible from standard linkage analysis, and also from the $NPD + \frac{1}{2} T$ formula.

The key to this situation is that the simple $M_{II}/2$ formula does not hold for very large distances. Once again, multiple exchanges are the culprit. We should include the equivalent of the NPD class, but there is no way to detect this class in centromere mapping. An M_{II} value of 66.7 percent can probably be directly equated with an RF of 50 percent.

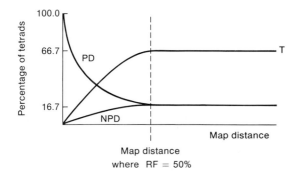

Figure 6-17. Frequency of various types of tetrads for linked loci of different linkage relationships.

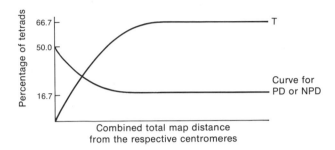

Figure 6-19. Frequency of various types of tetrads for unlinked loci.

Once any maximum is approached, there are always analytical problems to be overcome. Values are always rather unreliable, and they must not be taken literally. For example, we are worrying here about increasing a maximum of 33.3 to reach a value of 50, but the 50 itself is also unreliable because it may represent many more real map units—even hundreds! However, the preceding discussion shows that the two maxima are not inconsistent.

One convenient use of unordered tetrad analysis is that it provides a *direct* way of correcting mapping errors due to double crossovers. We will assume a genetic region of such a size that meioses have either no crossovers or a single crossover (SCO) or a double crossover (DCO), but never more. The key is the NPD asci, which should measure 1/4 of the DCO class (see Figure 6-3); so, working with frequencies,

$$DCO = 4NPD$$

What about the SCO class? Of course, T asci will be the result of single crossovers, but some T asci will result from double crossovers (see Figure 6-3 again); in fact, 1/2 of the double crossovers will result in T asci. Hence

$$SCO = T - 2NPD$$

In order to calculate a reasonably accurate estimate of m, the mean number of crossovers in the region, we must add the SCO frequency to twice the DCO frequency, so

$$m = (T - 2NPD) + 2(4NPD)$$
$$= T + 6NPD$$

We saw earlier that to convert m to map units we multiply by 50, so

corrected map distance (in m.u.) = 50(T + 6NPD)

This formula has an advantage over the mapping function in that it does not assume a lack of chiasma interference. Nevertheless, it should be evident that this formula and the

mapping function are alternative approaches to the same basic problem, which is correction for multiple crossovers.

Chromatid Interference

Does the occurrence of a crossover between two nonsister chromatids affect the probability of a second crossover between the *same* chromatids? As usual, the best hypothesis to test is a null hypothesis, which is that the second crossover will occur randomly between any pair of nonsister chromatids (Figure 6-20). The randomized second crossover should generate a 1:2:1 ratio of 2-strand:3-strand:4-strand doubles, and any deviation from that ratio can be considered interference between chromatids, or chromatid interference. Usually there is very little or no consistent interference of this sort when the analysis of double-exchange tetrads is performed using fungal asci.

Note that the RF limit of 50 percent applies only when there is no chromatid interference. Positive chromatid interference would favor the production of NPD tetrads in which all the products of meiosis are recombinant, at the expense of PD and T classes. Hence the RF could rise above 50 percent to a value dependent on the degree of chromatid interference.

Mitotic Segregation and Recombination

We normally think of segregation and recombination as meiotic phenomena, but they do occur (although less frequently) during mitosis. The presence of mitotic segregation and recombination can easily be demonstrated if the genetic system is appropriately chosen.

Mitotic Segregation

In genetics, the term **segregation** is used to describe the separation of two alleles constituting a heterozygote into

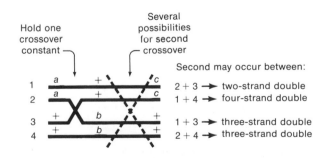

(All four possibilities give separate distinguishable ascus genotypes.)

Figure 6-20. Double crossovers can produce several distinctive patterns of alleles in the ascus, depending on the strands involved.

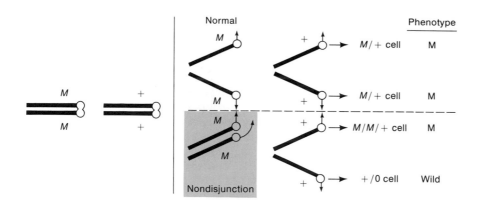

Figure 6-21. Mitotic nondisjunction can lead to phenotypic segregation—in this example, of M and $+$.

phenotypically distinguishable individuals or cells. We have seen segregation repeatedly, of course, in our meiotic analyses based on Mendel's first law. However, the alleles of a heterozygote occasionally can be seen to segregate when the heterozygous cell undergoes *mitotic* division. The following example clarifies the way in which this mitotic segregation is detected.

In the 1930s, C. B. Bridges was observing *Drosophila* females that were genotypically $M/+$ (M is a dominant allele that produces a phenotype of slender bristles). Some females had a patch, or **sector,** of wild-type bristles on a body of predominantly M phenotype. Thus the alleles of the heterozygote showed segregation at the phenotypic level. Bridges concluded that this segregation resulted from mitotic—that is, **somatic**—nondisjunction (Figure 6-21). In other heterozygotes, involving autosomal recessive genes and their wild-type alleles, patches of recessive phenotype on backgrounds of wild-type phenotype again were seen. These patches also can be explained by mitotic nondisjunction.

Other cases of segregation in the somatic tissue of a heterozygote have been found to be due to **mitotic chromosome loss.** Here the chromosome bearing the dominant allele somehow gets left behind when the daughter nuclei reconstitute after mitotic division (Figure 6-22).

Geneticists find two other terms useful in relation to such phenomena. First, **variegation** is the mere existence of different-looking sectors of somatic tissue, whatever the cause. Second, a **mosaic** is an individual composed of tissues of two or more different genotypes, often recognizable because of their different phenotypes.

Mitotic Crossing-Over

In 1936, Curt Stern showed that sectors in a mosaic are not always the result of nondisjunction or mitotic chromosome loss. He was working with the *Drosophila* sex-linked genes *y* (yellow) and *sn* (singed—short, curly bristles). He made a cross $+sn/+sn \times y+/Y$. The female progeny were predominantly wild-type in appearance, as expected. Some females had sectors of yellow tissue or of singed tissue; these could be explained by nondisjunction or chromosome loss. However, some females showed **twin spots.** A twin spot, in this example, is two adjacent sectors, one of yellow tissue and one of singed tissue, in a background of wild-type tissue (Figure 6.23). Stern reasoned that, because the twin sectors of a twin spot are adjacent, and because twin spots occurred too frequently to be chance juxtapositions of single spots, then twin sectors must be the reciprocal products of the same event. That event, he concluded, must have been a crossover between the $sn/+$ locus and the centromere during a mitotic division in which the homologous parental chromosomes had gratuitously been in a pairing conformation (Figure 6-24). Figure 6-24 demonstrates that a crossover between the marker loci could also have contributed to the yellow single-spot class.

Twin spots have been observed in other systems, including plants. All of these observations can be explained

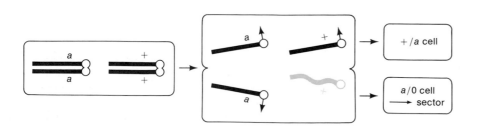

Figure 6-22. Chromosome loss at mitotic division can lead to phenotypic segregation—in this example, of a and $+$.

(a) Single yellow spot   (b) Twin spot   (c) Single singed spot

Figure 6-23. Segregation of body-surface phenotypes in *Drosophila* genotype $+sn/y+$, where *sn* is singed bristles and *y* is yellow body. (a) Single yellow spot. (b) Twin spot. (c) Single singed spot.

by mitotic crossing-over, which appears to be of quite general (although rare) occurrence.

The definition of mitotic recombination in general is similar to that of meiotic recombination. Compare the following definition with that on page 81.

Definition   Mitotic recombination (which must be studied in diploid cells) may be defined as any mitotic process that generates a diploid daughter cell with a combination of genes different from the diploid parental cell in which mitosis occurred.

Fungal Detection Systems

Fungi also are used extensively for the study of mitotic recombination and segregation. It is necessary, however, to generate diploid fungal cells in order to observe these mitotic phenomena. Diploids form spontaneously in many fungi. The one we examine is *Aspergillus*, a greenish mold. *Aspergillus* is a highly suitable organism for mitotic analysis for several reasons.

1. The hyphae of the fungus produce long chains of cells called asexual spores. These asexual spores are uninu-

cleate, and the phenotype of any individual spore is dependent only on the genotype of its own nucleus. This makes possible certain kinds of selective techniques.

2. If two haploid cultures are mixed, the hyphae fuse; both nuclear types are then present in a common cytoplasm. This condition is called a **heterokaryon.** Consider the following heterokaryon:

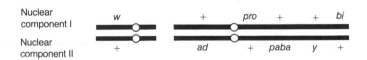

The alleles *ad, pro, paba,* and *bi* are all recessive to their wild-type counterparts, and each confers a requirement for a certain specific chemical supplement to permit growth. The alleles *w* and *y* produce white and yellow asexual spores, respectively, and are also recessive. Thus the heterokaryon does not require any supplement for growth, but (because of the phenotype autonomy just described in reason 1) the asexual spores are either yellow or white. Thus the heterokaryon looks yellowish-white, a kind of "pepper-and-salt" appearance.

3. In some heterokaryons, green sectors appear. Green is the normal wild-type color of the fungus, and the green coloration in the present example is the result of spontaneous production of a diploid nucleus, which has propagated to form the sector. The presence of the dominant y^+ and w^+ alleles in the same nucleus produces the wild-type coloration. Diploid asexual spores can be removed from the green sector, and diploid cultures can be prepared for study. Like the heterokaryon, the diploid cells require no growth supplements.

4. When the diploid is fully grown, rare sectors showing either white or yellow asexual spores can be observed. Some of these spores are diploid (recognized by their large diameter) and some are haploid (small diameter). Two types are particularly suitable for illustrating the phenomena at work: (a) white sectors with white hap-

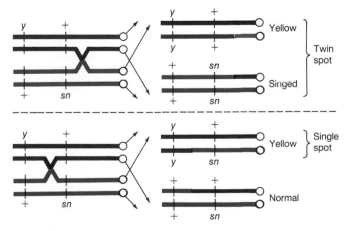

Figure 6-24. A mitotic crossover can lead to phenotypic segregation of the type shown in Figure 6-23.

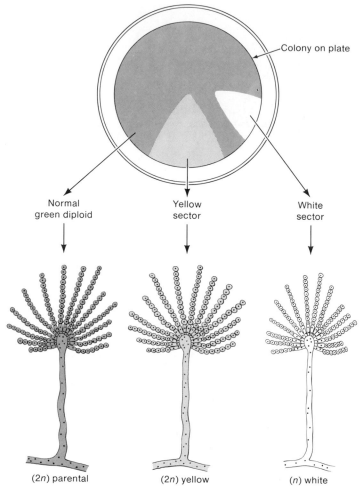

Colony on plate

Normal green diploid

Yellow sector

White sector

Chains of uninucleate asexual spores in sectors

(2n) parental

(2n) yellow

(n) white

Figure 6-25. Some sectors showing segregation in an *Aspergillus* diploid of genotype $+/w +/y$, where w is white and y is yellow asexual spores. Haploids are identified by smaller cell size.

(Yellow haploid and white diploid are also possible.)

loid spores; and (b) yellow sectors with yellow diploid spores (Figure 6-25).

Haploid White Sectors. If these sectors are isolated and tested, almost exactly one-half of them prove to have the genotype $w + pro + + bi$, and one-half show the genotype $w\,ad + paba\,y+$. Thus, the original diploid nucleus has somehow become haploid (a process known as **haploidization**), presumably by a process involving the progressive loss of one member of each chromosome pair. By looking at only white haploid spores, we automatically selected for the w-bearing chromosome. In half of the w sectors, the $+ pro + + bi$ chromosome is retained; in the other half, the $ad + paba\,y+$ chromosome is retained (Figure 6-26). In general, the recessive spore-color genes can be used to derive linkage information because haploidization is similar to independent assortment. You can see that this procedure involves selecting the chromosome bearing the spore-color marker and then observing which genes are retained with it and which are independent of it, and in what groupings.

Diploid Yellow Sectors. When a number of these sectors are examined, they usually prove to contain recombinant chromosomes. For example, one sector type examined was yel-

low and also required "paba" (*para*-aminobenzoic acid) for growth. Mitotic crossing-over explains this type (Figure 6-27). Notice that we must follow two spindle fibers going to each pole in mitotic analysis. Although one chromatid pair would normally *not* lie adjacent to its homologous

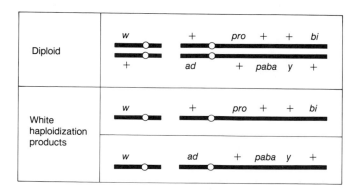

Diploid	w	$+$	pro	$+$	$+$	bi
	$+$	ad	$+$	$paba$	y	$+$
White haploidization products	w	$+$	pro	$+$	$+$	bi
	w	ad	$+$	$paba$	y	$+$

Figure 6-26. Genotype of an *Aspergillus* diploid, and the two white haploidization product genotypes possible for these marked chromosomes. (w = white, y = yellow; ad, pro, $paba$, and bi are recessive nutritional markers.)

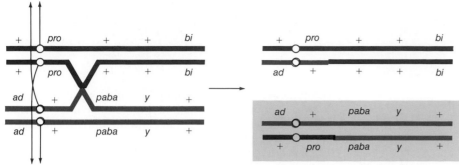

Figure 6-27. A mitotic crossover can produce a diploid yellow sector in the *Aspergillus* diploid shown.

chromatid pair, this *has* happened, presumably "accidentally." This yellow diploid arose from a mitotic exchange that obviously took place in the centromere-to-*paba* region; others would arise from mitotic exchange in the *paba*-to-*y* region (these would not require paba for growth). The relative frequencies of these two types would give a kind of mitotic linkage map for that region. Such mapping can be obtained for several fungi. As expected, the gene orders correspond to gene orders in meiotic maps, but, unexpectedly, the relative sizes of many of the intervals are very different when meiotic and mitotic maps are compared. Note that every locus from the point of crossing-over to the end of the chromosome arm is made homozygous by a mitotic crossover; this can give valuable mapping information and can be a lot quicker than a meiotic analysis.

Message Phenotypic sectoring (variegation) in somatic tissue can be due to mitotic segregation of a heterozygous gene pair (through nondisjunction or through chromosome loss) or to mitotic crossing-over.

In later chapters, we see that there are in fact several more genetic ways of producing variegation.

Mapping Human Chromosomes

Human beings do not readily submit themselves to traditional genetic analysis. Until recently, geneticists have had to rely on the study of family pedigrees in order to deduce linkage of various traits by inference from these hopelessly inadequate (from the geneticists' standpoint) data. Most of the analyses are concerned with the X chromosome; sex linkage is relatively easily shown in these cases, and testcrosses are not necessary because the male's phenotype reflects his X-chromosome genotype. (Another approach is illustrated in Problems 8, 19, and 24 of Chapter 5.) Recently, however, a technique has been developed that has revolutionized the mapping of both sex-linked and autosomal genes in humans. This technique uses human cells grown in culture (Figure 6-28).

There is a virus called Sendai that has a useful property. Normally, a virus has a specific point for attachment to and penetration of a host cell. Each Sendai virus has several

points of attachment, so that it can simultaneously attach to two different cells if they happen to be close together. A virus, though, is very small in comparison with a cell (similar to the comparison between the earth and the sun), so that the two cells to which it is attached are held very close together indeed. In fact, in many cases, the membranes of the two cells fuse together, and the two cells become one, a binucleate heterokaryon.

If suspensions of human and mouse cells are mixed together in the presence of Sendai virus (which has been inactivated by ultraviolet light), the virus can mediate fu-

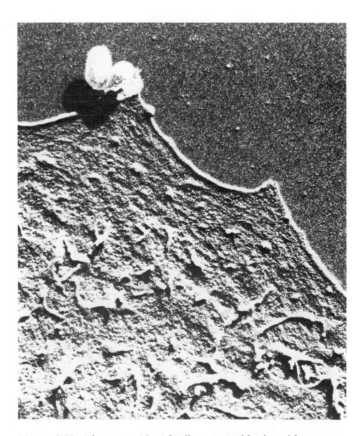

Figure 6-28. A human epithelial cell contrasted in size with two bacterial cells (*Escherichia coli*, from the human intestines). The wavy line is the edge of the human cell, of which only about one-eighth is shown. (Jack D. Griffith.)

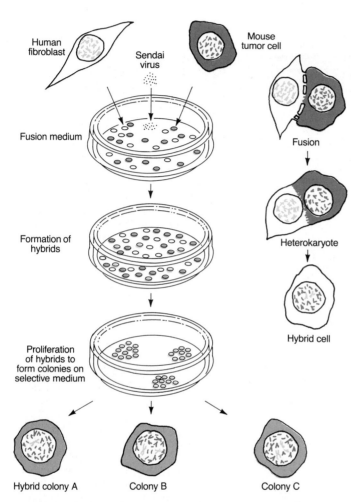

Human fibroblast

Sendai virus

Mouse tumor cell

Fusion medium

Fusion

Formation of hybrids

Heterokaryote

Proliferation of hybrids to form colonies on selective medium

Hybrid cell

Hybrid colony A   Colony B   Colony C

Figure 6-29. Cell-fusion techniques applied to human and mouse cells, producing colonies each containing a full mouse genome plus a few human chromosomes (lighter shade). A fibroblast is a cell from fibrous connective tissue. (From F. H. Ruddle and R. S. Kucherlapati, "Hybrid Cells and Human Genes." Copyright © 1974 by Scientific American, Inc. All rights reserved.)

sion of the two kinds of cells (Figure 6-29). Once the cells fuse, the nuclei can fuse to form a uninucleate cell line. Because the mouse and human chromosomes are very different in number and shape, the hybrid cells can be readily recognized. However, for some unknown reason, the human chromosomes are gradually eliminated from the hybrid as the cells divide (perhaps this is analogous to haploidization in *Aspergillus*). This process can be arrested to encourage the formation of a stable partial hybrid in the following way. The mouse cells that are used can be made genetically deficient in some function (usually a nutritional one) so that, for growth of cells to occur, the function must be supplied by the human genome. This selective technique usually results in the maintenance of hybrid cells that have a

complete set of mouse chromosomes and a small number of human chromosomes, which vary in number and type from hybrid to hybrid but always include the nutritionally sufficient human chromosome.

Luckily, this process can be followed under the microscope because mouse chromosomes can easily be distinguished from human chromosomes. Recently, this procedure has been made a lot easier by the development of stains (such as quinacrine and Giemsa) that reveal a pattern of "banding" within the chromosomes. The size and the position of these bands vary from chromosome to chromosome, but the banding patterns are highly specific and constant for each chromosome. Thus, for any hybrid, it is relatively easy to identify the human chromosomes that are present (Figure 6-30).

The mapping technique works as follows. If the human chromosome set contains a genetic marker (such as a gene that controls a specific cell-surface antigen, drug resistance, a nutritional requirement, or a protein variant), then the presence or absence of the genetic marker in each line of hybrid cells can be correlated with the presence or absence of certain human chromosomes in each line (Table 6-2). We can see that, in the different hybrid cell lines, genes 1 and 3 are always present or absent together. We conclude, then, that they are linked. Furthermore, the presence or absence of genes 1 and 3 is directly correlated with the presence or absence of chromosome 2, so we assume these genes are located on chromosome 2. By the same reasoning, gene 2 must be on chromosome 1, but the location of gene 4 cannot be assigned.

Large numbers of human genes have now been localized to specific chromosomes in this way, but of course we cannot derive a linkage map showing the order and distances between genes. Other tricks are needed; for example, the loss or gain of variously sized bits of a specific chromosome might be correlated with the presence or absence of genetic markers. A problem at the end of Chapter 8 encourages you to think through the kind of logic involved. However, the results of this kind of intrachromosomal mapping are so far not nearly as extensive as those on simple chromosome location (Figure 6-31).

■ **TABLE 6-2.** Comparison of five hybrid lines

		Hybrid cell lines				
		A	B	C	D	E
Human genes	1	+	−	−	+	−
	2	−	+	−	+	−
	3	+	−	−	+	−
	4	+	+	+	−	−
Human chromosomes	1	−	+	−	+	−
	2	+	−	−	+	−
	3	−	−	−	+	+

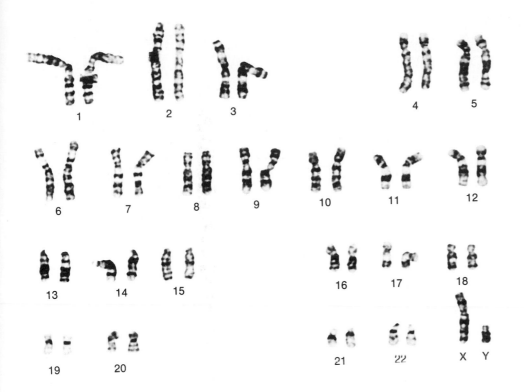

Figure 6-30. Karyotype of a human male. Note how size, centromere position, and banding pattern (produced by trypsin-Giemsa treatment) can be used to recognize specific human chromosomes. (Photograph by Fred Dill.)

Message   Mitotic as well as meiotic phenomena can give information on gene location in fruit flies, fungi, and humans.

In this chapter, we have considered more advanced treatments of transmission genetics, including mapping functions, tetrad analysis, and mitotic genetics. These genetic tools have enabled geneticists to test some of the assumptions of the chromosome theory of heredity and to learn more about how genetic material is passed from one generation to the next.

Summary

■ Because multiple crossovers are likely to occur when great distances separate loci, map distance between such loci is not linearly related to recombinant frequency. The ideal relationship between map distance and recombinant frequency is called the mapping function, which can be calculated by using the Poisson distribution.

Another useful genetic tool is tetrad analysis, which analyzes the four products of meiosis in those fungi and single-celled algae in which the four products of each meiosis are held together in a kind of bag. Tetrad analysis provides the opportunity to test directly some of the assumptions of the chromosome theory of heredity, to map centromeres as genetic loci, to investigate the possibility of chromatid interference, to examine the mechanisms of chromosome exchange, and to study abnormal chromosome sets.

Tetrads may be linear or unordered. Analysis of linear tetrads is particularly useful because it is possible to map loci in relation to their centromeres and to each other. In crosses involving two linked loci, the asci in a linear or unordered tetrad may be classified as parental ditype (PD), nonparental ditype (NPD), and tetratype (T). The number of PD asci in relation to the number of NPD asci provides a critical test for linkage; if the number of PD asci is greater than the number of NPD asci, the recombinant frequency must be less than 50 percent, and there must be linkage between the genes. If PD equals NPD, the proportion of T asci can be used to distinguish independent assortment from loose linkage.

Although segregation and recombination are normally thought of as meiotic phenomena, segregation and recombination do occasionally occur during mitosis. Mitotic segregation was first identified in the 1930s, when Bridges observed patches of M+ bristles on the body of a female *Drosophila* of predominantly M phenotype. He concluded that the patches were the result of abnormal chromosome segregation at the mitotic level. Around the same time, Stern observed twin spots in *Drosophila* and assumed they must be the reciprocal products of mitotic crossing-over. Fungi are also extensively used to study mitotic segregation and recombination.

Humans are generally unsuitable subjects for traditional genetic analysis. However, by using the Sendai virus to fuse human and mice cells, geneticists have been able to locate human genes on specific chromosomes.

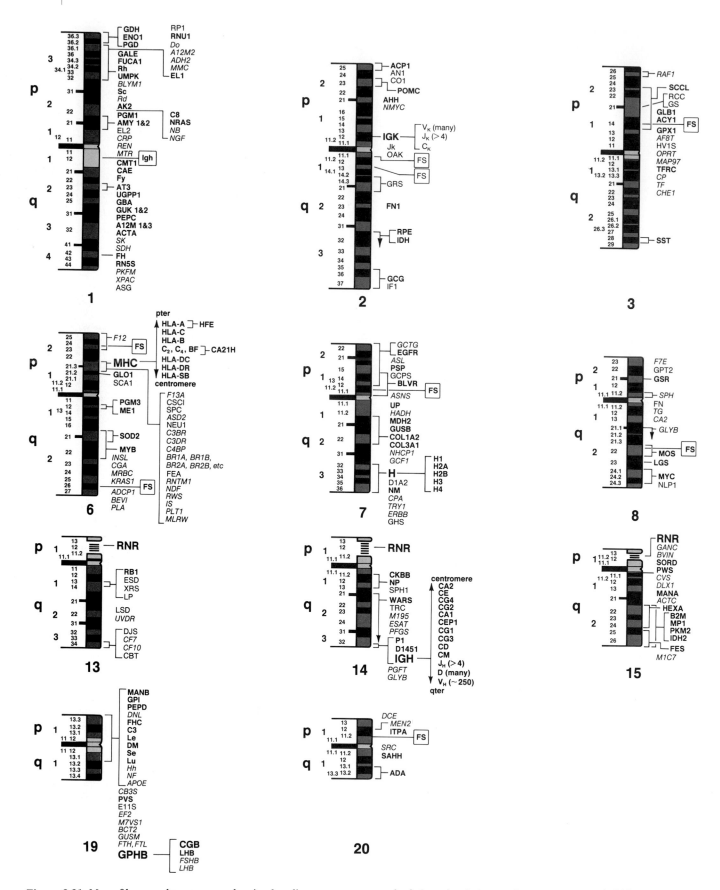

Figure 6-31. Map of human chromosomes showing banding patterns and the genetic markers that have been assigned to a particular chromosome or to a specific locus on a chromosome. For the 345 autosomal markers, 202 have been assigned by somatic hybridization, 67 by family studies, 14 by both, and 62 by other methods (p and q designate chromosome arms; bold letters designate gene families or clusters; italics represent provisional assignments). (From V. A. McKusick, in *Genetic Maps*, Vol. 2. Edited by S. J. O'Brien. Cold Spring Harbor, 1982.)

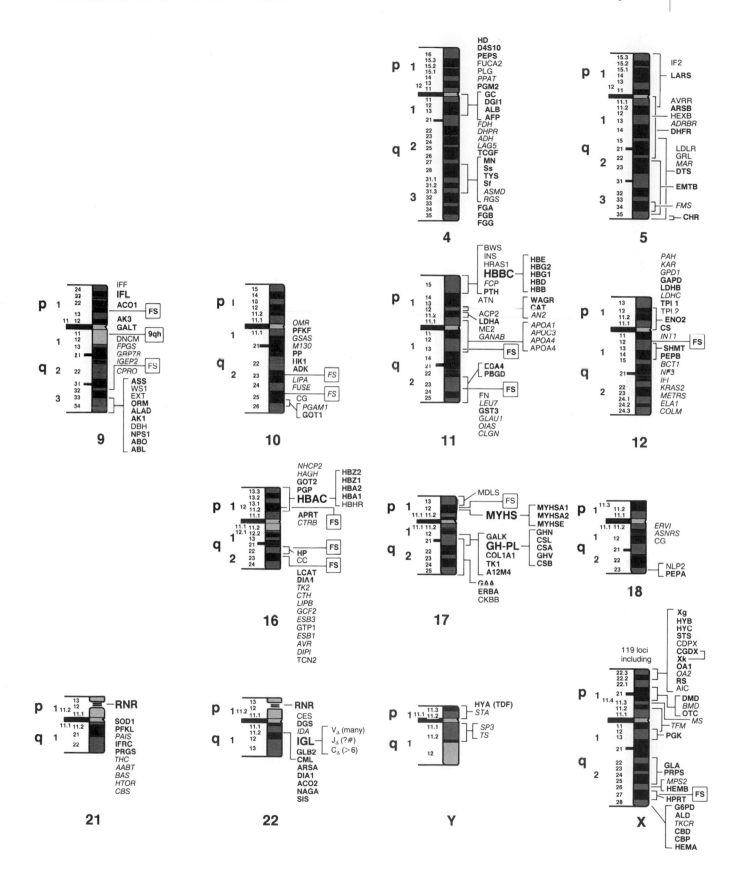

Problems

1. In haploid yeast, a cross between $arg^- ad^- nic^+ leu^+$ and $arg^+ ad^+ nic^- leu^-$ produces haploid sexual spores, and 20 of these are isolated at random. The resulting cultures are tested on various media as shown in Table 6-3 (where + means growth and − means no growth).

■ TABLE 6-3.

	Minimal medium plus			
Culture	Arginine, adenine, nicotinamide	Arginine, adenine, leucine	Arginine, nicotinamide, leucine	Adenine, nicotinamide, leucine
1	+	+	−	−
2	−	−	+	+
3	−	+	−	+
4	+	−	+	−
5	−	−	+	+
6	+	+	−	−
7	+	+	−	−
8	−	−	+	+
9	+	−	+	−
10	−	+	−	+
11	−	+	−	+
12	+	−	+	−
13	+	+	−	−
14	+	−	+	−
15	−	+	−	+
16	+	−	−	−
17	+	+	−	−
18	−	−	+	+
19	+	+	−	−
20	−	+	−	+

a. What can you say about the linkage arrangement of these genes?

b. What is the origin of culture 16?

2. Every Friday night, genetics student Jean Allele, exhausted by her studies, goes to the student's union bowling lane to relax. But even there she is haunted by her genetics studies. The rather modest bowling lane has only four bowling balls: two red and two blue. These are bowled at the pins, then collected and returned down the chute in random order, coming to rest at the end stop. Over the evening, Jean notices familiar patterns of the four balls as they come to rest at the stop. Compulsively, she counts the different patterns that occur. What patterns did she see, what were their frequencies, and what is the relevance of this matter to genetics? (This is not a trivial question.)

3. a. By using the map function, calculate how many real map units are indicated by a recombinant frequency of 20 percent. Remember that a mean of 1 equals 50 real map units.

   b. If you obtain an RF value of 45 percent in one experiment, what can you say about linkage? (The actual figures are 58, 52, 47, and 43 out of 200 progeny.)

*4. Complete Table 6-4 for a situation in Neurospora in which the *mean* number of crossovers between the a locus ($a/+$) and its centromere is equal to one per meiosis.

■ TABLE 6-4.

	Number of exchanges				
	0	1	2	3	4
Probability of this kind of meiosis?					
What proportion of each of these kinds of meiosis will result in an M_{II} pattern for $a/+$?					
What proportion of all asci from this cross will show an M_{II} pattern as a result of each of these kinds of meiosis?					

a. What is the total M_{II} frequency if the mean = 1?

b. Complete similar tables for means of 0.5, 2.0, and 4.0, and hence draw a mapping function for M_{II} frequency. (That is, plot the total M_{II} frequency against mean crossover frequency per meiosis.)

c. Why does the curve bend downward? How would you correct this?

*5. In a tetrad analysis the linkage arrangement of the $p/+$ and $q/+$ loci is as follows.

Assume that

In region (i), only two situations can occur at meiosis: no crossover (88 percent of meioses) or a single crossover (12 percent of meioses).

In region (ii), only two situations can occur at meiosis: no crossover (80 percent of meioses) or a single crossover (20 percent of meioses).

There is no interference (in other words, the situation in one region doesn't affect what is going on in the other region).

What proportion of tetrads will be of the following types? a. $M_I M_I$.PD   b. $M_I M_I$.NDP   c. $M_I M_{II}$.T   d. $M_{II} M_I$.T e. $M_{II} M_{II}$.PD   f. $M_{II} M_{II}$.NDP   g. $M_{II} M_{II}$.T (Note here the M pattern written first is the one that pertains to the $p/+$ locus.)

6. In *Neurospora*, the cross $+++ + \times a\,b\,c\,d$ is made (a, b, c, and d are linked in the order written). Draw crossover diagrams to illustrate how the following unordered (non-linear) ascus patterns could arise:

```
+ + c +     + b c d     + + c +     + + c +     + b + d
a b c +     + + + d     + b + d     + b + d     + b + d
+ b + d     a b c +     a + c +     a + c +     a + c +
a + + d     a + + +     a b + d     a b + d     a + c +

        + b c d     + b + d     + b + +     + b + d
        a b c +     + + + d     + b + +     a + c +
        + + + d     a b c +     a + c d     + b + d
        a + + +     a + c +     a + c d     a + c +
```

7. In *Neurospora*, crosses $a\,b \times ++$ (in which a and b represent different loci in each cross) are made. From each cross, 100 linear asci are analyzed, and the results shown in Table 6-5 are obtained. For each cross, map the genes in relation to each other and to their respective centromere(s).

Cross	Number of asci of type						
	a b a b + + + +	a + a + + b + b	a b a + + + + b	a b + b + + a +	a b + + + + a b	a + + b + b a +	a + + b + + a b
1	34	34	32	0	0	0	0
2	84	1	15	0	0	0	0
3	55	3	40	0	2	0	0
4	71	1	18	1	8	0	1
5	9	6	24	22	8	10	20
6	31	0	1	3	61	0	4
7	95	0	3	2	0	0	0
8	6	7	20	22	12	11	22
9	69	0	10	18	0	1	2
10	16	14	2	60	1	2	5
11	51	49	0	0	0	0	0

8. In *Neurospora*, the a locus is 5 m.u. from the centromere on chromosome 1. The b locus is 10 m.u. from the centromere on chromosome 7. From the cross of $a + \times + b$, determine the frequencies of the following: a. Parental ditype asci   b. Nonparental ditype asci   c. Tetratype asci d. Recombinant ascospores   e. Colonies growing from ascospores grown on minimal medium (inorganic salts, energy source, and vitamins; see Chapter 7) if a and b represent nutritional requirements (NOTE: don't bother with map-function complications here.)

9. The accompanying figure shows a germinated teliospore of the barley-smut fungus, *Ustilago hordei*, that has just undergone meiosis. Each haploid cell of the promycelium has undergone mitosis to form a sporidium. The four haploid sporidia are numbered in sequence, beginning with the terminal cell. The sporidia can be removed, in sequence, to establish haploid colonies, which are easy to maintain in the laboratory. Haploid colonies can be subcultured and combined in pairs; when this is done, compatible combinations result in the formation of dikaryons, and incompatible combinations do not. For one such set of haploid cultures, dikaryons were formed by the matings 1×2, 1×4, 3×2, and 3×4, but dikaryons were not formed by the matings 2×4 and 1×3.

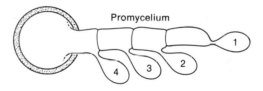

a. What can you conclude about the genetic determination of compatibility?

*b. Dikaryons of *U. hordei* are parasitic on cultivated barley. The four dikaryons listed in the problem, when inoculated into three different barley cultivars (varieties of barley), gave the results shown in Table 6-6. What can you conclude about the genetic determination of virulence (that is, the capacity of dikary-

Dikaryon	Disease on cultivar		
	A	B	C
1×2	None	Severe	None
1×4	Severe	None	None
3×2	Severe	None	None
3×4	Severe	None	Severe

ons to incite a severe disease reaction) on these cultivars?

c. Using your own system of symbols, assign genotypes to each of the four haploid cultures.

(Problem 9 courtesy of Clayton Person.)

10. In several nonlinear tetrad analyses, in which each experiment consists of a cross between different pairs of marked loci, the results shown in Table 6-7 were obtained.

■ TABLE 6-7.

Cross	PD	NPD	T
1	22	3	21
2	1	2	0
3	1	1	3
4	10	10	9
5	10	11	1
6	18	15	50

a. Deduce in each case if there is any indication of linkage (derive as much information as possible).

b. For cases of obvious linkage, assume there are no triple or higher-multiple crossovers and calculate map distance.

11. In an experiment with haploid yeast, you have two different cultures, each of which will grow on minimal medium (see Chapter 7) to which arginine has been added but will not grow on minimal medium alone. Using appropriate methods, you induce the two cultures to mate. The diploid cells then undergo meiosis and form unordered (nonlinear) tetrads. You examine a large number of these tetrads and record the data shown in Table 6-8.

■ TABLE 6-8.

Segregation ($arg^-:arg^+$)	Frequency (%)
4 : 0	40
3 : 1	20
2 : 2	40

a. Using symbols of your own choice, assign genotypes to the two parental cultures. For each of the three kinds of segregation, assign genotypes to the segregants.

b. Do these data lead to any specific conclusions about the mapping of genes? If so, what are your conclusions?

12. Four histidine loci are known in *Neurospora*. As shown here, each of the four loci is located on a different chromosome.

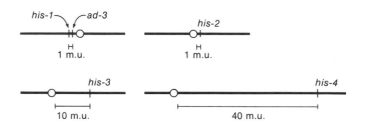

The *his-1* locus is closely linked (1 m.u.) to both *ad-3* and the centromere. The loci *his-2*, *his-3*, and *his-4* are 1, 10, and 40 m.u., respectively, from their centromeres. In your experiment, you begin with an *ad-3* line from which you recover a cell that also requires histidine. You wish now to determine which of the four histidine loci is involved. You cross the *ad-3 his-?* strain with wild-type (++) and analyze 10 nonlinear tetrads: two are PD, six are T, and two are NPD. From this result, which of the four *his* loci is most probably the one that changed from *his*⁺ to *his*?

(Problem 12 courtesy of Luke deLange.)

13. In the haploid ascomycete fungus *Sordaria*, the ascospores are normally black. Two ascospore-color mutants are isolated. When crossed to wild-type, mutant 1 gives asci that contain four black spores and four white spores. When crossed to wild-type, mutant 2 gives asci that contain four black spores and four tan spores. When mutants 1 and 2 are intercrossed, some asci contain four black and four white spores, some asci contain four tan and four white spores, and some asci contain four white and two black and two tan spores. Explain these data.

*14. In *Drosophila melanogaster*, two entire X chromosomes can be attached to the same centromere:

The two arms now behave as a single chromosome, called an attached X. Work out the inheritance of sex chromosomes in crosses of attached-X-bearing females with normal males. During meiosis, the duplicated attached-X chromosome segregates from its sister chromatids:

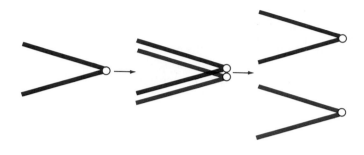

Crossing over can take place between nonsister chromatids of attached-X chromosomes. Suppose you have an attached-X chromosome of the following genotype:

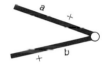

Diagram all the possible genotypic products and their phenotypes (a) from single crossovers between *a* and *b* and between *b* and the centromere; (b) from double exchanges between *a* and *b* and between *b* and the centromere. Make sure you consider all the possibilities. Describe how such a procedure represents a kind of tetrad analysis.

15. In soybeans, an incompletely dominant gene causes a "yellowish" appearance to the leaves. When yellowish heterozygotes are allowed to mature, some leaves show rare areas in which there is a patch of dark green (normal) tissue always adjacent to a patch of very pale yellow tissue, all in the yellowish background. Propose an explanation for these rare patches. (Invent symbols and draw diagrams.)

16. In *Aspergillus*, the genes *fw* and *cha* are closely linked on chromosome VIII. The allele *fw* gives fawn-colored conidia, and *cha* gives chartreuse-colored conidia. The normal color of the fungus is dark green. A diploid with *fw* and *cha* heterozygous in repulsion is plated. Most of the diploid colonies are dark green, but a few are bicolored, with one-half fawn and one-half chartreuse. Explain the origin of these bicolored colonies.

17. An *Aspergillus* diploid that is $++++/w\,a\,b\,c$ is haploidized, and many white haploids are scored for *a*, *b*, and *c*. The results are 25 percent $w\,a\,b\,c$; 25 percent $w+++$; 25 percent $w\,a+c$; and 25 percent $w+b+$. What linkage relations can you deduce from these frequencies? Sketch your conclusions.

18. In an *Aspergillus* diploid $++/y\,ribo$, the two loci are linked, but the order with respect to the centromere is not known. Yellow diploid segregants are obtained; 80 percent of them are ribo$^+$ and 20 percent are ribo-requiring. What is the most likely order?

19. An *Aspergillus* diploid is $+++/pro\,fpa\,paba$, in which *pro* is a recessive allele for proline requirement, *fpa* is a recessive allele for fluorophenylalanine resistance, and *paba* is a recessive allele for *para*-aminobenzoic acid (paba) requirement. By plating asexual spores on fluorophenylalanine, selection for resistant colonies can be made. Of 154 *diploid* resistant colonies, 35 require neither proline nor paba, 110 require paba, and 9 require both.

   a. What do these figures indicate?

   b. Sketch your conclusions in the form of a map.

   c. Some resistant colonies (not the ones described) are haploid. What would you predict their genotype to be?

20. Table 6-9 shows the only human chromosomes contained in three colonies of human/mouse hybrid cells. Five enzymes (α, β, γ, δ, and ϵ) are tested in each of the cell colonies, with the following results: α is active only in colony C; β is active in all three colonies; γ is active only in colonies B and C; δ is active only in colony B; and ϵ shows no activity in any colony. What can you say about the locations of the genes responsible for these enzyme activities?

■ **TABLE 6-9.**

Hybrid colony	Presence (+) or absence (−) of human chromosome							
	1	2	3	4	5	6	7	8
A	+	+	+	+	−	−	−	−
B	+	+	−	−	+	+	−	−
C	+	−	+	−	+	−	+	−

21. This question will start you thinking about the consequences of sister-chromatid exchange at meiosis. Imagine the diploid cell $A\,B/a\,b$, with its two linked gene pairs A/a and B/b.

   a. Draw a meiosis with a single crossover between the gene pairs. Now insert a single sister-chromatid exchange (SCE), involving only one sister pair, also anywhere between the gene pairs. Repeat, but this time put the single SCE outside the gene pairs. Does the SCE make any difference in either case?

b. Now draw a meiosis with a two-strand double crossover between the gene pairs. Then place a single SCE event (i) between a gene pair and the nearest crossover, (ii) between the two crossovers, and (iii) outside the gene pairs. Does the SCE make any difference in any case?

c. Repeat part b for both kinds of three-strand double crossovers, and for four-strand double crossovers.

d. Considering that the two-strand, three-strand, and four-strand double crossovers occur in a $1:2:1$ ratio, will single, randomly located SCE events affect the relative frequencies of PD, NPD, and T tetrad types?

CHAPTER 7

Gene Mutation

■ Genetic analysis would not be possible without **variants**—organisms that differ in a particular character. We have considered many examples where analyses have been performed in organisms that have different phenotypes connected with a particular character. Now we consider the origin of the variants. How, in fact, do genetic variants arise?

The simple answer to this question is that organisms have an inherent tendency to promote change from one hereditary state to another. This process is called **mutation.** We can recognize two basic levels of mutation.

1. **Gene mutation.** A gene can mutate from one allelic form to another. These changes occur at or within a single gene, so they sometimes are called **point mutations.**

2. **Chromosome mutation.** Segments of chromosomes, whole chromosomes, or even entire sets of chromosomes may be involved in genetic change, and this process is collectively called chromosomal mutation. Gene mutation is not necessarily involved in such a process; the effects of chromosomal mutation are due more to the new arrangements of chromosomes and of the genes they contain.

In this chapter we explore gene mutation; in Chapters 8 and 9 we consider chromosomal mutation.

In any consideration of the subject of change, a fixed reference point, or standard, is necessary. In genetics, that point is provided by the so-called wild-type. Remember that the wild-type gene may be a form actually isolated from nature or a form commonly used as a standard laboratory stock. Any change away from the standard form is called **forward mutation;** any change toward the standard form is called **reverse mutation, reversion,** or **back mutation.** For example

$$\left.\begin{array}{c} a^+ \longrightarrow a \\ D^+ \longrightarrow D \end{array}\right\} \text{forward mutation}$$

$$\left.\begin{array}{c} a \longrightarrow a^+ \\ D \longrightarrow D^+ \end{array}\right\} \text{reverse mutation}$$

The non-wild-type form of a gene usually is called a mutation. (To use the same word for the process and the product may sound wanton to you, but in practice little confusion arises!) Thus we can speak of a dominant mutation (such as D above) or a recessive mutation (such as a). Bear in mind how arbitrary these gene states are; the wild-type of today may have been a mutation in the evolutionary past, and vice versa.

Another useful term is **mutant.** This is, strictly speaking, an adjective and should properly precede a noun. A mutant individual or cell is one whose changed phenotype is attributable to the possession of a mutation. Sometimes the noun is left unstated; in this case, a mutant always means an individual or cell whose phenotype shows that it bears a mutation.

One final useful term is **mutation event,** the actual occurrence of a mutation.

Somatic Versus Germinal Mutation

Mutation can occur in either somatic or germinal tissue; these are called somatic and germinal mutations, respectively. The two types are diagrammed in Figure 7-1.

Somatic Mutation

Somatic mutation may lead to a sector, or **clone,** of identical mutant cells that can be recognized in the background of normal cells. The genetic system for the detection of somatic mutation must be such as to rule out the possibility that the sector is due to mitotic segregation or recombination. If the individual was a homozygous diploid, such sectoring is almost certainly due to mutation. The timing of a somatic mutation during development will determine the proportion of cells affected (Figure 7-2). A striking example of a somatic mutation is shown in Figure 7-3.

What about sexual transmission to progeny? In the organism in which the original mutation arises, there is little chance of transmission unless germinal tissue is involved. But in a cutting-propagated plant, the gamete will be either normal or mutant, depending on what cell line forms the germinal tissue.

Germinal Mutation

Germinal mutation occurs in tissue that ultimately will form sex cells. Then, if these mutant sex cells act in fertiliza-

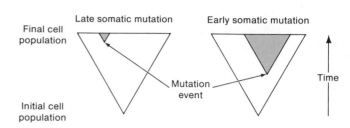

Figure 7-2. Early mutation produces a larger proportion of mutant cells in the growing population than does later mutation.

tion, the mutation will be passed on to the next generation. Of course, an individual of perfectly normal phenotype and of normal ancestry can harbor undetected mutant sex cells. These mutations can be detected only if they turn up in the zygote. Such a situation is thought to have occurred in Queen Victoria, who was almost certainly the origin of a germinal mutation to the X-linked recessive mutant allele for hemophilia (failure of the blood to clot). This mutation showed up in some of her male descendants.

At the operational level, the detection of germinal mutation depends on the ability to rule out meiotic segregation and recombination as possible causes.

Message   At the operational level, before any new variant hereditary state can be attributed to mutation, both segregation *and* recombination must be ruled out. This is true for somatic and for germinal mutation.

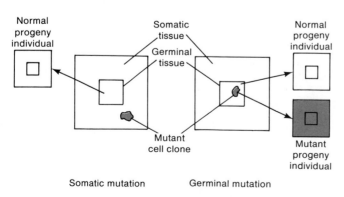

Figure 7-1. Diagrammatic representation of the differing consequences of somatic and germinal mutation.

Figure 7-3. Somatic mutation from red *(R)* to white *(r)* in a rose petal.

Figure 7-4. A rare morphological mutant in the thimbleberry, *Rubus parviflorus,* which arose spontaneously in nature. Left, three normal wild-type flowers; right, a flower from the mutant. The mutation causes a spectacular increase in the number of petals per flower. Such mutants have been used extensively in horticulture to increase the showiness of flowers.

Types of Mutations

What kinds of mutants are there? The phenotypic consequences of mutation may be so subtle as to require refined biochemical techniques to detect a difference from wild-type or so severe as to produce gross morphological defects or death. A rough classification follows, based only on the ways in which the mutations are recognized. This is by no means an attempt at a complete classification.

Morphological Mutations. *Morph* means "form." In this class are the mutations that affect the visible properties of an organism, usually the outward properties, such as shape, color, or size. Albino ascospores in *Neurospora,* curly wings in *Drosophila,* and dwarfism in peas are all considered morphological mutations. Some examples of morphological mutants are shown in Figures 7-4 and 7-5.

Lethal Mutations. Here the new allele is recognized through its lethal effects on the organism. Sometimes a primary cause of death is easy to identify — for example, in certain blood abnormalities. But often the gene is recognizable *only* by its effects on mortality.

Conditional Mutations. In this class, a mutant allele expresses the mutant phenotype under a certain condition called the **restrictive** condition but expresses a normal phenotype under another condition called the **permissive** condition. Temperature-conditional mutants have been the most frequently studied. For example, a certain class of mutations in *Drosophila* is known as "dominant heat-sensitive lethal." Heterozygotes in this class (say, H^+/H) are normal at 20°C (the permissive condition) but die if the temperature is raised to 30°C (the restrictive condition).

Many mutant organisms are less vigorous than normal

(a)   (b)

Figure 7-5. Plumage in Japanese quail. (a) Normal and (b) a rare mutant that arose spontaneously in a laboratory population of Japanese quail. The mutation is an autosomal recessive that interferes with the normal development of the feathers. (Courtesy of Janet Fulton.)

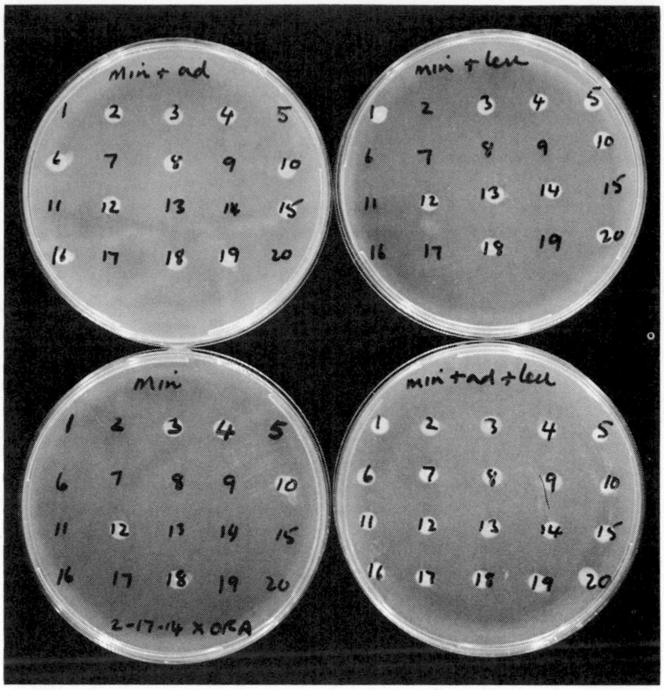

Figure 7-6. Testing for auxotrophy and prototrophy in the fungus *Neurospora crassa.* The process is illustrated here by testing the genotypes of 20 haploid cultures derived from a cross between an adenine-requiring auxotrophic mutant and a leucine-requiring auxotrophic mutant (thus the cross was *ad⁻ leu⁺ × ad⁺ leu⁻*). The cultures are tested by dipping a sterile needle into a culture tube (say, tube 1) and then touching the needle to the surface of each of four different media, where a few cells will adhere. If the cells proliferate, a colony is formed; colonies appear as white circles on the photograph. The four plates contain different combinations of adenine and leucine, where different genotypes produce different results. For example, culture 1 obviously requires leucine, but not adenine, so its genotype must be *ad⁺ leu⁻*. Four different genotypes are present in the 20 cultures. Min means the basic "minimal" medium of wild-type *Neurospora*, consisting of simple inorganic salts, an energy (carbon) source, and a nonnutritive gel called agar.

forms. For this reason, conditional mutants are handy in that many of them can be grown in permissive conditions and then shifted to restrictive conditions for study. There are other advantages to conditional mutations, as we shall see in following chapters.

Biochemical Mutations. This class is identified by the loss of, or a change in, some biochemical function of the cell. This change typically results in an inability to grow and proliferate. In many cases, however, growth of a mutant can be restored by supplementing the growth medium with a specific nutrient. Biochemical mutants have been extensively analyzed in microorganisms. Microorganisms, by and large, are **prototrophic**—that is, they are nutritionally self-sufficient and can exist on a substrate of simple inorganic salts and an energy source; such a growth medium is called a **minimal medium.** Biochemical mutants, however, often are **auxotrophic**—that is, they require supplementation with complex nutrients in order to grow. For example, in fungi, a certain class of biochemical mutants is recognized by the fact that they will not grow unless specifically supplemented with the important cellular chemical adenine. These auxotrophic mutants are called *ad*, or "ade-

nine-requiring." The method of auxotroph testing is shown in Figure 7-6.

Resistant Mutations. Here, the mutant cell or organism acquires the ability to grow in the presence of some specific inhibitor, such as cycloheximide or a pathogen, to which wild-types are susceptible. Such mutants have been extensively used because they are relatively easy to select for, as we shall see.

Table 7-1 illustrates detection of three of these mutation types. Clearly, the five classes are not mutually exclusive, nor do they cover all mutation types. Nevertheless, they are useful components in the vocabulary of mutation.

The Usefulness of Mutations

Mutation, as a biological process that has been occurring as long as there has been life on this planet, is certainly fascinating and worthy of study. Mutant alleles such as those mentioned in the previous section obviously are invaluable in the study of the process of mutation itself. In this connec-

■ **TABLE 7-1.** Operational basis for detection of mutant phenotype in three different types of mutations

Genotype	Conditional mutation (temperature-sensitive)		Auxotrophic mutation		Resistant mutation	
	Low temperature	High temperature	Without supplement	With supplement	Without agent	With agent
Wild-type	Normal	Normal	Growth	Growth	Growth	**No growth**
Mutant	Normal	**Mutant**	**No growth**	Growth	Growth	Growth

tion, they are used as genetic markers: they are used as representative genes, and their precise function is not particularly important except as a way to detect them.

In modern genetics, however, mutant genes have another important role, in which their precise function *is* important. We have already referred (in Chapter 2) to genetic dissection as an established approach to biological analysis. Mutant genes are like probes, which can be used to disassemble the constituent parts of a biological function and to examine their workings and interrelationships. Thus, it is of considerable interest to a biologist studying a particular function to have as many mutant forms affecting that function as possible. This has led to "mutant hunts" as an important prelude to any genetic dissection in biology. To identify a genetic variant is to identify a component of the process.

Message   Mutations can be used for two purposes: (1) to study the process of mutation itself and (2) to permit genetic dissection of biological function. The two main tools of genetic dissection are recombination dissection and mutational dissection.

Mutation Detection Systems

The tremendous stability and constancy of form of species from generation to generation suggest that mutation must be a rare process. This supposition has been confirmed, creating a problem for the geneticist trying to demonstrate mutation.

The prime need is for a detection system, designed in such a way that a mutant allele will make its presence known at the phenotypic level. Such a system ensures that any of the rare mutations that might occur will not be missed.

One of the main considerations here is that of dominance. The system must be set up so that recessive mutations will not be masked by a paired dominant normal allele. (Dominant mutations are less of a problem.) As an example, we can use one of the first detection systems ever set up—that used by Lewis Stadler in the 1920s to study mutation in corn from *C*, expressed phenotypically as a colored kernel, to *c*, expressed as a white kernel. Here we are dealing with the phenotype of the endosperm of the seed. If you check back to Figure 3-33 (page 55) you will see that this tissue is formed by the fusion of two identical haploid female nuclei with one haploid nucleus from the male pollen cell. Hence, the tissue has three chromosome sets (it is $3n$). This does not seriously complicate the genetic analysis because dominance generally still works in the presence of two recessive alleles.

Stadler crossed $cc\,♀ \times CC\,♂$ and simply examined thousands of individual kernels on the corn ears that resulted from this cross. Each kernel represents a progeny individ-

ual. In the absence of mutation, every kernel would be *Ccc* and show the colored phenotype. Therefore, the presence of a white kernel indicates mutation from *C* to *c* in the *CC* parent. Although laborious, this is a very straightforward and reliable approach (Figure 7-7).

This basic system can be extended to as many loci as can be conveniently made heterozygous in the same cross. For example,

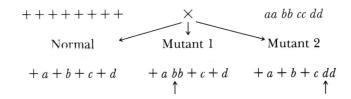

$$+ + + + + + + \qquad \times \qquad aa\ bb\ cc\ dd$$

Normal   Mutant 1   Mutant 2

$$+ a + b + c + d \qquad + a\ bb + c + d \qquad + a + b + c\ dd$$

By increasing the number of specific loci under study, the investigator increases the likelihood of detecting a mutation in the experiment. Hence, this type of test is called a **specific locus test** for detecting mutation. It has been used extensively in corn and in mammalian genetics.

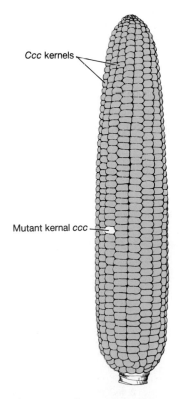

Figure 7-7. Detecting mutants by screening large numbers of progeny (kernels) in a corn cross of $cc♀ \times CC♂$.

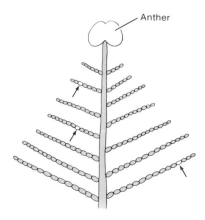

Anther

Figure 7-8. A *Tradescantia* stamen heterozygous for *P* (blue) and *p* (pink) alleles. In the chains that constitute the lateral hairs, some cells (marked by arrows) are mutant. Shading represents a blue color; lack of shading represents a pink color.

In *Tradescantia* plants of the vegetatively propagated strain called 02, there is a simple detection system for somatic mutations. These plants are heterozygous for dominant blue and recessive pink pigmentation alleles of one gene. The pigmentation is expressed in the flower parts: the petals and the stamens. In this plant, the stamens have hairs that are chains of single cells. Millions of single cells can be screened for pink cells representing somatic mutation of the blue to the pink allele (Figure 7-8).

In humans, mutation detection is theoretically simple but difficult in practice. For example, dominant mutations arising anew in a pedigree should be clearly recognizable. However, there is always the possibility that a person may carry the gene without expressing it; this possibility presents complications in genetic analysis. Thus, the most convincing cases of dominant mutations are for conditions known to have high penetrance and expressivity (see Chapter 4 for definitions of these terms). Autosomal recessive mutations, on the other hand, may go unnoticed because they can be transmitted for many generations without being manifested in the phenotype.

Haploids have a great advantage over diploids in mutation studies. Here the detection system is quite straightforward; any newly arising allele will announce its presence unhampered by any dominant partner allele. In fact, the question of dominance or recessiveness need never arise: there is what amounts to a built-in detection facility. Let's look at some examples. In some cases, a direct identification of mutants is possible. In *Neurospora*, for example, auxotrophic adenine-requiring mutants have been found to map at several loci. One of these gene loci (*ad-3*) is unique, in that auxotrophic mutants accumulate a purple pigment in their cells when grown on a low concentration of adenine. Thus auxotrophic mutants of this gene may be detected simply by allowing single asexual spores to grow into colonies on medium with limited adenine. The purple colonies may be identified easily among the normal white colonies.

What about other auxotrophs? Usually there are no visual pleiotrophic effects such as that with *ad-3*. The most commonly used detection technique is called replica plating, which we will examine later in this chapter.

How Common Are Mutations?

If a detection system is available, the investigator can set out to find mutations. One thing will become apparent: mutations are in general very rare. This is shown in Table 7-2, which presents some data collected by Stadler working with several corn loci. Mutation studies of this sort are a lot of work! Counting a million of *anything* is no small task. Another feature shown by these data is that different genes seem to generate different frequencies of mutations; a 500-fold range is seen in the corn results. Obviously, one of the prime requisites of mutation analysis is to be able to measure the tendency of different genes to mutate. Two terms are commonly used to quantify mutation.

1. **Mutation rate.** This is a number that represents an attempt to measure the probability of a specific kind of mutation *event* over a specific unit of time. This is obviously getting close to the intrinsic mutation tendency of a gene. The unit of time can be one of several. Instead of an actual time unit, such as hours or days, a

■ **TABLE 7-2.** Forward-mutation frequencies at some specific corn loci

Gene	Number of gametes tested	Number of mutations	Average per million gametes
$R \rightarrow r$	554,786	273	492.0
$I \rightarrow i$	265,391	28	106.0
$Pr \rightarrow pr$	647,102	7	11.0
$Su \rightarrow su$	1,678,736	4	2.4
$Y \rightarrow y$	1,745,280	4	2.2
$Sh \rightarrow sh$	2,469,285	3	1.2
$Wx \rightarrow wx$	1,503,744	0	0.0

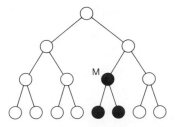

Figure 7-9. A simple cell pedigree showing a mutation at M.

unit such as an organismal generation, cell generation, or cell division is normally used. Consider the lineage of cells in Figure 7-9.

Obviously, only one mutation event (M) has occurred, so the numerator of a mutation rate is established. But what can be used as the denominator? The total opportunity for mutation, the "time" element, may be represented either by the total number of the lines in the diagram (14 total generations) or, alternatively, by the total number of actual cell divisions (7). Either is acceptable if stated clearly — for example, 1 mutation per 7 cell divisions. (Note that we are dealing with generations, not generation cycles, of which there are three.)

In practice, mutation rates are not easy to obtain in most organisms. The reason is that the precise number of proliferative steps, which generated a population of cells, must be very carefully monitored in some way. We shall see a specific example later in the chapter.

2. **Mutation frequency.** This is the frequency at which a specific kind of mutation (or mutant) is found in a population of cells or individuals. The cell population can be of gametes (in higher organisms), or of asexual spores, or of almost any other cell type. This variable is much easier to measure than mutation rate. In our example in Figure 7-9, the mutation frequency in the final population of 8 cells would be $2/8 = 0.25$.

Some mutation rates and frequencies are shown in Table 7-3.

Selective Systems

The rarity of mutations is a problem if the investigator is trying to amass a collection of a specific type for genetic study. Geneticists respond to this problem in two ways. One approach is to use **selective systems.** These are techniques

■ **TABLE** 7-3. Mutation rates or frequencies in various organisms

Organism	Mutation	Value	Units
Bacteriophage T2 (bacterial virus)	Lysis inhibition $r \rightarrow r^+$ Host range $h^+ \rightarrow h$	1×10^{-8} 3×10^{-9}	*Rate:* mutant genes per gene replication
Escherichia coli (bacterium)	Lactose fermentation $lac \rightarrow lac^+$ Histidine requirement $his^- \rightarrow his^+$ $his^+ \rightarrow his^-$	2×10^{-7} 4×10^{-8} 2×10^{-6}	*Rate:* mutant cells per cell division
Chlamydomonas reinhardtii (alga)	Streptomycin sensitivity $str\text{-}s \rightarrow str\text{-}r$	1×10^{-6}	
Neurospora crassa (fungus)	Inositol requirement $inos^- \rightarrow inos^+$ adenine requirement $ad^- \rightarrow ad^+$	8×10^{-8} 4×10^{-8}	*Frequency* per asexual spore
Corn	See Table 7-2		
Drosophila melanogaster (fruit fly)	Eye color $W \rightarrow w$	4×10^{-5}	
Mouse	Dilution $D \rightarrow d$	3×10^{-5}	
Human *to autosomal dominants*	Huntington's chorea Nail-patella syndrome Epiloia (predisposition to type of brain tumor) Multiple polyposis of large intestine Achondroplasia (dwarfism) Neurofibromatosis (predisposition to tumors of nervous system)	0.1×10^{-5} 0.2×10^{-5} $0.4\text{--}0.8 \times 10^{-5}$ $1\text{--}3 \times 10^{-5}$ $4\text{--}12 \times 10^{-5}$ $3\text{--}25 \times 10^{-5}$	*Frequency* per gamete
to X-linked recessives	Hemophilia A Duchenne's muscular dystrophy	$2\text{--}4 \times 10^{-5}$ $4\text{--}10 \times 10^{-5}$	
bone-marrow tissue-culture cells	Normal $\rightarrow$ azaguanine resistance	7×10^{-4}	*Rate:* mutant cells per cell division

SOURCE: R. Sager and F. J. Ryan, *Heredity,* Wiley, 1961.

specially designed to facilitate the picking out of the desired mutant types from among the rest of the individuals. The other approach is to try to increase the mutation rate using **mutagens,** agents that have the biological effect of inducing mutations above the background (or spontaneous) rate.

Message   Obtaining rare mutations is facilitated by the use of selective recovery systems and/or mutagens.

Selective systems are many and varied. Their scope is immense and is limited only by the ingenuity of the experimenter. But they all have one thing in common: elevated **resolving power.** That is, a selective system can automatically distinguish between (or resolve) two alternative states —in this case, mutant and nonmutant. In other words, the selective system lets the material, instead of the experimenter, do the resolving work. We shall see that resolving power is an important aspect of many areas of genetic analysis. It is especially important in allowing the experimenter to select rare events of any kind. (You will remember that rare exceptions are often the key to understanding the normal situation.) Most of the examples presented are from microorganisms. This doesn't mean that selective systems are impossible in higher organisms, but merely that selection can be used to much better advantage in microbes. A million spores or bacterial cells are easy to produce; but a million mice, or even a million fruit flies, involve a large-scale commitment of money, time, and laboratory space. Microbes appear frequently in the discussion that follows, so a few words on culturing and routine microbial manipulation are appropriate here.

Microbial Techniques

Microbes that we consider in this book are bacteria, fungi, and unicellular algae. All these can be regarded as haploid, but whereas fungi and algae are eukaryotic (having their chromosomes in a nucleus surrounded by a nuclear membrane), bacteria are **prokaryotic** (which means that their chromosomes are not enclosed in a separate compartment of any kind).

In liquid culture, these organisms proliferate as suspensions of individual cells. Each starting cell goes through repeated cell divisions so that, from each, a series of 2, 4, 8, 16, . . . descendant cells is produced. This exponential growth is limited by the availability of nutrients in the medium, but a dense suspension of millions of cells is soon produced. Fungi such as yeasts follow this pattern exactly, but a slightly different situation occurs in the mycelial fungi. Here the descendant cells remain attached as long chains called hyphae; thus a liquid culture started from asexual spores tends to look like tapioca pudding, with

Figure 7-10. Plating microbial cells. A cell suspension of appropriate density is being poured over the surface of a plate of medium. Each cell will ultimately produce a visible colony. This is one of the routine techniques used by microbial geneticists, referred to several times later in this book.

small fuzzy balls of hyphae in suspension, each originating from one spore.

In solid culture, usually on an agar-gel surface, descendant cells tend again to stay together, so that colonies are produced—one colony from each original cell in the suspension that is spread on the surface of the culture medium.

It is usually necessary to know how many cells you have in a culture. A suspension of cells may be counted by several methods.

1. **Microscope counts.** The suspension is placed in a chamber of known depth that is marked off in a grid of known dimensions. This device is known as a hemocytometer. The hemocytometer is placed under the microscope, and cells are counted directly.

2. **Turbidity.** Bacteria are too small to be counted conveniently under a light microscope, so they often are counted using turbidity measurements. The amount of light passing through suspensions of known density is measured, and a turbidity calibration curve is drawn. Suspensions of unknown density can then be checked off on this calibration curve.

3. **Colony-forming units.** Suspensions of known volume and appropriate dilution are **plated** (spread) on the surface of nutrient medium solidified with agar (Figure 7-10). Each cell will form a colony, and the colonies can be counted with the unaided eye.

4. **Electronic cell counters.**

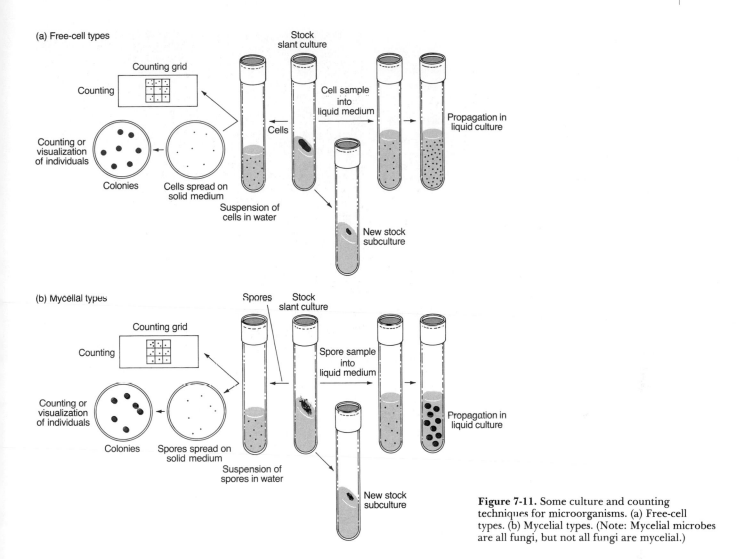

Figure 7-11. Some culture and counting techniques for microorganisms. (a) Free-cell types. (b) Mycelial types. (Note: Mycelial microbes are all fungi, but not all fungi are mycelial.)

Figure 7-11 summarizes these methods.

What kinds of phenotypes may be examined in microorganisms? Morphological mutations affecting color, shape, and size of colony are useful but of limited occurrence. Other characters have been far more useful—for example, auxotrophic mutations (can these cells grow without this specific supplement?), resistance mutations (can these cells grow on this growth inhibitor?), and substrate-utilization mutants (can these cells utilize this sugar as an energy source, as wild-types can?).

We now return to selective systems, and some examples thereof.

Reversion of Auxotrophs

For the detection of reversion of auxotrophy to prototrophy, there is a direct selection system. Take an adenine auxotroph, for example. A culture of the auxotrophic mutant is grown on adenine-containing medium. The cells are then plated on solid medium containing no adenine. The only cells that can proliferate (grow and divide) on this medium are adenine prototrophs, which must have arisen by back mutation in the original culture (Figure 7-12). For most genes (not only those concerned with nutrition), the rate of reversion is generally much lower than the rate of forward mutation. (We shall explore the reason for this later.)

Filtration Enrichment

Filtration enrichment is used in mycelial fungi to select specific auxotrophic mutants. A suspension of (predominantly) prototrophic spores is grown in liquid culture with no growth supplements. (Recall that such a minimal medium consists of inorganic salts and an energy source like sugar.) Any auxotrophic mutants that had arisen in the original culture will not grow in this medium, but prototrophs of course will. The prototrophic colonies may be filtered off using a glass-fiber filter, allowing the auxotrophic cells to pass through. Of course, these auxotrophs will be of several different types—some requiring A, some B, and so on. If we are specifically interested in adenine auxotrophs, then we plate the heterogeneous suspension that comes through the filter on medium supplemented with adenine. Only adenine auxotrophs will respond to this medium and form colonies (Figure 7-13).

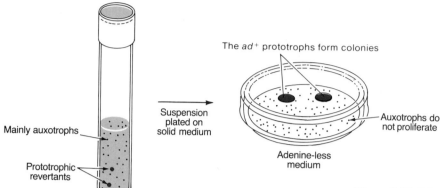

The *ad⁺* prototrophs form colonies

Mainly auxotrophs

Prototrophic revertants

Suspension plated on solid medium

Auxotrophs do not proliferate

Adenine-less medium

Figure 7-12. Selection for prototrophic revertants of auxotrophic mutants.

Penicillin Enrichment

An analogous technique is available for auxotroph selection in bacteria. Bacteria are in the main highly sensitive to the antibiotic penicillin, but only the proliferating cells are sensitive. If penicillin is added to a suspension of cells in liquid culture, all the prototrophs are killed because they proliferate, but the auxotrophs survive! The penicillin can be removed by washing the cells on a filter. Then, plating on medium supplemented with a specific chemical will reveal colonies of the auxotrophs specifically requiring that compound.

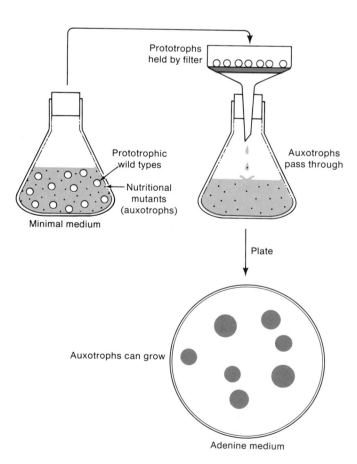

Prototrophs held by filter

Prototrophic wild types

Nutritional mutants (auxotrophs)

Minimal medium

Auxotrophs pass through

Plate

Auxotrophs can grow

Adenine medium

Resistance

Resistance to specific environmental agents not normally tolerated by wild-types is easily demonstrated in microorganisms. We use an example that was important historically in determining the nature of mutation.

Viruses, like most parasites, are highly specific with regard to the hosts they will parasitize. Some viruses are specific to bacteria; these are called either bacterial viruses, or **bacteriophages,** or **phages.** Phages have had a major role in the elucidation of our present level of understanding of molecular genetics. They appear frequently throughout the rest of the book. Although they are introduced properly in the chapter on bacterial genetics, we need them at this point to demonstrate resistance.

The gut bacterium *Escherichia coli* has many specific phages. One of these, called T1, was used in early bacterial mutation studies. T1 will attack and kill most *E. coli* cells, and a host of fresh viruses are liberated from the dead cell. T1 is a subcellular lollipop-shaped particle that can be seen only under an electron microscope, but the progress of phage infection can be followed on a plate by its effects. If a plate is spread with large numbers of bacteria (around 10^9) and phages, most of the bacteria will be killed. However, T1 phage-resistant bacterial cells survive and produce colonies that can be isolated. These individuals are called T-one resistant (*Ton^r*).

During these early studies on the selection of variants, the origin of these *Ton^r* bacterial mutants was questioned by Salvadore Luria and Max Delbrück (in 1943) in a classic experiment that was highly relevant to the study of mutation in general and, more specifically, to all selection experiments to follow. Although *Ton^r* individuals were obviously genuine mutants—after all, they represent a stable inherited phenotype—there was doubt about how they originated. Were the *Ton^r* colonies derived from cells that were genetically *Ton^r before* the exposure to T1 phage? (The *Ton^r* cells would have originated through random genetic

Figure 7-13. The filtration-enrichment method for selecting forward mutations to auxotrophy in filamentous organisms. (This example involves mutation to adenine requirement.)

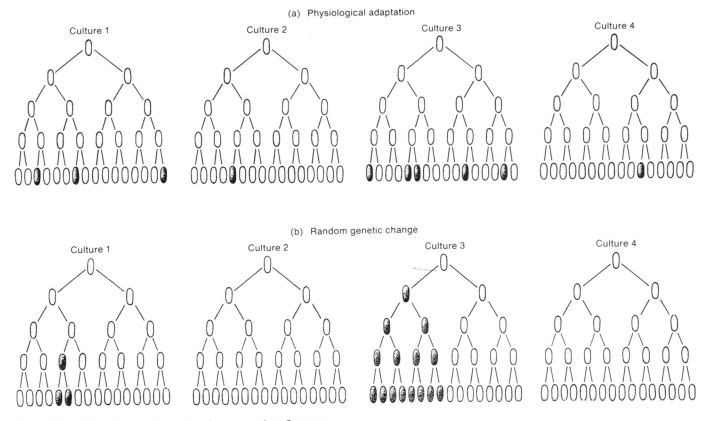

Figure 7-14. Cell pedigrees illustrating the expectations from two contrasting theories about the origin of resistant cells. (a) Physiological adaptation. (b) Random genetic change. (From G. S. Stent and R. Calendar, *Molecular Genetics*, 2d ed. Copyright © 1978 by W. H. Freeman and Company.)

change.) Or did the *Ton^r* genotype arise in response to the T1 exposure in a kind of physiological adaptation?

How is it possible to distinguish between these two alternatives? Let's assume that the resistant cells result from a random genetic change that can occur at any time during growth. If we initiate a bacterial culture with a small number of cells, and then the population increases, random genetic change to resistance to T1 phage could occur in any cell at any time. If we take a large number of small populations of cells and let each one expand into a large population, which is then exposed to T1 phage, the number of mutants in each population will vary considerably, depending on *when* the change occurred. On the other hand, if each cell has the same probability of becoming resistant by physiological adaptation, then in each population of cells there should be the same general frequency of survivors and little variation of that value (Figure 7-14).

Luria and Delbrück carried out such a test. Into each of 20 culture tubes containing 0.2 ml of medium and into one containing 10 ml, they introduced 10^3 *E. coli* cells per milliliter and incubated them until about 10^8 cells per milliliter were obtained. Each of the 20 0.2-ml cultures were spread on plates that had a dense layer of T1 phages. From the 10-ml "bulk" culture, 10 0.2-ml volumes were withdrawn and plated. Many colonies were T1-resistant, as shown in Table 7-4.

A tremendous amount of variation from plate to plate was seen in the individual 0.2-ml cultures, but not in the samples from the bulk culture (which represented a kind of control). This situation cannot be explained by physiological adaptation, because all the samples spread had the same approximate number of cells. The simplest explanation is random genetic change, occurring either early (large number of resistant cells), or late (few resistant cells), or not at all (no resistant cells) in the 0.2-ml cultures.

This elegant analysis suggests that the resistant cells are *selected* by the environmental agent (here, phages) rather than produced by it. Can the existence of mutants in a population *before* selection be directly demonstrated? This was done by means of the technique of **replica plating,** developed by Joshua Lederberg and Esther Lederberg in 1952. A sterile piece of velvet placed lightly on the surface of the petri plate will pick up cells wherever there is a colony (Figure 7-15). (Under a microscope, velvet looks like a series of needles, which explains why lint adheres to it so well and why it picks up colonies of cells.) On touching the velvet to another sterile plate, some of the cells clinging to the velvet will be inoculated onto the plate in the same relative positions as the colonies on the original "master" plate. This simple technique allows the investigator to grow cells on a nonselective medium (either with complete nutrients or free of antibiotics or phages) and then to transfer

■ **TABLE 7-4.** Results of Luria and Delbrück's test

Individual cultures		Bulk culture	
Culture number	Number of T1-resistant colonies	Culture number	Number of T1-resistant colonies
1	1	1	14
2	0		
3	3	2	15
4	0		
5	0	3	13
6	5		
7	0	4	21
8	5		
9	0	5	15
10	6		
11	107	6	14
12	0		
13	0	7	26
14	0		
15	1	8	16
16	0		
17	0	9	20
18	64		
19	0	10	13
20	35		
	Mean 11.3		Mean 16.7

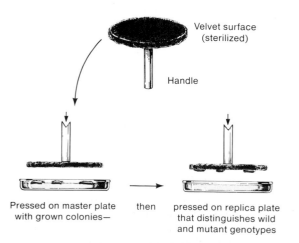

Velvet surface (sterilized)

Handle

Pressed on master plate with grown colonies— then pressed on replica plate that distinguishes wild and mutant genotypes

Figure 7-15. Replica-plating methodology. Replica plating is used to identify mutant colonies on a master plate, through their behavior on selective replica plates. (From G. S. Stent and R. Calendar, *Molecular Genetics*, 2d ed. Copyright © 1978 by W. H. Freeman and Co.)

a copy of the colonies to a selective medium (either minimal or plus antibiotics or phages), as shown in Figure 7-16. The cells from some of the colonies on the master plate form colonies when transferred to the selective plate, in which case cells from those colonies on the master plate can be retested. If they are found to be mutant (in this example, resistant), the investigator has proof that the mutation occurred *before* any selection was applied for the mutant. (It should be noted that there are some situations in which physiological adaptation can occur. The point for now is that mutations do not arise by physiological adaptation.)

Message   Mutation is a random process that can occur in any cell at any time.

Incidentally, replica plating has become an important technique of microbial genetics. In general, it is a way of retaining an original set of strains, on a master plate, while simultaneously subjecting them to a large battery of tests on various kinds of replica plates.

A Way of Calculating Mutation Rate

In passing let us see how Luria and Delbrück's test, called a **fluctuation test**, provides a way of calculating mutation rate, according to its strict definition. Consider the 20 cultures that were tested for T1 resistance. Here we have a situation that is well described by the Poisson distribution —a great opportunity for mutations to be found, but a large class having no mutations at all in the culture (11/20). Look back at Figure 7-9, and convince yourself that the number of cell divisions necessary to produce n cells is n minus the original number in the culture (it would be $8 - 1 = 7$ in the example in Figure 7-9). If n is very large, which it is in the fluctuation-test cultures, and the original number of cells was relatively very small, then a sufficiently accurate estimate of the number of cell divisions is given by n itself. If the mutation rate per cell division is μ, each culture tube may be expected to have entertained an average of μn mutation events. The Poisson distribution (see page 102) then tells us that the zero class (no mutants detectable) will equal $e^{-\mu n}$. Because we know that the zero class = 11/20 = 0.55 and that $n = 0.2 \times 10^8$, we can solve the following equation for μ:

$$0.55 = e^{-\mu(0.2 \times 10^8)}$$

We find that $\mu = 3 \times 10^{-8}$ mutation event per cell division. (Note that in the same data, the mutation frequency is $(1 + 3 + 5 + 5 + 6 + 107 + 1 + 64 + 35)/(20 \times 0.2 \times 10^8)$, which equals $227/(4 \times 10^8)$, or 5.7×10^{-7}.)

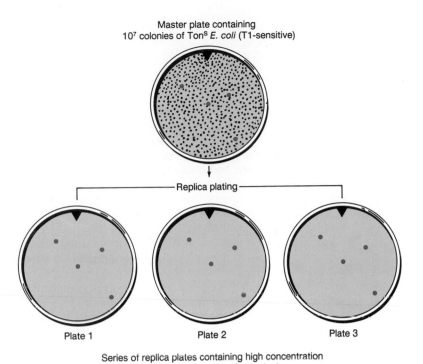

Master plate containing
10^7 colonies of Ton^s *E. coli* (T1-sensitive)

Replica plating

Plate 1   Plate 2   Plate 3

Series of replica plates containing high concentration
of T1 phage and four Ton^r colonies

Figure 7-16. Replica plating to demonstrate the presence of mutants before selection. The identical patterns on the replicas show that the resistant colonies are from the master. (From G. S. Stent and R. Calendar, *Molecular Genetics*, 2d ed. Copyright © 1978 by W. H. Freeman and Co.)

Microbial-Like Selection Techniques in Cell Culture of Higher Organisms

There are techniques for growing cells of higher organisms (animals and plants) in culture. A few cells taken from a specific tissue, including cancerous tissue, will proliferate much like microbial cells in culture. Furthermore, many of the techniques used for mutant induction and selection in microbes can also be used on these higher cells, permitting the flourishing of **somatic cell genetics** of higher organisms as an active area of research. The combination of these mutation-selection techniques with sophisticated techniques of cell fusion and hybridization now makes possible a wide variety of in vitro manipulation on higher cells, including human cells.

One extensively worked cell-culture system uses Chinese hamster ovary (CHO) cells. In this system (and in others), many mutant cell types have been isolated. Let's have a look at some examples. In the first place, dominant mutations are common. Dominance is defined in terms of the phenotype observed when the mutant cell line is fused with normal cells. Resistance to a particular drug—such as ouabain, α-amanitin, methotrexate, or colchicine—is an example of a dominant mutation. Dominant mutations are not surprising: we might expect to find *only* dominant mutations because the cells are diploid.

Nevertheless, recessive mutants are common, too! Resistance to lectins, 8-azaguanine, or methotrexate, auxotrophic requirement for glycine, proline, or lysine, and various temperature-sensitive lethals are all examples of recessive mutants. (Note that certain kinds of mutant phenotypes can be either dominant or recessive in different mutants.)

How is it possible that recessive mutants show up in diploid CHO cells? No one has the complete answer to this question. However, there is some evidence that, although the cells are predominantly diploid, they are hemizygous for very small sections of the genome. Recessive mutations would manifest themselves if they occurred in such regions. But whatever the mechanism of such mutations, their existence provides an invaluable tool for the mammalian-cell somatic geneticist.

Single cells of plants may also be grown in culture. Cells are plated on a synthetic medium containing appropriate combinations of plant hormones. The resulting colonies are called **calluses.** These calluses can be subdivided for further growth in culture, or they can be transferred to a different medium that promotes differentiation of roots and shoots. Such "plantlets" can then be potted in soil and grown into mature plants. In one application of this technique, selection was imposed for cell resistance to a toxin produced by a fungal plant parasite. Calluses growing on the toxin-containing plates were processed to produce plants that also showed resistance to the fungal toxin.

Mutation Induction

Compared with that in microorganisms, the task of finding mutations in multicellular organisms is tremendously complex. In 1928, Hermann J. Muller devised a method of searching for any lethal mutation on the X chromosome in *Drosophila*. He first constructed a chromosome called ClB, which carries a chromosomal inversion, labeled C for crossover suppressor (see Chapter 8); a lethal, l; and the dominant bar-eye marker, B. *ClB*/Y males die because of the hemizygosity for the lethal gene, but the chromosome can be maintained in heterozygous *ClB/+* females. By mating wild-type males with *ClB/+* females, he could then test for lethal mutations anywhere on the X chromosomes in samples of the male gametes by mating single *ClB/+* F$_1$ females with other wild-type males (Figure 7-17). We can see that, if a mutation has occurred on an X chromosome in one of the original male gametes sampled, then the F$_1$ female carrying that chromosome will not produce any viable male progeny. Note that only rarely will the new lethal mutation on the X chromosome be an allele of the lethal gene on the ClB chromosome (of course, when it is, the *ClB/l* female will die). The absence of males in a vial is very easily seen under low-power magnification and readily allows scoring for the presence of lethal mutations on the X chromosome. Muller found their spontaneous frequency to be about 1.5×10^{-3}, still a relatively low value for an entire chromosome with its many different genes.

Muller then asked whether there were any agents that would increase the rate of mutation. Using the ClB test, he scored for sex-linked lethal frequencies after irradiating males with X rays and discovered a striking increase; his results supplied the first experimental evidence of a mutagen—in this case, the X rays. Recall that a mutagen is an agent that causes mutation to occur at higher than spontaneous levels. Mutagens have been invaluable tools not only for studying the process of mutation itself but for increasing the yield of mutants for other genetic studies. It is now known that many kinds of radiation will increase mutations.

Table 7-5 shows the effects of several types of radiation in increasing mutation frequencies in *Drosophila*. To the list in Table 7-5 must be added ultraviolet (UV) radiation, which is also mutagenic. Radiation is often categorized as ionizing or nonionizing, depending on whether or not ions are produced in the tissue through which it passes. X rays

and γ (gamma) rays are often-used examples of the former, and UV radiation, of the latter.

The harnessing of nuclear energy for weapons and fuel has become a social issue because of the mutagenic effect of radiation. The pros and cons of the use of nuclear energy must be weighed by each of us individually, but here let us address a relevant point that is often poorly understood. For any organism, the vast majority of newly formed mutations are deleterious. But, we may ask, if organisms evolved through an advantage conferred by a mutant condition, why aren't many mutations an improvement? To answer this question, let's use an analogy often cited in this connection, in which a cell is compared to a highly complicated watch that has many delicate parts. This watch evolved through generations of minor changes in the design of the machine. If we expose the cogs and wheels by removing the back casing, close our eyes, and plunge a thick needle (analogous to a mutagen) into the workings, there is a remote possibility that this random hit will improve the efficiency of the watch, but the chances are overwhelmingly high that any change inflicted in this way will damage it. So it is with a cell or an organism. (We consider good molecular reasons for the detrimental nature of mutations in Chapter 12.)

Message   Most mutations are deleterious. Evolution is possible because of those very few that are not.

The kinds of gene mutations considered in this chapter are point mutations. (Recall that such mutations affect one point on the chromosome, the gene in question.) It is clear that, within a certain range of radiation dosage, point-mutation induction is linear—that is, if we double or halve the radiation level, the number of mutants produced will vary accordingly. From the kind of graph shown in Figure 7-18,

■ **TABLE 7-5.** Relative efficiencies of various types of radiation in producing mutations in *Drosophila*

Type of radiation	Sex-linked recessive lethals per 1000 roentgens*	Percentage of irradiated male X chromosomes
Visible light (spontaneous)	0.0015	0.15
X rays (25 Mev)	0.0170	1.70
β rays, γ rays, hard X rays	0.0290	2.90
Soft X rays	0.0250	2.50
Neutrons	0.0190	1.90
α rays	0.0084	0.84

* The roentgen (r) is a unit of radiation energy.

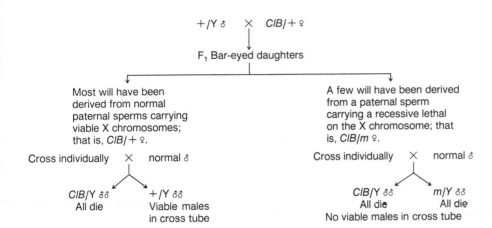

Figure 7-17. The ClB test for mutant detection in *Drosophila*. The symbol *m* represents a recessive lethal mutation anywhere on the X chromosome.

it is possible to extrapolate to very low radiation levels and to infer very low frequencies of mutation induction. Because exposure to radiation from X-ray machines, to radioactive fallout from bomb testing, and to contamination from nuclear plants is very low, it is possible to conclude that the effects are negligible. Yet every year 200 million new gametes form 100 million new babies in the world. In this very large annual "mutation experiment," even low mutation frequencies are potentially translatable into large numbers of mutant babies.

Radiation doses are cumulative. If a population of organisms is repeatedly exposed to radiation, the frequency of mutations induced will be in direct proportion to the *total amount* of radiation absorbed. However, there are exceptions to both additive and cumulative effects. For example, if mice given *x* rads (a biological measure of a dose of radiation) in one short burst (called an "acute" dose) are compared with those given the same dose gradually, over a protracted period of weeks or months (a "chronic" dose), significantly fewer mutations will be found in the chronically exposed group. This has been interpreted to mean that there is some form of repair of radiation-induced genetic damage with time.

Of even greater importance for geneticists was the discovery that certain chemicals also may be mutagenic. The first demonstration of chemical mutagenesis was made in 1947 by Charlotte Auerbach and J. M. Robson, who conducted experiments on mustard gases that were used earlier in gas warfare. (You might be interested to know that their discovery was kept from publication by the British military for several years.) This initial study opened a floodgate to research into the mutagenic effects of a wide variety of chemicals.

The mutagenicity of chemicals is an important phenomenon because, in many cases, the chemical reactions responsible for the mutagenic action of a compound can be determined, thereby providing a clue to the molecular basis of the mutation. Furthermore, many chemicals are much

less toxic to an organism than radiation is and yet give much higher frequencies of mutation. So, as a tool, chemical mutagens have been used to induce much of the wide array of mutants now available for genetic studies. Finally, great controversy now exists over the potential mutagenic effects

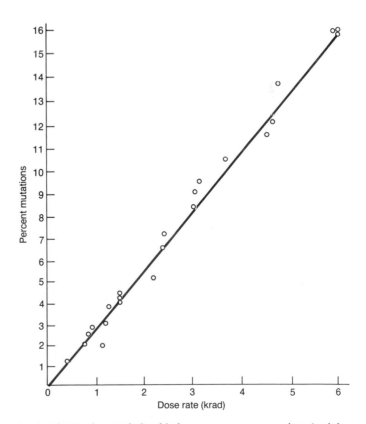

Figure 7-18. Linear relationship between percent mutations (mainly sex-linked recessive lethals) and X-ray dose in *Drosophila melanogaster*.

of a host of molecules in the human environment, ranging from caffeine to pollutants, pesticides, and LSD.

Mutagens in Genetic Analysis

Mutations are very useful. In the same way that we can learn how the engine of a car works by tinkering with its parts one at a time to see what effect each has, we can see how a cell works by altering its parts one at a time by means of induced mutations. The **mutation analysis** is a further aspect of the process we have called genetic dissection of living systems.

The first stage of any mutational dissection is the **mutant hunt.** Before embarking on a mutant hunt, the investigator usually has some specific biological process in mind. This process must be associated with some recognizable character of an organism. For example, the investigator might be interested in phototropic responses in algae — their tendency to swim toward the light. It would be comparatively easy to establish a selective system to recover mutants defective in this particular response. These mutants would then be tested for their single-gene inheritance, the number of different loci involved in the mutant set, and finally for specific cellular effects. In this way, the components of the response could be determined unambiguously.

The mutagenic agents are potent tools for the geneticist engaged in mutational dissection. Let's consider a few examples of the great usefulness of mutagens in such research.

First, Table 7-6 shows the relative frequencies of *ad-3* forward mutants in *Neurospora* after various mutagenic treatments. Note that recovery of a single mutant requires the testing of some 2.5 million cells without mutagenic treatment, whereas treatment with ICR-70 produces about one mutant in each 450 surviving cells tested. Table 7-7 provides another example of the great increase in available mutants obtained with an appropriate mutagen. The new term **supermutagen** has been introduced to describe some of these highly potent agents.

For a third example, we turn to *Drosophila*. Until the mid-1960s, most researchers working with *Drosophila* used radiation to induce mutations. Doses of 4000 roentgens produce lethal mutations in perhaps 10 to 11 percent of all X chromosomes of irradiated males. At higher doses, however, there is greater infertility of the treated flies. Furthermore, many of the mutations induced by X rays involve chromosome rearrangements, and these can greatly complicate the genetic analysis.

In contrast, the chemical ethyl methane sulfonate (EMS) induces mutations that show a vastly higher proportion of point mutations. This mutagen is very easily administered simply by placing adult flies on a filter pad saturated with a mixture of sugar and EMS. Simple ingestion of the EMS produces very large numbers of mutations. For example, males fed 0.025M EMS produce sperm carrying lethals on more than 70 percent of all X chromosomes and on virtually every chromosome 2 and chromosome 3. At these levels of mutation induction, it becomes quite feasible to screen for many mutations at specific loci or for defects with unusual phenotypes.

It is possible to screen mutagenized chromosomes immediately in the F_1 generation if the region of interest is hemizygous. The X chromosome can be tested in this way

■ **TABLE 7-6.** Forward-mutation frequencies obtained with various mutagens in *Neurospora*

Mutagenic treatment	Exposure time (minutes)	Survival (%)	Number of *ad-3* mutants per 10^6 survivors
No treatment (spontaneous rate)	–	100	~0.4
Amino purine (1 to 5 mg/ml)	During growth	100	3
Ethyl methane sulfonate (1%)	90	56	25
Nitrous acid (0.05 M)	160	23	128
X rays (2000 r/min)	18	16	259
Methyl methane sulfonate (20 mM)	300	26	350
UV rays (600 erg/mm² per min)	6	18	375
Nitrosoguanidine (25 μM)	240	65	1500
ICR-170 acridine mustard (5 μg/ml)	480	28	2287

NOTE: The assay measures the frequency of purple *ad-3* colonies among the white colonies produced by the wild-type *ad-3+*.

■ **TABLE 7-7.** The potency of various chemical mutagens for *his⁻* reversion in *Salmonella*

Mutagen	Revertants/nanomole	Ratio
1,2-Epoxybutane	0.006	1
Benzyl chloride	0.02	3
Methyl methane sulfonate	0.63	105
2-Naphthylamine	8.5	1400
2-Acetylaminofluorene	108	18,000
Aflatoxin B₁	7057	1,200,000
Furylfuramide (AF-2)	20,800	3,500,000

SOURCE: J. McCann and B. N. Ames, in *Advances in Modern Toxicology*, vol. 5. Edited by W. G. Flamm and M. A. Mehlman. Hemisphere Publishing Corp.

by crossing EMS-fed males with females carrying an attached-X chromosome and a Y chromosome ($\widehat{XX}$/Y). An attached-X ($\widehat{XX}$) is a compound chromosome formed by the fusing of two separate X chromosomes. It is inherited as a single unit. All F₁ males carry a mutagenized paternal X chromosome, and each fly represents a different treated sperm. Thus, if individual F₁ males are crossed with $\widehat{XX}$/Y females, each culture will represent a single cloned X. All F₁ zygotes carrying a sex-linked lethal will die, but any newly induced visible mutation will be expressed (Figure 7-19). In this way, it has been possible to select a wide range of behavioral and visible mutants involving a particular region of the genome; this approach is known as **saturating** the region. The F₁ flies can be reared at 22°C, and then clones of each individual X can be established at 22°C, 17°C, and 29°C to permit ready detection of heat-sensitive or cold-sensitive lethals. These temperature-sensitive (ts) lethals are found to represent about 10 to 12 percent of all EMS-induced lethals. We have already examined the utility of such conditional mutants in genetic analysis. Many labo-

$\widehat{XX}$/Y ♀ × X/Y ♂ (EMS-treated)

Sperm

		X*	Y*
Eggs	$\widehat{XX}$	$\widehat{XX}$ X* (dies)	$\widehat{XX}$/Y* ♀
	Y	X*/Y ♂	YY* (dies)

Figure 7-19. The use of attached-X chromosomes ($\widehat{XX}$) in *Drosophila* to facilitate the recovery of X-linked mutations. Sperm treated with EMS or another mutagen will fertilize eggs containing either the attached-X chromosome or a Y chromosome. The treated X chromosome from the male will show up as the hemizygous X of the sons, revealing phenotypically recessive mutations. (Recall that the ability to carry out this test is dependent on the mechanism of sex determination in *Drosophila*; see Chapters 3 and 19.) The asterisk (*) denotes the chromosome exposed to the mutagen.

ratories now routinely test for ts mutants in any *Drosophila* screening tests. Again, the approach is possible because large numbers of mutants are so easily obtained.

The recovery of ts lethals has a side benefit in simplifying laboratory procedures. One of the bothersome tasks involved in any large-scale *Drosophila* experiment is the need to separate all females from males within 12 hours after emergence from the pupae to prevent undesired mating. (Newly emerged males and females do not mate for 12 to 14 hours after emergence.) The tiresome procedure of collecting virgin females can be eliminated by using ts lethals (represented as l^{ts}) to produce unisexual cultures at will. For example, the cross $\widehat{XX}$/Y ♀ × l^{ts}/Y ♂ produces progeny of both sexes at permissive temperature. If the culture is shifted to restrictive temperature, the l^{ts}/Y males die, and only the females hatch. Similarly, homozygosis of an l^{ts} in an $\widehat{XX}$ chromosome will produce only wild-type males at restrictive temperatures.

Message The mutagen EMS has revolutionized the genetic versatility of *Drosophila* by providing a potent method for the recovery of a wide range of point mutants.

Mutation Breeding

Mutation has uses other than in mutational dissection of biological systems. We saw in Chapter 2 that one way of breeding a better crop plant is to make a hybrid and then select desired recombinants from the progeny generations. That approach makes use of the variation naturally found between available stocks or isolates from nature. Another way to generate variability for selection is to treat with a mutagen. In this way, the variability is produced through human intervention.

A variety of procedures may be used. Pollen may be mutagenized and then used in pollination. Dominant mutations will appear in the next generation, and further generations of selfing will reveal recessives. Alternatively, seeds may be mutagenized. A cell in a seed's enclosed embryo may become mutant, and then it may become part of germinal tissue or somatic tissue. If the mutation is in somatic tissue, any dominant mutations will show up in the plant derived from that seed (Figure 7-20), but this will be the end of the road for such mutations. Germinal mutations will show up in later generations, where they can be selected as appropriate. Figure 7-21 summarizes mutation breeding.

In this chapter, we have seen how gene mutation not only is of biological interest in itself but can also be put to a variety of experimental uses. In the next chapter, we shall see that much the same kind of statement can be made about chromosome mutation.

(a)

(b)   (c)

Figure 7-20. Irradiating seeds of *Collinsia grandiflora* with gamma rays to produce mutations in the embryo. (a) The effects of increasing dose (left to right) on survival and vigor. (b) A somatic mutation in a survivor, causing leaf-shape abnormalities. (c) Another somatic mutation causing a mutant sector. Germinal mutations also were recovered in the next generation.

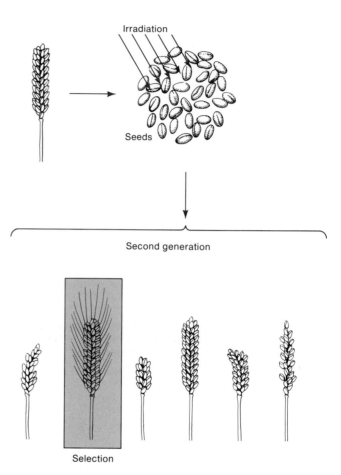

Figure 7-21. Mutation breeding in crops. (Courtesy of Björn Sigurbjörnsson, "Induced Mutations in Plants." Copyright © 1970 by Scientific American, Inc. All rights reserved.)

Summary

■ Gene mutation may occur in somatic cells or germinal cells. Within these two categories there are several kinds of mutations, including morphological, lethal, conditional, biochemical, and resistant mutations.

Mutations can be used to study the process of mutation itself or to permit genetic dissection of biological functions. In order to carry out such studies, however, it is necessary to have a system for detecting mutant alleles at the phenotypic level. In diploids, dominant mutations should be easily detected; recessive mutations, on the other hand, may never be manifested in the phenotype. For this reason, detection systems are much more straightforward in haploids, where the question of dominance does not arise.

Because mutations are rare, geneticists use selective systems or mutagens (or both) to obtain mutations. Selective systems automatically distinguish between mutant and nonmutant states and have been used mainly in microbes. Mutagens are valuable not only in studying the mechanisms of mutation but also for inducing mutations to be used in other genetic studies. In addition, mutagens are frequently used in crop breeding.

Problems

1. More than 10,000 new molecules are synthesized every year. Many of them could be mutagenic. How would you readily screen large numbers of compounds for their mutagenicity?

2. How would you use the replica-plating technique to select arginine-requiring mutants of haploid yeast?

3. Using the filtration-enrichment technique, you do all your filtering with minimal medium and do your final plating on complete medium that contains every known nutritional compound. How would you find out what *specific* nutrient is required? After replica plating onto every kind of medium supplement known to science, you still can't identify the nutritional requirement of your new yeast mutant. What could be the reason(s)?

4. *Meiotic (mei)* mutations are known in several organisms. The observable effect of this mutation on the phenotype is to cause a drastic disruption of the meiotic process, often producing only aborted meiotic products. In *Neurospora,* a cross is made between two strains called 1 (mating type *A*) and 2 (mating type *a*). The cross is perfectly fertile, with no spore abortion. Seven randomly selected progeny labeled 3 through 9 are intercrossed and crossed to the parental strains. Table 7-8 shows the fertility of the resulting progeny. In the table, F means fully fertile, and O means almost sterile (with many aborted white ascospores, and with the few normal spores showing reduced recombination throughout the genome). Explain these results in terms of a recessive *mei* mutation in one of the parental strains. Suggest a possible mode of action for the *mei* mutation at the cellular level.

■ TABLE 7-8.

Strains of mating type *a*	Strains of mating type *A*				
	1	3	4	5	6
2	F	F	O	F	O
7	F	F	O	F	O
8	F	F	O	F	O
9	F	F	F	F	F

5. An experiment is initiated to measure the reversion rate of an *ade-3* mutant allele in haploid yeast cells. One hundred tubes of liquid adenine-containing medium are each inoculated with a very small number of mutant cells and incubated until there are 10^6 cells per tube. Then the contents of each tube are spread over a separate plate of solid medium containing no adenine. The plates are observed after one day, and colonies are seen on 63 plates. Calculate the reversion rate of this allele per cell division.

6. Suppose that you want to determine whether caffeine induces mutations in higher organisms. Describe how you might do this (include control tests).

7. Certain mealybugs called coccids have a diploid number of 10. In cells of males, five of the chromosomes are always seen to be heterochromatic, and five are euchromatic. In female cells, all ten are always euchromatic. Spencer Brown and Walter Nelson-Rees gave large doses of X radiation to males and females and obtained the following results:

female (X-rayed) × male (non-X-rayed)
↓
no surviving progeny

female (non-X-rayed) × male (X-rayed)
↓
lots of male progeny
but no female progeny

Interpret these results. (NOTE: *heterochromatic* means densely staining and *euchromatic* means not densely staining.)

8. Assume that, in a leaf, an albino mutation is present in the inner meristem layers but not in the epidermal layer. During development, a few cells of the epidermis migrate into the photosynthetic layers of the leaf. What do you predict will be the appearance of the leaf? (NOTE: the epidermis normally has no chlorophyll.)

9. In corn, a single gene determines presence (*Wx*) or absence (*wx*) of amylose in the cell's starch. Cells that have *Wx* stain blue with iodine, and those that have only *wx* stain red. Design a system for studying frequency of rare mutations from *Wx* → *wx* without using acres of plants. (HINT: you might start by thinking of an easily studied cell type.)

10. A new high-yielding strain of wheat suffers from the disadvantages that it tends to "lodge" (fall over) during storms. You have an X-ray source (and a couple of years) to correct this defect. How would you proceed? State which part of the plant (or which stage of its life cycle) you would treat, what results you would look for, which generation you might expect your results in, and so forth.

11. Suppose that you cross a single male mouse from a homozygous wild-type stock with several homozygous black, virgin females. The F_1 consists of 38 wild-type females and males, and five black males and females. How can you explain this result?

12. Joe Smith accidentally receives a heavy dose of radiation in the gonadal region. Nine months later, his wife has a daughter, Mary. Mary appears perfectly normal, and she eventually marries a homozygous normal man. The accompanying figure shows their pedigree.

   a. What possible genetic mechanisms could explain these results?

   b. How would you prove which explanation is correct?

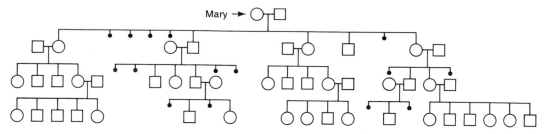

Mary →

• Early miscarriages, sex undetermined

13. A man employed for several years in a nuclear power plant becomes the father of a hemophiliac boy, the first in the extensive family pedigrees of both his own and his wife's ancestry. Another man, also employed for several years in the same plant, has an achondroplastic dwarf child, the first occurrence in his ancestry or in that of his wife. Both men sue their employer for damages. As a geneticist, you are asked to testify in court; what do you say about each situation? (NOTE: hemophilia is an X-linked recessive, and achondroplasia is an autosomal dominant.)

14. In a large maternity hospital in Copenhagen, there were 94,075 births. Ten of the infants were achondroplastic dwarfs. (Achondroplasia is an autosomal dominant showing virtually full penetrance.) Only two of the dwarfs had a dwarf parent. What is the mutation frequency to achondroplasia in gametes? Do you have to worry about reversion rates in this problem? Explain.

15. One of the jobs of the Hiroshima/Nagasaki Atomic Bomb Casualty Commission was to assess the genetic conse-quences of the blast. One of the first things they studied was the sex ratio in the offspring of the survivors. Why do you suppose they did this?

16. The government wants to build a nuclear reactor near the town of Poadnuck. The townspeople are very upset about the possibility of an accidental release of radioactivity and are putting up a stiff fight to keep it out. They call on you, a geneticist, to inform them about the biological hazards of an accident. What would you say in your speech?

17. The nuclear plant has been built and you are now a pro-fessor at Poadnuck State College. A radical group man-ages to infiltrate the plant and blow it up, releasing a large amount of radioactivity in the area. Fortunately, a thun-derstorm washes most of the radioisotopes to the ground, preventing widespread contamination. You set out imme-diately to determine the genetic effects of radiation. How do you go about it? (Remember, you must have controls.)

CHAPTER 8

Chromosome Mutation I: Changes in Chromosome Structure

■ The gene mutations discussed in Chapter 7 are not detectable by examination of chromosomes. A chromosome bearing a gene mutation looks the same as one bearing the normal allele. However, visible changes in the genome do occur regularly; such changes are called **chromosome mutations** or **chromosome aberrations.** We see in this chapter and the next that such changes may be detected not only with a microscope but also by standard genetic analysis.

Chromosome mutations are changes in the genome involving chromosome parts, whole chromosomes, or whole chromosome sets. Thus far we have treated the eukaryotic chromosome rather naively as merely a string of genes. A great deal is now known about the genetic organization of chromosomes (see Chapter 19), but there still are major gaps in our understanding at the molecular level. Luckily, the simplistic approach is not a major impediment in our understanding of chromosomes at the behavioral level. A large amount of information has been amassed about normal chromosome behavior and about how this behavior can go awry in the creation of chromosome mutations. This information has come from cytological and genetic studies, whose union constitutes the discipline of **cytogenetics.**

Genetics, perhaps more than any other field of biology, makes extensive use of deviations from the norm, and the study of chromosomes is no exception. Although this means of investigation may seem very esoteric to some, the findings have proved to be very important in applied biology—especially in agriculture, animal husbandry, and medicine. Many genetic tricks and devices used routinely by geneticists to build certain genotypes are discussed in this chapter. Finally, although this point is not given the attention it deserves, many of the aberrations we consider here have been important in building the theories of evolution and speciation.

The Topography of Chromosomes

Chromosome mutations may be detected either by appropriate genetic tests or, cytologically, simply by viewing the chromosomes under the microscope. Not all chromosome mutations can be detected cytologically because some are too small or subtle to produce any visible changes. Nevertheless, many cases are detectable in this way, and in this approach the cytogeneticist makes use of a variety of features of chromosomal topography that act as landmarks or chromosomal markers. Once the topography of the normal chromosomes is well known, then changes can be identified readily. The following features of chromosomes are commonly used as landmarks in cytogenetic analysis.

Chromosome Size.   There can be considerable variation in chromosome size within a genome. For example, in the human genome there is about a three- to fourfold range in

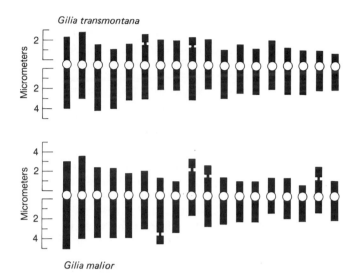

Figure 8-1. Chromosome diagram of two species of the plant genus *Gilia.* The chromosomes are arranged to show the characteristic arm ratios. Satellites are also shown.

size from chromosome 1 (the biggest) to chromosome 21 (the smallest) (see Figure 6-31). If individual chromosomes are difficult to identify on the basis of size alone, then at least groups of chromosomes of similar size may be defined, and a change can be pinpointed as involving, for example, "one of the chromosomes in size group A."

Centromere Position. The region of the centromere usually appears pinched; this region is called the **primary constriction.** The position of a centromere defines the ratio between the lengths of the two chromosome arms, and this ratio is a useful characteristic (Figure 8-1). Centromere positions can be categorized as **telocentric** (at one end), **metacentric** (in the middle), and **acrocentric** (off center). In addition to arm ratio, the centromere position determines the shape of chromosomes during anaphase, ranging from a rod through a J to a V (Figure 8-2). In some organisms, such as the Lepidoptera, centromeres are "diffuse," so that spindle fibers attach all along the chromosome. When such a chromosome is broken, both parts can still migrate to the poles. In contrast, a break in a chromosome with a single centromere results in a fragment having no centromere, which therefore cannot move to the pole. Chromosome segments lacking a centromere are called **acentric** (Figure 8-3).

The molecular structure of the centromeres of a few organisms, such as yeasts, is now known. This is also true for the tips of chromosomes, the **telomeres.** Although not morphologically distinct, the telomeres are crucial in maintaining the linear integrity of the chromosome. Such knowledge about molecular structure has permitted a new line of

research in yeast in which completely novel chromosomes can be synthesized, with a functional centromere, two telomeres, and any other genetic material of interest to the experimenter.

Position of Nucleolar Organizers. Different organisms are differently endowed with nucleoli, which range in number from one to many. The nucleoli contain ribosomal RNA, an important component of ribosomes. A common situation is to have two nucleoli in a diploid cell. The nucleoli are associated with secondary constrictions of the chromosomes, called **nucleolar organizers,** whose positions in the chromosome set are highly specific. Nucleolar organizers contain the genes for ribosomal RNA. Their positions can also be used as landmarks in cytogenetic analysis. A small piece of chromosome distal to the nucleolar organizer is called a **satellite.**

Chromomere Patterns. We have already encountered chromomeres in Chapter 5. They are visible during certain stages of cell division as beadlike localized thickenings of the chromosome.

Heterochromatin Patterns. When a chromosome is stained with standard reagents that react with DNA, such as Feulgen stain, distinct regions with different staining characteristics are visually revealed. Densely staining regions are designated **heterochromatin;** poorly staining regions, **euchromatin.** The distinction is thought to reflect the degree of compactness of the DNA in the chromosome. Heterochromatin can be **constitutive** or **facultative.** The constitutive type is a permanent feature of a specific chromosome location and is in this sense a hereditary feature; Figure 5-13 shows good examples of constitutive het-

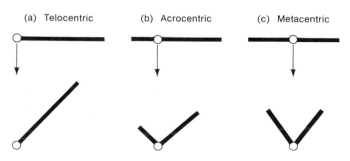

Figure 8-2. The classification of chromosomes by the position of the centromere. A telocentric chromosome has its centromere at one end. When the chromosome moves toward one pole of the cell during anaphase of cellular division, it appears as a simple rod. An acrocentric chromosome has its centromere somewhere between the end and the middle of the chromosome. During anaphase movement the chromosome will appear as a J. A metacentric chromosome has its centromere in the middle and will appear as a V during anaphase.

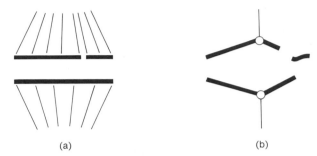

(a)   (b)

Figure 8-3. The spindle-fiber attachment to chromosomes. (a) An example of a relatively rare, diffuse centromere, with many spindle fibers attaching along the length of a single chromosome. A break in the chromosome will not result in the loss of any chromosomal material. (b) Spindle-fiber attachment to a single centromere; this is the more usual form. In this case, a break in the chromosome will result in an acentric fragment, which will be lost during cellular division.

erochromatin in the tomato. Facultative heterochromatin is a type that can be either present or absent at any particular chromosomal location. The patterns of heterochromatin and euchromatin along a chromosome constitute good cytogenetic markers. Heterochromatin is also of interest at the level of chromosome function because heterochromatic regions are for the most part genetically inert.

Banding Patterns.   Recently developed staining procedures have revealed several intricate chromosome banding systems in a wide range of organisms. Some of these systems are Q bands (produced by quinacrine hydrochloride), G bands (produced by Giemsa stain), and R bands (reversed Giemsa). An example of G bands in human chromosomes is shown in Figure 6-30.

A rather specialized kind of banding system, which has been used extensively by cytogeneticists for many years, is found in the so-called giant chromosomes in certain organs of the Diptera. In 1881, E. G. Balbiani had recorded peculiar structures in the nuclei of certain secretory cells of two-winged flies. These structures were long and sausage-shaped and marked by swellings and cross striations. Unfortunately, he did not recognize them as chromosomes, and his report remained buried in the literature. It was not until 1933 that Theophilus Painter, Ernst Heitz, and H. Bauer rediscovered them and realized these structures are in fact chromosomes.

In secretory tissues — such as Malpighian tubules, rectum, gut, footpads, and salivary glands of the Diptera — the chromosomes apparently replicate their genetic material many times without actual separation into distinct chromatids. Thus, as the chromosome increases in replicas, it elongates and thickens. *Drosophila melanogaster* has an *n* number of 4, and only four chromosomes are seen in the cells of such tissues because, for some reason, homologs are tightly paired. Furthermore, all four are joined at the **chromocenter,** which represents a coalescence of the heterochromatic areas around the centromeres of all four chromosome pairs. Salivary gland chromosomes are shown in Figure 8-4, in which L and R stand for arbitrarily assigned left and right arms.

Figure 8-4. *Drosophila* larval salivary chromosomes. Note that the two homologs of each chromosome pair have fused to form just one banded unit. The centromeres of all chromosomes are united at the common chromocenter. Thus, the telocentric X chromosome appears as a single unit, while the metacentric second and third chromosomes are seen as left (2L and 3L) and right (2R and 3R) portions. (Photograph by Tom Kaufman.)

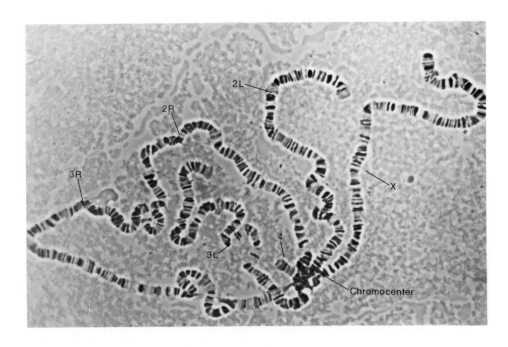

The formation of such giant chromosomes is by **endomitosis,** a process in which many chromosome replicas are produced but do not separate. The bundles of multiple replicas are called **polytene chromosomes.** The most commonly examined polytene chromosomes are in the salivary gland nuclei. These nuclei never divide. Along the chromosome length, characteristic stripes called **bands,** which vary in width and morphology, can be observed and identified. In addition, there are regions that may at times appear swollen (**puffs**) or greatly distended (**Balbiani rings**); these are presumed to correspond to regions of genetic activity. Recently, it has been found in *Drosophila* that, in general, each band contains the genetic material of a single gene. (However, the significance of the bands, such as Q and G bands, in human and other chromosomes is not known.) The polytene chromosomes corresponding to specific linkage groups have been identified through the use of chromosome aberrations. Such aberrations, as we shall see, have also been useful in specific localization of genes along the chromosomes.

So much for the cytological properties of *normal* chromosomes. We turn now to the properties of *abnormal* chromosomes: chromosome aberrations. These are classified into aberrations of chromosome structure (the subject of the rest of this chapter) and aberrations of chromosome number (the subject of Chapter 9).

Before we examine some abnormalities of chromosome structure, let us consider two important features of chromosome behavior that will be useful in understanding the abnormalities. First, during prophase I of meiosis, homologous regions of chromosomes show a very strong pairing affinity, and often go through considerable contortions in order to pair. This property accounts for many of the curious structures seen in cells containing one normal chromosome set plus an aberrant set. Similar pairing contortions between homologs are seen in polytene chromosomes, and equivalent shapes result. Second, changes in structure usually involve chromosome breakage; the broken chromosome ends are highly "reactive," showing a strong tendency to join with other broken ends. This property is not shown by the telomeres (the regular chromosome ends), however.

Types of Changes in Chromosome Structure

It is possible that a segment of a chromosome might be lost. For example, a chromosome described by a break and subsequent rejoining could result in

This type of change is called a **deletion** or a **deficiency.** The reciprocal of such a change would be its **duplication:**

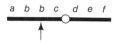

We can also conceive of a segment of a chromosome that has rotated 180 degrees and rejoined the chromosome as an **inversion:**

Finally, parts of two nonhomologous chromosomes might be exchanged to produce a **translocation:**

In fact, all of these types of chromosomal aberrations do occur, so we can examine their genetic and cytological properties. Collectively, this class of aberrations is known as **chromosome rearrangements.**

Deletions

Obviously, the occurrence of chromosomal rearrangements results from a break or disruption in the linear continuity of a chromosome. Deletions and duplications can be produced by the same event if breaks occur simultaneously at different points in two homologs, which can be visualized as occurring when the homologs overlap (Figure 8-5). This does not mean, however, that duplications and deletions are *always* reciprocal products of the same event.

In general, if a deletion is made homozygous, it is lethal. This suggests that most regions of the chromosomes are essential for normal viability and that complete elimination of any segment from the genome is deleterious. Even individuals heterozygous for deletions may not survive because the genome has been "fine-tuned" during evolution to require a specific balance or ratio of most genes; the presence of the deletion upsets this balance. Nevertheless, in some cases, individuals with relatively large deficiencies can survive if these deletions occur together with normal chromosomes. If meiotic chromosomes in such heterozy-

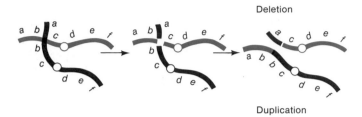

Deletion

Duplication

Figure 8-5. One possible way of producing deletions and duplications, by the reunion of broken homologs.

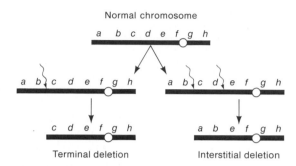

Normal chromosome

Terminal deletion   Interstitial deletion

Figure 8-7. Production of terminal and interstitial deletions. Chromosomes can be broken when struck by ionizing radiation (wavy arrows). A terminal deletion is formed when the end piece of a chromosome is lost. An interstitial deletion is formed when two breaks are induced. The acentric fragment (*cd*) is lost, while the terminal portion (*ab*) rejoins the main body of the chromosome.

gotes can be examined, the region of the deletion can be detected by the failure of the corresponding segment on the normal chromosome to pair properly; a "deletion loop" results (Figure 8-6). Deletion loops are also detected in polytene chromosomes, where the homologs are fused. Thus, deletions can be located on the chromosome by this technique.

Deletions of some chromosome regions produce their own unique phenotypes. A good example of this is a dominant notch-wing mutation in *Drosophila*. This is actually a small deletion and acts as a recessive lethal in this regard.

A good mutagen for inducing chromosome rearrangements of all kinds is ionizing radiation. This kind of radiation, of which X rays and γ rays are examples, is highly energetic and causes chromosome breaks. The way in which the breaks rejoin will determine the kind of rearrangement produced. In the case of deletion, a single break can cause a **terminal deletion,** and two breaks can produce an **interstitial deletion** (Figure 8-7).

But what of the genetic properties of deletions? Cytological detection of a "deletion loop" (for example, in salivary gland chromosomes of *Drosophila*) confirms its presence, but there are genetic criteria for inferring the presence of a deletion. One is the failure of the chromosome to survive as a homozygote, but that, of course, could also be

produced by any lethal gene. Another is the suppression of crossing-over in the region spanning the deficiency, but again this could occur with other aberrations, and small deficiencies may have only minor effects on crossing-over. The best criterion is that chromosomes with deletions can never revert to a normal condition. Another reliable criterion is the phenotypic expression of a recessive gene on a normal chromosome when the region in which it is located has been deleted from the homolog. Such **pseudodominance** (the expression of a recessive gene when present in a single dose) also allows the cytological localization of that gene when coupled with the chromosomal positioning of the deficiency loop. This technique permits a correlation between the genetic map (based on linkage analysis) and the cytological map (devised by marking the position of deficiency loops in specific cases of pseudodominance). By and large, the maps correspond well—a satisfying cytological endorsement of a purely genetic creation.

(a) Meiotic chromosomes   (b) Polytene chromosomes

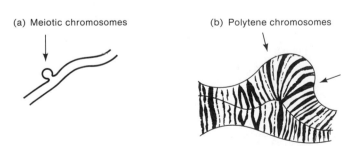

Figure 8-6. Cytogenetic configurations in a deletion heterozygote in *Drosophila*. (a) The "looped-out" portion of the meiotic chromosome is the normal form. The genes in this deletion loop have no alleles with which to pair during synapsis. (b) Since polytene chromosomes in *Drosophila* have specific banding patterns, the missing bands of the deleted chromosome can be observed in the deletion loop of the normal chromosome.

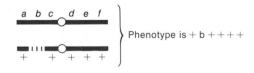

Phenotype is + b + + + +

Message   Deletion analysis proves that linkage maps are in fact reflections of chromosome maps.

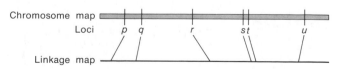

(a) Tandem 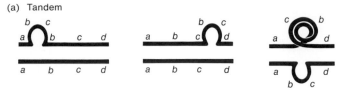 (b) Reverse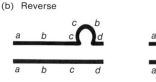

Figure 8-8. Possible pairing configurations in duplication heterozygotes. Duplicated segments may occur (a) in tandem or (b) in reverse order. There are several ways in which the homologs of duplicated heterozygotes may pair, illustrating the high affinity of homologous regions for pairing.

Conversely, pseudodominance can be used to map a small deletion. Consider an X chromosome in *Drosophila* carrying a recessive lethal suspected of being a deletion; let us call the chromosome "X?". We can cross X?-bearing females with males carrying different recessive genes known to reside in that interval. A map of genes in the tip region is

y	dor	br	gt		swa	w	rst		vt	
	0.3	0.3	0.3	0.4		0.2	0.2		0.6	

Suppose we get all wild-type flies in crosses between X?/X females and males carrying *y, dor, br, gt, rst,* or *vt* but get pseudodominance of *swa* and *w* with X? (that is, X?/*swa* is swa and X?/*w* is w). Then we have good genetic evidence for a deletion of the chromosome including at least the *swa* and *w* loci but not *gt* or *rst.*

Message Deletions are recognized genetically by (1) lack of revertability, (2) pseudodominance, and (3) recessive lethality, and cytologically by (4) deletion loops.

An interesting difference between animals and plants is revealed by deletions. In animals, a male that is heterozygous for a deletion chromosome and a normal one will produce functional sperm carrying each of the two chromosomes in approximately equal numbers. In other words, sperm seem to function to some extent regardless of their genetic content. In diploid plants, on the other hand, the pollen produced by a deletion heterozygote is of two types: functional pollen carrying the normal chromosome and nonfunctional (or aborted) pollen carrying the deficient homolog. Thus, pollen cells seem to be sensitive to changes in *amount* of chromosome material, and this might act to weed out deletions. The situation is somewhat different for polyploid plants, which are far more tolerant of pollen deletions. This is because there are several chromosome sets even in the pollen, and the loss of a segment in one of these sets is less crucial than it would be in a haploid pollen cell. Ovules, in either diploid or polyploid plants, also are quite tolerant of deletions. Presumably this is because of the nurturing effect of the surrounding maternal tissues.

Duplications

Duplications are very important chromosomal changes from the standpoint of evolution because they supply additional genetic material potentially capable of assuming new functions. Adjacent duplicated segments may occur in **tandem sequence** with respect to each other—*a bc bc d*—or in **reverse order**—*a bc cb d.* The pairing patterns obtained in these two sequences are different and illustrate the high affinity of homologous regions for pairing. Thus, chromosomes in meiotic nuclei containing a normal chromosome and a homolog with a duplication are seen to pair in the configurations shown in Figure 8-8. Alternatively, duplicated segments may be nonadjacent, either in the same chromosome or in separate chromosomes.

An organism that has evolved with a fixed number of genetic units would presumably be able to "spare" duplicated copies when they arise. Thus, loss or alteration of gene function due to changes in one of the duplicated genes would be covered by the duplicate copies. This provides an opportunity for divergence in function of genes, which

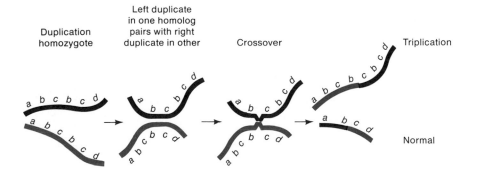

Duplication homozygote — Left duplicate in one homolog pairs with right duplicate in other — Crossover — Triplication — Normal

Figure 8-9. Generation of higher orders of duplications by asymmetric pairing and recombination in a duplication homozygote.

could be potentially advantageous. Indeed, in situations in which different gene products with related functions can be compared, such as the globins (which are discussed later), there is good evidence that they arose as duplicates of each other. Interestingly, once an adjacent tandem duplication arises in a population, homozygosity for such a duplication can result in higher orders of duplication by crossing-over when the chromosomes are **asymmetrically paired** (Figure 8-9).

Message   Duplications are important chromosomal alterations that supply additional genetic material capable of evolving new functions.

Duplications of certain genetic regions may produce specific phenotypes and act like a gene mutation. For example, the dominant mutation Bar in *Drosophila* produces a slitlike eye instead of the normal oval one. Cytologically, in the polytene chromosomes Bar was found to be in fact a tandem duplication that probably resulted from an **unequal crossover** (Figure 8-10). Evidence for the asymmetric pairing and crossing-over in *Drosophila* comes from studying homozygous Bar females. Occasionally, such females produce offspring with extremely small eyes called "double bar." They are found to carry three doses of the Bar region in tandem (Figure 8-11).

Figure 8-10. Production of bar-eye duplication by nonreciprocal crossing-over. Since this event will occur during meiosis, gametes containing the *deletion* chromosome will presumably die or produce an inviable zygote. The gamete containing the *Bar* duplication, however, will produce a male offspring with severely reduced eye size *(Bar)* or a female offspring with a slightly reduced eye size *(Bar* heterozygote).

In general, duplications are hard to detect and are rare. However, they are useful tools and can be generated from other aberrations by tricks that we shall learn later.

Duplications and deficiencies are detected in human chromosomes. As a matter of fact, some of the best evidence for the unequal crossover origin of tandem duplications (and their reciprocal deletions) comes from studies of the genes that determine the structure of the oxygen-transport molecule, hemoglobin, in humans. The hemoglobin molecule is composed of two different kinds of subunits or components. Furthermore, there are always two of each kind of subunit, so that there is a total of four subunits. The kinds of subunits that constitute hemoglobin are different

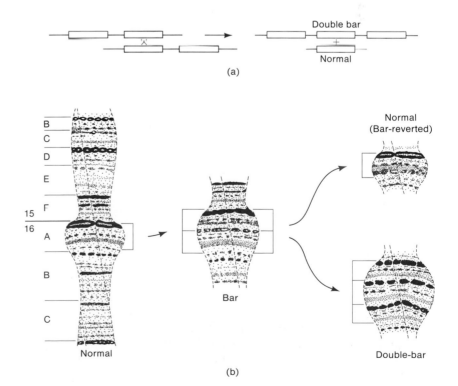

Figure 8-11. Production of double-bar (triplication) and bar-revertant (normal) chromosomes by asymmetric pairing and recombination in a duplication homozygote. (a) Diagrammatic representation. (b) Cytological representation. (Part b is from Bridges, *Science* 83:210, 1936.)

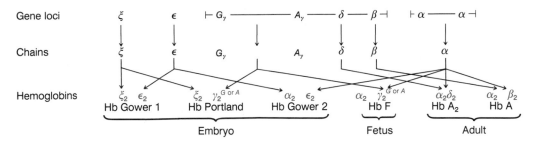

Gene loci ζ ϵ $\vdash G_\gamma$ ——— A_γ — δ — $\beta \dashv$ $\vdash \alpha$ ——— $\alpha \dashv$

Chains ζ ϵ G_γ A_γ δ β α

Hemoglobins $\zeta_2 \epsilon_2$ $\zeta_2 \epsilon_2$ $\gamma_2^{G\,or\,A}$ $\alpha_2 \epsilon_2$ $\alpha_2 \gamma_2^{G\,or\,A}$ $\alpha_2\delta_2$ $\alpha_2 \beta_2$

Hb Gower 1 — Hb Portland — Hb Gower 2 — Hb F — Hb A$_2$ — Hb A

Embryo — Fetus — Adult

Figure 8-12. Hemoglobin genes in humans. Each Greek letter represents a different gene locus and its type of hemoglobin subunit chain. These combine in different ways at different stages in development, as indicated, to yield functioning hemoglobin molecules. (From D. J. Weatherall and J. B. Clegg, "Recent Developments in Molecular Genetics of Human Hemoglobin," *Cell* 16, 1979. Copyright © 1979 by M.I.T. Press.)

at different stages of development. For example, the fetus has two alpha subunits and two gamma subunits ($\alpha_2\gamma_2$), whereas the adult has two alpha subunits and two beta subunits ($\alpha_2\beta_2$). The structures of these subunits are determined by different genes, some of which are linked and some not. The situation is summarized in Figure 8-12. It is the linked γ–δ–β group that provides the data we need on unequal crossover.

Some thalassemias (a kind of inherited blood disease) proved to involve hemoglobin subunits that are part δ and part β—Lepore hemoglobin—or part γ and part β—Kenya hemoglobin. The origin of these rare forms can be explained by the unequal crossover models shown in Figure 8-13. Also represented in the diagram are the reciprocal crossover products called anti-Lepore and anti-Kenya. It can be seen that the deletion types led to the anemic blood disease symptoms.

Multiple tandem (and nontandem) repeats of DNA are an inherent feature of normal eukaryotic chromosomes, as we shall see in Chapter 19. However, the origin of these repeats is in most cases not clear. It is also worth noting that some cancers are associated with the production of localized multiple repeats, appearing as homogeneously staining regions.

Visible deletions of chromosome segments in humans are always associated with major incapacities. For example, deletion of one-half of the short arm of chromosome 5 results in a syndrome characterized by severe mental retardation; this syndrome is called cri du chat (French, "cry of the cat") syndrome, because of the cat-like, mewing cry of affected infants. Figure 8-14 shows a pedigree involving cri du chat syndrome; examine it now, but don't worry about the details of the production of the deletion until after we have dealt with translocations. Deletions for certain other chromosomes also are found in humans, always associated with severe incapacity or with intrauterine lethality.

Inversions

Homozygosity for a chromosome carrying an inverted gene sequence will result in a linkage map with a different gene order. In a heterozygote having a chromosome that contains an inversion and one that is normal, there are important genetic and cytological effects. Because there is no net loss or gain of material, heterozygotes usually are perfectly viable. The location of the inverted segment can be recognized cytologically in the meiotic nuclei of such heterozygotes by the presence of an "inversion loop" in the paired homologs (Figure 8-15).

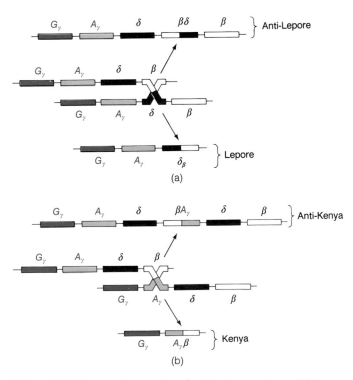

Figure 8-13. Proposed generation of variant human hemoglobin chains by unequal crossing-over in the γ-δ-β genetic region. (a) The Lepore variant. (b) The Kenya variant. These deletion types, not the Anti-Lepore and Anti-Kenya, result in anemia. (From D. J. Weatherall and J. B. Clegg, "Recent Developments in Molecular Genetics of Human Hemoglobin." *Cell* 16, 1979. Copyright © 1979 by M.I.T. Press.)

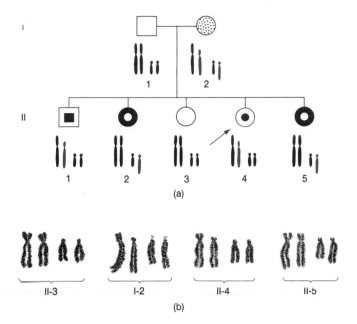

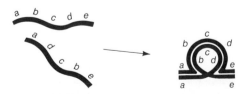

Figure 8-14. Cri du chat syndrome. (a) Pedigree with cases of the syndrome: I. Both parents are phenotypically normal. II. Of the offspring, II-1 and II-4 have cri du chat syndrome, II-2 and II-5 have the reciprocal chromosome abnormality, and II-3 is normal. Symbols represent different karyotypes, and the arrow points to the *proband* or affected individual with whom the study began. (b) Chromosomes 5 and 13 of four persons in the pedigree. (From J. Lejeune, J. Lafourcade, H. Berger, and R. Turpin, *Comptes Rendius. L'Academie des Sciences, Paris* 258, 1964.)

The location of the centromere relative to the inverted segment determines the genetic behavior of the chromosomes. If the centromere is not included in the inversion, the inversion is **paracentric,** whereas inversions spanning the centromere are **pericentric** (Figure 8-16).

What do inversions do genetically? In a heterozygote for a paracentric inversion, crossing-over within the inversion loop has the effect of connecting homologous centromeres in a **dicentric bridge,** as well as producing an acentric piece of chromosome—that is, one without a centromere (Figure 8-17). Thus, as the chromosomes separate during anaphase I, the disjoining centromeres will remain linked by means of the bridge. This orients the centromeres so that the noncrossover chromatids lie farthest apart. The acentric fragment cannot align itself or move, and consequently it will be lost. Remarkably, in *Drosophila* eggs and in plant megaspores, the dicentric bridge may remain intact

Figure 8-16. The location of the centromere relative to the inverted segment. If the centromere is not included in the inversion, the inversion is paracentric. Inversions including the centromere are pericentric.

long after anaphase I and, as the second meiotic division begins, the noncrossover chromatids are directed to the outermost nuclei (Figure 8-18). Thus, the two inner nuclei either will be linked by the dicentric bridge or will contain fragments of the bridge if it breaks, whereas the outer nuclei contain the noncrossover chromatids. Fertilization of a nucleus carrying the broken bridge should produce defective zygotes that die because they have an unbalanced set of genes. Consequently, in a testcross the recombinant chromosomes would end up in dead zygotes, and recombinant frequency would be lowered. However, in *Drosophila*, the presence of large inversions does not result in a large increase in zygotic mortality. The inner nuclei never participate in fertilization and only one of the outer nuclei can be the egg nucleus. Thus, we can see that the chromatids participating in a crossover event will be selectively retained in the central nuclei, thereby allowing recovery of the noncrossover chromatids in the egg nuclei. This remarkable suggestion based on genetic results was later confirmed cytologically in *Drosophila*. It has also been shown in plants. (How would you test this suggestion in *Neurospora* using tetrad analysis?) Nevertheless, the genetic consequence of inversion heterozygosity is the same—that is, the selective recovery of noncrossover chromatids from exchange tetrads. In addition, inversion heterozygotes often have mechanical pairing problems in the area of the inversion; this also reduces crossing-over and recombinant frequency in the vicinity.

Message   Although inversion heterozygosity does reduce the number of recombinants recovered, it in fact does so by two mechanisms: one by inhibiting the process of chromosome pairing in the vicinity of the inversion, and the other by selectively eliminating the products of crossovers in the inversion loop.

It is worth noting that paracentric inversions have been useful in studying crossing-over in organisms for which no genetic markers are known but which do have chromosomes that can be studied. Dicentric bridges are the consequence of crossovers within the inversion loop, so their frequency is related to the amount of crossing-over.

Figure 8-15. Inversion loop in paired homologs of an inversion heterozygote. Tight meiotic pairing produces this cytological configuration.

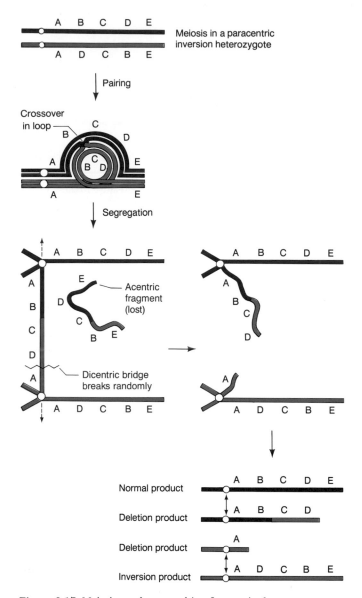

Figure 8-17. Meiotic products resulting from a single crossover within a heterozygous paracentric inversion loop. Crossing-over occurs in the four-strand stage (two identical chromatids connected to each centromere).

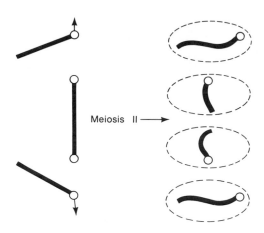

Figure 8-18. In some organisms, such as *Drosophila* and some plants, the dicentric bridge resulting from a single crossover within a heterozygous paracentric inversion loop will not break during anaphase I. As the second meiotic division begins, the noncrossover chromatids are directed to the outermost nuclei. Thus, the two inner nuclei either are linked by the dicentric bridge or contain fragments of the bridge if it breaks.

The net genetic effect of a pericentric inversion is the same as that of a paracentric one — that is, crossover products are not recovered — but for different reasons. In a pericentric inversion, because the centromeres are contained within the inverted region, disjunction of crossover chromosomes is normal. However, a crossover within the inversion produces chromatids that contain a duplication and a deficiency for different parts of the chromosome (Figure 8-19). In this case, fertilization of a nucleus carrying a crossover chromosome generally results in its elimination through zygotic mortality caused by an imbalance of genes. Again, the result is the selective recovery of noncrossover chromosomes as viable progeny.

To generate a duplication "on purpose," it is possible to use a pericentric inversion having one breakpoint at the

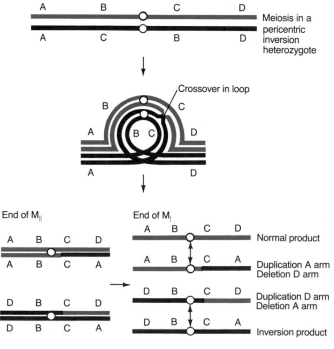

Figure 8-19. Meiotic products resulting from a meiosis with a single crossover within a heterozygous pericentric inversion loop.

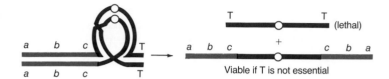

Figure 8-20. Generation of a viable nontandem duplication from a pericentric inversion close to a dispensable chromosome tip.

tip of the chromosome (Figure 8-20). A crossover in the loop produces a chromatid type in which the entire left arm is duplicated, and, if the tip is nonessential, a duplication stock is generated for investigation. Another way to make a duplication (and a deficiency) uses two paracentric inversions whose breakpoints overlap (Figure 8-21). (These tricks are possible only in genetically well-marked organisms.)

We have seen that genetic analysis and meiotic chromosome cytology are both good ways of detecting inversions. As with most rearrangements, there is also the possibility of detection through mitotic chromosome analysis. One of the key operational features is to look for new arm ratios (Figure 8-22). Note that the ratio of the long to the short arm has been changed from about 4 to about 1 by the pericentric inversion. (A pericentric inversion was the cause of the chromosome heteromorphism in the grasshoppers used by Carothers; see page 41.) *Paracentric* inversions are more difficult to detect, but they may be detected if banding or other chromosomal landmarks are available.

Translocations

Here we consider **reciprocal translocations,** the most common kind of translocation. A segment from one chromosome is exchanged with a segment from another nonhomologous one, so that in reality two translocation chromosomes are simultaneously achieved.

The exchange of chromosome parts between nonhomologs establishes new linkage relationships if the translocated chromosomes are homozygous and, as we shall see, even when heterozygous. Furthermore, translocations may drastically alter the size of a chromosome as well as the position of its centromere. For example,

Here a large metacentric chromosome is shortened by one-half its length to an acrocentric one, whereas the small chromosome becomes a large one. Examples in natural populations are known in which chromosome numbers have actually been changed by translocation between acrocentric chromosomes and the subsequent loss of the resulting small chromosome elements (Figure 8-23).

In heterozygotes having translocated and normal chromosomes, the genetic and cytological effects are important. Again, the pairing affinities of homologous regions dictate a characteristic configuration when all chromosomes are synapsed in meiosis. In Figure 8-24, which illustrates meiosis in a reciprocally translocated heterozygote, the configuration is that of a cross.

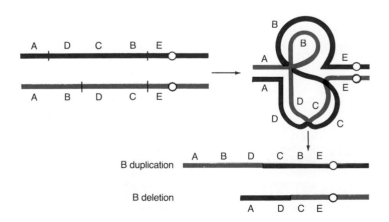

Figure 8-21. Generation of a nontandem duplication from two overlapping inversions.

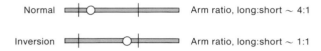

Normal		Arm ratio, long:short ~ 4:1
Inversion		Arm ratio, long:short ~ 1:1

Figure 8-22. The ratio of the lengths of the left and right arms of a chromosome can be changed by a pericentric inversion. Thus, changes in arm ratios can be used to detect pericentric inversions.

Remember, the configuration presented in the figure lies on the metaphase plate with the spindle fibers perpendicular to the page. Thus the centromeres would actually migrate up out of the page or down into it. Homologous paired centromeres disjoin, translocation or not. Because Mendel's second law still applies to *different paired centromeres,* there are two common patterns of disjunction. The segregation of each of the structurally normal chromosomes with one of the translocated ones (T_1 with N_2 and T_2 with N_1) is called **adjacent-1 segregation.** Both meiotic products are duplicated and deficient for different regions. On the other hand, the two normal chromosomes may segregate together, as do the reciprocal parts of the translocated ones to produce $T_1 + T_2$ and $N_1 + N_2$ products. This is called **alternate segregation.** There is another event called adjacent-2 segregation in which homologous centromeres migrate to the same pole, but in general this is a rare occurrence.

Semisterility in Plants.   Once again, in the study of rearrangements, a careful distinction must be made between animals and plants. In animals, the unbalanced products of adjacent-1 segregation in reciprocal translocation heterozygotes usually produce viable gametes. Thus, in *Drosophila,* for example, the gamete population is composed of approximately equal numbers of alternate and adjacent segregation meioses. However, in diploid plants, the T_1N_2 and T_2N_1 gametes normally abort, giving a situation known as semisterility. (Recall that semisterility in plants also can be produced in gametes containing deletions and in the products of crossovers in inversion loops.) Semisterility is often directly identifiable through the observation of a mixture of shriveled, abnormal pollen grains with normal pollen grains (Figure 8-25).

Even in *Drosophila* and other tolerant animals, the unbalanced gametes (when fertilized by normal gametes) give rise to unbalanced zygotes that tend not to survive unless the imbalance is for very small translocated regions.

Message   Translocations, inversions, and deletions produce semisterility by generating unbalanced meiotic products that may themselves be lethal or that may result in lethal zygotes.

Genetically, markers on nonhomologous chromosomes will appear to be linked if these chromosomes are involved in a translocation. Figure 8-26 shows a situation where a translocation heterozygote has been established by crossing an *aa bb* individual with a translocation bearing the wild-type genes. We shall assume that *a* and *b* are close to the translocation breakpoint. Upon testcrossing the heterozygote, the only viable progeny are those bearing the parental genotypes, so linkage is seen between loci on different chromosomes. In fact, if all four arms of the meiotic pairing structure are genetically marked, a cross-shaped linkage map will result. Such interlinkage group linkage is often a genetic giveaway for the presence of a translocation.

The Importance of Translocations for Humans.   Translocations are economically important as well. In agriculture, the occurrence of translocations in certain crop strains can reduce yields considerably because of the number of unbalanced zygotes formed. On the other hand, translocations are potentially useful: it has been proposed that the high incidence of inviable zygotes could be used to control insect pests by the introduction of translocations into the wild. Thus, 50 percent of the offspring of crosses between insects carrying the translocation and wild-types would die, and 10/16 of the progeny of crosses between translocation-bearing insects would die.

Translocations occur in humans, usually in association with a normal chromosome set in a translocation heterozygote. Down's syndrome (previously referred to as mongolism) can arise in the progeny of an individual heterozygous for a translocation involving chromosome 21. The heterozygous person is phenotypically normal (and is called a car-

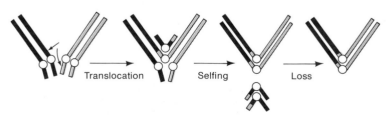

Translocation → Selfing → Loss

Figure 8-23. Genome restructuring by translocations. Small arrows indicate breakpoints in one homolog of each of two pairs of acrocentric chromosomes. The resulting fusion of the breaks yields one short metacentric and one long metacentric. If, as in plants, self-fertilization takes place (selfing), an offspring could be formed with only one pair of long metacentrics and one pair of short metacentrics. Under appropriate conditions, the short metacentric may be lost. Thus, we see a conversion from two acrocentric pairs of chromosomes to one pair of metacentrics.

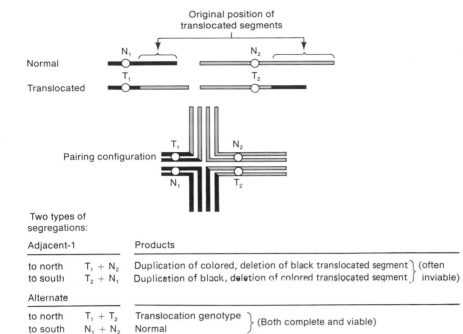

Two types of segregations:

Adjacent-1		Products	
to north	$T_1 + N_2$	Duplication of colored, deletion of black translocated segment	(often
to south	$T_2 + N_1$	Duplication of black, deletion of colored translocated segment	inviable)
Alternate			
to north	$T_1 + T_2$	Translocation genotype	(Both complete and viable)
to south	$N_1 + N_2$	Normal	

Figure 8-24. The meiotic products resulting from the two most commonly encountered chromosome segregation patterns in a reciprocal translocation heterozygote.

rier), but during meiosis an adjacent-1 segregation will produce gametes carrying duplicated parts of chromosome 21, and possibly a deficiency for some part of the other chromosome involved in the translocation. For unknown reasons, the extra chunk of chromosome 21 is the cause of Down's syndrome. Of the normal children of a carrier, one-half will themselves be carriers (Figure 8-27).

Later we shall examine another way in which Down's syndrome is generated. Bear in mind for now that under the present method there should be a high recurrence rate in the family pedigree involved: a translocation heterozygote or carrier can repeatedly produce children with Down's syndrome, and of course the carriers can do the same in subsequent generations. The other method does *not* show this recurrence within a family. The factors responsible for numerous other hereditary disorders have been traced to translocation heterozygosity in the parents —as, for example, in the cri du chat pedigree in Figure 8-14.

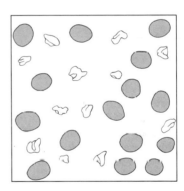

Figure 8-25. Sketch of normal and aborted pollen in a semisterile corn plant. The small, shriveled pollen grains contain aneuploid meiotic products of a reciprocal translocation heterozygote. The normal-shaped pollen grains, containing either the complete translocation genotype or normal chromosomes, will be functional in fertilization and development.

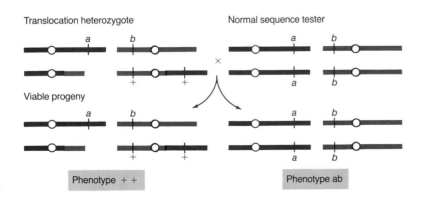

Figure 8-26. Inviability in some translocation progeny produces apparent genetic linkage because only parental types are recovered in the progeny. (This assumes *a* and *b* are close to the breakpoint.)

Cross $T_1T_2 \times N_1N_2$

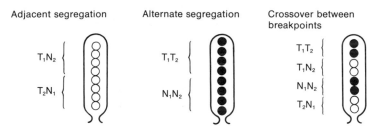

Adjacent segregation   Alternate segregation   Crossover between breakpoints

T_1N_2

T_2N_1

T_1T_2

N_1N_2

T_1T_2

T_1N_2

N_1N_2

T_2N_1

Figure 8-31. Consequences of various meioses in a cross of *Neurospora* heterozygous for a reciprocal translocation. White sexual spores abort; black are viable. T_1 and T_2 represent the respective translocated chromosomes; N_1 and N_2 represent the normal chromosomes. The 4 black – 4 white spores are produced by crossing-over between either centromere and the translocation breakpoint.

You may have noticed that little has been said in this chapter about how changes in chromosome structure are brought about. Unequal crossing-over has been considered as a mechanism for the production of tandem duplications, but what about the other rearrangements? Obviously, chromosome breakage is an integral part of most of the mechanisms for most rearrangements. Ionizing radiation, for example, is a potent inducer of chromosome breaks in the laboratory. However, such rearrangements also occur spontaneously in nature. Until quite recently, these were suggested to result from naturally occurring types of radiation, but it is now known that there are certain genetic factors — special regions in the DNA — that contribute in a major way to the instability of chromosomes. These regions can produce chromosome breaks and major rearrangements. A detailed look at this process must wait until Chapter 17, after we have dealt with the relevant molecular genetics.

Summary

■ The morphology of chromosomes provides a way of identifying them. Useful features are chromosome size, centromere position, nucleolar organizer position, and chromomere, heterochromatin, and banding patterns.

Four types of abnormalities of chromosome structure are deletions, duplications, inversions, and translocations. Deletions represent missing sections of chromosomes. If the region removed is essential to life, a homozygous deletion will be lethal. Heterozygous deletions can be nonlethal or lethal and can express recessive genes uncovered by the deletion.

Duplications can cause an imbalance in the genetic material, thereby producing a phenotypic effect in the organism. However, there is good evidence from a number of species, including humans, that duplications can lead to increased variety of gene functions. In other words, duplications can be a source of new material for evolution.

Inversions are caused by a 180-degree turn of a portion of a chromosome. In the homozygous state, these may cause little problem for an organism unless heterochromatin is involved and a position effect is thus exhibited. On the other hand, inversion heterozygotes often have pairing difficulties at meiosis, and an inversion loop may result. Crossing-over within the loop results in inviable products. The crossover products will be different for pericentric (spanning the centromere) and paracentric (not spanning the centromere) inversions.

Translocations involve relocation of a chromosomal segment to another position in the genome. In the heterozygous state, translocations produce duplication-deletion meiotic products, which can lead to unbalanced zygotes. New gene linkages can be produced by translocations. Both translocation and inversion heterozygotes can have reduced fertility.

Chromosome rearrangements are an important cause of ill health in human populations and are useful in engineering special strains of organisms in pure and applied biology.

Problems

1. The normal sequence of a certain *Drosophila* chromosome is 1 2 3 · 4 5 6 7 8 9, where the dot represents the centromere. Some chromosome aberrations were isolated that had the following structures: a. 1 2 3 · 4 7 6 5 8 9 b. 1 2 3 · 4 6 7 8 9 c. 1 6 5 4 · 3 2 7 8 9 d. 1 2 3 · 4 5 6-6 7 8 9. Give the correct name for each type, and draw diagrams to show how each would pair with the normal chromosome.

2. A *Neurospora* heterokaryon is established between nuclei of the genotypes shown in the following diagram in a common cytoplasm:

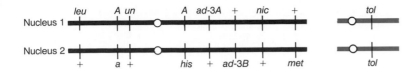

Here, *leu*, *his*, *ad*, *nic*, and *met* are all recessive alleles causing specific nutritional requirements for growth. *A* and *a* are the mating-type alleles (for a cross to occur one parent must be *A* and the other *a*). Usually, "*A* plus *a*" heterokaryons are incompatible, but the recessive mutant *tol* suppresses this incompatibility and permits heterokaryotic growth on vegetative medium. The allele *un* is recessive, prevents the fungus from growing at 37°C (it is a temperature-sensitive allele), and cannot be corrected nutritionally. This heterokaryon grows well on minimal medium, as do most of the cells derived mitotically from it. Some rare cells are found, however, that show the following traits:

They will not grow on minimal medium unless it is supplemented with leucine.

When the cells are transferred to a crossing medium, a cross does not occur (they will not self).

They will not grow when moved into a 37°C temperature, *even* if supplied with leucine.

When haploid wild-type *a* cells are added to these aberrant cells, a cross occurs, but the addition of *A* does not cause a cross.

From the cross with wild-type *a*, progeny with the genotype of nucleus 1 are recovered, but no alleles from nucleus 2 ever emerge from the cross.

Formulate an explanation for the origin of these strange cells in the original heterokaryon, and account for the observations concerning them.

3. Certain mice execute bizarre steps—in contrast to the normal gait for mice—and are called "waltzers." The difference between normals and waltzers is genetic, with waltzing being a recessive characteristic. W. H. Gates crossed waltzers with homozygous normals and found among several hundred normal progeny a single waltzing mouse, a ♀. When mated to a waltzing ♂, she produced all waltzing offspring. Mated to a homozygous normal ♂, she produced all normal progeny. Some ♂♂ and ♀♀ of this normal progeny were intercrossed, and there were no waltzing offspring among their progeny. Painter examined the chromosomes of waltzing mice that were derived from some of Gates' crosses and that showed a breeding behavior similar to that of the original, unusual waltzing ♀. He found that these individuals had 40 chromosomes, just as in normal mice or the usual waltzing mice. In the unusual waltzers, however, one member of a chromosome pair was abnormally short. Interpret these observations, both genetic and cytological, as completely as possible.

(Problem 3 is from A. M. Srb, R. D. Owen, and R. S. Edgar, *General Genetics*, 2d ed. Copyright © 1965 by W. H. Freeman and Co.)

4. In *Neurospora crassa*, mutants of the *ad-3B* gene are relatively easy to amass because they have a purple coloration

as well as requiring adenine. One hundred spontaneous *ad-3B* mutants were obtained in haploid cultures, and cells from each were plated on medium containing no adenine to test for reversion. Thirteen cultures produced no colonies, even after extensive platings involving a wide array of mutagens. What is the probable nature of these mutants? Account for both the lack of revertability and the haploid viability of these strains.

5. In *Drosophila*, five recessive lethal mutations are all shown to map on chromosome 2. The chromosomes bearing the lethal mutations are then each paired with a chromosome 2 from a stock having six recessive mutations (*h*, *i*, *j*, *k*, *l*, and *m*), which are distributed throughout the chromosome in that order. The appearance of the resulting flies is shown in Table 8-1, where M stands for mutant for any particular phenotype, and W stands for wild.

■ **TABLE 8-1.**

Lethal mutation	Chromosome-2 marker					
	h	*i*	*j*	*k*	*l*	*m*
1	M	M	W	W	W	W
2	W	W	W	M	M	W
3	W	W	W	W	W	M
4	W	W	W	M	M	M
5	W	W	W	W	W	W

a. What is the probable nature of the lethal mutations 1 through 4?

b. What can you say about the nature of the lethal mutation 5?

6. Two pure lines of corn showed different recombinant frequencies in the region from *P1* to *sm* on chromosome 6. The normal strain (A) shows an RF of 26 percent, and the abnormal strain (B) shows an RF of 8 percent. The two lines are crossed, producing hybrids that are semisterile.

a. Decide between an inversion and a deletion as possible causes of the low RF in the abnormal strain. List your reasons.

b. Sketch the approximate relation of the chromosome aberration to the genetic markers.

c. Why are the hybrids semisterile?

7. In the meiosis *P Bar Q* / *p Bar q*, the *P*/*p* and *Q*/*q* genes represent flanking markers very close to the left and right of a homozygous bar-eye mutation. In an appropriate testcross, some normal-eye and some double-bar types are recovered at low frequencies. These show the flanking marker combinations *Pq* or *pQ*. Explain the following with

diagrams: a. The origin of the rare normal and double-bar types b. The association with the flanking marker genotypes

8. In *Neurospora,* a nontandem duplication of the following type grows quite well as a haploid culture:

$$\underline{\qquad \underset{A\,B}{\qquad} \bullet \qquad \underset{b\,a}{\qquad}}$$

From such a culture, rare cells of the following constitution are detected:

$$\underline{\qquad \underset{A\,b}{\qquad} \bullet \qquad \underset{B\,a}{\qquad}}$$

a. What kinds of somatic pairing and crossover could produce such rare types?

b. What other kinds of rare types might you expect to find if you looked hard enough?

9. In *Drosophila,* a pure line is developed, carrying a duplication of the X-chromosome segment that contains the vermilion-eye gene. The stock is

$$\dfrac{v^+ \qquad v^-}{v^+ \qquad v^-}$$

and has wild-type eye color. Females of this stock are mated to nonduplicated vermilion males:

$$\dfrac{v^-}{Y}$$

The male offspring all have wild-type eye color, and the female offspring all have vermilion eyes. Explain why these are surprising results in regard to the theory of dominance. Explain the phenotype of the following: a. Female and male parents b. Female and male progeny

10. An aberrant corn plant gives the following results when testcrossed:

	Interval				
	d–f	*f–b*	*b–x*	*x–y*	*y–p*
Control RF values	5	18	23	12	6
Aberrant plant RF values	5	2	2	0	6

(The locus order is centromere-*d–f–b–x–y–p*.)

The aberrant plant is a healthy plant, but it produces far fewer normal ovules and pollen than the control.

a. Propose a hypothesis to account for the abnormal recombination and the abnormal fertility.

b. Explain with diagrams the origin of the recombinants, according to your hypothesis.

*11. In *Neurospora,* a cross is heterozygous for a paracentric inversion. The breakpoints of the inversion are known to be very close to two loci that recombine with an RF of 10 percent.

a. Using the mapping function $RF = \frac{1}{2}(1 - e^{-m})$, calculate the *mean* number of exchanges expected in the inversion loop per meiosis.

b. Use this mean frequency to calculate the frequency of meiosis with
   i. no exchanges in the loop
   ii. one exchange in the loop
   iii. two exchanges in the loop

   The Poisson formula is $e^{-m}\left(\dfrac{1}{0!} + \dfrac{m}{1!} + \dfrac{m^2}{2!} + \cdots\right)$.

c. Remembering that ascospores bearing deficient chromosome complements do not darken in *Neurospora,* predict how many light and dark ascospores you would find in eight-spored asci resulting from meioses in which there had been
   i. no crossovers in the loop
   ii. one crossover in the loop
   iii. two crossovers in the loop
   (Remember that there are three kinds of double crossovers, so the progeny population of asci from part iii could be heterogeneous.)

d. Using your predicted frequencies of zero, one, and two crossover meioses, what *overall* frequencies of the following asci would you find from this cross?
   i. 8 dark : 0 light
   ii. 0 dark : 8 light
   iii. 4 dark : 4 light
   (NOTE: your total from part should be less than 100 percent because triple and higher exchanges have been ignored, but it should be close to 100 percent because these events are rare. Simply make your total for this part equal your total for part b.)

12. A *Drosophila* geneticist has a strain of fruit flies that is true-breeding and wild-type. She crosses this strain with a multiply marked X-chromosome strain carrying the recessive genes *y* (yellow), *cv* (crossvein-less), *v* (vermilion), *f* (forked), and *car* (carnation), which are equally distributed along the X chromosome from one end to the other. She collects the heterozygous F_1 female offspring and mates them with *y cv v f B car* males. She gets the following classes among the male offspring:

1. *y cv v f car*
2. + + + + +
3. *y* + + + *car*

4. + *cv* *v* *f*   +
5. *y* *cv* + *f*   *car*
6. + + *v* +   +
7. *y* *cv* + +   *car*
8. + + *v* *f*   +
9. *y* + + *f*   *car*
10. + *cv* *v* +   +
11. *y* *cv* *v* *f* *B car*

a. How would you account for the results in classes 1 through 10?

b. How can you account for class 11? You should be able to give two ways.

c. How would you test your hypotheses?

(Problem 12 courtesy of Tom Kaufmann.)

*13. Suppose that you are given a *Drosophila* line from which you can get males or virgin females at any time. The line is homozygous for a second chromosome, which has an inversion to prevent crossing-over, a dominant gene *(Cu)* for curled wings, and a recessive gene (*pr*, purple) for dark eyes. The chromosome can be drawn as

You have irradiated sperm in a wild-type male and wish to determine whether recessive lethal mutations have been induced in chromosome 2. How would you determine this? (HINT: remember that each sperm carries a *different* irradiated second chromosome.) Indicate the kinds and number of flies used in each cross.

14. Predict the chromosomal shapes that would be produced at anaphase I of meiosis in a reciprocal translocation heterozygote undergoing: a. alternate segregations; b. adjacent-1 segregations.

15. In *Neurospora*, the genes *a* and *b* are on separate chromosomes. In a cross of a standard *a b* strain with a wild-type obtained from nature, the progeny are as follows: *a b*, 45 percent; ++, 45 percent; *a* +, 5 percent; + *b*, 5 percent. Interpret these results and explain the origin of all the progeny types under your hypothesis.

16. You discover a *Drosophila* male that is heterozygous for a reciprocal translocation between the second and third chromosomes, each break having occurred near the centromere (which for these chromosomes is near the center).

a. Draw a diagram showing how these chromosomes would synapse at meiosis.

b. You find that this fly has the recessive genes *bw* (brown eye) and *e* (ebony body) on the nontranslocated second and third chromosomes, respectively, and wild-type alleles on the translocated ones. It is mated with a female having normal chromosomes that is homozygous for *bw* and *e*. What type of offspring would be expected and in what ratio? (Zygotes with an extra chromosome arm or deficient for one do not survive. There is no crossing-over in *Drosophila* males.)

17. An *insertional* translocation consists of the insertion of a piece from the center of one chromosome into the middle of another (nonhomologous) chromosome. Thus

becomes

How will genomes heterozygous for such translocations pair at meiosis? In *Neurospora*, what spore abortion patterns will be produced and in what relative proportions in such translocation heterozygotes? (Remember, duplications survive and have dark spores, but deficiencies are light-spored.)

18. In *Neurospora*, the markers *ad-3* and *pan-2* are auxotrophic mutations located on chromosomes I and VI, respectively. An unusual *ad-3* line that arose in the laboratory gave the following results.

	Ascospore appearance	RF between *ad-3* and *pan-2*
1. Normal *ad-3* × normal *pan-2*	all black	50%
2. Abnormal *ad-3* × normal *pan-2*	about 1/2 black and 1/2 white (inviable)	1%

3. Of the black spores from cross 2, about half were completely normal and half repeated the same behavior as the original abnormal *ad-3* strain.

Explain all three results with the aid of clearly labeled diagrams. (NOTE: in *Neurospora*, ascospores with extra chromosomal material survive and are the normal black color, whereas ascospores lacking any chromosomal region are white and inviable.)

19. In corn, the following linkage arrangement holds in normal plants.

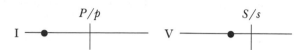

P = dark green
p = pale green
S = large ears
s = shrunken ears.

An original plant of genotype $Pp\ Ss$ had the expected phenotype of large ears, dark green, but gave unexpected results in crosses as follows:

On selfing, fertility was normal, but the frequency of $pp\ ss$ types was $1/4$, not $1/16$ as expected.

When crossed to a normal tester of genotype $pp\ ss$, the F_1 progeny were $1/2\ Pp\ Ss$ and $1/2\ pp\ ss$; fertility was normal.

When an $F_1\ Pp\ Ss$ plant was crossed to a normal $pp\ ss$ tester, it proved to be semisterile, but again the progeny were $1/2\ Pp\ Ss$ and $1/2\ pp\ ss$.

Explain these results, showing the full genotypes of the original plant, the tester, and the F_1 individuals. How would you test your hypothesis?

20. A corn plant pr/pr that has standard chromosomes is crossed with a plant homozygous for a reciprocal translocation between chromosomes 2 and 5 and for the Pr allele. The F_1 is semisterile and phenotypically Pr (a seed color). A backcross to the parent with standard chromosomes gives 764 semisterile Pr; 145 semisterile pr; 186 normal Pr; and 727 normal pr. What is the map distance of the Pr/pr locus from the translocation point?

21. In *Neurospora*, a reciprocal translocation of the following type is obtained:

The following cross is then made:

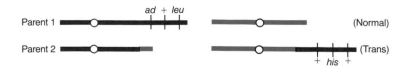

Assuming that the small, lightly shaded piece of the chromosome involved in the translocation does not carry any essential genes, how would you select products of meiosis that are duplicated for the translocated part of the solid chromosome?

22. Assume that, in a study of hybrid cells, three genes in humans have been assigned to chromosome 17. These genes are *a*, *b*, and *c* and are concerned with making the compounds a, b, and c—all of which are essential for growth. If $a^-\ b^-\ c^-$ mouse cells are fused with $a^+\ b^-\ c^+$ human cells, assume that you find a hybrid in which the only human component is the right arm of chromosome 17 (17R), translocated by some unknown mechanism to a mouse chromosome. The hybrid can make the compounds a, b, and c. Treatment of cells with adenovirus causes chromosome breaks. Assume that you can isolate 200 lines in which bits of the translocated 17R have been clipped off. These lines are tested for ability to make a, b, and c, and the results are:

Number	Can make
0	a only
0	b only
12	c only
0	a and b only
80	b and c only
0	a and c only
60	a, b, and c
48	nothing

a. How would these different types arise?

b. Are *a*, *b*, and *c* all on the right arm of 17?

c. If so, would you draw an approximate map indicating relative positions?

d. How would quinacrine dyes help you in this? (NOTE: this *kind* of approach has actually been used, although the details of this particular question are largely hypothetical.)

*23. Complex translocations often are found in natural plant populations. The best example is in the evening primrose, *Oenothera* ($2n = 14$). In this genus, the centromeres tend to be more or less in the middle of the chromosomes. Furthermore, chromosome breakage in the production of translocations tends to be close to or at the centromere.

The basic haploid chromosome set can be represented as follows, where a dot represents a centromere:

$$1^L \cdot 1^R \quad 2^L \cdot 2^R \quad 3^L \cdot 3^R \quad 4^L \cdot 4^R \quad 5^L \cdot 5^R \quad 6^L \cdot 6^R \quad 7^L \cdot 7^R$$

The species *O. lamarckiana* contains one basic haploid set as above, plus a haploid set bearing many translocations, as follows:

$$1^L \cdot 1^R \quad 3^L \cdot 5^R \quad 2^L \cdot 7^L \quad 6^R \cdot 5^L \quad 4^L \cdot 2^R \quad 7^R \cdot 3^R \quad 6^L \cdot 4^R$$

a. What patterns of chromosome pairing would you expect at meiosis if all homologous regions pair? (Draw a diagram.)

b. In *O. lamarckiana*, the segregation is always alternate. What are the cytological consequences of this?

c. *O. lamarckiana* always contains one "basic" plus one "translocated" set, as shown, never basic plus basic or translocated plus translocated. Can you think of a mechanism whereby the plant might maintain this situation?

d. Can you think of a reason why it is advantageous to the plant to maintain this situation?

24. Suppose that you are studying the cytogenetics of five closely related species of *Drosophila*. The accompanying figure shows the gene orders (the letters indicate genes identical in all five species) and chromosome pairs in each species that you find. Show how these species probably evolved from each other, describing the changes that occurred at each step. (NOTE: be sure to compare gene order carefully.)

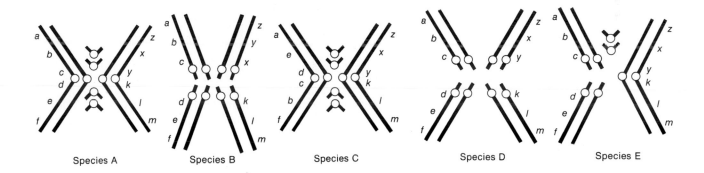

Species A   Species B   Species C   Species D   Species E

CHAPTER 9

Chromosome Mutation II: Changes in Chromosome Number

■ Like the structural aberrations treated in the last chapter, changes in chromosome number occur spontaneously in both natural and laboratory populations of organisms. Alternatively, they may be experimentally induced using certain standard mutagenic agents applied to appropriate cells or tissues. Either standard genetic tests or cytological examination may be used for the detection of such changes.

Changes in chromosome number are usually classified into those changes involving whole chromosome sets and those involving parts of chromosome sets. Before considering examples of these, we must define some useful terms. The number of chromosomes in a basic set is called the **monoploid number**, x. Organisms with multiples of the monoploid number of chromosomes are called **euploid.** Those euploid types whose number of sets is greater than two are called **polyploid.** Thus, $1x$ is **monoploid**, $2x$ is **diploid,** and the polyploid types are $3x$ **(triploid)**, $4x$ **(tetraploid)**, $5x$ **(pentaploid)**, $6x$ **(hexaploid)**, and so on. The haploid number (n), which we have already used extensively, refers strictly to the number of chromosomes in gametes. In most animals and many plants that we are familiar with, the haploid number and monoploid number are the same. Hence, n or x (or $2n$ or $2x$) can be used interchangeably. However, in certain plants such as modern wheat, n and x are different. Wheat has 42 chromosomes, but careful study reveals that it is hexaploid, with six rather similar but not identical sets of seven chromosomes. Hence, $6x = 42$, and $x = 7$. However, the gametes of wheat contain 21 chromosomes, so $2n = 42$, and $n = 21$.

Changes that involve parts of a chromosome set result in individuals that are **aneuploid** ("not euploid"). Addition of chromosomes produces individuals that are **hyperploid,** and subtraction results in those that are **hypoploid.** Changes involving one or a few chromosomes give rise to the following terms. In an organism that is predominantly diploid, $2n - 1$ is **monosomic**, $2n + 1$ is **trisomic**, $2n - 2$ is **nullisomic** (here the two lost are homologs), and $2n + 1 + 1$ is a **double trisomic.** In a haploid organism, $n + 1$ would be called a **disomic.** It can be seen that these terms refer to the number of copies of a particular type that are present in the aneuploid.

Now we can examine the genetic and cytological properties of these variants.

Abnormal Euploidy

Monoploids

In this section we shall consider monoploidy as an unusual condition. Monoploid individuals can arise spontaneously in natural populations as rare aberrations, but in several forms (such as bees, wasps, and ants) the males are normally monoploid, having been derived from unfertilized eggs.

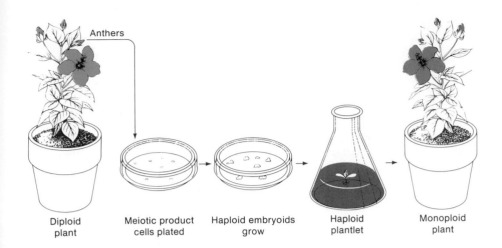

Figure 9-1. Generating a monoploid plant by tissue culture. Appropriately treated pollen grains (haploid) can be plated on agar containing certain plant hormones. Under these conditions, haploid embryoids will grow into monoploid plantlets. With another change in plant hormones, these plantlets will grow into mature monoploid plants with roots, stems, leaves, and flowers.

Anthers

Diploid plant — Meiotic product cells plated — Haploid embryoids grow — Haploid plantlet — Monoploid plant

In the germ cells of a monoploid, meiosis cannot occur normally because the chromosomes have no pairing partners. Thus monoploids are characteristically sterile. (However, meiosis can be bypassed in some monoploid animals, such as male honeybees, which produce gametes essentially by mitotic division.) If meiosis occurs and the single chromosomes segregate randomly, then the probability of their all going to one pole is $(1/2)^{x-1}$, where x is the number of chromosomes. This will determine the frequency of viable (whole-set) gametes, obviously a vanishingly small number if x is large.

Monoploids have a major role in modern approaches to plant breeding. Diploidy is an inherent nuisance in the induction and selection of new favorable plant mutations and of new combinations of genes already present. Monoploids provide a way around some of these problems. In some plants, monoploids may be artificially derived from the products of meiosis in the plant's anthers. A cell destined to become a pollen grain may be induced by cold treatment to grow instead into an **embryoid,** a small dividing mass of cells. The embryoid may be grown on agar to form a monoploid plantlet, which can then be potted in soil to mature (Figure 9-1).

Monoploids may be exploited in several ways. In one method, they are first examined for favorable traits or gene combinations. These may arise from heterozygosity already present in the parent or induced in the parent by mutagens. The monoploid can then be subjected to chromosome doubling to achieve a completely homozygous diploid with a normal meiosis, capable of providing seed. How is this achieved? Quite simply, by the application of a compound called **colchicine** to meristematic tissue. Colchicine, an alkaloid drug extracted from the autumn crocus, inhibits the mitotic spindle, so that cells with two chromosome sets are produced (Figure 9-2). These may proliferate to form a sector of diploid tissue that can be identified cytologically.

Another way the monoploid may be used is to treat its cells, basically like a population of haploid organisms, in a mutagenesis-and-selection procedure. The cells are isolated, their walls are removed by enzyme treatment, and they are treated with mutagen. They are then plated on selective medium—perhaps a toxic compound normally produced by one of the plant's parasites, or an insecticide—to select resistant cells. Resistant plantlets grow eventually into haploid plants, which can then be doubled (using colchicine) into a pure-breeding resistant type (Figure 9-3). These are potentially powerful techniques that can circumvent the normally slow process of what is basically meiotic plant breeding. The techniques have been successfully applied in several important crop plants, such as soybeans and tobacco. This is, of course, another aspect of somatic-cell genetics in higher organisms.

The anther technique for producing monoploids does not work in all organisms or in all genotypes of an organism. Another useful technique has been developed in barley, an important crop plant. When diploid barley, *Hordeum vulgare,* is pollinated using a diploid wild relative called *Hordeum bulbosum,* fertilization occurs, but during the ensuing somatic cell divisions, the chromosomes of *H. bulbosum* are preferentially eliminated from the zygote, resulting in a haploid embryo. (The haploidization process

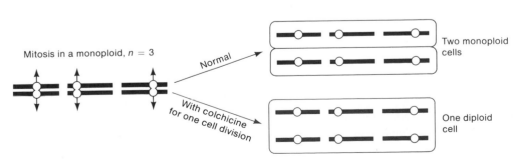

Mitosis in a monoploid, $n = 3$

Normal → Two monoploid cells

With colchicine for one cell division → One diploid cell

Figure 9-2. Using colchicine to generate a diploid from a monoploid. Colchicine added to mitotic cells during metaphase and anaphase disrupts spindle-fiber formation, thus preventing separation of chromatids after the centromere is split. A single cell is created containing pairs of identical chromosomes homozygous at all loci.

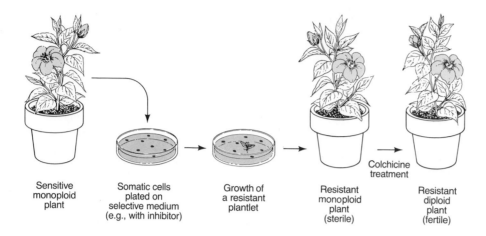

Figure 9-3. Using microbial techniques in plant engineering. Haploid cells have their cell walls removed enzymatically. The cells are then exposed to a mutagen and plated on an agar medium containing a selective agent, such as a toxic compound produced by a plant parasite. Only these cells containing a resistance mutation that allows the cells to live within the presence of this toxin will grow. After treatment with the appropriate plant hormones, they will grow into mature monoploid plants and, with proper colchicine treatment, can be converted into homozygous diploid plants.

Under the figure, left to right:
Sensitive monoploid plant
Somatic cells plated on selective medium (e.g., with inhibitor)
Growth of a resistant plantlet
Colchicine treatment
Resistant monoploid plant (sterile)
Resistant diploid plant (fertile)

appears to be caused by a genetic incompatibility between the chromosomes of the different species.) The resulting haploids can be doubled with colchicine. This approach has led to the rapid production and widespread planting of several new barley varieties. It is being used successfully in other species too.

Polyploids

Once into the realm of polyploids, we must distinguish between autopolyploids and allopolyploids. **Autopolyploids** are composed of multiple sets from within one species, whereas **allopolyploids** are composed of sets from different species. Allopolyploids form only between closely related species; however, the different chromosome sets are **homeologous** (only partially homologous), not fully homologous as they are in autopolyploids.

Triploids

Triploids are usually autopolyploids. They are constructed from the cross of a 4x (tetraploid) and a 2x (diploid). The 2x and the x gametes unite to form a 3x triploid.

Triploids also are characteristically sterile. The problem again involves pairing at meiosis. Although pairing can take place in several ways, it usually occurs between only two chromosomes at a time (Figure 9-4). The net result is always the same, an unbalanced segregation of one of the following types:

$$\frac{1+2}{3} \quad \text{or} \quad \frac{1+3}{2} \quad \text{or} \quad \frac{2+3}{1}$$

This happens for every chromosome threesome, and the probability of obtaining either a 2x or an x gamete is $(1/2)^{x-1}$, where x is the number of chromosomes in a set. The others will be unbalanced gametes, having two of one chromosome type, one of another, two of another, and so on, and most will be nonfunctional. Even if the gametes are functional, the resulting zygotes will be unbalanced. A practical application of the sterility associated with triploidy lies in the production of seedless varieties of watermelons and bananas.

Autotetraploids

Autotetraploids occur either naturally, by the spontaneous accidental doubling of a 2x genome to 4x, or artificially, through the use of colchicine. Autotetraploids are evident in many commercially important crop plants because, as with other polyploids, the larger number of chromosome sets is often associated with increased size of the plant. This is manifested in increased cell size, fruit size, stomata size, and so on (Figure 9-5).

Because 4 is an even number, autotetraploids can have a regular meiosis, although this is by no means always the case. The crucial factor is how the four chromosomes of one type pair and segregate. There are several possibilities, as shown in Figure 9-6. The two bivalent and the quadrivalent pairing modes tend to be most regular in segregation, but even here there is no guarantee of a 2 ↔ 2 segregation. If a regular 2 ↔ 2 segregation is achieved at each chromosome type, as is the case in some species, then a formal genetic analysis can be developed for autotetraploids.

Let's hypothesize an experiment in which colchicine is used to double the chromosomes of an *Aa* plant into an

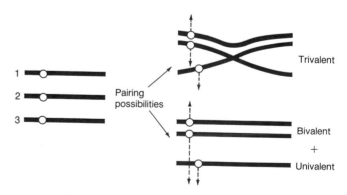

Figure 9-4. Meiotic pairing possibilities in a triploid. (Each chromosome is really two chromatids.) Pairing in meiosis with the resultant segregation always occurs between only two of the three homologs. The possibility that one gamete will receive the univalent of all chromosome sets is very small. Consequently, gametes of unbalanced chromosome number are produced, and sterility results.

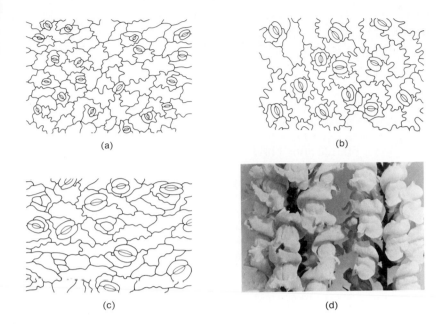

(a)

(b)

(c)

(d)

Figure 9-5. Epidermal leaf cells of tobacco plants showing increase in cell size, particularly evident in stomata size, with increase in autopolyploidy. (a) Diploid, (b) tetraploid, (c) octoploid. (From W. Williams, *Genetic Principles and Plant Breeding*, Blackwell Scientific Publications, Ltd.) (d) Diploid (right) and tetraploid (left) snapdragons. (W. Atlee Burpee Company.)

AAaa autotetraploid, which we will assume shows $2 \leftrightarrow 2$ segregation. We now have a further worry because autotetraploids give different genetic results in their progeny, depending on whether or not the locus concerned is tightly linked to the centromere. First we consider a centromeric gene. The three possible pairing and segregation patterns are presented in Figure 9-7; these occur by chance and with equal frequency. As the figure shows, the $2x$ gametes will be *Aa*, *AA*, or *aa*, and these will be produced in a ratio of $8:2:2$, or $4:1:1$. If such a plant is selfed, the probability of an *aaaa* phenotype in the offspring is obviously $1/6 \times 1/6 = 1/36$. In other words, a $35:1$ phenotypic ratio will be observed if *A* is fully dominant over three *a* alleles.

If, in the same kind of plant, a genetic locus *B/b* is very far removed from the centromere, crossing-over must be considered. This forces us to think in terms of chromatids instead of chromosomes, and we have four *B* chromatids

and four *b* chromatids (Figure 9-8). Because the number of crossovers in such a long region will be large, the genes will become effectively unlinked from their original centromeres, and the packaging of genes two at a time into gametes is very much like grabbing two balls at random from a bag of eight balls, four of one kind and four of another. The probability of picking two *b* genes is then

$$4/8 \text{ (the first one)} \times 3/7 \text{ (the second one)} = 12/56$$
$$= 3/14$$

So, in a selfing, the probability of a *bbbb* phenotype will equal $3/14 \times 3/14 = 9/196 \cong 1/22$. Hence there will be a $21:1$ phenotype ratio of $B---:bbbb$. For genetic loci of intermediate position, intermediate ratios will, of course, result.

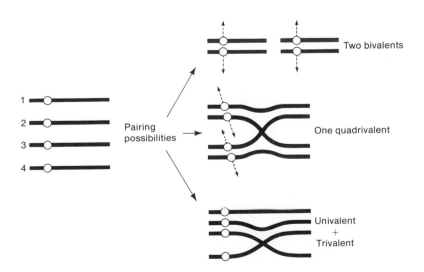

1
2
3
4

Pairing possibilities

Two bivalents

One quadrivalent

Univalent
+
Trivalent

Figure 9-6. Meiotic pairing possibilities in tetraploids. (Each chromosome is really two chromatids.) The four chromosomes of one type may pair as two bivalents or as a quadrivalent. Both of these possibilities can yield functional gametes. However, the four chromosomes may also pair in a univalent:trivalent combination, yielding nonfunctional gametes. Some tetraploids have adopted the first or second method as a routine in meiotic segregation and thus can function normally.

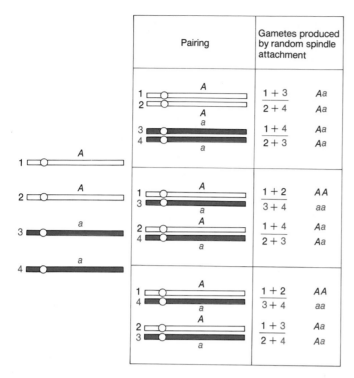

Figure 9-7. Genetic consequences in a tetraploid showing orderly pairing by bivalents. (Each chromosome is really two chromatids.) The locus is assumed to be close to the centromere. Self-fertilization could yield a variety of genotypes, including *aaaa*.

Allopolyploids

The "classical" allopolyploid was synthesized by G. Karpechenko in 1928. He wanted to make a fertile hybrid between the cabbage *(Brassica)* and the radish *(Raphanus)* that would have the leaves of the former and roots of the latter. Each of these species has 18 chromosomes, and they are related closely enough to allow intercrossing. A viable hybrid progeny individual was produced from seed. However, this hybrid was functionally sterile because the nine chromosomes from the cabbage parent were different enough from the radish chromosomes that homology was insufficient for normal synapsis and disjunction.

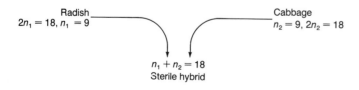

However, one day a few seeds were in fact produced by this (almost!) sterile hybrid. On planting, these seeds produced fertile individuals with 36 chromosomes. These individuals were allopolyploids. They had apparently been derived from spontaneous accidental chromosome doubling in the sterile hybrid, presumably in tissue that eventually became germinal and underwent meiosis. Thus, in $2n_1 + 2n_2$ tissue,

there is a pairing partner for each chromosome, and balanced gametes of the type $n_1 + n_2$ are produced. These fuse to give $2n_1 + 2n_2$ allopolyploid progeny, which are in turn fertile also. This kind of allopolyploid is sometimes called an **amphidiploid** (Figure 9-9). (Unfortunately for Karpechenko, his amphidiploid had the roots of a cabbage and the leaves of a radish.)

If the allopolyploid is crossed to either parent species, sterile offspring result. In the case of the cross to radish, these offspring would be $2n_1 + n_2$, constituted from an $n_1 + n_2$ gamete from the allopolyploid, and an n_1 gamete from the radish. Obviously, the n_2 chromosomes will have no pairing partners, so sterility will result. Consequently, Karpechenko had effectively created a new species, with no possibility of gene exchange with its parents. He called his new species *Raphanobrassica*.

Nowadays, allopolyploids are routinely synthesized as a major tool in plant breeding. The goal obviously is to combine some of the worthwhile features of both parental species into one type. This kind of endeavor is very uncertain, as Karpechenko found out. In fact, only one amphidiploid has ever been intentionally produced that is of potentially widespread use. This is *Triticale*, an amphidiploid between wheat *(Triticum, 2n = 6x = 42)* and rye *(Secale, 2n = 2x = 14)*. *Triticale* combines the high yields of wheat with the ruggedness of rye. A massive international *Triticale* testing program is now under way, and many breeders have great hopes for the future of this artificial amphidiploid. Figure 9-10 shows the procedure for synthesizing *Triticale*.

In nature, allopolyploidy seems to have been a major force in speciation of plants. There are many different examples. One particularly satisfying one is shown by the

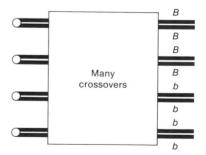

Figure 9-8. Highly diagrammatic representation of a tetraploid meiosis involving a heterozygous locus distant from the centromere. Although tetravalents may not form, the net effect of multiple crossovers in such a long region will be that the genes become effectively unhooked from their original centromeres. Genes are packaged two at a time into gametes, much as two balls may be grabbed at random from a bag containing eight balls, four of one kind and four of another.

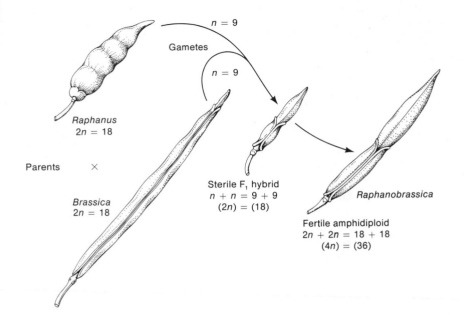

Figure 9-9. The origin of the amphidiploid (*Raphanobrassica*) formed from cabbage (*Brassica*) and radish (*Raphanus*). The production of the fertile amphidiploid in this case from the $2n = 18$ hybrid occurred in an accidental fashion, but one similar to the method of producing tetraploids by using colchicine. (From A. M. Srb, R. D. Owen, and R. S. Edgar, *General Genetics*, 2d ed. Copyright © 1965 by W. H. Freeman and Co. After Karpechenko, Z. *Indukt. Abst. Vererb.* 48:27, 1928.)

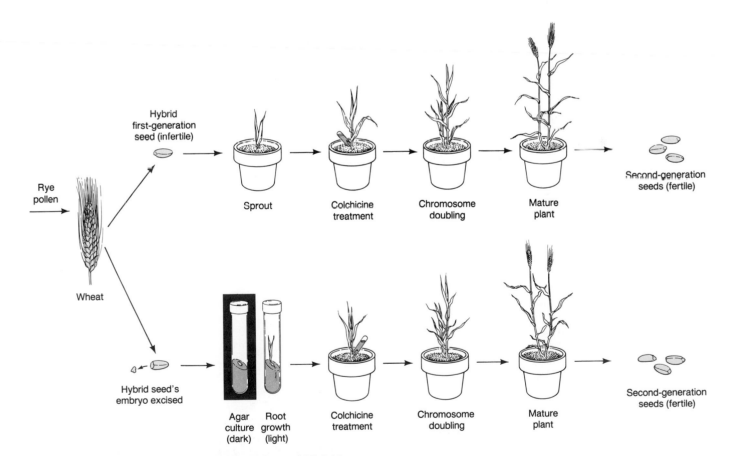

Figure 9-10. Techniques for the production of the amphidiploid *Triticale*. If the hybrid seed does not germinate, tissue culture (below) may be used to obtain a hybrid plant. (From Joseph H. Hulse and David Spurgeon, "Triticale." Copyright © 1974 by Scientific American, Inc. All rights reserved.)

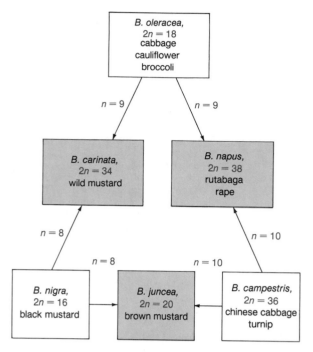

Figure 9-11. A species triangle, showing how amphidiploidy has been important in the production of new species of *Brassica*.

genus *Brassica,* as illustrated in Figure 9-11. Here three different parent species have been hybridized in all possible pair combinations to form new amphidiploid species. This has all taken place in nature, but *Brassica* amphidiploids also have been artificially synthesized (Figure 9-12).

A particularly interesting natural allopolyploid is bread wheat, *Triticum aestivum* ($2n = 6x = 42$). By a study of various wild relatives, it has been possible to reconstruct a probable evolutionary history of bread wheat (Figure 9-13). In a wheat meiosis, there are always 21 pairs of chromosomes. Furthermore, it has been possible to establish that any given chromosome has only one specific pairing partner (homologous pairing)—not five other potential ones (homeologous pairing). The suppression of such homeologous pairing (which would lead to much reduced stability of the species) is maintained by a gene *Ph* on the long arm of chromosome 5 of the B set. Thus, *Ph* ensures a diploid-like genetics for this basically hexaploid species. Without *Ph*, bread wheat could probably never have arisen. It is interesting to speculate on whether Western civilization could have arisen or progressed without this species— in other words, without *Ph*.

Somatic Allopolyploids from Cell Hybridization

Another innovative approach to plant breeding is to try to make allopolyploid-like hybrids by asexual methods. Theoretically, such a technique would permit combination of widely differing parental species. The technique does indeed work, but so far the only allopolyploids that have been produced are those that can also be made by the sexual methods we have considered already. The procedure is as follows. Cell suspensions of the two parental species are prepared and stripped of their cell walls by special enzyme

treatments. The stripped cells are called **protoplasts.** The two suspensions (protoplast suspensions) are combined with polyethylene glycol, which enhances protoplast fusion. The parental cells and the fused cells will proliferate to form colonies (in much the same way as microbes) on agar medium. If these colonies, or calluses, are examined, a fair percentage of them are found to be allopolyploid-like hybrids with chromosome number equal to the sum of the parental types. Thus, not only do the protoplast cell membranes fuse to form a kind of heterokaryon, but the nuclei fuse too.

A good example of an allopolyploid-like hybrid is com-

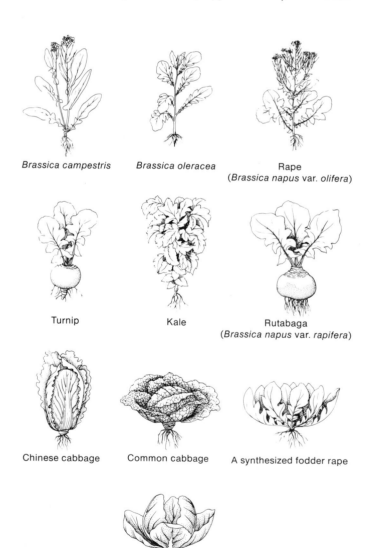

Figure 9-12. Some of the species from the species triangle of *Brassica* and two man-made *Brassica* amphidiploids. (Courtesy of H. Kihara, *Seiken Ziho* 20, 1968.)

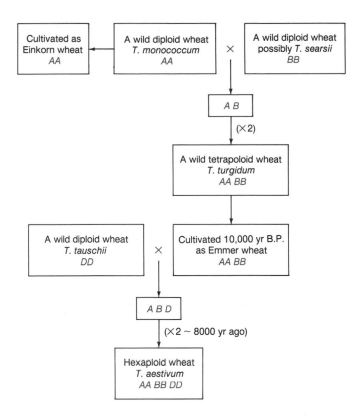

Figure 9-13. Diagram illustrating the proposed evolution of modern hexaploid wheat involving amphidiploid production at several points. *A, B,* and *D* are different chromosome sets.

mercial tobacco, *Nicotiana tabacum,* which has 48 chromosomes. This species of tobacco was originally found in nature as a spontaneously occurring amphidiploid. The two probable parents are *N. sylvestris* and *N. tomentosiformis,* each of which has 24 chromosomes. A sexual cross between *N. tabacum* and either of the other two gives a 36-chromosome hybrid in which there are 12 chromosome pairs plus 12 unpaired chromosomes. A cross between *N. sylvestris* and *N. tomentosiformis* gives a 24-chromosome hybrid in which there is no pairing at all. Hence, it appears that part of the *N. tabacum* genome is from *N. sylvestris* and part from *N. tomentosiformis.* This amphidiploid can be re-created either sexually, by processes involving colchicine as described previously, or somatically by cell fusion. When cells or the prospective parental species are fused, a 48-chromosome hybrid cell line is produced from which may be grown plants whose behavior is identical to that of *N. tabacum.* (Note that in the latter method, colchicine is not required, since the fusion product is already amphidiploid.)

The recovery of somatic hybrids may be enhanced if a selective system is available. For example, two different monoploid lines of *N. tabacum* had light-sensitive yellowish and light-sensitive whitish leaves, respectively. The hybrid calluses (diploid in this example) proved to be green and light-resistant, as a result of complementation between the parental genotypes. The calluses can be grown into plantlets, which then either are grafted onto a mature plant to develop or are themselves potted. The protocol for this experiment is illustrated in Figure 9-14.

Polyploidy in Animals

You will have noticed that all our examples of polyploidy have been from plants. Polyploid animals do exist, mainly in such lower organisms as flatworms, leeches, and brine shrimp. In some of these organisms, reproduction is **parthenogenetic** (not involving a normal meiotic sexual cycle). Progeny are produced essentially by mitotic division of parental cells. Parthenogenetic plants, such as dandelions, also are commonly polyploid. Furthermore, **endopolyploidy** (polyploidy of a somatic sector) also is common in plants, animals, and tumor cells. The reason for the rarity of polyploidy in higher animals is not known, but the most widely held hypothesis is that their complex sex-determining mechanisms depend on a delicate balance of chromosome numbers. In humans, polyploids always abort while still developing in the uterus.

Aneuploidy

Nullisomics (2n − 2)

Although nullisomy is a lethal condition in regular diploids, an organism like wheat (which "pretends" to be diploid but is fundamentally hexaploid) can tolerate nullisomy. In fact, all of the possible 21 wheat nullisomics have been produced; these are illustrated in Figure 9-15. Their appearances are different from normal wheat; furthermore, most of them show less vigorous growth.

Monosomics (2n − 1)

Monosomic chromosome complements are generally deleterious for two main reasons. First, the balance of chromosomes that is necessary for a finely tuned cellular homeostasis, carefully put together during evolution, is grossly disturbed. For example, if a genome consisting of two of each of chromosomes a, b, and c becomes monosomic for c (that is, 2a + 2b + 1c), the ratio of these chromosomes is changed from 1c : 1 (a + b) to 1c : 2 (a + b). Second, any deleterious recessive on the single remaining chromosome becomes hemizygous and may be directly expressed phenotypically. (Note that these are the same effects as those produced by deletions.)

Monosomics, trisomics (2n + 1), and other chromosome aneuploids are probably produced by nondisjunction during mitosis or meiosis. In meiosis it can happen at either the first or the second division (Figure 9-16). (You can ask yourself whether products of nondisjunction at these two times can be distinguished genetically.) If an n − 1 gamete is fertilized by an n gamete, a monosomic (2n − 1) zygote is produced; an n + 1 and an n gamete give a trisomic 2n + 1; and an n + 1 and an n + 1 give a tetrasomic if the same

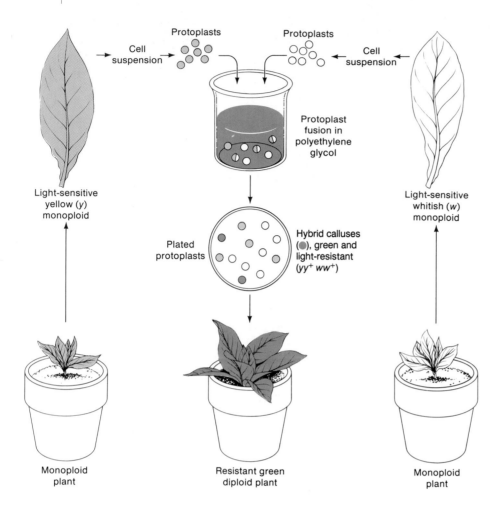

Figure 9-14. The use of cell hybridization in plant engineering of two strains of *Nicotiana tabacum*. One strain has light-sensitive yellowish leaves, and the other has light-sensitive whitish leaves. Protoplasts are produced by enzymatically stripping the cell walls from the leaf cells of each strain. Fusion of the protoplasts can occur, as indicated, and those that fuse as hybrids can be grown into calluses that are light resistant, as a result of recessiveness of the parental genotypes. The calluses, under the appropriate hormone regime, can be grown into green diploid plants.

chromosome is involved or a double trisomic if different chromosomes are involved, and so on.

In *Neurospora* (a haploid), the $n - 1$ meiotic products abort and do not darken like the normal ascospore; so M_I and M_{II} nondisjunctions are detected as asci with $4:4$ and $6:2$ ratios of normal to aborted spores. (Diagram the chromosome content of the various spores to convince yourself of the relation of the spore pattern to nondisjunction.) For loci on the aneuploid chromosomes, what ascus genotypes are produced?

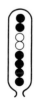 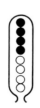

In humans, the sex-chromosome monosomic (44 autosomes + 1 X) produces a phenotype known as Turner's syndrome. Affected people have a characteristic, easily recognizable phenotype: they are sterile females, are short in stature, and often have a web of skin extending between the neck and shoulders. Their intelligence is near-normal, although some specific cognitive functions are defective. Their frequency is about 1 in 5000 female births. Monosomics for all autosomes die in utero.

If viable, nullisomics and monosomics are useful in locating newly found recessive genes on specific chromosomes in plants. In one such method, different monosomic lines lacking a different chromosome in each line are obtained. Homozygotes for the new gene are crossed with each monosomic line, and the progeny of each cross are inspected for expression of the recessive phenotype. The cross in which the phenotype appears identifies its chromosomal location. In nullisomics and monosomics, of course, $n - 1$ gametes are produced (see Figure 9-17 for monosomics). In general, these gametes tend to be more viable in a female parent than in a male. It is the union of these $n - 1$ gametes within n gametes, bearing the new mutation, that provides the crucial progeny types for the linkage test.

A similar approach can be used in humans. For example, two people whose vision is normal may produce a daughter who has Turner's syndrome and is also red-green color-blind. This shows that the allele for red-green color blindness is recessive, that it was on the X chromosome of the mother, and the nondisjunction must have occurred in the father. (Can you see why?)

Figure 9-15. The nullisomics of wheat. Although nullisomics are usually lethal in regular diploids, organisms like wheat, which "pretends" to be diploid but is fundamentally hexaploid, can tolerate nullisomy. Nullisomics, however, are less vigorous growers. (Courtesy of E. R. Sears.)

Trisomics $(2n + 1)$

In trisomics, trivalents are regularly seen (Figure 9-18; see also Figure 3-4, page 39). For genes that are tightly linked to the centromere of a trisomic chromosome set, the random segregations can be represented as shown in Figure 9-19 in a trisomic *Aaa*. All types occur equally frequently, and a gamete ratio of $1A:2Aa:2a:1aa$ is produced. Trisomics are sometimes recognized by these ratios, which are also useful in locating genes on chromosomes. We have already observed a complete set of trisomic lines in *Datura* (Figure 3-8). Once again, note that chromosome imbalance produces highly chromosome-specific deviations from the normal appearance.

In humans there are several examples of viable trisomics. The combination XXY (1/1000 male births) results in Klinefelter's syndrome, producing males that have lanky builds, are mentally retarded, and sterile. Another combination, XYY, also occurs in about 1 in 1000 male births. A lot of excitement was aroused when an attempt was made to link the XYY condition with a predisposition toward violence. This is still hotly debated, although it is now clear that an XYY condition in no way guarantees such behavior.

Nevertheless, several enterprising lawyers have attempted to use the XYY genotype as grounds for acquittal or compassion in crimes of violence. The XYY males are usually fertile.

We have already looked at the generation of Down's syndrome through adjacent segregation in translocation heterozygotes. Down's syndrome also occurs much more commonly as a result of nondisjunction during meiosis, and it is then called trisomy 21. In this form of Down's syndrome, there is generally no family history of the phenotype; however, the frequency of this form is dramatically higher among children born to older mothers (Figure 9-20). The overall incidence of this abnormality is about 0.15 percent of births.

Down's syndrome is a severely incapacitating condition. Affected individuals are mentally retarded, and about one-third die by the age of 10 years. Recent advances in mapping the human genome will allow the identification of precisely those genes on the long arm of chromosome 21 that must be trisomic to produce this syndrome; these advances offer some hope of a more precise understanding of its chemical nature and possible therapy. In humans, the only other two autosomal trisomics known to survive past

NONDISJUNCTION AT FIRST DIVISION

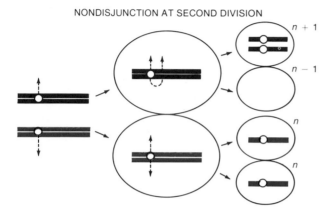

NONDISJUNCTION AT SECOND DIVISION

Figure 9-16. The origin of aneuploid gametes by nondisjunction at either the first or second meiotic division.

birth are individuals with trisomy 13 and trisomy 18. Affected children are even more severely handicapped, both mentally and physically, and rarely survive to 1 year of age.

Chromosome mutation in general plays a prominent role in determining genetic ill health in humans. Figure 9-21 summarizes the surprisingly high levels of various chromosomal abnormalities at different developmental

stages of the human organism. In fact, the incidence of chromosome mutations ranks close to that of gene mutations in human livebirths (Table 9-1). This is particularly surprising when we realize that virtually all chromosome mutations arise anew with each generation. This is in contrast to gene mutations, which (as we shall see in Chapter 23) owe their level of incidence to a complex interplay of mutation rates and environmental selection, acting over many generations of the history of the human species.

Somatic Aneuploids

Aneuploids can arise spontaneously in somatic tissue or tissue culture. In such cases, the initial result is a genetic mosaic of cell types. Good examples are provided by certain conditions in humans.

Sexual mosaics provide the first example. These are people whose bodies are a mixture of male and female tissue. One type of sexual mosaic is XO/XYY. This mosaic can be explained by postulating an XY zygote in which an early mitotic division involved a nondisjunction of the Y chromosomes, so that both went to one pole:

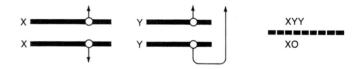

The phenotypic sex of such individuals depends upon where in the body the male and female sectors end up. In this case, if nondisjunction occurred at a later mitotic division, there would be a three-way mosaic XY/XO/XYY,

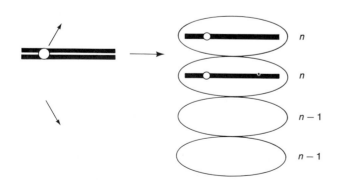

Figure 9-17. Behavior of a monosomic chromosome at meiosis. Two of the resulting haploid gametes will contain a normal set of chromosomes (n), while two will contain a set missing the monosomic chromosome of the parent ($n - 1$).

■ **TABLE 9-1.** Relative incidence of human ill health due to gene mutation and to chromosome mutation

Type of mutation	Percentage of live births
Gene mutation	
Autosomal dominant	0.90
Autosomal recessive	0.25
X-linked	0.05
Total gene mutation	1.20
Chromosome mutation	
Autosomal trisomies (mainly Down's syndrome)	0.14
Other unbalanced autosomal aberrations	0.06
Balanced autosomal aberrations	0.19
Sex chromosomes	
XYY, XXY, and other ♂♂	0.17
XO, XXX, and other ♀♀	0.05
Total chromosome mutation	0.61

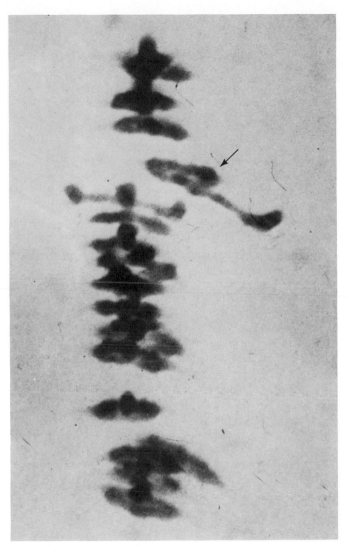

Figure 9-18. Chromosome pairing in a trisomic of wheat. The trivalent chromosome is shown by the arrow. (Courtesy of Clayton Person.)

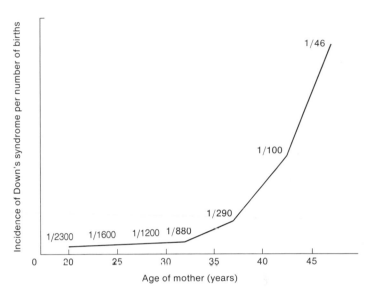

Figure 9-20. Maternal age and the production of Down's syndrome offspring. (From *Down's Anomaly* by L. S. Penrose and G. F. Smith. Little, Brown and Company, 1966.)

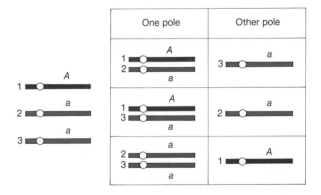

Figure 9-19. Genotypes of meiotic products of an *Aaa* trisomic. Three segregation patterns are equally likely.

which of course contains a clone of normal male cells as well. Other conditions of sexual mosaicism have different explanations; for example, XO/XX is probably due to chromosome loss in a female zygote, and XX/XY is probably the result of a double fertilization (fused twins).

Somatic aneuploidy and its resulting mosaics are often observed to occur in association with cancer. People suffering from chronic myeloid leukemia (CML), a cancer of the white blood cells, frequently contain cells with the so-called Philadelphia chromosome. This chromosome was once thought to represent an aneuploid condition, but it is now known to be a translocation product in which part of the long arm of chromosome 22 is attached to the long arm of chromosome 9. However, CML patients often show aneuploidy in addition to the Philadelphia chromosome. In one study of 67 people with CML, 33 proved to have an extra Philadelphia chromosome, and the rest had various aneuploidies; the most common aneuploidy was trisomy for the long arm of chromosome 17, which was detected in 28 people. Of 58 people with acute myeloid leukemia, 21 were shown to have aneuploidy for chromosome 8, 16 for chromosome 9, and 10 for chromosome 21. In another study of 15 patients with intestinal tumors, 12 had cells with abnormal chromosomes, usually at least some with trisomy for chromosome 8, 13, 15, 17, or 21. Of course, such studies merely establish correlations, and it is not clear whether the abnormalities are best thought of as cause or as effect of cancer.

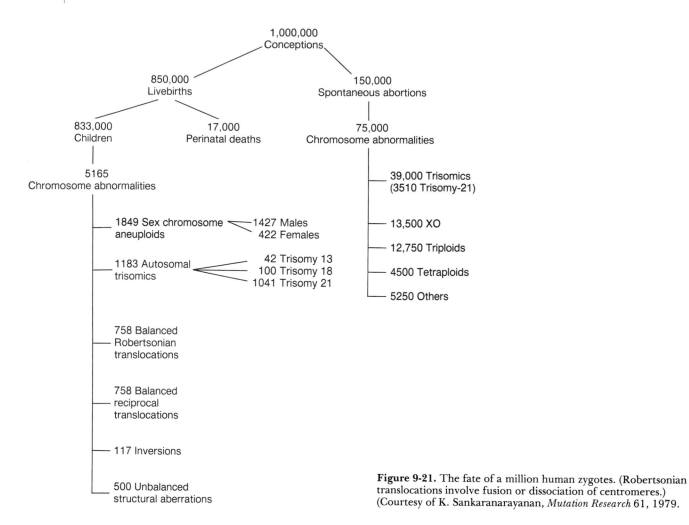

Figure 9-21. The fate of a million human zygotes. (Robertsonian translocations involve fusion or dissociation of centromeres.) (Courtesy of K. Sankaranarayanan, *Mutation Research* 61, 1979.

Figure 9-22. (a) Wheat. (b) *Aegilops umbellulata.* Both whole plants and seed heads are shown. (Courtesy of E. R. Sears.)

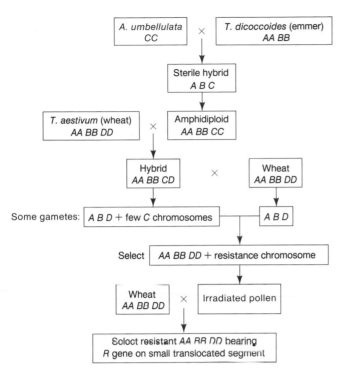

Figure 9-23. Summary of Sears' program for transferring rust resistance from *Aegilops* to wheat. *A, B, C,* and *D* represent chromosome sets of diverse origin. *R* represents the genetic determinant (single gene?) of resistance.

Chromosome Mechanics in Plant Breeding

Some of the material covered in this chapter may seem somewhat esoteric. The purpose of this section, then, is to provide convincing evidence that the details we have covered are of immense significance in the genetic engineering that is so necessary to produce and maintain new crop types in our hungry world. The sole experiment to be described, performed by E. R. Sears in the 1950s, concerns the transfer of a gene for leaf-rust resistance from a wild grass, *Aegilops umbellulata*, to bread wheat, which was highly susceptible to this disease. It is a classic experiment of its kind.

The first problem was that these two species (Figure 9-22) are not interfertile, so the feat of gene transfer seemed impossible. Sears sidestepped this problem with a **bridging cross,** in which *A. umbellulata* was crossed to a wild relative of bread wheat called emmer, *Triticum dicoc-*

coides. (Follow the process in Figure 9-23.) *A. umbellulata* is a diploid, $2n = 2x = 14$. We shall call its chromosome sets CC. *T. dicoccoides* is a tetraploid, $2n = 4x = 28$, with sets AABB. From this cross, the resulting sterile hybrid ABC was doubled into a fertile amphidiploid AABBCC with 42 chromosomes. This amphidiploid was fertile in crosses with wheat, which is represented as $2n = 6x = 42$, AABBDD. The offspring were, of course, AABBCD, and they were almost completely sterile because of pairing irregularities between the C and D sets. But crosses to wheat did produce a few rare seeds, some of which grew into resistant plants. Some of these were almost the desired types, having 43 chromosomes (42 of which were wheat, plus the one *Aegilops* chromosome bearing the resistance gene). Thus, in the AABBCD hybrid, some aberrant form of chromosome assortment had produced a gamete with 22 chromosomes: ABD plus one from the C group.

Unfortunately, the extra chromosome carried just too many undesirable *Aegilops* genes along with the good one, and the plants were weedy and low producers. So the *Aegilops* gene linkage had to be broken. Sears accomplished this by irradiating pollen of these plants and using it to pollinate wheat. He was looking for translocations of parts of the *Aegilops* chromosome tacked onto the wheat chromosomes. These were quite common, but only one turned out to be ideal. This was a very small *insertional* unidirection translocation (Figure 9-24). When bred to homozygosity, the resistant plants were indistinguishable from wheat.

Summary

■ Changes in chromosome number can involve whole sets, resulting in abnormal euploidy, or parts of chromosome sets, resulting in aneuploidy.

The most common abnormal euploids are polyploids —for example, triploids ($3x$) and tetraploids ($4x$). Odd numbers of sets lead to sterility because of unpaired chromosomes at meiosis, whereas even numbers of sets can produce standard (although abnormal) segregation ratios. Allopolyploids (polyploids formed by combining sets from different species) can be made by crossing and doubling progeny chromosomes with colchicine, or through somatic cell fusion. These techniques have important applications in crop breeding, since allopolyploids are effectively new species. Polyploidy can result in an organism of larger dimensions and this discovery has permitted important advances in horticulture and in crop breeding.

Aneuploids have also been important in the engineering of specific crop genotypes, although aneuploidy per se usually results in an unbalanced genotype with an abnormal phenotype. Examples of aneuploids are $2n - 1$ (monosomic) and $2n + 1$ (trisomic). Aneuploid conditions are well studied in humans—for example, Down's syndrome (tri-

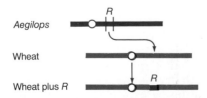

Figure 9-24. Translocation of *Aegilops R* segment to wheat using radiation as a means of breaking the chromosomes.

somy 21), Klinefelter's syndrome (XXY), and Turner's syndrome (XO). In fact, the spontaneous level of aneuploidy in humans is quite high; this is responsible for a major portion of genetically based ill health in human populations. Aneuploidy is believed to result in large part from chromosomal nondisjunction.

Problems

1. a. How would you synthesize a pentaploid (5x)?
    b. How would you synthesize a triploid of genotype Aaa?
    c. You have just obtained a rare recessive mutation a* in a diploid plant, which Mendelian analysis tells you is Aa*. From this plant, how would you synthesize a tetraploid of genotype AAa*a*?
    d. How would you synthesize a tetraploid of the type Aaaa?
    e. How would you synthesize a plant that is resistant to a chemical herbicide? (Assume that mutation to this trait is very infrequent.)

2. In corn, the part we eat (the kernel) is predominantly triploid tissue called endosperm. It is formed as follows. The haploid egg-cell nucleus divides to produce several identical nuclei, one of which acts as the gametic nucleus and two of which act as so-called polar nuclei. The pollen-cell nucleus also divides to form several identical haploid nuclei, one of which fuses with the gametic nucleus to produce the embryo, and one of which fuses with the two polar nuclei to form the endosperm. What are the constitutions of the endosperm types in the cross $Aa\,Bb\,♀ \times Aa\,Bb\,♂$? (Assume independent assortment.)

3. Allopolyploids are: a. not fertile at all; b. fertile only amongst themselves; c. fertile with one parent only; d. fertile with both parents only; e. fertile with both parents and themselves.

4. Tetraploid yeast can be created by fusing two diploid cells. These tetraploids will undergo meiosis like any other tetraploid and will produce four diploid products of meiosis. Assuming that homologous chromosomes synapse randomly in pairs and that there is no crossing-over in the gene–centromere interval, what nonlinear tetrads would be produced by a tetraploid of genotype BBbb? What would be the frequencies of the ascus types? (NOTE: this question involves tetrad analysis of tetraploid cells instead of the usual diploid cells.)

5. In a tetraploid AAaa, there is no pairing between chromosomes from the same parent. What phenotypic ratio will result from selfing? In another tetraploid BBbb, the only kind of pairing is between chromosomes from the same parent. What phenotypic ratio will result from selfing? (Assume that one parent carried the dominant allele and the other carried the recessive allele in each case.)

6. The New World cotton species *Gossypium hirsutum* has a 2n chromosome number of 52. The Old World species *G. thurberi* and *G. herbaceum* each have a 2n number of 26. Hybrids between these species show the following chromosome pairing arrangements at meiosis:

Hybrid	
G. hirsutum × *G. thurberi*	13 small pairs (bivalents) + 13 large univalents
G. hirsutum × *G. herbaceum*	13 large bivalents + 13 small univalents
G. thurberi × *G. herbaceum*	13 large univalents + 13 small univalents

Draw diagrams to interpret these observations phylogenetically, indicating clearly the relationships between the species. How would you go about proving that your interpretation is correct?

(Problem 6 is from A. M. Srb, R. D. Owen, and R. S. Edgar, *General Genetics*, 2d ed. Copyright © 1965 by W. H. Freeman and Co.)

7. An autotetraploid is heterozygous for two gene loci, FFff and GGgg, each locus affecting a different character and located on a different set of homologous chromosomes very close to their respective centromeres.

    a. What gametic genotypes will be produced by this individual, and in what proportions?

    b. If the individual is self-fertilized, what proportion of the progeny will have the genotype FFFf GGgg? the genotype ffff gggg?

8. Which of the following is *not* caused by meiotic nondisjunction? a. Turner's syndrome b. Down's syndrome c. Klinefelter's syndrome d. XYY syndrome e. Achondroplastic dwarfism

9. A patient with Turner's syndrome is found to be colorblind. Both her mother and father have normal vision. How can this be explained? Does this tell us whether nondisjunction occurred in the father or in the mother? If the color-blindness gene were close to the

centromere (it is not, in fact), would the clinical data tell us whether the nondisjunction occurred at the first or at the second meiotic division? Repeat the question, this time using a color-blind patient with Klinefelter's syndrome.

10. Individuals have been found who are color-blind in one eye but not in the other. What would this suggest if: a. these individuals were only or mostly females? b. they were only or mostly males? (Assume that this is an X-linked recessive trait.)

11. Down's syndrome men and women are able to mate with each other and have offspring, although this is rare. What chromosomal constitutions might be expected in the zygotes of such matings, and what would become of these zygotes?

12. When human sperms are treated with quinacrine dihydrochloride, about one-half of the sperms show a fluorescent spot thought to be the Y chromosome. About 1.2 percent of sperms, however, show two fluorescent spots. Some industrial workmen were exposed over about one year to the chemical dibromochloropropane. Their sperms were examined, and the frequency of sperms with two spots was found to be on average 3.8 percent. Propose an explanation of these results, and explain how you would test it.

13. People with Down's syndrome have about a 15-fold higher risk of leukemia. In the progression of the disease leukemia, complex chromosome aneuploidies usually are seen in the cancer cells. Discuss the possible relationship between these two statements.

14. In humans, the only autosomal trisomics that survive until birth are those for chromosome 13, 18, or 21. All three types are severely deformed. If you were a medical geneticist, how would you go about studying aneuploidy for the other chromosomes? Do you think aneuploids for the other chromosomes never occur, or are they very rare?

15. In British Columbia, between 1952 and 1972 the mean age of mothers of Down's syndrome babies fell from 34 years to 28 years. What are some possible causes of this population trend, and how could the related hypotheses be tested?

16. Several kinds of sexual mosaics are well documented in humans, some examples of which are given below. Suggest how each may have arisen.

   a. XX/XO (that is, there are two cell types in the body, XX and XO)

   b. XX/XXYY

   c. XO/XXX

   d. XX/XY

   e. XO/XX/XXX

17. The discovery of chromosome banding in eukaryotes has greatly improved our ability to distinguish various cytogenetic events. Particularly useful are banding polymorphisms, because the "morphs" can be used as chromosome markers. Consider chromosome 21 of humans. Assume that in one marriage the parents are $21^a 21^b$ ♀ × $21^c 21^d$ ♂, where a, b, c, and d stand for morphs of a polymorphism for this chromosome. (These morphs are forms of chromosome 21 that are cytologically distinguishable by virtue of minor variation in band size, position, and so forth.) Also assume that fetuses of the following types, where 42A stands for the rest of the autosomes, are produced:

   1. $42A + 21^b 21^b 21^c + XY$

   2. $42A + 21^a 21^b 21^d + XX$

   3. $42A + 21^b 21^d \quad + XY$

   4. $42A + 21^a 21^c 21^c + XX$

   5. $42A + 21^a 21^b \quad + XY$

   6. $42A + 21^a 21^c \quad + XYY$

   7. $(42A + 21^a + XY)(42A + 21^a 21^b 21^b + XY)$ (mosaic)

   8. $(42A + 21^a 21^c + XY)(42A + 21^b 21^d + XX)$ (mosaic)

In each case,

   a. State the genetic term for the condition.

   b. Describe with diagrams the events that gave rise to the condition.

   c. State in which individual the event(s) took place.

18. In tomatoes an attempt was made to assign five recessive genes to specific chromosomes using trisomics. Each homozygous mutant ($2n$) was crossed to three trisomics, involving chromosomes 1, 7, and 10. From these crosses, trisomic progeny (less vigorous) were selected. These trisomic progeny were backcrossed to the appropriate homozygous recessive, and *diploid* progeny from these crosses were examined. The results were as follows, where the ratios are of wild-type : mutant.

Trisomic chromosome	Gene				
	d	y	c	h	cot
1	48:55	72:29	56:50	53:54	32:28
7	52:56	52:48	52:51	58:56	81:40
10	45:42	36:33	28:32	96:50	20:17

Which of the genes can be assigned, and to which chromosomes? (Explain your answer fully.)

19. In a *Petunia* plant, the genes *A*, *B*, *C*, and *D* are very closely linked. A plant of genotype $a B c D/A b C d$ is irradiated with gamma rays and is then crossed to *aa bb cc dd*. In the progeny, plants of phenotype $A - B - C - D -$ are not rare. What are two possible modes of origin, and which is the more likely?

20. In *Neurospora*, a cross between the multiply marked chromosomes $a+c+e$ and $+b+d+$ gave one product of meiosis that grew on minimal medium (assume *a*, *b*, *c*, *d*, and *e* are nutritional markers). The rare colony was grown up, and some *asexual* spores were $a+c+e$ in genotype, some were $+b+d+$, and the rest grew on minimal medium. Explain the origin of the rare product of meiosis.

21. In *Sordaria brevicollis* (an ascomycete), the mutations b_1 and b_2 are closely linked complementing markers that result in buff-colored (light brown) ascospores. In the cross $b_1 \times b_2$, if one or both centromeres divide and separate precociously at the first division of meiosis, what patterns of spore colors would be produced in those asci? How could these asci be distinguished from normal asci and those in which nondisjunction had occurred? (NOTE: ascospores in this fungus are normally black; hypoploid ascospores are white; assume no crossing-over between b_1 and b_2.)

22. H. Sharat Chandra recovered triploids of mealybugs, *Planococcus* ($x = 5$). He found that, in the gonads, at the end of meiosis I all cells had 15 chromosomes, and at the end of meiosis II cells had variable numbers of chromosomes ranging from 0 to 15. How do you interpret these results?

23. In yeast, a diploid was made of genotype

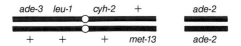

where all mutant alleles are recessive. On supplemented medium, the colonies are red (due to an accumulation of red pigment at the block caused by *ade-2* in adenine synthesis). However, a few colonies are one-half red and one-half white. (White is the normal yeast color.) These white sectors are also leucine-requiring and cycloheximide-resistant (*cyh* is the resistant allele). The red sectors did not require methionine.

a. Given that *ade-3* is an earlier adenine block than *ade-2*, what mechanism may have given rise to the sectored colonies?

b. How would you test the hypothesis?

24. An *Aspergillus* diploid is

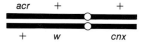

The diploid is green but produces rare white diploid sectors of three different genotypes:

(A) $\dfrac{acr \quad w \quad +}{+ \quad w \quad cnx}$ (B) $\dfrac{+ \quad w \quad +}{+ \quad w \quad cnx}$ (C) $\dfrac{+ \quad w \quad cnx}{+ \quad w \quad cnx}$

Which of these genotypes is most probably due to: a. mitotic crossing-over; b. mutation; c. mitotic nondisjunction? Explain.

25. Design a test system for detecting agents in the human environment that are potentially capable of causing aneuploidy in eukaryotes.

CHAPTER 10

DNA Structure

■ The elucidation of the structure of DNA by James Watson and Francis Crick was one of the most exciting discoveries in the history of genetics, since it paved the way for the understanding of gene action and heredity in molecular terms. Before we see how the analysis of DNA structure was carried out, let us review what was known about genes and DNA at the time that Watson and Crick began their historic collaboration.

1. Genes—the hereditary "factors" described by Mendel—were known to be associated with specific character traits, but their physical nature was not understood.

2. Genes were known to be carried on chromosomes.

3. The one-gene–one-enzyme theory (described more fully in Chapter 11) postulated that genes control the structure of proteins.

DNA: The Genetic Material

What was known about the molecular structure of the gene? Important observations and experiments led to the idea that deoxyribonucleic acid (DNA) is the primary genetic material.

1. The chromosomes, on which genes are located, were found to consist of DNA and protein.

2. Research by Frederick Griffith and subsequently by Oswald Avery and coworkers pointed to DNA as the genetic material. Their experiments showed that bacterial cells expressing one phenotype can be transformed into cells with a different phenotype, and that the transforming agent is DNA.

The Discovery of Transformation

A puzzling observation was made by Frederick Griffith in the course of experiments on the bacterium *Streptococcus pneumoniae* in 1928. This bacterium, which causes pneumonia in humans, is normally lethal in mice. However, different strains of this bacterial species have evolved that differ in virulence—in ability to cause disease or death. In his experiments, Griffith used two strains that are distinguishable by the appearance of colonies grown in laboratory culture. In one strain, a normal virulent type, the cells are enclosed in a polysaccharide capsule, giving colonies a smooth appearance; hence this strain is labeled S. In Griffith's other strain, a mutant nonvirulent type (that is, it grows in mice but is not lethal), the polysaccharide coat is absent, giving colonies a rough appearance; this strain is called R.

Griffith killed some virulent cells by boiling them and injected the heat-killed cells into mice. The mice survived, showing that the carcasses of the cells do not cause death. However, mice injected with a mixture of heat-killed virulent cells and live nonvirulent cells died. Furthermore, live cells could be recovered from the dead mice; these cells gave smooth colonies and were virulent upon subsequent injection. Somehow, the cell debris of the boiled S cells had converted the live R cells into live S cells. The process was called **transformation.** Griffith's experiment is summarized in Figure 10-1.

This same basic technique was also utilized to determine the nature of the **"transforming principle,"** the agent in the cell debris that is specifically responsible for transformation. In 1944, Oswald Avery, C. M. MacLeod, and M. McCarty separated the classes of molecules found in the debris of the dead S cells and tested them for transforming ability, one at a time. They showed first that the polysaccharides themselves do not transform the rough cells. Therefore, the polysaccharide coat, although no doubt concerned with the pathogenic reaction, is only the phenotypic expression of virulence. In screening the different groups, Avery and his colleagues found that only one class of molecules, DNA, induces transformation of R cells (Figure 10-2). They deduced that DNA is the agent that determines the polysaccharide character and hence the

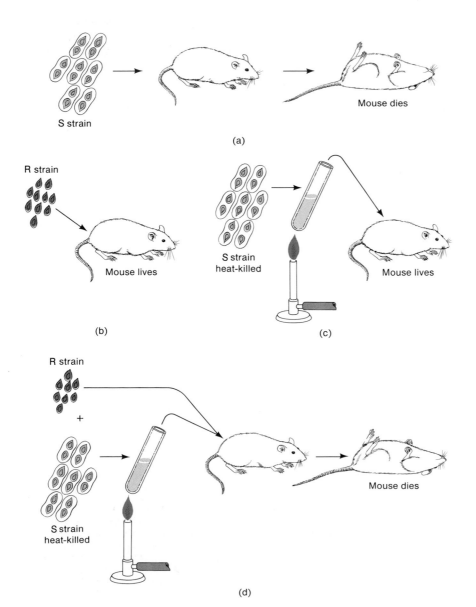

S strain

(a)

R strain

Mouse lives

S strain
heat-killed

Mouse lives

(b)

(c)

Mouse dies

R strain

+

S strain
heat-killed

Mouse dies

(d)

Figure 10-1. The first demonstration of bacterial transformation. (a) Mice die after injection with the virulent S strain. (b) Mice survive after injection with the R strain. (c) Mice survive after injection with heat-killed S strain. (d) Mice die after injection with a mixture of heat-killed S strain and live R strain. The heat-killed S strain somehow transforms the strain R to virulence. Parts a, b, and c act as control experiments for this demonstration. (From G. S. Stent and R. Calendar, *Molecular Genetics*, 2d ed. Copyright 1978 by W. H. Freeman and Co. After R. Sager and F. J. Ryan, *Cell Heredity*, Wiley, 1961.)

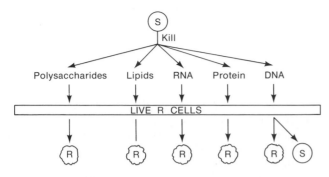

Figure 10-2. Demonstration that DNA is the transforming agent. DNA is the only agent that produces smooth (S) colonies when added to live R cells.

pathogenic character. Furthermore, it seems that providing R cells with S DNA is tantamount to providing these cells with S genes!

Message The demonstration that DNA is the transforming principle was the first demonstration that genes are composed of DNA.

The Hershey-Chase Experiment

Avery's experiments were definitive, but many scientists were very reluctant to accept DNA (rather than proteins) as the genetic material. The clincher was provided in 1952 by Alfred Hershey and Martha Chase using the phage (virus) T2. Phage infection obviously must involve the introduction into the bacterium of the specific information that dictates viral reproduction. The phage is relatively simple in molecular constitution. Most of its structure is protein, with

DNA contained inside the protein sheath of its "head."

Phosphorus is not found in proteins but is an integral part of DNA; conversely, sulfur is present in proteins but never in DNA. Hershey and Chase incorporated the radioisotope of phosphorus (^{32}P) into phage DNA, and that of sulfur (^{35}S) into the proteins of a separate phage culture. They then used each phage culture independently to infect *Escherichia coli* with many virus particles per cell. After sufficient time for injection to occur, they sheared the empty phage carcasses—called "ghosts"—off the bacterial cells by agitation in a kitchen blender. They used centrifugation to separate the bacterial cells from the phage ghosts and then measured the radioactivity in the two fractions. When the ^{32}P-labeled phages were used, most of the radioactivity ended up inside the bacterial cells, indicating that the phage DNA entered the cells. ^{32}P can also be recovered from phage progeny. When the ^{35}S labeled phages were used, most of the radioactive material ended up in the phage ghosts, indicating that the phage protein never enters the bacterial cell (Figure 10-3). The conclusion is inescapable: DNA is the hereditary material, and the phage proteins are mere structural packaging that is discarded after delivering the vital DNA to the bacterial cell.

Why such reluctance to accept this conclusion? DNA was thought to be a rather simple chemical. How could all the information about the wondrously variable protein structures (with their sequences of the 20 amino acids) be stored in such a simple molecule? How could such information be passed on, from one generation to the next? Clearly, the genetic material must have both the ability to encode specific information and the capacity for precise duplica-

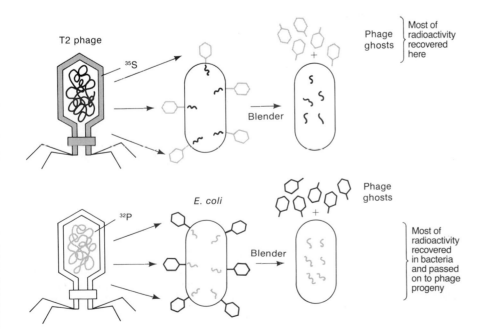

Figure 10-3. The Hershey-Chase experiment, which demonstrated that the genetic material of phage is DNA, not protein. The experiment uses two sets of T2 bacteriophage. In one set, the protein coat is labeled with radioactive sulfur (^{35}S) not found in DNA. In the other set, the DNA is labeled with radioactive phosphorus (^{32}P) not found in protein. Only the ^{32}P is injected into the *E. coli*, indicating that DNA is the agent necessary for the production of new phage.

tion of that information. What kind of structure could allow such complex functions in so simple a molecule?

The Structure of DNA

Although the DNA structure was not known, the basic building blocks of DNA had been known for many years. The basic elements of DNA had been isolated and determined by partly breaking up purified DNA. These studies showed that DNA is composed of only four basic molecules called **nucleotides,** which are identical except that each contains a different nitrogen base. Each nucleotide contains phosphate, sugar (of the deoxyribose type), and one

of the four bases (Figure 10-4). In the absence of the phosphate group, the base and the deoxyribose form a **nucleoside** rather than a nucleotide. The four bases are **adenine** (A), **guanine** (G), **cytosine** (C), and **thymine** (T). The full chemical names of the nucleotides are deoxyadenosine 5′-monophosphate (or deoxyadenylate, or dAMP), deoxyguanosine 5′-monophosphate (or deoxyguanylate, or dGMP), deoxycytidine 5′-monophosphate (or deoxycytidylate, or dCMP), and deoxythymidine 5′-monophosphate (or deoxythymidylate, or dTMP). However, it is more convenient just to refer to each nucleotide by the abbreviation of its base. Two of the bases, adenine and guanine, are similar in structure and are called **purines.** The other two bases, cytosine and thymine, also are similar and are called **pyrimidines.**

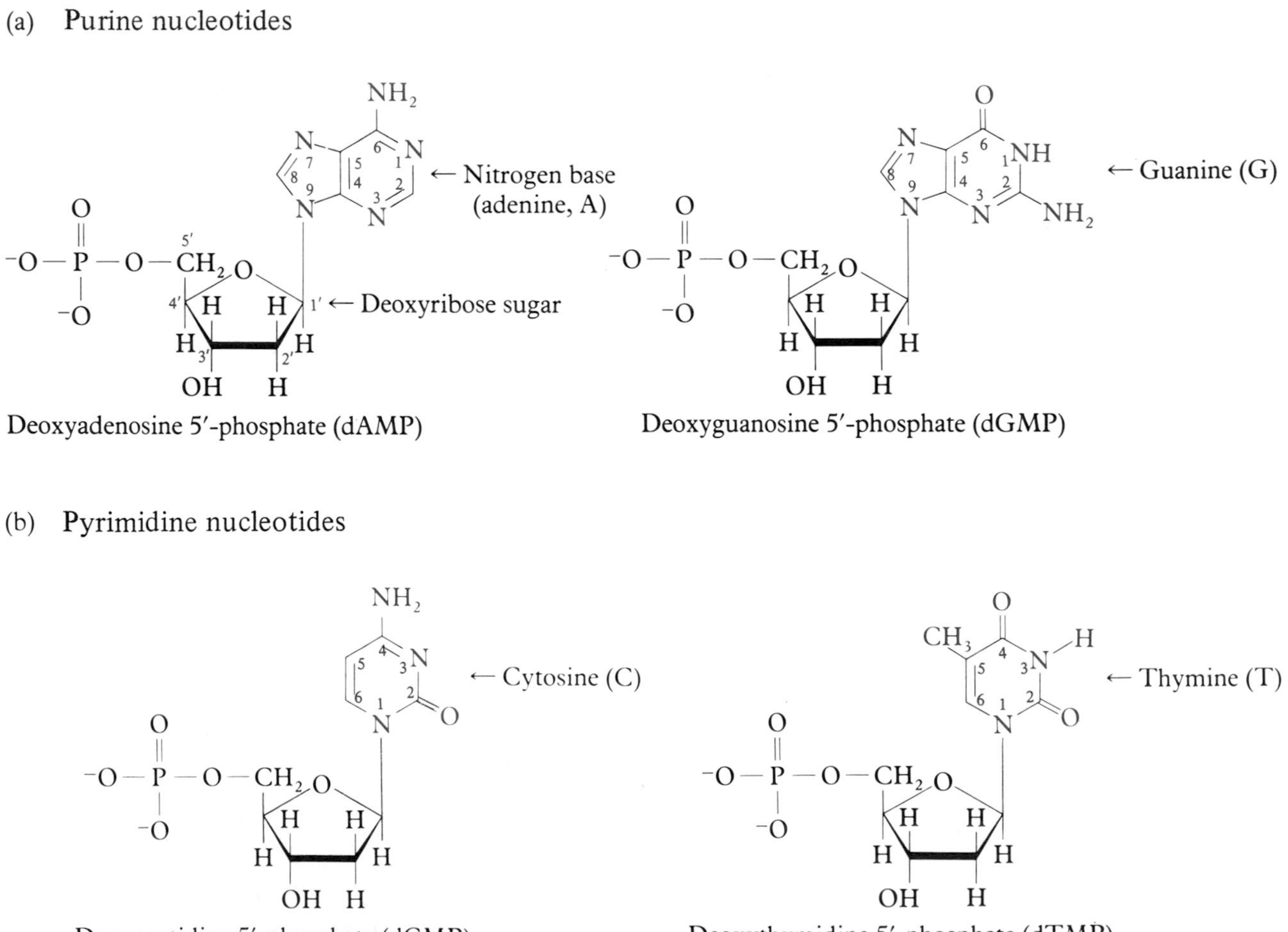

(a)   Purine nucleotides

Deoxyadenosine 5′-phosphate (dAMP)   Deoxyguanosine 5′-phosphate (dGMP)

(b)   Pyrimidine nucleotides

Deoxycytidine 5′-phosphate (dCMP)   Deoxythymidine 5′-phosphate (dTMP)

Figure 10-4. Chemical structure of the four nucleotides (two with purine bases and two with pyrimidine bases) that are the fundamental building blocks of DNA. The sugar is called deoxyribose because it is a variation of a common sugar, ribose, that has one more oxygen atom.

■ **TABLE 10-1.** Molar properties of bases (as moles of nitrogenous constituents per 100 g-atoms phosphate in hydrolysate) in DNAs from various sources

Organism	Tissue	Adenine	Thymine	Guanine	Cytosine	$\dfrac{A + T}{G + C}$
Escherichia coli (K12)	–	26.0	23.9	24.9	25.2	1.00
Diplococcus pneumoniae	–	29.8	31.6	20.5	18.0	1.59
Mycobacterium tuberculosis	–	15.1	14.6	34.9	35.4	0.42
Yeast	–	31.3	32.9	18.7	17.1	1.79
Paracentrotus lividus (sea urchin)	Sperm	32.8	32.1	17.7	18.4	1.85
Herring	Sperm	27.8	27.5	22.2	22.6	1.23
Rat	Bone marrow	28.6	28.4	21.4	21.5	1.33
Human	Thymus	30.9	29.4	19.9	19.8	1.52
Human	Liver	30.3	30.3	19.5	19.9	1.53
Human	Sperm	30.7	31.2	19.3	18.8	1.62

SOURCE: E. Chargaff and J. Davidson, eds., *The Nucleic Acids,* Academic Press, 1955.

After the central role of DNA in heredity became clear, many scientists set out to determine the exact structure of DNA. How can a molecule with such a limited range of different components possibly store the vast range of information about all the protein primary structures of the living organism? The first to succeed in finding a reasonable DNA structure were James Watson and Francis Crick in 1953. They worked from two kinds of clues. First, other researchers had amassed a lot of X-ray diffraction data on DNA structure. In such experiments, X rays are fired at DNA fibers, and the scatter of the rays from the fiber is observed by catching them on photographic film, where the X rays produce spots. The angle of scatter represented by each spot on the film gives information about the position of an atom or certain groups of atoms in the DNA molecule. This procedure is not simple to carry out (or to explain), and the interpretation of the spot patterns is very difficult. The available data suggested that DNA is long and skinny and that it has two similar parts that are parallel to one another and run along the length of the molecule. The X-ray data showed the molecule to be helical. Other regularities were present in the spot patterns, but no one had yet thought of a three-dimensional structure that could account for just those spot patterns.

The second set of clues available to Watson and Crick came from work done several years earlier by Erwin Chargaff. Studying a large selection of DNAs from different organisms (see Table 10-1), Chargaff found certain empirical rules about the amounts of each component of DNA.

1. The total amount of pyrimidine nucleotides (T + C) always equals the total amount of purine nucleotides (A + G).

2. The amount of T always equals the amount of A, and C always equals G. But the amount of A + T is not necessarily equal to the amount of G + C, as can be seen in the last column of Table 10-1. This latter ratio varies with the organism.

The structure that Watson and Crick derived from these clues is a double helix, looking rather like two interlocked bedsprings. Each bedspring (helix) is a chain of nucleotides held together by **phosphodiester bonds,** in which a phosphate group forms a bridge between —OH groups on two adjacent sugar residues. The two bedsprings (helices) are held together by **hydrogen bonds,** in which two electronegative atoms "share" a proton, between the bases. Figure 10-5 shows a part of this structure with the helices uncoiled. Figure 10-6 shows a simplified picture of the coiling, with each of the base pairs represented by a "stick" between the "ribbons" that represent the so-called "sugar-phosphate backbones" of the chains. In Figure 10-5, note that the two backbones run in opposite directions; they are said to be **antiparallel,** and (for reasons apparent in the figure) one is called $5' \rightarrow 3'$ and the other $3' \rightarrow 5'$.

In three dimensions, the bases actually form rather flat structures (more like steps in a ladder than like the sticks shown in Figure 10-6), and these flat bases stack on top of one another in the twisted structure of the double helix. This stacking of bases adds tremendously to the stability of the molecule by excluding water molecules from the spaces between the base pairs. (This phenomenon is very much like the stabilizing force that you can feel when you squeeze two plates of glass together underwater and then try to separate them.) Subsequently, it was realized that there were two forms of DNA in the fiber analyzed by diffraction. The *A* form is less hydrated than the *B* form. Figure 10-7 shows both the *A* and *B* forms in a schematic three-dimensional drawing. Note the stacking of bases as represented in this diagram. It is believed that the *B* form of DNA is the form found most frequently in living cells.

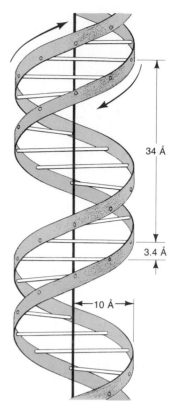

Figure 10-6. A simplified model showing the helical structure of DNA. The sticks represent base pairs, and the ribbons represent the sugar-phosphate backbones of the two antiparallel chains. In fact, the base pairs are more like flat "steps" than the round sticks shown here.

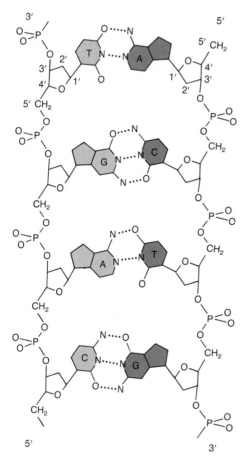

Figure 10-5. The DNA double helix, unrolled to show the sugar-phosphate backbones and base-pair rungs. The backbones run in opposite directions, and 5′ and 3′ ends are named for the orientation of the 5′ and 3′ carbon atoms of the sugar rings. Each base pair has one purine base, adenine (A) or guanine (G), and one pyrimidine base, thymine (T) or cytosine (C), connected by hydrogen bonds (*dotted lines*). (Figures 10-5, 10-7, 10-11, 10-12, and 10-13 from R. E. Dickerson, "The DNA Helix and How It Is Read." Copyright © 1983 by Scientific American, Inc. All rights reserved.)

The double helix accounted nicely for the X-ray data, and it also tied in very nicely with Chargaff's data. Studying models they made of the structure, Watson and Crick realized that the observed radius of the double helix (known from the X-ray data) would be explained if a purine base always pairs (by hydrogen bonding) with a pyrimidine base (Figure 10-8). Such pairing would account for the (A + G) = (T + C) regularity observed by Chargaff, but it would predict four possible pairings: T · · · A, T · · · G, C · · · A, and C · · · G. Chargaff's data, however, indicate that T pairs only with A and C pairs only with G.

Watson and Crick showed that only these two pairings have the necessary complementary "lock-and-key" shapes to permit efficient hydrogen bonding. Hydrogen bonds occur between hydrogen atoms with a small positive charge and acceptor atoms with a small negative charge. For example,

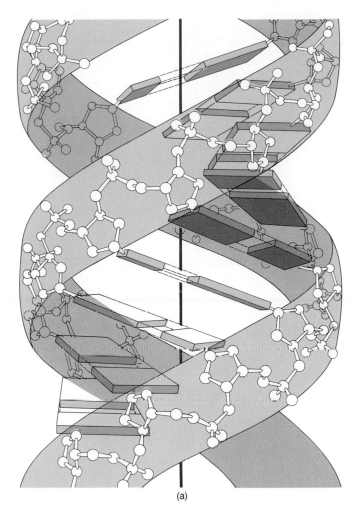

(a)

(b)

Figure 10-7. Schematic drawings of the structures of two forms of DNA. (a) *A* DNA. (b) *B* DNA. Analyses of DNA fibers by Struther Arnott and others provided the conceptual basis for these drawings. The sugar-phosphate backbones of the double helix are represented as ribbons and the runglike base pairs connecting them as planks. In *A* DNA the base pairs are tilted and are pulled away from the axis of the double helix. In *B* DNA, on the other hand, the base pairs sit astride the helix axis and are perpendicular to it.

Each hydrogen atom in the NH$_2$ group is slightly positive (δ^+) because the nitrogen atom tends to "hog" the electrons involved in the N—H bond, thereby leaving the hydrogen atom slightly short of electrons. The oxygen atom has six unbonded electrons in its outer shell, which form an electron cloud around it, making it slightly negative (δ^-). A hydrogen bond forms between one H and the O. Hydrogen bonds are quite weak (only about 3 percent of the strength of a covalent chemical bond), but this weakness (as we shall see) plays an important role in the hereditary function of the DNA molecule. One further important chemical fact: the hydrogen bond is much stronger if the participating atoms are "pointing at each other" in the ideal orientations.

Looking at the hydrogen-bonding potential between the various purine–pyrimidine pairs, we find that only two pairs have the necessary arrangement of δ^+ hydrogen atoms and δ^- acceptor atoms. These two are the T – A pair and the C – G pair, both of which show beautiful lock-and-key fit (Figure 10-9), providing just the proper "width" of

the base pair to explain the known radius of the DNA double helix.

Note that the C – G pair has three hydrogen bonds, whereas the T – A pair has only two. One would predict

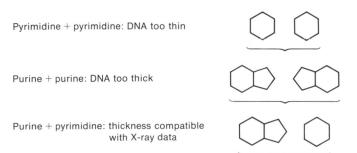

Pyrimidine + pyrimidine: DNA too thin

Purine + purine: DNA too thick

Purine + pyrimidine: thickness compatible with X-ray data

Figure 10-8. The pairing of purines with pyrimidines accounts exactly for the diameter of the DNA double helix as determined from X-ray data.

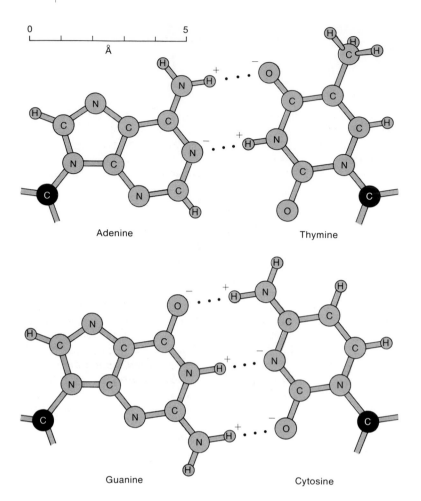

0   5
Å

Adenine   Thymine

Guanine   Cytosine

Figure 10-9. The lock-and-key hydrogen bonding between A and T and between G and C. (From G. S. Stent, *Molecular Biology of Bacterial Viruses.* Copyright © 1963 by W. H. Freeman and Co.)

that DNA containing many G–C pairs would be more stable than DNA containing many A–T pairs. In fact, this prediction is confirmed. We now have a neat explanation for the data of Chargaff in terms of DNA structure (Figure 10-10). We also have a structure that is consistent with the X-ray data. The stacking of the base pairs in the double helix results in two grooves in the sugar-phosphate backbones. These are termed the **major** and **minor** grooves and can be readily seen in the space-filling (three-dimensional) model in Figure 10-10.

Elucidation of the DNA structure caused a lot of excitement in genetics (and in all areas of biology) for two basic reasons:

1. The structure suggests an obvious way in which the molecule could be **duplicated,** or **replicated.** This essential property of a genetic molecule had been a mystery up until then.

2. The structure suggests that perhaps the *sequence* of nucleotide pairs in DNA is dictating the sequence of amino acids in the protein organized by that gene. In other words, there is some sort of **genetic code** whereby information in DNA is written as a sequence of nucleotide pairs and then translated into a different language of amino acid sequences in protein.

This basic information about DNA is now familiar to almost anyone who has read a biology text in elementary or high school, or even magazines and newspapers. It may seem trite and obvious. But try to put yourself back into the scene in 1953 and imagine the excitement! Until then, the evidence that the uninteresting DNA is the genetic molecule seemed disappointing and discouraging. But the Watson-Crick structure of DNA suddenly opened up the possibility of explaining two of the biggest "secrets" of life. James Watson has told the story of this discovery (from his own point of view, strongly questioned by others involved) in a fascinating book called *The Double Helix;* it reveals the intricate interplay of personality clashes, clever insights, hard work, and simple luck in such important scientific advances.

Alternate Structures

In addition to the *A* and *B* forms of DNA, a new form has been found in crystals of synthetically prepared DNA containing alternating purines and pyrimidines on the same strand. This Z DNA form has a zigzag-like backbone and represents a left-handed helix, whereas both *A* and *B* DNA represent right-handed helices. Figures 10-11, 10-12, and 10-13 compare these three forms using perspective drawings based on precise information obtained from crystal structures of short synthetic DNA sequences called **oligonucleotides.** Z DNA can be detected in living cells in certain stretches of the chromosomes. Regions of Z DNA may be involved in gene regulation in the cells of "higher" organisms.

Replication of DNA

Semiconservative Replication

Figure 10-14 diagrams the possible mechanism for DNA replication as proposed by Watson and Crick. Here, the sugar-phosphate backbones are represented by lines, and the sequence of base pairs is random. Let's imagine that the double helix is like a zipper that unzips starting at one end (the top in this figure). We can see that if this zipper analogy is valid, the unwinding of the two strands will expose single bases of either strand. Because the pairing requirements imposed by the DNA structure are strict, each exposed base will pair only with its *complementary* base. Because of this

base complementarity, each of the two single strands will act as a **template,** or mold, and will begin to reform a double helix identical to the one from which it was unzipped. The newly added nucleotides are assumed to come from a pool of free nucleotides that must be present in the cell.

If this model is correct, each daughter molecule should contain one parental nucleotide chain (black line in Figure 10-14) and one newly synthesized nucleotide chain (color line). This prediction has been tested in both prokaryotes and eukaryotes. A little thought shows that there are at least three different ways in which a parental DNA molecule might possibly be related to the daughter molecules. These hypothetical modes are called semiconservative (the Watson-Crick model), conservative, and dispersive (Figure 10-15). In **semiconservative** replication, each daughter duplex contains one parental and one newly synthesized strand. However, in **conservative** replication, one daughter duplex consists of two newly synthesized strands, while the parent duplex is conserved. **Dispersive** replication results in daughter duplexes that consist of strands containing only *segments* of parental DNA and newly synthesized DNA.

In 1958, Matthew Meselson and Franklin Stahl set out

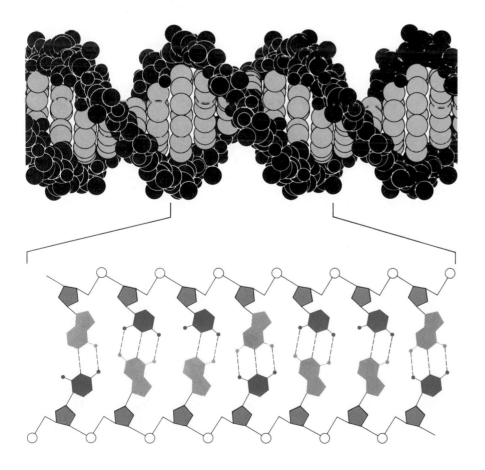

Figure 10-10. At the top is a space-filling model of the DNA (*B* form) double helix. At the bottom is an unwound representation of a short stretch of nucleotide pairs, showing how A–T and G–C pairing produces the Chargaff ratios. (Space-filling model from C. Yanofsky, "Gene Structure and Protein Structure." Copyright © 1967 by Scientific American, Inc. All rights reserved. Unwound structure based on A. Kornberg, "The Synthesis of DNA." Copyright © 1968 by Scientific American, Inc. All rights reserved.)

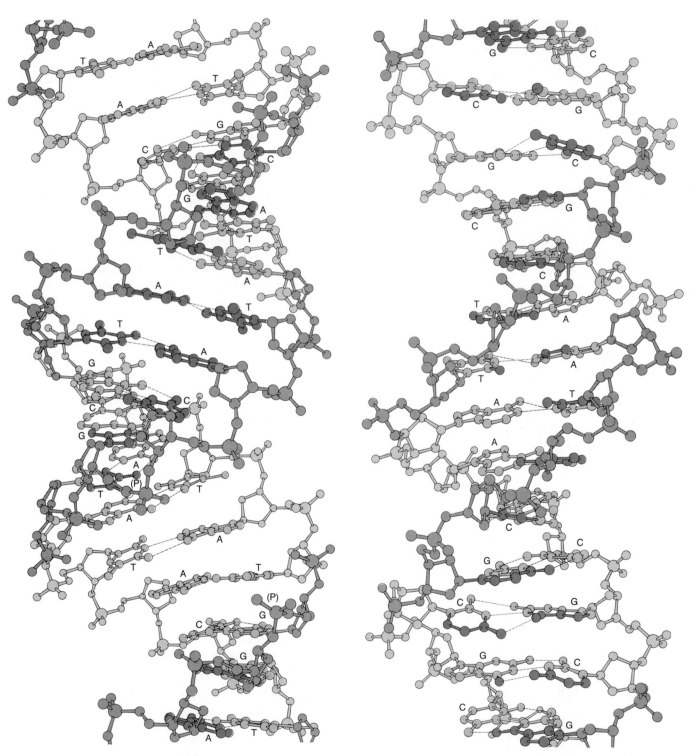

Figure 10-11. The *A*-DNA helix. This perspective drawing was generated from repetition of the central six bases of the octamer GGTATACC. Note how phosphate groups (P) on opposite chains face each other across the major groove.

Figure 10-12. The *B*-DNA helix. This perspective drawing was generated from repetition of the central 10 base pairs of the dodecamer CGCGAATTCGCG. Note the large twist relative to *A* DNA and how the twist improves the stacking of the bases along each backbone chain.

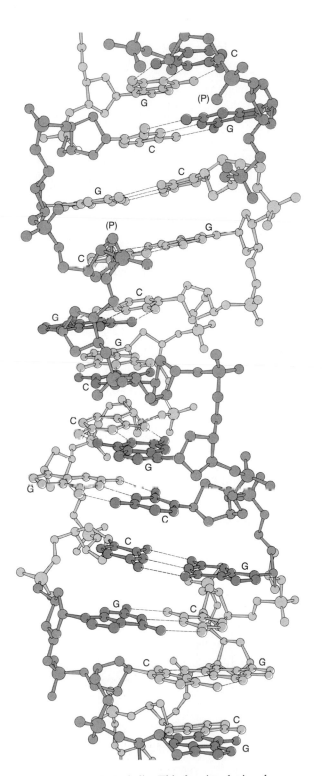

Figure 10-13. The Z-DNA helix. This drawing depicts the structure as a left-handed helix of alternating guanines and cytosines, generated from the central four base pairs of CGCGCG. Phosphate groups on different chains now face each other across the deep minor groove.

to distinguish among these possibilities in an experiment with *Escherichia coli*. They grew *E. coli* cells in a medium containing the heavy isotope of nitrogen (^{15}N) rather than the normal light (^{14}N) form. This isotope is inserted into the nitrogen bases, which then are incorporated into newly synthesized DNA strands. After many cell divisions in ^{15}N, the DNA of the cells is well labeled with the heavy isotope. The cells were then removed from the ^{15}N medium and put into ^{14}N medium; after one and two cell divisions, samples were taken. DNA was extracted from the cells in each of these samples and put into a solution of cesium chloride (CsCl) in an ultracentrifuge.

If cesium chloride is spun in a centrifuge at tremendously high speeds (50,000 rpm) for many hours, the salt ions tend to be pushed by centrifugal force toward the bottom of the tube. Ultimately, a **gradient** of Cs^+ and Cl^- ions is established in the tube, with the highest ion concentration at the bottom. Molecules of DNA in the solution also are pushed toward the bottom by centrifugal force. But, as they travel down the tube, they encounter the increasing salt concentration, which tends to push them back up because of DNA's buoyancy (or tendency to float). Thus, the DNA finally "settles" at some point in the tube where the centrifugal forces just balance the buoyancy of the molecules in the cesium chloride gradient. The buoyancy of DNA depends on its density (which in turn reflects the ratio of G–C to A–T base pairs). The presence of the heavier isotope of nitrogen changes the buoyant density of DNA. The DNA extracted from cells grown for several generations on ^{15}N medium can readily be distinguished from the DNA of cells grown on ^{14}N medium by the equilibrium position reached in a cesium chloride gradient. Such samples are commonly called "heavy" and "light" DNA, respectively.

Meselson and Stahl found that, one generation after the "heavy" cells were moved to ^{14}N medium, the DNA formed a single band with density intermediate between the densities of the heavy and light controls. After two generations in ^{14}N medium, the DNA formed two bands, one at the intermediate position and the other at the light position (Figure 10-16). This result would be expected from the semiconservative mode of replication, and in fact the result is compatible *only* with this mode *if* the experiment begins with chromosomes composed of individual double helices (Figure 10-17).

The Meselson-Stahl experiment on *E. coli* was essentially duplicated in 1958 by Herbert Taylor on the chromosomes of bean root-tip cells, using a cytological technique. He put root cells into a solution containing tritiated thymidine ([^3H]-thymidine)—that is, thymine nucleotide labeled with a radioactive hydrogen isotope called tritium. He allowed the cells to undergo mitosis in this solution, so that the [^3H]-thymidine could be incorporated into DNA. He then washed the tips and transferred them to a solution containing nonradioactive thymidine. Addition of colchi-

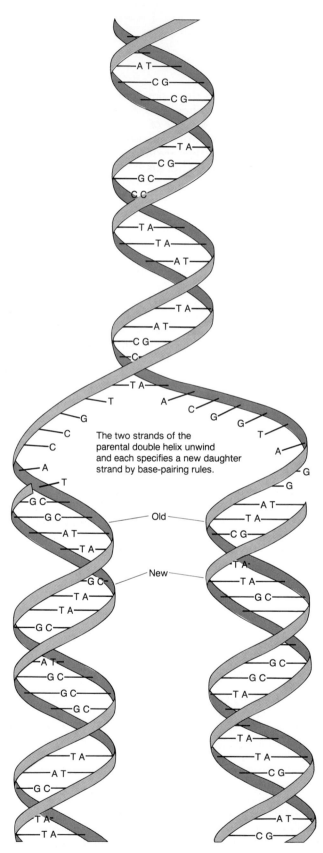

Figure 10-14. The model of DNA replication proposed by Watson and Crick is based on the hydrogen-bonding specificity of the base pairs.

The two strands of the parental double helix unwind and each specifies a new daughter strand by base-pairing rules.

Old

New

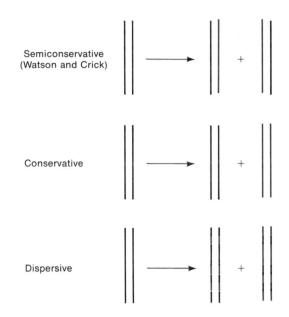

Semiconservative (Watson and Crick)

Conservative

Dispersive

Figure 10-15. Three alternative patterns for DNA replication. The Watson-Crick model would produce the first (semiconservative) pattern. Colored lines represent the newly synthesized strands.

cine to such a preparation inhibits the spindle apparatus so that chromosomes in metaphase fail to separate, and sister chromatids remain "tied together" by the centromere.

The cellular location of ^3H can be determined by **autoradiography.** As ^3H decays, it emits a beta particle (an energetic electron). If a layer of photographic emulsion is spread over a cell that contains ^3H, a chemical reaction takes place wherever a beta particle strikes the emulsion. The emulsion can then be developed like a photographic print, so that the emission track of the beta particle appears as a black spot or grain. The cell can also be stained, so that the structure of the cell is visible, to identify the location of the radioactivity. In effect, autoradiography is a process in which radioactive cell structures "take their own pictures."

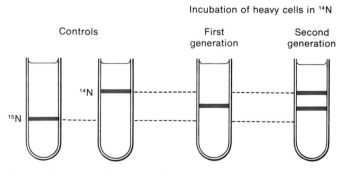

Incubation of heavy cells in ^{14}N

Controls

First generation

Second generation

^{14}N

^{15}N

Figure 10-16. Centrifugation of DNA in a cesium chloride gradient. Cultures grown for many generations in ^{15}N and ^{14}N media provide control positions for "heavy" and "light" DNA bands, respectively. When the cells grown in ^{15}N are transferred to a ^{14}N medium, the first generation produces an intermediate DNA band, and the second generation produces two bands, one intermediate and the other light.

Semiconservative

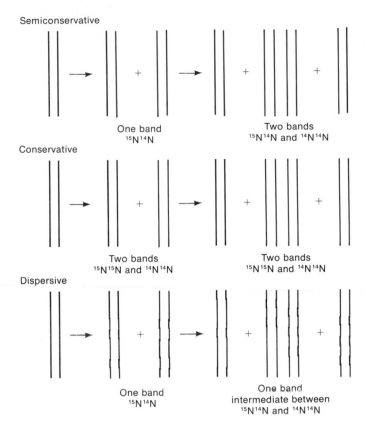

Figure 10-17. Only the semiconservative model of DNA replication predicts results like those shown in Figure 10-16: that is, a single intermediate band in the first generation and one intermediate and one light band in the second generation. (See Figure 10-15 for explanation of symbols.)

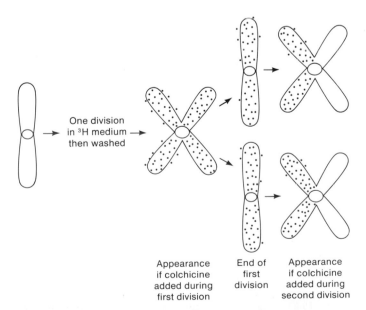

Figure 10-18. Diagrammatic representation of autoradiography of chromosomes from cells grown for one cell division in the presence of the radioactive hydrogen isotope ^3H (tritium). Each dot represents the track of a particle of radioactivity.

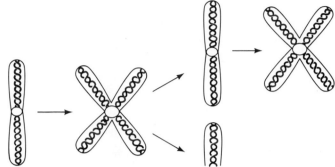

Figure 10-19. An explanation of Figure 10-18 at the DNA level. Colored lines represent radioactive strands.

Figure 10-18 shows the results observed when colchicine is added during the division in [^3H]-thymidine or during the subsequent mitotic division. It is possible to interpret these results by representing each chromatid as a single DNA molecule that replicates semiconservatively (Figure 10-19).

Using a more modern staining technique, it is now possible to visualize the semiconservative replication of chromosomes at mitosis without the aid of autoradiography. In this procedure, the chromosomes are allowed to go through two rounds of replication in bromodeoxyuridine. The chromosomes are then stained with fluorescent dye and Giemsa stain; this process produces so-called **harlequin chromosomes** (Figure 10-20). The DNA strands that are newly synthesized in bromodeoxyuridine stain differently from the "original" DNA strands. The basis of this pattern is exactly identical to that of Figure 10-19. (Note, in passing, that harlequin chromosomes are particularly favorable for the detection of sister-chromatid exchange at mitosis; two examples are seen in Figure 10-20.)

Using similar techniques, Taylor showed that chromosome replication at meiosis also is semiconservative. This result drove another nail in the coffin of the copy-choice theory of crossing-over (Chapter 5), which would require *conservative* chromosome replication at meiosis.

Figures 10-18 and 10-19 bring up one of the remaining great unsolved questions of genetics: Is a eukaryotic chromosome basically a single DNA molecule surrounded by a protein matrix? Two things strongly suggest that this is, in fact, the case. First, if there were many DNA molecules in the chromosome — whether side by side, or end to end, or randomly oriented — it would be almost impossible for the chromosome to replicate semiconservatively (with all of the label going into one chromatid as in Taylor's results). Look at Figure 10-21 and try to figure out how it could be done. Recent studies on isolated chromosomes and long DNA molecules are consistent with the suggestion that *each chro-*

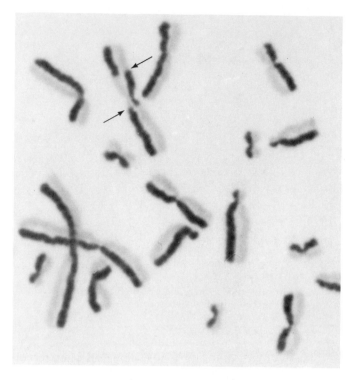

Figure 10-20. Harlequin chromosomes in a Chinese hamster ovary (CHO) cell. The procedure involves letting the chromosomes go through two rounds of replication in the presence of bromodeoxyuridine (BUdR), which replaces thymidine in the newly synthesized DNA. The chromosomes are then stained with a fluorescent dye and Giemsa stain, producing the appearance shown. The DNA strands that are newly replicated in BUdR stain differentially from the "original" DNA strands. A chromosome at the top has two sister chromatid exchanges. (Photo courtesy of Sheldon Wolff and Judy Bodycote.)

matid is a single molecule of DNA. That makes a very long molecule. There is enough DNA in a single human chromosome, for example, to stretch out to several inches in length. (That raises another interesting problem: How is this long molecule packed into the chromosome to permit easy replication?) The second fact supporting a single-molecule hypothesis is that DNA and genes behave as though they are attached end to end in a single string or thread that we call a linkage group. All genetic linkage data tell us that we need nothing more than a single linear array of genes per chromosome to explain the genetic facts.

As just mentioned, there is far too much DNA in a chromosome for it to extend linearly along the chromosome. It must be packed very efficiently into the chromosome. Current thinking (supported by good microscopic evidence) tends toward a process of coiling and supercoiling of the DNA. Twist a rubber band with your fingers and notice the way it coils; chromosomes may be like this. We return to these questions in Chapter 19.

The Replication Fork

A prediction of the Watson-Crick model of DNA replication is that a fork will be found in the DNA molecule during replication. In 1963, John Cairns tested this prediction by

allowing replicating DNA in bacterial cells to incorporate tritiated thymidine. Theoretically, each newly synthesized daughter molecule should then contain one radioactive ("hot") strand and another nonradioactive ("cold") strand. After varying intervals and varying numbers of replication cycles in "hot" medium, the DNA was extracted from the cells, put on a slide, and autoradiographed for examination under the electron microscope. After one replication cycle in [³H]-thymidine, rings of dots were seen in the autoradiograph and were interpreted as shown in Figure 10-22.

During the second replication cycle, the forks predicted by the model were indeed seen. Furthermore, the density of grains in the three segments was such that the interpretation shown in Figure 10-23 could be made. All sizes of these moon-shaped autoradiographic patterns were seen, corresponding to the progressive movement of the replication zipper, or fork, around the ring. Structures of the sort shown in Figure 10-23 are called theta (θ) structures.

Origin of Replication

In bacteria, replication begins from a fixed **origin** but then proceeds **bidirectionally** (with moving forks at both ends of the replicating piece), as shown in Figure 10-24. In higher cells, replication proceeds from multiple points of origin. Suppose that a eukaryotic cell is briefly exposed to [³H]-thymidine, in a step called a **pulse** exposure, and then provided an excess of "cold" thymidine, in a step called the **chase;** the DNA is then extracted, and autoradiographs are made. Figure 10-25 shows the results of such a procedure, with what appear to be distinct simultaneously replicating regions along the DNA molecule. Replication appears to begin at several different sites on these eukaryotic chromosomes. Similarly, a pulse-and-chase study of DNA replication in polytene (giant) chromosomes of *Drosophila*

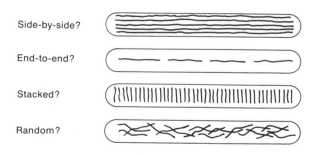

Side-by-side?

End-to-end?

Stacked?

Random?

Figure 10-21. Some theoretical alternative packing arrangements of DNA in a eukaryotic chromosome. Any of these models is hard to reconcile with the data supporting a semiconservative model of DNA replication. The question of the packaging of a long DNA molecule is considered in Chapter 19.

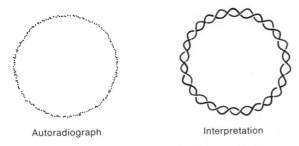

Autoradiograph   Interpretation

Figure 10-22. Autoradiograph of bacterial chromosome after one replication in tritiated thymidine. According to the semiconservative model of replication, one of the two strands should be radioactive. The interpretation of the autoradiograph is at the right.

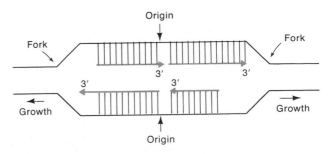

Figure 10-24. Diagrammatic representation of 3′ polymerization in bidirectional replication of DNA. (From A. Kornberg, *DNA Synthesis.* Copyright © 1974 by W. H. Freeman and Co.)

by autoradiography reveals many replication regions within single chromosome arms (Figure 10-26). As yet there is no firm proof that these regions are indeed different start points on a single DNA molecule; they could also be interpreted as evidence that the chromosome is made up of many separate DNA molecules. The structure of the eukaryotic chromosome still remains as one of the most exciting unresolved problems in genetics (see Chapter 19).

Enzymology of Replication

In the late 1950s, Arthur Kornberg succeeded in identifying and purifying an enzyme, DNA polymerase, that catalyzes the replication reaction:

$$\text{primer (parental) DNA} + \begin{array}{c} \text{dATP} \\ + \\ \text{dGTP} \\ + \\ \text{dCTP} \\ + \\ \text{dTTP} \end{array} \xrightarrow[\text{polymerase}]{\text{DNA}} \text{progeny DNA}$$

This reaction works only with the triphosphate forms of the nucleotides (such as deoxyadenosine triphosphate, or dATP). The total amount of DNA at the end of the reaction can be as much as 20 times the amount of original input DNA, so most of the DNA present at the end must be progeny DNA. Thus, an analysis of this final DNA mixture

can be regarded as largely indicative of the nature of the progeny DNA.

Although the process of replication appears simple in Figure 10-23, certain complexities arise.

1. The double helix must rotate in the process of replication, because the two strands are intertwined (or interlocked). This is accomplished with the aid of biological catalysts, or **enzymes,** called DNA **topoisomerases,** which convert rings of DNA from one topological form to another. For instance, one topoisomerase, DNA **gyrase,** can induce twisting and coiling of the DNA, called **supercoiling,** as shown in Figure 10-27. The supercoiled form may facilitate unwinding of the helix, as depicted in Figure 10-28. A **helicase,** the "rep" protein, is probably involved in actually unwinding the helix. The free single-stranded region would be subject to degradation, but it is protected by another protein termed the single-stranded DNA-binding (SSB) protein.

2. The simple notion of an unzipping molecule is inadequate. All of the known DNA polymerases synthesize new chains only in the 5′ to 3′ direction. (The enzyme first studied by Kornberg, now termed DNA polymerase I, is not the principal DNA replication enzyme, whereas the enzyme termed DNA polymerase III probably is.) It is now known that while one strand is synthesized continuously by DNA polymerase III, the other is synthesized in an interrupted fashion. For this

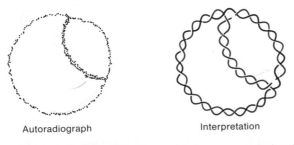

Autoradiograph   Interpretation

Figure 10-23. Autoradiograph of bacterial chromosome during the second round of replication in tritiated thymidine. In this theta structure, the newly replicated double helix that crosses the circle could show both strands as radioactive. The double thickness of the radioactive tracing on the autoradiogram appears to confirm this.

Autoradiogram

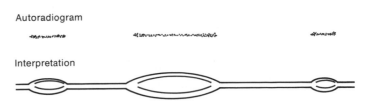

Interpretation

Figure 10-25. A replication pattern in DNA revealed by autoradiography. A cell was briefly exposed to ³H-thymidine (pulse) and then provided an excess of nonradioactive (cold) thymidine (chase). DNA is spread on a slide and autoradiographed. The interpretation shown in this figure is that there are several initiation points for replication within one double helix of DNA.

Figure 10-26. Replication pattern in a *Drosophila* chromosome revealed by autoradiography. Several points of replication are seen within a single chromosome, as indicated by the arrows.

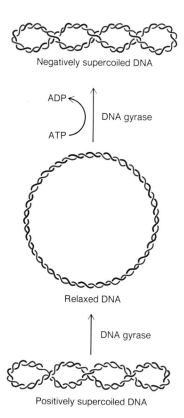

Figure 10-27. DNA-gyrase-catalyzed supercoiling. Replicating DNA generates "positive" supercoils, depicted at the bottom of the diagram, as a result of rapid rotation of the DNA at the replication fork. DNA gyrase can nick and close phosphodiester bonds, relieving the supercoiling, as shown here (relaxed DNA). Gyrase can also generate supercoils twisted in the opposite direction, termed "negative" supercoils; this arrangement facilitates unwinding of the helix (see Figure 10-28). (Modified from L. Stryer, *Biochemistry*. Copyright © 1983 by W. H. Freeman and Co.)

latter strand, DNA polymerase III initiates at many different points on the template, leaving gaps that are filled in by DNA polymerase I and then ligated by the enzyme DNA **ligase.**

3. DNA polymerase cannot begin a new chain on a single-stranded template without at least a short region of duplex, which serves as a primer. In bacteria, the enzyme **primase,** together with a second protein encoded by *dnaB*, synthesizes an RNA primer for DNA polymerase III.

Figure 10-29 summarizes many of the steps in DNA synthesis. The simultaneous synthesis of two new DNA chains is shown. On the left side of the diagram, the new strand is synthesized continuously, in the 5′ to 3′ direction, as the helix is unwound with the aid of the rep protein. Single-stranded regions are stabilized by the SSB protein. On the right side of the diagram, the new strand must be synthesized discontinuously, since all DNA polymerases synthesize in the 5′ to 3′ direction. Thus, as new portions of the old template become available, synthesis of fragments of the new strand can begin. This synthesis requires a primase to first synthesize a short RNA stretch that serves as a "primer" onto which DNA polymerase III adds on deoxynucleotides, before falling off. This process leaves gaps, as can be seen in the figure, that are filled in by DNA polymerase I, which also removes the short primer at the beginning of the double-stranded fragment that it has now reached. The enzyme DNA ligase then seals the final bond.

DNA and the Gene

We have now learned that DNA is the genetic material and consists of a linear sequence of nucleotide pairs. The obvious conclusion is that the allele maps represent a genetic equivalent of the nucleotide-pair sequences in DNA. We can validate this assumption if we can show that *the genetic maps are congruent with DNA maps.* This step was first taken using some elegant genetic and biochemical manipulations.

The DNA of the λ phage turns out to be a linear stretch of DNA that can be circularized because each 5′ end of the two strands has an extra terminal extension of 12 bases that is complementary to the other 5′ end (Figure 10-30). Because they are complementary, these ends can pair to join the DNA into a circle; they are known as "cohesive," or "sticky," ends.

When a linear object such as a DNA molecule is subjected to shear stress (say, by pipetting or stirring), the mechanics of the stress causes breaks to occur principally in the middle of the molecule. When DNA from the λ phage is sheared in half, the two halves happen to differ in G–C ratio, which means that their buoyant densities differ and they can be separated by centrifugation in CsCl. When the

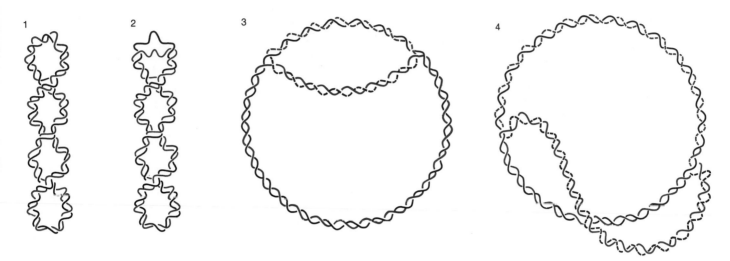

Figure 10-28. Replication of the information in the sequence of base pairs is necessary for a cell to divide. The replication of a double-stranded DNA ring may depend on the capacity of a topoisomerase to allow unwinding of the double helix. One of the common mechanisms for the duplication of a double-stranded ring is the manufacture of a new complementary strand for each original strand. For the new strands to be assembled the original strands must separate. In bacteria, gyrase negatively supercoils the ring (1). In the negatively supercoiled form the unwinding of the double helix is made easier. Unwinding is probably required for replication to begin in some organisms (2). Assembly of the new strands is begun using the original strands as templates (3). In order for replication to proceed the double helix must be progressively unwound. The unwinding may be accomplished by one or more topoisomerase molecules (4), after which the two double-stranded rings separate; each ring is made up of one original strand and one new strand. (From J. C. Wang, "DNA Topoisomerases." Copyright © 1982 by Scientific American, Inc. All rights reserved.)

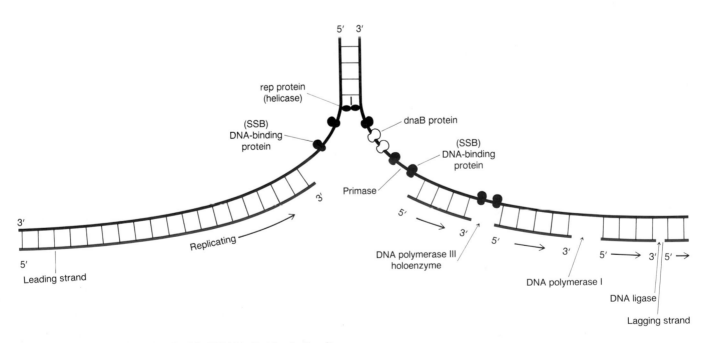

Figure 10-29. The enzymes involved in DNA replication in *E. coli*. (After A. Kornberg, *DNA Replication*. Copyright © 1980 by W. H. Freeman and Co.)

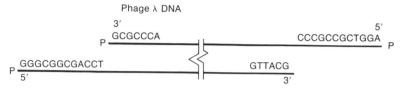

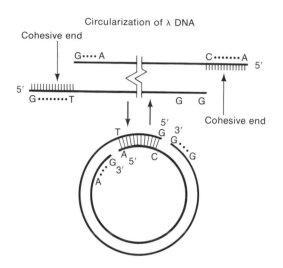

Figure 10-30. Circularization of DNA. The λ DNA is linear in the phage, but once in a host cell it circularizes as a prelude to insertion or replication. Circularization is achieved by joining the complementary ("sticky") single-stranded ends. (From A. Kornberg, *DNA Synthesis.* Copyright © 1974 by W. H. Freeman and Co.)

two half-molecules are separated, their genetic content can be assayed by introducing the DNA into bacteria in the following way. The DNA is introduced into the bacteria simultaneously upon infection with mutant phage λ. Recombination can occur between the phage DNA and the fragment as shown in Figure 10-31, in which *a* through *f* are phage genes. The introduced DNA can be incorporated into the normal λ DNA and "rescued" by inducing lysis, the rupture and death of a bacterial cell upon the release of phage progeny. You can see that, by using different strains, this technique can lead to analysis of the marker content of the DNA fractions. This is called a **marker-rescue experiment.** Such experiments demon-

strated that one particular half of the DNA molecule carries the information of one particular half of the linkage map.

Dale Kaiser and his associates separated one of the DNA halves carrying a cohesive end and attached the other end to chromatographic material over which DNA could be passed (Figure 10-32). The single-stranded ends dangle free like fish hooks. If the other half of the DNA is sheared into smaller and smaller molecules and then passed over the sticky ends, the complementary sequences will stick. These stuck pieces can be easily detached by raising the temperature to break the hydrogen bonds in the sticky ends. In this way, a series of fractions (of varying size) of one end of the λ DNA can be separated and tested for content by marker rescue. Kaiser and his associates showed that an unambiguous arrangement of genes on the DNA can be determined, and this sequence is completely congruent with the genetic map (Figure 10-33).

Message We are now justified in concluding that the sequence of bases in the DNA is indeed congruent with the gene map.

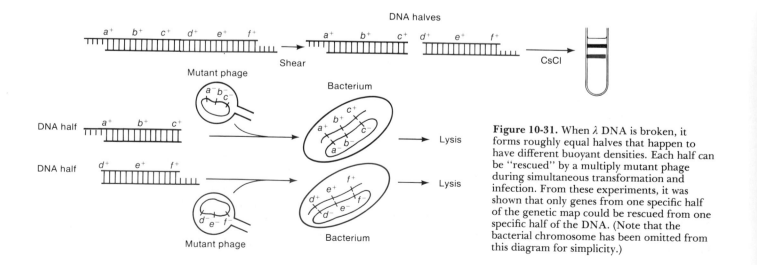

Figure 10-31. When λ DNA is broken, it forms roughly equal halves that happen to have different buoyant densities. Each half can be "rescued" by a multiply mutant phage during simultaneous transformation and infection. From these experiments, it was shown that only genes from one specific half of the genetic map could be rescued from one specific half of the DNA. (Note that the bacterial chromosome has been omitted from this diagram for simplicity.)

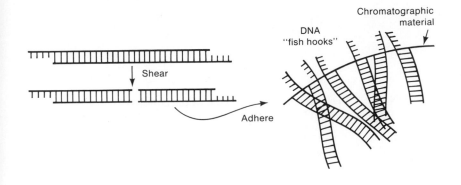

Figure 10-32. One specific sticky end can be used as a "fish hook" for the other sticky end plus any genes that may be attached to it. One-half of the λ phage DNA is attached to chromatographic material so that the cohesive or sticky ends are exposed. Any DNA passed over this chromatographic material that has single-stranded base sequences complementary to the "fish hook" cohesive ends will stick. Other DNA will pass through. Later, the "stuck" DNA can be removed from the chromatographic material by heating it to break the hydrogen bonds.

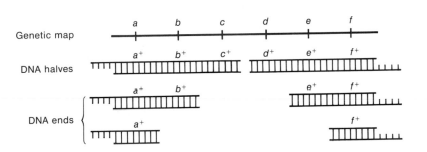

Figure 10-33. As the λ DNA is sheared progressively smaller and smaller, genes are lost to the fish hooks (Figure 10-32) in a progressive order, the same as their order on the genetic map.

Summary

■ Experimental work on the molecular nature of hereditary material has conclusively demonstrated that DNA (and not protein, RNA, or some other substance) is indeed the genetic material. Using data supplied by others, Watson and Crick created a double helical model with two DNA strands wound around each other running in antiparallel fashion. Specificity of binding the two strands together is based on the fit of adenine (A) to thymine (T) and guanine (G) to cytosine (C), the former pair held by two hydrogen bonds and the latter by three.

The Watson-Crick model shows how DNA can be replicated in an orderly fashion, a prime requirement for genetic material. Replication is accomplished semiconservatively; that is, one double helix is replicated into two identical helices, each with identical linear orders of nucleotides, and each of the two new double helices is composed of one old and one newly polymerized strand of DNA. This semiconservative replication occurs in both prokaryotes and eukaryotes.

Replication is achieved with the aid of several enzymes, including DNA polymerase, gyrase, and helicase. Replication starts at special regions of the DNA called origins of replication and proceeds down the DNA in both directions. Since DNA polymerase acts only in a 5′ → 3′ direction, one of the newly synthesized strands at each replication fork must be synthesized in short segments, then joined using the enzyme ligase. DNA polymerization cannot begin without a short primer, which is also synthesized with special enzymes.

The marker rescue technique was used to demonstrate that the sequence of genes on a chromosome corresponds exactly to the linear sequence of DNA, showing convincingly that the genetic and chemical entities are one and the same thing.

Problems

1. Assume that thymine makes up 15 percent of the bases in a specific DNA molecule. What percentage of the bases is cytosine?

2. Draw a graph of DNA content against time in a cell that undergoes mitosis and then meiosis.

3. Consider an *Escherichia coli* chromosome in which every nitrogen atom is labeled—that is, every nitrogen atom is the heavy isotope ^{15}N instead of the normal isotope ^{14}N. The chromosomes then are allowed to replicate in an environment in which all the nitrogen is ^{14}N. Using a solid line to represent a heavy polynucleotide chain and a dotted line for a light chain, sketch the following:

   a. The heavy parental chromosome and the products of the first replication after transfer to ^{14}N medium, assuming that the chromosome is one DNA double helix and that replication is semiconservative.

   b. Repeat part a, but assume conservative replication.

   c. Repeat part a, but assume that the chromosome is in fact two side-by-side double helices, each of which replicates semiconservatively.

   d. Repeat part c, but assume that each side-by-side double helix replicates conservatively and that the overall *chromosome* replication is semiconservative.

   e. Repeat part d, but assume that the overall chromosome replication is conservative.

   f. If the daughter chromosomes from the first division in ^{14}N are spun in a cesium chloride density gradient and a single band is obtained, which of possibilities a through e can be ruled out? Reconsider the Meselson-Stahl experiment: What does it *prove*?

4. R. Okazaki found that the immediate products of DNA replication in *E. coli* include single-stranded DNA fragments approximately 1000 nucleotides in length after the newly synthesized DNA is extracted and denatured. When he allowed DNA replication to proceed for a longer period of time, he found a lower frequency of these short fragments, and he found long single-stranded DNA chains after extraction and denaturation. Explain how this result might be related to the fact that all known DNA polymerases synthesize DNA only in a $5' \rightarrow 3'$ direction.

5. When plant and animal cells are given pulses of [³H]-thymidine at different times in the cell cycle, it is found that heterochromatic regions on chromosomes are invariably "late replicating." Can you suggest any biological significance this observation might have?

6. On the planet of Rama, the DNA is built of six nucleotide types: A, B, C, D, E, and F. A and B are called marzines; C and D are orsines; and E and F are pirines. The following rules are valid in all Raman DNAs:

   Total marzines = total orsines = total pirines

   A = C = E

   B = D = F

   a. Prepare a model for the structure of Raman DNA.

   b. On Rama, mitosis produces three daughter cells. Bearing this fact in mind, propose a replication scheme for your DNA model.

   c. Consider the process of meiosis on Rama. What comments or conclusions can you suggest?

7. If you extract the DNA of the coliphage ϕX174, you will find that its composition is 25 percent A, 33 percent T, 24 percent G, and 18 percent C. Does this make sense in terms of Chargaff's rules? How would you interpret this result? How might such a phage replicate its DNA?

8. The temperature at which a DNA sample denatures can be used to estimate the proportion of its nucleotide pairs that are G–C. What would be the basis for this determination, and what would a high denaturation temperature for a DNA sample indicate?

9. In 1960, Paul Doty and Julius Marmur observed that when DNA is heated to 100°C, all of the hydrogen bonds between the complementary strands are destroyed, and the DNA becomes single-stranded (this is called *melting*, or *denaturation*) (see the figure below). If the solution is cooled slowly, some double-stranded DNA is formed that is biologically normal (for example, it may have transforming ability). Presumably, this **reannealing,** or **renaturation,** process occurs when two single strands happen to collide in such a way that the complementing base sequences can align and reconstitute the original double helix, as shown in the figure below. This reannealing is very specific and precise, making it a very powerful tool because stretches of complementary base sequences in *different* DNAs also will anneal after melting and mixing. Thus the efficiency of annealing provides a measure of similarity between two different DNAs.

   Now suppose that you extract DNA from a small virus, denature it, and allow it to reanneal with DNA taken from other strains that carry a deletion, an inversion, or a duplication. What would you expect to see on inspection with an electron microscope?

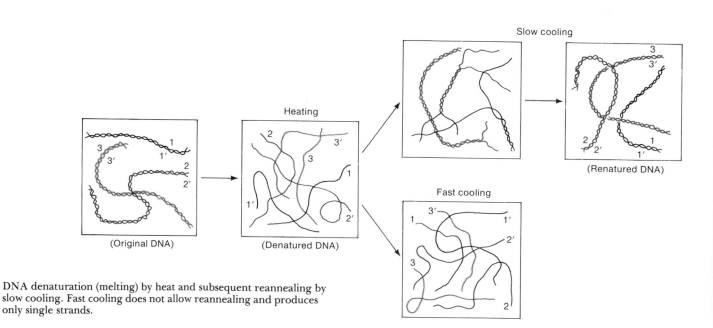

DNA denaturation (melting) by heat and subsequent reannealing by slow cooling. Fast cooling does not allow reannealing and produces only single strands.

10. DNA extracted from a mammal is heat-denatured and then slowly cooled to allow reannealing. The following graph shows the results obtained. There are two "shoulders" in the curve. The first shoulder indicates the presence of a very rapidly annealing part of the DNA—so rapid in fact, that it occurs before strand interactions take place.

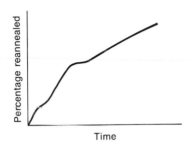

a. What could this part of the DNA be?

b. The second shoulder is a rapidly reannealing part as well. What does this evidence suggest?

11. Design tests to determine the physical relationship between highly repetitive and unique DNA sequences in chromosomes. (HINT: it is possible to vary the size of DNA molecules by the amount of shearing they are subjected to.)

12. In mice, there are viruses that are known to cause cancer. You have a pure preparation of virus DNA, a pure preparation of DNA from the chromosomes of mouse cancer cells, and pure DNA from chromosomes of normal mouse cells. Virus DNA will specifically anneal with cancer-cell DNA, but not with normal-cell DNA. Explore the possible genetic significance of this observation, its significance at the molecular level, and its medical significance.

13. Ruth Kavenaugh and Bruno Zimm have devised an elegant technique to measure the maximal length of the longest DNA molecules in solution. They studied DNA samples from the three *Drosophila* karyotypes shown in the accompanying figure. They found the longest molecules in karyotypes a and b to be of similar length and about twice the length of the longest in c. How would you interpret these results?

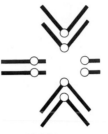

(a) Wild-type

(b) Pericentric inversion

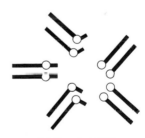

(c) Translocation

14. In the harlequin-chromosome technique, you allow *three* rounds of replication in bromodeoxyuridine and then stain the chromosomes. What result do you expect to obtain?

CHAPTER 11

The Nature of the Gene

■ What is the nature of the gene, and how do genes determine morphological and physiological aspects of an organism? For example, how is it that one allele of a gene can produce a wrinkled pea, whereas another allele of the gene produces a round, smooth pea? We now have a model for this relationship, which can be outlined as follows:

1. The characteristic features of an organism are determined by the phenotypes of its parts.

2. The phenotype of a part (say, an organ) is determined by the phenotypes of the tissues that make up the part.

3. The tissue phenotype is determined by the phenotypes of the cells that compose the tissue.

4. The phenotype of a cell is determined by its internal chemistry.

5. Each cell is a reaction vessel in which metabolic reactions are catalyzed by enzymes, so the enzymes control the internal chemistry of the cell.

6. Protein function depends on a specific three-dimensional structure, which in turn depends on a specific linear sequence of amino acids.

7. The enzymes present in a cell, as well as structural proteins, are determined by the genotype of the cell.

8. Genes specify the linear sequence of amino acids in polypeptides and thus determine phenotypes.

Let us examine the steps that have led to this crucial breakthrough in our understanding of heredity.

How Genes Work

The first clues to the nature of primary gene function came from studies of humans—unlikely subjects for genetic research. Early in this century, Archibald Garrod (a physician) noted that several hereditary human defects are produced by recessive mutations. Some of these defects can be traced directly to metabolic defects affecting the basic body chemistry; this observation led to the suggestion of "inborn errors" in metabolism. We know now, for example, that phenylketonuria, caused by an autosomal recessive allele, results from an inability to convert phenylalanine into tyrosine. Consequently, phenylalanine accumulates and is spontaneously converted into a toxic compound, phenylpyruvic acid. In a different character, it is the inability to convert tyrosine into the pigment melanin that produces an albino. In any case, the observations of Garrod focused attention on metabolic control by genes.

The One-Gene–One-Enzyme Hypothesis

Clarification of the actual function of genes came from research on *Neurospora* by George Beadle and Edward Tatum in the 1940s; they later received a Nobel prize for this work. After irradiation to produce mutations, ascospores were grown and the resulting cultures tested for their ability to grow on minimal medium. Wild-types can grow on minimal medium, but some cultures were unable to grow. However, the latter *could* grow when they were transferred to a medium containing certain specific chemical additives, showing that they were not dead. Some nongrowers responded to arginine, some to pyridoxine, and some to other specific chemicals. Each of these auxotrophic requirements was inherited as a single-gene mutation; each gave a 1 : 1 ratio when crossed with wild-type (recall that *Neurospora* is haploid).

Beadle and Tatum concentrated on a group of independently isolated arginine-requiring auxotrophic mutants. They set out to map the chromosomal location of each mutation. Eventually, all of the arginine (*arg*) mutations were mapped into three different locations on separate chromosomes; let's call these loci the *arg-1*, *arg-2*, and *arg-3* genes. Beadle and Tatum found that the auxotrophs for each of the three loci differ in their response to the chemical compounds ornithine and citrulline, which are related to arginine (Figure 11-1). The *arg-1* mutants will grow if supplied with either ornithine *or* citrulline *or* arginine in addition to the minimal medium. The *arg-2* mutants will grow on either arginine or citrulline but not on ornithine. The *arg-3* mutants can grow only when arginine is supplied.

It was known that related compounds are interconverted in cells by biological catalysts called enzymes. Beadle and Tatum and their colleagues proposed a biochemical model for such conversions in *Neurospora*:

$$\text{precursor} \xrightarrow{\text{enzyme X}} \text{ornithine} \xrightarrow{\text{enzyme Y}}$$
$$\text{citrulline} \xrightarrow{\text{enzyme Z}} \text{arginine}$$

Now suppose that the *arg-1* mutants have defective enzyme X, so that they are unable to convert the precursor into ornithine as the first step in producing arginine. However, having normal enzymes Y and Z, they are perfectly able to produce arginine if supplied with either ornithine or citrulline. By similar reasoning, we conclude that the *arg-2* mutants lack enzyme Y and that the *arg-3* mutants lack enzyme Z. Thus, a mutation at a particular gene is assumed to interfere with production of a single enzyme. The defective enzyme, then, creates a block in some biosynthetic pathway. The block can be circumvented by supplying to the cells any compound that normally comes *after* the block in the pathway. Note that this entire model was inferred from the properties of the mutant classes detected through ge-

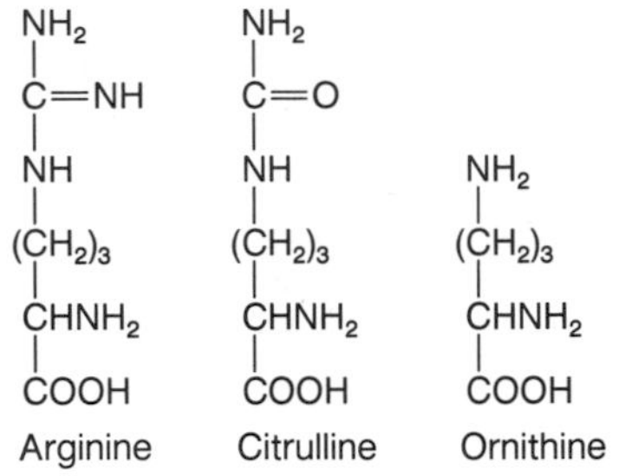

Figure 11-1. Chemical structures of arginine and the related compounds citrulline and ornithine. In the work of Beadle and Tatum, different *arg* auxotrophic mutants of *Neurospora* were found to grow when the medium was supplemented with citrulline or ornithine as an alternative to arginine.

netic analysis; only later were the existence of the pathway and the presence of defective enzymes demonstrated through independent biochemical evidence.

This model became known as the **one-gene–one-enzyme hypothesis.** It provided the first exciting insight into the function of genes: genes somehow are responsible for the function of enzymes, and each gene apparently controls one specific enzyme. Other researchers obtained similar results for other biosynthetic pathways, and the hypothesis soon achieved general acceptance. It is one of the great unifying concepts in biology, because it provided a bridge to bring together the concepts and research techniques of genetics and chemistry.

Message   Genes control biochemical reactions by controlling the production of enzymes.

We should pause to let the significance of this discovery sink in. Let us summarize what it established.

1. Biochemical reactions in vivo (in the living cell) occur as a series of discrete, stepwise reactions.

2. Each reaction is specifically catalyzed by a single enzyme.

3. Each enzyme is specified by a single gene.

Gene-Protein Relations

The one-gene–one-enzyme hypothesis is an impressive step forward in our understanding of gene function, but just *how* do genes control the functioning of enzymes? Enzymes belong to a general class of molecules called **pro-**

teins, and we must review the basic facts of protein structure in order to follow the next step in the study of gene function.

Protein Structure

In simple terms, a protein is a macromolecule composed of **amino acids** attached end to end in a linear string. The general formula for an amino acid is $H_2N - CHR - COOH$, in which the R group can be anything from a hydrogen atom (as in the amino acid glycine) to a complex ring (as in the amino acid tryptophan). There are 20 common amino acids in living organisms (Table 11-1), each having a different R group. Amino acids are linked together in proteins by covalent (chemical) bonds called **peptide bonds.** A peptide bond is formed through a condensation reaction that involves removal of a water molecule (Figure 11-2).

Several amino acids linked together by peptide bonds form a molecule called a **polypeptide;** proteins are large polypeptides of the kinds found in living organisms. The linear arrangement of amino acids in a polypeptide chain is called the **primary structure** of the protein. Figure 11-3

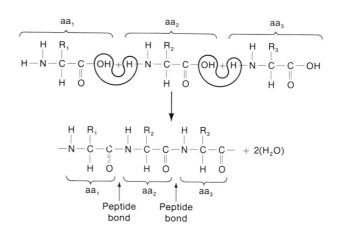

Figure 11-2. Formation of a polypeptide by the removal of water between amino acids to form peptide bonds. R_1, R_2, and R_3 represent side groups that differentiate the amino acids. R can be anything from a hydrogen atom (as in glycine) to a complex ring (as in tryptophan). Each aa indicates an amino acid.

shows the primary structures of beef insulin (a hormonal protein) and tryptophan synthetase (an enzyme). Many of the side groups of amino acids attract or repel one another in the protein, resulting in different types of **secondary structure** of the protein. Two of the basic periodic structures are the α-helix and the β-pleated sheet, which are depicted in Figures 11-4 and 11-5, respectively. Protein chains can also formulate a "β turn" (Figure 11-6), in which the direction of the amino acid chain is reversed. The protein chain can be further folded to form a **tertiary structure** (Figure 11-7). In many cases, a number of folded structures can associate to form a **quaternary structure** that is multimeric (composed of several separate polypeptide monomers; see Figures 11-8 and 11-9). Many proteins are basically compact "blobs"; such proteins are called globular proteins. Enzymes and antibodies are among the important globular proteins. Other, unfolded proteins, called fibrous proteins, are important components of such structures as hair and muscle.

Proteins act as biological catalysts, as hormones, and as structural elements in spindle fibers, hair, muscle, and so forth. Proteins play a very central role in living systems. If we purify a particular protein, we find that we can specify a particular ratio of the various amino acids for that specific protein. But the protein is not formed by a random hookup of fixed amounts of the various amino acids; it also has a characteristic sequence. For a small polypeptide, the amino acid sequence can be determined by clipping off one amino acid at a time and identifying it. However, large polypeptides cannot be readily "sequenced" in this way.

Frederick Sanger worked out a brilliant method for deducing the sequence of large polypeptides. There are several different **proteolytic enzymes** — enzymes that can

■ **TABLE 11-1.** The 20 amino acids common in living organisms

Amino acid	Three-letter abbreviation
Alanine	Ala
Arginine	Arg
Asparagine	Asn
Aspartic acid	Asp
Cysteine	Cys
Glutamine	Gln
Glutamic acid	Glu
Glycine	Gly
Histidine	His
Isoleucine	Ile
Leucine	Leu
Lysine	Lys
Methionine	Met
Phenylalanine	Phe
Proline	Pro
Serine	Ser
Threonine	Thr
Tryptophan	Trp
Tyrosine	Tyr
Valine	Val

Met-Glu-Arg-Tyr-Glu-Ser-Leu-Phe-Ala-Gln-Leu-Lys-Glu-Arg-Lys-Glu-Gly-Ala-Phe-Val- (10) (20)

Pro-Phe-Val-Thr-Leu-Gly-Asp-Pro-Gly-Ile-Glu-Gln-Ser-Leu-Lys-Ile-Ile-Asp-Thr-Leu- (30) (40)

Ile-Glu-Ala-Gly-Ala-Asp-Ala-Leu-Glu-Leu-Gly-Ile-Pro-Phe-Ser-Asp-Pro-Leu-Ala-Asp- (50) (60)

Gly-Pro-Thr-Ile-Gln-Asn-Ala-Thr-Leu-Arg-Ala-Phe-Ala-Ala-Gly-Val-Thr-Pro-Ala-Gln- (70) (80)

Cys-Phe-Glu-Met-Leu-Ala-Leu-Ile-Arg-Gln-Lys-His-Pro-Thr-Ile-Pro-Ile-Gly-Leu-Leu- (90) (100)

Met-Tyr-Ala-Asn-Leu-Val-Phe-Asn-Lys-Gly-Ile-Asp-Glu-Phe-Tyr-Ala-Gln-Cys-Glu-Lys- (110) (120)

Val-Gly-Val-Asp-Ser-Val-Leu-Val-Ala-Asp-Val-Pro-Val-Gln-Glu-Ser-Ala-Pro-Phe-Arg- (130) (140)

Gln-Ala-Ala-Leu-Arg-His-Asn-Val-Ala-Pro-Ile-Phe-Ile-Cys-Pro-Pro-Asn-Ala-Asp-Asp- (150) (160)

Asp-Leu-Leu-Arg-Gln-Ile-Ala-Ser-Tyr-Gly-Arg-Gly-Tyr-Thr-Tyr-Leu-Leu-Ser-Arg-Ala- (170) (180)

Gly-Val-Thr-Gly-Ala-Glu-Asn-Arg-Ala-Ala-Leu-Pro-Leu-Asn-His-Leu-Val-Ala-Lys-Leu- (190) (200)

Lys-Glu-Tyr-Asn-Ala-Ala-Pro-Pro-Leu-Gln-Gly-Phe-Gly-Ile-Ser-Ala-Pro-Asp-Gln-Val- (210) (220)

Lys-Ala-Ala-Ile-Asp-Ala-Gly-Ala-Ala-Gly-Ala-Ile-Ser-Gly-Ser-Ala-Ile-Val-Lys-Ile- (230) (240)

Ile-Glu-Gln-His-Asn-Ile-Glu-Pro-Glu-Lys-Met-Leu-Ala-Ala-Leu-Lys-Val-Phe-Val-Gln- (250) (260)

Pro-Met-Lys-Ala-Ala-Thr-Arg-Ser- (268)

(a)

A chain
Gly-Ile-Val-Glu-Gln-Cys-Cys-Ala-Ser-Val-Cys-Ser-Leu-Tyr-Gln-Leu-Glu-Asn-Tyr-Cys-Asn
(5) (10) (15) (21)

B chain
Phe-Val-Asn-Gln-His-Leu-Cys-Gly-Ser-His-Leu-Val-Glu-Ala-Leu-Tyr-Leu-Val-Cys-Gly-Glu-
(5) (10) (15) (20)

Arg-Gly-Phe-Phe-Tyr-Thr-Pro-Lys-Ala
(25) (30)

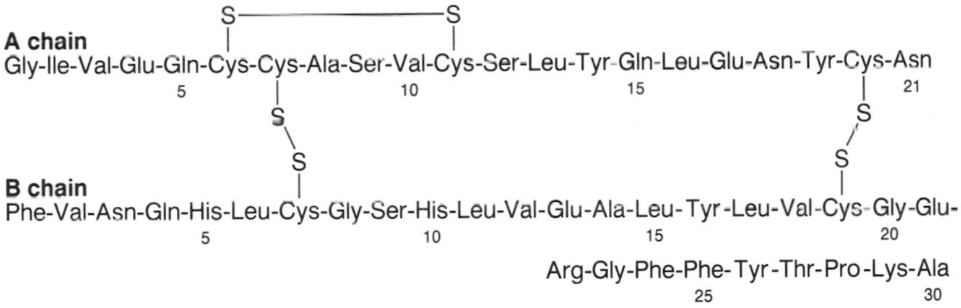

(b)

Figure 11-3. Primary sequences of two proteins. (a) The tryptophan synthetase A protein in *E. coli*. (b) Beef insulin protein. Note that the amino acid cysteine can form unique "sulfur bridges," since it contains sulfur.

break peptide bonds only between specific amino acids in proteins. Thus, a large protein can be broken by such enzymes into a number of smaller fragments. These fragments can be separated according to their migration speeds in a solvent on chromatographic paper. Because the speeds of mobility of different fragments may vary differently in various solvents, two-dimensional chromatography can be used to enhance the separation of the fragments (Figure 11-10). In this technique, the mixture is separated in one solvent; then the paper is turned 90 degrees and another solvent used.

When the paper is stained, the polypeptides appear as spots in a characteristic chromatographic pattern called the **fingerprint** of the protein. Each of the spots can be cut out

and the polypeptide fragments washed from the paper. Because each spot contains only small polypeptides, their amino acid sequences can easily be determined. Using different proteolytic enzymes to cleave the protein at different points, we can repeat the experiment to obtain other sets of fragments. The fragments from the different treatments will overlap (because the breaks have been made in different places with each treatment). The problem of solving the overall sequence then becomes one of fitting together the small-fragment sequences—almost like solving a tricky jigsaw or crossword puzzle (Figure 11-11).

Using this elegant technique, Sanger confirmed that the sequence of amino acids (as well as the amounts of the various amino acids) is specific to a particular protein. In

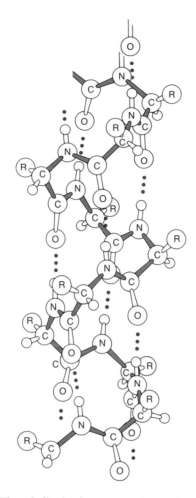

Figure 11-4. The α-helix that is a common basis of secondary protein structure. The backbone of the protein can be seen as the colored lines. Each R is a specific side group on one amino acid. Dots are hydrogen bonds, which are weak stabilizing bonds that maintain the helical shape. (Reprinted from Linus Pauling, *The Nature of the Chemical Bond.* Copyright 1939 and 1940 by Cornell University. Third edition © 1960 by Cornell University. Used by permission of Cornell University Press.)

other words, the amino acid sequence is what makes insulin insulin.

We can now examine some of the studies by Vernon Ingram (in 1957) on the globular protein hemoglobin—the molecule that transports oxygen in red blood cells. Hemoglobin is made up of four polypeptide chains. Hemoglobin A (HbA), the protein from normal adults, contains two identical chains of one type called α chains, and two identical chains of a second type called β chains. The α chain contains 141 amino acids, and the β chain contains 146. Ingram compared HbA, from normal people, with HbS, from people homozygous for the mutant gene that causes sickle-cell anemia. Using Sanger's technique, he found that the fingerprint of HbS differs from that of HbA in only one spot. Sequencing that spot from the two kinds of hemoglobin, Ingram found that only one amino acid in the fragment differs in the two kinds. Apparently, of all of the amino acids known to make up a hemoglobin molecule, a substitution of valine for glutamic acid at just one point in the chain is all that is needed to produce the defective hemoglobin (Figure 11-12). Unless patients with HbS receive medical attention, this single error in an amino acid in one protein will hasten their death. Figure 11-13 shows the sequence of events leading to the disease.

Notice what Ingram had accomplished. A gene mutation that is well established through genetic studies has been connected to an altered amino acid *sequence* in a protein. Subsequent studies identified numerous changes in hemoglobin, and each is the consequence of a single amino acid difference. Figure 11-14 shows a few examples. We conclude that one mutation in a gene corresponds to a change of one amino acid in the sequence of a protein.

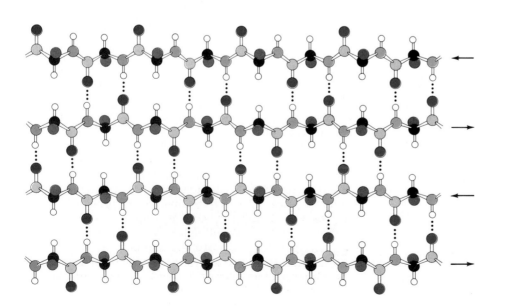

Figure 11-5. Antiparallel β-pleated sheet. Adjacent strands run in opposite directions. Hydrogen bonds between NH and CO groups of adjacent strands stabilize the structure. The side chains (shown in medium gray) are above and below the plane of the sheet. (From L. Stryer, *Biochemistry,* 3d ed. Copyright © 1983 by W. H. Freeman and Co.)

Figure 11-8. A model of the hemoglobin molecule (shown as contoured layers to provide a visualization of the three-dimensional shape). The different shadings indicate the different polypeptide chains that combine to form the quaternary structure of the protein. The disks are heme groups, complex structures containing iron. (After M. F. Perutz, "The Hemoglobin Molecule." Copyright © 1964 by Scientific American, Inc. All rights reserved.)

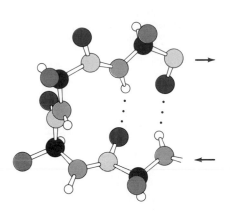

Figure 11-6. Structure of a β-turn. The CO group of residue 1 of the tetrapeptide shown here is hydrogen bonded to the NH group of residue 4, which results in a hairpin turn. (From L. Stryer, *Biochemistry,* 3d ed. Copyright © 1983 by W. H. Freeman and Co.)

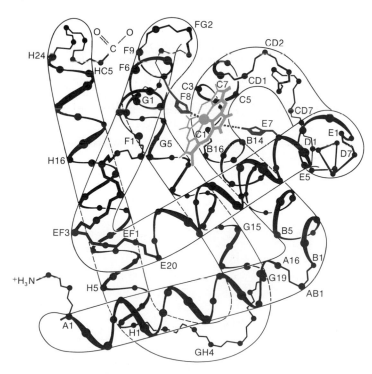

Figure 11-7. Folded tertiary structure of myoglobin, an oxygen-storage protein. Each dot represents an amino acid. The heme group, a cofactor that facilitates the binding of oxygen, is shown in pink. (From L. Stryer, *Biochemistry,* 2d ed. Copyright © 1981 by L. Stryer. Based on R. E. Dickerson, in *The Proteins,* 2d ed., vol. 2. Edited by H. Neurath. Academic Press, 1964.)

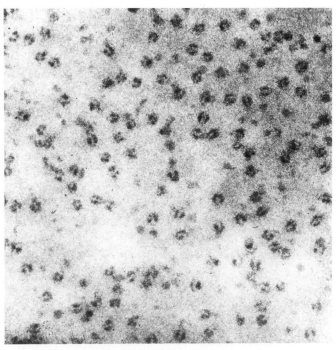

Figure 11-9. Electron micrograph of the enzyme aspartate transcarbamylase. Each small "glob" is an enzyme molecule. Note the quaternary structure; the enzyme is composed of subunits. (From Jack D. Griffith.)

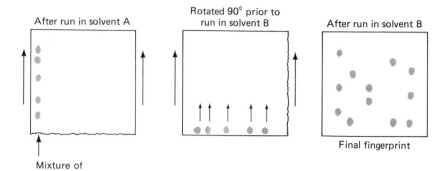

After run in solvent A

Rotated 90° prior to run in solvent B

After run in solvent B

Mixture of fragments spotted here

Final fingerprint

Figure 11-10. Two-dimensional chromatographic fingerprinting of a polypeptide fragment mixture. A protein is digested by a proteolytic enzyme into fragments that are only a few amino acids long. A piece of chromatographic filter paper is then spotted with this mixture and dipped into solvent A. As solvent A ascends the paper, some of the fragments are separated. The paper is then turned 90 degrees and, as solvent B ascends, further resolution of the fragments is obtained.

Message Genes determine the primary sequences of amino acids in specific proteins.

Protein Function

The genes truly are the master controllers of the cell. They not only dictate cell chemistry through the enzymes encoded by some genes, but also dictate biological architecture through the structural proteins encoded by other genes. Furthermore, the blueprints of such important proteins as hormones and hemoglobin are encoded in the structure of genes.

How can a single amino acid substitution, such as that in sickle-cell hemoglobin (Figure 11-13), have such a profound effect on protein function and the phenotype of an organism? Take enzymes, for example. Enzymes are known to do their job of catalysis by physically grappling with their substrate molecules, twisting or bending the molecules to make or break chemical bonds. Figure 11-15 shows the gastric digestion enzyme carboxypeptidase in its relaxed

position and after grappling with its substrate molecule, glycyltyrosine. The substrate molecule fits into a notch in the enzyme structure; this notch is called the **active site.** Figure 11-16 diagrams the general concept. (Note that here we have encountered the two basic types of reactions performed by enzymes: breakdown of substrate into simple products and synthesis of a complex product from one or more simpler substrates.)

Much of the "blob" structure of an enzyme is nonreactive material that simply supports the active site. We might expect that amino acid substitutions through most of the structure would have little effect, but that very specific amino acids are required for the part of the enzyme molecule that gives the precise shape to the active site. Hence the possibility arises that a functional enzyme would not require a *unique* amino acid sequence for the entire polypeptide. This has been demonstrated to be true in a number of systems in which the effects of different amino acid substitutions on the catalytic activity of an enzyme have been examined. It is clear that there are numerous positions in a polypeptide that can be filled by several alternative amino acids compatible with the enzyme function. At certain

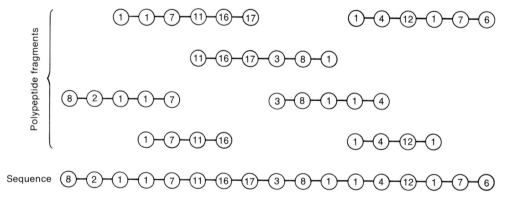

Figure 11-11. Alignment of polypeptide fragments to reconstruct an entire amino acid sequence. Different proteolytic enzymes can be used on the same protein to form different fingerprints. The amino acid sequence of each spot can be determined rather easily, and, because of overlap of amino acid sequences from different spots from different fingerprints, the entire amino acid sequence of the original protein can be determined. Using this procedure, it took Sanger about six years to determine the sequence of the insulin molecule, a relatively small protein.

Normal hemoglobin

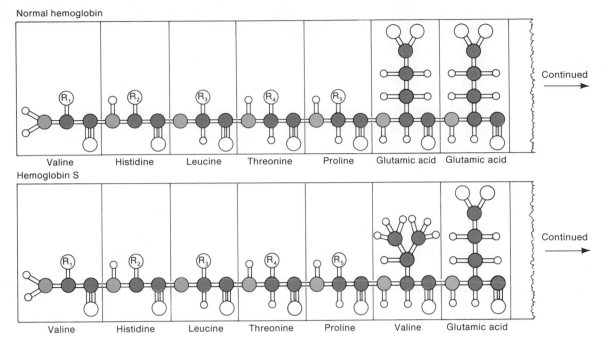

Valine   Histidine   Leucine   Threonine   Proline   Glutamic acid   Glutamic acid

Hemoglobin S

Valine   Histidine   Leucine   Threonine   Proline   Valine   Glutamic acid

Figure 11-12. The difference at the molecular level between normalcy and sickle-cell disease. Shown are only the first seven amino acids; all the rest not shown are identical. (From Anthony Cerami and Charles M. Peterson, "Cyanate and Sickle-Cell Disease." Copyright © 1975 by Scientific American, Inc. All rights reserved.)

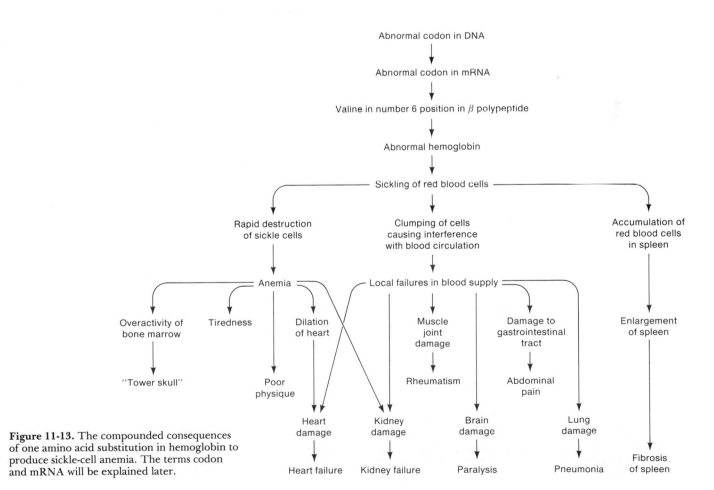

Figure 11-13. The compounded consequences of one amino acid substitution in hemoglobin to produce sickle-cell anemia. The terms codon and mRNA will be explained later.

Amino acid position	- 2 ----- 16--------- 43-------- 67------- 87 ------------132 ----143
Normal	His ---- Gly --------Glu ------- Val ------ Thr ------------Lys ---- His
Tokuchi	Tyr ───
Baltimore	───────Asp ────────────────────────────────
Galveston	─────────────── Ala ───────────────────────
Milwaukee	────────────────────────── Glu ────────────
Woolwich	──────────────────────────────────────Gln ────
Kenwood	── Asp

Figure 11-14. A variety of single amino acid substitutions in human hemoglobin. Amino acids at all residue positions except those indicated are normal. Each type of change causes disease. (Names indicate areas where cases were first identified.)

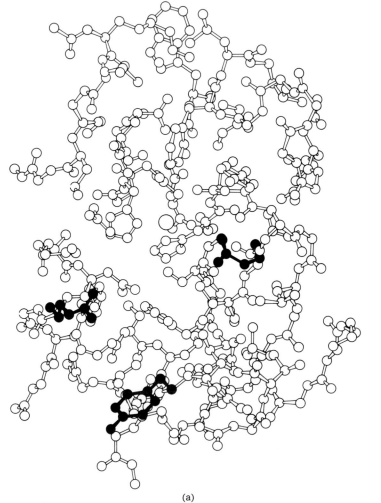

(a)

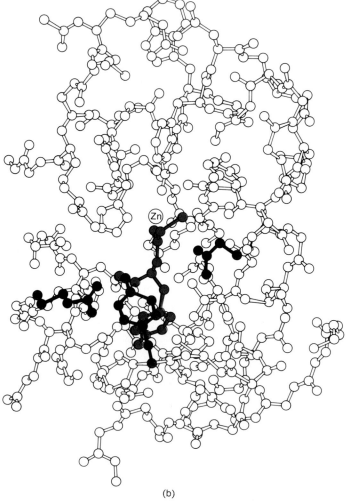

(b)

Figure 11-15. The active site of a specific enzyme, the digestive enzyme carboxypeptidase. (a) The enzyme without substrate. (b) The enzyme with its substrate (red) in position. Three crucial amino acids (black) have moved position to engage with the substrate. Carboxypeptidase carves up proteins in the diet. (From W. N. Lipscomb, *Proc. Robert A. Welch Found. Conf. Chem. Res.* 15:140–141, 1971.)

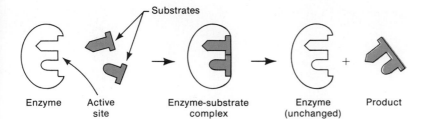

Figure 11-16. Diagrammatic representation of the action of a hypothetical enzyme in putting two substrate molecules together. The "lock-and-key" fit of the substrate into the enzyme's active site is very important in this model.

other positions in the polypeptide, only the wild-type amino acid will restore activity; in all likelihood, these amino acids form critical parts of the active sites. In Figure 11-15, some of these critical amino acids are indicated by gray shading.

Message Protein architecture is the key to gene function. A gene mutation typically results in substitution of a different amino acid into the polypeptide sequence of a protein. The new amino acid may have different chemical properties that are incompatible with the proper protein architecture at that particular position; in such a case, the mutation will lead to a nonfunctional protein.

Temperature-Sensitive Alleles

Recall that some mutants appear to be wild-type at normal temperatures but can be detected as mutants at high or low temperature. We can now explain such mutations by assuming that a substitution of an amino acid produces a protein that is functional at normal temperatures — called **permissive** temperatures — but is distorted and nonfunctional at high or low temperatures — called **restrictive** temperatures. Figure 11-17 shows a heat-sensitive example.

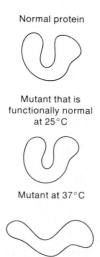

Normal protein

Mutant that is functionally normal at 25°C

Mutant at 37°C

Figure 11-17. Diagram of protein conformational distortion, probably the basis for temperature sensitivity in certain mutants. An amino acid substitution that has no significant effect at normal (permissive) temperatures may cause significant distortion at abnormal (restrictive) temperatures.

As we have seen, conditional mutations such as temperature-sensitive mutations can be very useful to geneticists. Stocks of the mutant culture can easily be maintained under permissive conditions, and the mutant phenotype can be studied intensively under restrictive conditions. Such mutants can be very useful in the genetic dissection of biological systems. For example, with a temperature-sensitive allele, the time at which a gene is acting can be determined by shifting to restrictive temperature at various times during development.

Enzymic Explanation of Genetic Ratios and Dominance

When the significance of the gene control of cellular chemistry became clear, a lot of other things fell into place. Many genetic generalizations now could be explained and tied together in a single conceptual model.

Most "classical" (Mendelian) gene-interaction ratios can be explained simply by the one-gene–one-enzyme concept. For example, recall the 9:7 F_2 dihybrid ratio for flower pigment:

P	$AA\,BB$ (purple) $\times$ $aa\,bb$ (white)		
F_1	$Aa\,Bb$ (purple)		
F_2	9	$A-B-$	(purple)
	3	$A-bb$	(white)
	3	$aa\,B-$	(white)
	1	$aa\,bb$	(white)

We can easily explain this result if we imagine a biosynthetic pathway leading ultimately to a purple petal pigment in which there are two colorless (white) precursors:

white precursor 1 $\xrightarrow{\text{enzyme A}}$ white precursor 2 $\xrightarrow{\text{enzyme B}}$ purple pigment

A allele   B allele

(Try to work out your own models to explain such ratios as 9:3:4 and 13:3.)

The meaning of dominance and recessiveness also becomes a little clearer in light of the biochemical model. In most cases, dominance represents the presence of enzyme

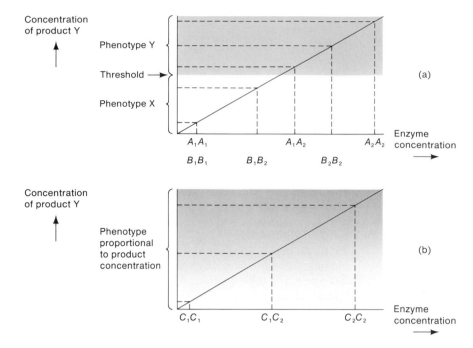

Figure 11-18. Hypothetical curves relating enzyme concentration to the amount of product. Two basic situations are possible. In (a), there is a threshold of the enzyme product above which a sharply contrasting phenotype, Y, is observed. Depending on where the levels in the three possible genotypes occur in relation to this threshold, the heterozygote will show either phenotype X (for example, B_1B_2) or Y (for example, A_1A_2). If the subscript 2 alleles are the active ones, you can see that the active allele (A_2) can be dominant, which is normally the case. Less frequently, the inactive allele (B_1) can be dominant. In (b) there is no threshold, and the heterozygote has an intermediate phenotype. This situation explains incomplete dominance.

function, whereas recessiveness represents the lack of enzyme function. A heterozygote has one dominant allele that can produce the functional enzyme:

precursor X $\longrightarrow$ product Y

enzyme A

allele A   allele a $\longrightarrow$ nonfunctional enzyme (does nothing)

If phenotype Y is due to the presence of product Y, and if phenotype X is due to the absence of product Y, then it is clear that the heterozygote will show phenotype Y, and allele A will be dominant over allele a.

However, this is not the only possible model. We can build-in the concept of a threshold. Suppose that phenotype Y is produced only when the concentration of product Y exceeds some threshold level. Suppose further that the homozygote AA produces more enzyme and hence more product than the heterozygote Aa. In this case, the phenotype of the heterozygote will depend upon the relationship between the threshold and the amount of product Y produced by the heterozygote. In Figure 11-18a, the heterozygote A_1A_2 does produce enough product Y to exceed the threshold, so the heterozygote has phenotype Y, and therefore A_2 is dominant over A_1. However, the situation could be like that shown for the alleles B_1 and B_2, where the heterozygote B_1B_2 does not exceed the threshold. In this case (which is less common), B_1 is dominant over B_2, and the dominant phenotype is the one involving a lack of product Y.

Figure 11-18b shows a situation in which no threshold exists. The heterozygote has an intermediate phenotype — exactly the situation observed in cases of incomplete dominance.

What determines whether a gene will behave like A, B, or C? Probably many interacting factors are involved: other genes, the chemical nature of the product, and (last but not least) the effect of the environment on that particular cell type. Finally, note that Figure 11-18 shows a simple linear relationship between enzyme concentration and the number of active alleles — but this need not be the case, as we shall see in Chapter 19.

The recessiveness of the *arg* mutants in *Neurospora* can be demonstrated by making heterokaryons between two *arg* mutants. If an *arg-1* mutant is placed on minimal medium with an *arg-2* mutant, the two cell types fuse and form a heterokaryon composed of both nuclear types in a common cytoplasm (Figure 11-19). The *arg-1* nuclei produce enzyme for one step, and the *arg-2* nuclei produce enzyme for the other step, so they combine their abilities to produce arginine in the shared cytoplasm.

The scale of involvement of the genes in controlling cellular metabolism is staggering. Most of us have boggled at the charts on laboratory walls showing the myriad interlocking, branched, and circular pathways along which the cell's chemical intermediates are shunted like parts on an assembly line. Bonds are broken, molecules cleaved, molecules united, groups added or removed, and so on. The key fact is that almost every step, represented by an arrow on the metabolic chart, is controlled (mediated) by an enzyme. And each of these enzymes is produced under the direction of a gene that specifies its function. Genes control the enzymes, and the enzymes control the chemical reactions that comprise metabolism. When we study a gene (or a few genes), we are focusing on one tiny corner of this vast network controlled by genes and their enzymes.

Humans provide some startling examples. Consider the list of specific enzyme-associated genetic diseases in Table 11-2, which suggests the magnitude of genetic involvement in human disease. Figure 11-20 shows a corner

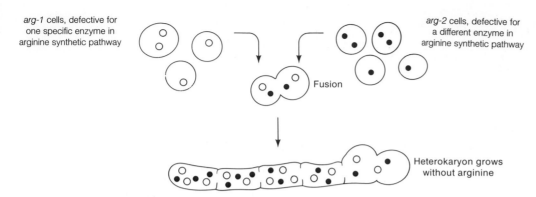

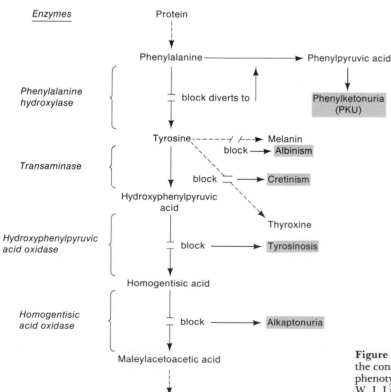

Figure 11-19. Formation of, and complementation in, a heterokaryon of *Neurospora*. Vegetative cells of this fungus can fuse, allowing the nuclei from the two strains to intermingle within the same cytoplasm. If each cell is blocked at a different point in a pathway, as are *arg-1* and *arg-2*, all functions are present in a heterokaryon and the *Neurospora* will grow; in other words, complementation takes place.

of the metabolic map to illustrate how a set of diseases, some of them common and familiar to us, can stem from blockage of adjacent steps in the pathways.

Genetic Fine Structure

Until the beginning of this chapter, our genetic and cytological analysis had led us to regard the chromosome as a linear (one-dimensional) array of genes, strung rather like beads on an unfastened necklace. Indeed, this model is sometimes called the bead theory. According to the bead theory, a gene is a unit of inheritance whose existence is recognized through its mutant alleles. All of these alleles affect a single phenotypic character, all map to one chromosomal locus, all give mutant phenotypes when paired, and all give Mendelian ratios when intercrossed. There are several points about the bead theory worth emphasizing:

Figure 11-20. One small part of the human metabolic map, showing the consequences of various specific enzyme failures. (Disease phenotypes are shown in colored boxes.) (After I. M. Lerner and W. J. Libby, *Heredity, Evolution, and Society,* 2d ed. Copyright © 1976 by W. H. Freeman and Co.)

■ **TABLE 11-2.** Enzymopathies: inherited disorders in which altered activity (usually deficiency) of a specific enzyme has been demonstrated in humans

Condition	Enzyme with deficient activity[1,2]
Acatalasia	Catalase
Acid phosphatase deficiency	Acid phosphatase
Adrenal hyperplasia I	20,21-Desmolase*
Adrenal hyperplasia II	3-β-Hydroxysteroid dehydrogenase*
Adrenal hyperplasia III	21-Hydroxylase*
Adrenal hyperplasia IV	11-β-Hydroxylase*
Adrenal hyperplasia V	17-Hydroxylase*
Albinism	Tyrosinase
Aldosterone deficiency	18-OH-Dehydrogenase
Alkaptonuria	Homogentisic acid oxidase
Angiokeratoma, diffuse (Fabry disease)	Ceramide trihexosidase
Apnea, drug-induced	Pseudocholinesterase
Argininemia	Arginase
Argininosuccinic aciduria	Argininosuccinase
Aspartylglycosaminuria	Specific hydrolase (AADG-ase)
Ataxia, intermittent	Pyruvate decarboxylase
Carnosinemia	Carnosinase
Citrullinemia	Arginosuccinic acid synthetase
Crigler-Najjar syndrome	Glucuronyl transferase
Cystathioninuria	Cystathionase
Disaccharide intolerance I	Invertase
Disaccharide intolerance II	Invertase, maltase
Disaccharide intolerance III	Lactase
Ehlers-Danlos syndrome, type V	Lysyl oxidase
Ehlers-Danlos syndrome, type VI	Collagen lysyl hydroxylase
Ehlers-Danlos syndrome, type VII	Procollagen peptidase
Fanconi panmyelopathy	Exonuclease*
Farber lipogranulomatosis	Ceramidase
Formininotransferase deficiency	Formininotransferase*
Fructose intolerance	Fructose 1-phosphate aldolase
Fructosuria	Hepatic fructokinase
Fucosidosis	α-L-Fucosidase
Galactokinase deficiency	Galactokinase
Galactose epimerase deficiency	Galactose epimerase
Galactosemia	Galactose 1-phosphate uridyl transferase
Gangliosidosis, generalized, type I GM	β-Galactosidase A, B, C
Gangliosidosis, GM$_1$, type II or juvenile form	β-Galactosidase B, C
Gangliosidosis, GM(3)	Acetylgalactosaminyl transferase
Gaucher disease	Glucocerebrosidase
Glycogen storage disease I	Glucose 6-phosphatase

Condition	Enzyme with deficient activity[1,2]
Glycogen storage disease II	α-1,4-Glucosidase
Glycogen storage disease III	Amylo-1,6-glucosidase
Glycogen storage disease IV	Amylo-(1,4 to 1,6)-transglucosidase
Glycogen storage disease V	Muscle phosphorylase
Glycogen storage disease VI	Liver phosphorylase*
Glycogen storage disease VII	Muscle phosphofructokinase
Glycogen storage disease VIII	Liver phosphorylase kinase
Gout	Hypoxanthine guanine phosphoribosyltransferase
	PPRP synthetase (increased activity)
Granulomatous disease	NADPH oxidase
Hemolytic anemia	Adenosine triphosphatase
	Adenylate kinase
	Aldolase A
	Diphosphoglycerate mutase
	γ-Glutamylcysteine synthetase
	Glucose 6-phosphate dehydrogenase
	Glutathione peroxidase
	Glutathione synthetase
	Hexokinase
	Hexosephosphate isomerase
	Phosphoglycerate kinase
	Pyrimidine 5'-nucleotidase
	Pyruvate kinase
	Trisephosphate isomerase
Histidinemia	Histidase
Homocystinuria I	Cystathionine synthetase
Homocystinuria II	N^5N^{10}-Methylenetetrahydrofolate reductase
β-Hydroxyisovaleric aciduria and methylcrotonylglysinuria	β-Methylcrotonyl CoA carboxylase*
Hydroxyprolinemia	Hydroxyproline oxidase
Hyperammonemia I	Ornithine transcarbamylase
Hyperammonemia II	Carbamyl phosphate synthetase
Hyperglycinemia, ketotic form	Propionyl CoA carboxylase*
Hyperglycinemia, nonketotic form	Glycine formininotransferase
Hyperlipoproteinemia, type I	Lipoprotein lipase
Hyperlysinemia	Lysine-ketoglutarate reductase
Hyperprolinemia I	Proline oxidase
Hyperprolinemia II	δ-1-Pyrroline-5-carboxylate dehydrogenase*
Hypoglycemia and acidosis	Fructose 1,6-diphosphatase

■ **TABLE 11-2.** *(Continued)*

Condition	Enzyme with deficient activity[1,2]
Hypophosphatasia	Alkaline phosphatase
Immunodeficiency disease	Adenosine deaminase
	Uridine monophosphate kinase
Intestinal lactase deficiency (adult)	Lactase
Isovalericacidemia	Isovaleric acid CoA dehydrogenase
Ketoacidosis, infantile	Succinyl CoA: 3-ketoacid CoA-transferase
Krabbe disease	A β-Galactosidase
Lactosyl ceramidosis	Lactosyl ceramidase
Leigh necrotizing encephalomyelopathy	Pyruvate carboxylase
Lipase deficiency, congenital	Lipase (pancreatic)
Lysine intolerance	L-Lysine: NAD-oxidoreductase
Male pseudohermaphroditism	Testicular 17,20-desmolase
	Testicular 17-ketosteroid dehydrogenase*
	α-Reductase*
Mannosidosis	α-Mannosidase
Maple sugar urine disease	Keto acid decarboxylase
Metachromatic leukodystrophy	Arylsulfatase A (sulfatide sulfatase)
Methemoglobinemia	NAD-methemoglobin reductase
Methylmalonicaciduria I (B$_{12}$-unresponsive)	Methylmalonic CoA mutase
Methylmalonicaciduria II (B$_{12}$-responsive)	Deoxyadenosyl transferase*
Methylmalonicaciduria III	Methylmalonyl-CoA racemase
Mucopolysaccharidosis I	α-L-Iduronidase
Mucopolysaccharidosis II	Sulfo-iduronide sulfatase
Mucopolysaccharidosis IIIA	Heparan sulfate sulfatase
Mucopolysaccharidosis IIIB	N-Acetyl-α-D-glucosaminidase
Mucopolysaccharidosis IV	6-Sulfatase*
Mucopolysaccharidosis VI	Arylsulfatase B
Mucopolysaccharidosis VII	β-Glucuronidase
Myeloperoxidase deficiency with disseminated candidiases	Myeloperoxidase (leukocyte)
Niemann–Pick disease	Sphingomyelinase
Norum disease	Lecithin cholesterol acetyltransferase (LCAT)
Ornithinemia	Ornithine ketoacid aminotransferase
Oroticaciduria I	Orotidylic pyrophosphorylase and orotidylic decarboxylase
Oroticaciduria II	Orotidylic decarboxylase
Oxalosis I (glycolic aciduria)	2-Oxoglutarate-glyoxylase carboligase

Condition	Enzyme with deficient activity[1,2]
Oxalosis II (glyceric aciduria)	D-Glycerate dehydrogenase
Pentosuria	Xylitol dehydrogenase (L-xylulose reductase)
Phenylketonuria	Phenylalanine hydroxylase
Porphyria, acute intermittent	Uroporphyrinogen I synthetase
Porphyria, congenital	Uroporphyrinogen III cosynthetase
Pulmonary emphysema and/or cirrhosis	α-1-Antitrypsin
Pyridoxine-dependent infantile convulsions	Glutamic acid decarboxylase
Pyridoxine-responsive anemia	δ-Aminolevulinic acid synthetase*
Pyruvate carboxylase	Pyruvate carboxylase
Refsum disease	Phytanic acid oxidase
Renal tubular acidosis with deafness	Carbonic anhydrase B
Richner-Hanhart syndrome	Tyrosine aminotransferase
Rickets, vitamin-D-dependent	25-Hydroxycholecalciferol*
Sandhoff disease (GM$_2$-gangliosidosis, type II)	Hexosaminidase A, B
Sarcosinemia	Sarcosine dehydrogenase*
Sulfite oxidase deficiency	Sulfite oxidase
Tay-Sachs disease	Hexosaminidase A
Thyroid hormonogenesis, defect in, II	Peroxidase*
Thyroid hormonogenesis, defect in, IV	Iodotyrosine dehalogenase (deiodinase)
Trypsinogen deficiency	Trypsinogen
Tyrosinemia I	*Para*-hydroxyphenylpyruvate oxidase
Tyrosinemia II	Tyrosine transaminase
Valinemia	Valine transaminase
Wolman disease	Acid lipase
Xanthinuria	Xanthine oxidase
Xanthurenic aciduria	Kynureninase
Xeroderma pigmentosum	Ultraviolet specific endonuclease
Xylosidase deficiency	Xylosidase

SOURCE: Victor A. McKusick, *Mendelian Inheritance in Man*, 4th ed., Johns Hopkins University Press, 1975.

[1] In some conditions marked * (as well as some not listed), deficiency of a particular enzyme is suspected but has not been proved by direct study of enzyme activity.

[2] The form of gout due to increased activity of PPRP is the only disorder listed that is due to *increased* enzyme activity.

1. The gene is viewed as a fundamental unit of *structure*, indivisible by crossing-over. Crossing-over occurs between genes (the beads in this model) but never within them.

2. The gene is viewed as a fundamental unit of *change*, or mutation. It changes from one allelic form to another, but there are no smaller components within it that can change.

3. The gene is viewed as the basic unit of *function*. Parts of a gene, if they exist, cannot function (although the precise function of the gene is not specified in this model).

However, the elucidation of the structure of DNA (Chapter 10), together with the realization that the gene consists of a sequence of nucleotides that encode the amino acid sequence of a protein, is at odds with the view that the gene is the smallest unit of mutation and of recombination. How can these two viewpoints be reconciled? Seymour Benzer's work in the 1950s showed that the bead theory was not correct. Benzer was able to use a genetic system where extremely small recombination percentages could be detected. He demonstrated that whereas a gene can be defined as a unit of function, a gene can be subdivided into a linear array of sites that are mutable and that can be recombined. The units of mutation and recombination can be correlated with single nucleotide pairs.

Benzer capitalized on the fantastic **resolving power** made possible by using selective systems for rare events in phages. He worked with the virulent *Escherichia coli* phage T4 (Figure 11-21) and a class of mutants that produces a phenotype called rapid lysis (*r*). Rapid-lysis strains produce large circular plaques (in contrast to the small and irregular plaques of normal phages). Genes at several different loci can mutate to cause rapid lysis. Benzer worked with the locus called *rII* for one important reason: all *rII* alleles are *conditional* lethals. That is, an *rII* mutant will grow and form large plaques of *E. coli* strain B, but it will not grow at all on the strain of *E. coli* that is lysogenic for λ called strain K(λ). (We need not worry now about the cause of the difference between these two *E. coli* strains.) In contrast, *rII*⁺ (wild-type) phages will grow and form small ragged plaques on both strains. Thus we have the relationships shown in Table 11-3.

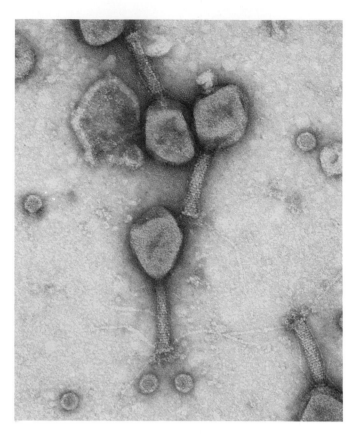

Figure 11-21. Enlargement of the *E. coli* phage T4 showing details of structure: note head, tail, and tail fibers. This was the phage used by Benzer in his experiments on the nature of the *rII* (rapid lysis) gene. (From Jack D. Griffith.)

This conditional growth of *rII* strains proved essential to the analysis because it allows the use of selective techniques to identify recombinants. Benzer started with an initial sample of eight independently derived *rII* mutant strains and set about crossing them in all possible combinations of pairs, simply by the double infection of *E. coli* B. He took the lysate (progeny phages) and plated onto "a lawn" of *E. coli* K(λ), on which the *rII* genotypes will not grow. But plaques *were* seen on K(λ), indicating that recombination had given rise to *rII*⁺ genotypes (Figure 11-22). The frequency of plaques was too large for them to be due to back-mutations. Furthermore, the alleles could be mapped unambiguously to the right or left of each other to give what we now call a gene map. In this case, the map units are the frequency of *rII*⁺ plaques.

$$rII^1 \quad rII^7 \quad rII^4 \quad rII^5 \quad rII^2 \quad rII^8 \quad rII^3 \quad rII^6$$

Recombination within a gene, called **intragenic recombination**, seems to be the rule rather than the exception. It can virtually always be found at any locus if a suitable selection system is available to detect recombinants. In other words, a mutant allele can be pictured as a length of genetic material (the gene) that has a damaged or non-wild part—that is, a **mutant site**—somewhere, and this partial damage is what causes the non-wild phenotype. Different

■ **TABLE 11-3.** Plaque phenotypes produced by different combinations of *E. coli* and phage strains

	E. coli strain	
T4 phage strain	B	K(λ)
rII	Large, round	No plaques
rII⁺	Small, ragged	Small, ragged

alleles have different phenotypic effects because they involve damage to different parts (sites) of the wild-type allele.

Thus, an allele a^1 can be represented as

$$+ + + + + * + + + + + + + + + + + + + + + + +$$

where the asterisk (*) represents the mutant site within an otherwise normal gene (denoted by the sites marked +). A cross between a^1 and another mutant allele a^2, in general, then, is something like this:

$$+ + + + + * + + + + + + + + + + + + + + + +$$

$$\times$$

$$+ + + + + + | | | | | + + + + * + + + + + +$$

and it is easy to see how

$$+ +$$

could be generated by a simple crossover anywhere between the two mutant sites.

Benzer showed, contrary to the classical view, that genes were not indivisible but could be subdivided by recombination. Extending his analysis to hundreds of rII alleles, Benzer found that the minimal recombinant frequency in a cross between a pair of different mutant alleles was 0.01 percent, even though his analytical system was capable of detecting recombinant frequencies as low as 0.0001 percent if they occurred. This led to the idea that genes were composed of small units, which Benzer named "recons," and that recombination could occur between but

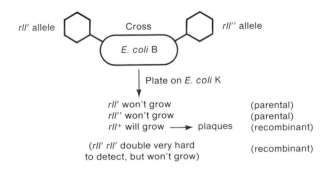

Figure 11-22. Selection of intragenic recombinants at the rII locus of phage T4. Mutants within the gene rII cannot grow on E. coli K. When two different phage carrying different alleles of rII infect the same bacterial cell, some progeny phage can grow on E. coli K; in other words, some progeny have become rII⁺. This result indicates that recombination has occurred *within* a single gene and not just between genes.

not within "recons." Thus, the "recon," rather than the gene, was the unit of recombination. The gene was assumed to be a completely linear sequence of "recons." Once again, a hypothetical entity (Benzer's "recon") was determined solely through genetic analysis—and once again it was soon to assume physical reality. The elucidation of the structure of DNA (Chapter 10) and subsequent detailed genetic analyses allowed the definition of the single nucleotide pair as the smallest unit of recombination. (The term "recon" is not in current usage.)

Message A gene is composed of units, originally called "recons," that are not divisible by recombination. Each unit consists of a single nucleotide pair.

The occurrence of intragenic recombination permits the construction of detailed gene maps. The relative frequencies of intragenic recombinants in crosses between various mutant alleles reveal the order and relative positions of the mutant sites within a gene. It should be noted that recombination within genes is the same as recombination between genes except that the scale is different. Figure 11-23 shows a detailed map of the rII region obtained by intragenic crosses.

Further advances in our understanding of intragenic recombination were made in the 1960s by Charles Yanofsky, who studied the enzyme tryptophan synthetase in E. coli. The enzyme catalyzes the conversion of indoleglycerol phosphate into tryptophan. Two genes, trpA and trpB, control the enzyme. Each gene controls a separate polypeptide; after the A and B polypeptides are produced, they combine to form the active enzyme (a multimeric protein). We concentrate here on the A gene.

Yanofsky isolated many A mutants, all of which required tryptophan in order to grow. He carefully performed genetic mapping studies by intercrossing the mutants and measuring the frequency of trp⁺ cells produced. Eventually he obtained a gene map. He crossed two trpA⁻ mutants (A23 and A46). These two mutant sites map very close together on the genetic map, and each involves an amino acid substitution at position 210 of the polypeptide (Figure 11-24). He plated the progeny of this cross on a medium that does not contain tryptophan; he found that about 0.002 percent of the progeny grew, indicating that they were trpA⁺ recombinants. Yanofsky extracted enzyme from the recombinants and determined the amino acid present at position 210. As Figure 11-24 shows, the recombinants matched the original wild-type.

This evidence demonstrates that the codon (the piece of gene coding for an amino acid) is composed of at least two recombination units—because we have just demonstrated recombination within the codon. Figure 11-25 shows a chromosomal or genic diagram of the cross that

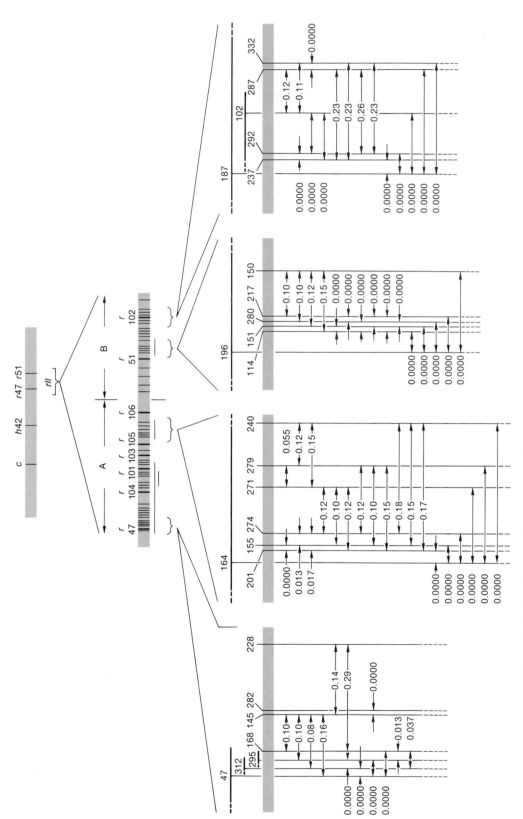

Figure 11-23. Detailed recombination map of the *rII* region of the phage T4 chromosome. The map unit is the percentage of *rII*⁺ recombinants in crosses between the *rII* mutants. Typical regions are progressively enlarged. Numbers on the map represent mutant sites. Note that the two portions of the *rII* region, A and B, are two different functional units of the region, as described in the text. After S. Benzer, *Proc. Natl. Acad. Sci. USA* 41:344, 1955. From G. S. Stent and R. Calendar, *Molecular Genetics*, 2d ed. Copyright © 1978 by W. H. Freeman and Co.)

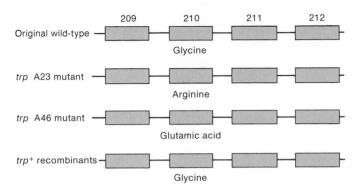

Figure 11-24. Intracodon recombination at codon 210. The mutants *trp* A23 and *trp* A46 each have a different amino acid at position 210, and each protein is nonfunctional. When these two mutants are mated, however, an occasional *trp*+ progeny individual occurs with functional tryptophan synthetase A protein. This occurrence indicates that genetic recombination can occur within the coding unit for one amino acid.

may make the concept a little clearer. The glycine codon is obtained from an arginine and a glutamic acid codon by crossing-over within the codons. We also know that this codon corresponds to at least two mutational sites, because the two mutant sites studied here map within the codon and affect the same amino acid position in the polypeptide.

Colinearity of Gene and Protein

The elucidation of the structure of DNA by Watson and Crick led to the realization that the structure of proteins must be encoded in the linear sequence of nucleotides in the DNA. The work by Ingram, and others, established that one mutation, and presumably the alteration of one nucleotide pair, alters one amino acid in a protein. Studies by Benzer and Yanofsky showed that intragenic recombination allowed the ordering of mutant sites within a gene. Is there any relationship between the linear sequence of mutant sites in a gene (inferred from genetic analysis) and the linear sequence of amino acids in a protein (determined biochemically)? The answer to this question was supplied by Yanofsky with his *trpA* system, described in the preceding section. At the same time that he compiled a gene map he also examined the A polypeptide produced by each mutant. His results were similar to those of Ingram for hemoglobin: each mutation has a defective polypeptide associated with a specific amino acid substitution at a specific point. However, Yanofsky was able to show an exciting correlation that

Ingram was not able to observe (owing to the limitations of the system). There is an exact match between the sequence of the mutant sites in the gene map of the A gene and the location of the corresponding altered amino acids in the A polypeptide chain. The farther apart two mutant sites are in map units, the more amino acids there are between the corresponding substitutions in the polypeptide (Figure 11-26). Thus, Yanofsky demonstrated **colinearity** between a gene and its corresponding polypeptide. Figure 11-27 shows the complete set of data.

Message There is a direct relationship between the linear sequence of amino acids in a protein and the linear structure of the gene.

Complementation

In another part of his studies Benzer made a discovery that relates to the gene as the unit of function (see page 220). Benzer found that although *rII* mutants cannot individually lyse *E. coli* K(λ) cells, certain pairs of mutants can somehow help or **complement** each other in a double infection of K(λ), leading to lysis of the cell (see Figure 11-28). We should realize at this point that such **complementation** tests are carried out routinely in the genetic analysis of diploid organisms, since all they involve is producing a heterozygote and looking at the phenotype. Benzer had to adapt the complementation test to phage by making the equivalent of a heterozygote through double infection. He was able to divide all the *rII* mutants he tested into two groups, A and B. Any member of group A will complement any member of group B, but no complementation is possible between any pair of alleles in the same group. Thus, it appeared that mutants in the A group are defective in some function that mutants in the B group can supply, and vice versa. Very interestingly, all alleles in group A mapped on one-half of the *rII* locus, and all those in group B mapped on the other half, as shown in Figure 11-29.

Mutations that fail to complement must be affecting the same unit of function. Those that do complement must affect different functional units. Benzer called this unit of function a **cistron.**

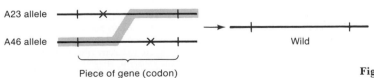

Figure 11-25. Intracodon recombination at codon 210. (Reciprocal not detected; × = mutant site.)

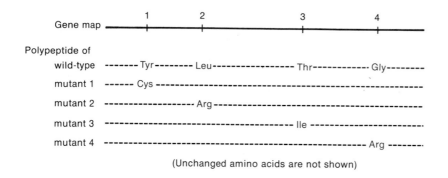

Gene map

Polypeptide of
wild-type ------- Tyr-------- Leu----------------- Thr----------- Gly--------

mutant 1 ------ Cys --

mutant 2 ------------------ Arg---------------------------------------

mutant 3 -- Ile ----------------

mutant 4 --- Arg -------.

(Unchanged amino acids are not shown)

Figure 11-26. Simplified representation of colinearity of gene mutations. The genetic map of point mutations (determined by recombinational analysis) corresponds linearly to the changed amino acids in the different mutants (determined by fingerprint analysis).

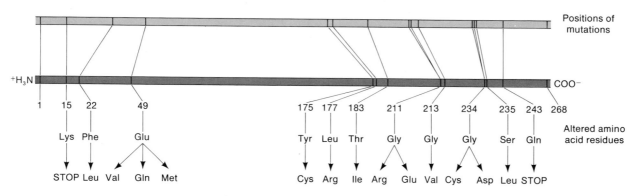

Figure 11-27. Actual colinearity shown in the A protein of tryptophan synthetase from *E. coli.* There is a linear correlation between the position of mutations and the altered amino acid residues. (Based on C. Yanofsky, "Gene Structure and Protein Structure." Copyright © 1967 by Scientific American. All rights reserved.)

Message   A cistron is a genetic region within which there is normally no complementation between mutations.

The cistron gets its name from the **cis-trans test,** which is performed to determine whether two mutant sites are within the same functional unit or are in different ones. In the cis-trans test, the complementation test is arranged with the mutant sites on the same chromosome (cis) or on opposite chromosomes (trans), as shown in Figure 11-30.

It is crucial to distinguish complementation from recombination. Recombination represents the creation of new genotypes by exchanging parts of chromosomes. Complementation is the effect produced by placing two genes in the same cell at the same time. There is no chromosomal rearrangement involved, but rather a mixing of gene products. Figure 11-31, which shows trans tests for two different *rII* mutant pairs, diagrams this difference. The arrangement shown in part (a) of the figure will allow phage growth

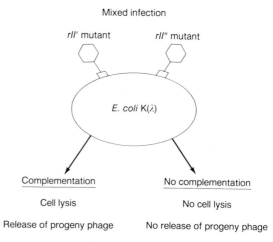

Figure 11-28. Complementation test: A schematic view of *rII* complementation. Two different mutants of *rII* are used to simultaneously infect *E. coli* K (mixed infection). Normally, an *rII* mutant cannot lyse *E. coli* K or generate progeny phage. However, if the two different mutants can complement, then lysis and phage growth will result. If the two *rII* mutants cannot complement one another, then no lysis or phage growth will result.

A group   B group

Figure 11-29. Gene map of *rII*.

and lysis (complementation) without rearrangement of phage chromosomes, whereas the mutant pair shown in (c) will not. Recombination can occur in each situation, as shown in (b) and (d).

How can we distinguish operationally between complementation and recombination? Fortunately, in the case of *rII* mutants, the incidence of recombination is never more than a few percent (see the map on page 222), and only rarely that high. Therefore, lysis will occur in only a very small fraction of the infected cells and will not interfere with the interpretation of the test. To distinguish definitively between these two possibilities, we could conduct an additional genetic analysis; in the case of *rII* mutants, we could analyze the genotype of the resulting progeny phage. Figure 11-32 shows how this is done. The phage resulting from a mixed infection of *E. coli* K(λ) are plated on both *E. coli* B and *E. coli* K(12). All phage grow on B, but only *rII*⁺ recombinants can form plaques on K. (Here, the multiplicity of infection — the ratio of phage to bacteria — is low, so that each bacterium is infected initially by no more than one phage; complementation cannot result in plaque formation in this situation.) If the progeny phage from the mixed infection of *E. coli* K(λ) had resulted from complementation, then virtually all of the phage would still be *rII* mutants and would not plate on K. However, if recombination had been required for phage growth and lysis during the mixed infection, then the analysis of the very low titer of progeny phage would show that about half are *rII*⁺ recombinants and would plate on K (Figure 11-32).

Of the different views of what a gene is according to the classical (bead) theory, the one aspect that has held up and seems most essential is the gene as a unit of function. We now see that the gene is equivalent to the cistron, and we

can consider it as a unit of function that can be defined experimentally by a cis-trans complementation test. There are occasional exceptions to this operational definition by the cis-trans test, such as for some genes with multimeric proteins, or for certain mutations that can affect expression of more than one gene. However, these do not upset the basic concept of the gene as a unit of function.

We now know that a cistron is a region of the genetic material that codes for one polypeptide chain. Therefore, the one-gene–one-enzyme hypothesis could be referred to more precisely as the one-cistron–one-polypeptide hypothesis, thus also emphasizing that cistrons (genes) can code for proteins other than enzymes.

Mutational Sites

Benzer extended his classic fine-structure analysis to the properties of mutational sites. An important tool for these studies is deletion mapping.

Deletion Mapping

The use of "deletion" mutants enabled Benzer to locate rapidly new mutant sites in his *rII* gene map. He found some special *rII* mutants that would not give recombinants when crossed with any of several other mutants (which had been shown to be different "recons") but would give recombinants when crossed to still others. He realized that such mutants behaved as if they involved short deletions within the *rII* region, and this model was supported by their lack of reversion. They could be used for rapid location of mutant sites in newly obtained mutant alleles. For example, consider the following gene map showing 12 identifiable mutant sites:

1   2   3   4   5   6   7   8   9   10   11   12

One special mutant D_1 fails to give *rII*⁺ recombinants when crossed with *1, 2, 3, 4, 5, 6, 7,* or *8*; therefore, D_1 behaves as if it involves a deletion of sites *1* through *8*:

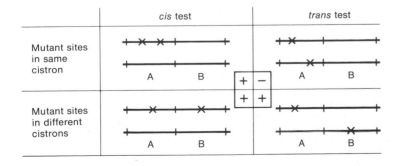

	cis test		trans test	
Mutant sites in same cistron				
	A B		A B	
Mutant sites in different cistrons				
	A B		A B	

+	−
+	+

Figure 11-30. The cis-trans test. A cistron is a genetic region within which there is no complementation between mutations. If two different *rII* mutant T4 phages infect the same bacterium (the trans configuration) and no growth of phage occurs, the mutants are said to be in the same cistron (*upper right box*). However, if complementation does occur (if progeny phage grow), the mutants are in different functional units or cistrons (*lower right box*). In the upper right box, only the B function can be expressed normally; in the lower right box, both A and B functions can be expressed normally. Plus represents a successful complementation; minus indicates no complementation; crosses represent mutant sites.

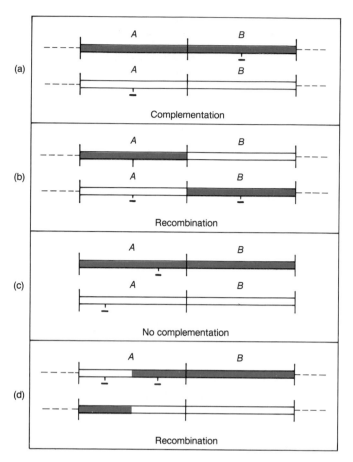

Figure 11-31. A comparison of the genetic consequences of complementation and recombination. (a) The mutant pairs can complement one another, since wild-type gene *A* and gene *B* products can mix in the cytoplasm. (b) If recombination occurred, then a rearrangement of the genomes would take place. (c) The mutant pairs cannot complement, since neither mutant can contribute a wild-type gene *A* product. (d) A relatively rare recombination event could result in a wild-type phage.

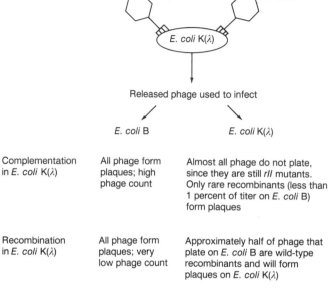

Figure 11-32. Analysis of phage resulting from mixed infection of *E. coli* K(λ). If complementation occurs between two *rII* mutants, then the progeny phage that are released will still be principally *rII* mutants, and they will fail to plate on *E. coli* K(λ) in single-infection experiments. If recombination but no complementation occurs, then there will be a sharply reduced yield of progeny phage, owing to the rarity of recombination. However, the few resulting phage will consist of approximately 50 percent wild-type recombinants, and they will form plaques on *E. coli* K(λ) in single-infection experiments.

Another special mutant D_2 fails to give rII^+ recombinants when crossed with *5, 6, 7, 8, 9, 10, 11,* or *12*; therefore, D_2 behaves as if it involves a deletion of sites *5* through *12*:

These overlapping deletions now define three areas of the gene; let us call them i, ii, and iii:

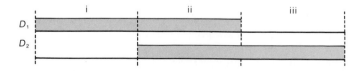

A new mutant that gives rII^+ recombinants when crossed with D_1 but not when crossed with D_2 must have its mutant site in area iii. One that gives rII^+ recombinants with D_2 but not with D_1 must have its mutant site in area i. A new mutant that does not give rII^+ recombinants with either D_1 or D_2 must have its mutant site in area ii. For example, consider a mutant in area iii crossed with D_1:

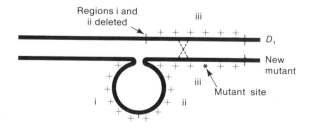

The more deletions there are in the tester set, the more areas can be uniquely designated, and the more rapidly new

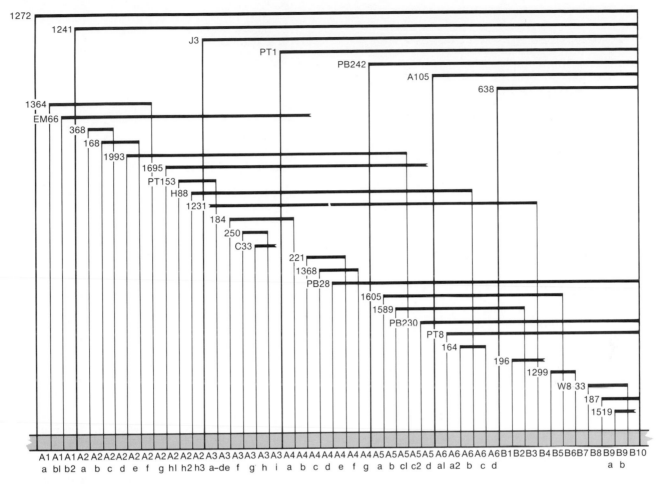

Figure 11-33. Detailed deletion map of the *rII* gene. Each deletion (*horizontal bar*) has an identification number. Along the bottom are the arbitrary identification numbers of the regions defined by the deletions. Note that some deletions extend out of the *rII* gene. (From G. S. Stent and R. Calendar, *Molecular Genetics*, 2d ed. Copyright © 1978 by W. H. Freeman and Co. After S. Benzer, *Proc. Natl. Acad. Sci. USA* 47:403, 1961.)

mutant sites can be located. Once assigned to a region, a mutant can be crossed with other alleles in the same region to obtain an accurate position. Figure 11-33 shows the complexity of Benzer's actual map.

Deletions themselves can be intercrossed and mapped just like point mutations. The deleted region is represented by a bar. If no wild-type recombinants are produced in a cross between different deletions, then the bars are shown as overlapping. A typical deletion map might be

Such deletion maps are useful in delineating regions of the gene to which new point mutations can be assigned.

The use of deletions enabled Benzer to define the **topology** of the gene (the manner in which the parts are interconnected). The gene is seen to consist of a linear array of mutable subelements. The next step was to examine the **topography** of the gene (differences in the properties of the subelements). Operationally, this is determined by asking whether all of the subelements or sites are equally mutable. For this study it was essential to work with the smallest mutable subelements possible. Instead of multisite mutations (deletions) that exhibited no reversion, revertible mutations were employed, since these probably represented small alterations, referred to as point mutations. Also, mutants with high reversion rates were discarded, since high reversion interferes with recombination tests. Each mutational site was first mapped into one of the short

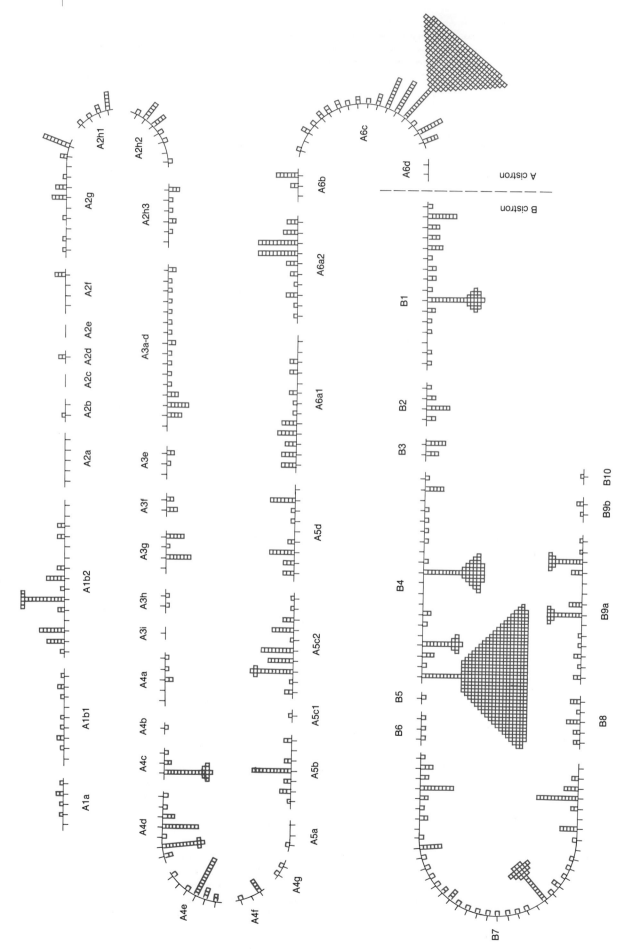

Figure 11-34. The distribution of 1612 spontaneous mutations in the *rII* cistrons. Each occurrence of an independent mutation is depicted by a square. When mutations are identical, the squares are drawn on top of one another. Many positions are represented by only a single square, whereas others have a large number of squares. These sites are termed hotspots. (From S. Benzer, *Proc. Natl. Acad. Sci. USA* 47:403–416, 1961.)

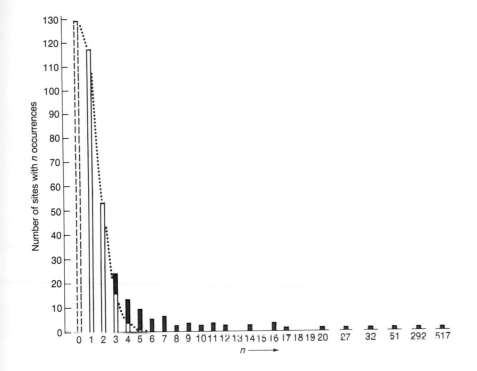

Figure 11-35. Distribution of occurrences of spontaneous mutations at various sites. The dotted line indicates a Poisson distribution fitted to the numbers of sites having one and two occurrences. This predicts a minimum estimate for the number of sites of comparable mutability that have zero occurrences due to chance (dashed column at $n = 0$). Solid bars indicate the minimum numbers of sites that have mutation rates significantly higher than the one- and two-occurrence class. (From S. Benzer, *Proc. Natl. Acad. Sci. USA* 47:403–416, 1961.)

deletion segments and then crossed against all of the other point mutations in the same interval. Two revertible mutations that failed to recombine with one another were concluded to represent recurrences of the same event.

Figure 11-34 shows the distribution of 1612 spontaneous mutations in the *rIIA* and *rIIB* cistrons. In Benzer's own words, "That the distribution is not random leaps to the eye." This extraordinary nonrandom distribution demonstrates that all sites are not equally mutable. Benzer termed sites that are more mutable than other sites **hotspots.** The most prominent hotspot is represented by over 500 repeated occurrences in the collection of 1612 mutations. By examining a Poisson distribution calculated to fit the number of sites having only one or two occurrences (Figure 11-35), it could be shown that at least 60 sites are truly more mutable than those with only one or two occurrences, and also that at least 129 sites were not observed at all (by chance) in this collection, even though they are equally mutable as those represented by one or two occurrences. The analysis was extended to include mutagen-induced mutations, with similar results. Namely, there were hotspots among the mutations generated by mutagenic agents (see Chapter 15).

From estimation of the physical size (and thus the number of base pairs) of the *rII* region and the determination of the number of mutational sites in the *rII* cistrons, the number of sites was calculated to be approximately one-fifth the number of nucleotide pairs. In other words, the smallest mutable site was five nucleotide pairs or less. The deciphering of the genetic code (Chapter 12), together with the work (described previously) by Ingram, Yanofsky, and others demonstrating that single amino acid substitutions resulted from single mutations, allowed the conclusion that a mutation could result from the alteration of a single nucleotide pair. (The direct sequencing of DNA, described in Chapter 14, has since confirmed these conclusions in many examples.)

Summary

■ The work of Beadle and Tatum in the 1940s showed that one gene codes for one protein. Further work by Benzer and others illustrated that the gene could be dissected into smaller and smaller pieces. A structural unit of mutation and one of recombination were identified and equated with a single nucleotide pair. A cistron is defined at the phenotypic level as a genetic region within which there is no complementation between mutations. This is the unit that codes for the structure of a single functional polypeptide. The gene is equivalent to the cistron.

The failure of an enzyme to function normally because of a mutation yields a variant phenotype. These variant phenotypes are often the basis of genetic disease in any organism, including humans. In order to understand how abnormal enzymes can cause phenotypic change, we need to understand the structure of proteins. Composed of a specific linear sequence of amino acids connected through peptide bonds, the proteins assume specific three-dimensional shapes as a result of the interaction of the 20 amino acids that in different combinations constitute the polypeptide chain. Different areas of this folded chain are sites for the attachment and interaction of substrates. Furthermore, many functional enzymes and other proteins are built by combining, in multimeric form, several polypeptide chains.

Specific amino acid changes can be detected in a protein by the technique of fingerprinting and amino acid sequencing. Work of this type has demonstrated colinearity between mutant sites on the genetic map and the positions of altered amino acids in a protein. Finally, and of importance to work to be discussed in the succeeding chapters, it has been shown that recombination takes place within a codon (a coding unit for one amino acid).

In contrast to the early days of genetics, when genes were represented as indivisible beads on a chain, we have now arrived at a far different picture of the gene. Multiple mutable sites exist, and recombination may occur anywhere within a gene. In addition, a closer connection between genotype and phenotype was realized when it was established that one cistron is responsible for the synthesis of one polypeptide.

Problems

1. A common weed, Saint-John's-wort, is toxic to albino animals. It also causes blisters on animals that have white areas of fur. Suggest a possible genetic basis for this reaction.

2. In humans, the disease galactosemia causes mental retardation at an early age because lactose in milk cannot be broken down, and this failure affects brain function. How would you provide a secondary cure for galactosemia? Would you expect this phenotype to be dominant or recessive?

3. Amniocentesis is a technique in which a hypodermic needle is inserted through the abdominal wall of a pregnant woman into the amnion, the sac that surrounds the developing embryo, to withdraw a small amount of amniotic fluid. This fluid contains cells that come from the embryo (not from the woman). The cells can be cultured; they will divide and grow to form a population of cells on which enzyme analyses and karyotype analyses can be performed. Of what use would this technique be to a genetic counselor? Name at least three specific conditions under which amniocentesis might be useful. (NOTE: this technique involves a small but real risk for the health of both woman and embryo; take this fact into account in your answer.)

4. Table 11-4 shows the ranges of enzyme activity (in units we need not worry about) observed for enzymes involved in two recessive metabolic diseases of humans. Similar information is available for many metabolic genetic diseases.

   a. Of what use is such information to a genetic counselor?

   b. Indicate any possible sources of ambiguity in interpreting studies of an individual patient.

   c. Reevaluate the concept of dominance in the light of such data.

■ TABLE 11-4.

| Disease | Enzyme involved | Range of enzyme activity | | |
		Patients	Parents of patients	Normal individuals
Acatalasemia	Catalase	0	1.2–2.7	4.3–6.2
Galactosemia	Gal-1-P uridyl transferase	0–6	9–30	25–40

5. Two albinos marry and have a normal child. How is this possible? Suggest at least two ways. (This question appeared first in Chapter 4. Reconsider it now in the light of biochemical pathways.)

6. In humans, PKU (phenylketonuria) is a disease caused by an enzyme inefficiency at step A in the following simplified reaction sequence, and AKU (alkaptonuria) is due to an enzyme inefficiency in one of the steps summarized as step B here:

$$\text{Phenylalanine} \xrightarrow{\ A\ } \text{Tyrosine} \xrightarrow{\ B\ } CO_2 + H_2O$$

A person with PKU marries a person with AKU. What phenotypes do you expect for their children? a. All normal; b. all having PKU only; c. all having AKU only; d. all having both PKU and AKU; e. some having AKU and some having PKU.

7. Three independently isolated tryptophan-requiring strains of yeast are called trpB, trpD, and trpE. Cell suspensions of each are streaked on a plate supplemented with just enough tryptophan to permit weak growth for a trp^- strain. The streaks are arranged in a triangular pattern so that they do not touch one another. Luxuriant growth is noted at both ends of the trpE streak and at one end of the trpD streak.

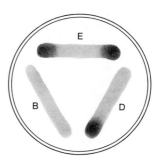

a. Do you think complementation is involved?

b. Explain briefly the patterns of luxuriant growth.

c. In what order in the tryptophan-synthesizing pathway are the enzymic steps defective in trpB, trpD, and trpE?

d. Why was it necessary to add a small amount of tryptophan to the medium in order to demonstrate such a growth pattern?

8. In *Drosophila* pupae, certain structures called imaginal disks can be detected as thickenings of the skin; after metamorphosis, these imaginal disks develop into specific organs of the adult fly. George Beadle and Boris Ephrussi devised a means of transplanting eye imaginal disks from one larva into another larval host. When the host metamorphoses into an adult, the transplant can be found as a colored eye located in its abdomen. They took two strains of flies that were phenotypically identical in having bright scarlet eyes: one because of the sex-linked mutant vermilion (*v*); the other because of cinnabar (*cn*) on chromosome 2. If *v* disks are transplanted into *v* hosts or *cn* disks into *cn* hosts, then the transplants develop as mutant scarlet eyes. Transplanted *cn* or *v* disks in wild-type hosts develop wild-type eye colors. A *cn* disk in a *v* host develops a mutant eye color, but a *v* disk in a *cn* host develops wild-type eye color. Explain these results and outline the experiments you would propose to test your explanation.

9. In *Drosophila*, the autosomal recessive *bw* causes a dark brown eye, and the unlinked autosomal recessive *st* causes a bright scarlet eye. A homozygote for both genes has a white eye. Thus we have the following correspondences between genotypes and phenotypes:

$$+/++/+ = \text{red eye (wild-type)}$$

$$+/+ \; bw/bw = \text{brown eye}$$

$$st/st +/+ = \text{scarlet eye}$$

$$st/st \; bw/bw = \text{white eye}$$

Construct a hypothetical biochemical pathway showing how the gene products interact and why the different mutant combinations have different phenotypes.

10. Several mutants are isolated, all of which require compound G for growth. The compounds (A through E) in the biosynthetic pathway are known, and each compound is tested for its ability to support the growth of each mutant (1 through 5). In the following table, + indicates growth and − indicates no growth:

		A	B	C	D	E	G
	1	−	−	−	+	−	+
	2	−	+	−	+	−	+
Mutant	3	−	−	−	−	−	+
	4	−	+	+	+	−	+
	5	+	+	+	+	−	+

a. What is the order of compounds A through E and G in the pathway?

b. At which point in the pathway is each mutant blocked?

c. Would a heterokaryon composed of double mutant 1,3 plus double mutant 2,4 grow on minimal medium? 1,3 plus 3,4? 1,2 plus 2,4 plus 1,4?

11. In *Neurospora* (a haploid), assume that two genes participate in the synthesis of valine. Their mutant alleles are called *val-1* and *val-2*, and their wild-type alleles are called *val-1*+ and *val-2*+. These two genes are linked on the same chromosome, and a crossover occurs between them on the average in one of every two meioses.

a. In what proportion of meioses are there no crossovers between the genes?

b. Use the map function to determine the recombinant frequency between these two genes.

c. Progeny from the cross *val-1 val-2*+ × *val-1*+ *val-2* are plated on medium containing no valine. What proportion of the progeny will grow?

d. The *val-1 val-2*+ strains accumulate intermediate compound B, and the *val-1*+ *val-2* strains accumulate intermediate A. The *val-1 val-2*+ strains will grow on valine or A, but the *val-1*+ *val-2* strains grow only on valine and not on B. Show the pathway order of A and B in relation to valine, and indicate which gene controls each conversion.

12. In a certain plant, the flower petals are normally purple. Two recessive mutations arise in separate plants and are found to be on different chromosomes. Mutation 1 (m_1) gives blue petals when homozygous ($m_1 m_1$). Mutation 2 (m_2) gives red petals when homozygous ($m_2 m_2$). Biochemists working on the synthesis of flower pigments in this species have already described the following pathway:

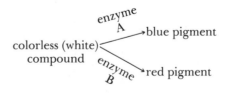

a. Which mutant would you expect to be deficient in enzyme-A activity?

b. A plant has genotype $M_1 m_1 M_2 m_2$. What do you expect its phenotype to be?

c. If the plant of part b is selfed, what colors of progeny are expected, and in what proportions?

d. Why are these mutants recessive?

13. In sweet peas, the synthesis of purple anthocyanin pigment in the petals is controlled by two genes, *B* and *D*. The pathway is

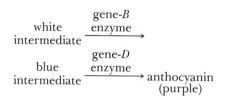

   a. What color petals would you expect in a pure-breeding plant unable to catalyze the first reaction?

   b. What color petals would you expect in a pure-breeding plant unable to catalyze the second reaction?

   c. If the plants of parts a and b are crossed, what color petals would the F_1 plants have?

   d. What ratio of purple : blue : white plants would you expect in the F_2?

14. Various pairs of *rII* mutants of phage T4 are tested in *E. coli* in both the cis and trans positions. Comparisons are made of the average number of phage particles produced per bacterium (a measure called the "burst size"). Table 11-5 shows a hypothetical set of results for six different *r* mutants: *rU*, *rV*, *rW*, *rX*, *rY*, and *rZ*. If we assign *rV* to the A cistron, what are the locations of the other five *rII* mutations with respect to the A and B cistrons?

■ **TABLE 11-5.**

Cis genotypes	Burst size	Trans genotypes	Burst size
rU rV/++	250	rU+/+rV	258
rW rX/++	255	rW+/+rX	252
rY rZ/++	245	rY+/+rZ	0
rU rW/++	260	rU+/+rW	250
rU rX/++	270	rU+/+rX	0
rU rY/++	253	rU+/+rY	0
rU rZ/++	250	rU+/+rZ	0
rV rW/++	270	rV+/+rW	0
rV rX/++	263	rV+/+rX	270
rV rY/++	240	rV+/+rY	250
rV rZ/++	274	rV+/+rZ	260
rW rY/++	260	rW+/+rY	240
rW rZ/++	250	rW+/+rZ	255

(Problem 14 is from M. Strickberger, *Genetics.* Copyright © 1968 by Monroe W. Strickberger. Reprinted with permission of Macmillan Publishing Co., Inc.)

15. There is evidence that occasionally during meiosis either one or both homologous centromeres will divide and segregate precociously at the first division rather than at the second division (as is the normal situation). In *Neurospora*, *pan2* alleles produce a pale ascospore, aborted ascospores are completely colorless, and normal ascospores are black. In a cross between two complementing alleles *pan2x* × *pan2y*, what ratios of black : pale : colorless would you expect in asci resulting from precocious division of: a. one centromere? b. both centromeres? (Assume that *pan2* is near the centromere.)

16. *Protozoon mirabilis* is a hypothetical single-celled haploid green alga. It orients to light by means of a red "eye-spot." Fourteen "white-eye-spot" mutants (*eye⁻*) are isolated after mutation by selecting cells that do not move toward the light. It is possible to fuse haploid cells to make diploid individuals. The 14 *eye⁻* mutants are paired in all combinations, and the color of the eye-spot is scored in each. Table 11-6 shows the results, where + indicates a red eye-spot and − indicates a white eye-spot.

■ **TABLE 11-6.**

	1	2	3	4	5	6	7	8	9	10	11	12	13	14
1	−	+	+	+	−	+	+	−	−	+	+	+	+	−
2	+	−	−	−	+	+	+	+	+	+	+	−	+	−
3	+	−	−	−	+	+	+	+	+	+	+	−	+	−
4	+	−	−	−	+	+	+	+	+	+	+	−	+	−
5	−	+	+	+	−	+	+	−	−	+	+	+	+	−
6	+	+	+	+	+	−	−	+	+	−	−	+	−	−
7	+	+	+	+	+	−	−	+	+	−	−	+	−	−
8	−	+	+	+	−	+	+	−	−	+	+	+	+	−
9	−	+	+	+	−	+	+	−	−	+	+	+	+	−
10	+	+	+	+	+	−	−	+	+	−	−	+	−	−
11	+	+	+	+	+	−	−	+	+	−	−	+	−	−
12	+	−	−	−	+	+	+	+	+	+	+	−	+	−
13	+	+	+	+	+	−	−	+	+	−	−	+	−	−
14	−	−	−	−	−	−	−	−	−	−	−	−	−	−

   a. Mutant 14 obviously is different from the rest. Why might this be?

   b. Excluding mutant 14, how many complementation groups are there, and which mutants are in which group?

   c. Three crosses are made with the results shown in Table 11-7. Explain these genetic ratios with symbols.

   d. How many genetic loci are involved altogether, and which of the 14 mutants are at each locus?

   e. What is the linkage arrangement of the loci? (Draw a map.)

■ TABLE 11-7.

Mutants crossed	Number of progeny		
	eye^+	eye^-	Total
1 × 2	31	89	120
2 × 6	5	113	118
1 × 14	0	97	97

17. You have the following map of the *rII* locus:

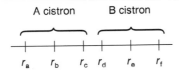

You detect a new mutation r_x, and you find that it does not complement any of the mutants in the A or B cistron. You find that wild-type recombinants are obtained in crosses with r_a, r_b, r_e, and r_f, but not with r_c or r_d. Suggest possible explanations for these results. Describe tests you would use to choose between the explanations.

18. The following map shows four deletions (1 through 4) involving the *rIIA* cistron of phage T4

1 ——

2 ————————

3   ————————

4   ————

Five point mutations (*a* through *e*) in *rIIA* are tested against these four deletion mutants for their ability to give r^+ recombinants; the results are as follows:

	a	b	c	d	e
1	+	+	−	+	+
2	+	+	−	−	−
3	−	−	+	−	+
4	+	−	+	+	+

a. What is the order of the point mutants?

b. Another strain of T4 has a point mutation in the *rIIB* cistron. This strain is mixed in turn with each of the *rIIA* deletion mutants, and the mixtures are used to infect *E. coli* K(λ) at a multiplicity of infection great enough that each host cell will be infected by at least one *rIIA* and one *rIIB* mutant. A normal plaque is formed with deletions 1, 2, and 3, but no plaque forms with deletion 4. Given that the B cistron is to the right of A, explain the behavior of deletion 4. Does your explanation affect your answer to part a?

19. In a phage, a set of deletions is intercrossed in pairwise combinations. The following results are obtained (with a plus indicating that wild-type recombinants are obtained from that cross):

	1	2	3	4	5
1	−	+	−	+	−
2	+	−	+	+	−
3	−	+	−	−	−
4	+	+	−	−	+
5	−	−	−	+	−

a. Construct a deletion map from this table.

b. The first geneticists to do a deletion-mapping analysis in the mythical schmoo-phage SH4 (which lyses schmoos) came up with this unique set of data:

	1	2	3	4
1	−	−	+	−
2	−	−	−	+
3	+	−	−	−
4	−	+	−	−

Show why this is a unique result by drawing the only deletion map that is compatible with this table. (Don't let your mind be shackled by conventional expectations.)

20. In a haploid eukaryote, four alleles of the *cys-2* gene are obtained. Each requires cysteine, and all map to the same locus. The four strains bearing these mutant alleles are crossed to wild-types to obtain a set of eight cultures representing the four mutant alleles in association with each mating type. Then the mutant alleles can be intercrossed in all pairwise combinations. The haploid meiotic products from each cross are plated on medium containing no cysteine. In some crosses, cys^+ prototrophs are observed at low frequencies. The results are the following, with the numbers representing the frequencies of cys^+ colonies per 10^4 meiotic products plated:

		Mating type A′			
		1	2	3	4
Mating type A″	1	0	14	2	20
	2	14	0	12	6
	3	2	12	0	18
	4	20	6	18	0

a. Draw a map of the four mutant sites within the *cys-2* gene. Provide a measurement of the relative intersite distances.

b. Do you see any evidence that mutation might be involved in the production of the prototrophs?

21. In *Neurospora*, there is a gene controlling the production of adenine, and mutants in this gene are called *ad-3* mutants. The *his-2* locus is 2.0 m.u. to the left, and the *nic-2* locus is 3.0 m.u. to the right of the *ad-3* locus (*his-2* controls histidine, and *nic-2* controls nicotinamide). Thus, the genetic map is

```
his-2          ad-3              nic-2
——+————————————+——————————————————+——
      2 m.u.          3 m.u.
```

Three different *ad-3* auxotrophs are detected: *ad-3*^{a}, *ad-3*^{b}, and *ad-3*^{c}. (Use *a*, *b*, and *c* as labels.) The following crosses are made:

Cross 1: *his-2*$^+$ *a nic-2*$^+$ × *his-2 b nic-2*

Cross 2: *his-2*$^+$ *a nic-2* × *his-2 c nic-2*$^+$

Cross 3: *his-2 b nic-2* × *his-2*$^+$ *c nic-2*$^+$

The ascospores are then plated on minimal medium containing histidine and nicotinamide, and *ad-3*$^+$ prototrophs are picked up. Table 11-8 shows the results obtained. What is the map order of the *ad-3* mutants and the genetic distance between them?

■ **TABLE 11-8.**

Genotype of *ad-3*$^+$ recombinants	Number of *ad-3*$^+$ spores picked up		
	Cross 1	Cross 2	Cross 3
his-2 + *nic-2*	0	6	0
his-2$^+$ + *nic-2*$^+$	0	0	0
his-2 + *nic-2*$^+$	15	0	5
his-2$^+$ + *nic-2*	0	0	0
Total ascospores scored	41,236	38,421	43,600

22. The *Notch* locus of *Drosophila* is assumed to be a single cistron. William Welshons has recovered two classes of *Notch* mutants. Class I mutants show a dominant effect on the wings, bristles, and eyes, and the mutation acts as a recessive lethal. Class II mutations are all nonlethal, and all have recessive mutant phenotypes affecting eyes, bristles, or wings. Heterozygotes for a class I and a class II mutation are viable, but they exhibit the dominant phenotype of the class I mutant and the recessive phenotype of the class II mutant. Construct an explanation, and describe ways to test your model.

23. In a hypothetical diploid organism, squareness of cells is due to a threshold effect such that more than 50 units of "square factor" per cell will produce a square phenotype, whereas less than 50 will produce a round phenotype. Allele *s*^{f} is a functional gene that actively synthesizes square factor. Each *s*^{f} allele contributes 40 units of square factor; thus, *s*^{f}*s*^{f} homozygotes have 80 units and are phenotypically square. A mutant allele (*s*^{n}) arises; it is nonfunctional, contributing no square factor at all. Which allele will show dominance, *s*^{f} or *s*^{n}? Are functional alleles necessarily always dominant? In a system such as this one, how might a specific allele become changed in evolution so that its phenotype shows recessive inheritance at generation 0 and dominant inheritance at a later generation?

24. Some genes in humans are known to have a multiple (or "pleiotropic") effect on phenotype. Does this constitute an invalidation of the one-gene–one-enzyme hypothesis? Explain.

25. Consider the following three biochemical sequences in *Neurospora* (genes controlling particular reactions through the catalyzing enzymes are indicated for some reactions):

$$\text{glutamate} \xrightarrow{pro\text{-}3} \text{GSA} \longrightarrow \longrightarrow \text{proline}$$

$$\text{precursor X} \xrightarrow{arg\text{-}3} \text{CAP} \xrightarrow[\text{(OTCase)}]{arg\text{-}12} \text{citrulline} \longrightarrow \text{arginine}$$
ornithine

$$\text{precursor Y} \xrightarrow{pyr\text{-}3a} \text{CAP} \xrightarrow[\text{(ATCase)}]{pyr\text{-}3d} \text{ureidosuccinate} \longrightarrow \text{pyrimidine}$$
aspartic acid

(CAP is carbamyl phosphate; note that it occurs in two of these sequences.)

a. The *arg-3* mutants require arginine, and the *pyr-3a* mutants require pyrimidine. Because CAP is found in *both* sequences, what does this observation suggest?

b. The gene *pyr-3* seems to control two consecutive enzymic conversions. How does this fact fit with your answer to part a? What can you suggest about the probable structure of the *pyr-3* enzyme?

c. The *arg-12* mutants partially suppress *pyr-3a* mutants, and the *pyr-3d* mutants partially suppress *arg-3* mutants. Is this consistent with your answer for part a?

d. All *pro-3* mutants require proline, but an *arg-12 pro-3* genotype does not require proline, and in this case label added as ornithine ends up in GSA and proline. The conversion of ornithine to GSA is catalyzed by the enzyme ornithine transaminase (OTA). Why do you think *pro-3* single mutants do not have access to ornithine?

e.   In rats, enzyme blocks corresponding to *pyr-3a* do *not* lead to pyrimidine requirement. Compare rats and *Neurospora* in this regard.

26.   Explain how Benzer was able to calculate the number of sites with zero occurrences, as depicted in Figure 11-35.

27.   In *Collinsia parviflora* the petal color is normally purple. Four recessive mutations were induced, each of which produced white petals and was recessive. The four pure-breeding lines were then intercrossed in the following combinations, with the results indicated.

Mutants crosses	F_1	F_2
1×2	all purple	1/2 purple, 1/2 white
1×3	all purple	9/16 purple, 7/16 white
1×4	all white	all white

a.   Explain all these results clearly, using diagrams wherever possible.

b.   What F_1 and F_2 do you predict from crosses of 2×3 and 2×4?

DNA Function

■ The genetic information embodied in DNA can either be copied into more DNA during replication or be translated into protein. These are the processes of information transfer that constitute DNA function. We considered replication in some detail in Chapter 10. Let us now explore the way that genetic information is turned into protein. Only a part of this story was revealed through purely genetic analysis—mutants have been useful, of course, but only as tools to shortcut a lot of the biochemical work. However, the kind of reasoning used by molecular biologists in investigating this aspect of DNA function illustrates an analytical approach also characteristic of work in genetics.

Transcription

It soon became evident that information is not transferred directly from DNA into protein. Another nucleic acid, ribonucleic acid (RNA), is necessary as an intermediary. Early investigators had good reasons for thinking this. For one thing, DNA is found in the nucleus (of eukaryotic cells), whereas protein is known to be synthesized in the cytoplasm. If cells are fed radioactive RNA precursors, the labeled RNA shows up first of all in the nucleus, indicating that the RNA is synthesized there. In a pulse-chase experiment, a brief "pulse" of labeling is followed by a "chase" of nonlabeled RNA precursors. In samples taken after the chase, the labeled RNA is found in the cytoplasm (Figure 12-1). Apparently, the RNA is synthesized in the nucleus and then moves into the cytoplasm. Thus it is a good candidate as an information-transfer intermediary between DNA and protein.

In 1957, Elliot Volkin and Lawrence Astrachan made a significant observation. They found that one of the most striking molecular changes when *E. coli* is infected with the phage T2 is a rapid burst of RNA synthesis. Furthermore, this phage-induced RNA "turns over" rapidly, as shown in the following experiment. The infected bacteria are first pulsed with radioactive uracil (a specific precursor of RNA). The bacteria are then chased with cold uracil; the RNA recovered shortly after the pulse is labeled, but that recovered somewhat later after the chase is unlabeled, indicating that the RNA has a very short lifetime. Finally, when the nucleotide contents of *E. coli* and T2 DNA are compared with the nucleotide content of the induced RNA, and RNA is found to be very similar to the phage DNA.

The tentative conclusion is that RNA is synthesized from DNA and that it passes into the cytoplasm where it is somehow used to synthesize protein. We can outline three stages of information transfer: **replication, transcription,** and **translation** (Figure 12-2).

Although RNA is a long-chain macromolecule of nucleic acid (as is DNA), it has very different properties. First,

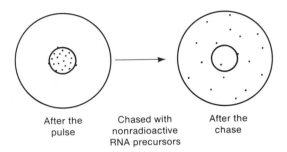

After the
pulse
Chased with
nonradioactive
RNA precursors
After the
chase

Figure 12-1. RNA synthesized during one short time period is labeled by feeding the cell a brief "pulse" of radioactive RNA precursors, followed by a "chase" of nonradioactive precursors. In an autoradiograph, the labeled RNA appears as dark grains, showing that the RNA moves from the nucleus to the cytoplasm. Apparently, the RNA is synthesized in the nucleus (*small circle*) and then moves out into the cytoplasm.

RNA is single-stranded, not a double helix. Second, RNA has ribose sugar rather than deoxyribose in its nucleotides (hence its name):

ribose

deoxyribose

Third, RNA has the pyrimidine base **uracil** (abbreviated U) instead of thymine. However, uracil does form hydrogen bonds with adenine just as thymine does.

uracil

No one is absolutely sure why RNA has uracil instead of thymine or why it has ribose instead of deoxyribose. The most important aspect of RNA is that it is single-stranded, but otherwise it is very similar in structure to DNA. This suggests that transcription may be based on the complementarity of bases, which was also the key to DNA replica-

■ TABLE 12-1. Nucleotide ratios in various DNAs and in their transcripts (in vitro)

DNA source	$\dfrac{(A + T)}{(G + C)}$ of DNA	$\dfrac{(A + U)}{(G + C)}$ of RNA synthesized
T2 phage	1.84	1.86
Cow	1.35	1.40
Micrococcus (bacterium)	0.39	0.49

tion. A transcription enzyme, RNA polymerase, could perform the transcription in a fashion quite similar to replication (Figure 12-3).

In fact, this model of transcription is confirmed cytologically (Figure 12-4). The fact that RNA can be synthesized with DNA acting as a template is demonstrated by synthesis in vitro of RNA from nucleotides in the presence of DNA, using an extractable RNA polymerase. Whatever the source of DNA used, the RNA synthesized has an $(A + U)/(G + C)$ ratio similar to the $(A + T)/(G + C)$ ratio of the DNA (Table 12-1). This experiment does not indicate whether the RNA is synthesized from both DNA strands or just from one, but it does indicate that the linear frequency of the A–T pairs (in comparison with the G–C pairs) in DNA is precisely mirrored in the relative abundance of $(A + U)$ in the RNA. (These points are difficult to grasp without drawing some diagrams; Problem 2 at the end of this chapter provides some opportunities to clarify these notions.)

To test the complementarity of DNA with RNA, investigators can apply the specificity and precision of nucleic acid hybridization. DNA can be denatured and mixed with RNA formed from it. On slow cooling, some of the RNA strands anneal with complementary DNA to form a DNA:RNA hybrid. The DNA:RNA hybrid differs in density from the DNA:DNA duplex, so its presence can be detected by ultracentrifugation in cesium chloride. Nucleic acids will anneal in this way only if there are stretches of base-sequence complementarity, so the experiment does prove that the RNA transcript is complementary in base sequence to the parent DNA.

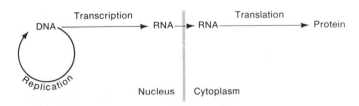

Figure 12-2. The three processes of information transfer: replication, transcription, and translation.

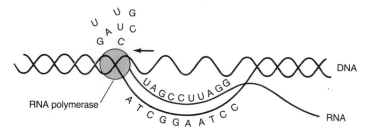

Figure 12-3. Synthesis of RNA on a single-stranded DNA template using free nucleotides. The process is catalyzed by RNA polymerase. Uracil (U) pairs with adenine (A).

Can we determine whether RNA is synthesized from only one or from both of the DNA strands? It seems reasonable that only one strand would be used, because transcription of RNA from both strands would produce two complementary RNA strands from the same stretch of DNA, and these presumably would produce two different kinds of protein (with different amino acid sequences). In fact, a great deal of chemical evidence confirms that transcription takes place on only one of the DNA strands (though not necessarily the same strand throughout the entire chromosome).

The hybridization experiment can be extended to explore this problem. If the two strands of DNA have distinctly different purine : pyrimidine ratios, they can be purified separately because they have different densities in cesium chloride. The RNA made from a stretch of DNA can be purified and annealed separately to each of the strands to see whether it is complementary to only one. J. Marmur and his colleagues were able to separate the strands of DNA from the *B. subtilis* phage SP8. They denatured the DNA, cooled it rapidly to prevent reannealing of the strands, and then separated the strands in cesium chloride. They showed that the SP8 RNA hybridizes to only one of the two strands, thus proving that transcription is **asymmetrical**—that is, it occurs only on one DNA strand.

RNA is transcribed from a single strand of DNA at a time. However, the same strand is not necessarily transcribed throughout the entire chromosome or through all stages of the life cycle. The RNA produced at different stages in the cycle of a phage hybridizes to different parts of the chromosome, showing the different genes that are activated at each stage. In λ phage, each of the two DNA strands is partially transcribed at a different stage (Figure 12-5). In phage T7, however, the same strand is transcribed for both early-acting and late-acting genes (Figure 12-6). In

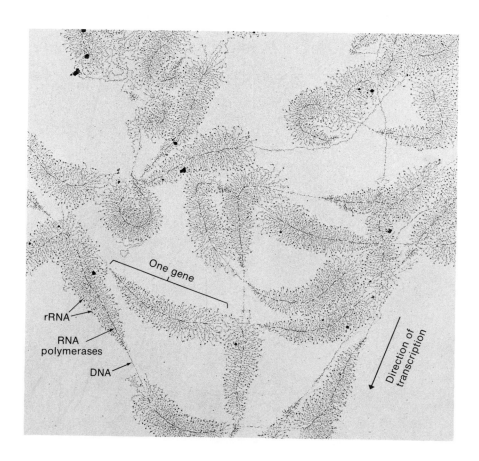

Figure 12-4. Tandemly repeated ribosomal RNA genes being transcribed in the nucleolus of *Triturus viridiscens* (an amphibian). Along each gene, many RNA polymerase molecules are attached and transcribing in one direction. The growing RNA molecules appear as threads extending out from the DNA backbone. The shorter RNA molecules are nearer the beginning of transcription; the longer ones have almost been completed, hence the "Christmas tree" appearance. (Photograph by O. L. Miller, Jr., and Barbara A. Hamkalo.)

nu1 A W B C nu3 D E FI FII Z U V G T H M L K I J   b2 int xis red γ cIII N rex cI cro cII O P Q S R

Figure 12-5. Map of λ phage DNA, with arrows indicating direction of transcription into mRNA. The upper arrows indicate transcription from one DNA strand, and the lower arrows indicate transcription from the other strand. The DNA is circular during transcription, so the lower two arrows are actually one stretch of transcription. (From G. S. Stent and R. Calendar, *Molecular Genetics*, 2d ed. Copyright © 1978 by W. H. Freeman and Co.)

any case, the RNA always is synthesized in the 5' → 3' direction (Figure 12-7).

In most prokaryotes, a single RNA polymerase species transcribes all types of RNA, whereas in higher eukaryotes, three different RNA polymerases transcribe different classes of RNA. All polymerases recognize signals to initiate and terminate transcription. The region of the DNA recognized by RNA polymerase, and within which the polymerase binds and initiates transcription, is termed the **promoter.** We shall describe RNA polymerases and transcription initiation and termination signals in more detail in Chapter 18.

Translation

The information-bearing RNA is appropriately called **messenger RNA** (mRNA). It acts as a copy of information from the DNA in the nucleus, sent out to direct protein synthesis in the cytoplasm (rather like a copy of a blueprint sent from the executive office to the production department). If you mix mRNA and all 20 amino acids in a test tube and hope to make protein, you will be disappointed. Other components are needed; the discovery of the nature of these components provided the key to understanding the mechanism of translation.

Another important experimental tool is involved in this part of our story: sucrose density-gradient centrifugation. The cesium chloride gradient discussed earlier is created by ultracentrifugation of a uniform solution. However, the sucrose gradient is created in a test tube by layering successively lower concentrations of sucrose solution, one on top of the other. The material to be studied is carefully placed on top. When the solution is centrifuged in a machine that allows the test tube to swivel freely, the sedimenting material travels through the gradient at different rates that are related to the sizes and shapes of the

molecules. Larger molecules migrate farther in a given period of time than do smaller molecules. The separated molecules can be collected individually by collecting sequential drops from a small opening in the bottom of the tube (Figure 12-8). The time that a fraction takes to move the fixed distance to the tube bottom indicates its position or sedimentation (S) value, which is a measure of the size of the molecules in the fraction.

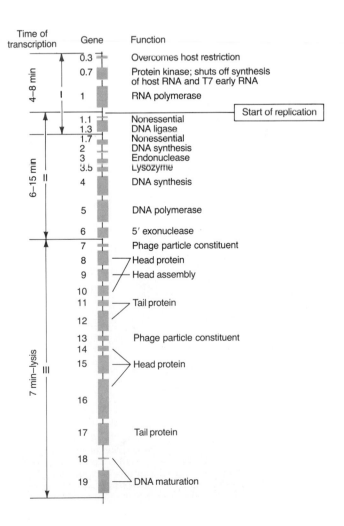

Time of transcription	Gene	Function
4–8 min (I)	0.3	Overcomes host restriction
	0.7	Protein kinase; shuts off synthesis of host RNA and T7 early RNA
	1	RNA polymerase
		Start of replication
6–15 min (II)	1.1	Nonessential
	1.3	DNA ligase
	1.7	Nonessential
	2	DNA synthesis
	3	Endonuclease
	3.5	Lysozyme
	4	DNA synthesis
	5	DNA polymerase
	6	5' exonuclease
7 min—lysis (III)	7	Phage particle constituent
	8	Head protein
	9	Head assembly
	10	
	11	Tail protein
	12	
	13	Phage particle constituent
	14	
	15	Head protein
	16	
	17	Tail protein
	18	
	19	DNA maturation

Figure 12-6. The various parts of the T7-phage genome are transcribed at various times during the phage growth cycle. (After G. S. Stent and R. Calendar, *Molecular Genetics*, 2d ed. Copyright © 1978 by W. H. Freeman and Co.)

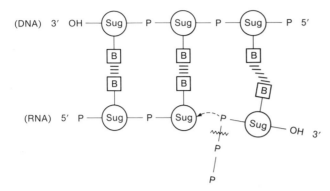

Figure 12-7. Chain elongation during transcription. A nucleoside triphosphate is aligning at the 3′ growing point. Two phosphate groups (P) will be lost as the phosphodiester bond is synthesized. (B = base; Sug = sugar.)

Ribosomes, on the other hand, are cellular organelles. They are composed of very complex aggregations of ribosomal proteins and **ribosomal RNA** (rRNA) components. In *E. coli*, for instance, at least three separate RNA molecules can be distinguished by size in ribosomes: 23S, 16S, and 5S. The precise function of ribosomes is still the subject of much research; the story of how we have learned what we do know is a fascinating one that lies outside the scope of this book. We do not know precisely how rRNA is bound up with the protein components or how each component functions. Under the electron microscope, a ribosome appears as a "blob." On chemical treatment, the blob splits into two main subblobs (50S and 30S in *E. coli*), and we represent it by the simplified symbol shown in Figure 12-10.

Both rRNA and tRNA molecules will form RNA:DNA hybrids in vitro, indicating that they are transcribed from the DNA. Figure 12-11 diagrams an exploded view of the components of an *E. coli* ribosome, giving some idea of their relative sizes. Table 12-2 summarizes the main types of RNA that can be found in a typical protein-synthesizing system.

Other components are needed to make protein synthesis work in vitro. These include several enzymes (aminoacyl-tRNA synthetases and peptidyl transferase), several mysterious protein "factors" whose role is probably enzymic, and a chemical source of energy. The energy donor is needed because an orderly structure is being created out of a mess of components—a process that requires energy because the system must lose entropy (a measure of disorder or randomness).

Using the separatory powers of the sucrose-gradient technique, it is possible to identify several macromolecules and macromolecule aggregates in a typical protein-synthesizing system. The main components are **transfer RNA** (tRNA), **ribosomes,** and messenger RNA (mRNA). Transfer RNA is a class of small (4S) RNA molecules of rather similar type and function. In fact, complete nucleotide sequences have been determined for some tRNA molecules; they all appear to have some hydrogen-bonded regions and some single-stranded regions, and they form variations of a cloverleaf structure (Figure 12-9).

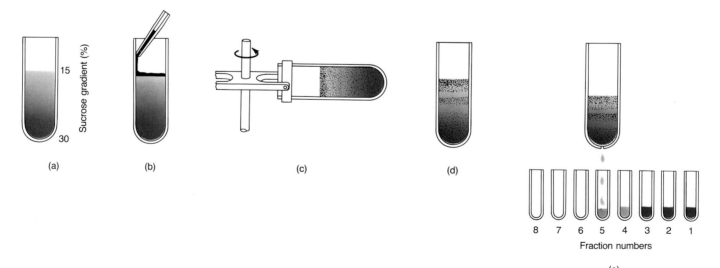

Figure 12-8. The sucrose-gradient technique. (a) A sucrose density gradient created in a centrifuge tube by layering of solutions of differing density. (b) The sample to be tested is placed on top of the gradient. (c) Centrifugation causes the various components (fractions) of the sample to sediment differentially. (d) The different fractions appear as bands in the centrifuged gradient. (e) The different bands can be collected separately by collecting samples from the bottom of the tube at fixed time intervals. The S value for the fraction is based on its position in the gradient, which is determined by the time at which it drips from the bottom of the tube. (From A. Rich, "Polyribosomes." Copyright © 1963 by Scientific American, Inc. All rights reserved.)

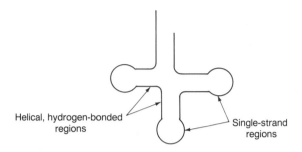

Helical, hydrogen-bonded regions

Single-strand regions

Figure 12-9. The cloverleaf structure of tRNA.

Figure 12-10. The simplified "two-blob" representation of the ribosome.

We can regard protein synthesis as a chemical reaction, and we shall take this approach at first. Then we shall take a three-dimensional look at the physical interactions of the major components.

1. Each amino acid (aa) is attached to a tRNA molecule that is specific to that amino acid by a high-energy bond derived from GTP. The process is catalyzed by a specific enzyme called a synthetase (the tRNA is said to be "charged" when the amino acid is attached). There is a separate synthetase for each amino acid.

$$aa_1 + tRNA_1 + GTP \xrightarrow{\text{synthetase}_1} aa_1 - tRNA_1 + GDP$$

2. The energy of the charged tRNA is converted into a peptide bond linking the amino acid to another on the ribosome:

$$aa_1 - tRNA_1 + aa_2 - tRNA_2 \xrightarrow[\text{on a} \atop \text{ribosome}]{\text{peptidyl transferase}}$$

$$\underbrace{aa_1 - aa_2}_{\substack{\text{small} \\ \text{polypeptide}}} - tRNA_2 + tRNA_1 \text{ released}$$

3. New amino acids are linked by means of a peptide bond to the growing chain:

$$aa_3 - tRNA_3 + aa_1 - aa_2 - tRNA_2 \longrightarrow$$

$$\underbrace{aa_1 - aa_2 - aa_3}_{\substack{\text{larger} \\ \text{polypeptide}}} - tRNA_3 + tRNA_2 \text{ released}$$

4. This process continues until aa_n (the final amino acid) is added. Of course, the whole thing works only in the presence of mRNA, ribosomes, several additional protein factors, enzymes, and inorganic ions.

To visualize this incredible process, we must recognize the main interacting sites of the components. We begin with tRNA. Is it the tRNA or the amino acid that recognizes the portion of the mRNA, termed a **codon,** that codes for a specific amino acid? A very convincing experiment answered this question. In the experiment, cysteinyl tRNA ($tRNA_{Cys}$, the tRNA specific for cysteine) charged with cysteine was treated with nickel hydride, which converted the cysteine (while still bound to $tRNA_{Cys}$) into another amino acid, alanine, without affecting the tRNA:

$$\text{cysteine} - tRNA_{Cys} \xrightarrow{\text{nickel hydride}} \text{alanine} - tRNA_{Cys}$$

Protein synthesized with this hybrid species had alanine

■ **TABLE 12-2.** RNA molecules in *E. coli*

Type	Relative amount in cell (%)	Sedimentation coefficient (S)	Molecular weight	Number of nucleotides
Ribosomal RNA (rRNA)	80	23	1.2×10^6	3700
		16	0.55×10^6	1700
		5	3.6×10^4	120
Transfer RNA (tRNA)	15	4	2.5×10^4	75
Messenger RNA (mRNA)	5		Heterogeneous	

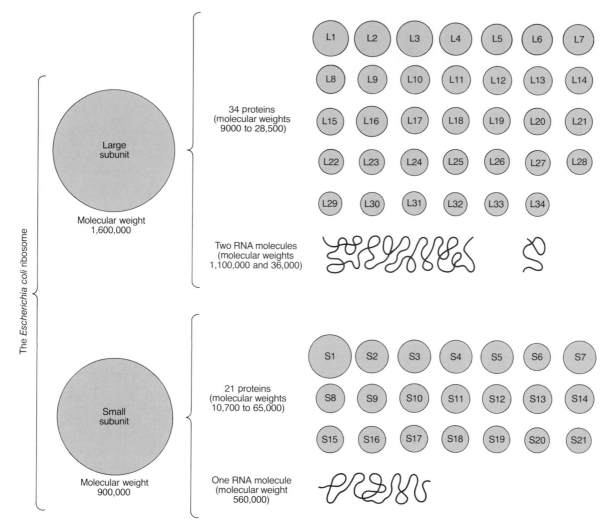

The *Escherichia coli* ribosome

Large subunit — Molecular weight 1,600,000

34 proteins (molecular weights 9000 to 28,500)

Two RNA molecules (molecular weights 1,100,000 and 36,000)

Small subunit — Molecular weight 900,000

21 proteins (molecular weights 10,700 to 65,000)

One RNA molecule (molecular weight 560,000)

Figure 12-11. The parts of a ribosome of *E. coli,* showing the complexity of what is the single most important entity in all biological synthesis. The precise roles of the parts are not understood. Peptidyl transferase, the enzyme activity responsible for the formation of peptide bonds between incoming amino acids and the growing polypeptide chain, appears to be built into the ribosome. (From Donald M. Engelman and Peter B. Moore, "Neutron-scattering Studies of the Ribosome." Copyright © 1976 by Scientific American, Inc. All rights reserved.)

wherever we would expect cysteine. Thus the experiment demonstrated that the amino acids are illiterate; they are inserted at the proper position because the tRNA "adaptors" recognize the mRNA codons and insert their attached amino acids appropriately. We expect, then, to find some site on the tRNA that recognizes the mRNA codon, presumably by complementary base pairing.

Figure 12-12a shows several sites of tRNA in terms of function. The site that recognizes an mRNA codon is called the **anticodon;** its bases are complementary to the bases of the codon. Another operationally identifiable site is the amino acid–binding region. The other arms probably assist in binding the tRNA to the ribosome. Figure 12-12b shows a specific tRNA (yeast alanine tRNA). The "flattened" cloverleafs shown in these diagrams are not the nor-

mal conformation of tRNA molecules; tRNA normally exists as an L-shaped folded cloverleaf, as shown in Figure 12-12c. These diagrams are supported by very sophisticated chemical analysis of tRNA nucleotide sequences and by X-ray crystallographic data on the overall shape of the molecule.

Where does tRNA come from? If radioactive tRNA is put into a cell nucleus in which the DNA has been partially denatured by heating, the radioactivity appears (by autoradiography) in localized regions of the chromosomes. These regions probably reflect the location of **tRNA genes;** they are regions of DNA that produce tRNA rather than producing mRNA that will produce a protein. The labeled tRNA hybridizes to these sites because of the complementarity of base sequences between the tRNA and its parent

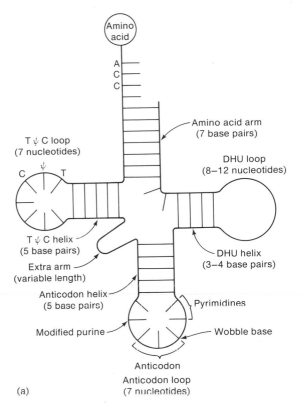

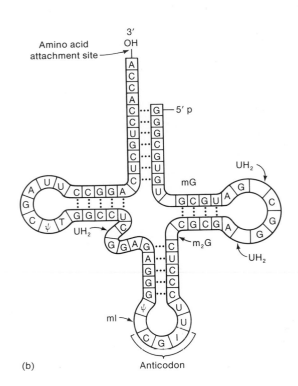

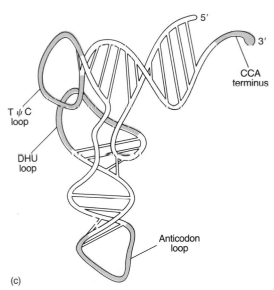

Figure 12-12. Structure of transfer RNA. (a) The functional areas of a generalized tRNA molecule. (b) The specific sequence of yeast alanine tRNA. Arrows indicate several kinds of rare modified bases. (c) The actual three-dimensional structure of yeast phenylalanine tRNA. The symbols ψ, UH$_2$, mG, m$_2$G, mI, and DHU are abbreviations for modified bases. (Part a from S. Arnott, "The Structure of Transfer RNA," *Progress in Biophysics and Molecular Biology* 22 (1971):186, parts b, c from L. Stryer, *Biochemistry*, 2d ed., copyright © 1981 by W. H. Freeman and Co.; part c based on a drawing by Dr. Sung-Hou Kim.)

gene. A similar situation holds for rRNA. Thus we see that even the one-gene–one-polypeptide idea is not completely valid. Some genes do not code for protein; rather, they specify RNA components of the translational apparatus.

Message Some genes code for proteins; other genes have RNA (tRNA or rRNA) as their final product.

How does tRNA get its fancy shape? It probably folds up spontaneously into a conformation that produces maximal stability. Transfer RNA contains many "odd" or modified bases (such as pseudouracil, ψ) in its nucleotides, and these might play a role in folding. These bases have also been implicated in other tRNA functions.

Now we turn to the ribosomes, which have several sites that we can predict from our model of translation, including binding sites for mRNA and tRNA. By adding radioactive tRNA to a solution of ribosomes and measuring how much of it becomes bound to the ribosomes, we could calculate that there are two tRNA-binding sites per ribosome.

There also is an mRNA-binding site, and the enzyme peptidyl transferase is built up into the ribosome (Figure 12-13).

We can now assemble all of the components in a diagram: Figure 12-14 shows an amino acid being added to a growing polypeptide. The ribosome "moves along" the mRNA strand. As each new codon enters the ribosome, conditions are right for the insertion of the appropriate aa-tRNA complex in the amino acid–binding site (A site) and for the formation of a bond between the amino acid in the A site and the polypeptide being held to a tRNA in the polypeptide-binding site (P site). When the peptide bond is formed, the tRNA in the P site is liberated, and the new

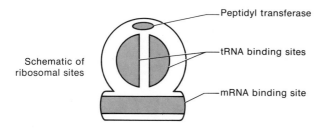

Figure 12-13. A diagrammatic representation of some important functional regions of the ribosome.

tRNA-polypeptide complex moves into the unoccupied P site as the ribosome moves farther along the mRNA. Figure 12-15 depicts in three dimensions the formation of the peptide bond on the ribosome.

Much of the model shown in Figure 12-14 was constructed by inference based on genetic and chemical analyses. Its validity was gratifyingly demonstrated recently by electron micrographs of the process of protein synthesis in an *E. coli* gene. You can see in Figure 12-16 that protein synthesis in this prokaryotic organism does not wait for the completion of mRNA synthesis. As soon as part of the mRNA is synthesized, ribosomes attach to it and begin

translation! Protein synthesis in eukaryotes is different, because mRNA is made in the nucleus and then shipped to the cytoplasm for translation; thus, transcription and translation in the eukaryote are separated in both time and space.

In Figure 12-14, a few imaginary codons have been inserted as illustrations of the process. Of course, this was the general notion in the minds of the investigators at the time also, but the knowledge of *which* specific codons represented *which* specific amino acids had to await another round of sophisticated investigations. This work came to be known as "cracking the genetic code."

The Genetic Code

If genes are segments of DNA, and if DNA is just a string of nucleotide pairs, then how does the sequence of nucleotide pairs dictate the sequence of amino acids in protein? The analogy to a code springs to mind at once. The cracking of the genetic code is the story of the rest of this chapter. The experimentation was sophisticated and swift, and it did not take long for the code to be deciphered once its existence was strongly indicated.

Simple logic tells us that if nucleotide pairs are the *letters* in a code, then a combination of letters could form

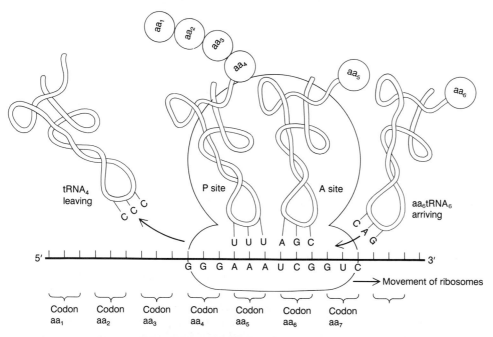

Figure 12-14. Mechanism of the addition of a single amino acid to the growing polypeptide chain during translation of mRNA. Amino acid 6 is being added; amino acids 1 through 5 are already part of the growing polypeptide. The A site is the amino acid binding site; the P site is the polypeptide binding site.

words representing different amino acids. We must ask whether the code is overlapping or nonoverlapping. Then we must ask how many letters make up a word—a codon—and which specific codon or codons represent each specific amino acid.

Overlapping Versus Nonoverlapping Code

Figure 12-17 shows the difference between an overlapping and a nonoverlapping code. In the example given a three-letter or **triplet** code is shown. For the nonoverlapping code, consecutive amino acids are specified by consecutive code words (codons) that do not overlap, as shown in the bottom of the figure. For an overlapping code, consecutive amino acids are encoded by sets of bases (the codons) that overlap, as shown in the top portion of the figure. Thus, for the sequence ATTGCTCAG, for a nonoverlapping code, the first three amino acids are encoded by the three triplets ATT, GCT, and CAG, respectively. However, for an overlapping code, the first three amino acids are encoded by the triplets ATT, TTG, and TGC, if the overlap is a single base as shown in the figure.

By 1961 it was already clear that the code was nonoverlapping. The analysis of mutationally altered proteins, in particular the nitrous acid–generated mutants of tobacco mosaic virus, showed that only a single amino acid changes at one time in one region of the protein. This is predicted by a nonoverlapping code. As you can see from Figure 12-17, an overlapping code predicts that a single base change would alter as many as three amino acids at adjacent positions in the protein.

It should be noted that while the use of an overlapping *code* was ruled out by the analysis of single proteins, nothing precluded the use of alternate reading frames to encode amino acids in two different proteins. In the example just given, one protein might be encoded by the series of codons that reads ATT, GCT, CAG, CTT, and so on. A second protein might be encoded by codons that are shifted over by one base and therefore read TTG, CTC, AGC, TTG, and so on. This would be an example of storing the information encoding two different proteins in two different reading frames, while still using a genetic code that is read in a nonoverlapping manner during the translation of a specific protein. Some examples of such information storage have been found, as we shall see in Chapter 14.

Number of Letters in the Code

Reading a DNA molecule from one particular end, one nucleotide pair at a time, only four nucleotide pairs can be encountered:

$$-A- \quad -T- \quad -G- \quad \text{and} \quad -C-$$
$$-T- \quad -A- \quad -C- \quad \quad\quad -G-$$

Thus, if the words are one letter long, then only four words are possible. This cannot be the genetic code because we must have a word for each of the 20 amino acids commonly found in cellular proteins. If the words are two letters long, then $4^2 = 16$ words are possible—for example,

$$-AT- \quad \text{or} \quad -CT- \quad \text{or} \quad -CC-$$
$$-TA- \quad \quad\quad -GA- \quad \quad\quad -GG-$$

where the length of the DNA molecule runs across the page (with one strand shown at the top and the other at the bottom). This vocabulary still is not large enough.

If the words are three letters long, then $4^3 = 64$ words are possible—for example,

$$-ATT- \quad \text{or} \quad -GCG- \quad \text{or} \quad -TGC-$$
$$-TAA- \quad \quad\quad -CGC- \quad \quad\quad -ACG-$$

This code would provide more than enough words to describe the amino acids. We can conclude that the code word must consist of at least three nucleotide pairs. However, if all words are "triplets," we have a considerable excess of possible words over the 20 needed to name the common amino acids.

Convincing proof that a codon is, in fact, three letters long (and no more than three) came from beautiful genetic experiments first reported in 1961 and later extended by Crick and Brenner and their coworkers, using mutants in the *rII* locus of T4 phage. Mutations causing the rII phenotype (see Chapter 11) were induced using a chemical called proflavin, which was thought to act by the addition or deletion of single nucleotide pairs in DNA. (This assumption is based on experimental evidence not presented here.) The following examples illustrate the action of proflavin:

$$
\begin{array}{ccc}
& & \downarrow \\
\text{Insertion} & & -ATCTAGTCT- \\
& \nearrow & -TAGATCAGA- \\
-ATCTGTCT- & & \\
-TAGACAGA- & & \\
& \searrow & -ATCTGTT- \\
\text{Deletion} & & -TAGACAA- \\
& & \uparrow
\end{array}
$$

Then, starting with one particular proflavin-induced mutation called FCO, Crick and his colleagues again used proflavin to induce "reversions" that were detected by their wild-type plaques on *E. coli* strain K(λ). Genetic analysis of these plaques revealed that the "revertants" were not identical to true wild types, thereby suggesting that the back mutation was not an exact reversal of the original forward mutation. In fact, the reversion was found to be caused by the presence of a *second mutation* at a different site from—but in the same cistron as—that of FCO; this second mutation "suppressed" mutant expression of the original FCO. A **suppressor mutation** counteracts or suppresses the effects of another mutation.

1. A suppressor mutation is at a different site from that of the mutation it counteracts. Therefore, the original mutation can be recovered by genetic crosses between the wild-type and the "revertant," since the revertant carries both the suppressor and the original mutation.

2. A suppressor mutation may be within the same gene as the mutation it suppresses (internal suppressor), as in the example just given, or it may be in a different gene (external suppressor).

3. Different suppressors may exert their effects in different ways. For instance, some suppressors act at the level of transcription, others at the level of translation, and others by altering the physiology of the cell.

The suppressor mutation could be separated from the original forward mutation by recombination. Surprisingly,

when this was done, the suppressor was shown to be an *rII* mutation by itself (Figure 12-18).

How can we explain these results? *If* the cistron is "read" from both ends, then the two proflavin-induced mutations should still give a mutant phenotype when combined:

$$rII \qquad\qquad rII \qquad\qquad rII$$
$$\longrightarrow \ \longleftarrow \qquad \longrightarrow \ \longleftarrow \qquad \longrightarrow \ \longleftarrow$$
$$\underline{\quad\; | \quad\quad} \qquad \underline{\quad\; | \quad\quad} \qquad \underline{\quad\; | | \quad}$$
$$r_a \qquad\qquad\quad r_b \qquad\qquad\quad r_a \ r_b$$

However, if reading is polarized—that is, if the cistron is read from one end only—then the original proflavin-induced addition or deletion could be mutant because it interrupts a normal reading mechanism that establishes the groups of bases to be read as words. For example, if each three nucleotide pairs make a word, then the "reading frame" might be established by taking the first three pairs from the end as the first word, the next three pairs as the second word, and so on. In that case, a proflavin-induced addition or deletion of a single pair would shift the reading frame from that point on, causing all following words to be

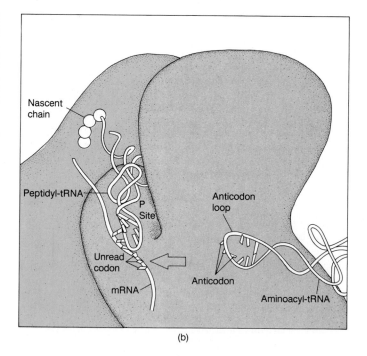

(a)

(b)

Figure 12-15. Hypothetical molecular mechanism for the synthesis of a protein by a ribosome is shown in a sequence of drawings that begins on these two pages and continues on the next page. (a) The entire ribosome. The color indicates the large subunit of the ribosome, and the gray depicts the small subunit. The black square indicates the part of the ribosome that appears in each of the following drawings. (b) The events that begin an iteration of the elongation cycle. A peptidyl-tRNA is bound to the small subunit's P site; it bears a nascent protein chain that is shown as entering the

large subunit. The anticodon of the peptidyl-tRNA is bound to a codon of the mRNA. The codon was translated in the preceding iteration of the cycle. An aminoacyl-tRNA draws near the small subunit. GTP and the elongation factor EF-Tu, which accompany the tRNA, are not depicted. (c) The arriving tRNA has bound itself to the R site; its anticodon becomes bound to the next unread codon. The anticodon is part of a loop of seven bases. Five of them are stacked; these are the five that lie nearest the end of the tRNA designated the 5' end. (d) Protein synthesis continues. Here the

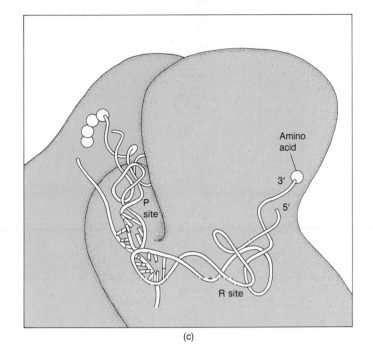

(c)

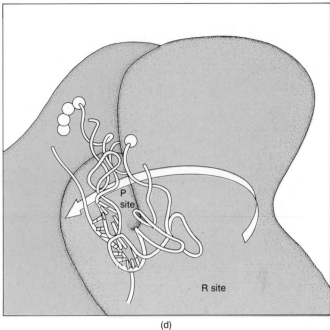

(d)

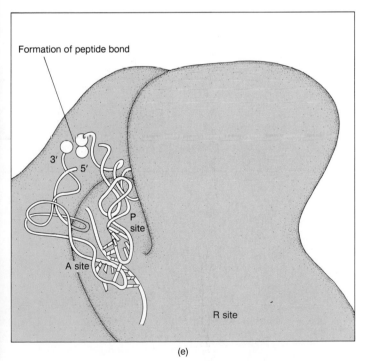

(e)

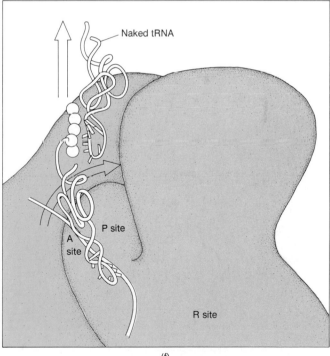

(f)

aminoacyl-tRNA has begun to flip into a position that will bind it to the A site. The flip constitutes a test of the strength of the binding between the codon and the anticodon; hence it improves the likelihood that the arriving amino acid is the one the code requires. (e) The aminoacyl-tRNA has arrived at the A site. The five stacked bases in the anticodon loop are now the ones that lie closest to the 3′ end of the molecule. This change allows the tRNA to flip without tugging on the mRNA. The proper alignment of the tRNAs on the mRNA may be ensured by a bond between bases that forms a bridge between the two anticodon loops. The large subunit can now transfer the nascent chain to the amino acid on the aminoacyl-tRNA. (f) The cycle is completed. The naked tRNA is expelled; the A-site tRNA takes its place at the P site, and the mRNA is repositioned for the arrival of the next aminoacyl-tRNA. Neither GTP nor the elongation factor EF-G, both of which act in these final events, is shown. (After J. Lake, "The Ribosome." Copyright © 1981 by Scientific American, Inc. All rights reserved.)

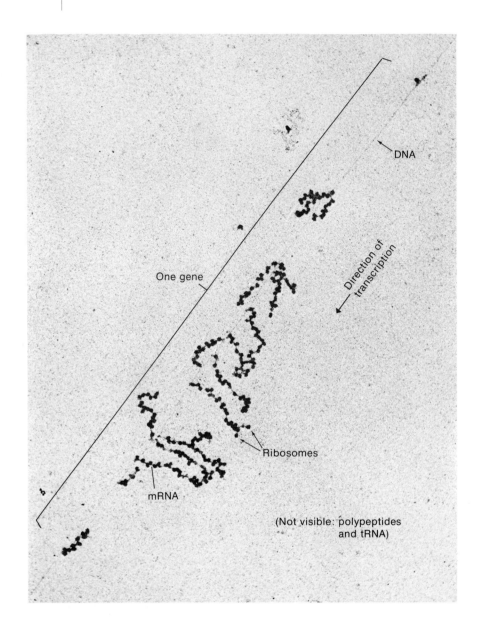

Figure 12-16. A gene of *E. coli* being simultaneously transcribed and translated. (Electron micrograph by O. L. Miller, Jr., and Barbara A. Hamkalo.)

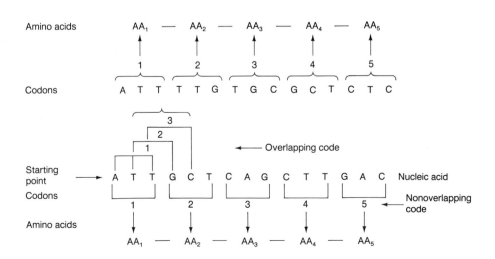

Figure 12-17. Difference between an overlapping and a nonoverlapping code. The case illustrated is for a code with three letters (a triplet code). In a nonoverlapping code, a protein is translated by reading codons that do not share any of the same nucleotides. An overlapping code uses codons that employ some of the same nucleotides as other codons for the translation of a single protein, as shown in the top of the diagram.

Figure 12-18. The suppressor of an initial *rII* mutation is shown to be an *rII* mutation itself after separation by crossing-over. The original mutant, FCO, was induced by proflavin. Later, when the FCO strain was treated with proflavin again, a revertant was found, which on first appearance seemed to be wild-type. However, it was found that a second mutation within the *rII* region had been induced, and the double mutant, *rII' rII''*, was shown not to be quite identical to the original wild-type.

misread. Such a **frame-shift mutation** could reduce most of the genetic message to gibberish. However, the proper reading frame could be restored by a compensatory insertion or deletion somewhere else, giving only a short stretch of gibberish between the two. Consider the following example that uses three-letter English words to represent the codons:

THE FAT CAT ATE THE BIG RAT

Delete C: THE FAT ATA TET HEB IGR AT

Insert A: THE FAT ATA ATE THE BIG RAT

The insertion suppresses the effect of the deletion by restoring most of the sense of the sentence. By itself, however, the insertion also disrupts the sentence:

THE FAT CAT AAT ETH EBI GRA T

If we assume that the FCO mutant is caused by an addition, then the second (suppressor) mutant would have to be a deletion, because this would restore the reading frame of the gene as we have seen (a second insertion would not correct the frame). In the following diagrams, we use a hypothetical nucleotide chain to represent DNA for simplicity, realizing that the complementary chain is automatically dictated by the specificity of the base pairing. We also assume that the code words are three letters long and that the words are read in one direction (left to right in our diagrams).

wild-type message

CAT CAT CAT CAT CAT

rII' message: distal words
changed (x) by frame-
shift mutation (words
marked ✓ are unaffected)

Addition ⟶

CAT ACA TCA TCA TCA T

✓   x   x   x   x

rII' rII'' message: few
words wrong, but
reading frame restored
for later words

Deletion ⟶

CAT ACA TCT CAT CAT

✓   x   x   ✓   ✓

The few wrong words in the suppressed genotype could account for the fact that the "revertants" (suppressed phenotypes) that Crick and his associates recovered did not look exactly like the true wild-types phenotypically.

We have assumed here that the original frame-shift mutation was an addition, but the explanation works just as well if we assume that the original FCO mutation is a deletion and the suppressor is an addition. If the FCO is defined as plus, then suppressor mutations are automatically minus; hence, proflavin-induced mutations are also called sign mutations. Experiments confirmed that a plus cannot suppress a plus, nor can a minus suppress a minus. In other words, two mutations of the same sign never act as suppressors of each other. However, very interestingly, it was found that combinations of *three* pluses or *three* minuses can act together to restore a wild-type phenotype. This observation provided the first experimental confirmation that a word in the genetic code consists of three successive nucleotide pairs, or a triplet. This is because three additions or three deletions within a gene would automatically restore the reading frame if the words are triplets. For example,

Deletions

↓ ↓   ↓
CAT CAT CAT CAT CAT CAT CAT
CAT ACA TAT CAT CAT CAT

✓   x   x   ✓   ✓   ✓

Crick's work also suggested that the code is **degenerate.** That expression is not a moral indictment! It simply means that each of the 64 triplets must have some meaning within the code, so that at least some amino acids must be specified by two or more different triplets. If only 20 triplets were used (with the other 44 being nonsense), then most frame-shift mutations would be expected to produce nonsense words, which presumably would stop the protein-building process. However, if all triplets specify some amino acid, then the changed words would simply result in the insertion of incorrect ("gibberish") amino acids into the protein. Thus, Crick reasoned that many or all amino acids must have several different names in the base-pair code; this hypothesis was later confirmed biochemically.

Proof that the genetic deductions about proflavin were correct came from an analysis of proflavin-induced mutants in a gene whose protein product could be analyzed. George Streisinger worked with the gene that controls the enzyme lysozyme, whose amino acid sequence is known. He induced a mutation in the gene with proflavin and selected for proflavin-induced "revertants," which were shown genetically to be double mutants (with mutations of opposite sign). When the protein of the double mutant was analyzed, a stretch of "gibberish" amino acids lay between two wild-type ends, just as predicted:

Wild-type   – Thr – Lys – Ser – Pro – Ser – Leu – Asn – Ala –

"Revertant" – Thr – Lys – Val – His – His – Leu – Met – Ala – type

Let us summarize what the work up to this point demonstrated about the genetic code.

1.   The code is nonoverlapping.

2.   Three bases code for an amino acid. These triplets are termed codons.

3.   The code is read from a fixed starting point and continues to the end of the coding sequence. There are no "commas" that would serve to allow realignment of codon selection during translation. We know this because a single frame-shift anywhere in the coding sequence alters the codon alignment for the rest of the sequence.

4.   The code is degenerate, in that some amino acids are specified by more than one codon.

Cracking the Code

The actual deciphering of the genetic code — determining the amino acid specified by each triplet — is one of the most exciting breakthroughs of the past two decades. Once the necessary experimental techniques became available, the genetic code was broken in a rush.

The first breakthrough was the discovery of how to make synthetic mRNA. If the nucleotides of RNA are mixed with a special enzyme (polynucleotide phosphorylase), a single-stranded RNA is formed in the reaction. No DNA is needed for this synthesis, and so the nucleotides are incorporated at random. The ability to synthesize mRNA offered the exciting prospect of creating specific RNA sequences and then seeing what kinds of amino acids were incorporated when acting as mRNA. The first synthetic messenger obtained was poly-U ($\cdots$ – U – U – U – U – $\cdots$), made by reacting only uracil nucleotides with the RNA-synthesizing enzyme. In 1961, Marshall Nirenberg and Heinrich Mathaei mixed poly-U with the protein-synthesizing machinery of *E. coli* (ribosomes, aminoacyl tRNAs, a source of chemical energy, several enzymes, and a few other things) in vitro and *observed the formation of a protein!* Of course, the main excitement centered on the question of the amino acid sequence of this protein. It proved to be polyphenylalanine — that is, a string of phenylalanine molecules attached to form a polypeptide. Thus, the triplet UUU must code for phenylalanine:

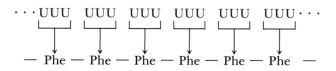

This type of analysis was extended by mixing nucleotides in a known fixed proportion when making synthetic mRNA. In one experiment, the nucleotides uracil and guanine were mixed in a ratio of 3 : 1. If they are incorporated at random into synthetic mRNA, then we can calculate the relative frequency at which each triplet will appear in the sequence (Table 12-3). The amino acids produced by this RNA in the protein-synthesizing system in vitro should reflect the same distribution of probabilities. In fact, the ratios of amino acids in the protein produced were those shown in Table 12-4. From this evidence, we deduce that codons consisting of one guanine and two uracils (G + 2U) code for valine, leucine, and cysteine, although we cannot distinguish the specific sequence for each of these amino acids. Similarly, one uracil and two guanines (U + 2G)

■ **TABLE 12-3.** Expected frequencies of various codons in synthetic mRNA composed of 3/4 uracil and 1/4 guanine

Codon	Probability	Ratio
UUU	$p(\text{UUU}) = 3/4 \times 3/4 \times 3/4 = 27/64$	1.00
UUG	$p(\text{UUG}) = 3/4 \times 3/4 \times 1/4 = 9/64$	0.33
UGU	$p(\text{UGU}) = 3/4 \times 1/4 \times 3/4 = 9/64$	0.33
GUU	$p(\text{GUU}) = 1/4 \times 3/4 \times 3/4 = 9/64$	0.33
UGG	$p(\text{UGG}) = 3/4 \times 1/4 \times 1/4 = 3/64$	0.11
GGU	$p(\text{GGU}) = 1/4 \times 1/4 \times 3/4 = 3/64$	0.11
GUG	$p(\text{GUG}) = 1/4 \times 3/4 \times 1/4 = 3/64$	0.11
GGG	$p(\text{GGG}) = 1/4 \times 1/4 \times 1/4 = 1/64$	0.03

■ **TABLE** 12-4. Observed frequencies of various amino acids in protein translated from mRNA composed of 3/4 uracil and 1/4 guanine

Amino acid	Ratio
Phenylalanine	1.00
Leucine	0.37
Valine	0.36
Cysteine	0.35
Tryptophan	0.14
Glycine	0.12

must code for tryptophan, glycine, and perhaps one other. It looks as though the Watson-Crick model is correct in predicting the importance of the precise sequence (not just the ratios of bases). Many provisional assignments (such as those just outlined for G and U) were soon obtained, primarily by groups working with Nirenberg or with Severo Ochoa.

Specific code words were finally deciphered through two kinds of experiments. The first involved making "mini mRNAs," each only three nucleotides in length. These, of course, are too short to promote translation into protein, but they do stimulate the binding of aminoacyl tRNAs (aa-tRNAs) to ribosomes in a kind of abortive attempt at translation. One can make a specific mini mRNA and determine *which* aminoacyl tRNA it will bind to ribosomes.

For example, the G + 2U problem discussed previously can be resolved by using the following mini mRNAs:

GUU   stimulates binding of valyl tRNA$_{Val}$

UUG   stimulates binding of leucyl tRNA$_{Leu}$

UGU   stimulates binding of cysteinyl tRNA$_{Cys}$

Analogous mini RNAs provided a virtually complete cracking of all the $4^3 = 64$ possible codons.

The second kind of experiment that was useful in cracking the code involved the use of "repeating copolymers." For instance, the copolymer designated $(AGA)_n$, which is a long sequence of $\cdots$ AGAAGAAGAA-GAAGA $\cdots$, was used to stimulate polypeptide synthesis in vitro. From the sequence of the resulting polypeptides, and the possible triplets that could occur in the respective RNA copolymer, many code words could be verified. This kind of experiment is detailed in Problem 10 at the end of this chapter. In solving it, you can pretend that you are H. Gobind Khorana, who received a Nobel prize for directing the experiments.

Figure 12-19 gives the code dictionary of 64 words. You should inspect this figure carefully for long periods of

time in which you ponder the miracle of molecular genetics. Such an inspection should reveal several points that require further explanation.

Multiple Codons for a Single Amino Acid

First, you will note that the number of codons for a single amino acid varies, ranging from one (tryptophan = UGG) to as many as six (serine = UCU or UCA or UCG or UCC or AGU or AGC). Why? The answer is complex but not difficult, and it can be divided into two parts.

1. Certain amino acids can be brought to the ribosome by several *alternative* tRNA types (species) having different anticodons, whereas certain other amino acids are brought to the ribosome by only one tRNA.

2. Certain tRNA species can bring their specific amino acids in response to several codons, not just one, through a loose kind of base pairing at one end of the codon and anticodon. This sloppy pairing is called **wobble.**

We had better consider wobble first, and it will lead us into a discussion of the various species of tRNA. Wobble is caused by a third nucleotide of the anticodon (at the 5′ end) that is not quite aligned. This out-of-line nucleotide sometimes can form hydrogen bonds not only with its normal complementary nucleotide in the third position of the codon but also with a different nucleotide in that position. Crick established certain "wobble rules" that dictate which

Second letter

		U	C	A	G	
First letter	U	UUU ⎫ Phe UUC ⎬ UUA ⎫ Leu UUG ⎭	UCU ⎫ UCC ⎬ Ser UCA UCG ⎭	UAU ⎫ Tyr UAC ⎬ UAA Stop UAG Stop	UGU ⎫ Cys UGC ⎬ UGA Stop UGG Trp	U C A G
	C	CUU ⎫ CUC ⎬ Leu CUA CUG ⎭	CCU ⎫ CCC ⎬ Pro CCA CCG ⎭	CAU ⎫ His CAC ⎬ CAA ⎫ Gln CAG ⎭	CGU ⎫ CGC ⎬ Arg CGA CGG ⎭	U C A G
	A	AUU ⎫ AUC ⎬ Ile AUA ⎭ AUG Met	ACU ⎫ ACC ⎬ Thr ACA ACG ⎭	AAU ⎫ Asn AAC ⎬ AAA ⎫ Lys AAG ⎭	AGU ⎫ Ser AGC ⎬ AGA ⎫ Arg AGG ⎭	U C A G
	G	GUU ⎫ GUC ⎬ Val GUA GUG ⎭	GCU ⎫ GCC ⎬ Ala GCA GCG ⎭	GAU ⎫ Asp GAC ⎬ GAA ⎫ Glu GAG ⎭	GGU ⎫ GGC ⎬ Gly GGA GGG ⎭	U C A G

Third letter

Figure 12-19. The genetic code.

■ **TABLE 12-5.** Codon-anticodon pairings allowed by the wobble rules

5' end of anticodon	3' end of codon
G	U or C
C	G only
A	U only
U	A or G
I	U, C, or A

nucleotides can and which cannot form new hydrogen-bonded associations through wobble (Table 12-5). In Table 12-5, inosine (I) is one of the rare bases found in tRNA, often in the anticodon.

Figure 12-20 shows the possible codons that one tRNA serine species can recognize. As the wobble rules indicate, G can pair with U or with C. Table 12-6 lists all the codons for serine and shows how different tRNAs can service these codons. This is a good example of the effects of wobble in the genetic code.

Sometimes there can be an additional tRNA species that we represent as $tRNA_{Ser_4}$; it has an anticodon identical with any one of the three anticodons shown in Table 12-6, but it differs in its nucleotide sequence elsewhere in the tRNA molecule. These four tRNAs are called **isoaccepting tRNAs** because they accept the same amino acid, but they are probably all transcribed from different tRNA genes.

Stop Codons

The second point you may have noticed in Figure 12-19 is that some codons do not specify an amino acid at all. These codons are labeled as **stop codons.** They can be regarded as something like periods or commas punctuating the message encoded in the DNA.

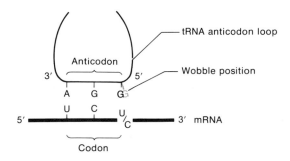

Figure 12-20. In the third site (5' end) of the anticodon, G can take either of two wobble positions, thus being able to pair with either U or C. This means that a single tRNA species carrying an amino acid (in this case, serine) can recognize two codons in the mRNA, UCU and UCC.

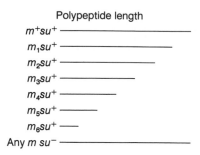

Figure 12-21. Polypeptide-chain lengths of phage-T4 head protein in wild-type (*top*) and various amber mutants (*m*). An amber suppressor (*su*) leads to phenotypic development of the wild-type chain.

One of the first indications of the existence of stop codons came in 1965 from work by Sidney Brenner with the T4 phage. Brenner analyzed certain mutations (m_1 through m_6) in a single cistron that controls the head protein of the phage. These mutants had two things in common. First, the head protein of each mutant was a shorter polypeptide chain than that of the wild-type. Second, the presence of a suppressor mutation (*su*) in the host chromosome would cause the phage to develop a head protein of normal (wild-type) chain length despite the presence of the *m* mutation (Figure 12-21).

Brenner examined the ends of the shortened proteins and compared them with wild-type protein, recording for each mutant the next amino acid that *would* have been inserted to continue the wild-type chain. These amino acids for the six mutations were glutamine, lysine, glutamic acid, tyrosine, tryptophan, and serine. There is no immediately obvious pattern to these results, but Brenner brilliantly deduced that certain codons for each of these amino acids are similar in that each of them can mutate to the codon UAG by a single change in a DNA nucleotide pair. He therefore postulated that UAG is a stop (or termination) codon, a signal to the translation mechanism that the protein is now complete.

UAG was the first stop codon deciphered, and it is called the **amber codon.** Mutants that are defective because

■ **TABLE 12-6.** Different tRNAs that can service codons for serine

Codon	tRNA	Anticodon
UCU UCC	$tRNA_{Ser_1}$	AGG + wobble
UCA UCG	$tRNA_{Ser_2}$	AGU + wobble
AGU AGC	$tRNA_{Ser_3}$	UCG + wobble

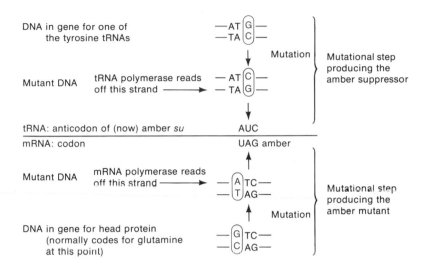

DNA in gene for one of the tyrosine tRNAs   —AT⌐G⌐— —TA⌐C⌐—

Mutant DNA   tRNA polymerase reads off this strand ⟶   — AT⌐C⌐— — TA⌐G⌐—

Mutation

Mutational step producing the amber suppressor

tRNA: anticodon of (now) amber *su*   AUC

mRNA: codon   UAG amber

Mutant DNA   mRNA polymerase reads off this strand ⟶   —⌐A⌐TC— —⌐T⌐AG—

Mutational step producing the amber mutant

Mutation

DNA in gene for head protein (normally codes for glutamine at this point)   —⌐G⌐TC— —⌐C⌐AG—

Figure 12-22. Mutation can produce an amber suppressor (*top*) that counteracts the effect of the amber mutant codon (*bottom*). Amber mutations occur when the base sequence in the DNA is changed from a codon representing an amino acid to one representing a stop signal. Suppressor mutations are mutations in genes coding for specific tRNA molecules. One nucleotide in the anticodon of the tRNA is changed so that the tRNA molecule will now recognize the mutant stop signal and insert an amino acid at that point. Translation can thus continue through the entire gene. See also Figure 12-23.

of the presence of an abnormal amber codon are called amber mutants, and their suppressors are amber suppressors. UGA, the **opal codon,** and UAA, the **ocher codon,** are also stop codons and also have suppressors. Stop codons often are called **nonsense** codons because they designate no amino acid, but their sense is real enough (it is unfortunate that this misnomer persists). **Missense** mutations, on the other hand, are those that lead to a change in a single amino acid in the translated polypeptide. Not surprisingly, stop codons do not act as mini mRNAs in binding aa-tRNA to ribosomes *in vitro*

Message   A missense mutation changes a codon so that it stands for a different amino acid. A nonsense mutation changes a codon so that it means "stop" to the translation system.

It is interesting to consider the nonsense suppressor mutations, many of which now are known to be mutations in the anticodon loop of specific tRNAs that allow recognition of a nonsense codon in mRNA. Thus an amino acid is inserted in response to the stop codon, and translation continues past that triplet. Figure 12-22 shows an example for m_1 in the T4 head-protein analysis. The amber mutation replaces the codon for glutamine by a stop codon, which by itself would prematurely cut off the protein at this position. The suppressor mutation produces a $tRNA_{Tyr}$ with an anticodon that complements that mutant stop codon. This mutant tRNA inserts tyrosine in the protein, so that translation continues past the m_1 stop codon. The suppressed m_1 mutant thus does not have a fully wild-type protein, because one glutamine has been replaced by a tyrosine. Obviously, the insertion of tyrosine is not the critical factor

that restores protein activity (probably any of a variety of amino acids would suffice in this case). The important thing is that some amino acid *is* inserted, and the translation apparatus trundles by and completes the rest of the protein (see Figure 12-23).

Two questions often are asked at this point:

1. What is doing the job of putting tyrosine where tyrosine should be when the gene for tyrosine tRNA becomes a nonsense suppressor? Remember that there typically are several isoaccepting tRNA forms (and hence several $tRNA_{Tyr}$ genes) and that two of these may have the same anticodon loop. The "other" (one or more) wild-type $tRNA_{Tyr}$ gene takes over when a suppressor locus is created from the first.

2. What happens to normal stop signals (indicating the ends of normal proteins) when nonsense suppressors are present? First of all, suppression is not 100 percent efficient. The range of suppression efficiencies varies from less than 1 to greater than 50 percent, depending on the suppressor used and the specific site being acted on. Suppression can be affected by the surrounding nucleotide sequence, and in a number of cases nonsense suppression at the natural end of a coding sequence is less efficient than suppression at many internal nonsense sites created by mutation. Also, the normal end of a protein is often signaled by two different consecutive stop codons.

Start Codon

The third point regarding Figure 12-19 is that a single codon (AUG) acts as a **start codon**—rather like the capital letter indicating the start of a sentence. This codon also acts

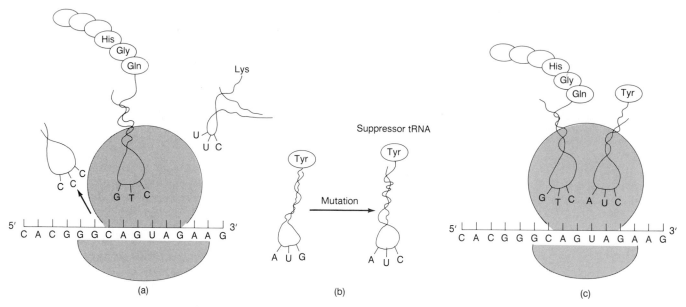

Figure 12-23. (a) A schematic view of translation. Here, the translation apparatus cannot go past a nonsense (UAG in this case) codon, because there is no tRNA that can recognize the UAG triplet. This leads to the termination of protein synthesis and to the subsequent release of the polypeptide fragment. This release is promoted by protein factors that are not shown here. (b) The molecular consequences of a mutation that alters the anticodon of a tyrosine tRNA. This tRNA can now read the UAG codon. (c) The suppression of the UAG codon by the altered tRNA, which now permits chain elongation. At the ribosome, the codons of an mRNA molecule base-pair with the anticodons of RNAs, which are charged with amino acids. (From James D. Watson, John Tooze, and David T. Kurtz, *Recombinant DNA: A Short Course.* Copyright © 1983 by W. H. Freeman and Co.)

as the codon for the amino acid methionine. In *E. coli* and in most other organisms, the first amino acid in any newly synthesized polypeptide always is one called *N*-formylmethionine. It is inserted not by tRNA$_{Met}$, however, but by an initiator tRNA called tRNA$_{N\text{-f-Met}}$. This initiator tRNA has the normal methionine anticodon, but it inserts *N*-formylmethionine rather than methionine in the polypeptide chain (Figure 12-24). Either the formyl group or a sequence in the tRNA apparently mimics a polypeptide chain; at least the ribosome recognizes some specific signal and shifts one codon to amino acid position 2. Methionine won't cause this shift; if methionyl tRNA$_{Met}$ inserts, nothing

happens. The system then must wait until the Met–tRNA$_{Met}$ diffuses away and an *N*-f-Met–tRNA$_{N\text{-f-Met}}$ chances along to get things going. Similarly, when AUG occurs in the middle of a protein, *N*-f-Met–tRNA$_{N\text{-f-Met}}$ cannot form a peptide bond with the growing chain, so the system must wait for Met–tRNA$_{Met}$. In *E. coli*, GUG and perhaps UUG can serve as initiation codons in some cases. When this occurs, these triplets are recognized by *N*-f-Met–tRNA$_{N\text{-f-Met}}$, and methionine appears as the first amino acid in the chain.

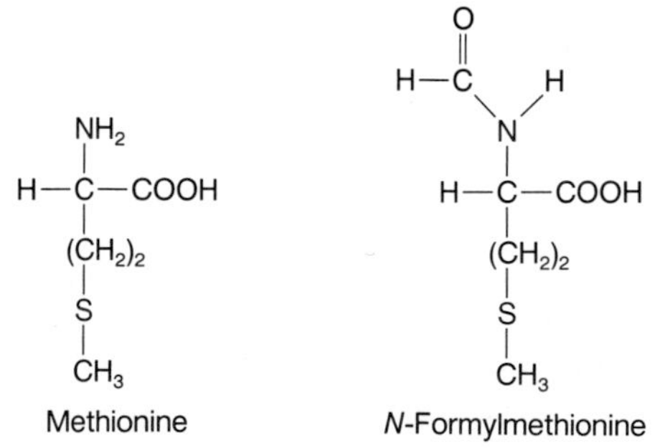

Unsolved Problems

The ribosome is an immensely challenging structure. Very little is known about the precise arrangement of the ribosomal protein and rRNA subunits, or about how they unite to grapple physically with the mRNA, the tRNA, the amino acid, and the peptide chain. The role of rRNA has always been a mystery. The role of the proteins can be visualized much like a complex enzyme, but the occurrence of what is normally an informational molecule in this structure is baffling. There is evidence now suggesting that the rRNA is crucial in the binding of various translational components (such as tRNA and in RNA) to the ribosome. This role must be nonspecific with respect to the tRNA species because a ribosome is basically a nonspecific translational apparatus. Ribosomal RNA is the most abundant RNA in a cell and obviously serves a crucial cell function. It is known to be synthesized in the nucleolus in a repetitive tandem array of rRNA genes, synthesized off the chromosomal region known as the **nucleolar organizer.**

Figure 12-24. The structures of methionine (Met) and *N*-formylmethionine (*N*-f-Met). A tRNA bearing *N*-f-Met can initiate a polypeptide chain but cannot be inserted in a growing chain; a tRNA bearing Met can be inserted in a growing chain but will not initiate a new chain. Both of these tRNAs bear the same anticodon complementing the codon AUG.

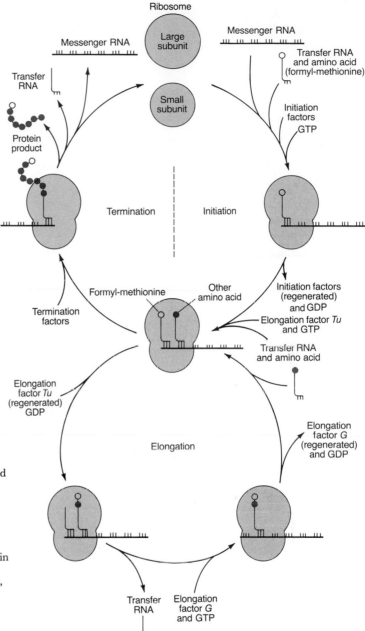

Figure 12-25. The transactions of the ribosome. At initiation, the ribosome recognizes the starting point in a segment of mRNA and binds a molecule of tRNA bearing a single amino acid. In all bacterial proteins, this first amino acid is *N*-formylmethionine. In elongation, a second amino acid is linked to the first one. The ribosome then shifts its position on the mRNA molecule, and the elongation cycle is repeated. When the stop codon is reached, the chain of amino acids folds spontaneously to form a protein. Subsequently, the ribosome splits into its two subunits, which rejoin before a new segment of mRNA is translated. Protein synthesis is facilitated by a number of catalytic proteins (initiation, elongation, and termination factors) and by guanosine triphosphate (GTP), a small molecule that releases energy when it is converted into guanosine diphosphate (GDP). (From Donald M. Engelman and Peter B. Moore, "Neutron-scattering Studies of the Ribosome." Copyright © 1976 by Scientific American, Inc. All rights reserved.)

We have followed a highly simplified version of protein synthesis. There are several other components or "factors" required for the system to work. Figure 12-25 summarizes the action of some of them.

There are many other chemical mysteries surrounding protein synthesis. In eukaryotic cells, for example, mRNA is transcribed in the nucleus as **heterogeneous nuclear RNA** (HnRNA), which is much longer than the final messenger and also acquires a 3′ tail of about 150 to 200 adenine nucleotides (a **poly-A tail**). The mRNA is enzymatically chopped out of the HnRNA, although the poly-A tail remains. We consider these processes in more detail in Chapter 19.

Our discussion has been limited chiefly to microbes, but the amazing fact is that the information-transfer, coding, and translation processes are virtually identical in all organisms that have been studied. For example, all of the different single amino acid substitutions known to occur in human hemoglobin result from single nucleotide-pair substitutions based on the genetic code derived from *E. coli* (Table 12-7). Such observations suggest that the genetic code is shared by all organisms. Furthermore, an information-bearing molecule, such as rabbit red-blood-cell mRNA, which is predominantly hemoglobin gene transcript, will be translated in an alien environment (such as a frog egg) into rabbit hemoglobin (Figure 12-26). Apparently, the translation apparatus is functionally the same in a wide range of different organisms.

■ **TABLE 12-7.** Mutations in human hemoglobin, in *E. coli* tryptophan synthetase, and in tobacco-mosaic-virus (TMV) coat protein

Protein	Amino acid substitution	Inferred codon change
Hemoglobin	Glu ⟶ Val	GAA ⟶ GUA
Hemoglobin	Glu ⟶ Lys	GAA ⟶ AAA
Hemoglobin	Glu ⟶ Gly	GAA ⟶ GGA
Tryptophan synthetase	Gly ⟶ Arg	GGA ⟶ AGA
Tryptophan synthetase	Gly ⟶ Glu	GGA ⟶ GAA
Tryptophan synthetase	Glu ⟶ Ala	GAA ⟶ GCA
TMV coat protein	Leu ⟶ Phe	CUU ⟶ UUU
TMV coat protein	Glu ⟶ Gly	GAA ⟶ GGA
TMV coat protein	Pro ⟶ Ser	CCC ⟶ UCC

SOURCE: L. Stryer, *Biochemistry*, 2d ed. Copyright © 1981 by W. H. Freeman and Co.

Sequencing techniques at the protein, RNA, and DNA (see Chapter 14) levels have verified that the genetic code is universal in all organisms studied to date, ranging from viruses and bacteria to humans. One exception involves mitochondrial DNA (see also Chapter 20). Two codons are translated differently here, owing to the properties of tRNAs that are confined to the mitochondrial system. Thus, whereas AUA is normally translated as isoleucine, it is read as methionine in the mitochondria. Also, the mammalian mitochondria translate UGA as tryptophan, whereas UGA normally specifies a chain terminating codon. In yeast, the mitochondria translate UGA as tryptophan, as in mammalian mitochondria, but they translate AUA as isoleucine, like bacterial systems. As we shall see from genetic engineering experiments in Chapter 14, DNA is DNA no matter what its origin. The nature and message of the DNA represent a universal language of life on earth.

Does this interspecific equivalence of parts in the genetic apparatus indicate a common evolutionary ancestry for all life forms on earth? Or does it simply reflect the fact that this is the only workable biochemical option in the earth environment (biochemical predestination)? Whatever the answer, the wonderful uniformity of the molecular basis of life on earth is firmly established. Minor variations do exist, but they do not detract from the central uniformity of the mechanism that we have described.

Message The processes of information storage, replication, transcription, and translation are fundamentally similar in all living systems. In demonstrating this fact, molecular genetics has provided a powerful unifying force in biology. We now know some of the tricks that life uses to achieve persistent order in a randomizing universe.

This chapter and Chapters 10 and 11 have described the development of the central theory of molecular genetics. A linear sequence of nucleotides in DNA is transcribed into a comparable linear sequence of nucleotides in mRNA. This mRNA sequence then is translated into an amino acid sequence in protein by a complex translational apparatus. The protein thus made has importance to the organism either as a structural component (such as hair, muscle, or skin protein) or as a regulator of the body chemistry (such as enzymes or hemoglobin). Figure 12-27 summarizes the structural relationship between DNA and protein.

Summary

■ We have discovered in earlier chapters that DNA is the genetic material and is responsible for directing the synthesis of proteins. The first clue to how DNA accomplishes this feat came from eukaryotes, when it was shown that RNA is synthesized in the nucleus and then transferred to the cytoplasm. However, most of the details of this transfer of information from DNA to protein were worked out with experiments in bacteria and phage.

RNA is synthesized from only one strand of a double-stranded DNA helix. This transcription is catalyzed by an enzyme, RNA polymerase, and follows rules similar to those followed in replication: A complements with T, G with C, and U (uracil) with A. Ribose is the sugar used in RNA, and uracil replaces thymine. Extraction of RNA from a cell yields three basic varieties: ribosomal, transfer, and messenger RNA. The three sizes of ribosomal RNA (rRNA) combine with an array of specific proteins to form ribosomes that are the machines used for protein synthesis (translation). Transfer RNAs (tRNA) are a group of rather

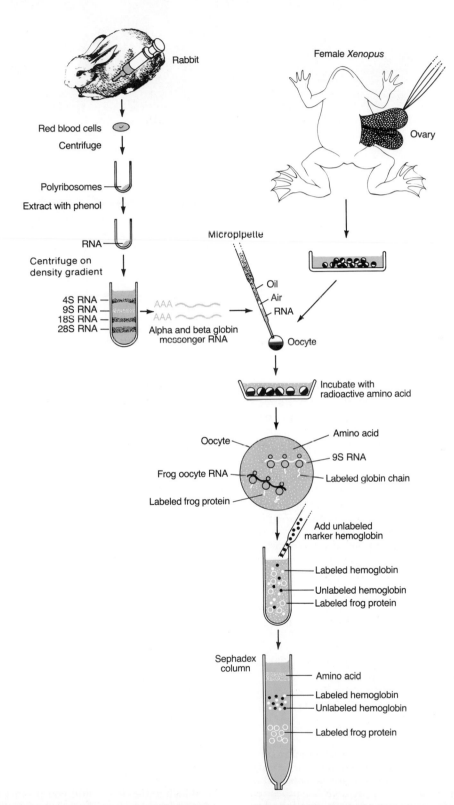

Figure 12-26. Rabbit hemoglobin mRNA is translated into rabbit hemoglobin in a frog *(Xenopus)* egg. This translation occurs with the *Xenopus* translation apparatus. This experiment is one of many that point toward the uniformity of the genetic molecular mechanism in all forms of life. (Sephadex is a separatory material used in chromatography.) (From C. Lane, "Rabbit Hemoglobin from Frog Eggs." Copyright © 1976 by Scientific American, Inc. All rights reserved.)

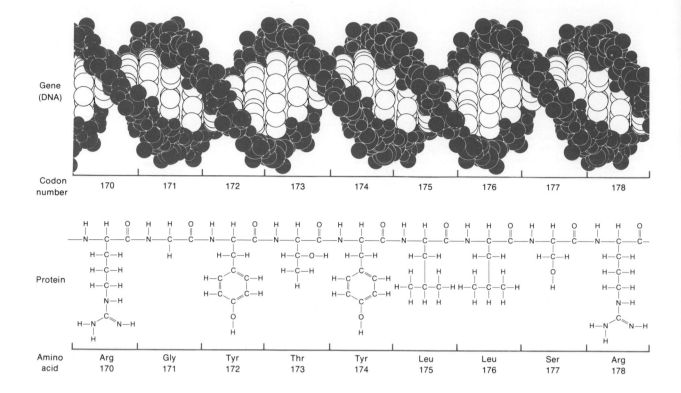

small RNA molecules, each with specificity for a particular amino acid; they carry the amino acids to the ribosome, where they can be attached to a growing polypeptide.

Messenger RNA (mRNA) molecules are of many sizes and base sequences. These are the molecules that contain information for the structure of proteins. The sequence of codons in mRNA determines the sequence of amino acids that will comprise a polypeptide. Each codon is specific for one amino acid, but several different codons may code for the same amino acid; that is, there is redundancy in the genetic code. In addition, there are three codons for which there are no tRNAs, and these stop codons terminate the process of translation. Figure 12-28 summarizes the way that genetic information is turned into protein.

The processes of information storage, replication, transcription, and translation are fundamentally similar in all living organisms. In demonstrating this similarity, molecular genetics has provided a powerful unifying force in biology.

Problems

1. The two strands of phage λ differ from each other in their G–C content. Because of this property, they can be separated in an alkaline cesium chloride gradient (the alkalinity denatures the double helix). When RNA synthesized by phage λ is isolated from infected cells, it is found to form DNA-RNA hybrids with both strands of λ DNA. What does this tell you? Formulate some testable predictions.

2. The data in Table 12-8 represent the base compositions of two double-stranded DNA sources and their RNA products in experiments conducted in vitro.

   a. From these data, can you determine whether the RNA of these species is copied from a single strand or from both strands of the DNA?

   b. Explain how you can tell whether the RNA itself is single-stranded or double-stranded.

   (Problem 2 is reprinted with permission of Macmillan Publishing Co., Inc., from M. Strickberger, *Genetics.* Copyright © 1968, Monroe W. Strickberger.)

3. Before the true nature of the genetic coding process was fully understood, it was proposed that the message might be read in overlapping triplets. For example, the sequence GCAUC might be read as GCA CAU AUC:

   G C A U C

   Devise an experimental test of this idea.

4. In protein-synthesizing systems in vitro, the addition of a specific human mRNA to *E. coli* translational apparatus (ribosomes, tRNA, and so forth) stimulates the synthesis of a protein very much like that specified by the mRNA. What does this result show?

5. Which anticodon would you predict for a tRNA species carrying isoleucine? Is there more than one possible answer?

6. a. In how many cases in the genetic code would you *fail*

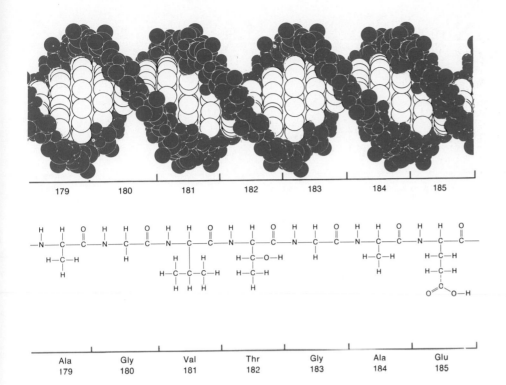

Figure 12-27. The colinearity of DNA (gene) and polypeptide (protein). The figure shows a stretch of 16 amino acids from the *E. coli* protein called tryptophan synthetase A. (From C. Yanofsky, "Gene Structure and Protein Structure." Copyright © 1967 by Scientific American, Inc. All rights reserved.)

to know the amino acid specified by a codon if you know only the first two nucleotides of the codon?

b. In how many cases would you fail to know the first two nucleotides of the codon if you know which amino acid is specified by it?

7. Deduce what the six wild-type codons may have been in the mutants that led Brenner to infer the nature of the amber codon UAG.

8. If a polyribonucleotide contains equal amounts of randomly positioned adenine and uracil bases, what proportion of its triplets would code for: a. phenylalanine? b. isoleucine? c. leucine? d. tyrosine?

9. You have synthesized three different messenger RNAs with bases incorporated in random sequence in the following ratios: a. 1U:5C; b. 1A:1C:4U; c. 1A:1C:1G:1U. In a protein-synthesizing system in vitro, indicate the identities and proportions of amino acids that will be incorporated into proteins when each of these mRNAs is tested. (Use Figure 12-19.)

10. One of the techniques that was used to decipher the genetic code was to synthesize polypeptides in vitro, using synthetic mRNA with various repeating base sequences —for example, (AGA)$_n$, which could be written out as AGAAGAAGAAGAAGA . . . . Sometimes the synthesized polypeptide contained just one amino acid (a homopolymer), and sometimes it contained more than one (a heteropolymer), depending on the repeating sequence used. Furthermore, sometimes different polypeptides were made from the same synthetic mRNA, suggesting that the initiation of protein synthesis in the system in vitro does not always start on the end nucleotide of the messenger. For example, from (AGA)$_n$, three polypeptides may have been made: aa$_1$ homopolymer (abbreviated aa$_1$-aa$_1$), aa$_2$ homopolymer (aa$_2$-aa$_2$), and aa$_3$ homopolymer (aa$_3$-aa$_3$). These probably correspond to the following readings derived by starting at different places in the sequence:

AGA AGA AGA AGA . . .

GAA GAA GAA GAA . . .

AAG AAG AAG AAG . . .

Table 12-9 shows the actual results in the experiment done by Khorana.

■ TABLE 12-8.

Species	DNA base ratio	RNA base ratios	
	(A + T)/(G + C)	(A + U)/(G + C)	(A + G)/(U + C)
Bacillus subtilis	1.36	1.30	1.02
Escherichia coli	1.00	0.98	0.80

Chromosomal DNA

Recognition sequences for RNA polymerase
(promoter)

(a)

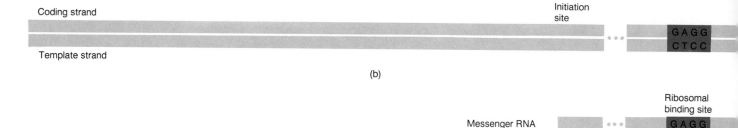

Coding strand

Initiation
site

Template strand

(b)

Ribosomal
binding site

Messenger RNA

Translation

Protein chain

(c)

Figure 12-28. Genetic information is stored in the double helix of DNA. (a) Each strand of the helix is a chain of nucleotides, each comprising a deoxyribose sugar and a phosphate group, which form the strand's backbone, as well as one of four bases: adenine (A), guanine (G), thymine (T), and cytosine (C). The information is encoded in the sequence of the bases along a strand. The complementarity of the bases (A always pairs with T, and G with C)

is the basis of the replication of DNA from generation to generation and of its expression (shown here for bacterial DNA) as protein. (b) and (c) Expression begins with the transcription of the DNA base sequence into a strand of messenger RNA, which corresponds to the coding strand of the DNA except for the fact that uracil (U) replaces thymine. Transcription into RNA and translation into protein are regulated by special sequences (red) in the DNA and

■ TABLE 12-9.

Synthetic mRNA	Polypeptide(s) synthesized
$(UC)_n$	(Ser–Leu)
$(UG)_n$	(Val–Cys)
$(AC)_n$	(Thr–His)
$(AG)_n$	(Arg–Glu)
$(UUC)_n$	(Ser–Ser) and (Leu–Leu) and (Phe–Phe)
$(UUG)_n$	(Leu–Leu) and (Val–Val) and (Cys–Cys)
$(AAG)_n$	(Arg–Arg) and (Lys–Lys) and (Glu–Glu)
$(CAA)_n$	(Thr–Thr) and (Asn–Asn) and (Gln–Gln)
$(UAC)_n$	(Thr–Thr) and (Leu–Leu) and (Tyr–Tyr)
$(AUC)_n$	(Ile–Ile) and (Ser–Ser) and (His–His)
$(GUA)_n$	(Ser–Ser) and (Val–Val)
$(GAU)_n$	(Asp–Asp) and (Met–Met)
$(UAUC)_n$	(Tyr–Leu–Ser–Ile)
$(UUAC)_n$	(Leu–Leu–Thr–Tyr)
$(GAUA)_n$	None
$(GUAA)_n$	None

NOTE: the order in which the polypeptides or amino acids are listed is not significant except for $(UAUC)_n$ and $(UUAC)_n$.

a. Why do $(GUA)_n$ and $(GAU)_n$ each code for only two homopolypeptides?

b. Why do $(GAUA)_n$ and $(GUAA)_n$ fail to stimulate synthesis?

c. Assign an amino acid to each triplet in the following list. Bear in mind that there often are several codons for a single amino acid, and that the first two letters in a codon usually are the important ones (but that the third letter is occasionally significant). Also remember that some very different-looking codons sometimes code for the same amino acid. Try to carry out this task without consulting Figure 12-19.

AUG	GAU	UUG	AAC
GUG	UUC	UUA	CAA
GUU	CUC	AUC	AGA
GUA	CUU	UAU	GAG
UGU	CUA	UAC	GAA
CAC	UCU	ACU	UAG
ACA	AGU	AAG	UGA

To solve this problem requires both logic and trial and

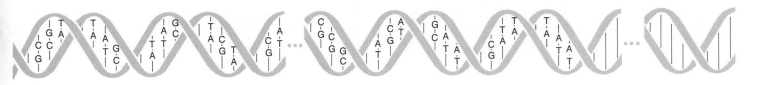

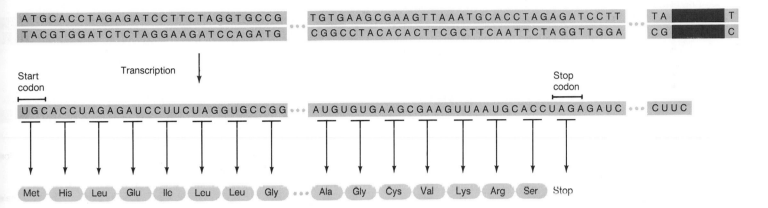

Coding sequence of structural gene
(average length about 1000 base pairs)

Termination region

```
ATGCACCTAGAGATCCTTCTAGGTGCCG      TGTGAAGCGAAGTTAAATGCACCTAGAGATCCTT   TA        T
TACGTGGATCTCTAGGAAGATCCAGATG      CGGCCTACACACTTCGCTTCAATTCTAGGTTGGA   CG        C
```

Start codon

Transcription

Stop codon

```
UGCACCUAGAGAUCCUUCUAGGUGCCGG ··· AUGUGUGAAGCGAAGUUAAUGCACCUAGAGAUC ··· CUUC
```

Met His Leu Glu Ile Leu Leu Gly ··· Ala Gly Cys Val Lys Arg Ser Stop

the RNA, respectively. The transcribing enzyme, RNA polymerase, binds to a promoter region before a transcription-initiation site; beyond the end of the structural gene a termination region causes the polymerase to cease transcription. Messenger RNA is translated on the cellular organelles called ribosomes; each triplet of bases (codon) encodes a particular amino acid and specifies its incorporation into the growing protein chain. A ribosomal binding site on the RNA allows translation to begin at a "start" codon, which is always AUG for the amino acid methionine (Met). Translation proceeds until a "stop" codon is reached (UAA is one of three possibilities), which signals the end of translation and detachment of the completed protein chain from the ribosome.

error. Don't be disheartened: Khorana received a Nobel prize for doing it. Good luck!

(Problem 10 is from J. Kuspira and G. W. Walker, *Genetics: Questions and Problems*, McGraw-Hill, 1973.)

11. You are studying a gene in *E. coli* that specifies a protein, part of whose sequence is

    –Ala–Pro–Trp–Ser–Glu–Lys–Cys–His–

    You recover a series of mutants for this gene that show no enzyme activity. Isolating the mutant enzyme products, you find the following sequences:

    Mutant 1 –Ala–Pro–Trp–Arg–Glu–Lys–Cys–His–

    Mutant 2 –Ala–Pro–

    Mutant 3 –Ala–Pro–Gly–Val–Lys–Asn–Cys–His–

    Mutant 4 –Ala–Pro–Trp–Phe–Phe–Thr–Cys–His–

    What is the molecular basis for each mutation? What is the DNA sequence that specifies this part of the protein?

12. A single nucleotide addition and a single nucleotide deletion approximately 15 sites apart in the DNA cause a protein change in sequence from

    –Lys–Ser–Pro–Ser–Leu–Asn–Ala–Ala–Lys–

    to

    –Lys–Val–His–His–Leu–Met–Ala–Ala–Lys–

    a. What are the old and the new mRNA nucleotide sequences? (Use Figure 12-19.)

    b. Which nucleotide has been added and which has been deleted?

    (Problem 12 is from W. D. Stansfield, *Theory and Problems of Genetics*, McGraw-Hill, 1969.)

13. A mutational event inserts an extra nucleotide pair into DNA. Which of the following do you expect? a. No protein product at all b. A protein in which one amino acid is changed c. A protein in which three amino acids are changed d. A protein in which two amino acids are changed e. A protein in which most amino acids following the site of the insertion are changed

14. Suppressors of frame-shift mutations are now known. Propose a mechanism for their action.

15. Using Figure 12-19, complete the following table. As-

sume that reading is from left to right and that the columns represent transcriptional and translational alignments.

C									DNA double helix
				T	G	A			
	C	A			U				mRNA transcribed
						G	C	A	Appropriate tRNA anticodon
		Trp							Amino acids incorporated into protein

16. Consider the gene that specifies the structure of hemoglobin. Arrange the following events in the most likely sequence in which they would occur:

  a. Anemia is observed.

  b. The shape of the oxygen-binding site is altered.

  c. An incorrect codon is transcribed into hemoglobin mRNA.

  d. The ovum (female gamete) receives a high radiation dose.

  e. An incorrect codon is generated in the DNA of the hemoglobin gene.

  f. A mother (an X-ray technician) accidentally steps in front of an operating X-ray generator.

  g. A child dies.

  h. The oxygen-transport capacity of the body is severely impaired.

  i. The tRNA anticodon that lines up is one of a type that brings an unsuitable amino acid.

  j. Nucleotide-pair substitution occurs in the DNA of the gene for hemoglobin.

17. The comparison of physical distances with map distances is facilitated by our knowledge of the genetic code. The code permits us to "translate" numbers of amino acids in a protein into numbers of nucleotides in a corresponding stretch of DNA.

  a. Consider two mutant forms of a particular enzyme in *Neurospora*. The two proteins are known to differ at only two positions in their polypeptide chains. The two positions are separated by 40 other amino acids. Crosses of the two mutants regularly give a recombinant frequency of 1.0×10^{-5} for the two mutations. Approximately how many nucleotides in *Neurospora* lie between a pair of markers that give a recombinant frequency of 10^{-5}?

  b. Consider two other mutant forms of the enzyme. Each has the normal (wild-type) number of amino acids, but these enzymes differ from each other and from the wild-type enzyme at amino acid 68 in the polypeptide chain. The wild-type protein has arginine at position 68, whereas one mutant has glutamine and the other has serine. When mutants 1 and 2 are crossed, six kinds of offspring differing in the amino acid at position 68 are observed. Two of these are parental types in which glutamine or serine is present at position 68, and one has arginine like the wild type. Three novel types—having lysine, asparagine, or histidine—make up the remainder. Table 12-10 shows the frequencies of these classes in the progeny of the cross. Deduce the nucleotide sequences at codon 68 for each of the six types. What is the frequency of recombinants for crosses in which the markers are at adjacent positions in the DNA?

■ **TABLE 12-10.**

Amino acid at position 68	Frequency among offspring of the cross
Gln	about 0.50
Ser	about 0.50
Arg	4.0×10^{-7}
His	2.0×10^{-7}
Asn	1.0×10^{-11}
Lys	2.0×10^{-7}

(Problem 17 is from Franklin W. Stahl, *The Mechanics of Inheritance*, 2d ed., p. 192. Copyright © 1969, Prentice-

Hall, Inc., Englewood Cliffs, New Jersey. Reprinted by permission.)

18. An induced cell mutant is isolated from a hamster tissue culture because of its resistance to α-amanitin (a poison derived from a fungus). Electrophoresis shows that the mutant has an altered RNA polymerase; *just one* electrophoretic band is in a position different from that of the wild-type polymerase. The cells are presumed to be diploid. What does this experiment tell you about ways to detect recessive mutants in such cells?

19. A double-stranded DNA molecule with the following sequence produces, in vivo, a polypeptide that is five amino acids long.

a. Which strand of DNA is transcribed? and in which direction?

b. Label the 5′ and the 3′ ends of each strand.

c. If an inversion occurred between the second and third triplets from the left and right ends, respectively, and the same strand of DNA was transcribed, how long would the resultant polypeptide be?

d. Assume that the original molecule is intact and that transcription occurs on the bottom strand from left to right. Give the base sequence and label the 5′ and 3′ ends of the anticodon that inserts the *fourth* amino acid into the nascent polypeptide. What is this amino acid?

TAC ATG ATC ATT TCA CGG AAT TTC TAG CAT GTA
ATG TAC TAG TAA AGT GCC TTA AAG ATC GTA CAT

CHAPTER 13

Recombination in Bacteria and Their Viruses

■ In the last few chapters we have seen examples of recombination in bacteria or phages. Now we consider the tools of genetic analysis in these organisms. A very large part of the history of genetics and of current genetic analysis (particularly molecular genetics) is concerned with prokaryotic organisms and viruses, as we have seen. Viruses are a problem for biologists to classify. They aren't cells, and they cannot grow or multiply alone; they must parasitize living cells, using the cells' metabolic machinery to reproduce. Nevertheless, they do have hereditary properties and can be used for genetic analysis. Although viruses share some of the definitive properties of organisms, many biologists regard them as distinct entities that in some sense are not fully alive.

Prokaryotic organisms and viruses have very simple chromosomes (compared with those of eukaryotes) that are not contained within a nuclear membrane. Nor do these chromosomes undergo mitosis or meiosis. However, although the ways in which they undergo reproduction may seem strange, there are stages that are analogous to meiosis. The approach to genetic analysis of recombination in these organisms is surprisingly similar to that for eukaryotes. Although they are treated in separate chapters here, there is no fundamental difference between the two systems.

The prokaryotes are bacteria and blue-green algae (now classified as "cyanobacteria"). Among the viruses, the best-studied are those that parasitize bacteria; they are called bacterial viruses, or **bacteriophages**—often simply called **phages.** The pioneering work with bacteriophages has led to a great deal of recent research on tumor-causing viruses and other kinds of viruses in animals and plants, and these are now becoming better understood at the genetic level.

The early history of genetics (from 1900 to around 1945) is dominated by the stunning successes in deciphering the basic rules of genetics in higher organisms—animals and plants. The "middle years" (roughly 1945 to 1965) were dominated by study of bacteria and phage. Recently, the trend is toward a return to study of higher organisms, applying the information and techniques learned from the simpler systems. Thus, bacterial and phage genetics represents a crucial pivotal point in the advance of genetics.

Bacteria and viruses have obvious medical importance. Furthermore, they are very important in the ecosystem of our planet, representing a highly successful occupation of many diverse kinds of ecological niches. Their very simplicity makes them attractive for the study of the most basic cellular and molecular processes. But how is it possible to study inheritance in organisms too small to be seen without a microscope?

Bacteria can be grown in two ways—in a liquid medium or on a solid surface such as an agar gel—so long as basic nutritive ingredients are supplied. In liquid medium, the bacteria divide by binary fission; they multiply geometrically until the nutrients are exhausted or until toxic factors (waste products) accumulate to levels that halt the population growth. A small amount of such a liquid culture can be pipetted onto a petri plate containing an agar medium and spread evenly on the surface with a sterile spreader. Each cell then reproduces by fission. Because the cells are immobilized in the gel, all of the daughter cells remain together in a clump. Soon this mass of more than 10^7 cells becomes visible to the naked eye as a **colony.** This process is called **plating** (Figure 13-1). If the sample initially plated contains very few cells, then each distinct colony on the plate will derive from a single original cell. Such colonies whose members share a single genetic ancestor are known as **clones.**

For many characters, the phenotype of a clone can be determined readily through visual inspection or simple chemical tests. This phenotype can then be assigned to the original cell of the clone, so the frequencies of various phenotypes in the pipetted sample can be determined.

Bacterial Conjugation

To fully appreciate the reasoning behind early experiments in bacterial genetics, you must try to grasp the level of understanding that existed at the time. It was not known whether bacteria have regular mechanisms for exchanging genetic information, nor even whether they have chromosomes. Indeed, about all that was known was that fairly stable true-breeding lines could be established with different phenotypes (usually involving different nutritional requirements) and that new forms occasionally appeared in these lines, apparently as the result of mutation.

The Discovery of Bacterial Gene Transfer

Starting from this lack of knowledge, it is easy to see that experimental questions regarding the very fundamentals of bacterial inheritance were needed. For example, can bacteria exchange hereditary information? That is, do they possess any processes similar to sex and recombination? This question was answered in 1946 by the elegantly simple experimental work of Joshua Lederberg and Edward Tatum. They studied two strains of *Escherichia coli* with different nutritional requirements: strain A would grow on "minimal medium" (a medium containing only inorganic salts, a carbon source, and water) only if the medium were supplemented with methionine and biotin; strain B would grow on minimal medium only if it were supplemented with threonine, leucine, and thiamine. Thus we can designate strain A as *met⁻ bio⁻ thr⁺ leu⁺ thi⁺* and strain B as *met⁺ bio⁺ thr⁻ leu⁻ thi⁻*. It was perhaps presumptuous even to use gene symbols to designate these phenotypes because it was not proved that they were determined by single genes.

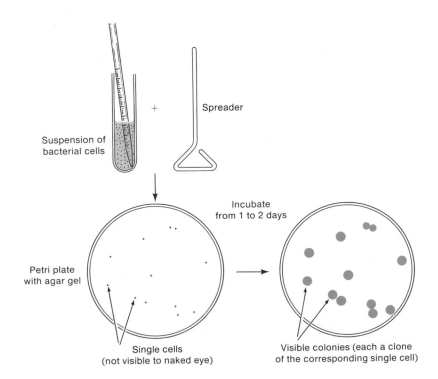

Figure 13-1. Methods of growing bacteria in the laboratory. A few bacterial cells that have been grown in a liquid medium containing nutrients can be spread on an agar medium, also containing the appropriate nutrients. Each of these original cells will divide many times by binary fission and eventually give rise to a colony. All cells in a colony, being derived from a single cell, will have the same genotype and phenotype.

Suspension of bacterial cells

Spreader

Petri plate with agar gel

Incubate from 1 to 2 days

Single cells (not visible to naked eye)

Visible colonies (each a clone of the corresponding single cell)

Of course, no linkage relationship was intended in writing the symbols in a specific order. The symbolism was merely a convenience.

In their experiment, Lederberg and Tatum plated bacteria into dishes containing only unsupplemented minimal medium. Some of the dishes were plated with only strain-A bacteria, some with only strain-B bacteria, and some with a mixture of strain-A and strain-B bacteria, which had been incubated together for several hours in a liquid medium containing all of the supplements (Figure 13-2). The plates that received the mixture of strain A and strain B produced growing colonies with a frequency of 1 for every 10,000,000 cells plated (or, in scientific notation, 1×10^{-7}). Because only prototrophic $met^+ bio^+ thr^+ leu^+ thi^+$ bacteria can grow on minimal medium, this observation suggests that some form of recombination of genes has occurred.

Now, if you are thinking critically about this experiment (as you should be), you might object: "But what about the possibility that these wild-type colonies were produced by mutation?" The answer is that, if the results were due to mutation, then wild-type colonies should have been obtained when the strain-A and strain-B bacteria were plated *by themselves* onto the minimal medium. But they weren't. Therefore, we conclude that the wild-type colonies were produced by an exchange of genetic material between the two strains.

It could be suggested that the cells of the two strains do not really exchange genes but instead leak substances that the other cells can absorb and use for growing (this won't seem so farfetched later). This possibility of "cross-feeding" was ruled out by Bernard Davis. He constructed a U tube in which the two arms were separated by a fine filter. The pores of the filter were too small to allow bacteria through, but they were large enough to allow the easy passage of the fluid medium and any dissolved substances (Figure 13-3). Strain A was put in one arm and strain B in the other. After they had been incubated for a while, the content of each arm was tested for cells able to grow on minimal medium, and none were found. In other words, *physical contact* between the two strains was needed for wild-type cells to form. It looked as though some kind of gene transfer was involved, and genetic **recombinants** were indeed produced.

Early Attempts to Identify Linkage in Bacteria

Having seen that bacteria can exchange genetic material, as can higher organisms, Lederberg and Tatum hypothesized that the bacterial genes might be organized into linkage groups, as are those of higher organisms. They recognized that two possibilities exist: either the bacterial genes are not organized into linkage groups (in which case something like Mendel's law of independent assortment would apply to all combinations of gene pairs) or, alternatively, the bacterial

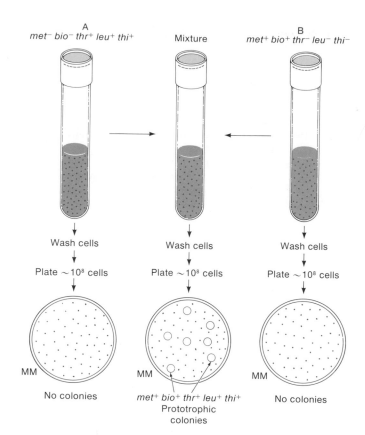

Figure 13-2. Demonstration by Lederberg and Tatum of genetic recombination occurring between bacterial cells. Cells of type A or type B cannot grow on an unsupplemented medium, since each carries mutations and lacks the ability to synthesize constituents needed for cell growth. When they are mixed for a few hours and then plated, however, a few colonies appear on the agar plate. These colonies derive from single cells in which exchange of genetic material has occurred, and they are thus capable of synthesizing all required constituents of metabolism.

genes are organized into linkage groups (in which case departures from independent assortment could be detected). Furthermore, they recognized that a simple, two-step extension of their work with strain A and strain B could be used to test for independent assortment.

In step one, they crossed A with B and then plated onto minimal medium supplemented with biotin. Any surviving colonies *must* be $met^+ thr^+ leu^+ thi^+$ at these four loci but *could* be either bio^+ or bio^-, because either of these can grow when biotin is supplied. Thus, step one produced many colonies that could be designated as $bio^? met^+ thr^+ leu^+ thi^+$. In step two, they reasoned that, if the loci are unlinked, then their assortment must be independent, and about one-half of the $bio^?$ colonies should be bio^+ and the other one-half bio^-. (Why? Because one-half of the "parental" alleles were bio^+ and one-half bio^-.) On the other hand, if the biotin locus is linked to any of the other four loci, then there should be a great departure from the 1 : 1 ratio. Specifically, if the biotin locus is linked to the methionine locus, they expected to see an excess of bio^+ over bio^- alleles (because they selected for the met^+ allele from strain B, and that would pull the linked bio^+ allele along). If the biotin

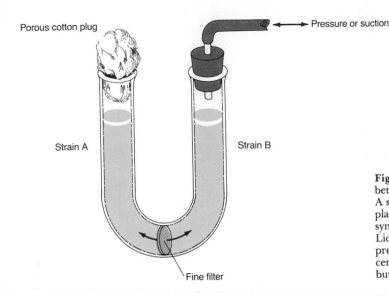

Porous cotton plug

Strain A

Strain B

Pressure or suction

Fine filter

Figure 13-3. Experiment demonstrating that physical contact between bacterial cells is needed for genetic recombination to occur. A strain of bacteria unable to grow on unsupplemented medium is placed in one arm of the U tube. A strain genetically unable to synthesize different required metabolites is placed in the other side. Liquid may be transferred between the arms by the application of pressure or suction, but bacterial cells cannot pass through the center filter. After several hours of incubation, the cells are plated, but no colonies grow on the agar medium.

locus is linked to any of the other three loci, they expected to see an excess of bio^- over bio^+ alleles (because the selection for the $thr^+ leu^+ thi^+$ alleles from strain A would pull the linked bio^- along). To determine how many of the $bio^?$ colonies were + and how many were −, Lederberg and Tatum simply plated samples of them on minimal medium: if they grew, they were bio^+; if not, they were bio^-. Finally, to generate additional data, they repeated the whole procedure using each of the other supplements in turn. Their results are shown in Table 13-1.

The data clearly show linkage, because the allele frequencies at each of the unselected loci show great departures from a 1 : 1 ratio. By noting whether the departure from 1 : 1 is toward an excess of + alleles or an excess of − alleles, Lederberg and Tatum were able to determine the linkage arrangements among the loci. (As explained previously, the excess of bio^+ over bio^- suggests that the biotin and the methionine loci are linked. To test your understanding of the experiment, you should try to work out the linkage arrangements among the other loci.)

Discovery of the Fertility Factor, F

The experiments discussed previously represent a complicated way to do a genetic analysis. In fact, Lederberg found it increasingly difficult to interpret his data. In 1953, William Hayes made a remarkable discovery. He verified the results of Lederberg and Tatum, using a similar cross:

strain A   strain B

$met^- thr^+ leu^+ thi^+ \times met^+ thr^- leu^- thi^-$

In a further experiment, Hayes treated one of the strains with the antibiotic streptomycin (which does not kill immediately but which prevents cell division) before mixing in the other strain. When he treated strain A with the streptomycin, washed out the streptomycin, mixed in strain B, and then plated the culture on minimal medium, he obtained the same frequency of colonies as he obtained in the control experiment with both strains untreated. However, when he

treated strain B with streptomycin, washed out the streptomycin, mixed in strain A, and then plated the culture on minimal medium, he obtained no colonies.

How can these asymmetrical results be explained? It would seem that the ability of strain-B cells to divide is crucial to the production of the colonies on minimal medium, whereas it does not matter whether or not the strain-A cells can divide. One interpretation is that the genetic transfer is nonreciprocal: cells of strain A donate genetic material to cells of strain B, which then can divide to produce colonies containing genes from both strains.

Message   The transfer of genetic material in *E. coli* is not reciprocal. One cell acts as the **donor,** and the other cell acts as the **recipient.**

In Hayes' experimental strains, the donor could still transmit genes after exposure to streptomycin, but the recipient could not divide to produce colonies if it had been exposed to streptomycin. This kind of unidirectional transfer of genes was originally analogized to a sexual dif-

■ **TABLE 13-1.** Allele frequencies observed by Lederberg and Tatum in cross A × B

A: $met^- bio^- thr^+ leu^+ thi^+$

B: $met^+ bio^+ thr^- leu^- thi^-$

Medium supplement	Genotype of surviving colonies	Allele frequencies at the unselected (?) locus	
		+	−
Biotin	$met^+ bio^? thr^+ leu^+ thi^+$	60	10
Threonine	$met^+ bio^+ thr^? leu^+ thi^+$	37	9
Leucine	$met^+ bio^+ thr^+ leu^? thi^+$	51	5
Thiamine	$met^+ bio^+ thr^+ leu^+ thi^?$	8	79

ference, with the donor being termed "male" and the recipient "female." Although the terms "male" and "female" still persist, it should be stressed that this type of gene transfer is not sexual reproduction. In gene transfer, one organism receives genetic information by a donor; this recipient is changed by that information. In sexual reproduction two organisms donate equally (or nearly so) to the formation of a new organism, but only in exceptional cases is either parent changed.

By accident, Hayes discovered a variant of his original strain A (male) that would not produce recombinants upon crossing with the B strain (female). Had the A males changed into females? In his analysis of this sterile variant, Hayes discovered a central but surprising component of the fertility of *E. coli*. The original A male strain, and hence the sterile variant, were sensitive to streptomycin (*str*^{s}). By plating the sterile variant on medium containing streptomycin, Hayes isolated a streptomycin-resistant mutant (*str*^{r}), which proved to be very useful in solving the genetic jigsaw puzzle.

Hayes mixed the sterile A *str*^{r} cells with the fertile A male *str*^{s} cells and then plated on a medium containing streptomycin. He found that as many as one-third of the A *str*^{r} cells had become fertile and could cross with B females (Figure 13-4). Hayes explained these bizarre results by suggesting that maleness (or donor ability) is itself a hereditary state imposed by a **fertility factor,** or F. Females lack F and therefore are recipients. Thus, females can be designated F$^-$, and males F$^+$. The sterile A-strain variant must have lost F and become F$^-$, and the original pedigree must have been that shown in Figure 13-5. In other words, the variant strain (which was sterile as a male parent) had in fact become female, as which it was perfectly fertile.

Recombinant genotypes for marker genes are relatively rare in bacteria crosses, but the F factor apparently is transmitted very effectively at physical contact, or **conjugation.** Male fertile *str*^{r} cells were recovered very soon after mixing with F$^+$ *str*^{s}. There seems to be a kind of **infectious transfer** of the F factor that takes place far more quickly than the regular exchange of marker genes. The physical nature of the F factor was elucidated much later, but these early experiments showed clearly that it is some kind of errant particle not closely tied to the marker genes.

In F$^+$ × F$^-$ crosses, Hayes found that the progeny selected as recombinants for specific marker genes generally tend to contain the remaining (unselected) alleles of the F$^-$ parent. This is true regardless of the particular marker alleles used and regardless of their coupling or repulsion arrangement. These results suggest a nonreciprocal exchange of genetic material between the parents of a cross. Further substantiation came in a difficult experiment where F$^+$ and F$^-$ cells were separated using a micromanipulator; only the F$^-$ cells ever showed a recombinant phenotype of any kind. The process involved in these crosses obviously is quite different from any kind of meiosis and

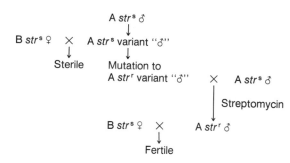

Figure 13-4. Pedigree involving an apparently sterile bacterial variant. The original cross of strain A (streptomycin-sensitive recipient) to strain B (streptomycin-sensitive donor) was sterile. However, a rare variant, or mutant, of strain A to streptomycin resistance allowed Hayes to cross this variant to the "normal" streptomycin-sensitive strain A. If this cross was plated on a medium containing streptomycin, only the streptomycin-resistant progeny would grow. These, he discovered, could then be crossed to strain-B cells, yielding fertile offspring. From these and other data, Hayes concluded that maleness in these bacteria was determined by a factor called F, which could be passed to the female during conjugation, converting her to a male.

fertilization. Is it possible that only *part* of the F$^+$ chromosome is being transferred into the F$^-$ cell?

The big break in solving the puzzle came when Luca Cavalli-Sforza obtained a new kind of male from an F$^+$ strain. On crossing with F$^-$ females, this new strain produced a thousand times more recombinants for marker genes than did its progenitor. Cavalli-Sforza called this derivative an **Hfr** strain (for *high frequency of recombination*). (It later became known as Hfr C, to distinguish it from a similar strain, Hfr H, found by Hayes.)

You will appreciate that, in the cells resulting from an F$^+$ × F$^-$ cross, a large proportion of the F$^-$ parents are found to have been converted to F$^+$ by infectious transfer of the fertility particle. However, in the Hfr × F$^-$ crosses, virtually none of the F$^-$ parents are converted to F$^+$ or to

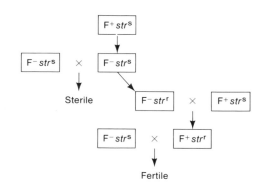

Figure 13-5. Symbolic explanation of pedigree in Figure 13-4.

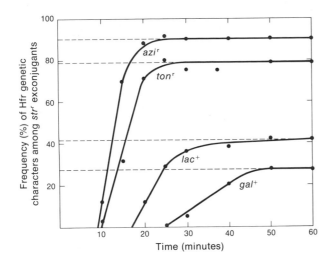

Figure 13-6. Interrupted mating/conjugation experiments with *E. coli.* F⁻ cells that were *str*ʳ were crossed with Hfr cells that were *str*ˢ. The F⁻ cells had a number of mutants (indicated by *azi, ton, lac, gal*) that prevented them from carrying out specific metabolic steps. However, the Hfr cells were capable of carrying out all these steps. At different times after the cells were mixed, samples were withdrawn, disrupted in a blender in order to break conjugation between cells, and plated on media containing streptomycin. The antibiotic killed the Hfr cells but allowed the F⁻ cells to grow and to be tested for their ability to carry out the four metabolic steps. Transfer of the donor allele of each of these steps is obviously dependent on the time that conjugation is allowed to continue. (From E. L. Wollman, F. Jacob, and W. Hayes, *Cold Spring Harbor Symposia on Quantitative Biology* 21:141, 1956.)

Hfr. Thus, infectious transfer of the factor F does not seem to occur in these crosses, even though recombination of markers is manyfold more efficient than in F⁺ × F⁻ crosses. Perhaps at this point you can understand why most geneticists until the late 1950s tried to ignore bacterial genetics!

Determining Linkage From Interrupted-Mating Experiments

The clues all began to fit together in 1957 when Ellie Wollman and François Jacob investigated the pattern of transmission of Hfr genes to F⁻ cells during a cross. They crossed Hfr *str*ˢ *a⁺ b⁺ c⁺ d⁺* with F⁻ *str*ʳ *a⁻ b⁻ c⁻ d⁻*. At specific time intervals after mixing, they removed samples. Each of these samples was put into a kitchen blender for a few seconds to disrupt the mating cell pairs; it then was plated onto medium containing streptomycin to kill the Hfr donor cells. This is called an **interrupted-mating** procedure. The *str*ʳ cells then were tested for the presence of marker alleles from the donor. Those *str*ʳ cells that bear donor marker alleles must have been involved in conjugation; such cells are called **exconjugants.** Figure 13-6 shows a plot of the results; *azi*ʳ, *ton*ʳ, *lac⁺*, and *gal⁺* correspond to the *a⁺, b⁺, c⁺,* and *d⁺* mentioned in our generalized description of the experiment.

The most striking thing about these results is that each donor allele first appears in the F⁻ recipients at a specific time after mating begins. Furthermore, the donor alleles appear in a specific sequence. Finally, the maximal yield of cells containing a specific donor allele is smaller for the donor markers that enter later. Putting all these observations together, we obtain an interpretation of the results.

Message   The Hfr chromosome is transferred to the F⁻ cell in a linear fashion, beginning at a specific point (called the origin, or O). The farther a gene is from O, the later it is transferred to the F⁻. For "later" genes, it is more likely that the transfer process will stop before they are transferred.

Wollman and Jacob realized that it would be easy to construct linkage maps from the interrupted-mating results, using as a measure of "distance" the time at which the donor alleles first appear after mating. The units of distance in this case are minutes. Thus, if *b⁺* begins to enter the F⁻ cell 10 minutes after *a⁺* begins to enter, then *a⁺* and *b⁺* are 10 units apart (Figure 13-7). Like the maps based on crossover frequencies, these linkage maps are purely genetic constructions; at the time, they had no known physical basis.

Chromosome Circularity

When Wollman and Jacob allowed Hfr × F⁻ crosses to continue for as long as 2 hours before blending, they found that some of the exconjugants were converted into Hfr. In other words, the fertility factor conferring maleness (or donor ability) is eventually transmitted, but at a very low efficiency and apparently as the last element of the linear "chromosome." We now have the following picture:

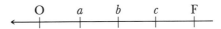

However, when several different Hfr linkage maps were derived by interrupted-mating and "time-of-entry" studies using different separately derived Hfr strains, the maps differed from strain to strain:

Hfr H	O *thr pro lac pur gal his gly thi* F
1	O *thr thi gly his gal pur lac pro* F
2	O *pro thr thi gly his gal pur lac* F
3	O *pur lac pro thr thi gly his gal* F
AB 312	O *thi thr pro lac pur gal his gly* F

At first glance, there seems to be a random reshuffling of genes. However, a pattern does exist; the genes are not thrown together at random in each strain. For example, note that in every case the *his* gene has *gal* on one side and

Figure 13-7. Chromosome map from Figure 13-6. A linkage map can be constructed for the *E. coli* chromosome from interrupted-mating studies, using the time at which the donor alleles first appear after mating. The units of distance are given in minutes.

gly on the other. Similar statements can be made about each gene, except when it appears at one end or the other of the linkage map. The order in which the genes are transferred is not constant. For example, in two Hfr strains the *his* gene is transferred before the *gly* gene (*his* is closer to O), but in three strains the *gly* gene is transferred before the *his* gene.

A startling hypothesis was proposed to account for these results. Suppose that, in an F⁺ male, F is a small cytoplasmic element (and therefore easily transferred to an F⁻ cell on conjugation). If the "chromosome" of the F⁺ male is a **ring**, then any of the linear Hfr chromosomes could be generated simply by inserting F at some particular place in the ring (Figure 13-8).

Several additional experiments demonstrated that Hfr strains did result from the insertion of F into the chromosome.

1. The presence of F between chromosomal markers donated very early and very late was indicated by the disruption of linkage between the chromosomal markers. This could be demonstrated in phage P1 transduction experiments (see the subsequent section on transduction).

2. Altered F factors, termed F′ factors, carrying regions of the chromosome including both late and early markers could be recovered at low frequency from Hfr strains. (The properties of F′ factors are described in a subsequent section.)

Chromosome circularity was a wildly implausible concept inferred solely from the genetic data; confirmation of its physical reality came only years later. Apparently, the insertion of F determines polarity, with the end opposite F being the origin. How might we explain F attachment? Wollman and Jacob suggested that some kind of crossover event between F and the chromosome might generate the Hfr chromosome. Alan Campbell then came up with a brilliant extension of that idea. He proposed that F, like the chromosome, is circular. Hence, a crossover between the two rings would produce a single larger ring with F inserted (Figure 13-9).

Now suppose that F consists of three different regions, as shown in Figure 13-10. The bacterial chromosome is pictured as having several regions of pairing homology with the pairing region of F. Then different Hfr chromosomes would easily be generated by crossovers at these different sites. This direct-crossover model of integration, depicted in Figure 13-11, was subsequently confirmed—but only for certain Hfr's. It is now known that integration can also be mediated by a series of **insertion elements,** which are sequences of DNA that can promote the integration of genetic particles such as F into many different regions of the chromosome, in the absence of homology. (We consider such insertion elements in detail in Chapter 17.)

The fertility factor thus exists in two states: as a free cytoplasmic element F that is easily transferred to F⁻ recipients and as an integrated part of a circular chromosome that is transmitted only very late in conjugation. The word **episome** was coined for a genetic particle having such a pair of states. A cell containing F in the first state is called an F⁺ cell; a cell containing F in the second state is an Hfr cell; and a cell lacking F is an F⁻ cell.

It is important to note the functional distinctions between Hfr and F⁺ cells. All Hfr cells can donate, and they do so from a fixed point. Markers donated early

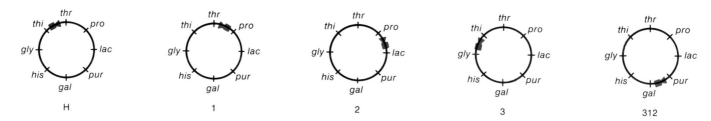

▶■ = F

▶ = origin (first to enter)

■ = terminus (last to enter)

Figure 13-8. Circularity of the *E. coli* chromosome. By using different Hfr strains (H, 1, 2, 3, 312), which have the fertility factor inserted into the chromosome at different points, interrupted-mating experiments indicate that the chromosome is circular. The mobilization points in the various strains are shown.

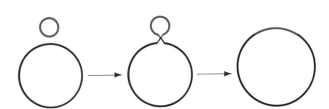

Figure 13-9. Attachment of F factor by crossing-over between two rings.

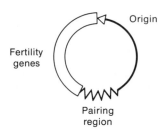

Figure 13-10. The three hypothetical regions of the circular F-factor chromosome.

by an Hfr appear 1000 times more frequently in recipients than do the same markers transferred from an F⁺ population, and very late markers are transferred at about a 10-fold higher frequency. This gradient of transfer for early and late markers is not seen in the low-level transfer manifested by an F⁺ population; all markers are transferred at similar frequencies.

One explanation for the infrequent recombinants in an F⁺ × F⁻ cross is that they are the result of rare insertions of the F factor to produce a subpopulation of Hfr cells. But, if this were the case, we would expect to see some gradient of transfer in different F⁺ populations. The absence of such a gradient has led to the suggestion that the F⁺-mediated transfer is due primarily to transient integration of F into many different points, at a higher frequency than that seen for the more stable integrations generating detectable Hfr's.

Message   An **episome** is a genetic factor in bacteria that can exist either as an element in the cytoplasm or as an integrated part of a chromosome. The F factor is an episome.

Infectious elements other than F have been found in *E. coli* and other bacteria. Some are episomes that integrate into the ring chromosome as the F factor does. Others, called **plasmids,** do not integrate into the ring. Episomes and plasmids are of central importance in the mechanics of genetic engineering, and we shall consider them in more detail later in this book.

Does an Hfr die after donating its chromosome to an F⁻ cell? The answer is no (unless the culture is treated with streptomycin). There is evidence that the Hfr chromosome replicates shortly before or during conjugation, transferring a single strand to the F⁻ cell, which is then replicated in the F⁻ cell. This ensures a complete chromosome for the donor after mating. Finally, we assume that the F⁻ chromosome also is circular, because F⁻ is readily converted into an F⁺ from which an Hfr can be derived.

The picture emerges of a circular Hfr unwinding a copy of its chromosome, which is then transferred in a linear fashion into the F⁻ cell. How is the transfer achieved? Electron-microscope studies show that Hfr and F⁺ cells have **conjugation tubes,** or **F pili** (singular, pilus), protruding from their cell walls. These tubes are hollow, and they almost certainly represent the path of chromosome transfer to the F⁻ cell, which has no pili. It is evidently the

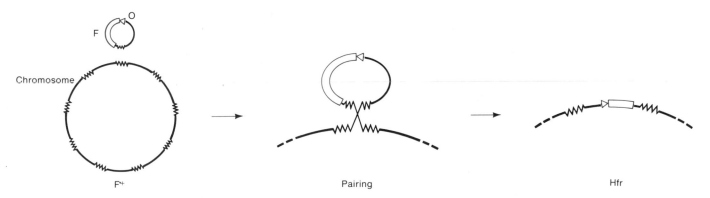

Figure 13-11. Model for the insertion of F factor into the *E. coli* chromosome. If the F factor is considered to be circular, then an area of the fertility factor may have regions of pairing homology for different regions of the circular *E. coli* chromosome. Crossover between the F factor and the chromosome could thus insert the F factor into various points on the chromosome. (Jagged lines represent possible regions of homology; the arrow indicates the direction of transfer from the origin, O.)

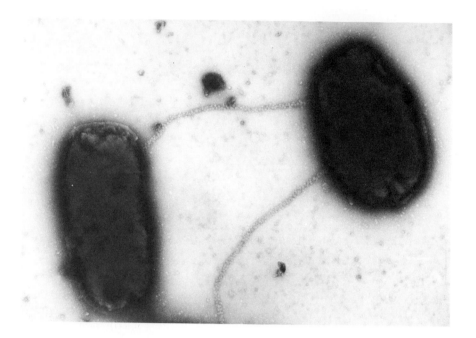

Figure 13-12. Electron micrograph of a cross between two *E. coli* cells (×34,300). The pili of the Hfr cell (not present in the F⁻ cell) have been visualized through the addition of viruses, which attach specifically to them. (Electron micrograph by David P. Allison, Biology Division, Oak Ridge National Laboratory.)

pili that are fractured during an interrupted-mating experiment, breaking the donor chromosome. Figure 13-12 shows conjugating bacteria, and Figure 13-13 is a diagrammatic representation of the passage of the chromosome.

We can now summarize the various aspects of the conjugational cycle in *E. coli* (Figure 13-14).

Recombination Between Marker Genes After Transfer

Thus far we have studied only the process of transfer of genetic information between individuals in a cross. This transfer was inferred from the existence of recombinants produced from the cross. However, before a stable recombinant can be produced, obviously the transferred genes must be "integrated" or incorporated into the host's genome by an exchange mechanism. We now consider some of the special properties of this exchange event. Genetic exchange in prokaryotes does not take place between two whole genomes (as it does in eukaryotes); rather, it takes place between one *complete* genome, called the F⁻ **endogenote,** and an *incomplete* one, called the donor **exogenote.** What we have in fact is a partial diploid, or **merozygote.** Bacterial genetics is merozygote genetics. Figure 13-15a is a diagram of a merozygote.

It is obvious that a single "crossover" would not be very useful in generating viable recombinants, because the ring is broken to produce a strange, partially diploid linear

chromosome (Figure 13-15b). To keep the ring intact, there must be an even number of crossovers (Figure 13-15c). The fragment produced in such a crossover is only a partial genome; in most cases, it is lost during subsequent cell growth. (We say "in most cases" because there are ways to maintain "stable partial diploids.") Hence, it is obvious that reciprocal products of recombination do not survive — only one does. A further unique property of bacterial exchange, then, is that we must forget about reciprocal exchange products.

Message   In the merozygote genetics of bacteria, we generally are concerned with double crossovers, and we do not expect reciprocal recombinants.

Higher-Resolution Mapping by Recombinant Frequency in Bacterial Crosses

Interrupted-mating experiments are ideal to obtain a rough overall set of gene locations over the entire map. In other words, this technique is useful for **low-resolution** mapping. Some other methods are needed in order to obtain a higher resolution between marker loci that are quite close together. For "distances" of less than about two minutes, the interrupted-mating method is not reliable (it does

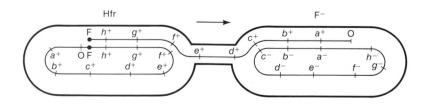

Figure 13-13. Diagrammatic representation of the sequential transfer of genes in a bacterial cross. (F = fertility factor; O = origin.)

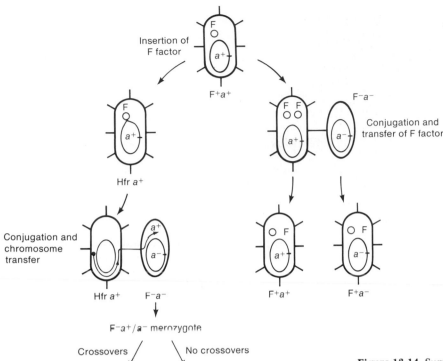

Figure 13-14. Summary of the various events that occur in the conjugational cycle of *E. coli*.

not produce consistent results). Here we consider one approach to this problem, based on measuring the frequency of recombinants. We saw earlier that the first attempts to map in this way were failures. With the wisdom of hindsight, we can now see why they failed, and we can compensate for the problems.

The basic problem was the confusion due to the merozygotic nature of bacterial reproduction. In our RF calculations for eukaryotes, we assumed (quite rightly) an opportunity for recombination between two genes in a diploid

cell. In merozygotes, however, only partial diploids exist. In the merozygote, some genes don't even get into the act! Our analysis must involve two steps in the process. We need methods that allow us to measure first the *potential* opportunity for recombination (resulting from gene transfer) and then the *actual* recombination that occurs.

In the interrupted-mating experiment considered earlier, the genes *ade* and *leu* are about 2 minutes apart, with *ade* entering after *leu*. Let's use these genes to illustrate the approach. This method relies on selecting the Hfr marker that enters last and then testing these individuals for the presence or absence of the male marker that entered ahead of it. Because the unselected marker had to enter first, we can safely assume that it was part of the merozygote. In the present example, we select *ade+* exconjugants and see which of them are *leu+* and which *leu−*. In the *leu−* exconjugants, we know that one crossover has occurred between these gene pairs. We need not worry about the location of the other crossover of the double crossover; we are concentrating on the kind that breaks up the *ade+ leu+* linkage. Figure 13-16 diagrams the two crossover patterns that lead to the two *ade+* types. Let (*ade+ leu−*) represent the frequency of this genotype; this is the frequency of types arising from a crossover between *ade* and *leu*. The total frequency of *ade+* types is (*ade+ leu+*) + (*ade+ leu−*). The fraction

$$\frac{(ade^+\,leu^-)}{(ade^+\,leu^+) + (ade^+\,leu^-)}$$

obviously will be related to the distance separating the two loci, and we can call this the recombinant frequency. In *E. coli*, 1 minute on the map equals about 20 percent recombinants calculated in this manner.

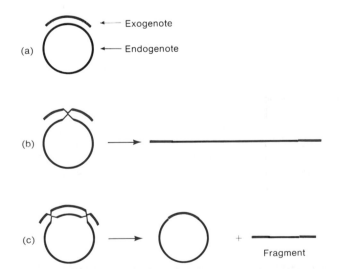

Figure 13-15. Crossover between exogenote and endogenote in a merozygote. (a) The merozygote. (b) A single crossover leads to a partially diploid linear chromosome. (c) An even number of crossovers leads to a ring plus a linear fragment.

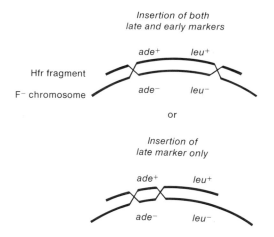

Insertion of both late and early markers

ade⁺   leu⁺

Hfr fragment

F⁻ chromosome   ade⁻   leu⁻

or

Insertion of late marker only

ade⁺   leu⁺

ade⁻   leu⁻

Figure 13-16. Incorporation of a later marker (ade^+) into the F⁻ *E. coli* chromosome. The early marker (leu^+) may or may not be inserted. Whether or not it will be inserted depends on recombination between the Hfr fragment and the F⁻ chromosome at the appropriate place.

This and similar techniques can be used to study most of the merozygote systems in bacteria (and in phage transduction, as we shall see later). You are probably beginning to appreciate the fact that bacteria do things quite differently from eukaryotes. But even though their analysis bears little superficial resemblance to that of eukaryotes, the principles of mapping are very similar. The underlying genetic approach is much the same, whether we are studying humans, peas, flies, or bacteria.

Deriving Gene Order

In many cases, loci are so close together that it becomes difficult to order them in relation to a third locus. For example, consider three loci linked in this way:

a b

c

The RF between a and b under most experimental conditions will be more or less the same as that between a and c. Is the order a-b-c or a-c-b? One technique often used is to make a pair of reciprocal crosses, using the same marker genotypes as both donor and recipient. Figure 13-17 shows the crossover events needed to generate prototrophs from the cross $a\,b\,c^+ \times a^+\,b^+\,c$, depending on the order of the loci.

Obviously, if the reciprocal crosses give dramatically different frequencies of wild-type survivors on minimal medium, then we know that the order is a-c-b. If we observe no difference in frequencies between the reciprocal crosses, then the order must be a-b-c. Once again, this same princi-

ple can be used in other bacterial and phage mapping systems.

Infectious Marker-Gene Transfer by Episomes

Now that we understand the F⁻, F⁺, and Hfr states, we can understand the initially confusing results of recombination work in *E. coli*. Knowing all this, Edward Adelberg began in 1959 to do recombination experiments with an Hfr strain. However, the particular Hfr strain he used kept producing F⁺ cells, so the recombination frequencies were not very large. He called this particular fertility factor F′ to signify a difference from the normal F, for the following reasons:

1. The F′-bearing F⁺ strain reverted back to an Hfr strain quite often.

2. F′ always integrated at the *same place* to give back the original Hfr chromosome (remember that randomly selected Hfr derivatives from F⁺ males have origins at many different positions).

How could these properties of F′ be explained? The answer came from the recovery of a new F′ from an Hfr strain in which the lac^+ locus was near the end of the Hfr chromosome (that is, was transferred very late). Using this Hfr lac^+ strain, Jacob and Adelberg found an F⁺ derivative that transferred lac^+ to F⁻ lac^- recipients at a very high frequency. Furthermore, the recipients, which became

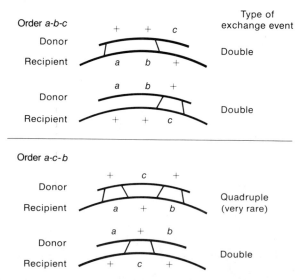

Order a-b-c Type of exchange event

+   + c

Donor

Recipient a b +   Double

a b +

Donor

Recipient   +   + c Double

Order a-c-b

+ c +

Donor

Recipient a + b Quadruple (very rare)

a + b

Donor

Recipient   + c +   Double

Figure 13-17. Inferring gene order from the relative frequencies of recombinants in reciprocal crosses involving parental genotypes $a\,b+ \times ++c$. If the order is a-b-c, the frequency of $+++$ progeny from the reciprocal crosses will be approximately equal. However, if the order is a-c-b, the frequencies will be quite different.

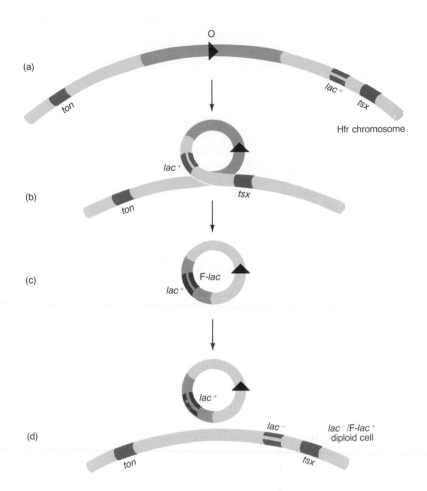

(a)

ton

O

lac⁺   tsx

Hfr chromosome

(b)

lac⁺

ton   tsx

(c)

F-lac

lac⁺

(d)

lac⁺

lac⁻   lac⁻/F-lac⁺
          diploid cell

ton   tsx

Figure 13-18. Origin and reintegration of the F′ (or F-*lac*) factor. (a) F factor inserted in an Hfr strain between the *ton* and *lac⁺* alleles. (b) Abnormal "outlooping" (separation of F factor) to include *lac* locus. (c) The F-*lac⁺* particle (= F′). (d) Constitution of an F-*lac⁺*/*lac⁻* partial diploid produced by the transfer of the F-*lac⁺* particle into an F⁻ *lac⁻* recipient. (From G. S. Stent and R. Calendar, *Molecular Genetics,* 2d ed. Copyright © 1978 by W. H. Freeman and Co.)

F⁺ *lac⁺* phenotypically, occasionally (at a frequency of 1 × 10⁻³) produced F⁻ *lac⁻* daughter cells. Thus, the genotype of the recipients appears to be F′ *lac⁺*/*lac⁻*.

Now we have the clue: F′ is a cytoplasmic element that carries a part of the bacterial chromosome. Its origin and reintegration can be visualized as shown in Figure 13-18. This F′ is known as F-*lac*. Because F-*lac⁺*/*lac⁻* cells are *lac⁺* in phenotype, we know that *lac⁺* is dominant over *lac⁻*. As we shall see later, the dominance-recessive relationship between alleles can be a very useful bit of information in interpretations of gene function. Partial diploidy, called **merodiploidy,** for specific segments of the genome can be made with an array of F′ derivatives from Hfr strains. The F′ cells can be selected by looking for infectious transfer of normally late genes in a specific Hfr strain.

The use of F′ elements to create partial diploids is called **sexduction,** or F′-duction. Some F′ strains can carry very large parts (up to one-quarter) of the bacterial chromosome; if appropriate markers are used, the merozygotes generated can be used for recombination studies. Figure 13-19 shows some of the F′ factors that have been characterized.

Message During conjugation between an Hfr donor and an F⁻ recipient, the genes of the donor are transmitted linearly, with the inserted fertility factor transferring last.

During conjugation between an F′ donor carrying an F′ plasmid and an F⁻ recipient, a specific part of the donor genome may be transmitted infectiously to F⁻ cells, carried on the plasmid. This part was originally adjacent to the F locus in an Hfr strain from which the F⁺ was derived.

As mentioned earlier, F is by no means the only kind of episome. In *E. coli* and other intestinal bacterial species, a variety of inherited characters may be transferred in an infectious manner from cell to cell. Some of these characters are colicin production (colicin is a poison that kills other bacteria) and certain antibiotic resistances. In some cases, these episomes may be transferred between bacterial species. Furthermore, these episomes can "pick up" other bacterial genes and transfer them simultaneously in a manner resembling sexduction. These episomes and plasmids are important tools for genetic engineering, and we shall encounter them again in Chapter 14.

Bacterial Transformation

The conversion of one genotype into another by the introduction of exogenous DNA is termed **transformation.** The discovery of transformation in 1928 by Frederick Griffith, and the demonstration in 1944 by Avery, McLeod, and

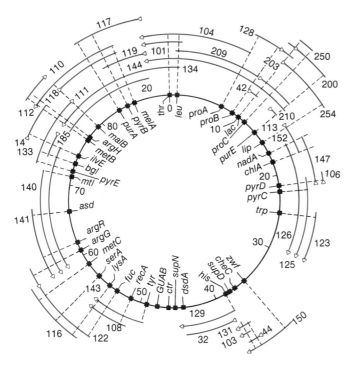

Figure 13-19. Some of the F′ factors derived from *E. coli* are shown, together with the regions of the bacterial chromosome that they carry. Markers such as *trp, thr,* and *leu* are indicated on the circular *E. coli* map, which is delineated into 90 minutes (referring to the time of entry of different genes in an Hfr × F⁻ cross, beginning at an arbitrary point). The F′ factors transfer markers in a fixed direction, as indicated by the direction of the arrow, and form a fixed point, as shown by the placement of the arrow. (Courtesy of B. Low and J. Falkinham. (From with permission from *Handbook of Microbiology.* Edited by A. I. Laskin and H. Lechevalier. Chemical Rubber Co., Cleveland, Ohio, 1972.)

McCarty that the "transforming principle" was DNA, are milestones in the elucidation of the molecular nature of genes (see Chapter 10).

After it was shown that DNA is the agent that determines the polysaccharide character in *Streptococcus pneumoniae* (page 186), transformation was subsequently demonstrated for other genes, such as those for drug resistance (Figure 13-20) and prototrophy, and in several bacterial species.

It seems that the transforming principle, or DNA, is actually physically incorporated into the bacterial chromosome by a physical breakage-and-insertion process quite similar to crossing-over. Thus, if radioactively labeled DNA from an *arg*⁺ bacterial culture is added to unlabeled *arg*⁻ cells, the *arg*⁺ transformants (selected by plating on minimal medium) can be shown to contain some of the radioactivity. We shall examine a molecular model for this in Chapter 16. For now, let's consider transformation simply as a genetic analytic tool.

Linkage Information from Transformation

Transformation has been a very handy tool in several areas of bacterial research. We shall learn later how it is used in some of the modern techniques of genetic engineering.

Here we examine its usefulness in providing linkage information.

When DNA (the bacterial chromosome) is extracted for transformation experiments, some breakage into smaller pieces is inevitable. The closer together two donor genes are located, then the greater is the chance that they will be carried on the same piece of transforming DNA and hence will cause a **double transformation.** Conversely, if genes are widely separated on the chromosome, then they will be carried on separate transforming segments, and the frequency of double transformants will equal the product of the single-transformation frequencies. Thus, it should be possible to test for close linkage by testing for a departure from the product rule.

Unfortunately, the situation is made more complex by several factors, most important of which is that not all cells in a population of bacteria are competent to be transformed. Because single transformations are expressed as proportions, the success of the product rule obviously depends on the absolute size of these proportions. There are ways of calculating the proportion of competent cells, but we need not detour into that subject now. You can sharpen your skills in transformation analysis in one of the problems at the end of the chapter, which assumes 100 percent competence.

Phage Genetics

Most bacteria are susceptible to attack by bacteriophages (a name that literally means "eaters of bacteria"). A phage consists of a nucleic acid "chromosome" (DNA or RNA) surrounded by a coat of protein molecules. One well-studied set of strains of phage are identified as T1, T2, and so

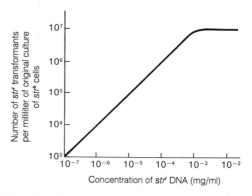

Figure 13-20. The genetic transfer of streptomycin resistance (*str*ʳ) into streptomycin-sensitive (*str*ˢ) cells of *E. coli.* The recovery of *str*ʳ transformants among *str*ˢ cells depends on the concentration of *str*ʳ DNA. (From G. S. Stent and R. Calendar, *Molecular Genetics,* 2d ed. Copyright © 1978 by W. H. Freeman and Co.)

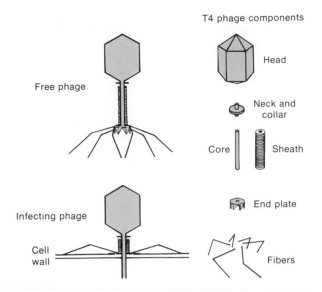

T4 phage components

Free phage

Head

Neck and collar

Core Sheath

Infecting phage

End plate

Cell wall

Fibers

Figure 13-21. Phage T4, shown in its free state and in the process of infecting a cell of *E. coli*. On the right, a phage has been diagrammatically exploded to show its highly ordered structure in three dimensions. (From R. S. Edgar and R. H. Epstein, "The Genetics of a Bacterial Virus." Copyright © 1965 by Scientific American, Inc. All rights reserved.)

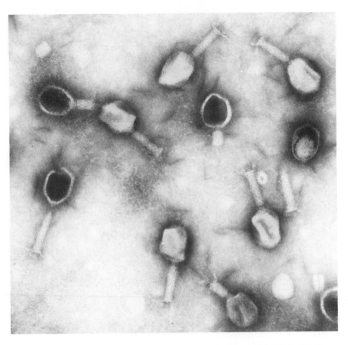

Figure 13-22. Mature particles of the *E. coli* phage T4 (×97,500). (From Grant Heilman.)

on. Figures 13-21 and 13-22 show the complicated structure of a phage belonging to the class called T-even phages (T2, T4, and so on).

The Phage Cross

A phage attaches to a bacterium and injects its genetic material into the bacterial cytoplasm (Figure 13-23a). The phage genetic information then takes over the machinery of the bacterial cell by turning off the synthesis of bacterial components and redirecting the bacterial synthetic material to make more phage components (Figure 13-23b). (The use of the word information is interesting in this connection; it literally means "to give form." And of course, that is precisely the role of the genetic material: to provide blueprints for the construction of form. In the present discussion, the form is the elegantly symmetrical structure of the new phages.) Ultimately, many phage descendants are released when the bacterial cell wall breaks open. The process of breaking open is called **lysis.**

But how can we study inheritance in phages when they are so small that they are visible only with the electron microscope? In this case, we cannot produce a visible colony by plating. One phage character we can examine involves the effects of the phage on bacteria. When a phage lyses a bacterium, progeny phages infect neighboring bacteria, and these in turn lyse and infect other bacteria. This is an exponentially explosive phenomenon (an exponential increase in the number of lysed cells). Very soon after starting an experiment of this type (overnight), the effects are visible to the naked eye: a clear area, or **plaque,** is present on the opaque lawn of bacteria on the surface of a dish of solid medium (Figure 13-24). Depending on the phage genotype, such plaques can be large or small, fuzzy or sharp, and

so forth. Thus, **plaque morphology** is a phage character that can be analyzed. Recall how Benzer used plaque morphology to distinguish *rII* mutants from wild-type T4 phage (Chapter 11, page 220).

Another phage phenotype that can be analyzed genetically is **host range.** Certain strains of bacteria are immune to adsorption (attachment) or injection by phages. Phages, in turn, may differ in the spectra of bacterial strains they can infect and lyse.

A phage cross can be illustrated by a cross of T2 phages originally studied by Alfred Hershey. These phages of *E. coli* are of a type called **virulent;** they are committed to a simple cycle of infection and lysis. The genotypes of the two parental strains of T2 phage in Hershey's cross were $h^- r^+ \times h^+ r^-$. The alleles are identified by the following characters: h^- can infect two different *E. coli* strains (which we can call strains 1 and 2); h^+ can infect only strain 1; r^- rapidly lyses cells, thereby producing large plaques; and r^+ slowly lyses cells, thus producing small plaques.

In the cross, strain 1 is infected with both parental T2 phage genotypes at a concentration—called **multiplicity of infection,** which is the ratio of phages to bacteria— sufficiently high to ensure a high proportion of cells that are simultaneously infected by both phage types. This kind of infection (Figure 13-25) is called a **mixed infection,** or **double infection.** The phage lysate (the progeny phage) is then analyzed by spreading it onto a bacterial lawn composed of a mixture of strains 1 and 2. Four plaque types are distinguishable (Figure 13-26 and Table 13-2). These four genotypes can easily be scored as parental (the first two in Table 13-2) and recombinant, and an RF can be calculated:

$$RF = \frac{(h^+ r^+) + (h^- r^-)}{\text{total plaques}}$$

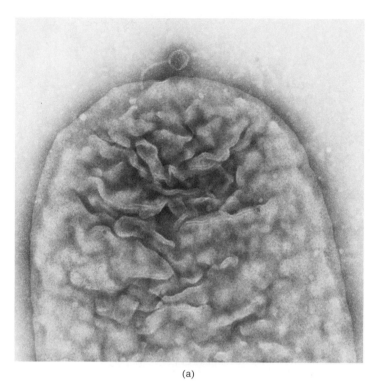

(a)

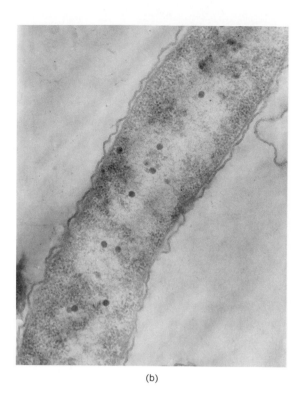

(b)

Figure 13-23. (a) A bacteriophage (called λ) attached to an *E. coli* cell and injecting its genetic material. (b) Progeny particles of phage λ maturing inside an *E. coli* cell. (From Jack D. Griffith.)

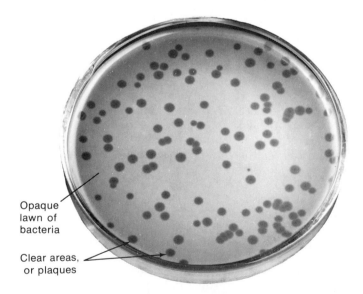

Opaque lawn of bacteria

Clear areas, or plaques

Figure 13-24. The appearance of phage plaques. Individual phage are spread on an agar medium that contains a fully grown "lawn" of *E. coli*. Each phage infects one bacterial cell, producing 100 or more progeny phage that burst the *E. coli* cell and infect neighboring cells. They, in turn, are exploded with progeny, and the process continues until a clear area, or plaque, appears on the opaque lawn of bacterial cells. (From G. S. Stent, *Molecular Biology of Bacterial Viruses.* Copyright © 1963 by W. H. Freeman and Co.)

If we assume that entire phage genomes recombine, then we are not faced with a merozygotic situation as in a bacterial cross. Presumably, then, single exchanges can occur and produce viable reciprocal products. However, phage crosses are subject to several complications that are only mentioned here. First, several **rounds of exchange** can potentially occur within the host. Because hundreds of phages can be released from a single infected cell, each parental infecting phage can be duplicated many times. If recombination does not occur at one specific time in the lytic cycle, then a recombinant produced shortly after infection may undergo further exchange at later times. Second, recombination can occur between genetically similar phages as well as between different types. Thus $P_1 \times P_1$ and $P_2 \times P_2$ occur in addition to $P_1 \times P_2$. For both of these reasons, recombinants from phage crosses are a consequence of a **population** of events rather than defined, single-step exchange events. Nevertheless, *other things being equal,* the RF calculation given does represent a valid index of map distance in phages.

Circularity of the T2 Genetic Map

Hershey obtained several different T2 strains with the rapid-lysis phenotype; he called their genotypes *r1, r2,* and

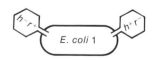

Figure 13-25. A double infection of *E. coli* by phages.

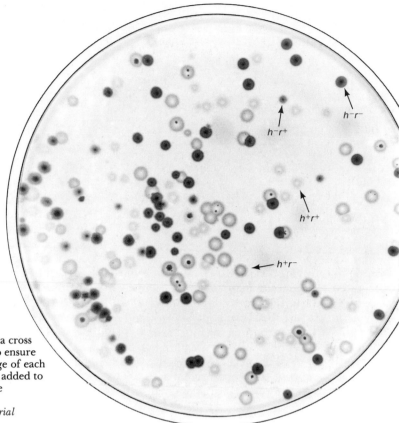

Figure 13-26. Plaque phenotypes produced by progeny of a cross $h^- r^+ \times h^+ r^-$. Enough phage of each genotype are added to ensure that most bacterial cells are infected with at least one phage of each genotype. After lysis, the progeny phage are collected and added to an appropriate *E. coli* lawn. Four plaque phenotypes can be differentiated, representing two parental types and two recombinants. (From G. S. Stent, *Molecular Biology of Bacterial Viruses.* Copyright © 1963 by W. H. Freeman and Co.)

so forth (in the order of discovery). Let's indicate three different *r* strains as r_a, r_b, and r_c and make the cross $r_x^- h^+ \times r_x^+ h^-$ (where r_x represents one of the *r* genes). Table 13-3 shows the results. We can construct a linkage map in just the same way that Sturtevant constructed the original eukaryote maps in *Drosophila.* The parental types ($r^- h^+$ and $r^+ h^-$) occur with the highest frequencies, although not with equal frequency. The two recombinant classes, however, are equally frequent. We can construct linkage maps for each cross (Figure 13-27a). The different recombination values indicate that the loci for the three *r* genes are in different places on the chromosome, so there are four possible linkage maps (Figure 13-27b).

Can we distinguish among these alternatives? First, let's take only r_b, r_c, and h and ask whether the order is r_c-h-r_b or h-r_c-r_b. We can make the cross $r_c^- r_b^+ \times r_c^+ r_b^-$ and compare the RF with the value of 12.3 obtained for the $r_b - h$ interval. From this comparison, we find that h is located between r_b and r_c (r_c-h-r_b).

Now we ask whether r_a lies on the side of h next to r_b or on the side next to r_c. The data from crosses of r_a with r_b

■ **TABLE 13-2.** Progeny-phage plaque types from cross $h^- r^+ \times h^+ r^-$

Phenotype	Inferred genotype
Clear and small	$h^- r^+$
Cloudy and large	$h^+ r^-$
Cloudy and small	$h^+ r^+$
Clear and large	$h^- r^-$

NOTE: clearness is produced by the h^- allele, which allows infection of *both* bacterial strains in the lawn; cloudiness is produced by the h^+ allele, which limits infection to the cells of strain 1.

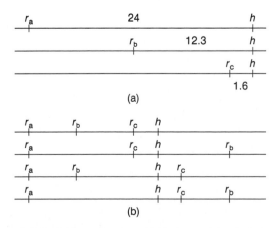

Figure 13-27. (a) Distances between gene pairs for each cross in Table 13-3. (b) The various possible linkage relations inferred from the distances of part (a).

■ **TABLE 13-3.** Frequency of progeny-phage types in crosses involving several r mutants and an h mutant

Cross	Percentage of each genotype			
	r^-h^+	r^+h^-	r^+h^+	r^-h^-
$r_a^-h^+ \times r_a^+h^-$	34.0	42.0	12.0	12.0
$r_b^-h^+ \times r_b^+h^-$	32.0	56.0	5.9	6.4
$r_c^-h^+ \times r_c^+h^-$	39.0	59.0	0.7	0.9

and r_c do not provide a clear-cut resolution of the answer. After intensive genetic mapping with many different strains of T2, the answer turns out to be that *both* alternative maps are correct. How can both r_a-r_c-h-r_b and r_c-h-r_b-r_a be correct? We have encountered a similar situation before, and the answer is similar. Like the bacterial map, the linkage map of T2 is circular, as shown in Figure 13-28a. The total genetic length of the T2 linkage map is about 1500 m.u. Figure 13-28b shows a more complete map for another T-even phage.

In the bacterial and phage experiments we have considered, the data are initially confusing. However, once the novelty of the conditions for "crossing" is understood, the analysis of recombination and the construction of linkage maps are fairly straightforward procedures.

Message Recombination between phage chromosomes can be studied by bringing the parental chromosomes together in one host cell through double infection. Progeny phages can be examined for parental versus recombinant genotypes.

Lysogeny

In the 1920s, long before *E. coli* became the darling of microbial geneticists, some interesting results were obtained in the study of phage infections. Some bacterial strains are resistant to infection by certain phages, but these resistant bacteria will cause lysis of nonresistant bacteria when the two bacterial strains are mixed together. The resistant bacteria that induce lysis in other cells are said to be **lysogenic.** Apparently, the lysogenic bacteria somehow "carry" the phages while remaining immune to their lysing action. When nonlysogenic bacteria are infected with phages from a lysogenic strain, a small fraction of the infected cells do not lyse but instead become lysogenic themselves. Little attention was paid to this phenomenon after some studies seemed to show that the lysogenic bacteria are simply contaminated with external phages that can be removed by careful purification.

However, in the mid-1940s, André Lwoff examined lysogenic strains of *Bacillus megaterium* and carefully followed the lysogenic behavior of a lysogenic strain through many cell divisions. Carefully observing his culture, he separated each pair of daughter cells immediately after division; one cell was put into a culture, while the other was observed until it in turn divided. In this way, Lwoff obtained 19 cultures representing 19 generations (19 consecutive cell divisions). All 19 cultures were lysogenic, but tests of the medium showed no free phage at any time during these divisions, thus confirming that lysogenic behavior is a character that persists through reproduction in the absence of free phage.

On rare occasions, Lwoff observed spontaneous lysis in one of the cells in his cultures. When the medium was spread on a lawn of nonlysogenic cells after one of these spontaneous lyses, plaques appeared, thus showing that free phages had been released in the lysis. Lwoff was able to propose a hypothesis to explain all his observations. Each bacterium of the lysogenic strain contains a noninfective factor that is passed from generation to generation, but this factor can occasionally give rise to the production of infective phage (without the presence of free phage in the medium). He called this factor the **prophage** because it somehow seems to be able to *induce* the formation of a "litter" of infective phage. Later studies showed that a variety of agents, such as ultraviolet light or certain chemicals, can induce lysis in a large fraction of a population of lysogenic bacteria.

We can now set forth a model to explain the observations. A lysogenic bacterium contains a prophage, which somehow protects the cell against **superinfection** from free phages and which is duplicated and passed to daughter cells during division. In a small fraction of the lysogenic cells, the

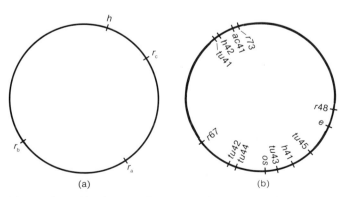

Figure 13-28. Circular maps for T-even phage. (a) Simple linkage map for T2 phage. (b) Map of phage T4, inferred from crosses of nonlethal mutants r (rapid lysis), h (host range), ac (acridine resistance), tu (turbid plaques), os (resistance to osmotic shock), and e (lysis defective).

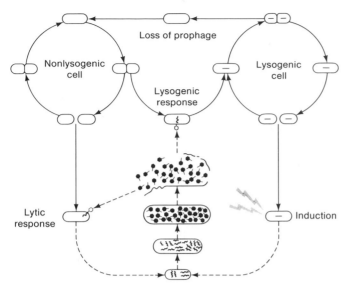

Loss of prophage

Nonlysogenic cell

Lysogenic cell

Lysogenic response

Lytic response

Induction

Figure 13-29. Alternative cell cycles associated with a temperate phage and its host. (From A. Lwoff, *Bacteriological Reviews* 17:269, 1953.)

certain time in mating) are not recovered. Furthermore, lysogenic exconjugants are almost never recovered from this reciprocal cross. What is the explanation? The observations make sense if the λ prophage is behaving like a bacterial gene locus — that is, as part of the bacterial chromosome. In the cross of a lysogenic Hfr with a nonlysogenic F⁻ recipient, the entry of the λ prophage into the cytoplasm of a nonimmune cell triggers the prophage into a lytic cycle; this is called **zygotic induction**. In interrupted-mating experiments, the λ prophage proves always to enter the F⁻ cell at a specific time, closely linked to the *gal* locus. We can assign the λ prophage to a specific locus next to the *gal* region.

Entry of the λ prophage into an F⁻ cell immediately induces the lytic cycle. But in the cross Hfr(λ) × F⁻(λ), any recombinants are readily recovered (that is, no induction of the prophage occurs). It would seem that the cytoplasm of the F⁻ cell must exist in two different states (depending on

prophage is induced to produce infective phage. This process robs the cell of its protection against phage; it lyses and releases infective phage into the medium, thus infecting any nonlysogenic cells present in the culture.

Phages can be categorized into two types. Those for which there are no lysogenic bacteria are called virulent phages (resistant bacterial mutants may exist for these phages, but their resistance is not due to lysogeny). Those phages capable of lysogenizing bacteria are called **temperate phages** (resistance to superinfection is in fact an "immunity" conferred by the presence of the prophage). Figure 13-29 diagrams the life cycle of a typical temperate phage.

The Genetic Basis of Lysogeny

What is the nature of the prophage? Upon induction, the prophage is capable of directing production of complete mature phage, so all of the phage genome must be present in the prophage. But is the prophage a small particle free in the bacterial cytoplasm, or is it somehow associated with the bacterial genome? By a fortuitous happenstance, the original strain of *E. coli* used by Lederberg and Tatum (page 265) proved to be lysogenic for a temperate phage called **lambda (λ).** Phage λ has become the most intensively studied and best-characterized phage (Figure 13-30). Crosses between F⁺ and F⁻ cells yielded interesting results. It turns out that F⁺ × F⁻(λ) crosses yield recombinant lysogenic recipients, whereas the reciprocal cross F⁺(λ) × F⁻ almost never gives lysogenic recombinants.

These results became understandable when Hfr strains were discovered. In the cross Hfr × F⁻(λ), lysogenic F⁻ exconjugants with Hfr genes are readily recovered. However, in the reciprocal cross Hfr(λ) × F⁻, the early genes from the Hfr are recovered among the exconjugants, but recombinants for late markers (those expected to transfer after a

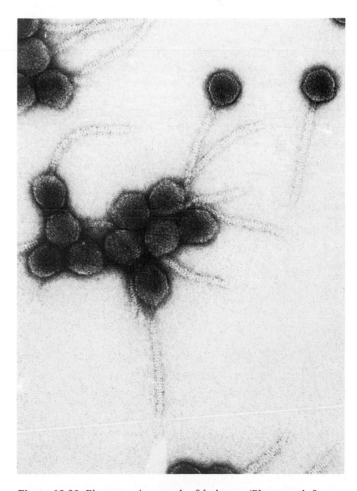

Figure 13-30. Electron micrograph of λ phages. (Photograph from Jack D. Griffith.)

whether the cell contains a λ prophage), so that contact between an entering prophage and the cytoplasm of a non-immune cell immediately induces the lytic cycle. Perhaps some cytoplasmic factor specified by the prophage somehow represses the multiplication of the virus. Entry of the prophage into a nonlysogenic environment immediately dilutes this repressing factor, and therefore the virus reproduces. But if the virus specifies the repressing factor, then why doesn't it shut itself off again? Perhaps it does, because a fraction of infected cells do become lysogenic. There may be a race between the λ gene signals for reproduction and those specifying a shutdown. The model of a phage-directed cytoplasmic repressor nicely explains immunity, because any superinfecting phage would immediately encounter a repressor and be inactivated.

How is the prophage attached to the bacterial genome? In the days before chromosome circularity was known, two models seemed possible. These models are shown in Figure 13-31.

The clue for a choice between these models came from a mutant strain of λ. A large section of the chromosome was deleted in this strain, and it could not lysogenize, although it could reproduce. Perhaps the deleted region (which obviously does not contain the genes for λ production) is a region of homology with the bacterial chromosome (the Campbell model again). Crossing-over between the λ and *E. coli* chromosomes at such a region could incorporate the entire λ genome at a specific point (and as a continuous part) of the *E. coli* chromosome (Figure 13-32).

Can this simple model of lysogeny be tested? The attraction of Campbell's proposal is that it does make testable predictions, and λ gives us a chance to test those predictions.

1. Physical integration of the prophage should increase the genetic distance between flanking bacterial

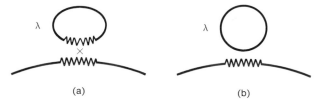

Figure 13-32. Models of λ affinity for the bacterial chromosome: (a) in the normal phage; (b) in a phage mutant showing deletion.

markers (Figure 13-33). In fact, time-of-entry or recombination distances between the bacterial genes *are* increased by lysogeny.

2. Some deletions of bacterial segments adjacent to the prophage site should delete phage genes (Figure 13-34). Experimental studies do confirm this prediction.

The phenomenon of lysogeny is a very successful way for a temperate phage to avoid "eating itself out of house and home." Lysogenic cells can perpetuate and carry the phages around. We shall consider lysogeny and the integration of the λ phage into the host chromosome in more detail in Chapters 16 and 18.

Transduction

Some phages are able to carry bacterial genes from one bacterial cell to another in a process called **transduction.** There are two kinds of transduction: generalized and specialized.

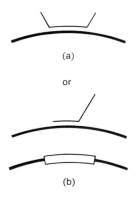

Figure 13-31. Two conceivable models of prophage attachment. (a) Pairing association. (b) Physical incorporation. (Thick line = *E. coli* chromosome; thin line = phage chromosome.)

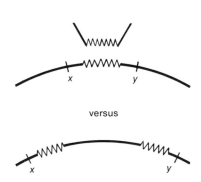

Figure 13-33. Insertion of λ genome into the *E. coli* chromosome splits the attachment region, increasing the distance between markers *x* and *y*.

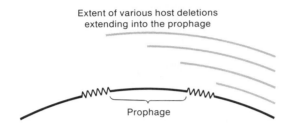

Extent of various host deletions
extending into the prophage

Prophage

Figure 13-34. Host deletions may delete genes from an adjacent prophage.

Generalized Transduction

In 1951, Joshua Lederberg and Norton Zinder were testing for recombination in the bacterium *Salmonella typhimurium*, using the techniques that had been successful with *E. coli*. They used two different strains: one was *phe⁻ trp⁻ tyr⁻* and the other was *met⁻ his⁻*. (We won't worry about the nature of these markers except to note that the mutant alleles confer nutritional requirements.) When they plated either strain on minimal medium, they observed no wild-type cells. However, after mixing the two strains, they found wild-type cells at a frequency of about 1 in 10⁵. Thus far, the situation seems similar to that for recombination in *E. coli*.

However, in this case, the experimenters also recovered recombinants from a U-tube experiment, in which cell contact (conjugation) was prevented by a filter. Varying the size of the pores in the filter separating the two arms, they found that the agent responsible for recombination is about

the size of the virus P22, a known temperate phage of *Salmonella*. Further studies supported the suggestion that the vector of recombination is indeed P22. The filterable agent and P22 are identical in properties of size, sensitivity to antiserum, and immunity to hydrolytic enzymes. Thus, Lederberg and Zinder, instead of confirming conjugation in *Salmonella,* had discovered a new type of gene transfer mediated by a virus. They called this process transduction. Somehow, some virus particles during the lytic cycle pick up bacterial genes, which are then transferred to another host, where the virus inserts its contents. Transduction has subsequently been shown to be quite common among both temperate and virulent phages.

How are transducing phages produced? In 1965, K. Ikeda and J. Tomizawa threw light on this question in some experiments on the temperate *E. coli* phage P1. They found that, when a nonlysogenic donor cell is lysed by P1, the bacterial chromosome is broken up into small pieces. Occasionally, the forming phage particles mistakenly incorporate a length of *pure* bacterial DNA into a phage head. This is the origin of the transducing phage. A similar process can occur when the prophage of P1 is induced. Because it is the phage coat proteins that determine the phage's ability to attack a cell, such viruses or transducing particles can bind to a bacterial cell and inject their contents, which now happen to be donor bacterial genes. When the contents of a transducing phage are injected into a recipient cell, a merodiploid situation is created in which the transduced genes can be incorporated by recombination (Figure 13-35).

From such merozygotes, we can derive linkage information about bacterial genes. Transduction from an *a⁺ b⁺* donor to an *a⁻ b⁻* recipient produces various transductants

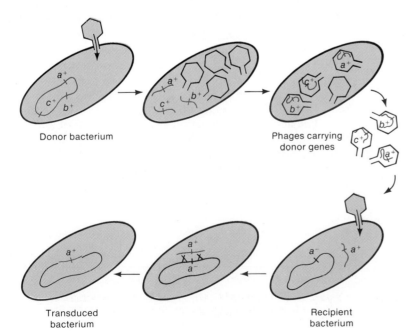

Donor bacterium

Phages carrying
donor genes

Transduced
bacterium

Recipient
bacterium

Figure 13-35. The mechanism of generalized transduction. In reality, only a minority of phage progeny would carry donor genes.

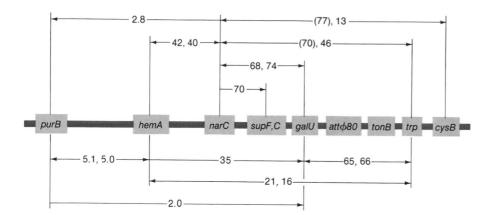

Figure 13-36. Genetic map of the *purB* to *cysB* region of *E. coli* determined by P1 cotransduction. The numbers given are the averages in percent for cotransduction frequencies obtained in several experiments. Where transduction crosses were performed in both directions, the head of each arrow points to the selective marker and the corresponding linkage nearest to it. The values in parentheses are considered unreliable owing to interference from the nonselective marker. (Redrawn from J. R. Guest, *Molecular and General Genetics* 105:285, 1969.)

for a^+ and b^+. We can obtain linkage information from the ratio

$$\frac{\text{single-gene transductants}}{\text{total transductants}} = \frac{(a^+ b^-)}{(a^+ b^-) + (a^+ b^+)}$$

$$\text{or} \quad \frac{(a^- b^+)}{(a^- b^+) + (a^+ b^+)}$$

Presumably, the chance of either a^+ or b^+ being included individually in the transducing phage is proportional to the distance between them. If they are close together, they will usually be picked up and transduced by the phage together. Of course, the method gives linkage values only if the genes under test *are* close enough together for *both* to be included in the transducing phage and thus form an $a^+ b^+$ transductant, called a **cotransductant.** Linkages are usually expressed as cotransduction frequencies, as shown in Figure 13-36. However, even the failure to find cotransductants provides some linkage information in a negative sense. Thus transduction joins the battery of modes of genetic transfer in bacteria—along with conjugation, infectious transfer of episomes, and transformation.

The phages P1 and P22 belong to a group that shows generalized transduction, that is, they transfer virtually any gene of the host chromosome. As prophages, P22 probably inserts into the host chromosome, and P1 remains free like a large plasmid. But both transduce by faulty headstuffing during lysis.

We can estimate the size of the piece of host chromosome that a phage can pick up from the following type of experiment using P1 phage:

donor *leu⁺ thr⁺ azi*ʳ ⟶ recipient *leu⁻ thr⁻ azi*ˢ

We can select for one or more donor markers in the recipient and then (in true merozygote-genetics style) look for the presence of the other unselected markers, as outlined in Table 13-4. Experiment 1 in the table tells us that *leu* is relatively close to *azi* and distant from *thr*, but we are left with two possibilities:

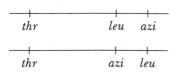

Experiment 2 tells us that *leu* is closer to *thr* than is *azi*, so the map must be

By selecting for *thr⁺* and *leu⁺* in the transducing phage in experiment 3, we see that the transduced piece of genetic material never includes the *azi* locus. If enough markers were studied to produce a more complete linkage map, we could estimate the size of a transduced segment. Such experiments indicate that P1 cotransduction occurs within approximately 1.5 min of the *E. coli* chromosome map. (One min, or minute, equals the length of chromosome transferred by an Hfr in one minute's time at 37°C.)

Specialized Transduction

Another class called **specialized,** or **restricted,** transducing phages carry only restricted parts of the bacterial chromosome. We look now at this process of specialized transduction.

Lambda is a good example of a specialized transducer. You will recall that as a prophage, λ always inserts next to the *gal* region of the *E. coli* host chromosome. In transduction experiments, λ can transduce only the *gal* gene and another closely linked gene, *bio*. Let's follow a typical experiment and try to visualize the mechanism of λ transduction, as diagrammed in Figure 13-37. In Figure 13-37a we see a schematic representation of the production of a lysogen. The actual recombination between regions of λ and the bacterial chromosome is catalyzed by a specific enzyme system, described more fully in Chapter 16. For now, it is important to know only that the phage and bacterial integration regions are not completely identical, so the integra-

■ **TABLE 13-4.** Accompanying markers in specific P1 transductions

Experiment	Selected marker(s)	Unselected markers
1	*leu⁺*	50% are *azi*ʳ; 2% are *thr⁺*
2	*thr⁺*	3% are *leu⁺*; 0% are *azi*ʳ
3	*leu⁺* and *thr⁺*	0% are *azi*ʳ

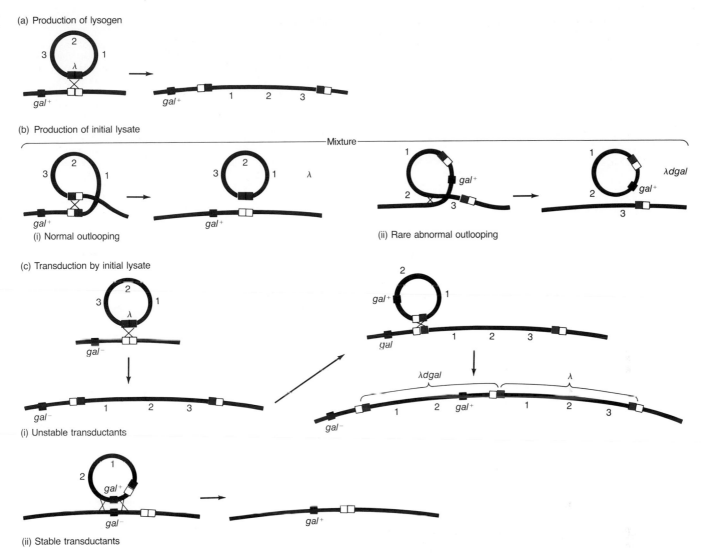

Figure 13-37. Transduction mechanisms in phage λ. (a) The production of a lysogen by crossing-over in a specialized region. (b) The lysogenic bacterial culture can produce normal λ, or, rarely, an abnormal particle, λdgal, which is the transducing particle. (c) Transduction by the mixed lysate can produce either stable transductants, by crossovers flanking the gal gene, or unstable transductants, by the incorporation of λ and λdgal. The open double squares are bacterial integration sites, the colored double squares are λ-phage integration sites, and the pairs of open and colored double squares are hybrid integration sites, partly derived from the bacterial site and partly from the λ site.

tion of λ results in two hybrid sites, as shown. We can induce the lytic cycle with ultraviolet light and produce a lysate (progeny phage population), as depicted in Figure 13-37b. The normal outlooping of the prophage restores the original phage integration site. These phage can integrate normally upon subsequent infection of a strain that is not lysogenic for λ (see Figure 13-37a). As seen in Figure 13-37b, very rare abnormal outlooping can result in phage particles that now carry the gal genes. These particles are defective in that some genes have been left behind in the host; consequently, they are called λdgal (λ-defective gal). The λdgal particle has a λ body and can infect bacteria, but it is also defective in its integration site. The hybrid integration site left in λdgal does not provide a correct substrate for the enzyme that promotes recombination between the phage and bacterial integration sites. Therefore, efficient integration cannot occur in a single infection of E. coli by

λdgal. However, coinfection with a wild-type phage results in efficient integration of the λdgal phage. The second phage is often termed a **helper** phage. In general, the helper phage provides something that is required for integration into the host chromosome. In this case, the role of the helper phage is to provide, after its own integration, a hybrid attachment site (see Figure 13-37c, i), which does serve as an effective integration site for the λdgal phage. (It is a characteristic of the integration enzyme system that a hybrid attachment site cannot mediate integration with a normal bacterial integration site, whereas it can with another hybrid site.)

In practice, the lysate of λ produced originally (Figure 13-37b) can be used to infect a gal⁻ recipient culture that is nonlysogenic for λ. These infected cells are plated on minimal medium, and rare gal⁺ transductants are the only ones to grow and produce colonies. A few percent of these trans-

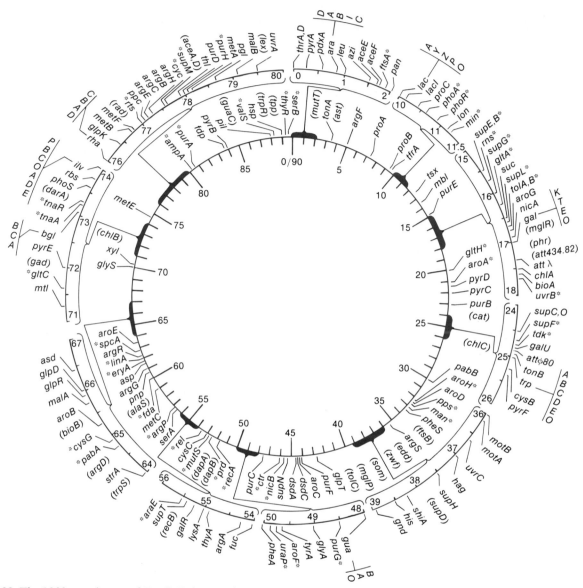

Figure 13-38. The 1963 genetic map of *E. coli.* Units are minutes (timed from an arbitrarily located origin). (From G. S. Stent, *Molecular Biology of Bacterial Viruses.* Copyright © 1963 by W. H. Freeman and Co.)

ductants are stable *gal*⁺ types, all their descendants being *gal*⁺, too. Most of these are due to recombination between the *gal* regions of the λ*dgal* and the recipient chromosome, as shown in Figure 13-37c, ii. The vast majority of the transductants are unstable; that is, they segregate out *gal*⁻ progeny cells as well as *gal*⁺ cells. The unstable types are double lysogens (Figure 13-37c, i). If an unstable culture is lysed and used as a *gal*⁺ donor in transduction, a very high frequency of transduction is obtained. This lysate is called a high-frequency transduction (HFT) lysate. HFT lysates contain a significant fraction of specialized λ*dgal*-transducing phage, since each lysogen already contained a λ*dgal* phage, and induction results in the excision and propagation of both λ*dgal* and helper phage. This is in contrast to the original single lysogen (Figure 13-37a), which upon in-

Figure 13-39. Linear scale drawings representing the circular map of *E. coli* K12 (pages 287 and 288). The time scale of 100 min, beginning arbitrarily with zero at the *thr* locus, is based on the results of interrupted-conjugation experiments. Parentheses around a gene symbol indicate that the position of the marker is not well known and may have been determined only within 5 to 10 min. An asterisk indicates that a marker has been mapped more precisely but that its position with respect to nearby markers is not known. Arrows above genes and sets of genes (see Chapter 18) indicate the direction of transcription of these loci. Parentheses around a set of genes indicate that, although the direction of transcription of the genes in the set is known, the orientation of the genes on the chromosome is not known. (From B. J. Bachmann, *Microbiol. Rev.* 47:180–230, 1983.)

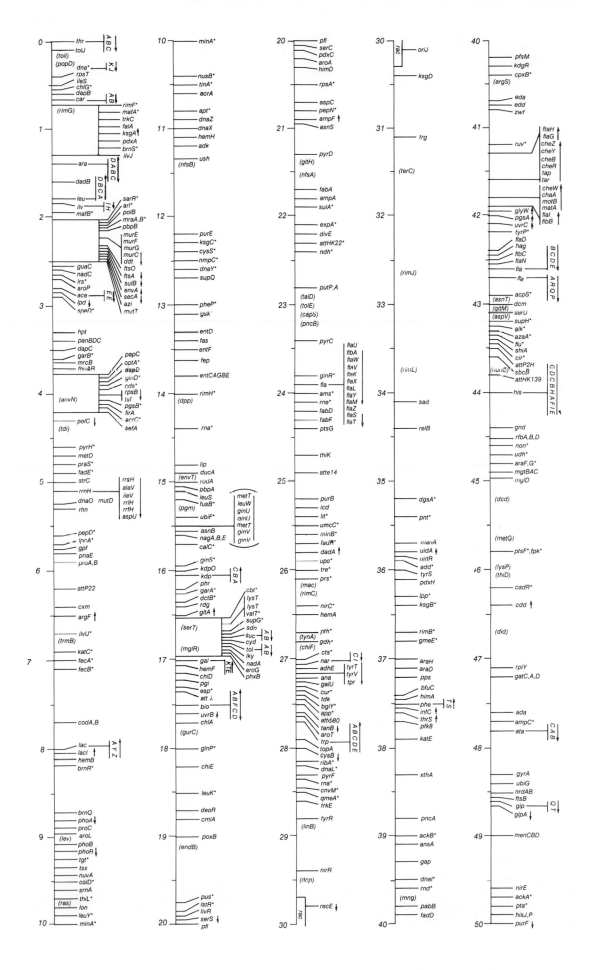

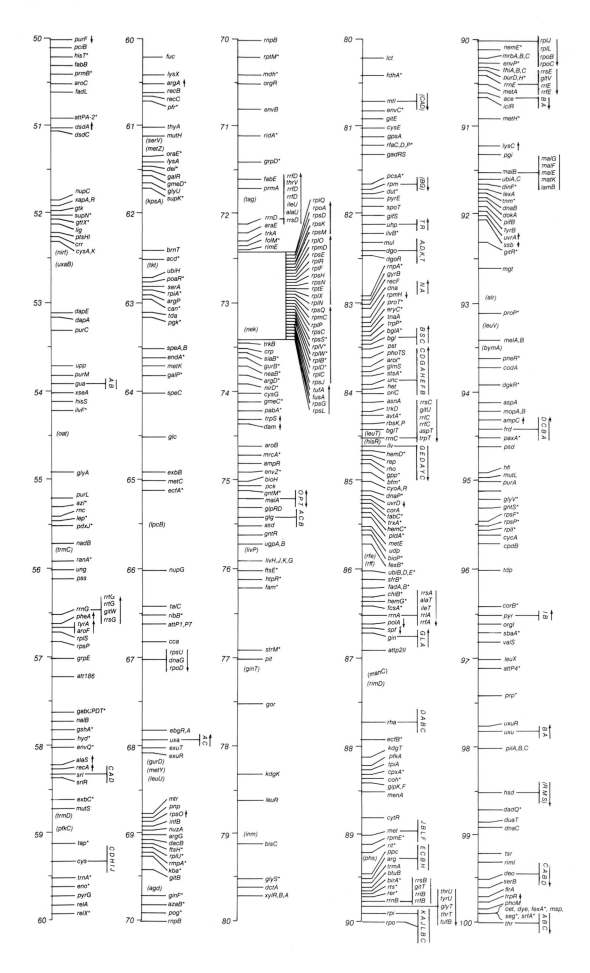

duction yielded *λdgal* phage at a very low frequency (Figure 13-37b).

Message Transduction occurs when bacteriophage pick up host genes prior to lysis. Generalized transduction is mediated by phage particles that have accidentally incorporated a piece of bacterial chromosome during phage packaging. This can occur in the lytic cycle of some virulent and temperate phages, or when lysogenic temperate phages are induced to lysis. Specialized transduction is mediated by temperate phages, whose prophages always are inserted at one specific bacterial locus. The transducing phage in this case is produced by faulty separation of the prophage from the bacterial chromosome, so that the prophage includes both bacterial and phage genes.

Some very detailed chromosome maps for bacteria have been obtained by combining the mapping techniques of interrupted mating, recombination mapping, transformation, and transduction. Today, new markers are typically mapped first into a segment of about 10 to 15 map minutes by using a series of Hfr's that transfer from different points around the chromosome. This allows selection of markers, within the interval, to be used for P1 cotransduction. The complexity of the *E. coli* map derived by 1963 already illustrated the power and sophistication of genetic analysis at its best. As shown in Figure 13-38, the 1963 map detailed the position of approximately 100 genes. After 20 years of further refinement, the 1983 map, which is adjusted to a scale of 100 min, depicts the position of over 1000 genes! A portion of this map is shown in Figure 13-39. More bacterial and phage genetics are discussed in subsequent chapters.

Summary

■ Advances in microbial genetics within the past four decades have provided the foundation for the recent advances in molecular biology (discussed in the next several chapters). Early in this period, it was discovered that gene transfer and recombination occur between different mating types in several bacteria. However, in bacteria, genetic material is passed in only one direction, from a donor cell (F⁺ or Hfr) to a recipient cell (F⁻). Donor ability is determined by the presence in the cell of a fertility (F) factor acting as an episome.

On occasion, the F factor present in a free state in F⁺ cells can integrate into the *E. coli* chromosome and form an Hfr. When this occurs, gene transfer and subsequent recombination take place. Furthermore, since the F factor can insert at different places on the host chromosome, investigators were able to show that the *E. coli* chromosome is a single circle. Interruptions of the transfer at different times has provided geneticists with a new method for constructing a linkage map of the single chromosome of *E. coli* and other similar bacteria.

Genetic traits can also be transferred from one bacterial cell to another in the form of purified DNA. This process of transformation in bacterial cells was the first demonstration that DNA is the genetic material. For transformation to occur, DNA must be taken into a recipient cell, and then recombination between a recipient chromosome and the incorporated DNA must take place.

Bacteria also have viral diseases, caused by bacteriophage. Phages can affect bacteria in two ways. The phage chromosome may enter the bacterial cell and, using the bacterial metabolic machinery, produce progeny phage and burst the host bacteria. The new phage can then infect other cells. If two phages of different genotypes infect the same host, recombination between their chromosomes can take place during this lytic process. Mapping the genetic loci through these recombinational events has led to the discovery that phage chromosomes can also be circular.

In another infection method, lysogeny, the injected phage lies dormant in the bacterial cell. In many cases the prophage incorporates into the host chromosome and replicates with it. Either spontaneously or under appropriate stimulation, the dormant phage (prophage) can lyse the bacterial host cell.

Phages can carry bacterial genes from a donor to a recipient. In generalized transduction, pure host DNA is incorporated into the phage head during lysis. In restricted transduction, faulty outlooping of the prophage from a unique chromosomal locus results in the inclusion of some host DNA into the phage head.

Figure 13-40 summarizes transduction, transformation, and conjugation.

Problems

1. A microbial geneticist isolates a new mutation in *E. coli* and wishes to map its chromosomal location. She uses interrupted-mating experiments with Hfr strains and generalized transduction experiments with phage P1. Explain why each technique by itself is insufficient for accurate mapping.

2. Four *E. coli* strains of genotype $a^+ b^-$ are labeled 1, 2, 3, and 4. Four strains of genotype $a^- b^+$ are labeled 5, 6, 7, and 8. The two genotypes are mixed in all possible combinations and (after incubation) plated to determine the frequency of $a^+ b^+$ recombinants. The following results were obtained, where M = many recombinants, L = low numbers of recombinants, and O = no recombinants.

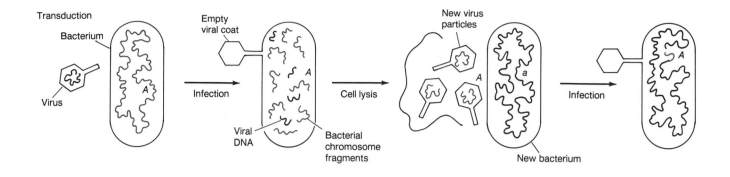

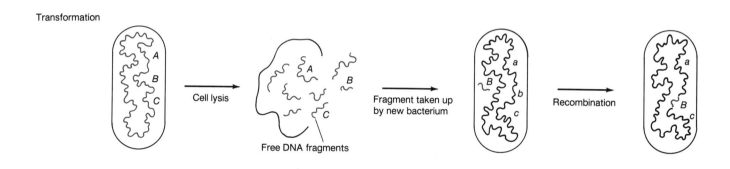

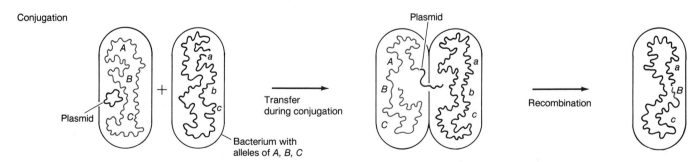

Figure 13-40. Recombination in bacteria requires the introduction into a bacterial cell of an allele obtained from another cell. In transduction, an infecting phage, or bacterial virus, picks up a bacterial-DNA segment carrying allele *A* and incorporates it instead of viral DNA into the virus particle. When such a particle infects another cell, the bacterial-DNA segment recombines with a homologous segment, thereby exchanging allele *A* for allele *a*. In transformation, a DNA segment bearing allele *B* is taken up from the environment by a cell whose chromosome carries allele *b*; the alleles are exchanged by homologous recombination. In conjugation, a plasmid inhabiting one bacterial cell can transfer the bacterium's chromosome, during cell-to-cell contact, to another cell whose chromosome carries alleles of genes on the transferred chromosome; again allele *B* is exchanged for allele *b* by recombination between homologous DNA segments. (From S. N. Cohen and J. A. Shapiro, "Transposable Genetic Elements." Copyright © 1980 by Scientific American, Inc. All rights reserved.)

	1	2	3	4
5	O	M	M	O
6	O	M	M	O
7	L	O	O	M
8	O	L	L	O

On the basis of these results, assign a sex type (either Hfr, F$^+$, or F$^-$) to each of the strains.

3. In *E. coli*, four Hfr strains donate the markers shown in the order given:

strain 1	Q	W	D	M	T
strain 2	A	X	P	T	M
strain 3	B	N	C	A	X
strain 4	B	Q	W	D	M

All these Hfr strains are derived from the same F$^+$ strain. What is the order of these markers on the circular chromosome of the original F$^+$?

4. An Hfr strain with genotype $a^+ b^+ c^+ d^-$ *str*^{S} is mated with a female strain of genotype $a^- b^- c^- d^+$ *str*^{r}. At various times, the culture is shaken violently to separate mating pairs, and the cells are plated on agar of the following three types (where nutrient A allows the growth of a^- cells, and so on; a plus indicates the presence of each nutrient, and a minus indicates its absence):

Agar type	str	A	B	C	D
1	+	+	+	−	+
2	+	−	+	+	+
3	+	+	−	+	+

a. What donor genes are being selected on each type of agar?

b. Table 13-5 shows the number of colonies on each type of agar for samples taken at various times after mixing of the strains. Using this information, determine the order of the genes *a*, *b*, and *c*.

c. One hundred colonies from each of the 25-minute plates are picked and transferred to a dish containing agar with all of the nutrients except D. The numbers of colonies that grow on this medium are 89 for the sample from agar type 1; 51 for the sample from agar type 2; and 8 for the sample from agar type 3. Using these data, fit gene *d* into the sequence of *a*, *b*, and *c*.

d. On agar containing C and streptomycin but no A or B, at what sampling time would you expect colonies to first appear?

(Problem 4 is from D. Freifelder, *Molecular Biology and Biochemistry*. Copyright © 1978 by W. H. Freeman and Co.)

■ **TABLE 13-5.**

Time of sampling (minutes)	Number of colonies on agar of type		
	1	2	3
0	0	0	0
5	0	0	0
7.5	100	0	0
10	200	0	0
12.5	300	0	75
15	400	0	150
17.5	400	50	225
20	400	100	250
25	400	100	250

5. You are given two strains of *E. coli*. One is an Hfr strain and is *arg*$^+$ *ala*$^+$ *glu*$^+$ *pro*$^+$ *leu*$^+$ T^S; the other is F$^-$ and is *arg*$^-$ *ala*$^-$ *glu*$^-$ *pro*$^-$ *leu*$^-$ T^r. The markers are all nutritional except T, which determines sensitivity or resistance to phage T1. The order of entry is that given, with *arg*$^+$ entering the recipient first and T^S last. You find that the F$^-$ strain dies when exposed to penicillin (*pen*^{S}), but the Hfr does not (*pen*^{r}). How would you locate the locus for *pen* on the bacterial chromosome with respect to *arg*, *ala*, *glu*, *pro*, and *leu*? Formulate your answer in logical, well-explained steps, illustrated with explicit diagrams where possible.

6. A cross is made between Hfr *met*$^+$ *thi*$^+$ *pur*$^+$ × F$^-$ *met*$^-$ *thi*$^-$ *pur*$^-$. Interrupted-mating studies show that *met*$^+$ enters the recipient last, so *met*$^+$ exconjugants are selected on medium containing thi and pur only. These exconjugants are tested for the presence of *thi*$^+$ and *pur*$^+$. The following numbers of individuals are found with each genotype:

met$^+$ *thi*$^+$ *pur*$^+$	280
met$^+$ *thi*$^+$ *pur*$^-$	0
met$^+$ *thi*$^-$ *pur*$^+$	6
met$^+$ *thi*$^-$ *pur*$^-$	52

a. Why was met left out of the selection medium?

b. What is the gene order?

c. What are the map distances in recombination units?

d. Why are there no individuals of the *met*$^+$ *thi*$^+$ *pur*$^-$ genotype?

7. In the cross Hfr *aro*$^+$ *arg*$^+$ *ery*^{r} *str*^{S} × F$^-$ *aro*$^-$ *arg*$^-$ *ery*^{S} *str*^{r}, the markers are transferred in the order given (with *aro*$^+$ entering first), but the first three genes are very close together. Exconjugants are plated on medium containing

str (streptomycin, to contraselect Hfr cells), ery (erythromycin), arg (arginine), and aro (aromatic amino acids). Three hundred colonies from these plates are isolated and tested for growth on various media, with the following results. On ery only, 263 strains grow. On ery + arg, 264 strains grow. On ery + aro, 290 strains grow. On ery + arg + aro, 300 strains grow.

a. Draw up a list of genotypes and indicate the number of individuals of each.

b. Calculate the recombination frequencies.

c. Calculate the ratio of the size of the *arg*-to-*aro* region to the size of the *ery*-to-*arg* region.

8. You make the following *E. coli* cross: Hfr $Z_1^- ade^+ str^s \times F^-$ $Z_2^- ade^- str^r$, in which *str* determines resistance or sensitivity to streptomycin, *ade* determines adenine requirement for growth, and Z_1 and Z_2 are two very close sites whose Z^- alleles cause an inability to use lactose as an energy source. After about an hour, the mixture is plated on medium containing streptomycin, with glucose as the energy source. Many of the ade^+ colonies that grow are found to be capable of using lactose. However, hardly any of the ade^+ colonies from the reciprocal cross Hfr $Z_2^- ade^+ str^s \times F^- Z_1^- ade^- str^r$ are found to be capable of using lactose. What is the order of the Z_1 and Z_2 sites in relation to the *ade* locus? (Note that the *str* locus is terminal.)

9. Jacob selected eight closely linked *lac⁻* mutations (called *lac-1* through *lac-8*) and then attempted to order the mutations with respect to the outside markers *pro* (proline) and *ade* (adenine) by performing a pair of reciprocal crosses for each pair of *lac* mutants:

Cross A   Hfr *pro⁻ lac-x ade⁺* × F⁻ *pro⁺ lac-y ade⁻*

Cross B   Hfr *pro⁻ lac-y ade⁺* × F⁻ *pro⁺ lac-x ade⁻*

In all cases, prototrophs are selected by plating on minimal medium with lactose as the only carbon source. Table 13-6 shows the number of colonies in the two crosses for each pair of mutants. Determine the relative order of the mutations.

(Problem 9 is from Burton S. Guttman, *Biological Principles*. Copyright © 1971, W. A. Benjamin, Inc., Menlo Park, California.)

10. Linkage maps in an Hfr bacterial strain are calculated in units of minutes, the number of minutes between genes indicating the length of time it takes for the second gene to follow the first after conjugation. In making such maps, microbial geneticists assume that the bacterial chromosome is transferred from Hfr to F⁻ at a constant rate. Thus, two genes separated by 10 minutes near the origin end are assumed to be the same *physical* distance apart as two genes separated by 10 minutes near the F-attachment end. Suggest a critical experiment to test the validity of this assumption.

11. A particular Hfr strain normally transmits the pro^+ marker as the last one during conjugation. In a cross of this strain with an F⁻ strain, some pro^+ recombinants are recovered early in the mating process. When these pro^+ cells are mixed with F⁻ cells, the majority of the latter are converted to pro^+ cells that also carry the F factor. Explain these results.

12. F′ strains in *E. coli* are derived from Hfr strains. In some cases, these F′ strains show a high rate of integration back into the bacterial chromosome. Furthermore, the site of integration often is the same site that the sex factor occupied in the original Hfr strain (before production of the F′ strains). Explain these results.

13. You have two *E. coli* strains, F⁻ $str^r ala^-$ and Hfr $str^s ala^+$, in which the F factor is inserted close to ala^+. Devise a screening test to detect F′ ala^+ sexductants.

14. *Streptococcus pneumoniae* cells of genotype $str^s mtl^-$ are transformed by donor DNA of genotype $str^r mtl^+$ and (in a separate experiment) by a mixture of two DNAs with genotypes $str^r mtl^-$ and $str^s mtl^+$. Table 13-7 shows the results.

a. What does the first line of the table tell you? Why?

b. What does the second line of the table tell you? Why?

■ TABLE 13-7.

Transforming DNA	Percentage of cells transformed to		
	$str^r mtl^-$	$str^s mtl^+$	$str^r mtl^+$
$str^r mtl^+$	4.3	0.40	0.17
$str^r mtl^- + str^s mtl^+$	2.8	0.85	0.0066

15. A transformation experiment is performed with a donor strain that is resistant to four drugs: A, B, C, and D. The recipient is sensitive to all four drugs. The treated recipient-cell population is divided up and plated on media con-

■ TABLE 13-6.

x	y	Cross A	Cross B	x	y	Cross A	Cross B
1	2	173	27	1	8	226	40
1	3	156	34	2	3	24	187
1	4	46	218	2	8	153	17
1	5	30	197	3	6	20	175
1	6	168	32	4	5	205	17
1	7	37	215	5	7	199	34

taining various combinations of the drugs. Table 13-8 shows the results.

■ **TABLE 13-8.**

Drug(s) added	Number of colonies	Drug(s) added	Number of colonies
None	10,000	BC	51
A	1156	BD	49
B	1148	CD	786
C	1161	ABC	30
D	1139	ABD	42
AB	46	ACD	630
AC	640	BCD	36
AD	942	ABCD	30

a. One of the genes obviously is quite distant from the other three, which appear to be tightly (closely) linked. Which is the distant gene?

b. What is the probable order of the three tightly linked genes?

(Problem 15 is from Franklin Stahl, *The Mechanics of Inheritance*, 2d ed. Copyright © 1969, Prentice-Hall, Englewood Cliffs, New Jersey. Reprinted by permission.)

16. In the bacteriophage T4, gene *a* is 1.0 m.u. from gene *b*, which is 0.2 m.u. from gene *c*. The gene order is *a-b-c*. In a recombination experiment, you recover five double crossovers between *a* and *c* from 100,000 progeny viruses. Is it correct to conclude that interference is negative?

17. You have infected *E. coli* cells with two strains of T 4 virus. One strain is minute (*m*), rapid lysis (*r*), and turbid (*tu*); the other is wild-type for all three markers. The lytic products of this infection are plated and classified. Of 10,342 plaques, the following numbers are classified as each genotype

m r tu	3467	*m + +*	520
+ + +	3729	*+ r tu*	474
m r +	853	*+ r +*	172
m + tu	162	*+ + tu*	965

a. Determine the linkage distances between *m* and *r*, between *r* and *tu*, and between *m* and *tu*.

b. What linkage order would you suggest for the three genes?

c. What is the coefficient of coincidence in this cross, and what does it signify?

(Problem 17 is reprinted with the permission of Macmillan Publishing Co., Inc., from Monroe W. Strickberger, *Genetics.* Copyright © 1968, Monroe W. Strickberger.)

18. Using P22 as a generalized transducing phage grown on a *pur⁺pro⁺his⁺* bacterial donor, a recipient strain of genotype *pur⁻pro⁻his⁻* is infected and incubated. Later, transductants for each donor gene are selected individually. In experiment I, *pur⁺* transductants are selected. In experiment II, *pro⁺* transductants are selected. In experiment III, *his⁺* transductants are selected.

a. What media are used for these selection experiments?

b. Next, the transductants are examined for the presence of unselected donor markers, with the following results:

I	II	III
pro⁻ his⁻ 87%	*pur⁻ his⁻* 43%	*pur⁻ pro⁻* 21%
pro⁺ his⁻ 0%	*pur⁺ his⁻* 0%	*pur⁺ pro⁻* 15%
pro⁻ his⁺ 10%	*pur⁻ his⁺* 55%	*pur⁻ pro⁺* 60%
pro⁺ his⁺ 3%	*pur⁺ his⁺* 2%	*pur⁺ pro⁺* 4%

What is the order of the bacterial genes?

c. Which two genes are closest together?

d. On the basis of the order you have proposed, explain the relative proportions of genotypes observed in experiment II.

(Problem 18 courtesy of D. Freifelder, *Molecular Biology and Biochemistry.* Copyright © 1978 by W. H. Freeman and Co.)

19. Although most λ-mediated *gal⁺* transductants are unstable, a small percentage of these transductants in fact are completely stable. Control experiments show that these stable transductants are not produced by mutation. What is the likely origin of these types?

20. An *ade⁺ arg⁺ cys⁺ his⁺ leu⁺ pro⁺* bacterial strain is known to be lysogenic for a newly discovered phage, but the site of the prophage is not known. The accompanying figure shows the bacterial map. The lysogenic strain is used as a source of the phage, and the phages are added to a bacterial strain of genotype *ade⁻ arg⁻ cys⁻ his⁻ leu⁻ pro⁻*. After a short incubation, samples of these bacteria are plated on six different media, whose supplementation is indicated in Table 13-9. The table also shows whether or not colonies were observed on the various media.

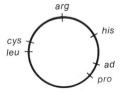

■ **TABLE 13-9.**

Medium	Nutrient supplementation in medium						Presence of colonies
	ade	arg	cys	his	leu	pro	
1	−	+	+	+	+	+	N
2	+	−	+	+	+	+	N
3	+	+	−	+	+	+	C
4	+	+	+	−	+	+	N
5	+	+	+	+	−	+	C
6	+	+	+	+	+	−	N

NOTE: + indicates the presence of a nutrient supplement: N indicates no colonies; C indicates colonies present.

a. What genetic process is at work here?

b. What is the approximate locus of the prophage?

21. You have two strains of λ that can lysogenize *E. coli;* the following figure shows their linkage maps.

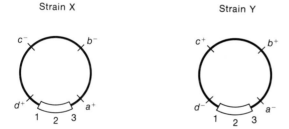

Strain X   Strain Y

The segment shown at the bottom of the chromosome and designated 1-2-3 is the region responsible for pairing and crossing-over with the *E. coli* chromosome. (Keep the markers on all your drawings.)

a. Diagram the way in which strain X is inserted into the *E. coli* chromosome (so that the *E. coli* is lysogenized).

b. It is possible to superinfect the bacteria lysogenic for strain X by using strain Y. A certain percentage of these superinfected bacteria become "doubly" lysogenic (that is, lysogenic for both strains). Diagram how this will occur. (Don't worry about how double lysogens are detected.)

c. Diagram how the two λ prophages can pair.

d. It is possible to recover crossover products between the two prophages. Diagram a crossover event and the consequences.

22. You have three strains of *E. coli.* Strain A is F′ *cys⁺trp1/ cys⁺trp1* (that is, both the F′ and the chromosome carry *cys⁺* and *trp1,* an allele for tryptophan requirement).

Strain B is F⁻ *cys⁺trp2 Z* (this strain requires cysteine for growth and carries *trp2,* another allele causing a tryptophan requirement; the strain also is lysogenic for the generalized transducing phage Z). Strain C is F⁻ *cys⁺trp1* (it is an F⁻ derivative of strain A that has lost the F′).

a. How would you determine whether *trp1* and *trp2* are alleles of the same locus? (Describe the crosses and the results expected.)

b. Suppose that *trp1* and *trp2* are allelic and that the *cys* locus is cotransduced with the *trp* locus. Using phage Z to transduce genes from strain C to strain B, how would you determine the genetic order of *cys, trp1,* and *trp2?*

23. A generalized transducing phage is used to transduce an $a^- b^- c^- d^- e^-$ recipient strain of *E. coli* with an $a^+ b^+ c^+ d^+ e^+$ donor. The recipient culture is plated on various media with the results shown in Table 13-10. What can you conclude about the linkage and order of the genes?

■ **TABLE 13-10.**

Compounds added to minimal medium	Presence (+) or absence (−) of colonies
C D E	−
B D E	−
B C E	+
B C D	+
A D E	−
A C E	−
A C D	−
A B E	−
A B D	+
A B C	−

NOTE: the allele a^- determines a requirement for A as a nutrient, and so forth.

24. In a generalized transducing system using P1 phage, the donor was $pur^+ nad^+ pdx^-$, and the recipient was $pur^- nad^- pdx^+$. The donor allele pur^+ was initially selected after transduction, and 50 pur^+ transductants were then scored for the other alleles present. The results were as follows:

Genotype	Number of colonies
$nad^+ pdx^+$	3
$nad^+ pdx^-$	10
$nad^- pdx^+$	24
$nad^- pdx^-$	13
	50

a. What is the cotransduction frequency for *pur* and *nad*?

b. What is the cotransduction frequency for *pur* and *pdx*?

c. Which of the unselected loci is closest to *pur*?

d. Are *nad* and *pdx* on the same side or on opposite sides of *pur*? Explain. (Draw the exchanges needed to produce the various transformant classes under either order to see which requires the minimum number to produce the results obtained.)

25. In a generalized transduction experiment, phages were collected from an *E. coli* donor strain of genotype *cys⁺ leu⁺ thr⁺* and used to transduce a recipient of genotype *cys⁻ leu⁻ thr⁻*. Initially, the treated recipient population was plated on minimal medium supplemented with leucine and threonine. Many colonies were obtained.

a. What are the possible genotypes of these colonies?

b. These colonies were replica-plated onto three different media: (1) minimal plus threonine only, (2) minimal plus leucine only, and (3) minimal. Give the genotypes that could in theory grow on these three media.

c. It was observed that 56 percent of the original colonies grew on (1), 5 percent grew on (2), and no colonies grew on (3). What were the actual genotypes of the colonies on (1), (2), and (3)?

d. Draw a map showing the order of the three genes and which of the two outer genes is closer to the middle gene.

CHAPTER 14

Manipulation of DNA

■ We are now in the midst of a new era in genetics, made possible by the techniques of molecular genetics and the uses of recombinant DNA. Many of the standard methods of genetic analysis have been replaced by biochemical and DNA-sequence analyses that were inconceivable before the early 1970s. In fact, the whole approach to the study of the genetic makeup of higher organisms has been altered by recombinant-DNA techniques. Avenues of study have been opened up to the molecular geneticist at a level of resolution never dreamed possible just a decade before. Let us look at the new arsenal of methods at the disposal of the modern molecular biologist and at the principles upon which they are based and see how these techniques are being used to understand heredity, evolution, gene control, and human diseases.

It is interesting to note that many of the operational criteria used in molecular biology are identical to those used by geneticists working at the level of organisms:

1. Recognizable differences (comparable to phenotypes) must exist so that the genetic molecules under study can be distinguished from one another.

2. There must be techniques that permit the study of individual molecules or groups of molecules over time — that is, ways to follow the fate of individuals or particular groups.

3. There must be quantitative measures of the molecules involved (comparable to progeny counts or frequencies).

4. There must be ways to mix and even to hybridize the molecules in different combinations (equivalent to crosses in organisms).

5. There must be controls for comparison and standardization of results.

This chapter presents experiments that do not require genetic crosses but that nevertheless involve similar processes of manipulation. First we examine manipulation of DNA before recombinant-DNA techniques were available, and then we consider more advanced methodologies.

The Power of Base Complementarity

Denaturation of DNA by Heat

The hydrogen bonds that link complementary base pairs are disrupted by high temperature. Because a G–C pair has three hydrogen bonds, whereas an A–T pair has only two, the **melting point** (defined as the temperature at which one-half of the DNA sample is no longer hydrogen bonded) is directly proportional to the G–C content (Figure 14-1). Thus, any experimental technique that allows separation of

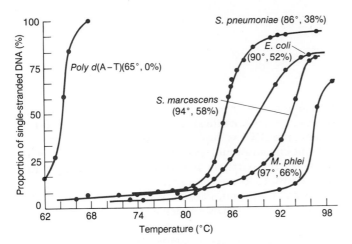

Figure 14-1. Denaturation of DNA from different sources at various temperatures. In parentheses for each sample, the first value is the melting temperature (at which one-half of the DNA molecules have been denatured), and the second value is the percentage of base pairs in the sample that are G–C pairs. There is an obvious relationship between G–C content and melting temperature. (From J. Marmur and P. Doty, *Nature* 183:1427, 1959.)

single-stranded from double-stranded DNA will permit separation of molecules with different melting points and hence with different G–C contents.

Message The relative G–C content of DNA can be inferred from its melting temperature. DNA with a relatively higher content of A–T is denatured (melted) at a lower temperature than is DNA with a greater amount of G–C.

Within a DNA molecule, the proportion of G–C versus A–T pairs may vary along the length of the molecule. Partial denaturation can be produced by a hydrogen-bond-breaking agent, such as high temperature, and the

denatured regions within the molecule can then be mapped.

The positions and sizes of the melted regions can be reproducibly identified in a population of identical molecules, thus indicating that such maps do reflect the base composition within the molecules. In 1976, David Wolstenholme used the heat denaturation of AT-rich regions to map the mitochrondrial DNAs of different *Drosophila* species.

The histone genes provide another example of differing melting points. Histones are the basic proteins found in association with nuclear DNA. They are rich in arginine and lysine, whose codons are relatively rich in G–C pairs, so the histone genes should have a greater density than other parts of the chromosome. This density difference permits isolation of the histone genes. Furthermore, the histone genes should resist heat denaturation. Indeed, the segments of DNA that code for five histones in sea urchins occur in a single region, with each gene separated from the next by an AT-rich "spacer" that denatures at lower temperatures (Figure 14-2).

Message Regions within DNA that are relatively rich in A–T pairs denature at a lower temperature than the surrounding regions. Denaturation maps show the effects of these intramolecular differences in melting temperature.

Reassociation of Complementary Single Strands

In completely denatured DNA, all strands are single. These single strands can reassociate by random collisions that permit matching between complementary sequences. The spe-

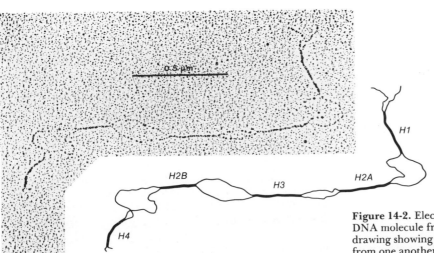

Figure 14-2. Electron micrograph of a partially denatured (at 61°C) DNA molecule from the histone genes of the sea urchin, with a drawing showing the sequence of the histone genes (*H*), separated from one another by the denatured AT-rich spacers. (From R. Portmann and M. Birnstiel, *Nature* 246:31, 1976.)

cific matching of strands after reannealing can be demonstrated by testing the biological activity of reformed duplexes in bacterial transformation.

An important use of reassociation is the physical mapping of deletions or of regions of nucleotide differences in heteroduplexes formed by DNA from different sources. For example, the position and size of a deletion can be determined by annealing DNA from a deletion mutant with DNA from wild-type, as shown in Figure 14-3. Figure 14-4 shows an electron micrograph of such a heteroduplex. In the same way, hybridization of DNA sequences from sources that are related evolutionarily provides a visual indication of the extent of divergence in the nucleotide sequences.

Message Strand matching by base complementarity is the property that makes DNA accessible to manipulation. The remarkable specificity of complementary base-sequence recognition provides a powerful tool for actually comparing base sequences in heteroduplexes.

Locating DNA Sequences on Chromosomes

Can the base sequences of a purified nucleic acid be used to locate those sequences of DNA within a chromosome that are complementary to them? In the late 1960s, Mary Lou

Pardue and Joseph Gall made use of the giant chromosomes of *Drosophila* salivary glands to answer this question. Because the DNA is duplicated several hundredfold in the polytene chromosome, specific nucleic acids have many potential pairing partners at a complementary site. Suppose that we wish to locate the genes coding for an RNA.

The chromosomes are initially squashed and fixed on the slides. Then the DNA is denatured with a mild alkaline treatment that breaks hydrogen bonds without liberating the DNA from the chromosome. The single strands are prevented from renaturing by treatment with formamide, which combines with free amino groups and inhibits duplex re-formation. Now radioactive RNA is incubated on the chromosomes. After sufficient time for hybridization, the excess label is washed off, single-stranded RNA is removed by treatment with ribonuclease (which breaks single-stranded RNA into nucleotides while leaving untouched any RNA that is double-stranded or paired to DNA), and a photographic emulsion is placed onto the chromosomes to locate DNA-RNA hybrids in an autoradiograph.

In this way, it was possible to locate the DNA that codes for 18S and 28S ribosomal RNA in the chromocenter (Figure 14-5). The locus for 5S ribosomal RNA is at 56EF in the right arm of chromosome 2. Several sites for tRNA genes have now been identified by localization on chromosomes in situ. RNA made from highly repetitive sequences of DNA (by a procedure we shall consider later in this chapter) has been used to show the centromere position of this redundant DNA in mammalian chromosomes (Figure 14-6).

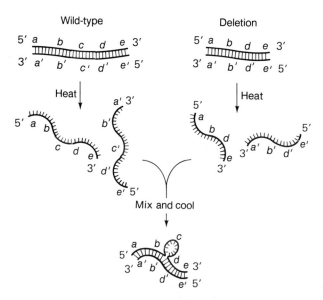

Figure 14-3. Formation of a hereoduplex with deletion and normal DNA.

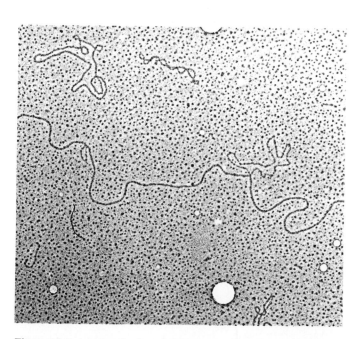

Figure 14-4. A heteroduplex of deletion and wild-type DNA of phage T4. Two different deletion loops are visible. (From T. Homyk.)

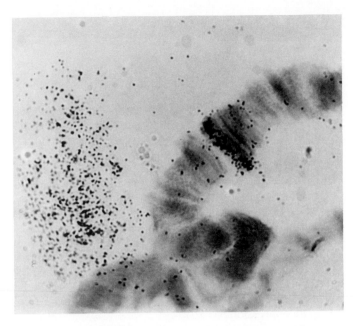

Figure 14-5. Autoradiograph showing ribosomal RNA binding to the chromocenter and at 56F,F in the right arm of chromosome 2. (From T. Grigliatti et al., *Cold Spring Harbor Symposia on Quantitative Biology* 38:461, 1974.)

Message Chromosome positions of the DNA complementary to specific RNAs can be identified by hybridization to chromosomes in situ.

Isolation of Specific DNA Sequences

In order to probe the properties of DNA in relation to specific functions, we must separate specific classes or segments of DNA from the rest. Several techniques are now available to accomplish this task.

1. One of the earliest techniques was the separation of a rapidly annealing portion of mammalian DNA that represents highly redundant sequences from the more slowly annealing unique segments that are present only in single copies per genome. This separation is accomplished on nitrocellulose filters or columns of hydroxyapatite. The amount of highly repetitive sequences varies greatly, ranging from 0 percent in many prokaryotes to 30 or 40 percent in some eukaryotes. The highly repetitive sequences involve repetitions of a short basic unit. For example, in the guinea pig, the repeating unit is

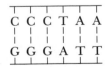

2. Because the highly redundant sequence is a repetition of a short unit, the ratio of GC to AT in such segments

may deviate considerably from the ratio for the bulk of the organism's DNA. Because the equilibrium position of DNA in a cesium chloride gradient is determined by its GC content, DNA fragments with different buoyant densities can be identified as **satellites** of the main DNA band in the gradient (Figure 14-7). The satellite DNA may be more or less dense than the main band.

These two methods provide DNA fractions whose physical properties distinguish them from the main DNA component. The challenge then is to try to find biological functions for these fractions. But are there ways of purifying DNA sequences whose function is already known—sequences that therefore are of specific interest? Such methodologies do exist, and they can provide the most useful kind of information.

3. A very effective method for separating small plasmids (episomes) from the bacterial chromosomes was developed in 1967 by Jerome Vinograd. The molecule ethidium (Figure 14-8) can insert itself between bases of a DNA molecule if the molecule is sufficiently flexible to untwist a bit, thereby providing the space for ethidium to squeeze in. When DNA has ethidium bound to it, this complex has a density less than that of the pure

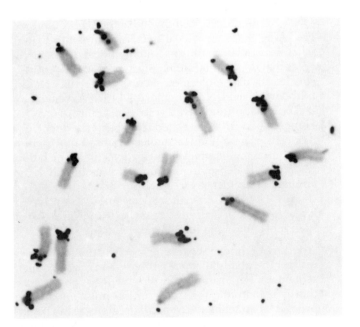

Figure 14-6. Autoradiograph of mouse metaphase chromosomes hybridized in situ with radioactive RNA made from highly redundant mouse DNA. The RNA sequences seem to be present in all chromosomes and to be concentrated in the region immediately adjacent to the centromere. (From M. L. Pardue and J. Gall, *Chromosomes Today* 3:47, 1971.)

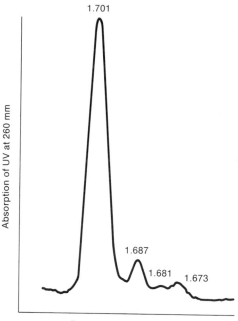

Figure 14-7. Distribution of *Drosophila melanogaster* DNA in a cesium chloride density gradient that separates DNA molecules of differing G–C content. The DNA was prepared in such a manner that it was fragmented into approximately 25-kb segments. The bulk of the DNA appears at 1.701 g/cm³ in the gradient, but there are several satellite bands with a lower buoyant density. The DNA was prepared in such a manner that it was fragmented into sizes of approximately 25 kb. (From S. A. Endow, M. L. Polan, and J. G. Gall, *Journal of Molecular Biology* 96:670, 1975. Copyright © 1975 Academic Press, Inc., London, Ltd.)

DNA. Vinograd realized that a bacterial chromosome is so long that mechanical stress will break the DNA when it is isolated, thus producing linear DNA molecules that do allow ethidium intercalation. In contrast, smaller circular molecules, such as the fertility factor, mitochrondrial DNA, or chloroplast DNA, remain intact on isolation and have a restricted ability to untwist. Hence, when DNA is isolated from bacterial or eukaryotic cells, the large linear molecules bind much more ethidium than the small circular molecules, which thus remain more dense. In a cesium chloride gradient, the circular molecules are readily purified and collected (Figure 14-9). As we shall see, episomes have played a key role in manipulation of genes, so the purification of such molecules is an important technique.

4. Another method of separating specific DNA sequences utilizes the ability of some proteins to recognize such sequences. For example, the enzyme RNA polymerase that is responsible for transcription must initiate the process by attachment to specific regions at the beginnings of genes. After a preparation of DNA is exposed to RNA polymerases, the mixture can be digested with a nuclease that breaks down the DNA chains. Those sequences to which the enzyme is bound are physically sheltered from the nucleolytic action, so they can be recovered intact after the nuclease treatment. In prin-

ciple, any DNA sequence that is bound by a specific protein can be recovered in this manner. This is the principle that permitted the purification of the beginning of the *lacZ* gene, which is regulated by the *lac* repressor protein (see Chapter 18). The DNA segment protected by repressor is 24 base pairs in length. Note that the regions indicated by the lines are symmetrical when read 5′ → 3′ (with a few intervening base pairs that do not fit the pattern). As the amino acid sequences and three-dimensional structures of proteins are determined, along with the base sequences of the DNA sites they recognize, we shall learn about the factors responsible for the specificity of the DNA-protein interactions that appear to be the key to regulation of gene expression.

5. An important tool for the isolation of specific DNA sequences resulted from a study of tumor-causing viruses. Thus far, we have assumed a unidirectional relationship between DNA, RNA, and protein: DNA directs the synthesis of RNA, which in turn specifies protein production (shown as DNA → RNA → protein). The ability of RNA to function both as the hereditary information and as the molecule to be translated is shown by the existence of viruses that contain only RNA. An exception to the DNA → RNA → protein rule was discovered with animal tumor viruses known to carry only RNA. Normal cells cultured in vitro and infected with the virus are "transformed" phenotypically into tumor-like cells. However, such transformed cells normally do not produce infective viruses. It was suggested that the genetic material of the virus is integrated like a prophage into the DNA of the transformed cells. But if the virus genome is RNA, how can it integrate into chromosomal DNA?

In the early 1960s, Howard Temin proposed a mechanism by suggesting that the information in the viral RNA is "transcribed" into DNA that is then inserted into the host cell's genome. In 1970, Temin and David Baltimore independently discovered an enzyme that catalyzes this step; it is called **reverse transcriptase.** The existence of reverse transcriptase

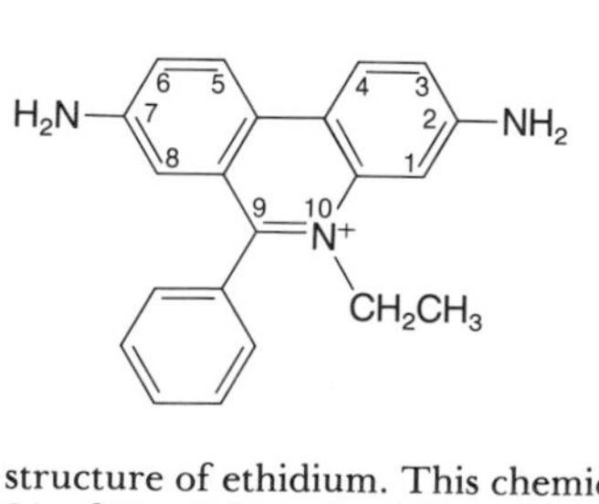

Figure 14-8. The structure of ethidium. This chemical can be used to separate the DNA of *E. coli* from the DNA of its episomes.

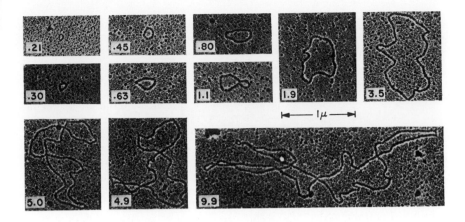

Figure 14-9. Electron micrographs of circular DNA from HeLa cells. The number in each micrograph is the length of the molecule in microns. These may be similar to episomes isolated from bacterial cells. (From R. Radloff, W. Bauer, and J. Vinograd, *Proc. Natl. Acad. Sci. USA* 57:1514, 1967.)

requires an amendment of the central dogma to DNA $\rightleftharpoons$ RNA $\rightarrow$ protein, and it provides a tool for making DNA that complements any RNA that can be purified. Cell biologists have long recognized that cells that are specialized to carry out a specific function typically contain large quantities of a single gene product. For example, the silk-producing cells in the glands of a silkworm produce large quantities of silk protein, fibroin; cells in the mammalian pancreas excrete insulin; red blood cells (erythrocytes) are rich in hemoglobin; cells in chick oviducts make a great deal of ovalbumin; and so on. Isolation of RNA from such specialized cells provides a sample that is enriched for a specific mRNA. Thus, pure hemoglobin mRNA can readily be prepared from immature red blood cells (reticulocytes). With reverse transcriptase, cDNA (DNA complementary to the mRNA) is formed in vitro from the mRNA. The cDNA can be subjected to sequence analysis or used to recover complementary sequences from total cellular DNA or from preparations of RNA by the formation of hybrids. When the cDNA is hybridized with RNA, DNA:RNA hybrids reveal the existence of large RNA transcripts, which are precursors of the active mRNA.

6. Recombinant DNA techniques, described in the following section, allow the isolation of many specific DNA sequences.

Message   There are several techniques for isolating specific classes of DNA from a heterogeneous population of molecules. This isolation allows us to focus on a restricted part of the genome, just as geneticists used various techniques to isolate specific loci for genetic analysis.

Recombinant DNA and Genetic Engineering

Let us first look at the larger picture and ask what recombinant DNA is, how it is created, and why it is so important to molecular biology. The complexity of eukaryotic genomes makes detailed analysis of gene structure and gene regula-

tion extremely difficult. However, the ability to break up chromosomes into small fragments, to isolate and analyze these fragments individually, and even to manipulate them opens up many areas of study. This is one of the goals of recombinant DNA research: to isolate distinct fragments of DNA and to recombine them into a smaller genome much more amenable to analysis than the original genome from which the DNA fragments came. There are a number of methods for creating such **recombinant DNA molecules,** as we shall see later. Usually the vehicle, or **vector,** into which the DNA fragment has been incorporated is capable of selective replication at some stage, thus allowing the amplification of specific segments of DNA. The increased amounts of DNA of the segment under study greatly facilitate detailed molecular analysis. Bacteria are frequently employed as the host for maintenance and amplification of recombinant DNA molecules. The process by which a specific segment of DNA is selectively amplified in a bacterial cell is termed **cloning.** This is depicted in Figure 14-10, in which a piece of foreign DNA is inserted into a small plasmid in vitro (see later), and the plasmid is introduced by transformation into a host *E. coli* cell where it can be maintained by selecting for an antibiotic resistance gene present on the plasmid. We shall examine different methods of cloning after we first consider the discoveries that led to the methodology for creating recombinant DNA molecules.

Restriction Enzymes

The Phenomenon of Host Restriction.   We have already seen that a bacterial genotype determines the cell's susceptibility to infection by various phages. Similarly, a phage's genotype determines the range of bacterial cells that it can infect. Clearly, host and parasite have each evolved genetic strategies for coping with the other.

Let's consider the infective capacity of phages grown in bacteria of different genotypes. For example, suppose that a hypothetical phage X is found in two bacterial strains, A and B. We'll label phage from these two sources as X.A and X.B, respectively. Suppose that we use X.A to infect strain B, and we use X.B to infect strain A. We find that X.B phages do poorly at infecting A cells, whereas X.A phages infect both strains equally well (Figure 14-11). When the few X.B phages that are recovered from A are used to

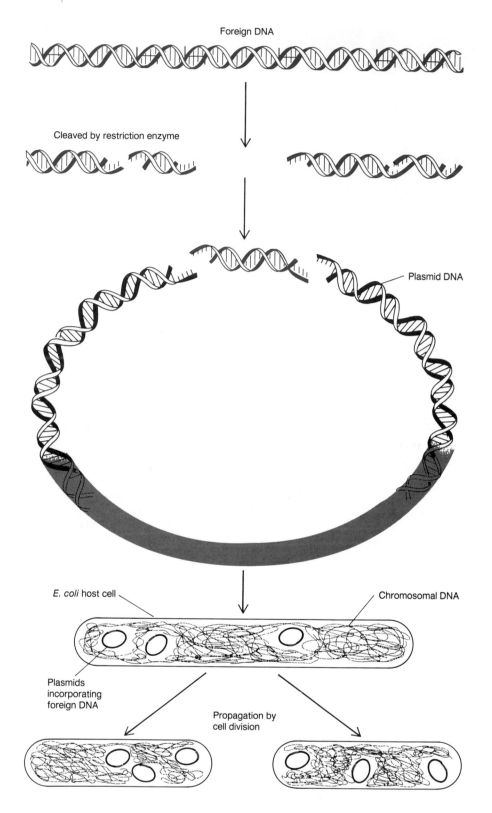

Foreign DNA

Cleaved by restriction enzyme

Plasmid DNA

E. coli host cell

Chromosomal DNA

Plasmids
incorporating
foreign DNA

Propagation by
cell division

Figure 14-10. A recombinant-DNA technique that makes it possible for the first time to introduce deliberately nucleotide sequences from the DNA of one strain or species of organism into the DNA of another. The DNA of the "foreign" organism is first fragmented in one of a number of ways. In the example shown here, restriction enzymes (described in the text) are used to fragment the foreign DNA and also to cut the circular plasmid DNA. After recombining the foreign DNA with the plasmid DNA, the circular form of the plasmid can be restored, and the structure can be inserted into a suitable host. (From C. Grobstein, "The Recombinant DNA Debate." Copyright © 1977 by Scientific American, Inc. All rights reserved.)

infect strain A, they are found to be *fully infective!* Perhaps some A-infecting mutants already existed in the X.B population, and selection has now isolated them. However, when the phages are allowed to infect strain B again, and then returned to strain A, we find that they are once again poorly infective in strain A. We have not isolated an A-infecting pure-breeding strain of X.B phages.

Apparently, the host range of the phage depends on the bacterial strain in which it matured, not on the phage's

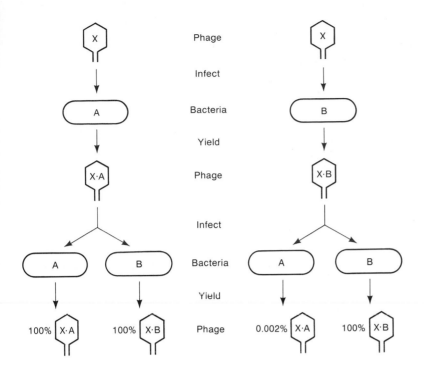

Figure 14-11. Infectivity of hypothetical phage X from two different bacterial strains, A and B. Phages derived from strain B are poorly infective on strain A, whereas phages derived from strain A infect both strains equally well. The percentages indicate the efficiency of plaque formation on each host.

genotype. In other words, the host genotype apparently modifies the phage's particle without altering the DNA sequence in the phage. It would seem that the small number of phages released in the restricting cross are produced in a few cells whose physiological state happens to be tolerant of the infective particle.

DNA Modification.   But what restricts phage X.B from multiplying in strain A? The mature phage is able to attach to the bacterial cell wall and to inject its DNA into the cell. The factor that prevents it from reproducing is the nucleolytic activity of a host enzyme (nuclease) that breaks the phage DNA into a number of noninfective fragments. The host cell seems to have a defense system that destroys unfamiliar DNA! But what protects the host DNA and the infective X.A phage DNA from this nuclease? The answer to this question revealed the nature of the phage-modification process.

Enzymes exist that modify specific bases at specific sequences *without altering the coding properties of those bases.* For example, in certain bacterial strains, cytosine and adenine are altered by the addition of a methyl group to the forms shown in Figure 14-12. In the 1960s, Werner Arber was able to show that the alteration of cytosine and adenine by addition of a methyl group (a process called methylation) is responsible for protection of the DNA from nuclease activity. He showed that mutations involving replacement of a normally methylating base by a base that cannot be methylated results in a loss of protection from the nuclease action. The total number of bases that are methylated is very small, so these particular bases must occupy very specific regions that are attacked by the nucleases. In our example, bacterium A evidently has the capacity to modify DNA whereas B does not.

The phenomenon of host restriction is due to the action of nucleases that degrade any DNA not specifically modified for protection from the nucleases of a given host cell.

Message   There are two interrelated processes involved in the phenomenon of host restriction: the **restriction** of phage multiplication by enzymic destruction of invading viral DNA, and the **modification** of phage DNA to render it immune to effects of the restriction enzymes.

Specificity of Restriction Enzymes.   The next step in understanding restriction phenomena did not come until 1970, when Hamilton Smith made great progress in his studies of the restriction enzyme from *Haemophilus influenzae.* This enzyme, called HindII, cuts T7 phage DNA into 40 specific fragments. What do the cleavage sites have in common? To find out, Smith took the mixture of fragments and marked the 5' ends by attaching the radioisotope ^{32}P. He then used hydrolyzing enzymes to break the labeled fragments into

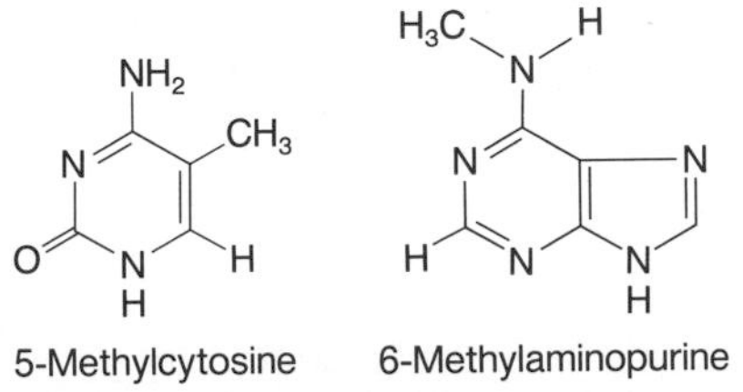

5-Methylcytosine   6-Methylaminopurine

Figure 14-12. Forms of cytosine and adenine that have been modified by the addition of a methyl group (methylation). Such methylation does not change the coding capacity of the DNA but does protect the DNA from attack by some highly specific nucleases.

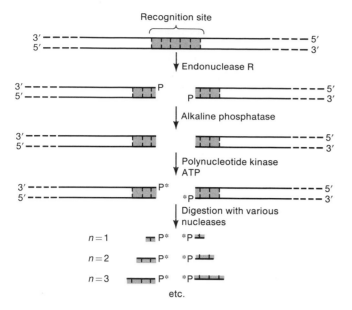

Figure 14-13. Smith's method for identifying the bases at the *HindII* recognition site. The T7 DNA is cleaved by HindII (endonuclease R), which leaves a phosphate on the 5′ end of the cleaved strands. This phosphate is removed with alkaline phosphatase, and then polynucleotide kinase is used to catalyze the attachment to the 5′ end of a radioactive phosphorus atom in a phosphate group (*P) from labeled ATP. Various nucleases are then used to cleave the fragments into smaller fragments of varying lengths. The labeled fragments are separated, and their base sequences are identified. (From J. T. Kelly, Jr., and H. O. Smith, *Journal of Molecular Biology* 51:397, 1970. Copyright © 1970 Academic Press, Inc., London, Ltd.)

still smaller pieces (Figure 14-13). He was able to separate the labeled end fragments in small segments only a few nucleotides long, so that he could determine the base sequence of each fragment.

Smith found that the label was always attached to an adenine or a guanine (the purines). Fragments with labeled adenine were always A–A or A–A–C; fragments with labeled guanine were always G–A or G–A–C. Smith suggested that such fragments could be produced if the enzyme cleaves only at the points indicated by the arrows in the following specific sequence (where Py represents a pyrimidine and Pu represents a purine):

$$5' \quad -G-T-Py-Pu-A-C- \quad 3'$$
$$3' \quad -C-A-Pu-Py-T-G- \quad 5'$$

Note the rotational symmetry of this sequence: a rotation of 180 degrees around the dot in the center leaves the sequence unchanged. Verify that cleavage at the arrows will produce just the 5′-end fragments that Smith identified: Pu–A– and Pu–A–C–. HindII apparently is very specific in identifying the sequence at which it will cleave. Furthermore, Smith showed that the host-induced methylation that confers protection from HindII activity occurs at this

same cleavage site: protection from cleavage by HindII is obtained when the adenines one base away from the cleavage site are methylated (m):

$$5' \quad -G-T-Py-Pu-\overset{m}{A}-C- \quad 3'$$
$$3' \quad -C-A-\underset{m}{Pu}-Py-T-G- \quad 5'$$

Studies of other restriction enzymes produced similar results. For example, the enzyme EcoRI is produced by a gene on an R plasmid in *E. coli*. EcoRI cleaves the circular DNA of SV40 (a small mammalian virus) at only one site, thus converting the DNA ring into a linear molecule that has sticky ends like those of linear λ DNA. The sequence at the cleavage site for EcoRI is

$$5' \quad -G-A-A-\overset{m}{T}-T-C- \quad 3'$$
$$3' \quad -C-T-T-A-\underset{m}{A}-G- \quad 5'$$

Again the sequence is rotationally symmetrical, but in this case the cuts are staggered and therefore produce "sticky ends" (Figure 14-14). Once again, methylation of adenines near the cleavage site provides protection against the cleaving action (the methylated bases are indicated in the sequence, although, of course, *either* methylation *or* cleavage would occur at such a sequence, *not* both). Comparing the sequences in the two strands for the *EcoRI* site (recalling that each is read in the opposite direction), you can see that the sequences are the same. In semantics, a sentence reading the same forward or backward (such as ABLE WAS I ERE I SAW ELBA) is called a **palindrome,** and this name is used to describe DNA sequences such as the one in the *EcoRI* site.

These studies have opened an explosively expanding area. Dozens of restriction enzymes with different sequence specificities have now been identified, some of which are shown in Table 14-1. Most restriction enzymes

Figure 14-14. Cleavage of SV40 DNA by the restriction enzyme EcoRI produces a linear DNA with sticky ends.

■ TABLE 14-1. Recognition, cleavage, and modification sites for various restriction enzymes

Enzyme	Source organism	Restriction site	ϕX174	λ	SV40
			Number of cleavage sites in DNA from		
EcoRI	*Escherichia coli*	5′ –G–A–A–T–T–C– –C–T–T–A–A–G– 5′	0	5	1
EcoRII	*E. coli*	5′ –G–C–C–T–G–G–C– –C–G–G–A–C–C–G– 5′	2	>35	16
HindII	*Hemophilus influenzae*	5′ –G–T–Py–Pu–A–C– –C–A–Pu–Py–T–G– 5′	13	34	7
HindIII	*H. influenzae*	5′ –A–A–G–C–T–T– –T–T–C–G–A–A– 5′	0	6	6
HaeIII	*H. aegyptius*	5′ –G–G–C–C– –C–C–G–G– 5′	11	>50	19
HpaII	*H. parainfluenzae*	5′ –C–C–G–G– –G–G–C–C– 5′	5	>50	1
PstI	*Providencia stuartii*	5′ –C–T–G–C–A–G– –G–A–C–G–T–C– 5′	1	18	2
SmaI	*Serratia marcescens*	5′ –C–C–C–G–G–G– –G–G–G–C–C–C– 5′	0	3	0
BamI	*Bacillus amyloliquefaciens*	5′ –G–G–A–T–C–C– –C–C–T–A–G–G– 5′	0	5	1
BgIII	*B. globiggi*	5′ –A–G–A–T–C–T– –T–C–T–A–G–A– 5′	0	5	0

NOTE: an asterisk (*) is commonly used to indicate methylation sites rather than the m used here (to avoid confusion with radioactive labeling).

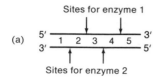

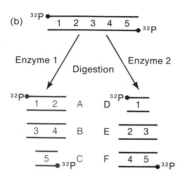

Figure 14-15. (a) A hypothetical DNA with recognition sites for two different restriction enzymes. (b) After labeling of the 5' ends, digestion of the DNA by enzyme 1 produces fragments A, B, and C, whereas digestion of the DNA by enzyme 2 produces fragments D, E, and F. The fragments can be separated electrophoretically, and the end fragments can be identified by the radioactive labeling.

recognize specific palindromic sequences. Restriction enzymes are powerful tools for analysis, because they can locate specific base sequences and cut the DNA in a very specific way. Now we are ready to see how we can approach the task of genetic engineering.

Message Restriction enzymes provide a way of cleaving DNA from any source at a specific sequence, thereby producing a heterogeneous population of fragments with identical ends.

Restriction-Enzyme Mapping. The restriction-enzyme target sites can be used as markers for DNA, just as the bubbles of AT-rich melt regions are used. The DNA from a specific source is subjected to successive digestion by different restriction enzymes. When the fragments are separated electrophoretically on polyacrylamide gels, the "map" of the restriction sites can be deduced, as shown in Figures 14-15 to 14-17.

For example, consider a hypothetical DNA molecule having the distribution of restriction sites shown in Figure 14-15a. The 3' ends can be labeled with ^{32}P before the DNA is cleaved by each enzyme in separate samples, as illustrated in Figure 14-15b. The resulting fragments are separated on gels. The recovery of three fragments after treatment with each restriction enzyme shows that there are two recognition sites for each enzyme. The absence of radioactivity in fragments B and E shows that these are the center pieces.

The relative positions of the recognition sites can be determined by taking the fragments from one enzyme treatment and treating these fragments with the other enzyme (Figure 14-16). If smaller subfragments are produced

by the second treatment, we know that the original fragments contained sites for the second enzyme. The number of subfragments produced by this double treatment is always one more than the total number of restriction sites (for both enzymes). We now compare the subfragments and determine overlaps, as shown in Figure 14-16. For example, the subfragment 2 is obtained by further breakdown of both fragments A and E, so we know that A and E must overlap. (The similarity of subfragments in the two experiments is indicated by similar positions on the electrophoretic gel.) With this kind of reasoning (Figure 14-16c), we conclude that the overlapping order of fragments in the original DNA must have been DAEBFC.

We know that fragments D and A are both end fragments (because of the radioactive labeling). They share subfragment 1, so we can place subfragment 1 at the end of

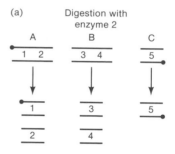

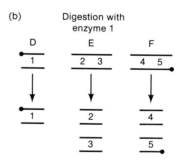

Figure 14-16. (a) Fragments A, B, and C, obtained from the original DNA by digestion with enzyme 1, are now digested with enzyme 2, producing subfragments 1 through 5. (b) The fragments obtained by digestion with enzyme 2 are now digested with enzyme 1 to produce subfragments 1 through 5. (c) Comparison of the subfragments (identified by position on the electrophoretic gel) obtained from each fragment indicates which fragments must overlap (indicated here by vertical lines).

our map. Fragments A and E share subfragment 2, so we place subfragment 2 next in the map. Proceeding in this way, we map the subfragments on the original DNA, as in Figure 14-17. We know that the original treatment with enzyme 2 separated fragments D and E, so we conclude that a site for enzyme 2 lies between subfragments 1 and 2. With similar reasoning, we can locate the other restriction-enzyme sites on the map. The final map at the bottom of Figure 14-17 is, of course, identical to the one shown in Figure 14-15a (which would not have been known in a real experiment). You may find it useful to review this reasoning to be sure you see how the map could be constructed in a real experiment where the order of subfragments is not known initially.

In 1976, Smith and Birnstiel developed a similar method for locating the restriction-enzyme sites. This method utilizes the ability to distinguish between DNA molecules of differing length. Suppose that we have a circular DNA molecule with a single *EcoRI* site, so that the molecule can be converted into a linear rod by treatment with EcoRI (Figure 14-18). Several samples are each partially digested (using concentrations such that around one of every 50 sites is actually recognized and cleaved) by one of a series of test enzymes, producing different populations of DNA fragments of varying lengths. These fragments can be separated on gels, where they migrate in order of increasing length. By reading across the gels from the bottom up, we can obtain the order of cleavage sites. A map of enzyme sites can now be prepared. Furthermore, the distances that the various fragments migrate in the gels pro-

vide a measurement of their sizes, so that the relative distances between cleavage sites can also be determined. Restriction-enzyme maps prepared in this way can be very detailed, as Figure 14-19 illustrates. With such maps, specific segments can be identified and separated for further analysis.

Message The relative order of restriction-enzyme cleavage sites on a DNA molecule can be determined, providing a new kind of chromosome map. Furthermore, the number of nucleotides between any two sites can be estimated from the size of the fragments obtained in the analysis.

Formation of Recombinant DNA

There are several methods for creating recombinant DNA molecules. Each exploits the properties of different enzymes.

Direct Generation of Sticky Ends. This technique utilizes the restriction enzymes described in the preceding sections. Restriction enzymes can cleave DNA from any source at a specific sequence. In the most favorable cases, "sticky ends" are generated, which will anneal to the sticky ends generated in other DNA molecules (the vectors; see later) cleaved with the same restriction enzyme. Recall the cloning procedure depicted schematically in Figure 14-10. Now we can consider the formation of the recombinant plasmid in more detail, as shown in Figure 14-20a. In this example, the plasmid called SC101 carries one *EcoRI* restriction site, so digestion with the restriction enzyme EcoRI converts the circular plasmid DNA to a linear molecule with single-stranded sticky ends. DNA from any other source (say, *Drosophila*) can be treated with EcoRI enzyme to produce a population of fragments carrying the same sticky sequence at the fragment ends. When the two populations are mixed, the DNAs from the two sources can combine as duplexes form between their sticky ends. The annealed fragments can then be linked permanently by the enzyme DNA ligase (Figure 14-20b).

Tailing. The enzyme **terminal transferase** from calf thymus can be used to generate sticky ends on DNA fragments. This enzyme catalyzes the addition of nucleotide "tails" to the 3′ end of DNA chains. Therefore, if dA (deoxyadenine) residues are added to one DNA fragment (let us say the vector), and dT residues are added to the other fragment (in this case, the fragment to be inserted into the vector), then the two fragments can anneal and subsequently be joined by DNA ligase, as shown in Figure 14-21. Alternatively, poly-G and poly-C tails can be added to the respective fragments at the 3′ ends.

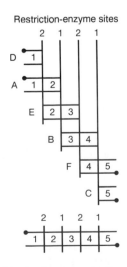

Figure 14-17. Arranging the fragments in the order indicated by their overlapping subfragments, we obtain the map of the restriction-enzyme sites along the DNA (*bottom*). Compare this map to Figure 14-15a (which, of course, would not be known at the beginning of such an analysis).

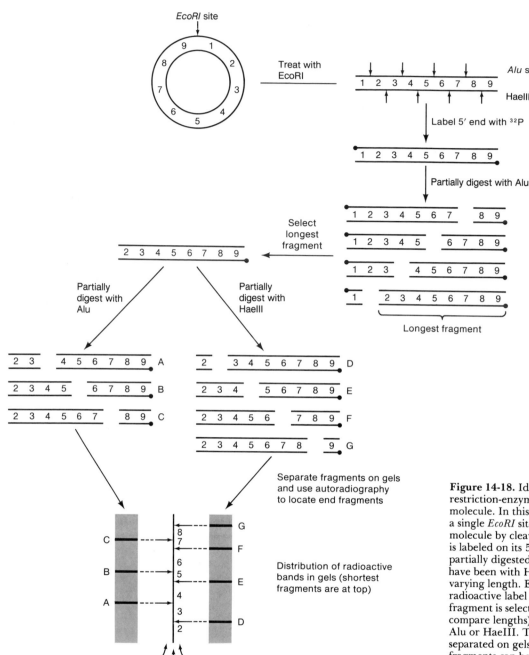

Figure 14-18. Identification of the sequence of restriction-enzyme sites in a circular DNA molecule. In this example, the ring of DNA with a single *EcoRI* site is opened into a linear molecule by cleavage with EcoRI. The molecule is labeled on its 5′ ends with ^{32}P and then partially digested with Alu (it could just as easily have been with HaeIII) to produce fragments of varying length. Each fragment now carries the radioactive label at only one end. The longest fragment is selected (after testing on a gel to compare lengths), and it is partially digested with Alu or HaeIII. The new sets of fragments are separated on gels. The location of the labeled fragments can be determined by autoradiography of gels. The sequence of restriction sites can now be read in order as the two gels are compared.

Blunt-End Ligation. Under appropriate conditions, T4 DNA ligase can join fragments containing blunt ends. Although less useful for direct cloning, this reaction permits the addition of synthetically prepared DNA duplexes that contain restriction sites. These DNA **linkers** are very useful, since they allow the creation of restriction sites that are then cleaved with the appropriate enzyme to generate a fragment containing cohesive ends. This procedure facilitates the cloning of fragments containing blunt ends.

Vectors

Cloning vehicles, or vectors, are used to enable replication of cloned fragments. The following general features are common to the most frequently employed vectors:

1. A small, well-characterized molecule

2. An origin of replication within the molecule enabling replication of itself and of the inserted fragment

3. The ability to selectively recover the hybrid molecule

There are numerous vectors in current usage.

Plasmids. Plasmids, which as we saw in Chapter 13 are small, circular DNA molecules, can be introduced into cells

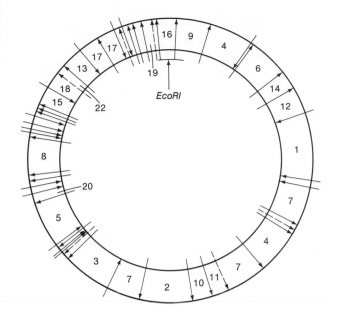

Figure 14-19. Restriction-enzyme cleavage map of SV40 phage DNA. Arrows pointing outward indicate sites for Alu (restriction enzyme from *Arthrobacter luteus*), and arrows pointing inward indicate sites for HaeIII (from *Hemophilus aegyptius*). (From Yang et al., *European Journal of Biochemistry* 61:119, 1976.)

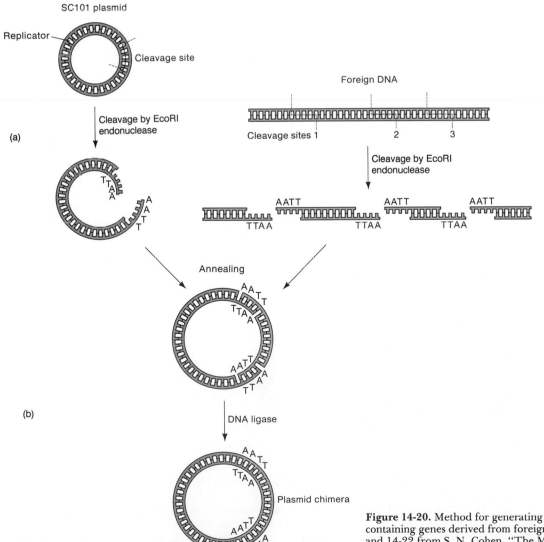

Figure 14-20. Method for generating a chimeric DNA plasmid containing genes derived from foreign DNA. (Figures 14-20, 14-21, and 14-22 from S. N. Cohen, "The Manipulation of Genes." Copyright © 1975 by Scientific American, Inc. All rights reserved.)

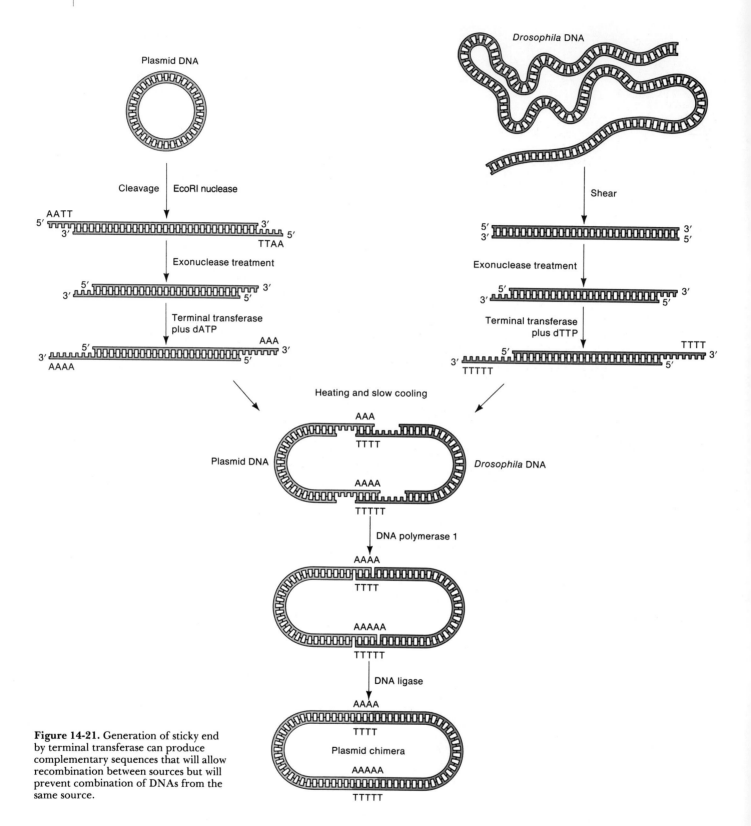

Figure 14-21. Generation of sticky end by terminal transferase can produce complementary sequences that will allow recombination between sources but will prevent combination of DNAs from the same source.

by transformation, since bacteria like *E. coli* can be made permeable to DNA by treatment with calcium chloride (Figure 14-22). Plasmids can almost be considered as mini-chromosomes that replicate autonomously in the cell. They offer several advantages as vectors, the most important of which is the ability to confer antibiotic resistance to the host cell. This allows direct selection for cells that receive and

maintain recombinant DNA plasmids. Different antibiotic-resistance genes can be introduced into plasmids to facilitate these selections. For instance, the commonly used plasmid PBR322 carries the genes conferring resistance to ampicillin and tetracycline. Other commonly used antibiotic-resistance genes are those for chloramphenicol and kanamycin. Plasmids also allow the amplification of cloned

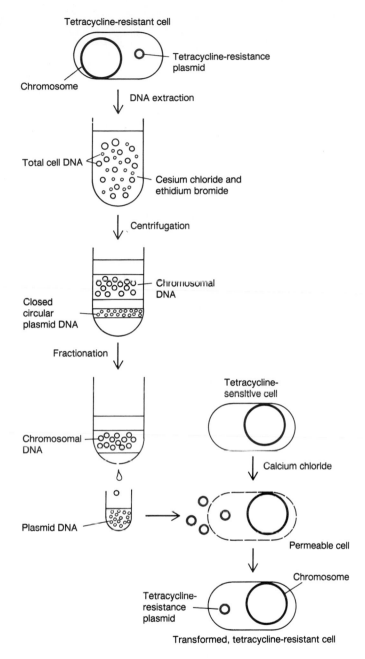

Figure 14-22. Plasmid DNA can be introduced into a bacterial cell by the procedure called transformation. Plasmids carrying genes for resistance to the antibiotic tetracycline (top left) are separated from bacterial chromosomal DNA. Because differential binding of ethidium bromide by the two DNA species makes the circular plasmid DNA denser than the chromosomal DNA, the plasmids form a distinct band on centrifugation in a cesium chloride gradient and can be separated (bottom left).

DNA, since some plasmids are present in 20 to 50 copies during cell growth, and after the arrest of protein synthesis as many as 1000 copies per cell of the plasmid can be generated.

Phage λ.   Derivatives of phage λ (lambda) are convenient for cloning larger fragments of DNA in the 15 to 20 kb (kilobases; one kilobase is a thousand bases) range, since continuously replicating plasmids that contain large inserts

of foreign DNA tend to lose the insert, selection favoring smaller plasmids. Phage-λ heads will package a DNA molecule about 45 kb in length; this property can be used to select for inserts of DNA that replace a central portion of the phage genome that is required for prophage integration and lysogenization but is not required for replication of λ in *E. coli* (Figure 14-23).

Single-Stranded Phage.   Single-stranded phages can be used as cloning vectors, since upon infection of *E. coli* the single infecting strand is converted to a double-stranded replicative form, which can be isolated and used for cloning. The advantages of such phage as cloning vehicles is that upon reinfection of suitable hosts the phage particles that are generated are single stranded and can serve as ready substrates for the rapid dideoxy DNA sequencing technique developed by Sanger (see the following section). M13 is the phage most widely used for this purpose.

Expression Vectors.   Specialized vectors have been constructed for specific purposes. One set of expression vectors affords the opportunity to express the cloned sequences by fusing them to the appropriate transcription and translation start signals. This allows the foreign DNA to be expressed in the respective host. (We shall consider aspects of some of these vectors later.) For instance, some vectors have restriction sites located just next to the control region for the *lac* operon, which has been spliced into the vector. This allows expression of the cloned gene by using

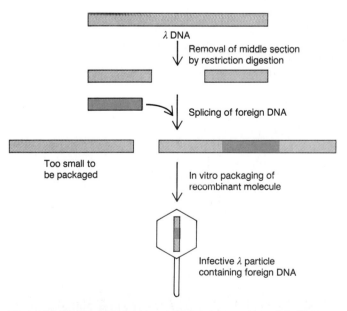

Figure 14-23. Use of λ phage as a cloning vector. Altered λ phage containing conveniently situated restriction sites are used to allow selection for a 45-kb-long packaged molecule containing an insert. (After L. Stryer, *Biochemistry.* Copyright © 1981 by W. H. Freeman and Co.)

the *lac* transcription and translation start signal and, in some cases, even allows the expression to be controlled by the *lac* repressor. (See Chapter 18 for a description of gene control by the *lac* repressor.) Similarly, certain plasmids that allow expression in yeast are being used. Some vectors are bifunctional, allowing expression in two different hosts. For example, a certain plasmid contains the origin of replication of the plasmid PBR322 and of the animal virus SV40. These origins allow replication in *E. coli* and some cultured mammalian cell lines, respectively. These plasmids are called **shuttle vectors,** because they can transfer genes back and forth from one type of cell to another.

Cloning Strategies

Cloning genes involves attaching the desired DNA fragment to the appropriate vector molecule and then propagating the recombinant DNA molecule in a suitable host. We have already examined methods for generating recombinant DNA molecules, as well as different vector systems. However, these techniques must still be used in conjunction with strategies for isolating and recognizing the gene or genetic region to be cloned. As molecular geneticists attempt to analyze very complex eukaryotic genomes, sophisticated methods and strategies become very important.

There are two basic approaches to cloning a specific gene. The first approach involves cloning all the fragments from a restriction digest nonselectively, and then screening for the desired gene. The nonselective method for cloning random DNA fragments from a higher organism into bacteria is called **shotgunning.** The entire collection represents a **gene bank,** or **gene library,** which can now be screened for specific genes (Figure 14-24). All of the plasmids or phage comprising a gene library together represent the entire genome of an organism, with each different plasmid or phage carrying a different small fragment from the genome.

How can we determine whether our gene bank is large enough to contain any unique sequence of interest with a high degree of certainty? Louise Clark and John Carbon, who first constructed a gene bank representing the entire *E. coli* genome, have applied the following formula to help tabulate the relevant probabilities.

$$P = 1 - (1-f)^N \quad \text{or} \quad N = \frac{\ln(1-P)}{\ln(1-f)}$$

where *P* equals the probability that a given unique DNA sequence is present in a collection of *N* transformant colonies and *f* is the fraction of the total genome used as a source for each fragment. Clearly *f* will depend on the size of the fragments and the complexity of the genome. Table 14-2 depicts the results from several genomes at several levels of probability.

The above formula applies to cases where the length *x*

of the DNA sequence being sought is small in relation to the length *L* of the cloned DNA fragments. Otherwise, a corrected value of *f* or *f'* could be used where $f' = [1 - (x/L)](f)$.

The second approach to cloning involves first using a purified probe for the gene in question to select the appropriate restriction fragment from the entire collection of fragments, and then cloning that specific fragment.

Detection of Cloned Genes

Southern Blotting. One of the most valuable techniques for identifying cloned genes is **Southern blotting,** which is depicted in Figure 14-25. This technique exploits the properties of gel electrophoresis and nitrocellulose filters. Single-stranded but not double-stranded DNA can stick to nitrocellulose. During electrophoresis on agarose gels, DNA fragments from restriction digests will migrate according to their size. They can be transferred to nitrocellulose by a buffer flow, after denaturation, and immobilized on the filters in a pattern that mirrors their positions in the agarose gel. ^{32}P-labeled DNA or RNA probes are then used for hybridization with the affixed DNA on the filters. The probes are denatured to allow annealing with the single-stranded restriction fragments that are anchored on the gel. Unlabeled single-stranded DNA from an unrelated source is used to first saturate the remaining sites on the nitrocellulose to prevent nonspecific binding of the single-stranded probe, which can now bind to the filter only by annealing to complementary DNA fragments. The position of bands that anneal to the probes is revealed by autoradiography.

cDNA. Among the most efficient probes for screening for cloned genes are **cDNA clones.** Although, in principle, mRNA for the gene in question can be used as a probe, it is

Figure 14-24. (a) A genomic library can be established by cloning genes in bacteriophage λ. When a "lawn" of bacteria in a culture dish is infected by a large number of different hybrid phages, each phage in the lawn is inhabited by a single clone of phages descended from the original infecting phage. Each clone carries a different fragment of cellular DNA. The problem now is to identify the clone carrying a particular gene of interest by probing the clones with DNA or RNA known to be related to the desired gene. The plaque pattern is transferred to a nitrocellulose filter and the phage protein is dissolved, leaving the recombinant DNA. (b) The filter is incubated with a radioactively labeled probe: a DNA copy of the messenger RNA representing the desired gene. The probe hybridizes with any recombinant DNA incorporating a matching DNA sequence, and the position of the clone having the DNA is revealed by autoradiography. Now the desired clone can be selected from the culture medium and transferred to a fresh bacterial host, so that a pure gene can be manufactured. (After R. A. Weinberg, "A Molecular Basis of Cancer," and P. Leder, "The Genetics of Antibody Diversity." Copyright © 1982, 1983 by Scientific American, Inc. All rights reserved.)

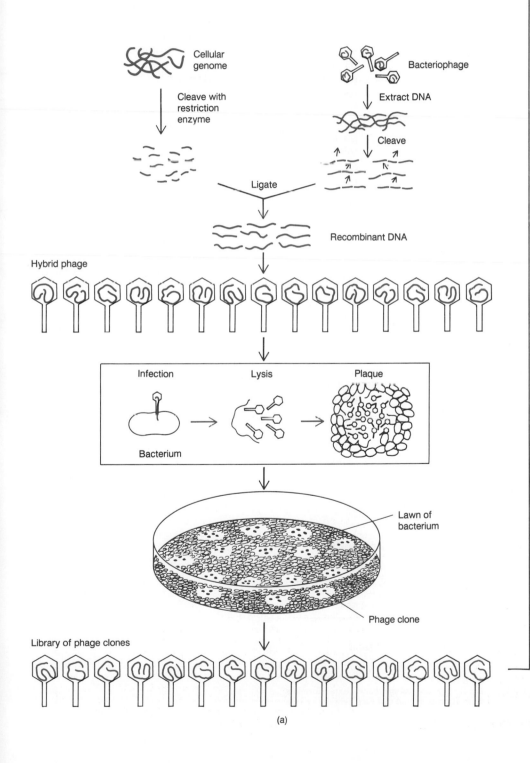

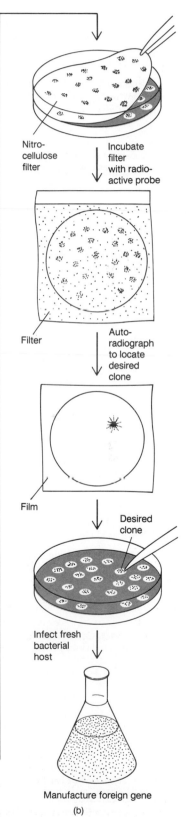

Cellular genome

Cleave with restriction enzyme

Bacteriophage

Extract DNA

Cleave

Ligate

Recombinant DNA

Hybrid phage

Infection   Lysis   Plaque

Bacterium

Lawn of bacterium

Phage clone

Library of phage clones

(a)

Nitro-cellulose filter

Incubate filter with radio-active probe

Filter

Auto-radiograph to locate desired clone

Film

Desired clone

Infect fresh bacterial host

Manufacture foreign gene

(b)

Mouse

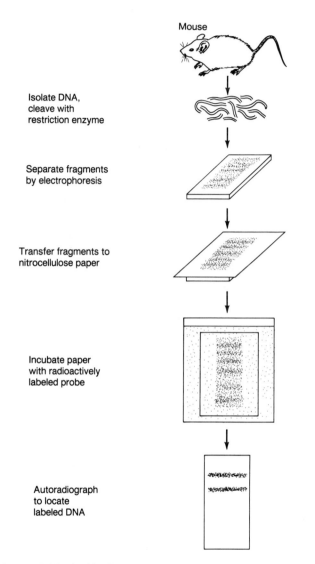

Isolate DNA,
cleave with
restriction enzyme

Separate fragments
by electrophoresis

Transfer fragments to
nitrocellulose paper

Incubate paper
with radioactively
labeled probe

Autoradiograph
to locate
labeled DNA

Figure 14-25. The blotting technique developed by E. M. Southern. (See description in text.) (From P. Leder, "The Genetics of Antibody Diversity." Copyright ©1982 by Scientific American, Inc. All rights reserved.)

difficult to obtain sufficiently pure mRNA. However, the enzyme reverse transcriptase can be used to make a DNA copy of the partially purified mRNAs, as described earlier (page 300), which in turn can program the synthesis of a complementary strand (see Figure 14-26). The resulting DNA duplex is termed complementary DNA (cDNA). It is relatively easy to purify individual cDNA fragments. The total population of cDNA fragments can be joined to plasmids so that each plasmid receives only one fragment, and bacterial cells can be transformed so that each cell receives only one plasmid. Clones derived from single cells can be tested for which unique cDNA is present. Amplified DNA is purified and denatured and then used to trap the corresponding mRNAs on a nitrocellulose filter. The mRNA purified in this manner is used to program a cell-free protein synthesis system, to allow identification of the protein encoded in the complementary mRNA, and thus the gene present in the cloned mRNA. The purified cDNA can itself be used as a probe to screen colonies directly from a gene library, since replica plating techniques have been developed which employ nitrocellulose filters to detect hybridization of DNA from colonies with specific probes. Then all of the cloned fragments containing parts of the gene sequence used in the probe can be detected. When partial digests are used to generate the restriction fragments used to establish the gene library, there will be fragments of different sizes containing the gene in question, and the larger region surrounding the sequences contained in the probe can therefore be analyzed.

The isolation of cDNA is therefore a crucial step in screening genomic libraries. Some RNAs are easily purified because of their particular size (i.e., rRNA, tRNA, 5S RNA), thus facilitating the cloning of genes encoding these RNAs. Other RNAs are obtainable by virtue of their abundant expression at a specific time or in a particular tissue — for example, the mRNA that encodes the silk protein, fibroin, in the glands of the silkworm. Also, in some cases the gene product is relatively conserved in evolution, so that

■ **TABLE 14-2.** Colony "bank" sizes N needed to contain a particular hybrid plasmid transformant at various probability levels

DNA source	Average size of DNA fragment cloned (dal)	"Bank" size N, number of colonies		
		$P = 0.90$	$P = 0.95$	$P = 0.99$
E. coli	8.5×10^6	720	940	1440
Yeast	1×10^7	2300	3000	4600
Drosophila	1×10^7	23,000	30,000	46,000

The above calculations are based on the formula $P = 1 - (1 - f)^N$ and assume that each transformant colony in the "bank" arises from an independent transformation event and that each hybrid molecule transforms with the same efficiency.
From L. Clarke and J. Carbon, *Cell*, 9:91–99, 1976.

isolation of a gene from one organism makes possible its isolation from another, as exemplified by globins, histones, and actin. Sometimes the respective mRNA is rare and difficult to enrich. One technique exploits the possibilities of synthetic oligonucleotides. In cases where part or all of the amino acid sequence of the protein encoded by the gene in question has been determined, a series of 15- to 20-base-pair-long oligonucleotides is synthesized, corresponding to each of the possible DNA coding sequences predicted by a stretch of the protein sequence. These are then used as probes in the manner described previously.

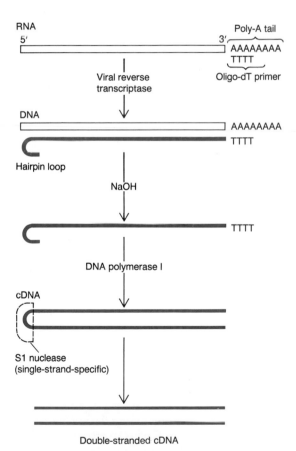

Figure 14-26. The synthesis of double-stranded cDNA from mRNA. A short oligo-dT chain is hybridized to the poly-A tail of an mRNA strand. The oligo-T segment serves as a primer for the action of reverse transcriptase, which uses the mRNA as a template for the synthesis of a complementary DNA strand. The resulting cDNA ends in a hairpin loop. Once the mRNA strand is degraded by treatment with NaOH, the hairpin loop becomes a primer for DNA polymerase I, which completes the paired DNA strand. The loop is then cleaved by S1 nuclease to produce a double-stranded cDNA molecule. (Figures 14-26 and 14-27 from J. D. Watson, J. Tooze, and D. T. Kurtz, *Recombinant DNA: A Short Course.* Copyright © 1983 by W. H. Freeman and Co.)

It should be stressed that cDNA clones are copies of mature mRNA, whereas genomic clones represent the actual structure of a gene. By analysis of cDNA clones and genomic clones it is possible to elucidate what portion of a (eukaryotic) gene is transcribed, what parts of the gene are represented in the transcript after processing, and whether any structural rearrangement is associated with the expression of particular genes. One important point to note here is that eukaryotic genes often contain intervening sequences (introns) that do not end up in the mature mRNA. Hence cDNA and genomic DNA can be quite different in size. Chapter 19 describes eukaryotic gene structure and expression in more detail.

Gene Expression. Screening can also be achieved by testing directly for production of a protein encoded by the cloned gene. The set of expression vectors described in the preceding section is designed for this purpose. Proteins with immunological activity can be rapidly detected in bacterial colonies with replica-plating techniques.

Chromosome Walking

How can we analyze very large segments of DNA from a eukaryotic genome when the segments are much larger than the maximum size of fragments that can be cloned in any individual vector? Figure 14-27 outlines a procedure termed "chromosome walking," which makes possible the dissection of large regions of DNA. In this method a cloned portion of eukaryotic DNA is used to screen recombinant DNA clones from the same eukaryotic genome library for other clones containing neighboring sequences. It is important to note that many gene libraries are generated by partial digestion with a restriction enzyme, so that relatively large fragments can be represented. Many of these fragments will contain internal, uncleaved restriction sites. Also, some regions of the genome will be present on different-size fragments.

In the example shown in Figure 14-27, eukaryotic DNA is cut with the restriction enzyme EcoRI and cloned into a λ vector. Recombinant phage containing the "A" gene are identified with an "A" gene probe. The cloned DNA is recut into smaller fragments with a different restriction enzyme and these pieces are themselves "subcloned" into a plasmid vector. When the subcloned fragment is different from the initial probe ("A" in this case), it can be used to detect other fragments in the original library that contain part of the region carried in the first λ clone. Thus, in Figure 14-27, the subcloned "α" probe is used to identify an overlapping λ recombinant. Subsequent subcloning of different small fragments allows the generation of a series of overlapping clones as shown in the bottom of Figure 14-27. In this manner we literally "walk" around the chromosome. One drawback to this method is the re-

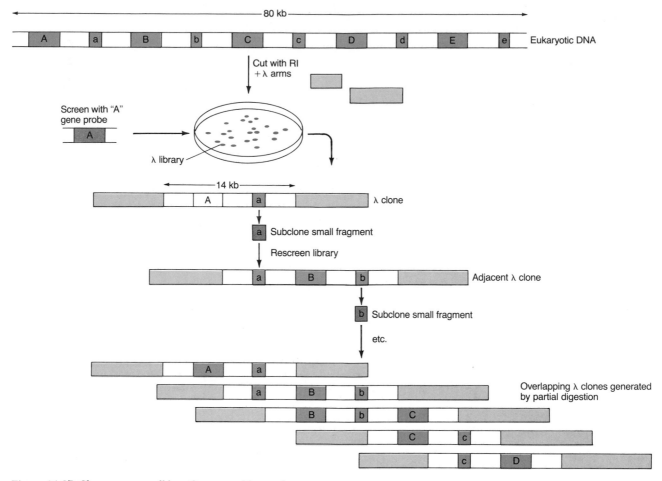

Figure 14-27. Chromosome walking. One recombinant phage obtained from a library made by the partial EcoRI digest of a eukaryotic genome can be used to isolate another recombinant containing a neighboring segment of eukaryotic DNA, as described in the text.

quirement that each DNA segment used is not repeated elsewhere in the genome. Therefore, chromosome walking has been used most successfully in *Drosophila,* where repeated sequences are less prevalent than in the DNAs of other higher cells.

Message Recombinant DNA molecules can be made by joining nonhomologous DNAs from virtually any sources. This technique offers the possibility of bypassing all biological restraints to genetic exchange and mixing — even permitting combination of genes from widely differing species.

DNA Sequence Determination

The technology for DNA manipulation that we have considered is extensive; combined with a technique for identifying the bases in isolated fragments, it opens the way for genetic engineering. A mere decade ago, the ability to de-

termine base sequences easily seemed a long way in the future. Today, however, "DNA sequencing" is performed as routinely as genetic crosses.

We do know what sequence is recognized by each restriction enzyme, so an extensive restriction-enzyme map such as that in Figure 14-19 represents the distribution of known short sequences along the DNA. Ideally, we would like to take each DNA fragment, tag the end with a radioactive label, and then clip it off with an enzyme for identification. However, repeating this process over and over to identify several hundred nucleotides in a typical eukaryotic DNA fragment is far too laborious and time-consuming. So long as only this approach was available, the sequencing of a small piece of DNA was a major task, and genetic manipulation as a routine procedure was impossible.

The art of DNA sequencing advanced explosively after 1975, when new techniques were developed that made the task astonishingly simple. The crucial technique involves placing single-stranded DNA on a special gel material (acrylamide or agarose) and subjecting it to an electric cur-

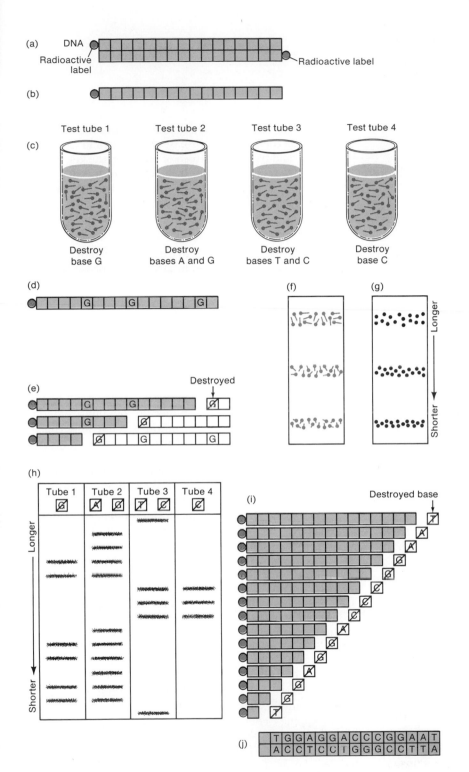

Figure 14-28. Procedure for sequencing DNA, devised by Maxam and Gilbert. (a) The 3′ end of each strand is labeled with ^{32}P. (b) The strands are separated, and one specific strand is retained. (c) The strands are separated into four equivalent fractions and placed in four test tubes. Each tube is treated with a different reagent that selectively destroys one or two of the four bases. The concentration is adjusted so that only a small proportion of the target bases is attacked, thereby generating a population of fragments of different lengths. (d) A hypothetical example: a strand containing three G bases. (e) After treatment in test tube 1, this strand yields a population of labeled fragments of three different lengths. (f) The fragments are separated on a gel. (g) The bands of labeled fragments are identified by autoradiography. (h) Comparison of the bands produced by labeled fragments from the four different treatments provides a display of successively shorter fragments when read from top to bottom on the gels. (i) The appearance of the band on one or two particular gels indicates which base was destroyed to yield the fragment. (j) The sequence of base pairs in the original DNA can then be inferred. (From W. Gilbert and L. Villa-Komaroff, "Useful Proteins from Recombinant Bacteria." Copyright © 1980 by Scientific American, Inc. All rights reserved.)

rent to separate strands on the basis of their lengths. (The use of this technique has already been mentioned in the discussion of restriction-enzyme mapping.) The mobility of a strand is inversely proportional to the logarithm of its length. This technique is so sensitive that fragments differing in length by only a single nucleotide can be separated.

One of the requirements for DNA sequencing is the ability to obtain particular fragments of DNA. There is a strong interdependence of DNA cloning and DNA se-

quencing technology, since DNA cloning provides large amounts of specific DNA fragments.

A widely used method is that advanced by Maxam and Gilbert. They label the 3′ ends of DNA with ^{32}P and then separate one strand from the other to yield a population of identical strands labeled on one end. They then divide the mixture into four samples, each of which is subjected to a different chemical reagent that destroys one or two specific bases (Figure 14-28). The four reagents destroy (1) only G,

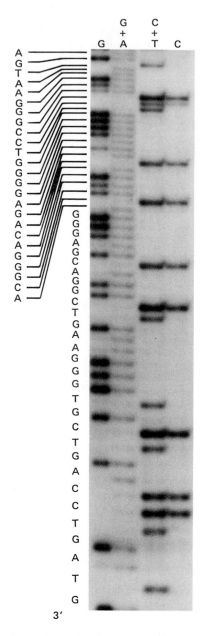

Figure 14-29. Autoradiograph of a Maxam-Gilbert sequencing gel, showing a portion of a sequence of nucleotides located between the two α-globin genes of human DNA. The DNA fragment was labeled at the 3' end and subjected to degradation by methods that cleave at G, C, G and A, C and T (cleavage reactions need not be specific to a *single* base to provide the necessary information). The sequence that can be read from the gel is indicated at the left. (Courtesy of John Hess and C.-K. James Shen, University of California, Davis. From F. J. Ayala and J. A. Kiger, Jr., *Modern Genetics*, 2d ed. Benjamin/Cummings Publishing Company, 1984.)

(2) only C, (3) A and G, or (4) T and C. The loss of a base makes the sugar-phosphate backbone more likely to break at that point. The reagent concentration is adjusted so that only about one in 50 of the target bases is destroyed. The procedure is similar to that outlined for restriction-enzyme mapping in Figure 14-18. It results in a mixture of different-sized pieces carrying the ^{32}P label. When these are separated in the different lanes of a gel, they can be arranged in order of length, and the base destroyed at each site can be

determined by noting in which lane or lanes the band appears. Thus the sequence of bases in the strand can quite simply be read from the pattern of bands on the gel. Figure 14-29 shows an actual gel used to determine a portion of a sequence of nucleotides located between the two α-globin genes of human DNA.

Message It is now possible to carry out rapid determination of nucleotide sequences in DNA. This procedure has become so routine that many hundreds of sequences are known, and the number of known sequences increases daily.

Fred Sanger developed a different sequencing method, with which he and his associates set out to determine the complete nucleotide sequence of φX174 DNA, which codes for nine proteins in this virus. They completed this *tour de force* in 1977. The molecule contains just under 5400 nucleotides! This investigation was not undertaken solely to achieve the sequencing of a remarkably long DNA molecule; it also sought to resolve an interesting paradox. From the molecular weight of the nine proteins encoded in the φX174 DNA, the number of nucleotides required for the coding can be estimated. That estimate is significantly higher than the number of nucleotides indicated by physical properties of the DNA. It was hoped that knowledge of the complete sequence would lead to an explanation of this puzzle.

Different teams within Sanger's laboratory group worked on the sequencing of different fragments of the φX174 chromosome. The paradox of the "missing nucleotides" was quickly resolved in a surprising way. Within the coding sequence for one protein, a second protein code proved to exist with a different reading frame! Another pair of such "overlapping" genes was discovered by another team. It should be pointed out that the use of two different reading frames to encode two different proteins (each encoded in one reading frame) does *not* constitute an "overlapping" code (see Chapter 12). The *genetic* map of φX174 has thus been completed by the evidence from the molecular study (Figure 14-30). Figure 14-31 shows the consequences of the overlapping genes *D* and *E*.

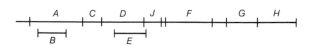

Figure 14-30. The genetic map of the virus φX174, including overlapping genes.

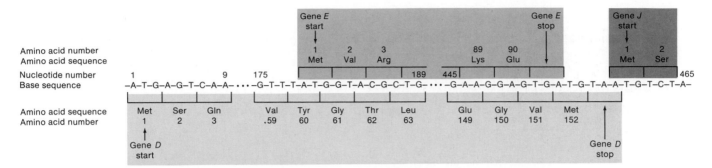

Figure 14-31. The beginnings and ends of genes D and E (and of their corresponding proteins) in the DNA of ϕX174. The nucleotide sequence is numbered from the start triplet of gene D. The E gene begins at nucleotide 179, with its triplet sequence offset from the reading frame of gene D. Gene E is completely contained within gene D and codes for a protein about 60 percent as large as the protein of gene D. The final base in the stop triplet for gene D is used as the first base of the start triplet for gene J.

Message A single stretch of nucleotides can be read in more than one way by initiating reading of the sequence in two different reading frames that are offset from each other.

The concept of overlapping genes with offset reading frames had earlier been discarded because it raises problems about the simultaneous evolution of the two proteins. However, once undeniable evidence of such overlapping genes was available for ϕX174, old observations were reassessed and new studies undertaken, and there is now evidence indicating the existence of overlapping genes in other organisms, including *E. coli*. Note that a single point mutation within the region of overlap will produce amino acid substitutions in two different proteins; this creates an interesting problem for researchers studying the evolutionary effects of various mutations. (What happens if a certain mutation is favorable for one protein but unfavorable for the other?)

Sanger's original method for sequencing DNA utilizes DNA polymerase to increase DNA chain length. It has been termed the "plus-minus" method. Subsequently, however, Sanger developed a much more powerful method utilizing single-stranded DNA and **dideoxy** nucleotides (see Figure 14-32). The respective triphosphates can be incorporated into a growing chain, but they terminate synthesis, since they do not permit bond formation with the next nucleotide triphosphate. With four reaction tubes, each containing a small amount of one of the four dideoxy nucleotide triphosphates, the sequence of a DNA molecule can be determined by examining the size of terminated

fragments obtained from each reaction on acrylamide gels. With this technique, the entire 48,513 base-pair sequence of bacteriophage λ was determined by Sanger's group.

Because of the ease with which DNA can be sequenced, it now is often convenient to infer the amino acid sequence of a protein by determining the sequence of codons in the gene that encodes it, although this is not always this simple, as we shall see when we consider the structure of eukaryotic genes in Chapter 19.

Gene Synthesis

We now have methods to determine the sequence of nucleotides in a DNA. Is it possible to synthesize a DNA of some desired sequence from scratch? (We might determine

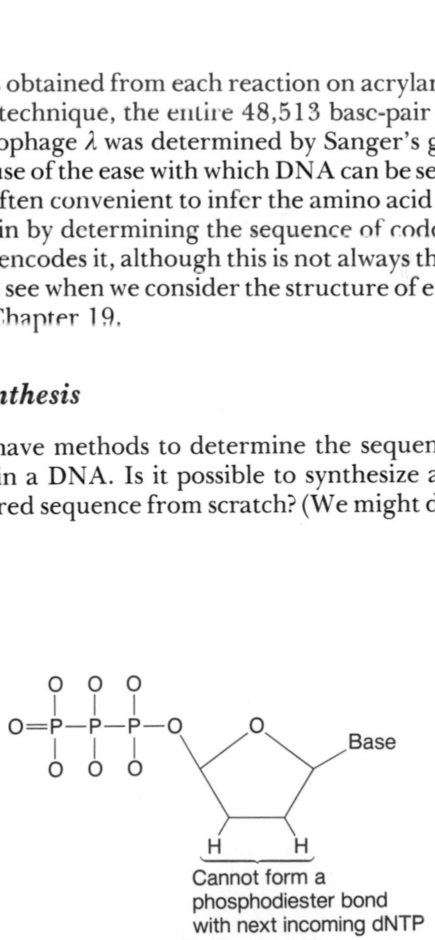

Cannot form a
phosphodiester bond
with next incoming dNTP

Figure 14-32. The structure of 2′,3′-dideoxy nucleotides, which are employed in the Sanger DNA sequencing method.

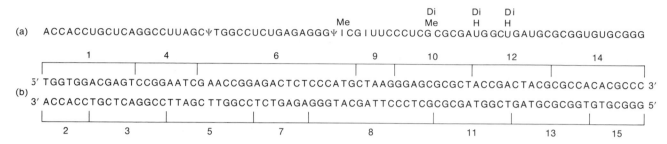

(a) ACCACCUGCUCAGGCCUUAGCΨTGGCCUCUGAGAGGGΨICGIUUCCCUCGCGCGAUGGCUGAUGCGCGGUGUGCGGG

(b)
5′ TGGTGGACGAGTCCGGAATCG AACCGGAGACTCTCCCATGCTAAGGGAGCGCGCTACCGACTACGCGCCACACGCCC 3′

3′ ACCACCTGCTCAGGCCTTAGC TTGGCCTCTGAGAGGGTACGATTCCCTCGCGCGATGGCTGATGCGCGGTGTGCGGG 5′

Figure 14-33. (a) The base sequence of the major alanine tRNA from yeast. (b) The base sequence of the DNA coding for the alanine tRNA. The segments used by Khorana in synthesizing this DNA molecule are indicated by the numbers. The segments were then annealed and connected with a ligase.

a desired DNA sequence by finding the amino acid sequence of a desired protein or by determining the nucleotide sequence of an RNA that codes for a desired protein.) Suppose we wish to construct a DNA that has the sequence

$$T-A-G-C-C-T-C-C-A-G-T-A-A-T$$
$$A-T-C-G-G-A-G-G-T-C-A-T-T-A$$

We might set out to construct the bottom strand, with the intention of later synthesizing the complementary strand through normal replication reactions. We add the nucleotides of A and T to an appropriate reaction mix to obtain the A – T dinucleotide, but we must stop the reaction very quickly before A – T – T or A – T – A is formed. Therefore, the yield of the A – T polymer is only a fraction of the amount of A and T supplied. We then add the A – T and C to an appropriate reaction mix, and again must stop the reaction quickly to avoid forming polymers longer than the desired A – T – C. Thus the yield of A – T – C represents only a percentage of the A – T. At each step, we have a low yield, and this obviously imposes harsh limits on the length of strands that can be constructed in vitro. Such stepwise synthesis of long-chain polynucleotides is impossible.

In the mid-1960s, Gobind Khorana attempted to synthesize the DNA coding for an alanine tRNA molecule whose sequence had been determined by Robert Holley. Figure 14-33a shows the sequence of bases in the tRNA, which must be dictated by the DNA sequence shown in Figure 14-33b. Khorana developed a method that bypassed the need to synthesize the entire sequence by the stepwise approach just discussed. He synthesized short polynucleotides of each strand by adding one base at a time. The short fragments were selected to have overlapping complementary sequences. For example, he first synthesized the fragment G – G – T – G – G – A – C – G – A – G – T, and then the fragments C – C – A – C – C and T – G – C – T – C – A – G – G – C – C. When the first two fragments are mixed, the

complementary sequences anneal to form a double helix with a single-stranded end:

$$G-G-T-G-G-A-C-G-A-G-T$$
$$C-C-A-C-C$$

When the third fragment is added, it anneals to the sticky end and produces a new sticky end:

$$G-G-T-G-G-A-C-G-A-G-T$$
$$C-C-A-C-C \quad T-G-C-T-C-A-G-G-C-C$$

A fourth fragment can then be synthesized to overlap this sticky end and extend beyond. The entire sequence can be "stitched together" in this fashion, obtaining a double helix composed of short fragments. The ends of the fragments then can be linked by the enzyme ligase (Figure 14-34).

As Khorana developed this methodology, it became clear that the gene specifying the tRNA extends beyond the limits indicated by the length of the mature tRNA molecule. He did eventually construct the entire tRNA gene (Figure 14-35). Appended to each end of his artificial gene was a cohesive terminus of – T – T – A – A complementary to EcoRI-induced ends so that he could insert the complete gene into λ DNA (Figure 14-36). When the gene was inserted into *E. coli* by the λ vector, the bacterial cell did

Figure 14-34. Treatment with the enzyme ligase leads to formation of an uninterrupted DNA molecule. In effect, the ligase works its way along the molecule and bonds together any consecutive nucleotides that are not joined in one strand or the other.

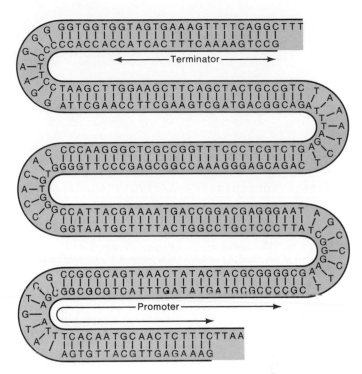

synthesize the tRNA. This verified that the start and termination signals inferred to exist did, in fact, work.

Message By construction of short nucleotide sequences which overlap with complementary sequences, large DNA duplexes can be generated.

Applications of Recombinant DNA Technology

Synthesis of Eukaryotic Proteins and Hormones

The Khorana method no longer is needed because there are easier methods to recover specific pieces of DNA. However, it remains an elegant and sophisticated technique, and it was applied by Herbert Boyer's group to make the gene coding for a small human growth-regulating hormone, somatostatin. The hormone is a short polypeptide with the sequence shown in Figure 14-37. Boyer's group synthesized the gene using overlapping fragments, and they added a triplet specifying methionine and an *EcoRI* cleavage site on the amino end. On the other end, they placed two consecutive stop triplets and a *BamHI* site (Figure 14-38). The entire gene was inserted into a plasmid carrying the bacterial gene β-galactosidase, within which there is an *EcoRI* site. The other end of the somatostatin gene hybridized with a *BamHI* site elsewhere in the plasmid. The *E. coli* selected by their possession of the plasmid were found to produce a protein chimera containing part of β-galactosidase fused to somatostatin via a methionine residue. Methionine is cleaved by cyanogen bromide, so the active hormone could be liberated by such treatment (Figure 14-39).

Techniques such as this already have been used to produce recombinant plasmids bearing DNA sequences for

Figure 14-36. The complete sequence of the alanine tRNA gene constructed by Khorana's group. Note the sticky ends that were added to permit insertion in the λ DNA after that DNA was cleaved by EcoRI. (From Graham Chedd, "The Making of a Gene." This first appeared in *New Society*, London, the weekly review of the social sciences, 30 September 1976. Reprinted with permission of New Science Publications.)

human insulin, growth hormone, interferon, and blood-clotting factors. Commercially profitable quantities of such human proteins can be obtained from bacterial cultures.

Message Recombinant DNA technology is sufficiently advanced to allow economically profitable production of human proteins through direct engineering of the genetic content of microorganisms.

Genetic Engineering in Plants

How can we introduce useful genes into plants? One obvious problem is recognizing the gene or genes that control important properties, such as nitrogen fixation. A second problem is characterizing vector systems that permit

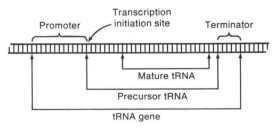

Figure 14-35. The DNA regions included in a complete tRNA gene. The promoter site is the region where the RNA polymerase attaches to begin transcription. Transcription begins at the initiation site and ends at a termination sequence. The precursor tRNA that is transcribed is larger than the active tRNA, which is produced by removing segments from the beginning and end of the precursor molecule.

H₂N—Ala—Gly—Cys—Lys—Asn—Phe—Phe
               | Trp
               S   Lys
               |
               S
               |
OH—Cys—Ser—Thr—Phe—Thr

Figure 14-37. The amino acid sequence of the hormone somatostatin.

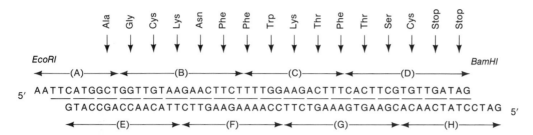

Figure 14-38. The overlapping complementary sequences synthesized to produce the somatostatin gene. A triplet specifying methionine was added to the 5' end of the somatostatin coding region (inferred from the amino acid sequence), and, adjacent to this, an *EcoRI* restriction sequence was added. A *BamHI* restriction sequence was added at the other end of the "artificial" gene. (Figures 14-38 and 14-39 from K. Itakura et al., "Expression in *Escherichia coli* of a Chemically Synthesized Gene for the Hormone Somatostatin." *Science* 198:1056–1063, 1977. Copyright © 1977 by the American Association for the Advancement of Science.)

transfer of genes into plant cells. In this regard, a set of plasmids detected in the bacterium *Agrobacterium tumefaciens* has generated a lot of excitement. *A. tumefaciens* can infect certain plant varieties and induce **crown galls,** tumor-like growths that have often been compared to mammalian cancerous tumors. The "transformation" of plant cells to crown galls is mediated by a plasmid, termed the **Ti plasmid** (for *tumor-inducing*). Certain genes on the plasmid are integrated into the plant genome, causing transformation. Therefore, the Ti plasmids are natural vectors for introducing genetic material into the plant genome.

Ti Plasmids. The Ti plasmids are circular DNA molecules that contain about 200,000 base pairs. However, only a 20,000-base-pair portion of the plasmid, termed the **T DNA** segment, is required for tumor induction (see Figure 14-40). Southern blot hybridization (Figure 14-25) has revealed T DNA segments integrated into the chromosomes of transformed plant cells, where they are stably inherited during successive generations. The integrated T DNA maintains the transformed state. Because only the T DNA segment is transferred from the Ti plasmid to the infected host genome, it is possible that the T DNA is a transposable genetic element (see Chapter 17), but it is still not clear how this region is transferred to the plant chromosome.

Ti plasmids are useful as vectors, because DNA incorporated by genetic engineering into the T DNA segment will be cotransferred with the rest of the T DNA segment into the host plant chromosome. Because *Agrobacteria* have a broad host range, this type of cotransfer opens up many possibilities for genetic engineering in plants. Ti plasmids carrying specific genes can be used to transform plant cells after being introduced by *Agrobacterium* into treated wounds of whole plants or else into protoplasts in culture.

Plant protoplasts produced by digesting the plant cell wall can be cultured and then used to regenerate whole plants in some cases. Selective media have been developed that allow preferential growth of transformed cells. Therefore, cultured cells transformed with certain Ti-plasmid derivatives can regenerate whole plants carrying the T DNA segment. When foreign genes are transcribed by the resident T DNA promoters, these genes are expressed in the resulting transformed plant. These advances have now opened up possibilities for future genetic engineering in plants.

Although Ti plasmids offer one way of introducing genes into plants, only dicotyledons can be transformed by *Agrobacterium.* Therefore, different vector systems are being sought for introducing cloned genes into monocotyledons such as wheat and corn.

Mutagenesis in vitro

This is an exciting time in genetics, since for the first time in history we can program the alteration of the genetic material. The late 1970s and early 1980s saw the development of techniques that permit the introduction of point mutations, deletions and insertions into segments of cloned DNA, and that also allow alteration of specific base pairs. By directing specific mutations into predetermined segments of DNA, we make possible many experiments.

Base substitutions can be introduced into cloned DNA after the generation of short, single-stranded regions, as summarized in Figure 14-41. Single-stranded regions are produced either by using limited exonuclease III digestion following restriction enzyme cleavage, or else by exploiting the exonuclease activity of the *E. coli* DNA polymerase I enzyme. The single-stranded regions allow bisulfite ions to deaminate cytosine to uracil, which leads to C-to-T transi-

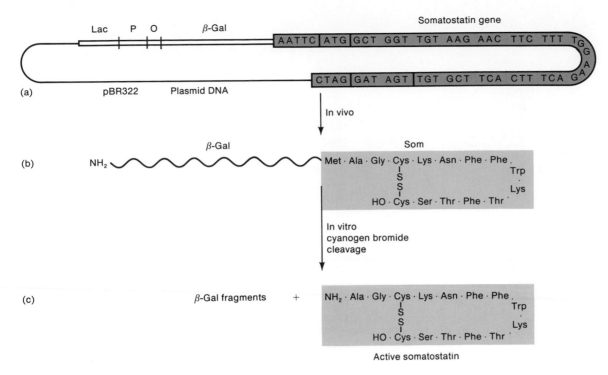

Figure 14-39. Production of somatostatin by *E. coli*. (a) The plasmid carrying the synthetic DNA sequence is added to the bacterial cell. (b) A chimeric polypeptide is produced. (c) The desired somatostatin is liberated by treatment with cyanogen bromide.

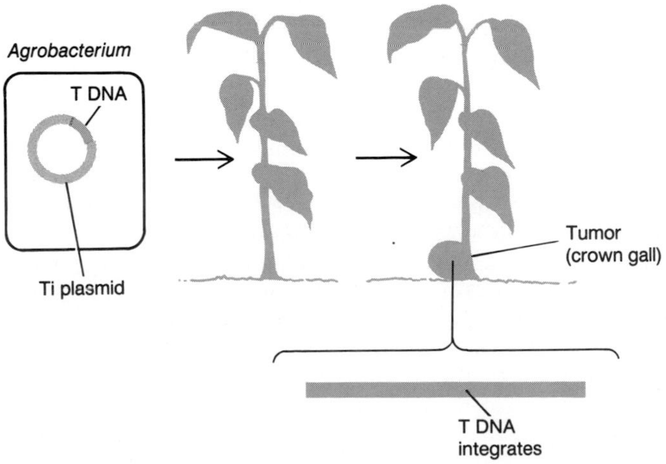

tions, as described in Chapter 15. After treatment with bisulfite, the plasmid is recircularized by polymerase I and ligase.

Alternatively, the incorporation of base analogs can be employed. This is done when short single-stranded gaps are created within a duplex (without cleaving both strands). The gap is then repaired using a modified form of DNA polymerase I (see Chapter 10), together with three nucleotide triphosphates and *N*-4-hydroxycytosine in place of T (actually, dTTP). Both tautomeric forms of *N*-4-hydroxycytosine (keto and enol) are prevalent, allowing pairing with either G or A. The analog is incorporated in place of T but can also pair with G. Therefore, this in vitro method results in T-to-C transitions (Figure 14-42).

Less specific changes can be effected at single-stranded gaps, by carrying out the polymerization reaction in the absence of one of the four deoxynucleotide triphosphates, since at a low rate in vitro polymerases will add nucleotides at random across from the base complementary to the missing base.

Site-Directed Mutagenesis

The preceding methods describe specific or random base substitutions generated in vitro in cloned DNA. However, they all involve short regions surrounding a favorable restriction site. How can we create mutations at specific places that do not happen to be so favorably situated? There is a powerful method for creating specific mutations that circumvents this limitation. This technique employs short, **synthetic oligonucleotides,** approximately 15 base pairs in length, which can be constructed reasonably quickly by

Figure 14-40. Certain species of *Agrobacterium* infect plants and cause crown galls, lumps or calli of tumor tissue. The tumor-inducing agent is a plasmid (the Ti plasmid) that integrates some of its DNA (the T, or transforming, DNA) into the host cell chromosome. (Figures 14-40, 14-41, 14-43, and 14-46 from J. D. Watson, J. Tooze, and D. T. Kurtz, *Recombinant DNA: A Short Course.* Copyright © 1983 by W. H. Freeman and Co.)

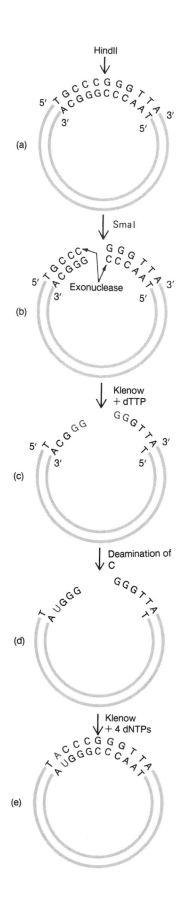

current procedures. As a first step the gene of interest is cloned into a single-stranded phage vector, such as the phage M13. The synthetic oligonucleotide serves as a primer for the in vitro synthesis of the complementary strand of the M13 vector (see Figure 14-43). Any desired specific base change can be programmed into the sequence of the synthetic primer. Although there will be a mispaired base when the synthetic oligonucleotide hybridizes with the complementary sequence on the M13 vector, one or two mismatched bases can be tolerated when hybridization occurs at low temperature and at high salt. After DNA synthesis mediated by DNA polymerase in vitro, the M13 is replicated in *E. coli*, in which case many of the resulting phage will be the desired mutant. It should be noted that the synthetic oligonucleotide can be used as a labeled probe to distinguish wild-type from mutant phage by hybridization. The mismatched base will still allow the primer to hybridize with both types of phage at low temperature, but only with the complementary mutant phage at high temperature. This method has been used to create an amber (UAG) suppressor from a human tRNA by converting the anticodon to a sequence that recognizes the UAG triplet instead of the AAA triplet (lysine codon), as depicted in Figures 14-43 and 14-44.

Genetic Diseases

Recessive mutations that follow Mendelian inheritance are responsible for over 500 genetic diseases. Homozygous individuals resulting from marriages involving two carriers of the same recessive trait will be affected by the disease. Screening cells derived from the fetus offers the possibility of predicting genetic defects at an early enough stage to allow the option of abortion to prevent the birth of afflicted individuals. The enzymes or proteins that are altered or missing in a number of genetic diseases are known (refer to the list of "inborn errors of metabolism" in Table 11-2). To detect such genetic defects, fetal cells are taken from the amniotic fluid, separated from other components, and cultured, allowing analysis of chromosomes, proteins, and enzymic reactions, and other biochemical properties. This process, termed **amniocentesis** (see Figure 14-45), can already pinpoint a series of known disorders. Table 14-3 lists

Figure 14-41. Creation of a substitution mutant through deamination of cytosine. A restriction enzyme site, in this case *SmaI*, is treated with a modified form of DNA polymerase I, termed the Klenow fragment, in the presence of dATP; 3′ → 5′ digestion of single strands then occurs until an A residue is encountered. Deamination of C residues on exposed single strands is effected by the addition of bisulfite. The molecule is now repaired by the addition of all four dNTPs and the Klenow fragment. The result in this case is the alteration of a G–C base pair to an A–U base pair.

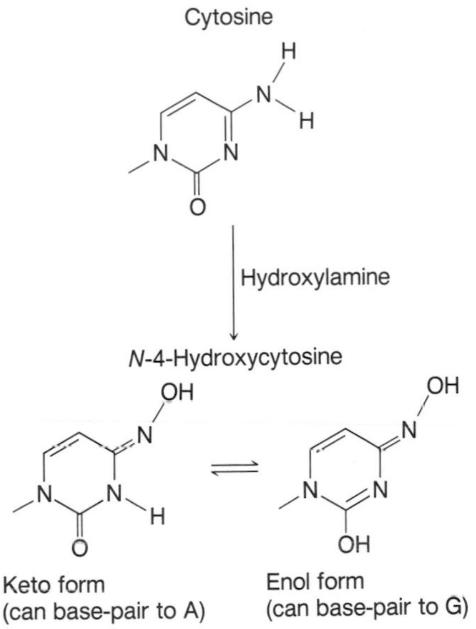

Cytosine

↓ Hydroxylamine

N-4-Hydroxycytosine

Keto form
(can base-pair to A)

Enol form
(can base-pair to G)

Figure 14-42. The formation of *N*-4-hydroxycytosine with hydroxylamine.

examples of genetic diseases that can be detected by amniocentesis. Relying on physiological properties or on the presence or absence of enzymic activity in cultured fetal cells limits the screening procedure to those disorders that affect characters or proteins expressed in the cultured cells. The use of recombinant DNA greatly increases our ability to screen for genetic diseases, however, since we can analyze the DNA directly. In principle, if we could clone out the gene being tested and compare its sequence with that of a cloned normal gene, we could determine whether suspected defects were present. Of course, this would be a very laborious procedure, so shortcuts have to be devised to allow more rapid screening. Three useful techniques that have been used for this purpose involve searching for alteration of restriction sites by the genetic defect itself, linkage of the mutation in question to altered restriction sites, and probing for altered sequences with synthetic oligonucleotides.

Alterations of Restriction Sites

Sickle-cell anemia is an example of a genetic disease that is caused by a well-characterized alteration. Affecting approximately 0.25 percent of U.S. blacks, the disease results from an altered hemoglobin due to the substitutions of a valine residue for a glutamic acid residue at position 6 in the β-globin chain (see also Chapter 11). The GAG-to-GTG change eliminates a cleavage site for the restriction enzyme MstII, which cuts the sequence CCTNAGG (where N represents any of the four bases). The change from CCT<u>GA</u>GG to CCT<u>GT</u>GG can thus be recognized by Southern blotting (see Figure 14-25) using labeled β-globin cDNA as a probe, since the DNA derived from sickle-cell

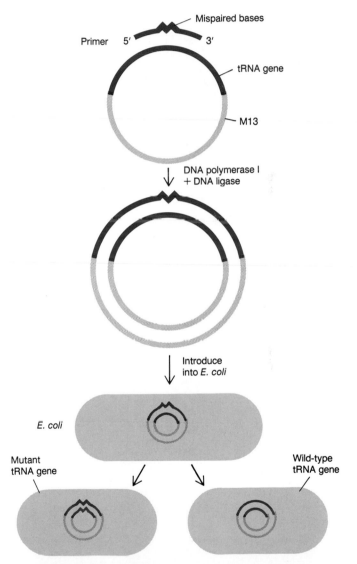

Figure 14-43. Creation of a substitution mutant by use of a synthetic oligonucleotide. The 12- to-15-base oligonucleotide is constructed so that it is complementary to a region of a DNA strand, but with one or two mismatches. When mixed with a clone of the complementary strand, the oligonucleotide will anneal to it even though the match is not exact, as long as the hybridization conditions are not stringent and the mismatches are in the middle of the oligonucleotide segment. The segment then serves as a primer for DNA polymerase I, which synthesizes the remainder of the complementary strand. When the resulting double-stranded molecule is introduced into *E. coli*, the molecule replicates to re-create either the original wild-type sequence or the mutant sequence.

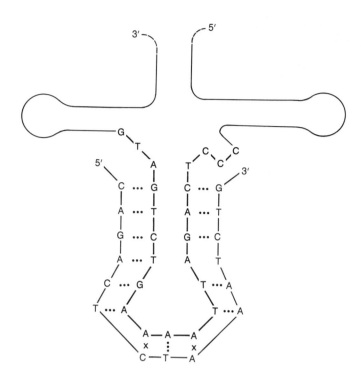

Figure 14-44. Sequences of the antisense strand (the strand that is not transcribed) of the tRNA gene at the anticodon stem and loop, and the synthetic pentadecamer with the two-base-pair mismatch (x) at the anticodon. (After G. F. Temple, et al., *Nature* 296:537, 1982.)

■ **TABLE 14-3.** Some common genetic diseases*

Inborn errors of metabolism	Approximate incidence among live births
1. Cystic fibrosis (mutated gene unknown)	1/1600 Caucasians
2. Duchenne muscular dystrophy (mutated gene unknown)	1/3000 boys (X-linked)
3. Gaucher's disease (defective glucocerebrosidase)	1/2500 Ashkenazi Jews, 1/75,000 others
4. Tay-Sachs disease (defective hexosaminidase A)	1/3500 Ashkenazi Jews, 1/35,000 others
5. Essential pentosuria (a benign condition)	1/2000 Ashkenazi Jews, 1/50,000 others
6. Classic hemophilia (defective clotting factor VIII)	1/10,000 boys (X-linked)
7. Phenylketonuria (defective phenylalanine hydroxylase)	1/5000 among Celtic Irish, 1/15,000 others
8. Cystinuria (mutated gene unknown)	1/15,000
9. Metachromatic leukodystrophy (defective arylsulfatase A)	1/40,000
10. Galactosemia (defective galactose 1-phosphate uridyl transferase)	1/40,000

Hemoglobinopathies	Approximate incidence among live births
1. Sickle-cell anemia (defective β-globin chain)	1/400 U.S. blacks. In some West African populations the frequency of heterozygotes is 40%.
2. β-Thalassemia (defective β-globin chain)	1/400 among some Mediterranean populations

* Although the vast majority of the over 500 recognized recessive genetic diseases are extremely rare, in combination they represent an enormous burden of human suffering. As is consistent with Mendelian mutations, the incidence of some of these diseases is much higher in certain racial groups than in others.
Source: J. D. Watson, J. Tooze, and D. T. Kurtz, *Recombinant DNA: A Short Course.* Copyright © 1983 by W. H. Freeman and Co.

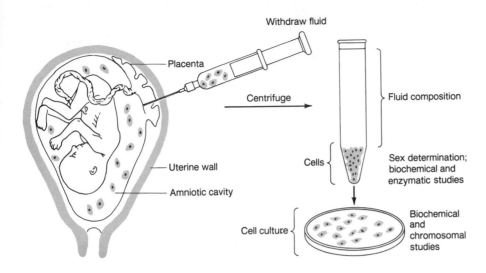

Figure 14-45. Amniocentesis.

carriers will lack one fragment contained in the DNA from normal individuals.

Linkage to Altered Restriction Site

What if a genetic defect itself does not alter a restriction site? Sometimes linkage to a restriction site alteration can be measured. Some of the polymorphic loci in the human genome result in restriction site changes. If linkage between such a **restriction site polymorphism** and a genetic defect can be established, then this can be used in prenatal diagnosis. This method is diagrammed in Figure 14-45. Linkage to restriction site changes is simply doing on the DNA level the same type of analysis that has already been applied in fully developed organisms: namely, the rise of an identifiable character to give additional information about the genotype of an individual. For instance, color blindness is used to yield information about the state of the locus governing the disease hemophilia on the X chromosome (see Problem 24 in Chapter 5). Because the Cb (color blindness) locus is closely linked to the Hb (hemophilia) locus, the probability of the presence of the Hb alleles in a color-blind individual can be determined, provided the genotype of the parents is known. The example given in Figure 14-46 employs the same principle. However, instead of determining color blindness we are determining the restriction-enzyme cleavage pattern of the DNA.

Probing for Altered Sequences

When a genetic disorder can be attributed to a specific nucleotide change in all cases, then synthetic-oligonucleotide probes can identify that change. The best example is alpha-antitrypsin deficiency, which leads to greatly increased probability for developing pulmonary emphysema, and results from a single base change at a known position. Using a synthetic oligonucleotide as a probe that contains the wild-type sequence in the relevant region of the gene, Southern blot analysis (see Figure 14-25) can distinguish between DNA containing the wild-type or the mutant sequence, since at higher temperatures a complementary sequence will hybridize, whereas a sequence containing even a single mismatched base will not.

Recombinant DNA and Social Responsibility

Recombinant DNA techniques have revolutionized biology with their revelations about gene and chromosome organization, and they promise enormous potential benefits for humanity. However, as scientists began to exploit these techniques in the early 1970s, some scientists (and some other people) began to express concern about the possible hazards of manipulating gene segments. For example, SV40 is a mammalian virus known to cause cancer in monkeys. E. coli is a bacterium that normally lives in the human digestive tract. When DNA from SV40 is inserted into E. coli, is it possible that a carcinogenic bacterium might be produced, escape, and thrive as a parasite in humans? Others have wondered whether the combination of genes from eukaryotes with prokaryotic cells might generate new types of pathogenic organisms against which humans would

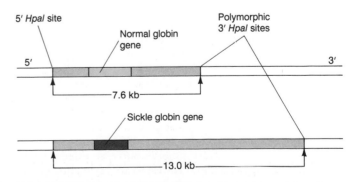

Figure 14-46. *HpaI*-site polymorphism is diagnostic for the sickle β-globin gene in humans.

have no natural defenses. Of course, the question of whether such fears are reasonable could be settled definitively only by carrying out the experiments to explore the possible results.

In an unprecedented step, 11 eminent molecular biologists published a letter in 1974 pointing out some of their concerns about potential biohazards of work with recombinant DNA. They called for the development of guidelines to regulate such research. They asked scientists to observe a moratorium on certain kinds of experiments deemed particularly hazardous (cloning genes for toxins or cancer-causing agents). For the first time in history, a group of scientists publicly declared certain areas of scientific inquiry to be "off limits" and called for possible restrictions on such research.

The call for a moratorium attracted widespread public notice and caused many people to conclude that recombinant DNA research is dangerous. Under considerable public pressure, the National Institutes of Health (NIH) in the United States set out to establish categories of biohazards and guidelines for conducting experiments in each category. Eventually (on June 23, 1976), the NIH announced categories for experiments based on their potential hazards and defined four categories of physical conditions to contain the experiments. These conditions range from the P1 requirements of standard sterile techniques and common-sense precautions to the P4 facilities with the most extreme precautions against the escape of any organisms. Standards were set as well for biological restrictions that would minimize the chances of escape. For example, special strains of genetically enfeebled *E. coli* were constructed to use as recipients of recombinant DNA. These bacteria would not survive except in special laboratory conditions.

Over the decade of the 1970s, evidence accumulated to indicate that the biohazards of recombinant DNA research are not as serious as some had feared. Meanwhile, increasing impatience built up in the scientific community about the delays in scientific progress and the regulation of scientific research by those with no training in the field. The NIH guidelines have now been relaxed significantly, and the use of recombinant DNA techniques has become routine laboratory practice.

Nonetheless, the turmoil about recombinant DNA did raise important social issues. For example, what is the social responsibility of scientists who are developing powerful new technologies? Should the people who are doing the experiments be the ones who set the guidelines? At what point should the public have an input? Who should be legally liable for any accidental damage that results from scientific research? Should limits be placed on the freedom of scientists to design and conduct research projects? Should a scientist attempt to foresee possible adverse effects from future use of discoveries and refuse to advance knowledge in certain directions that might have unfortunate applications?

Other kinds of questions are raised by the controversy over recombinant DNA. Can we predict with confidence the properties of an organism modified by inserting DNA from a totally unrelated source? Can there be deleterious effects that will not be detected until large populations have been exposed for years (as was the case with oral contraceptives)? In the long run, will increasing sophistication in DNA manipulation inevitably lead to genetic manipulation of human beings? If so, who will decide the conditions?

Although much of the worry about dangers of recombinant DNA research has been laid to rest, the issue has served to raise far more profound questions about the relationship between science and society. These questions have not been answered satisfactorily, and they are likely to persist and become even more important in the coming years.

Summary

■ The highly specific pairing of complementary bases (to form A–T and G–C pairs) permits the experimental manipulation of DNA. A DNA strand can recognize a complementary strand and anneal with it to renature a double helix or to produce DNA:RNA duplexes.

Because even a short polynucleotide has a sequence that is relatively unlikely to occur by chance, base pairing provides a highly specific method of matching strands. (If all four bases have an equal probability of occurring at any position, then a specific sequence n bases in length should occur with a frequency of $1/4^n$. For example, a particular sequence 5 bases long should occur by chance only about once in 1000 such segments.)

By annealing single strands into double helices, it is possible to identify the sites of chromosomal DNA that are complementary to RNA, to compare DNAs from different sources, and to isolate the DNA that codes for specific RNAs. Studies using DNA:DNA and DNA:RNA hybrids have revealed the existence in eukaryotes of highly redundant short sequences of DNA and of large sections of DNA that do not code for amino acids but are inserted into genes between regions that do code for amino acids.

Synthetic genes have been constructed by producing short polynucleotides with regions of overlapping complementarity. In this way, a longer duplex can be formed by annealing several short overlapping strands and then using ligase to seal the gaps between adjacent ends.

Restriction enzymes recognize specific nucleotide sequences and cleave the DNA molecule at such sites; they provide a powerful tool for fragmenting DNA in a controlled fashion. Coupled with electrophoretic gels that permit separation of strands varying in length (by as little as a single base), restriction enzymes have made genetic engineering simple. Large DNA molecules can be cut into small fragments; the fragments can be separated, and their base sequences determined. Such a study determined the entire base sequence for the DNA of the phage ϕX174 and revealed the surprising fact that some genes are contained within other genes (but using offset reading frames).

Recombinant DNA is produced by linking DNA fragments with sticky ends. That is, two molecules are prepared with complementary single-stranded ends, and these ends are then annealed. A gene from a eukaryote can be isolated or constructed and then inserted into the DNA of a bacterial plasmid. This recombinant DNA can then be inserted into bacteria, where the recombinant plasmid can persist as a self-replicating cytoplasmic entity. DNA coding for human proteins has been constructed or isolated and inserted into bacteria, where the human protein is produced in significant quantity.

Recombinant DNA technology provides powerful insights into the structure and regulation of genes. It also offers promise as a way to produce modified organisms that will have great benefits for humans. However, like any powerful new technique, genetic engineering also involves potential hazards for society that must be assessed carefully.

Problems

1. The bacteriophage ϕX174 has in its head a single strand of DNA as its genetic material. Upon infection of a bacterial cell, the phage forms a complementary strand on the infective strand to yield a double-stranded replicative form (RF). Design an experiment using ϕX174 to determine whether or not transcription occurs on both strands of the RF double helix.

2. After irradiation of wild-type T4 phages, an *rII* mutation is recovered that fails to complement with mutants in either the A or the B cistron. DNAs from the mutant and the wild-type strains are mixed, heat-denatured, and cooled slowly to allow reannealing. What hybrid molecules would be seen if the *rII* mutation is: a. a double point mutation? b. a deletion? c. an inversion? d. a transposition? e. a tandem duplication?

3. Suppose that the actual function of the *rII* locus is not known. How would you go about determining its primary gene products? Assume that some techniques not presently available may become available in the future.

4. Noboru Sueoka showed that some species of crabs contain DNA, of which 30 percent is dAT, a polymer of alternating sequences of adenine and thymine. Suppose that you want to study the cell biology of crab dAT. How would you show: a. where it is located in the cell? b. if it is nuclear, in which chromosomes it is located? c. whether there are other DNA sequences linked to the dAT?

5. In 1975, Norman Davidson and his colleagues isolated *Drosophila* DNA and sheared it into pieces. The DNA was then denatured into single strands and allowed to renature for a very short period. The DNA was then filtered through a hydroxyapatite column, which retains double-helical DNA while allowing single strands to pass through. About once in every 40 to 80 thousand bases (kilobases), they recovered a double-helical structure ranging in size from very short to more than 15 kb. In many cases the structure had the following appearance:

These researchers found around 2000 to 4000 such structures per genome. What is the explanation of these structures?

6. In 1973, Eric Davidson and his associates took DNA from *Xenopus* and broke it into pieces a few kb in length. The DNA was then denatured and allowed to anneal under conditions in which only redundant sequences anneal. The double-stranded sequences were retained on hydroxyapatite columns and then inspected by electron microscope. They obtained such duplexes as those in the accompanying figure.

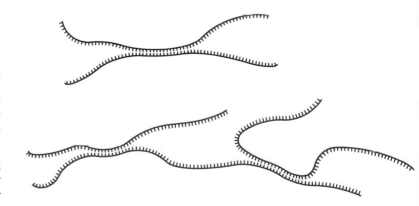

On the average, the duplexes were 0.3 kb in length, and the separation between duplexes was around 0.8 kb. Interpret these results.

7. You have a purified DNA molecule, and you wish to map restriction-enzyme sites along its length. After digestion with EcoRI, you obtain four fragments: 1, 2, 3, and 4.

After digestion of each of these fragments with HindII, you find that fragment 3 yields two subfragments (3_1 and 3_2), and fragment 2 yields three (2_1, 2_2, and 2_3). After digestion of the entire DNA molecule with HindII, you recover four pieces: A, B, C, and D. When these pieces are treated with EcoRI, piece D yields fragments 1 and 3_1, A yields 3_2 and 2_1, and B yields 2_3 and 4. The C piece is identical to 2_2. Draw a restriction map of this DNA.

8. After treating *Drosophila* DNA with restriction enzyme, the fragments are attached to plasmids and selected as clones in *E. coli*. Using this "shotgun" technique, David Hogness has recovered every DNA sequence of *Drosophila* in a cloned line.

   a. How would you go about identifying the clone that contains DNA from a particular chromosome region of interest to you?

   b. How would you identify a clone coding for a specific tRNA?

9. You have isolated and cloned a segment of DNA that is known to be a unique sequence in the genome. It maps near the tip of the X chromosome. It is about 10 kb in length. You label the 5′ ends with ^{32}P and cleave the molecule with EcoRI. You obtain two fragments, one that is 8.5 kb, and the other, 1.5 kb. You separate the 8.5 kb fragments into two fractions, partially digesting one with *Hae* and the other with HindII. You then separate each sample on an agarose gel. You obtain the following results by autoradiography (the origin is at the bottom):

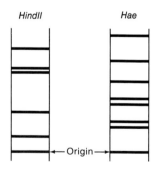

Draw a restriction-enzyme map of the complete (10-kb) molecule.

10. As shown at the top of the accompanying autoradiographs, the Maxam-Gilbert technique has been used for sequencing each of two DNA fragments from the *a* mating-type locus in yeast. The bases above each gel are the ones attacked by the reagent. What is the base sequence of these two DNA fragments?

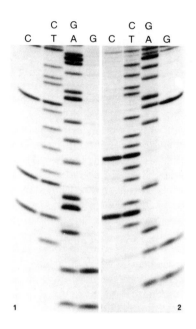

11. Suppose that a specific tRNA is encoded by six tandemly duplicated tRNA genes. You don't know what phenotype a tRNA mutation would yield. Design experiments to determine whether there are spacers between the tRNA genes and how the cluster of genes is transcribed. How could you detect mutations in these genes?

12. What result would you expect when adenine is substituted for guanine at nucleotide position 181 of the *D* gene in ϕX174? (See Figure 14-30.)

13. Design an experiment to allow the purification of DNA sequences in the Y chromosome.

14. Calculate the average distances, in nucleotide pairs, between the restriction sites in the organism X for the following restriction enzymes.

AluI	5′ AGCT 3′
	3′ TCGA 5′
EcoRI	5′ GAATTC 3′
	3′ CTTAAG 5′
AcyI	5′ G Pu CG Py C 3′
	3′ C Py GC Pu G 5′

   (NOTE: Py = any pyrimidine; Pu = any purine.)

15. Genes *A* and *B*, which map on yeast chromosome 4, were used as genetic markers in a study of two different haploid populations of yeast. The two populations expressed different allelic forms of the genes: in population 1, gene *A* gave *A1* and gene *B* gave *B1*; in population 2, gene *A* gave *A2* and gene *B* gave *B2*. These alleles were distinguished by the HindIII restriction map of the DNA in the region of the genes:

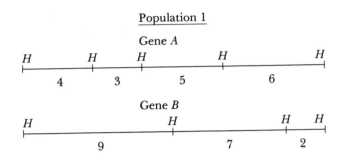

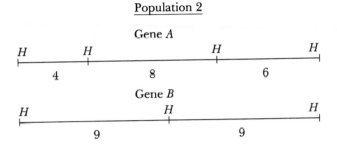

The tetrad products were examined, and the DNA fragments corresponding to genes A and B, respectively, are given for each type:

Spore type	Frequency	DNA (HindIII fragments)	
		Gene A	Gene B
1	15%	4, 3, 5, 6	9, 9
2	15%	4, 8, 6	9, 7, 2
3	35%	4, 3, 5, 6	9, 7, 2
4	35%	4, 8, 6	9, 9

a. What are the allele types of the tetrad products?

b. How did they arise?

c. Draw a linkage map.

(Problem 15 courtesy of Joan McPherson.)

16. a. A fragment of mouse DNA with EcoRI sticky ends carries the gene M. This DNA fragment of 8 kb is inserted into the bacterial plasmid pBR322 at the *EcoRI* site. The recombinant plasmid was cleaved with three different restriction enzymes, and the patterns of ethidium bromide fragments following electrophoresis on agarose gels were as shown in the accompanying figure.

A Southern blot was prepared from gel (iii). Which fragments would hybridize to a probe (^{32}P) of pBR plasmid DNA?

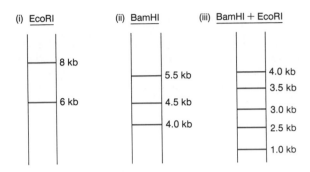

b. Gene X is carried on a plasmid consisting of 5300 nucleotide pairs (5300 bp). Cleavage of the plasmid with the restriction enzyme BamHI enzyme gives fragments 1, 2, and 3, as indicated in the diagram ($B = BamHI$ restriction site):

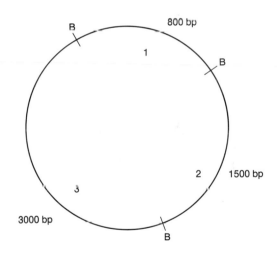

Tandem copies of gene X are contained within a single BamHI fragment. If gene X encodes a protein X of 400 amino acids, indicate the approximate positions and orientations of the gene-X copies.

(Problem 16 courtesy of Joan McPherson.)

17. A linear fragment of DNA was cleaved with the individual restriction enzymes HindIII and SmaI, and then with a combination of the two enzymes. The fragments obtained were

HindIII alone	2.5 kb, 5.0 kb
SmaI alone	2.0 kb, 5.5 kb
Together	2.5 kb, 3.0 kb, 2.0 kb

a. Draw the restriction map.

b. The mixture of fragments produced by the combined enzymes was next cleaved with the enzyme EcoRI, resulting in the loss of the 3-kb fragment (band stained with ethidium bromide on an agarose gel) and the appearance of a band stained with ethidium bromide of 1.5 kb. Mark the *EcoRI* cleavage site on the restriction map.

(Problem 17 courtesy of Joan McPherson.)

18. A viral DNA fragment carrying a specific gene, *V*, was transfected (introduced into the cell by transformation) into a muscle-cell culture. Following incubation with ^{32}P-labeled ribonucleotides, the virus-encoded RNA product was isolated at two timed intervals. The radiolabeled viral RNA was treated as follows: First, it was hybridized to a specific cDNA previously constructed from viral-gene-*V* mature mRNA. Second, the hybrid was treated with RNAase. Finally, the hybrid was denatured and electrophoresed on a gel, which was then subjected to autoradiography. The following results suggest that the pathologic nature of the virus is time-related (number of nucleotides is indicated on the bands observed):

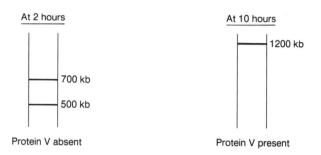

a. What is the size of the mature mRNA for gene *V*?

b. Draw a diagram of each hybrid and indicate what the illustrated bands represent.

c. Why is protein V not produced until after 2 hours?

(Problem 18 courtesy of Joan McPherson.)

CHAPTER 15

Mechanisms of Genetic Change I: Gene Mutation

■ Genetic change can result from a number of processes. Consider an individual organism that represents a variant from an established control population. What mechanism could have produced the change that created this variant individual? The following are four possibilities:

1. Gene mutation
2. Recombination
3. Transposable genetic elements
4. Chromosomal rearrangements

In previous chapters we considered genetic changes merely as useful and interesting phenomena—we did not probe deeply into how such changes come about. Let us now examine, at the molecular level, the processes themselves that lead to each type of genetic change. This chapter explores the mechanisms of gene mutation; Chapter 16 describes the events leading to recombination; and Chapter 17 introduces the concept of transposable genetic elements, which can effect genetic change by moving from one chromosomal location to another. Although some chromosomal rearrangements can result from recombination and from transposable elements, many rearrangement events occur by mechanisms that are not yet understood.

To understand mechanisms of gene mutation requires analysis at the level of DNA and protein molecules. Preceding chapters have described models for DNA and protein structure and have discussed the nature of mutations that alter these structures. Table 15-1 draws together this information to provide an explanation of the nature of gene mutation at the molecular level.

Technical advances in the mid-1970s ushered in an exciting new era in molecular genetics, permitting for the first time the direct determination of the sequence of large segments of DNA and also the sequence changes resulting from mutations. This has greatly increased our understanding of the pathways that lead to mutagenesis and has even allowed unraveling of the mysteries of mutational hotspots (see page 299). Much work until now on the molecular basis of mutation has been carried out in single-cell bacteria and their viruses. Let us review some of the recent findings of these studies. We shall also consider biological repair mechanisms, since repair systems play a key role in mutagenesis.

The Molecular Basis of Gene Mutations

Gene mutations can arise spontaneously or they can be induced. **Spontaneous mutations** occur in all cells. **Induced mutations** are produced when an organism is treated with a mutagenic agent, or mutagen; such muta-

■ TABLE 15-1. Summary of changes at the molecular level in gene mutations

Type of mutation	Result and example(s)
Forward mutations	
Single nucleotide-pair (base-pair) substitutions	
At DNA level	
Transition	Purine replaced by a different purine, or pyrimidine replaced by a different pyrimidine:
	AT $\longrightarrow$ GC GC $\longrightarrow$ AT CG $\longrightarrow$ TA TA $\longrightarrow$ CG
Transversion	Purine replaced by a pyrimidine, or pyrimidine replaced by a purine:
	AT $\longrightarrow$ CG AT $\longrightarrow$ TA GC $\longrightarrow$ TA GC $\longrightarrow$ CG
	TA $\longrightarrow$ GC TA $\longrightarrow$ AT CG $\longrightarrow$ AT CG $\longrightarrow$ GC
At protein level	
Silent mutation	Triplet codes for same amino acid:
	AGG $\longrightarrow$ CGG
	both code for Arg
Neutral mutation	Triplet codes for different but functionally equivalent amino acid:
	AAA $\longrightarrow$ AGA
	changing basic Lys to basic Arg
	(at many positions will not alter protein function)
Missense mutation	Triplet codes for a different and nonfunctional amino acid.
Nonsense mutation	Triplet codes for chain termination:
	CAG $\longrightarrow$ UAG
	changing from a codon for Gln to amber termination codon
Single nucleotide-pair addition or deletion: frame-shift mutation	Any addition or deletion of base pairs that is not a multiple of three results in a frame-shift in DNA segments that code for proteins.
Intragenic addition or deletion of several to many nucleotide pairs	
Reverse mutations	
Exact reversion	AAA (Lys) $\xrightarrow{\text{forward}}$ GAA (Glu) $\xrightarrow{\text{reverse}}$ AAA (Lys)
	wild-type mutant wild-type
Equivalent reversion	UCC (Ser) $\xrightarrow{\text{forward}}$ UGC (Cys) $\xrightarrow{\text{reverse}}$ AGC (Ser)
	wild-type mutant wild-type
	CGC (Arg, basic) $\xrightarrow{\text{forward}}$ CCC (Pro, not basic) $\xrightarrow{\text{reverse}}$ CAC (His, basic)
	wild-type mutant pseudo-wild-type
Suppressor mutations	
Frame-shift of opposite sign at second site within gene	CATCATCATCATCATCAT
	(+) (−)
	↓ ↓
	CATXCA TATCATCATCAT
	✓ X X ✓ ✓ ✓
Second-site missense mutation	Still not fully understood at level of protein function, but explained in terms of a second distortion that restores a more or less wild-type protein conformation after a primary distortion

■ **TABLE 15-1.** (*Continued*)

Type of mutation	Result and example(s)
Extragenic suppressor mutations	
Nonsense suppressors	Gene (e.g., for tyrosine tRNA) undergoes mutational event in its anticodon region that enables it to recognize and align with a mutant nonsense codon (e.g., amber UAG) to insert an amino acid (here, tyrosine) and permit completion of the translation.
Missense suppressors	A heterogeneous set of mutations whose molecular mechanisms are not fully understood. One missense suppressor in *E. coli* is an abnormal tRNA that carries glycine but inserts it in response to arginine codons. Though *normal* arginine codons also mistranslated, observed mutations not lethal, probably because of low efficiency of abnormal substitution.
Frame-shift suppressors	Very few examples found; in one, a four-nucleotide anticodon in a single tRNA can "read" a four-letter codon caused by a single nucleotide-pair insertion.
Physiological suppressors	A defect in one chemical pathway is circumvented by another mutation—for example, one that opens up another chemical pathway to the same result, or one that permits more efficient transport of a compound produced in small quantities because of the original mutation. Thus, these mutations act as one form of missense suppressors; a very heterogeneous group.

tions are typically recovered at much higher frequencies than the spontaneous mutations.

Spontaneous Mutations

Spontaneous mutations arise from a variety of sources, including errors in DNA replication, spontaneous lesions, and even transposable genetic elements (discussed in Chapter 17).

Errors in DNA Replication. An error in DNA replication can allow an illegitimate nucleotide pair (say, A – C) to form during DNA replication, leading to a base substitution. Each of the bases in DNA can appear in one of two forms, called **tautomers,** which are in equilibrium. The keto form of each base is present in normal DNA, whereas the rarer imino and enol forms of the bases are not (see Figure 15-1). The ability of the wrong tautomer of one of the standard bases to mispair and cause mutations during DNA replication was first noted by Watson and Crick when they formulated their model for the structure of DNA (Chapter 10). Figure 15-2 demonstrates some possible mispairs resulting from changes of one tautomer to another, termed **tautomeric shifts.** Such mispairs would lead (Figure 15-3) to **transition** mutations, in which a purine is substituted for a purine or a pyrimidine for a pyrimidine (see Table 15-1). The bacterial DNA polymerase III (Chapter 10) has an editing capacity that recognizes such mismatches and excises them, thus greatly reducing the observed mutations. (Another repair system described later in this chapter cor-

rects many of the mismatched bases that pass through the polymerase checking function.)

TRANSVERSIONS. **Transversion** mutations, in which a pyrimidine is substituted for a purine or vice versa, cannot be generated by the mismatches depicted in Figure 15-2. Can you see why? With bases in the DNA in the normal orientation, the creation of a transversion by a replication error would require, at some point during replication, the mispairing of a purine with a purine, or a pyrimidine with a pyrimidine. However, the dimensions of the DNA double helix forbid such mispairing on steric grounds. (Refer to some of the figures in Chapter 10 to verify this.) Although mispairing schemes using other rare forms of different bases have been proposed, it is presently unclear how spontaneous transversions are generated.

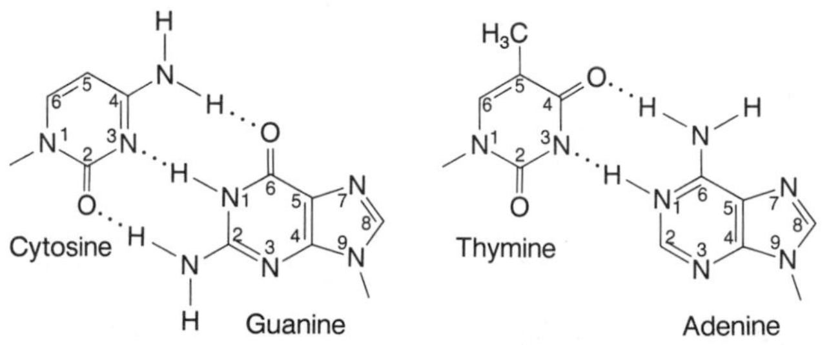

Figure 15-1. Base pairs in DNA. The normal Watson-Crick base pairs are shown.

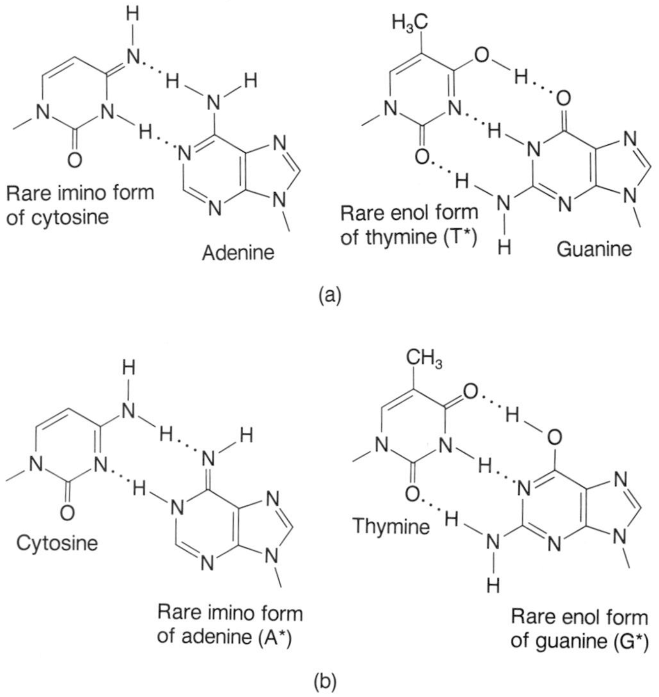

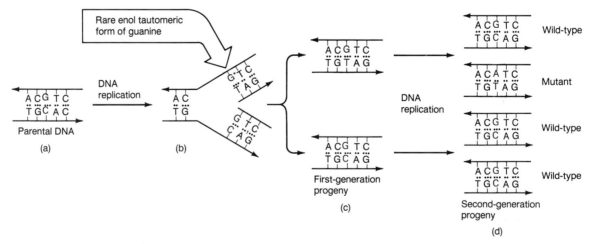

Figure 15-2. Mismatched bases. Mispairs resulting from rare tautomeric forms of the pyrimidines are shown in (a); mispairs resulting from rare tautomeric forms of the purines are shown in (b).

FRAME-SHIFT MUTATIONS. Replication errors can also lead to frame-shift mutations. Recall from Chapter 12 that such mutations result in greatly altered proteins.

In the mid-1960s, George Streisinger and coworkers deduced the nucleotide sequence surrounding different sites of frame-shift mutations in the lysozyme gene of phage T4. They found that these mutations often occurred at repeated sequences and formulated a model to account for frame-shifts during DNA synthesis. In the Streisinger model (Figure 15-4), frame-shifts arise when loops in single-stranded regions are stabilized by "slipped mispairing" of repeated sequences. With the advent of DNA sequencing in the mid 1970s, such models could be tested directly. J. Miller and coworkers examined mutational **hotspots** in the *lacI* gene of *E. coli*. (Recall from Chapter 10 that Benzer had demonstrated in 1961 the existence of such hotspots, sites in a gene that are much more mutable than other sites.) The *lacI* work showed that certain hotspots resulted from repeated sequences, just as predicted by the Streisinger model. Figure 15-5 depicts the distribution of spontaneous mutations in the *lacI* gene. Compare this with the distribution seen by Benzer in the *rII* genes of T4 (page 228). Note how one or two mutational sites dominate the distribution in both cases. In *lacI*, a four-base-pair sequence repeated three times in tandem is the cause of the hotspots (for simplicity, only one strand of the double strand of DNA is indicated):

Figure 15-3. Mutation via tautomeric shifts in the bases of DNA. (a) In the example diagrammed, a guanine undergoes a tautomeric shift to its rare enol form (G*) at the time of replication. (b) In its enol form, it pairs with thymine. (c) and (d) During the next replication, the guanine shifts back to its more stable keto form. The thymine incorporated opposite the enol form of guanine, seen in (b), directs the incorporation of adenine during the subsequent replication, shown in (c) and (d). The net result is a GC → AT mutation. If a guanine undergoes a tautomeric shift from the common keto form to the rare enol form at the time of incorporation (as a nucleoside triphosphate, rather than in the template strand as diagrammed here), it will be incorporated opposite thymine in the template strand and cause an AT → GC mutation. (From E. J. Gardner and D. P. Snustad, *Principles of Genetics*, 5th ed., John Wiley & Sons, New York, 1984.)

5′–GTCTGG CTGG CTGG CTGG C–3′

FS5, FS25, FS45, FS65

wild-type   GTCTGG CTGG CTGG C

FS2 | *FS84*

GTCTGG CTGG C

The major hotspot, represented here by the mutations *FS5, FS25, FS45,* and *FS65*, results from the addition of one extra set of the four bases CTGG to one strand of the DNA. This hotspot reverts at a high rate, losing the extra set of four bases. The minor hotspot, represented here by the mutations *FS2* and *FS84*, results from the loss of one set of the four bases CTGG. This latter mutant does not readily regain the lost set of four base pairs. How can the Streisinger model explain these observations? Remember that the model predicts that the frequency of a particular frameshift is dependent on the number of base pairs that can be formed during slipped mispairing. The wild-type sequence shown for the *lacI* gene can slip out one CTGG sequence and stabilize this by forming nine base pairs. (Can you work this out by applying the model in Figure 15-4 to the sequence shown for *lacI*?) Whether a deletion or addition is generated depends on whether the slippage occurs on the template or on the newly synthesized strand. In a similar fashion, the addition mutant can slip out one CTGG sequence and stabilize this with 13 base pairs (verify this for the *FS5* sequence shown for *lacI*), explaining the rapid reversion of mutations such as *FS5*. However, there are only five base pairs available to stabilize a slipped-out CTGG in the deletion mutant, thus accounting for the infrequent reversion of mutations such as *FS2* in the sequence shown for *lacI*.

DELETIONS.   Deletions represent a sizable fraction of spontaneous mutations, as you can visualize from Figure 15-5. Deletions of up to several thousand base pairs in size have been studied extensively at the DNA sequence level.

The majority, although not all, of the deletions occur at short-sequence repeats. Figure 15-6 shows the results for the first 12 deletions analyzed at the DNA sequence level, presented by Miller and coworkers in 1978. Further studies have shown that hotspots for deletions involve the longest sequences that are repeated.

There are several mechanisms that could account for deletion formation. Deletions may be generated as replication errors. For example, an extension of the Streisinger model of slipped mispairing (Figure 15-4) could explain why deletions predominate at short repeated sequences. Alternatively, recombinational mechanisms (described in Chapter 16) by one or a number of cellular enzyme systems that recognize short-sequence repeats could generate deletions.

Spontaneous Lesions.   In addition to replication errors, **spontaneous lesions** can also generate mutations. Two of the most frequent spontaneous lesions result from depurination and deamination. **Depurination,** the more common of the two, involves the interruption of the glycosidic bond between base and deoxyribose and subsequent loss of a guanine or an adenine residue from the DNA (Figure 15-7). A mammalian cell spontaneously loses about 10,000 purines from its DNA during a 20-hour generation period at 37°C. If these lesions were to persist, they would result in significant genetic damage, since during replication the resulting **apurinic** sites cannot specify a base complementary to the original purine. However, as we shall see later in the chapter, efficient repair systems remove apurinic sites. Under certain conditions (described later), a base can be inserted across from an apurinic site; this will frequently result in a mutation.

Deamination of cytosine yields uracil (Figure 15-8a). Unrepaired uracil residues will pair with adenine during replication, resulting in the conversion of a G–C pair to an A–T pair (a transition). One of the repair enzymes in the cell, uracil-DNA glycosylase, recognizes uracil residues in

Addition

DNA synthesis →

(a) 5′ . . . CGTTTT
       . . . . . .
    3′ . . . GCAAAAACGTAC . . .

          GT
(b) 5′ . . . C TTT
       . . . .
    3′ . . . GCAAAAACGTAC . . .

          GT
(c) 5′ . . . C TTTTTGCATG
       . . . .
    3′ . . . GCAAAAACGTAC . . .

Deletion

DNA synthesis →

(d) 5′ . . . CTGAGAGA
       . . . .
    3′ . . . GACTCTCTCTCTGCA . . .

(e) 5′ . . . CTGAGAGA
       . . . .
    3′ . . . GACTCTCTCTGCA . . .
                              CT
(f) 5′ . . . CTGAGAGAGACGT . . .
    3′ . . . GACTCTCTCTGCA . . .
                              CT

Figure 15-4. A simplified version of the Streisinger model for frame-shift formation. (a) to (c) During DNA synthesis the newly synthesized strand slips, looping out several base pairs. This loop is stabilized by the pairing afforded by the repetitive-sequence unit—the single A bases in this case. An addition will result at the next round of replication. (d) to (f) If instead of the newly synthesized strand, the template strand slips, then a deletion would result. Here the repeating unit is a C–T. After slippage, a deletion of two base pairs would result at the next round of replication.

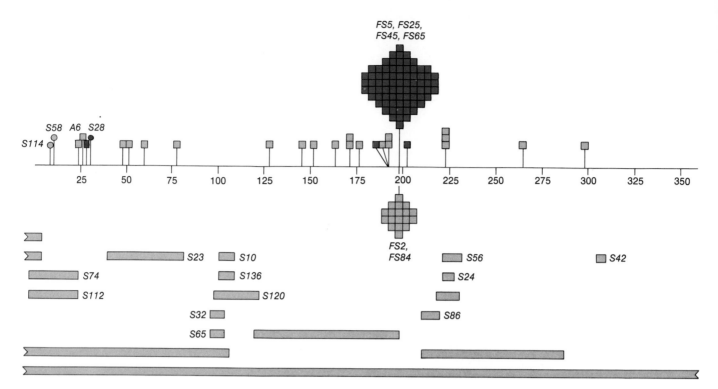

Figure 15-5. The distribution of 140 spontaneous mutations in *lacI*. Each occurrence of a point mutation is indicated by a box. Colored boxes depict fast-reverting mutations. Deletions are represented below the *I* map, which is given in terms of the amino acid number in the corresponding *I*-encoded *lac* repressor. Allele numbers refer to mutations that have been analyzed at the DNA sequence level. The mutations *S114* and *S58* result from the insertion of transposable elements (see Chapter 17). (From P. J. Farabaugh, U. Schmeissner, M. Hofer, and J. H. Miller, *Journal of Molecular Biology* 126: 847–857.)

the DNA and excises them, leaving a gap that is subsequently filled in (see following section, Biological Repair Mechanisms). An exciting discovery in 1978 revealed that the specificity of this repair enzyme was the cause of one type of mutational hotspot! DNA sequence analysis of GC → AT (GC-to-AT) transition hotspots in the *lacI* gene showed that 5-methylcytosine residues occurred at the position of each hotspot. (Certain bases in prokaryotes and eukaryotes are methylated; see page 305.) Some of the

actual data from this study are shown in Figure 15-9. The height of each bar on the graph represents the frequency of mutations at each of a number of sites. It can be seen that the position of 5-methylcytosine residues correlates nicely with the most mutable sites. This is because the deamination of 5-methylcytosine (shown in Figure 15-8b) generates thymine (5-methyluracil), which is not recognized by the enzyme uracil-DNA glycosylase and thus is not repaired. Therefore, C-to-T transitions generated by deamination

```
                          S74, S112      75 bases
                       _____  _____

CAATTCAGG GTGGTGAA TGTGAAACC------CGC GTGGTGAA CCAGG
          _____
```

Site (no. of b.p.)	Sequence repeat	Bases deleted	Occurrences	
20 to 95	GTGGTGAA	75	2	S74, S112
146 to 269	GCGGCGAT	123	1	S23
331 to 351	AAGCGGCG	20	2	S10, S136
316 to 338	GTCGA	22	2	S32, S65
694 to 707	CA	13	1	S24
694 to 719	CA	25	1	S56
943 to 956	G	13	1	S42
322 to 393	None	71	1	S120
658 to 685	None	27	1	S86

Figure 15-6. Deletions in *lacI*. Deletions occur as indicated by the colored bars at the top of the figure. One of the sequence repeats and all the intervening DNA is deleted, leaving one copy of the repeated sequence. All mutations were analyzed by direct DNA sequence determination. (From P. J. Farabaugh, et al., *Journal of Molecular Biology* 126: 847–857.)

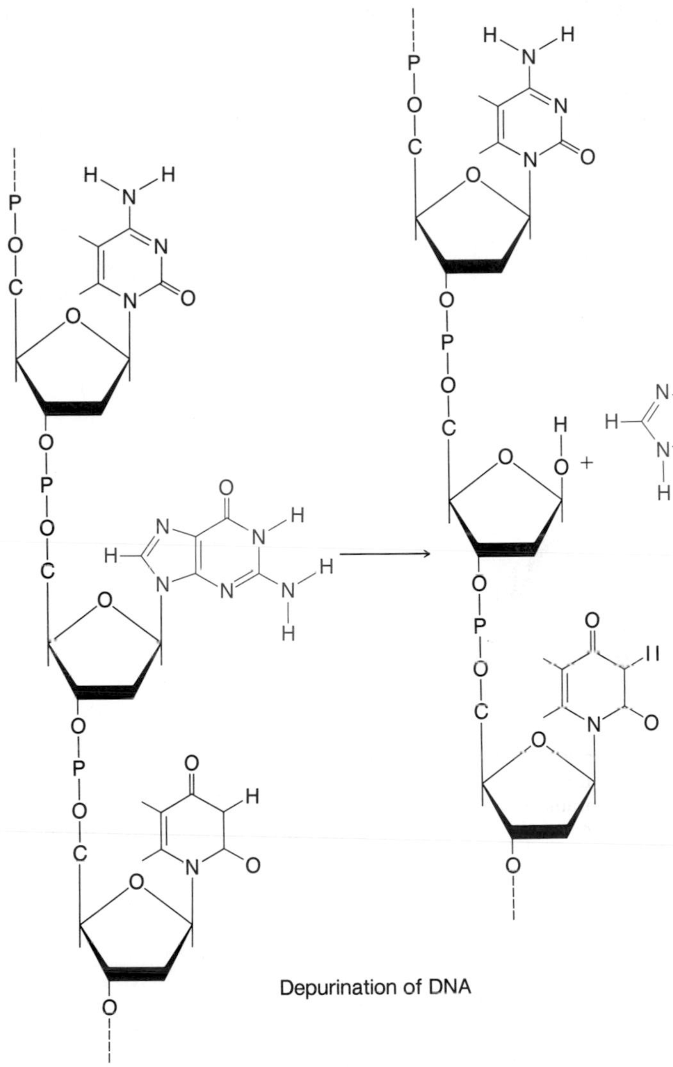

Figure 15-7. The loss of a purine residue from a single strand of DNA. The sugar-phosphate backbone is left intact.

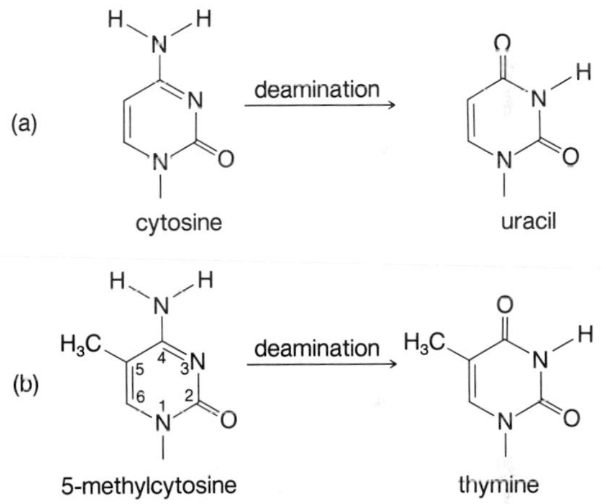

Figure 15-8. Deamination of cytosine and 5-methylcytosine, (a) Cytosine; (b) 5-methylcytosine.

are detected more frequently at 5-methylcytosine sites, which occur both in bacteria and in higher cells.

The insertion of certain "transposable elements" into genes represents an additional source of spontaneous mutations, as we shall see in Chapter 17.

Message Spontaneous mutations can be generated by different processes. Replication errors and spontaneous lesions generate most of the base-substitution and frame-shift mutations. Replication errors may also cause deletions that occur in the absence of mutagenic treatment.

Induced Mutagenesis

When we observe the distribution of mutations induced by different mutagens, we see a distinct specificity that is char-

acteristic of each mutagen. Such **mutational specificity** was first noted in the *rII* system, by Benzer in 1961. Specificity arises from a "preference" both for certain *types* of mutations (for example, GC → AT transitions) and for certain mutational *sites*, termed hotspots. Because of the recent advances allowing the determination of DNA sequences, we can now visualize mutational specificity at the molecular level. Figure 15-10 shows the mutational specificity in *lacI* for three mutagens described later: ethylmethanesulfonate (EMS), ultraviolet (UV) light, and aflatoxin B_1 (AFB_1). In this diagram the distribution of base-substitution mutations that create chain-terminating UAG codons is seen. Figure 15-10 is similar to Figure 11-34, which shows the distribution of mutations in *rII*, except that the specific sequence changes are known for each site, allowing the diagram to be broken down into each category of substitution.

Figure 15-10 reveals the two components of muta-

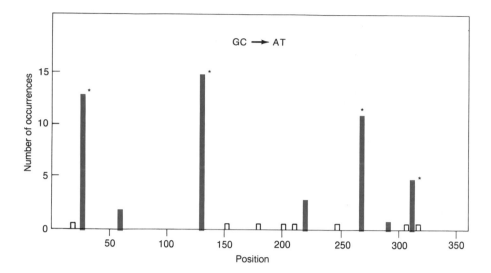

Figure 15-9. 5-Methylcytosine hotspots in *E. coli.* Nonsense mutations occurring at 15 different sites and in *lacI* were scored. All result from the GC → AT transition. The asterisks (*) mark the position of 5-methylcytosines. Open bars depict sites at which the GC → AT change could be detected but at which no mutations occurred in this particular collection. It can be seen that 5-methylcytosine residues are hotspots for the GC → AT transition. Of 50 independently occurring mutations, 44 were at the four 5-methylcytosine sites, and only six were at the 11 unmethylated cytosines. (From C. Coulondre et al., *Nature* 274:775– 780, 1978.)

tional specificity. First of all, each mutagen shown favors a specific category of substitution. For example, EMS favors GC → AT transitions, whereas AFB₁ favors GC → TA transversions. This is related to the different mechanisms of mutagenesis. Secondly, even within the same category there are large differences in mutation rate. This can be seen best with UV light for the GC-to-AT changes. Some aspect of the surrounding DNA sequence must cause these differences. In some cases the cause of mutational hotspots can be determined by DNA sequence studies, as previously described for 5-methylcytosine residues and for certain frame-shift sites (see Figures 15-5 and 15-9). In many examples of mutagen-induced hotspots, however, the precise reason for high mutability of specific sites is still unknown.

Mutagens induce mutations by at least three different mechanisms. They can either replace a base in the DNA, alter a base so that it specifically mispairs with another base, or else damage a base so that it can no longer pair with any base under normal conditions.

Incorporation of Base Analogs. Some chemical compounds are sufficiently similar to the normal nitrogen bases of DNA so that they occasionally are incorporated into DNA in place of normal bases; such compounds are called **base analogs.** Once in place, these bases have pairing properties unlike those of the bases they replace, and thus they can produce mutations by causing insertions of incorrect nucleotides opposite them during replication. The original base analog exists in only a single strand, but it can cause a nucleotide-pair substitution that is replicated in all DNA copies descended from the original strand.

For example, 5-bromouracil (5-BU) is an analog of thymine that has bromine at the C-5 position in place of the CH₃ group found in thymine. This change does not involve the atoms that take place in hydrogen bonding during base pairing, but the presence of the bromine significantly alters the distribution of electrons in the base. The normal structure—the keto form—of the 5-BU undergoes a relatively frequent change to the enol form (Figure 15-11). (We have encountered such tautomeric shifts

before; recall Figures 15-2 and 15-3.) The enol form has hydrogen-bonding properties almost identical to those of cytosine! Thus, the nature of the pair formed during replication will depend on the form of 5-BU at the moment of pairing (Figure 15-12). 5-BU causes almost exclusively transitions, as is predicted in Figures 15-11 and 15-12.

Another widely used analog is 2-aminopurine (2-AP), which is an analog of adenine that can pair with thymine but can also mispair with cytosine. Therefore, when 2-AP is incorporated into DNA as adenine, it can generate AT → GC transitions by mispairing with cytosine during subsequent replications. Or, if 2-AP is incorporated by mispairing with cytosine, then GC → AT transitions will result. Genetic studies have shown that 2-AP is very specific for transitions.

Specific Mispairing. Some mutagens are not incorporated into the DNA but instead alter a base, causing specific mispairing. Certain **alkylating agents,** such as ethylmethanesulfonate (EMS) and the widely used nitrosoguanidine (NG), operate via this pathway.

$$O=N-N\overset{\underset{\displaystyle CH_3}{|}}{\underset{\underset{\displaystyle H}{|}}{\underset{\displaystyle N}{\overset{\displaystyle C}{\|}}}}N\overset{\displaystyle H}{\underset{\displaystyle NO_2}{}}$$

$$C_2H_5-O-\overset{\overset{\displaystyle O}{\|}}{\underset{\underset{\displaystyle O}{\|}}{S}}-H_3C$$

EMS   NG

Although such agents add alkyl groups (an ethyl group in the case of EMS and a methyl group in the case of NG) to many positions on all four bases, mutagenicity is best correlated with an addition to the oxygen at the 6 position of guanine, creating O-6-alkylguanine. This leads to direct mispairing with thymine, as shown in Figure 15-13, and would result in GC → AT transitions at the next round of replication. As expected, determinations of mutagenic

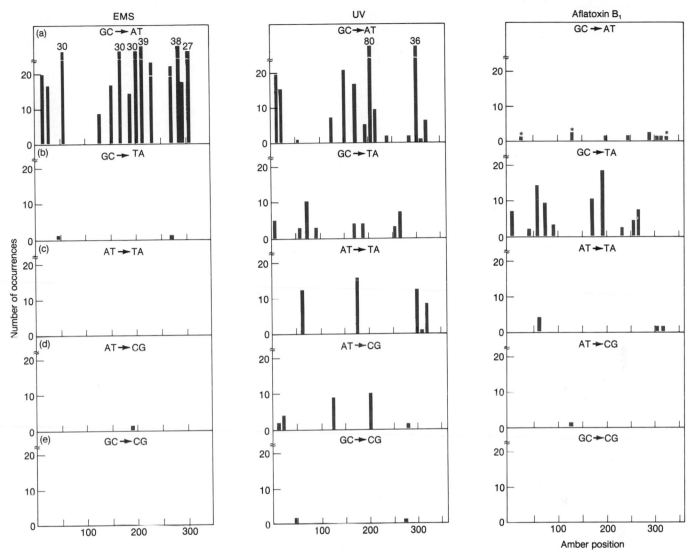

Figure 15-10. Specificity of mutagens. The distribution of mutations among 36 sites in the *lacI* gene is shown for three mutagens: EMS, UV light, and aflatoxin B_1. The height of each bar represents the number of occurrences of mutations at the respective site. Some hotspots are shown offscale, with the number of occurrences indicated directly alongside the respective peak. For instance, in the UV-generated collection, one site resulting from a GC → AT transition is represented by 80 occurrences. Each mutational site generates an amber (UAG) codon in the corresponding mRNA. The mutations are arranged according to the type of base substitution involved. Asterisks mark the position of 5-methylcytosines. (Redrawn from C. Coulondre and J. H. Miller, *Journal of Molecular Biology* 117:577–606, 1977; and P. L. Foster et al., *Proc. of the Natl. Acad. Sci. USA,* 80:2695–98, 1983.)

specificity for EMS and NG show a strong preference for GC → AT transitions. (Verify this by consulting the data for EMS shown in Figure 15-10.)

Hydroxylamine (HA) is a specific inducer of GC → AT transitions. This specific effect is observed particularly in phage and *Neurospora;* the effects of HA are less specific in *E. coli.* Its structure is

$$\begin{matrix} H \\ \quad \diagdown \\ \quad \quad N\!-\!OH \\ \quad \diagup \\ H \end{matrix}$$

The relative specificity of HA is very probably due to the fact that it preferentially hydroxylates the amino nitrogen bound to C-4 of cytosine, causing the cytosine to bind like thymine (Figure 15-14). *N*-4-hydroxycytosine prepared in vitro has the same ability to pair with thymine and cause mutations (see Chapter 14), which strongly supports the proposed mechanism.

Other examples of mutagens that specifically alter bases are those that deaminate cytosine to uracil. For instance, bisulfite isons convert cytosine to uracil, as does nitrous acid (NA). The uracil residue, if unrepaired (as shown earlier in Figure 15-8), will pair with adenine instead of guanine, generating a C-to-T transition. Nitrous acid

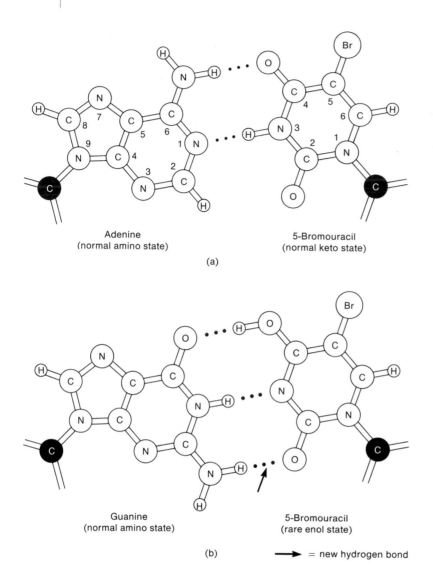

Adenine
(normal amino state)

5-Bromouracil
(normal keto state)

(a)

Guanine
(normal amino state)

5-Bromouracil
(rare enol state)

(b)   ⟶ = new hydrogen bond

Figure 15-11. The alternative pairing possibilities for 5-bromouracil (5-BU). 5-BU is an analog of thymine that can be mistakenly incorporated into DNA as a base. It has a bromine atom in place of the methyl group. (a) In its normal keto state, 5-BU mimics the pairing behavior of the thymine it replaces, pairing with adenine. (b) The presence of the bromine atom, however, causes a relatively frequent redistribution of electrons so that 5-BU can spend part of its existence in the rare enol form. In this state, it pairs with guanine, mimicking the behavior of cytosine, and can thus induce mutations during replication.

also deaminates adenine to generate hypoxanthine, which can form A–C mispairs (see Figure 15-15).

The **intercalating agents** form another important class of DNA modifiers. This group of compounds includes proflavin, acridine organge, and a class of chemicals termed ICR compounds (see Figure 15-16). These agents are planar molecules, which mimic base pairs and are able to slip themselves in between the stacked nitrogen bases at the core of the DNA double helix in a process called **intercalation** (Figure 15-16). In this intercalated position the agent can cause single-nucleotide-pair insertions or deletions. Intercalating agents may also stack between bases in single-stranded DNA; in so doing they may stabilize bases that are looped out during frame-shift formation, as depicted in the Streisinger model in Figure 15-4. A model for the actions of such agents is shown in Figure 15-17.

Replication Bypass: The SOS System. A large number of mutagens require the operation of host enzyme systems in bacteria (and presumably in mammalian cells as well) in order to generate viable mutants. These mutagens damage one or more bases so that specific pairing is no longer possible. The damaged bases, if left unrepaired, block replication because DNA synthesis will not proceed past a base that cannot specify its complementary base by hydrogen bonding. This is for good reason, since the insertion of bases across from noncoding lesions would lead to frequent mutations. The **bypass** of such replication blocks requires the activation of a special system, termed the **SOS system.** Therefore, mutagens that generate noncoding lesions are dependent on the SOS system for their action. The category of SOS-dependent mutagens is important, since it includes most carcinogens, such as ultraviolet light, benzo(a)pyrene and aflatoxin B_1 (see later). The name SOS is derived from the idea that this system is induced as an emergency response to prevent cell death in the presence of significant DNA damage. (This "induction" is really the activation of gene expression, which is described more fully in Chapter 18.) SOS induction is a last resort, allowing the cell to trade a certain level of mutagenesis for ultimate survival. Figure 15-18 depicts the bypass of a noncoding lesion.

(a)   Transition 1   AT ⟶ GC

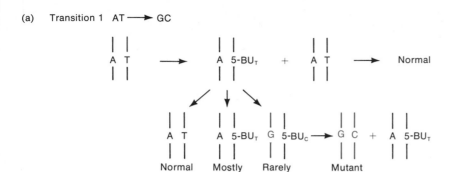

(b)   Transition 2   GC ⟶ AT

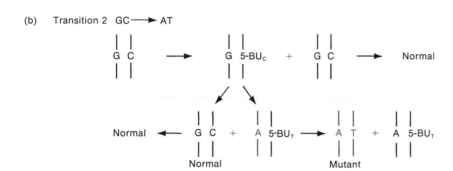

Figure 15-12. The mechanism of 5-BU mutagenesis. (a) In its keto state, 5-BU pairs like thymine (this state indicated as 5-BU$_T$). (b) In its enol state, 5-BU pairs like cytosine (this state indicated as 5-BU$_C$). In (a), 5-BU is incorporated across from adenine and subsequently mispairs with guanine, resulting in AT → GC transitions. In (b), 5-BU is misincorporated across from guanine and subsequently pairs with adenine, resulting in GC → AT transitions.

How is the SOS system involved in the recovery of mutants induced by certain mutagens? One hypothesis was that induction of the SOS system lowers the fidelity of DNA replication so much (in order to permit bypass of noncoding lesions) that many replication errors occur, even for undamaged DNA. This hypothesis could be tested, since it predicted that most mutations generated by different SOS-dependent mutagens would be similar, rather than specific to each mutagen. Most mutations would result from the action of the SOS system itself on undamaged DNA. The mutagen would then play an indirect role, that of inducing the SOS system. Studies of mutational specificity, however, have shown this is not the case. Thus, a series of different SOS-dependent mutagens have markedly different specificities. You can see this by comparing the specificities of ultraviolet (UV) light and aflatoxin B$_1$ in Figure 15-10. Each mutagen induces a unique distribution of mutations. Therefore, the mutations must be generated in response to specific damaged base pairs. The type of lesion differs in many cases. Some of the most widely studied lesions include UV photoproducts, apurinic sites, and bulky chemical additions on specific bases.

Exactly how the SOS bypass system functions is not clear, although it is known to be dependent on at least two genes: *recA* (which is also involved in general recombination, as described in Chapter 16) and *umuC*. (Chapter 18 describes the control of the induction of the SOS system.)

Ultraviolet (UV) light generates a number of photoproducts in DNA. Two different lesions occurring at adjacent pyrimidine residues have been most strongly correlated with mutagenesis. The "cyclobutane-type dimer" and the "6-4 photoproduct" shown in Figure 15-19 interfere with normal base pairing. Induction of the SOS system is required for mutagenesis. Insertion of bases across from

UV photoproducts leads most frequently to transition mutations, but other base substitutions (transversions) and frame-shifts are also stimulated by UV light, as are duplications and deletions. The mutagenic specificity of UV light is illustrated in Figure 15-10.

Figure 15-13. Alkylation-induced specific mispairing. The alkylation (in this case ethylation generated by EMS) of the O-6 position of guanine and also the O-4 position of thymine can lead to direct mispairing with thymine and guanine, respectively, as shown here. In bacteria, where mutations have been analyzed in great detail, the principal mutations detected are GC → AT transitions, indicating that the O-6 alkylation of guanine is most relevant to mutagenesis.

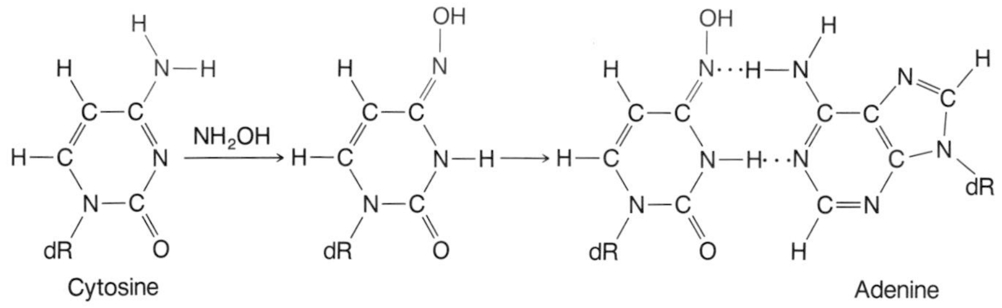

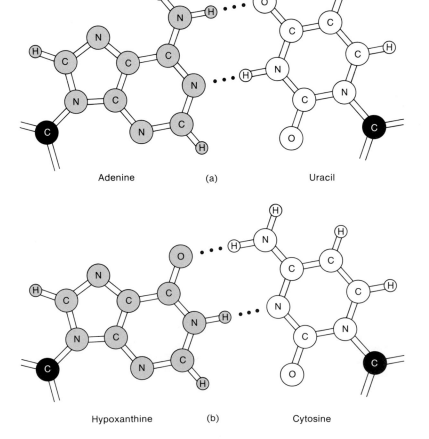

Figure 15-14. A possible explanation for the GC → AT specificity of HA in some organisms. Cytosine is modified to pair like thymine, resulting in a GC → AT transition.

Aflatoxin B$_1$ (AFB$_1$) is a powerful carcinogen, which generates apurinic sites following the formation of an addition product at the N-7 position of guanine (Figure 15-20). Studies with apurinic sites generated in vitro have demonstrated a requirement for the SOS system and have also shown that bypass of these sites leads to the preferential insertion of an adenine across from an apurinic site. This predicts that agents that cause depurination at guanine residues should induce preferentially GC → TA transversions. Can you see why the insertion of an adenine across from an apurinic site derived from a guanine would generate this

substitution at the next round of replication? Figure 15-10 shows the genetic analysis of many base substitutions induced by AFB$_1$. You can verify that most of the substitutions are indeed GC → TA transversions.

AFB$_1$ is a member of a class of chemical carcinogens that generate bulky addition products by binding covalently to DNA. Other examples include the diolepoxides of benzo(a)pyrene, a compound produced by internal combustion engines. For many different compounds it is not yet clear *which* DNA addition products play the principal role in mutagenesis. In some cases, the mutagenic specificity

Adenine   (a)   Uracil

Hypoxanthine   (b)   Cytosine

Figure 15-15. Nitrous acid (NA) mutagenesis. (a) NA deaminates cytosine to form uracil, which bonds like thymine. (b) NA deaminates adenine to form hypoxanthine, which bonds like guanine. These altered bonding patterns can lead to mutations. For example, AT may become GC, or GC may become AT. (From E. Freese, in *Structure and Function of Genetic Elements,* Brookhaven Symposia in Biology, No. 12, Brookhaven National Laboratory, Upton, N.Y., 1959.)

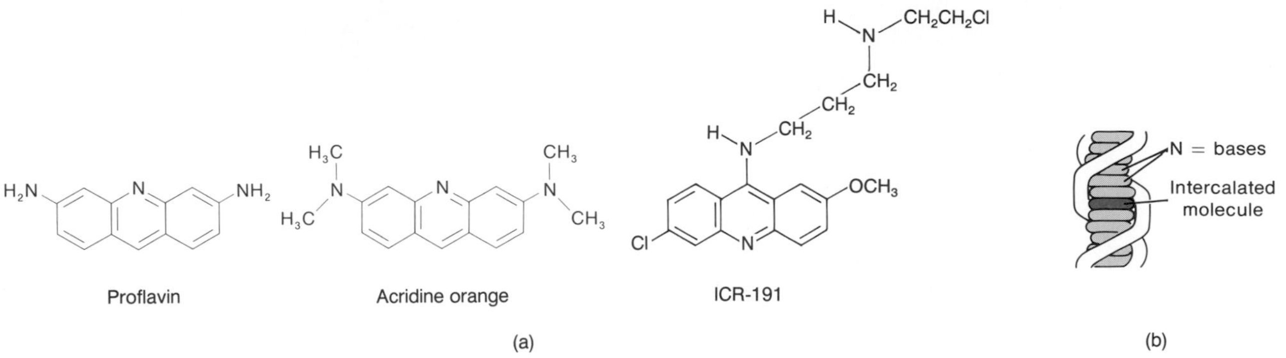

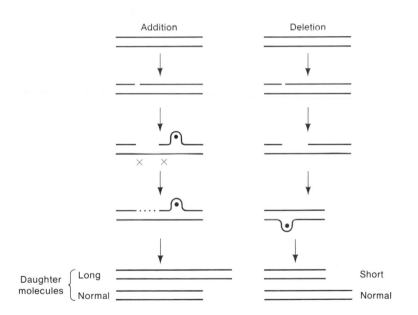

Figure 15-16. Intercalating agents. (a) Structures of the common agents proflavin, acridine orange, and ICR-191. (b) An intercalating agent slips between the stack of bases at the center of the DNA molecule. This occurrence can lead to single-nucleotide-pair insertions and deletions. (From L. S. Lerman, *Proc. Natl. Acad. Sci. USA* 49:94, 1963.)

Figure 15-17. Model for the action of intercalating agents to cause short deletions or insertions. In this model, we assume that the agents are active only during DNA processing (repair or recombination), when they insert into a single-stranded loop and stabilize it. (See also Figures 15-4 and 15-16.) For an addition to occur, the loop can form only if there is a short repeat length of complementary sequence (indicated by X).

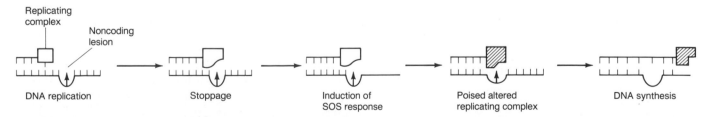

Figure 15-18. The SOS bypass system. This highly schematic diagram represents the stoppage of DNA replication in response to a noncoding lesion. The SOS system relieves this blockage, perhaps by altering the replicating complex.

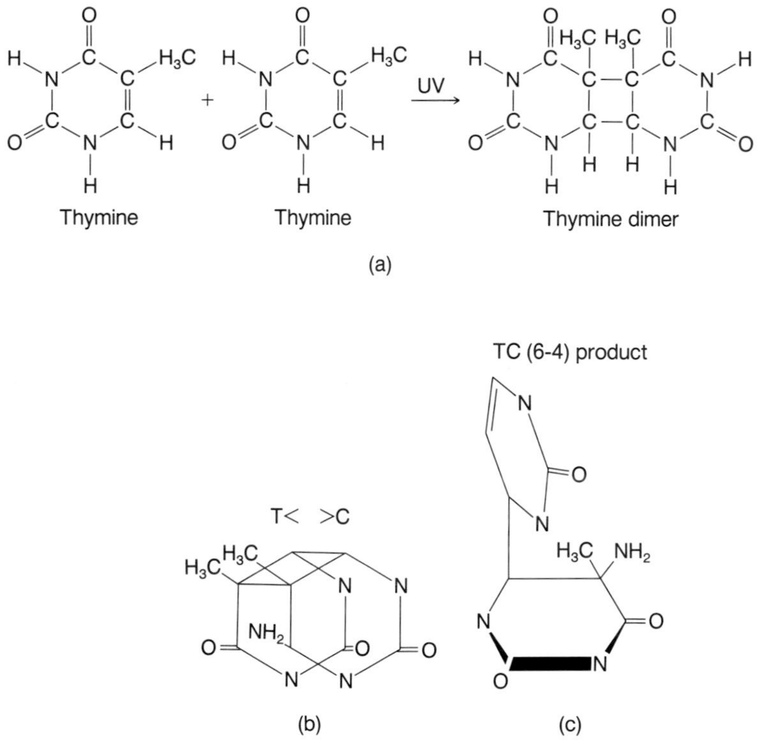

(a)

Thymine + Thymine --UV--> Thymine dimer

TC (6-4) product

T< >C

(b) **(c)**

Figure 15-19. UV photoproducts. (a) Cyclobutane-pyrimidine dimer of T and T, (b) three-dimensional view of dimer of T and C, (c) the 6-4 photo product of T and C.

suggests that depurination may represent an intermediate step in mutagenesis; in others, the question of which mechanism is operating is completely open.

Message Mutagens induce mutations by a variety of mechanisms. The active participation of an enzyme system, termed the SOS system, is required to convert some DNA damage into mutations that are recovered in viable cells.

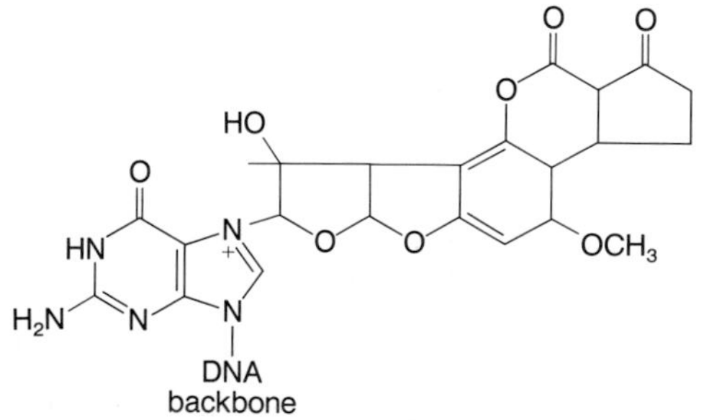

DNA backbone

Figure 15-20. The binding of metabolically activated aflatoxin B$_1$ to DNA (see text).

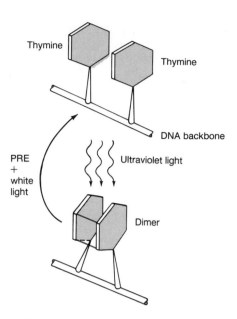

Figure 15-21. Illustration of thymine dimerization between adjacent thymine bases in a single strand of DNA. (PRE stands for photoreactivating enzyme.) (After J. D. Watson, *Molecular Biology of the Gene,* 3d ed., W. A. Benjamin, Menlo Park, Cal., 1976.)

Biological Repair Mechanisms

Living cells have numerous repair systems to deal with damage to the genetic material. The activity of repair enzymes is essential for maintaining the stability of the genome. Some enzymatic systems directly remove lesions, whereas others first excise bases and then fill in the resulting gaps. Certain systems even operate after DNA replication has generated mismatched bases. Although repair mechanisms have been more completely characterized in bacteria, counterparts in higher cells have also been described. Let us consider some of the known systems.

Direct Removal of Lesions

The direct removal of lesions by enzymes has been well documented in two systems. In the first system, the photodimers generated by UV light (Figure 15-19) are split in the presence of white light by photoreactivating enzyme (PRE), to restore the normal pyrimidine bases. These events are diagrammed in Figure 15-21.

The second system involves the enzyme alkyltransferase, which removes certain alkyl groups added to the O-6 position of guanine (see Figure 15-13) by agents such as NG and EMS. The damaged nucleotide is not released from the DNA. Instead, the alkyl group is transferred to a cysteine residue in the enzyme itself, as shown in Figure 15-22. Alkyltransferases have been found both in bacteria and in human cells.

Excision of Damaged Base Pairs

Excision Repair. A general excision-repair system has been well studied in *E. coli,* in which it is encoded by three

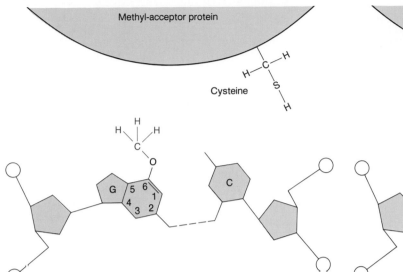

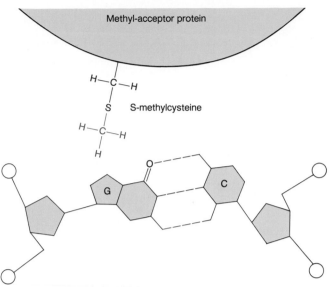

Figure 15-22. Methylation of one site in a guanine by the chemical agent nitrosoguanidine (NG) is repaired by a novel process. The NG adds a methyl group (CH_3) to various sites in DNA, including an oxygen atom at position 6 of guanine (left), disrupting the guanine's hydrogen bonding to a cytosine. Here the repair is accomplished by a protein that is synthesized in the cell during a period of adaptation when the cell is exposed to a low level of NG. A cysteine (one of the 20 amino acids) on the protein acts as a methyl acceptor: it binds the CH_3 group, thereby restoring the guanine to its original state (right). (From P. Howard-Flanders, "Inducible Repair of DNA." Copyright © 1981 by Scientific American, Inc. All rights reserved.)

genes: *uvrA, uvrB,* and *uvrC.* This system removes many damaged base pairs that cause a recognizable distortion of the DNA double helix. The excision produces a gap, which is then filled in by DNA polymerase I and DNA ligase, as shown in Figure 15-23. The system excises the principal UV photoproducts (Figure 15-19), as well as the bulky chemical additions resulting from the binding of compounds such as AFB_1 and epoxides of benzo(a)pyrene.

A human disease caused by a deficiency in one of the excision-repair enzymes is xeroderma pigmentosum (Figure 15-24). This recessive hereditary disease involves formation of skin cancers after exposure to the UV rays in sunlight. The unrepaired DNA damage presumably results in cancer. The difference in UV photosensitivity between normal and diseased cells is evident from the survival curves in Figure 15-25.

Excision-repair systems that remove specific lesions are also known. Two such systems are the AP endonuclease repair pathway and the DNA glycolase repair pathway.

AP Endonuclease Repair Pathway.   All cells have endonucleases that attack the sites left after spontaneous loss of single purine or pyrimidine residues. For convenience, the apurinic and the apyrimidinic sites are termed **AP sites,** since they are biochemically equivalent (see Figure 15-7). The **AP endonucleases** are vital to the cell, since, as was noted earlier, spontaneous depurination is a relatively frequent event. These enzymes introduce chain breaks by cleaving the phosphodiester bonds at AP sites. This initi-

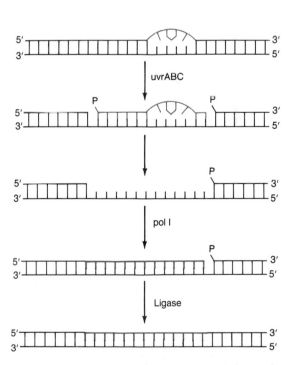

Figure 15-23. A model for nucleotide-excision repair in *E. coli.* UvrABC nuclease hydrolyzes the eighth phosphodiester bond 5′ and the fourth phosphodiester bond 3′ to the pyrimidine dimer, producing a 12-nucleotide-long single-stranded DNA fragment and 3′-OH and 5′-phosphoryl termini. The oligonucleotide carrying the damage is removed, and the resulting gap is filled by DNA polymerase I (pol I) and sealed by DNA ligase. This diagram shows the removal of a 12-nucleotide fragment. The uvrABC nuclease also generates oligonucleotides 13 bases long. (From A. Sancar and W. D. Rupp., *Cell* 33:249–260.)

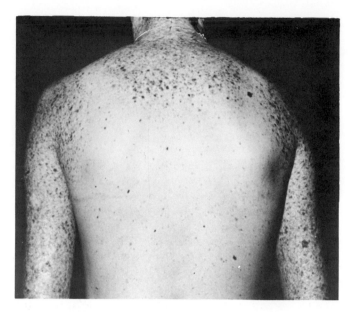

Figure 15-24. Skin cancer in the inherited human disease xeroderma pigmentosum. This recessive hereditary disease is caused by a deficiency in one of the excision-repair enzymes, which leads to the formation of skin cancers upon exposure of the skin to the UV rays in sunlight. (From Dirk Bootsma, Erasmus University, Rotterdam.)

an AP site, the AP endonucleases can complete the restoration to wild-type. The enzymes that excise specific damaged bases are called DNA glycosylases.

DNA Glycosylase Repair Pathway. **DNA glycosylases** do not cleave phosphodiester bonds, but instead cleave N-glycosidic (base-sugar) bonds, liberating the altered base and generating an AP site (Figure 15-27). The AP site resulting from glycosylase action is subsequently repaired by the pathway shown in Figure 15-26. Namely, AP endonucleases cleave the phosphodiester bond, and exonuclease excision is followed by repair mediated by DNA polymerase and ligase (Figure 15-26). Uracil DNA glycosylase (shown in the specific example in Figure 15-27) removes uracil from DNA. Uracil residues result from deamination of cytosine (Figure 15-8) and can lead to a C-to-T transition if unrepaired. It is possible that the pairing partner of adenine in DNA is thymine (5-methyluracil), rather than uracil, in order to allow recognition and excision of the uracil

ates an excision-repair process mediated by an exonuclease, DNA polymerase I, and DNA ligase, as pictured in Figure 15-26. (The last two steps are identical to the corresponding steps in the previously mentioned excision repair shown in Figure 15-24.)

The efficiency of the AP endonuclease repair pathway allows it to be used as the final step of other repair pathways. Thus, if damaged base pairs can be excised, leaving

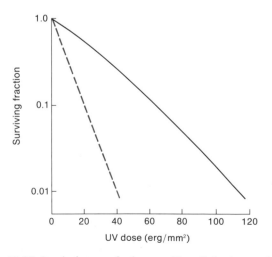

Figure 15-25. Survival curves for human skin cells in tissue culture after exposure to various dosages of UV radiation. The solid line shows the curve for normal cells; the dashed line shows the survival curve for cells from an individual with xeroderma pigmentosum. (After J. E. Cleaver, *Advances in Radiation Biology*, Vol. 4, 1974.)

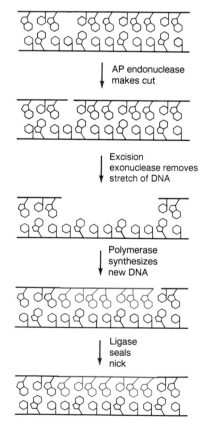

Figure 15-26. Repair of AP sites. AP endonucleases recognize AP sites and cut the phosphodiester bond. A stretch of DNA is removed by an exonuclease, and the resulting gap is filled in by DNA polymerase I and DNA ligase. (After B. Lewin, *Genes*, Wiley, New York, 1983, p. 561.)

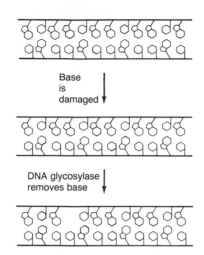

Figure 15-27. Action of DNA glycosylases. Glycosylases remove altered bases and leave an AP site. The AP site is subsequently excised by the AP endonucleases diagrammed in Figure 15-26. (After B. Lewin, *Genes*, Wiley, New York, 1983, p. 561.)

residues that result from spontaneous deamination of cytosine. If uracil were a normal constituent of DNA, such repair would not be possible. There is also a glycosylase that recognizes and excises hypoxanthine, the deamination product of adenine.

Different glycosylases have been described that remove alkylated bases (such as 3-methyladenine, 3-methylguanine, and 7-methylguanine), ring-opened purines, and, in some organisms, UV photodimers. New glycosylases are still being discovered.

Post-Replication Repair

Mismatch Repair System. Errors introduced during DNA replication can be repaired by a sophisticated repair system that can recognize certain mispaired bases. One of the mispaired bases can be excised, and repair synthesis can be accomplished by using the other strand as a template. In order to do this, however, there must be a mechanism for recognizing the strand carrying the correct information. For reversing errors that occur during replication, the ability to recognize the original template strand is crucial. For this purpose the cell takes advantage of DNA methylation. The enzyme adenine methylase catalyzes the addition of a methyl group to the N-6 position of adenines, which are part of a $\begin{smallmatrix}5'-G-A-T-C-3'\\3'-C-T-A-G-5'\end{smallmatrix}$ sequence in *E. coli*, where this system has been well studied. Immediately after replication of a $\begin{smallmatrix}\text{m}\\5'-G-A-T-C-3'\\3'-C-T-A-G-5'\\\text{m}\end{smallmatrix}$ sequence, the newly synthesized strand will not be methylated. The unmethylated strand is distinguished by the repair system that recognizes mismatched bases. This **mismatch repair system** excises incorrect bases from the newly synthesized strand, as depicted in Figure 15-28.

Recombinational Repair. The *recA* gene, which is involved in SOS bypass (see Figure 15-18), is also involved in a post-replication recombinational repair. The DNA replication system stalls at a UV photodimer or other blocking lesion, leaving a single-stranded gap. In recombinational repair, this gap is patched by DNA cut from the sister molecule (see Figure 15-29a). This process seems to lead to few errors. SOS bypass is, however, highly mutagenic, as described earlier. Here the replication system continues past the lesion (Figures 15-18 and 15-29b), accepting noncomplementary nucleotides for new strand synthesis.

Message Repair enzymes play a crucial role in reducing genetic damage in living cells. Many different repair pathways have been characterized (Table 15-2 summarizes these pathways).

Mutators

As the preceding description of repair processes indicates, normal cells are programmed for error avoidance. The repair processes are so efficient that the observed base-substitution rate is as low as 10^{-10} to 10^{-9} per base pair per cell per generation. However, mutant strains have been detected with an increased spontaneous mutation rate. Such strains are termed **mutators.** In many cases the mutator phenotype is due to a defective repair system. In *E. coli* the mutator loci *mutH*, *mutL*, and *mutS* affect components of the post-replication mismatch repair system, as does the *dam* locus, which specifies the enzyme deoxyadenosine methylase. Dam⁻ strains cannot methylate adenines at

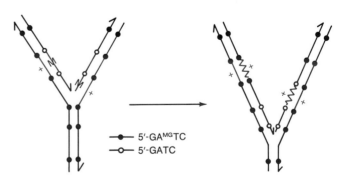

Figure 15-28. Mismatch correction in replicational heteroduplexes: sequence conservation by strand-directed mismatch repair. Mismatched base pairs (+/M) arising as replicational errors (mutations M) are corrected by excision and resynthesis (ᐱᐱ). Only the newly synthesized strands segments proximal to the replication fork contain unmethylated GATC sequences (–O–) and therefore are subject to efficient mismatch repair. (From F. Bourguignon-Van Horen et al., *Biochimie* 64:559–564, 1982.)

Postreplication recombination repair.

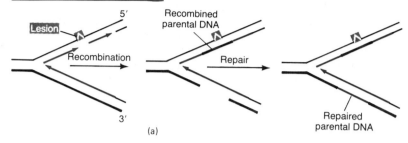

(a)

Error-prone (SOS) replication (dimer bypass)

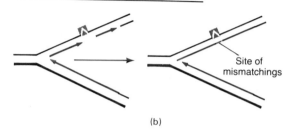

(b)

Figure 15-29. Schemes for recombination repair or lesion bypass. (a) Postreplication recombination repair. (b) SOS bypass. (From A. Kornberg, *DNA Replication.* Copyright © 1980 by W. H. Freeman and Co.)

■ **TABLE 15-2.** Repair systems in *E. coli*

General mode of operation	Example	Type of lesion repaired	Mechanism
Direct removal of lesions	Alkyltransferases	O-6-alkylguanine	Transfer alkyl group from O-6-guanine to cysteine residue on transferase
	Photoreactivating enzyme (PRE)	UV photodimers	Splits dimers in the presence of white light
General excision	*uvrABC*-encoded exonuclease system	Lesions causing distortions in double helix, such as UV photoproducts, and bulky chemical adducts	Makes endonucleolytic cut on either side of lesion; resulting gap is repaired by DNA polymerase I and DNA ligase
Specific excision	AP endonuclease	AP sites	Makes endonucleolytic cut; exonuclease creases gap, which is repaired by polymerase I and ligase
	DNA glycosylases	Certain altered bases, such as deaminated bases (uracil, hypoxanthine), certain methylated bases, ring-opened purines, and other modified bases	Removes base, creating AP site, which is repaired by AP endonucleases
Postreplication	Mismatch-repair system	Replication errors resulting in base-pair mismatches	This system recognizes which strand is correct by detecting methylated A residues that are part of the 5'-GATC-3' sequence, and then excises bases from the newly synthesized strand when a mismatch is detected
	Recombinational repair	Lesions that block replication and result in single-stranded gaps	Recombinational exchange
	SOS system	Lesions that block replication	Allow replication bypass of blocking lesion, resulting in frequent mutations across from lesion

GATC sequences, and the mismatch repair system can no longer discriminate between the template and the newly synthesized strands. This leads to a higher spontaneous mutation rate.

Ung⁻ mutants are missing the enzyme uracil DNA glycosylase. These mutants cannot repair cytosine deaminations and have elevated levels of $C \rightarrow T$ transitions. The *mutD* locus is responsible for a very high rate of mutagenesis, at least three orders of magnitude higher than normal. Mutations at this locus affect the proofreading function of DNA polymerase III.

Not all mutators are well understood. For instance, the *mutT* locus raises the level of only $AT \rightarrow CG$ transversions, for reasons that are still not clear.

Reversion Analysis

In this chapter we have considered the different pathways leading to mutagenesis and have observed that mutagenic processes are often very specific. We can now begin to see how reversion analysis can tell us something about the nature of a mutation or something about the action of a mutagen. For example, if a mutation cannot be reverted by action of the mutagen that induced it, then the mutagen must have some relatively specific unilateral action. In the case of a mutation induced by hydroxylamine (HA), it would be reasonable to expect that the original mutation is $GC \rightarrow AT$, which of course cannot be reverted by another specific $GC \rightarrow AT$ event. Similarly, mutations that can be reverted by proflavin are in all likelihood frame-shift mutations, those induced by nitrous acid (NA) mutations (which are transitions) should not be revertible by proflavin. Transversions are not as easy to detect by reversion, but they are known definitely to be common among spontaneous mutations, as shown by studies of DNA and protein sequencing. Thus, in the reversion test, if a mutation does revert spontaneously but does not revert in response to a transition mutagen or a frame-shift mutagen, then by elimination it is probably a transversion. Note that the kinds of logic employed in the reversion test rely heavily on the assumption that the reversion events are not due to suppressors or transposable elements; either of these would make inference from reversion more difficult. Table 15-3 summarizes some reversion expectations based on simple assumptions.

The system outlined in Table 15-3 is intended merely to illustrate the kinds of inferences possible from reversion analysis. Recall that mutagen specificities depend on the organism, the genotype, the gene studied, and perhaps even the *region* of the gene studied.

The Ames Test

There is increasing awareness of a correlation between mutagenicity and carcinogenicity. One study showed that 157 of 175 known carcinogens are also mutagens (a ratio of 90 percent). The somatic-notation theory of cancer holds that these agents cause cancer by inducing mutation of somatic cells. This means that mutagenesis is of great relevance to our society. We are faced not only with the genetic time bomb of germinal mutation, with its potential for increasing inherited disease over the long term, but also with somatic genetic disease of cancer with its overwhelming immediacy. The modern environment exposes each individual to a wide variety of chemicals in drugs, cosmetics, food preservatives, pesticides, compounds used in industry, pollutants, and so on. Many of these compounds have been shown to be carcinogenic and mutagenic (Figure 15-30). Examples include the food preservative AF-2, the food fumigant ethylene dibromide, the antischistosome drug hycanthone, several hair-dye additives, and the industrial compound vinyl chloride; all are potent, and some have subsequently been subjected to government control. However, hundreds of new chemicals and products appear on the market each week. How can such vast numbers of new

■ **TABLE 15-3.** Different types of point mutations theoretically distinguishable by their reversion behaviors in response to a battery of specific mutagens

Mutation	Reversion mutagen			
	NA	HA or EMS	Proflavin	Spontaneous
Transition, GC ⟶ AT	+	−	−	+
Transition, AT ⟶ GC	+	+	−	+
Transversion	−	−	−	+
Frame-shift	−	−	+	+

NOTE: a plus (+) indicates a measurable rate of reversion due to a given mutagen. NA = nitrous acid; HA = hydroxylamine; EMS = ethylmethanesulfonate.

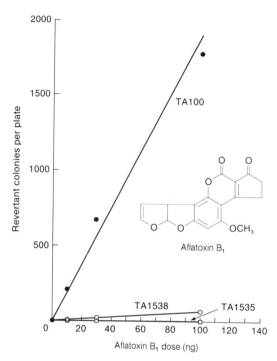

Figure 15-30. The mutagenicity in the Ames test of aflatoxin B_1, which is also a potent carcinogen. TA100, TA1538, and TA1535 are strains of *Salmonella* bearing different *his* auxotrophic mutations. The *Salmonella* strain TA100 is a *his* mutant strain that is highly sensitive to reversion through base-pair substitution. The strains TA1535 and TA1538 are *his* mutant strains sensitive to reversion through frame-shift mutation. The results of this test show that aflatoxin B_1 is a potent mutagen causing base-pair substitutions but not frame-shifts. This is the Ames test used to detect mutagens. (From J. McCann and B. N. Ames, in *Advances in Modern Toxicology*, Vol. 5, W. G. Flamm and M. A. Mehlman, eds., Hemisphere Publishing Corp.)

agents be tested for carcinogenicity before much of the population has been exposed to them?

Many test systems have been devised to screen for carcinogenicity. These are time-consuming tests, typically involving laborious research with small mammals. More rapid tests do exist that make use of microbes (such as fungi or bacteria) and test for mutagenicity rather than carcinogenicity. The most widely used test was developed in the 1970s by Bruce Ames, using *Salmonella typhimurium*. This **Ames test** uses two auxotrophic histidine mutations, which revert by different molecular mechanisms. Further properties were genetically engineered into these strains to make them suitable for mutagen detection. First, they carry a mutation that inactivates the excision-repair system. Second, they carry a mutation eliminating the protective lipopolysaccharide coating of wild-type *Salmonella*, so that any escaping bacteria will be unable to survive in such natural (but chemically hostile) environments as sewers or intestines.

Bacteria are evolutionarily a long way removed from humans. Can the results of such a test in bacteria have any real significance in detecting chemicals dangerous for humans? First, we have seen that the genetic and chemical nature of DNA is identical in all organisms, so that a compound acting as a mutagen in one organism is likely to have some mutagenic effects in other organisms. Second, Ames

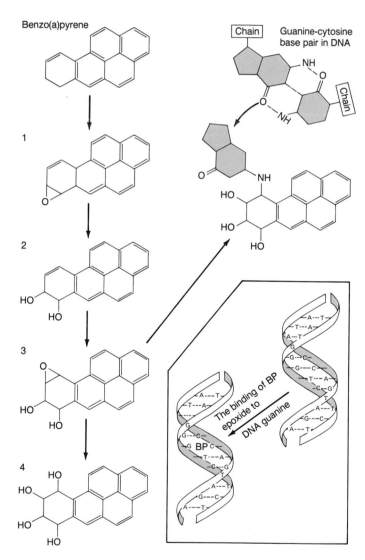

Figure 15-31. The detoxification and metabolic activation of benzo(a)pyrene. The detoxification of the carcinogen benzo(a)pyrene (BP) goes through several steps, as it is made more water-soluble prior to excretion. One of the intermediates in this process (3) is capable of reacting with guanine in DNA (upper right of the diagram). This leads to a distortion of the DNA molecule and mutations as described in the text. Benzo(a)pyrene is therefore a mutagen for any cell that has the enzymes that produce this intermediate. (After I. B. Weinstein et al., *Science* 193: 592–595, 1976. From J. Cairns, *Cancer: Science and Society*. Copyright © 1978 by W. H. Freeman and Co.)

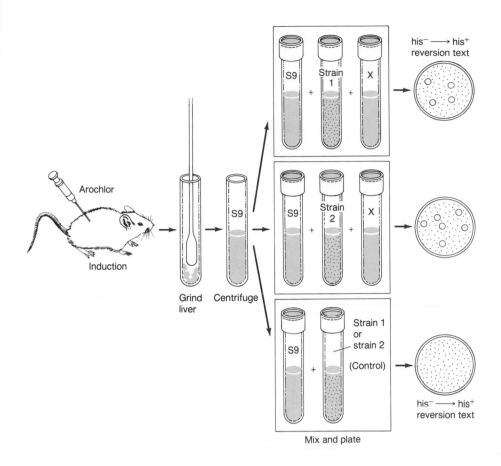

Figure 15-32. Summary of the procedure used for the Ames test. First, rat liver enzymes are mobilized by injecting the animals with Aroclor. (Enzymes from the liver are used because it carries out the processes of detoxifying and toxifying body chemicals.) The rat liver is then homogenized, and the supernatant of solubilized rat liver enzymes (S9) is added to a suspension of auxotrophic bacteria in a solution of the potential carcinogen (X). This mixture is plated on a medium containing no histidine, and revertants of mutant strains 1 and 2 are looked for. A control experiment containing no potential carcinogen is always run simultaneously. The presence of revertants indicates that the chemical is a mutagen and possibly a carcinogen as well.

devised a way to simulate the human metabolism in the bacterial system. Much of the important processing of ingested chemicals in mammals occurs in the liver, where externally derived compounds normally are detoxified or broken down. In some cases, the action of liver enzymes can create a toxic or mutagenic compound from a substance that was not originally dangerous, as shown in Figure 15-31. Ames set out to incorporate the mammalian liver enzymes in his bacterial test system.

Rat livers are normally used for this purpose. First, the liver enzymes are mobilized by injection of Arochlor, a polychlorinated biphenyl (PCB), into the rats. The rats are then killed, and their livers are homogenized and centrifuged to remove cell debris. The supernatant, called S9 mix, contains the solubilized batteries of rat liver enzymes. The S9 mix is added to a suspension of auxotrophic bacteria in a solution of the suspected carcinogen being tested. The solution is then plated on a medium containing no histidine, and later the plates are scored for colonies of revertants (Figure 15-32).

The Ames test has detected potential carcinogens among a wide variety of heterogeneous types of chemicals. Of course, chemicals detected by this test can be regarded not only as potential carcinogens (sources of somatic mutations) but also as possible causes of mutations in germinal cells. Because the test system is so simple and inexpensive, many laboratories throughout the world now routinely test large numbers of potentially hazardous compounds for mutagenicity and potential carcinogenicity.

Summary

■ Gene mutations can arise by many different processes. Spontaneous mutations can result from replication errors, or from spontaneous lesions such as those generated by deamination or depurination. (Recombination and transposable elements can also result in altered genes, as described in Chapters 16 and 17.) Mutagens can increase the frequency of mutations. Some of these agents act by mimicking a base but then pairing differently during DNA replication. Others alter bases in the DNA and convert them to derivatives that pair differently. A third class of mutagens, which includes most carcinogens, damages DNA in such a way that replication is blocked. The activation of an enzymatic pathway, termed the SOS system, is required to replicate past the blocking lesions. This results in mutations that appear mainly across from the blocking lesion. Repair enzymes present in living cells greatly minimize genetic damage, thus averting many mutations. Mutant organisms lacking certain repair enzymes have higher mutation rates than normal.

Our knowledge of the molecular basis of mutation can be exploited for useful purposes. One example is the Ames test, which utilizes mutant bacterial strains to test compounds in the environment for mutagenic activity. Because of the correlation between mutagenicity and carcinogenicity, the identification of potential carcinogens in the environment can be achieved by this rapid assay.

Problems

1. Differentiate between the following pairs:
   a. Transitions and transversions
   b. Silent and neutral mutations
   c. Missense and nonsense mutations
   d. Frame-shift and nonsense mutations

2. Why are frame-shift mutations more likely to result in proteins lacking normal function than nonsense mutations?

3. Describe the Streisinger model for frame-shift formation. Show how this model can explain mutational hotspots in the *lacI* gene of *E. coli*.

4. Diagram two different mechanisms for deletion formation. How do DNA sequencing experiments suggest these possibilities?

5. Describe two spontaneous lesions that can lead to mutations.

6. Compare the mechanism of action of 5-bromouracil (5-BU) with ethylmethanesulfonate (EMS) in causing mutations. Explain the specificity of mutagenesis for each agent in light of the proposed mechanism.

7. Compare the two different systems involved in the repair of AP sites and in the removal of bulky chemical adducts.

8. Describe the repair systems that operate after replication.

9. Normal ("tight") auxotrophic mutants will not grow at all in the absence of the appropriate supplement to the medium. However, in mutant hunts for auxotrophic mutants, it is common to find some mutants (called "leaky") that grow very slowly in the absence of the appropriate supplement but normally in the presence of the supplement. Propose an explanation for the molecular nature of the leaky mutants.

10. Strain A of *Neurospora* contains an *ad-3* mutation that reverts spontaneously at a rate of 10^{-6}. Strain A is crossed with a newly acquired wild-type isolate, and *ad-3* strains are recovered from the progeny. When 28 different *ad-3* progeny strains are examined, 13 lines are found to revert at the rate of 10^{-6}, but the remaining 15 lines revert at the rate of 10^{-3}. Formulate a hypothesis to account for these findings, and outline an experimental program to test your hypothesis.

11. a. Why is it not possible to induce nonsense mutations (represented at the mRNA level by the triplets UAG, UAA, and UGA) by treating wild-type strains with mutagens that cause only AT → GC or TA → CG transitions in DNA?

   b. Hydroxylamine (HA) causes only GC → AT or CG → TA transitions in DNA. Will HA produce nonsense mutations in wild-type strains?
   c. Will HA treatment revert nonsense mutations?

12. Several auxotrophic point mutants in *Neurospora* are treated with various agents to see if reversion will occur. Table 15-4 shows the results (with + indicating reversion).

■ TABLE 15-4.

Mutant	Mutagen			
	5-BU	HA	Proflavin	Spontaneous
1	−	−	−	−
2	−	−	+	+
3	+	−	−	+
4	−	−	−	+
5	+	+	−	+

   a. For each of the five mutants, describe the nature of the original mutation event (not the reversion) at the molecular level. Be as specific as possible.

   b. For each of the five mutants, name a possible mutagen that could have caused the original mutation event (spontaneous mutation is not an acceptable answer).

   c. In the reversion experiment for mutant 5, a particularly interesting prototrophic derivative is obtained. When this type is crossed to a standard wild-type strain, the progeny consists of 90 percent prototrophs and 10 percent auxotrophs. Provide a full explanation, including a precise reason for the frequencies observed.

13. You are using nitrous acid to "revert" mutant *nic-2* alleles in *Neurospora*. You treat cells and plate them on medium without nicotinamide and look for prototrophic colonies. You obtain the following results for two mutant alleles. Explain these results at the molecular level, and indicate how you would test your hypotheses.

   a. With *nic-2* allele 1, you obtain no prototrophs at all.

   b. With *nic-2* allele 2, you obtain three prototrophic colonies, and you cross each separately with a wild-type strain. From the cross prototroph A × wild-type, you obtain 100 progeny and all are prototrophic. From the cross prototroph B × wild-type, you obtain 100 progeny, of which 78 are prototrophic and 22 are nicotinamide requiring. From the cross prototroph C × wild-type, you obtain 1000 progeny, of which 996 are prototrophic and 4 are nicotinamide-requiring.

14. Devise very clever screening procedures for detecting the following:

a. Nerve mutants in *Drosophila*

b. Mutants lacking flagella in a haploid unicellular alga

c. Supercolossal-sized mutants in bacteria

d. Mutants that overproduce the black compound me-lanine in haploid fungus cultures (which normally are white)

e. Individual humans (in large populations) whose eyes polarize incoming light

f. Negatively phototropic *Drosophila* or unicellular algae

g. UV-sensitive mutants in haploid yeast

CHAPTER 16

Mechanisms of Genetic Change II: Recombination

■ A normal crossover (a reciprocal intrachromosomal recombination event) is really an extraordinary process. Somehow the genetic material from one parental chromosome and the genetic material from the other parental chromosome are "cut up and pasted together" during each meiosis, and this is done with complete reciprocity. In other words, neither chromosome gains or loses any genes in the process. In fact, it is probably correct to say that neither chromosome gains or loses even one nucleotide in the exchange. How is this remarkable precision attained? We do not know for sure, but many interesting phenomena provide important clues about the nature of the answer.

General Homologous Recombination

Breakage and Reunion of DNA Molecules

Throughout our analysis of linkage, we implicitly assumed that crossing-over occurs by some process of breakage and reunion of chromatids. The evidence against the copy-choice hypothesis (Chapter 5) provides good *indirect* evidence in favor of breakage and reunion. Furthermore, there is good genetic and cytological evidence that crossing-over occurs during prophase of meiosis rather than during interphase, when chromosomal DNA is replicating. A small amount of DNA synthesis does occur during prophase, but certainly chromosome replication is not associated with crossing-over. One of the first direct proofs that chromosomes (albeit viral chromosomes) can break and rejoin came from experiments on λ phage done in 1961 by Matthew Meselson and Jean Weigle.

Meselson and Weigle multiply infected *E. coli* with two strains of λ. One strain had the genetic markers c and mi at one end of the chromosome, and this chromosome was "heavy" because the phages were produced from cells growing in heavy isotopes of carbon (^{13}C) and nitrogen (^{15}N). The other strain was $++$ for the markers and had "light" DNA because it was harvested from cells grown on the normal light isotopes ^{12}C and ^{14}N. The two DNAs (chromosomes) can be represented as shown in Figure 16-1a. The multiply infected cells were now incubated in light medium until they lysed.

The progeny phage released from the cells were spun in a cesium chloride density gradient. A wide band was obtained, indicating that the virus DNAs ranged in density from the heavy parental value to the light parental value, with a great many intermediate densities (Figure 16-1b). Interestingly, some recombinant phages were recovered with density values very close to the heavy parental value. They were of genotype $c+$, and they must have arisen through an exchange event between the two markers (Figure 16-1c). The heavy density of the chromosome would be expected because only the small tip of the chromosome

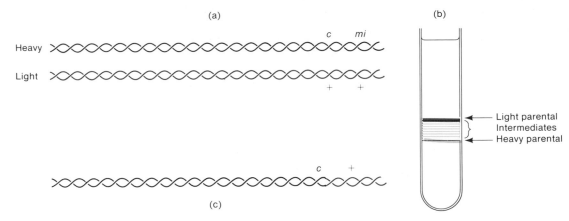

Figure 16-1. Evidence for chromosome breakage and reunion in λ phage. (a) The chromosomes of the two λ strains used to multiply infect *E. coli*. (b) Bands produced when progeny phage are spun in a cesium chloride density gradient. The fact that intermediate densities are obtained indicates a range of chromosome compositions with partly light and partly heavy components. (c) The chromosome of the heavy *c* + progeny resulting from crossover between the two markers. The density of this crossover product confirms that the crossover involved a physical breakage and reunion of the DNA.

carrying the *mi*+ allele would come from the "light" parental chromosome. When heavy + + phage were crossed with light *c mi*, the heavy recombinants were found to be +*mi*, and the light recombinants were found to be *c*+, as expected. These results can be explained in only one way: the recombination event must have occurred through the physical breakage and reunion of DNA. Of course, it is unwise to extrapolate from viral to eukaryotic chromosomes. However, this evidence shows that the breakage and reunion of DNA strands is a chemical possibility.

Chiasmata: The Crossover Points

In Chapter 5, we made the simple assumption that chiasmata are the actual sites of crossovers. Mapping analysis gives indirect support for this idea: since an average of one crossover per meiosis produces 50 genetic map units, there should be correlation between the size of the genetic map of a chromosome and the observed mean number of chiasmata per meiosis. This correlation has been made in well-mapped organisms.

However, the harlequin chromosome staining technique (see Chapter 10) has made it possible to test the idea directly. In 1978, C. Tease and G. H. Jones prepared harlequin chromosomes in meioses of the locust. You will remember that the harlequin technique produces sister chromatids, one of which is dark and the other light. When a crossover occurs, it can involve two dark, two light, or a dark and a light nonsister chromatid. This latter situation is crucial because mixed (part dark and part light) crossover chromatids are produced. Tease and Jones found that the dark/light transition occurred right at the chiasma, proving beyond reasonable doubt that these are the sites of crossing-over, and settling a question that had been unresolved since the early part of the century (Figure 16-2).

A Crossover Model

Much of the available information on the mechanism of intrachromosomal recombination, especially at the chemical level, has come from study of bacteria and phage. In addition, we shall consider information of a different kind based on genetic analysis of eukaryotes. We shall be studying what can be called the genetics of genetics! Several clues about recombination mechanisms have emerged in studies of eukaryotes.

Clue 1: Chromatid Conversion and Half-Chromatid Conversion. Much information about recombination in eukaryotes has come from studies of fungi. There is one good

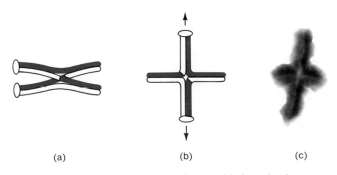

(a)   (b)   (c)

Figure 16-2. Crossing-over between dark- and light-stained nonsister chromatids in a meiosis in the locust. (a) Representation of the chiasma. (b) The best stage for observing is when the centromeres have pulled apart slightly, forming a cross-shaped structure with the chiasma at the center. (c) Photograph of the stage shown in (b). (Photo courtesy of C. Tease and G. H. Jones, *Chromosoma* 69:163–178, 1978.)

+	+	m	+	+	+
+	+	m	+	+	+
+	+	m	+	+	+
+	+	m	+	m	m
m	+	m	+	m	+
m	+	m	m	m	m
m	m	+	m	m	m
m	m	+	m	m	m
4:4	6:2	2:6	5:3	3:5	3:1:1:3

(Note: 3:1:1:3 = aberrant 4:4.)

Normal	Chromatid conversion	Half-chromatid conversion

Figure 16-3. Rare aberrant allele ratios observed in a cross of type + × m in fungi. (Ascus genotypes are represented here.) When the Mendelian ratio of 4:4 is not obtained, some of the alleles in the cross have been converted to the opposite allele. In some asci, it appears that the entire chromatid has been converted (6:2 or 2:6 ratios). In others, it appears that only half-chromatids have been converted (5:3, 3:5, or 3:1:1:3 ratios).

reason for this: the ascus. All products of a single meiosis can be recovered and examined, so that records of each meiosis can be kept quite precisely in terms of the total genetic information being lost or gained. Because we can recover all four products of a specific meiosis, we can make inferences about events occurring during that meiosis with a high degree of confidence. The ascus represents a tight system of internally self-consistent controls.

Non-Mendelian allele ratios are detectable in some asci. Mendel would have predicted 4:4 segregations for all monohybrid crosses, but other ratios are obtained very rarely (in 0.1 to 1 percent of all asci, depending on the fungus species). Figure 16-3 gives the most common aberrant ratios obtained. It appears as though some genes in the cross have been "converted" to the opposite allele (Figure

16-4). The process therefore became known as **gene conversion;** it can occur only where there is heterozygosity for two different alleles of a gene. In some asci, the entire chromatid in meiosis seems to have converted; this process is called **chromatid conversion.** In other asci, only half of the chromatid seems to have converted, so the process is called **half-chromatid conversion.** In half-chromatid conversions, different members of a spore pair have different genotypes. Recall that each spore pair is produced by mitosis from a single product of meiosis. Half-chromatid conversion implies that two strands of one double helix carry information for two different alleles at the conclusion of meiosis. Following the next mitotic division to form a spore pair, the two strands segregate to separate nuclei.

It should be emphasized that alleles heterozygous at other loci in the same cross typically segregate 4:4, so the aberrant ratios are not the results of accidents of isolation. The process of conversion cannot be mutation, because the process is directional: the allele that is converted always changes to the other specific allele involved in the cross. This specificity has been confirmed in molecular studies on the gene products of converted alleles.

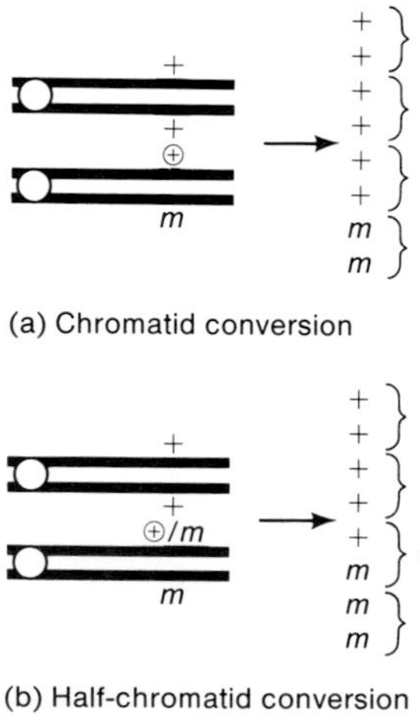

Clue 2: Polarity. In genes for which accurate allele maps are available, we can compare the conversion frequencies of alleles at various positions within the gene. In almost every case, the sites closer to one end show higher frequencies than do those farther away from that end. In other words, there is a gradient, or **polarity,** of conversion frequencies along the gene.

Figure 16-4. Gene conversions are inferred from the patterns of alleles observed in asci. (a) In a chromatid conversion, the allele on one chromatid seems somehow to have been converted to an allele like those on the other chromatid pair. The converted allele is shown by the symbol ⊕. One spore pair is of the opposite genotype from that expected in Mendelian segregation. (b) In a half-chromatid conversion, one spore pair (*) has nonidentical alleles. Somehow, one chromatid seems to be "half-converted," giving rise to one spore of the original genotype and one spore converted to the other allele.

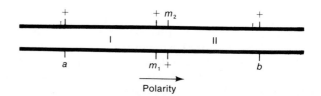

Figure 16-5. Diagram of chromatids involved in a cross. The arrow indicates the polarity of gene conversion in the *m* locus, pointing toward the end with lower conversion frequency.

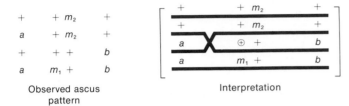

Observed ascus pattern | Interpretation

Figure 16-6. A specific ascus pattern can be explained by both a crossover and a chromatid conversion. In this case, a conversion of $m_1 \rightarrow +$ is accompanied by a crossover in the region between a and m_1.

Clue 3: Conversion and Crossing-Over. In heteroallelic crosses where the locus under study is closely flanked by other genetically marked loci, the conversion event is very often (about 50 percent of the time) accompanied by an exchange in one of the flanking regions. This exchange nearly always occurs on the side nearest the allele that has converted. Furthermore, it almost always involves the chromatid in which conversion has occurred.

For example, consider the chromatids diagrammed in Figure 16-5. Suppose the polarity is such that alleles toward the left end of the chromatid convert more often than those toward the right end. The cross diagrammed here is between $a^+ m_2 b^+$ and $a m_1 b$, where m_1 and m_2 are different alleles of the m locus, and a and b represent closely linked flanking markers. If we look at asci in which conversion has occurred at the m_1 site (the most frequent kind of conversion in this locus), we find that one-half of these asci will also have a crossover in region I, and one-half will have no crossover. In the smaller number of asci showing gene conversion at the m_2 site, one-half will also have a crossover in region II, and one-half will have no crossover. Such events are detected in ascus genotypes like that shown in Figure 16-6, which can be interpreted as a conversion of $m_1 \rightarrow +$, accompanied by a crossover in region I. (If this is a nutritional locus—say, for arginine requirement—see if you can figure out how the genotypes $m_1 +$, $+ m_2$, and $m_1 m_2$ would be distinguished from each other.)

Clue 4: Co-conversion. In some asci, a single conversion event seems to include several sites at once. In a heteroallelic cross, this event is called a **co-conversion** (Figure 16-7). The frequency of co-conversion increases as the distance between alleles decreases.

The Holliday Model. A recombination model has been constructed that accounts for all of these clues. It was originally formulated by Robin Holliday and has subsequently been modified by others. The **Holliday model** is typical of the various recombination models that have been proposed both for eukaryotes and for prokaryotes. The concept of hybrid or "heteroduplex" DNA put forth in this model provides a useful way of expressing the present state of

knowledge about crossing-over. Figure 16-8 depicts the Holliday model in its entirety. It is based on the creation of a cross-bridge that can migrate along the two heteroduplex strands ("branch migration") and the subsequent splicing of the intermediate structure in one of two ways to yield different types of recombinant molecules. Let us examine the aspects of this model in detail.

We can set up a hypothetical cross of $+ \times m$, in which the $+$ site corresponds to a G–C nucleotide pair, and the m site corresponds to a transition mutation A–T (Figure 16-9). The four chromatids are represented as four DNA double helices. The arrows indicate the directions of the DNA strands ($5' \rightarrow 3'$). Also shown is a hypothetical fixed breakage point—perhaps a recognition site for an endonuclease enzyme (its significance will become clear). The fixed breakage points of two nonsister molecules now become the site of phosphodiester-bond breakage (Figure 16-10), and the broken strands unravel away from the fixed breakage point for some distance. The unraveled strands have the same directionality (arrows), so they can rejoin at each other's breakage points through the action of an enzyme, ligase (Figure 16-11). We now have two sets of heteroduplex DNA (the double strands that include both solid and shaded parts) containing illegitimate purine-pyrimidine pairs, G–T and C–A. (We shall return to these later.) Note that the structure generated in Figure 16-11 can be rotated to generate a planar molecule, as depicted in Figure 16-8i.

The tangle at the exchange point is now resolved by "nicking." We can assume that strands 2 and 3 break and rejoin in one-half of the cases (Figure 16-12a). In the other one-half of the cases, strands 1 and 4 break and rejoin (Figure 16-12b). Thus we see that the result can be either a crossover or a noncrossover situation (as depicted in Figure 16-8j and k), with respect to flanking markers, but that two regions of heteroduplex DNA exist in either case.

The heteroduplex DNA, which contains mismatched base pairs, is unstable. The mismatched nucleotides could

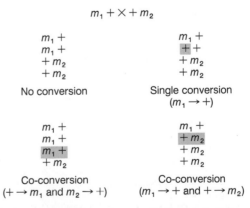

$$m_1 + \times + m_2$$

No conversion

Single conversion $(m_1 \rightarrow +)$

Co-conversion $(+ \rightarrow m_1$ and $m_2 \rightarrow +)$

Co-conversion $(m_1 \rightarrow +$ and $+ \rightarrow m_2)$

Figure 16-7. Sample ascus patterns obtained from a single conversion and co-conversions.

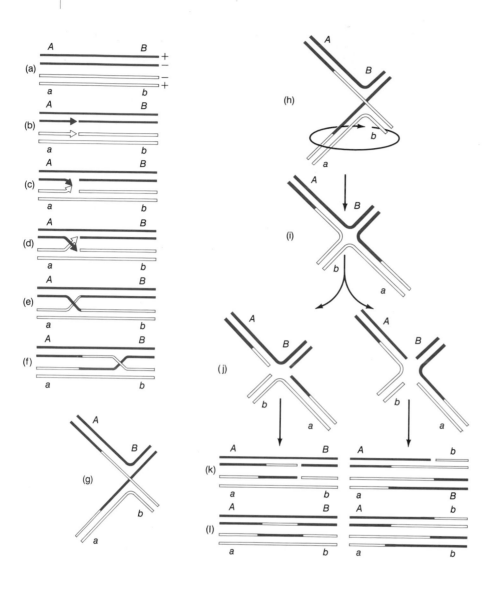

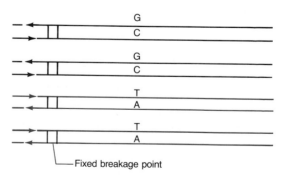

Figure 16-8. A prototype mechanism for genetic recombination. (a). Two homologous double helices are aligned. (b) The two + or two − strands are cut. (c) The free ends leave the complementary strands to which they had been hydrogen-bonded. (d) The free ends become associated with the complementary strands in the homologous double helix. (e) Ligation creates partially heteroduplex double helices. This is the Holliday structure. (f) Migration of the branch point occurs by continuing strand transfer by the two polynucleotide chains involved in the crossover. (g) The Holliday structure shown in an extended form. (h) The rotation of the structure shown in (g) can yield the form depicted in (i). Resolution of the structure shown in (i) can proceed in two ways, depending on the points of enzymatic cleavage, yielding the structures shown in (j), which can be depicted as shown in (k), and repaired to the forms shown in (l). (From H. Potter, D. Dressler, *Cold Spring Harbor Symposium of Quantitative Biology* 43:1979, p. 970. Cold Spring Harbor Laboratory, Cold Spring Harbor, New York.)

produce a distortion in the DNA at these points, which is recognized by a repair system, much as the excision-repair system recognizes and removes the thymine dimers induced by UV light. For example, the G–T pair could be repaired in either of two ways (Figure 16-13). Thus, the correction of heteroduplex DNA by such a system could result in either a wild-type or a mutant allele in a chromatid. Failure to correct the mismatched nucleotides would lead to a "hybrid" chromatid that (on replication) would generate two different daughter chromatids, and hence the two different spore-pair members observed in half-chromatid conversion.

The various observed aberrant ratios can be produced by the events listed in Table 16-1, which deals only with correction (and hence conversion) from the hybrid $m/+$ to +. The symbols m and + are used for simplicity instead of the nucleotides used in Figure 16-9 through 16-13. Similar ratios can be developed for the correction of heteroduplex DNA to m.

This concept of heteroduplex DNA does account for most of the phenomena that we have called clues.

Figure 16-9. In this and the following figures, each double helix represents a meiotic chromatid in a cross + × m. Black lines represent one parent, and colored lines represent the other. This figure illustrates the normal synapsis arrangement of the four chromatids during prophase of the first meiotic division. Arrows represent the direction of the antiparallel DNA strands. A fixed breakage point, perhaps a recognition site for an endonuclease enzyme, is also represented.

■ **TABLE 16-1.** Correction of one or both heteroduplex DNA molecules can explain a variety of aberrant allele ratios in an octad

DNA strands at start of meiosis	Strands at heteroduplex DNA stage	No correction	One heteroduplex DNA corrected to +	Both heteroduplex DNAs corrected to +
_m_	_m_	} 3 m	} 3 m	} 2 m
_m_	_m_			
_m_	_m_			} 6 +
_m_	_+_	} 1 +		
_+_	_m_	} 1 m	} 5 +	
_+_	_+_			
_+_	_+_	} 3 +		
_+_	_+_			
		Aberrant 4:4	5:3	6:2

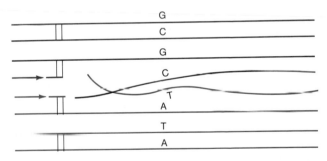

Figure 16-10. Breakage of equivalent strands and unwinding. The broken strands unravel away from the fixed breakage point for some distance and can rejoin at one another's breakage point by means of a ligase enzyme.

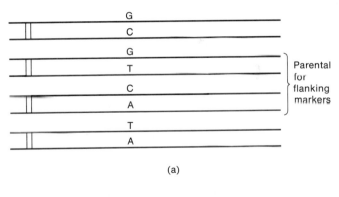

(a)

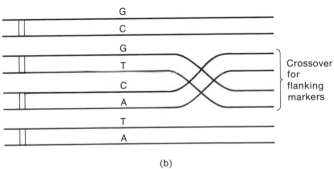

(b)

Figure 16-12. Resolution of the half-chromatid chiasma. (a) In one-half of the cases, resolution will yield a parental conformation for flanking markers. (b) In the other one-half of the cases, resolution will yield a recombinant conformation for flanking markers.

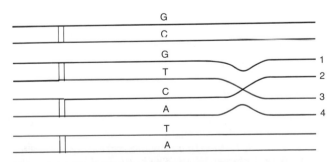

Figure 16-11. Formation of a half-chromatid chiasma and two stretches of heteroduplex DNA extending between the breakpoint and the half-chromatid chiasma. The heteroduplex DNA contains illegitimate base pairs, in this example GT and CA.

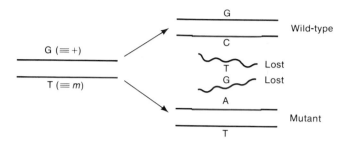

Figure 16-13. Correction of mispaired nucleotides in heteroduplex DNA to either wild-type or mutant pairs. Heteroduplex DNA containing mismatched base pairs is unstable. The mispaired nucleotides could produce a distortion in the DNA at these points that will be recognized by a repair system much like the excision-repair system for UV-induced damage that removes thymine dimers.

1. Aberrant ratios are explained as a consequence of the generation and subsequent mismatch repair of regions of heteroduplex DNA in the process of crossing-over.

2. Polarity is explained because a heterozygous site will be included more often in heteroduplex DNA if it is located nearer the fixed breakage point.

3. The association of crossing-over with about one-half of the cases of gene conversion is explained by the resolution of the exchange point in two equally likely ways. The ascus used to illustrate clue 3 (Figure 16-6) can be explained as shown in Figure 16-14. (Any conversion of the m_2 allele must be explained by assuming that heteroduplex DNA sometimes "filters in" from some distant breakage point to the right.)

4. Co-conversion is explained by the location of both sites in the region of heteroduplex DNA and by the excision of both in the same excision-repair act. This double excision obviously converts both sites to the same parental type.

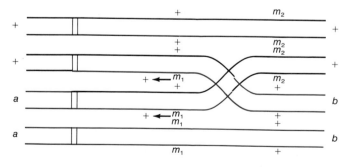

Figure 16-14. An explanation of the ascus in Figure 16-6 in terms of the heteroduplex DNA model. Arrows represent the direction of correction of the heteroduplex DNA.

Message The phenomenon of gene conversion provides clues that lead to a heteroduplex DNA model to explain the mechanism of crossing-over. Mendelian (1 : 1) allele ratios are normally observed in crosses because it is only rarely that a heterozygous locus is the precise point of chromosome exchange. (Remember that asci showing gene conversion at a heterozygous locus are relatively rare, on the order of 1 percent.)

The Holliday model does formally account for many of the observed features of recombination. Many of the individual steps comprising the Holliday model have been demonstrated to occur in vivo or in vitro, such as nicking, strand displacement, branch migration, repair synthesis, and ligation. Recently, H. Potter and D. Dressler have shown that DNA intermediates of the type predicted by the Holliday model can be found in recombining phages or plasmids. Figure 16-15 shows an electron micrograph of a recombinant molecule; it is formally equivalent to the central pair of DNA double helices in Figure 16-11, with two arms rotated to produce the central single-stranded "square" (see also Figure 16-8i).

Recombination itself is a biological process and as such is amenable to analysis by genetic dissection. By isolating mutants defective in some stage of recombination, much light has been shed on the enzymology of recombination. In *E. coli* the products of three genes involved in general recombination, the *recA*, *recB*, and *recC* genes, have been well characterized, as has the single-stranded DNA-binding (SSB) protein. Mutants deficient in any of these proteins have reduced levels of recombination.

An initial step in recombination is probably the nicking and unwinding of a DNA duplex by a protein complex encoded by *recB* and *recC*. The SSB protein, which also is involved in DNA replication (Chapter 10), can bind to and stabilize the single strands that are generated. The *recA*-encoded protein, which also plays a role in the induction of the SOS repair system (see Chapters 15 and 18), can bind to single strands and catalyze their invasion of a duplex and subsequent displacement of the corresponding strand from the duplex. These events are depicted in Figure 16-16.

Site-Specific Recombination

Phage Integration

The bacteriophage λ (lambda) integrates and excises via a pathway utilizing enzymes that recognize specific sites on the λ and on the *E. coli* chromosome and catalyze recombination events between them. These attachment, or *att*, sites contain short regions of homology, as pictured in Figure 16-17. The homologous region of 15 base pairs is only part of each *att* site. The integration reaction is catalyzed by the

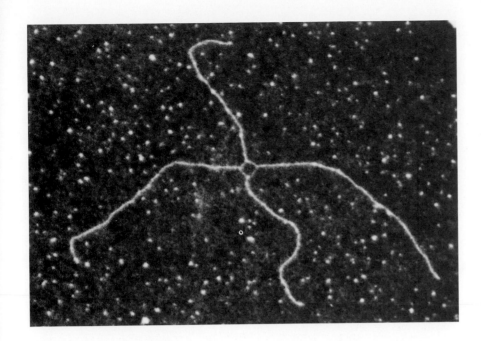

Figure 16-15. Recombination intermediate from recombination between plasmids. Shown are four double helical arms and a single-stranded diamond uniting them. This is the same kind of intermediate as that postulated in the heteroduplex DNA model for recombination in eukaryotes and is formally equivalent to the structure shown in Figure 16-8i. (Courtesy of H. Potter and D. Dressler.)

λ-encoded **Int** protein, in cooperation with a host protein, while the excision reaction requires these two proteins plus the λ-encoded **Xis** enzyme.

Control of Gene Expression

Several genomes use site-specific recombination systems to control surface antigens or host-range phenotypes. One of the best-characterized systems involves phase variation in the bacterium *Salmonella*. The surface flagella can be one of two types in these strains, termed H1 or H2. The conversion frequency of one type to another is 10^{-3}. This high rate of transition from one "phase" to another is caused by the unique arrangement of genes controlling the H1 and H2 loci (Figure 16-18). When the *H2* gene is actively expressed, a protein termed a repressor is also synthesized, which prevents transcription of the *H1* gene (Figure 16-8a).

(We shall consider repressors and gene control in more detail in Chapter 18.) Failure to transcribe the *H2* gene and *H1* repressor gene results in the failure to repress *H1* gene expression (Figure 16-18c). The orientation of the intervening genetic segment determines which of the two systems is transcribed, since it contains the transcription-initiation, or "promoter," sites that activate the respective gene systems. The site-specific recombination event (Figure 16-18b) is catalyzed by the Hin protein encoded by the invertible segment. The Hin protein acts on two 14-base-pair homologous segments in opposite orientation ("inverted repeats"). Recombination at inverted repeats yields an inversion.

Phages *mu* (see Chapter 17) and P1 (Chapter 13) have a similar site-specific recombination system that controls host range by allowing a switch from one surface protein to another. The respective *gin* and *cin* genes for *mu* and P1 are closely related to the *hin* gene of *Salmonella*.

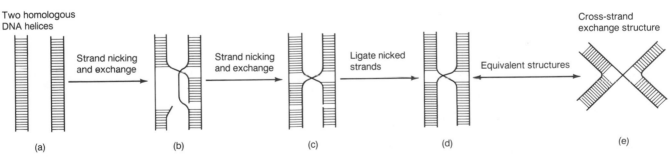

(a)   (b)   (c)   (d)   (e)

Figure 16-16. A schematic view of some of the steps in recombination. (a) The pairing of two homologous duplexes. (b) A nick is made by the RecB,C nuclease. The helix is partially unwound, and the single-stranded region is extended and stabilized by the SSB protein. The RecA protein catalyzes the invasion by the single strand of the duplex. The SSB protein aids in keeping the single strand free. The arrow points to the position of the next nick.

(c) After nicking by the RecB,C nuclease, the free single strand from the second duplex can anneal with the first duplex. (d) RNA ligase can seal this structure. (e) After a 180-degree rotation, this structure is that depicted in Figures 16-8i and 16-15. (After B. Alberts et al., *Molecular Biology of the Cell.* Garland Publishing, New York, 1983, p. 245.)

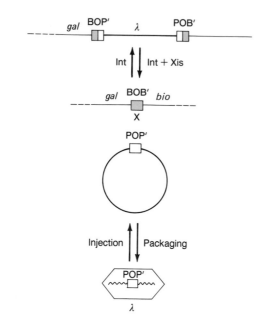

Figure 16-17. λ integration and excision. The λ and *E. coli* chromosomes contain attachment sites that are recognized by the λ integration and excision enzymes. These sites share a short region of homology, indicated by O, but also contain regions flanking the homology that are different. The flanking bacterial sequences are designated B and B', and the flanking phage sequences are designated P and P'. The bacterial attachment site is therefore designated BOB', and the phage attachment site POP'.

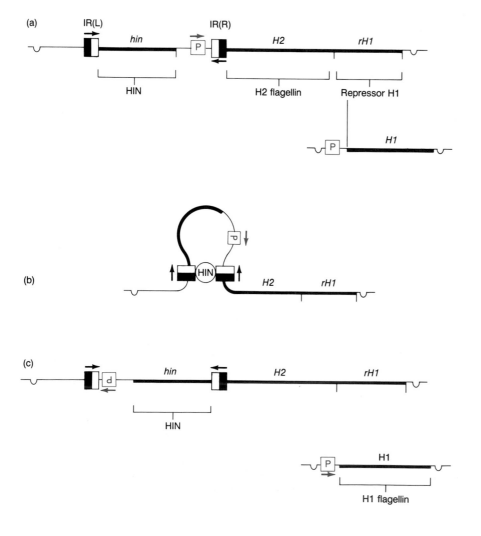

Figure 16-18. Genetic rearrangement controls flagellar phase transition. Inversion of a region of DNA of approximately 1000 base pairs adjacent to the *H2* operon alternately couples and uncouples a promoter element (b). When the promoter is coupled to the gene set *H2*, flagellin is synthesized as well as the product of the *rhI* gene that repressed *H1* expression (a; *H2* on, *H1* off). When the promoter is uncoupled from the *H2* gene set, no *rhI* gene product is synthesized, and the *H1* gene is expressed (c; *H2* off, *H1* on). IR(L) and IR(R) describe the cis-acting sites in inverted repeat configurations in which a reciprocal recombination event resulting in inversion takes place. The *hin* gene product is encoded by a sequence within the inversion region and is required for inversion. The fate of DNA sequences rearranged by inversion can be followed by referring to the black areas of the IR boxes. Note that IR(L) and IR(R) are defined for the *H2* (on) position. (After M. Silverman and M. Simon, *Mobile Genetic Elements*, edited by J. A. Shapiro, Academic Press, 1983.)

Summary

■ We are now beginning to understand the molecular processes behind recombination, which produces new gene combinations by exchanging homologous chromosomes. Both genetic and physical evidence have led to a heteroduplex DNA model to explain the mechanism of crossing-over. The process of recombination itself is under genetic control: there are genes that affect the efficiency of recombination. Several enzymes, including those encoded by the *recA*, *recB*, and *recC* genes, have been implicated in the recombination process in bacteria such as *E. coli*.

Problems

1. Many mutagens increase the frequency of sister-chromatid exchange. Discuss possible explanations for this observation.

2. Mutations in locus *46* of the Ascomycete fungus *Ascobolus* produce light-colored ascospores; let's call them *a* mutants. In the following crosses between different *a* mutants, asci are observed for the appearance of dark wild-type spores. In each cross, all such asci were of the genotypes indicated:

$$a_1 \times a_2 \qquad a_1 \times a_3 \qquad a_2 \times a_3$$

$$
\begin{array}{ccc}
a_1+ & a_1+ & a_2+ \\
++ & a_1+ & a_2+ \\
+a_2 & ++ & ++ \\
+a_2 & +a_3 & +a_3 \\
\end{array}
$$

Interpret these results in light of the models discussed in this chapter.

3. In the cross $A\,m_1\,m_2\,B \times a\,m_3\,b$, the order of the mutant sites m_1, m_2, and m_3 is unknown in relation to each other and to A/a and B/b. One nonlinear conversion ascus is obtained:

$$
\begin{array}{lll}
A & m_1\,m_2 & B \\
A & m_1 & b \\
a & m_1\,m_2 & B \\
a & m_3 & b \\
\end{array}
$$

Interpret this result in the light of the heteroduplex DNA theory, and derive as much information as possible about the order of the sites.

4. In the cross $a_1 \times a_2$ (alleles of one locus), the following acus is obtained. Deduce what events may have produced it (at the molecular level).

$$
\begin{array}{l}
a_1+ \\
a_1\,a_2 \\
a_1\,a_2 \\
+a_2 \\
\end{array}
$$

5. G. Leblon and J.-L. Rossignol have made the following observations in *Ascobolus*. Single nucleotide-pair insertion or deletion mutations show gene conversions of the 6:2 or 2:6 type, rarely 5:3, 3:5, or 3:1:1:3. Base-pair transition mutations show gene conversion of the 3:5, 5:3, or 3:1:1:3 type, rarely 6:2 or 2:6.

   a. In terms of the hybrid DNA model, propose an explanation for these observations.

   b. Furthermore, they have shown that there are far less 6:2 than 2:6 for insertions and far more 6:2 than 2:6 for deletions (where the ratios are $+:m$). Explain these results in terms of heteroduplex DNA. (You might also perhaps think about excision of thymine dimers.)

   c. Finally, they have shown that, when a frame-shift mutation is combined in a meiosis with a transition mutation at the same locus in a *cis* configuration, the asci showing *joint* conversion are all 6:2 or 2:6 for *both* sites—that is, the frame-shift conversion pattern seems to have "imposed its will" on the transition site. Propose an explanation for this.

6. At the *grey* locus in the Ascomycete fungus *Sordaria*, the cross $+ \times g_1$ is made. In this cross, heteroduplex DNA sometimes extends across the site of heterozygosity, and two heteroduplex DNA molecules are formed (as discussed in this chapter). However, correction of heteroduplex DNA is not 100 percent efficient. In fact, 30 percent of all heteroduplex are not corrected at all, whereas 50 percent are corrected to +, and 20 percent are corrected to g_1. What proportion of aberrant-ratio asci will be: a. 6:2? b. 2:6? c. 3:1:1:3? d. 5:3? e. 3:5?

7. Noreen Murray crossed α and β, two alleles of the *me-2* locus in *Neurospora*. Included in the cross were two markers, *trp* and *pan*, which flank *me-2* each at a distance of 5 m.u. The ascospores were plated onto a medium containing tryptophan and pantothenate but no methionine. The methionine prototrophs that grew were isolated and scored for the flanking markers, yielding the results shown in Table 16-2. Interpret these results in light of the models presented in this chapter. Be sure to account for the asymmetries in the classes.

8. In *Neurospora*, the cross $A\,x \times a\,y$ is made, in which *x* and *y* are alleles of the *his-1* locus, and *A* and *a* are mating-type alleles. The recombinant frequency between the *his-1* alleles is measured by prototroph frequency when asco-

■ TABLE 16-2.

Cross	Genotype of $me\text{-}2^+$ prototrophs			
	$trp+$	$+pan$	$trp\,pan$	$++$
$trp\,\alpha+ \times +\beta\,pan$	26	59	16	56
$trp\,\beta+ \times +\alpha\,pan$	84	23	87	15

spores are plated on medium lacking histidine; it is measured as 10^{-5}. Progeny of parental genotype are backcrossed to the parents, with the following results. All $a\,y$ progeny backcrossed to the $A\,x$ parent show prototroph frequencies of 10^{-5}. When $A\,x$ progeny are backcrossed to the $a\,y$ parent, two prototroph frequencies are obtained: one-half of the crosses show 10^{-5}, but the other one-half show the much higher frequency of 10^{-2}. Propose an explanation for these results, and describe a research program to test your hypothesis. (NOTE: intragenic recombination is a *meiotic* function that occurs in a diploid cell. Thus, even though this is a haploid organism, dominance and recessiveness could be involved in this question.)

CHAPTER 17

Mechanisms of Genetic Change III: Transposable Genetic Elements

■ Genetic studies of maize, beginning in the late 1930s (see page 380), yielded results that greatly upset the classical picture of genes residing only at their fixed loci on the main chromosome. The research literature began to carry reports suggesting the existence of genetic elements of the main chromosomes that can somehow mobilize themselves and move from one location to another. These findings were viewed with skepticism for many years, but now it is clear that we must find a place for such mobile genetic elements in the genetic scheme of things. Such mobile elements have turned up often enough in experimental genetics to warrant separate discussion here, although their functions are only beginning to be understood at the molecular level. However, the special methods applied to their detection and analysis add another interesting chapter to the science of genetics.

A variety of colorful names (some of which help to describe their properties) have been applied to these genetic elements: controlling elements, cassettes, jumping genes, roving genes, mobile genes, mobile genetic elements, and transposons. We choose the term **transposable genetic elements,** which is formally most correct and embraces the entire family of types. The term transposition has long been used in genetics to describe transfer of chromosomal segments from one position to another in major structural rearrangements. In the present context, what is being transposed seems to be a gene, or a small number of linked genes, or a gene-sized fragment. Collectively, this size of genetic entity can be called a **genetic element.**

Transposable genetic elements seem to be able to move to new positions within the same chromosome or even to move to a different chromosome. The normal genetic role of these elements is not known with certainty. They have been detected genetically through the abnormalities they produce in the activities and structures of the genes near the sites to which they move. A variety of physical techniques have been used for their detection as well. Transposable genetic elements have been found in phages, bacteria, fungi, higher plants, viruses, and insects.

Although transposable elements were first detected in eukaryotes, the molecular nature of transposable genetic elements was first understood in bacteria and phage. Therefore, let us begin with the information derived from the original studies in these prokaryotes.

Transposable Genetic Elements in Prokaryotes

Several distinct types of transposable genetic elements were originally distinguished in bacteria, although geneticists now consider them as members of the same general category of transposable elements found in all organisms.

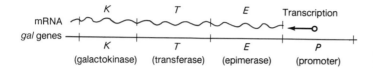

Figure 17-1. The *gal* genes of *E. coli.* Galactokinase, transferase, and epimerase are structural genes of the galactose gene set. The promoter controls their transcription into a single mRNA molecule.

Insertion Sequences

Insertion sequences, or **insertion-sequence (IS) elements,** were first found in *E. coli* in the *gal* genes, a set of three genes involved in the metabolism of the sugar galactose. This set of genes consists of three adjacent genes (for epimerase, transferase, and kinase), which are transcribed together from the same "promoter," (see Chapter 18) as shown in Figure 17-1.

The IS elements were found in mutants that had been selected by their deficiency in kinase activity. These mutations were found to map at various sites throughout the gene set. In any particular mutant, the mutant site might map somewhere in the kinase itself, or in the transferase, or in the epimerase. Each mutation obviously affects all structural gene functions transcriptionally "downstream" in the set. Such **polar mutations** were not new (these are also described in Chapter 18), but this particular *kind* was new. The mutants were observed to be capable of spontaneous reversion to wild-type (showing that the mutation was not a deletion), but the reversion rate was not increased by any mutagen. Thus, they did not seem to be frame-shifts or any form of point mutation, either! If not deletions or frameshifts or point mutations, what were they?

Recall that the phage λ inserts next to the *gal* operon and that it is a simple matter to obtain λ*dgal* phage particles that have picked up the *gal* region. (Review the material on this topic in Chapter 13.) Let us represent one of the polar mutations by the symbol *gal*ᵐ. The λ*dgal*ᵐ phages were isolated from the polar mutants, and their DNA was used to synthesize radioactive RNA in vitro. Certain fragments of this RNA were found consistently to hybridize with the mutant DNA but not with wild-type DNA. This must mean that the mutant contains an extra piece of DNA. These particular λ*dgal*ᵐ RNA fragments would also hybridize to DNA from other polar mutants, showing that the same bit of DNA has been inserted in different places in the different polar mutants.

By hybridizing denatured λ*dgal*ᵐ DNA to denatured λ*dgal*⁺ DNA, the extra piece of DNA could actually be located under the electron microscope. Some of the DNA molecules that form in the mixture are heteroduplexes between one mutant and one wild-type strand. Normally, such heteroduplexes under the electron microscope are indistinguishable from parental DNA molecules; however, in the case of the DNA involving the polar mutants, each heteroduplex showed a single-stranded buckle, or loop (Figure 17-2). This single-stranded buckle confirmed the pres-

ence of an inserted sequence in the λ*dgal*ᵐ DNA that has no complementary sequence in the λ*dgal*⁺ DNA. The length of this single-stranded loop could be calibrated by including standard-sized marker DNA in the preparation. It proved to be approximately 800 nucleotides in length.

We now have a model indicating that the polar mutations of the *gal* genes involve the insertion of an extra bit of DNA (800 base pairs long) anywhere within the gene set. This insertion sequence was later called IS1 after different insertion sequences were identified in other mutants. For example, IS2 is 1350 base pairs long. Table 17-1 lists some of the insertion sequences and their sizes.

Because of the base sequence, the two strands of λ*dgal*⁺ DNA happen to have different buoyant densities. After DNA denaturation, they can be recovered separately in the ultracentrifuge. In some cases, the *same* strands from two different IS1 mutants would form an unexpected hybrid with each other. Under the electron microscope, these hybrids had a peculiar appearance—a double-stranded region with four single-stranded tails (Figure 17-3). This observation was explained by assuming that the IS1 elements

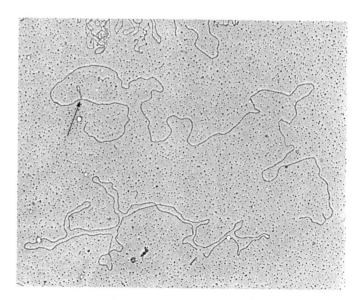

Figure 17-2. Electron micrograph of a λ*dgal*⁺/λ*dgal*ᵐ DNA heteroduplex. The single-stranded loop (arrow) is caused by the presence of an insertion sequence in λ*dgal*ᵐ. (From A. Ahmed and D. Scraba, *Mol. Gen. Genet.* 136:233, 1975.)

■ **TABLE 17-1.** Prokaryotic insertion elements

Insertion sequence	(1) Normal occurrence in *E. coli*	(2) Length (bp)	(3) Inverted repeat (bp)
IS1	5–8 copies on chromosome	768	18/23
IS2	5 on chromosome, 1 on F	1327	32/41
IS3	5 on chromosome, 2 on F	1400	32/38
IS4	1 or 2 copies on chromosome	1400	16/18
IS5	Unknown	1250	short
Gamma-delta	One on F, one or more on chromosome	5700	35
pSC101 segment	On plasmid pSC101	200	30/36

SOURCE: Tables 17-1 and 17-3 from M. P. Calos and J. H. Miller. *Cell:* 20, 579–595, 1980.

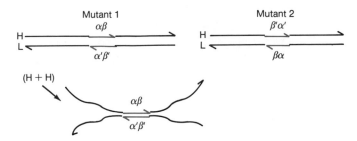

Figure 17-4. A model to explain the heteroduplex DNA structure of Figure 17-3. IS1 is represented by the colored lines; α and β represent the ends of the IS1 molecule; H and L represent the strands of *λdgal* DNA with high and low buoyant density, respectively. The hybrid can be explained by assuming that the IS1 sequence is inserted in opposite directions in the two mutants.

are inserted in opposite directions in the two mutants (Figure 17-4).

We now know that the genome of the standard wild-type *E. coli* is rich in IS elements: it contains eight copies of IS1, five copies of IS2, and copies of other less-well-studied IS types as well (see Table 17-1). It should be emphasized that the sudden appearance of an insertion sequence at any given locus under study means that these elements are truly mobile, with a capability for transposition throughout the genome. Presumably, they produce a mutation or some other detectable alteration of normal cell function only when they happen to end up in an "abnormal" position, such as the middle of a structural gene. The effects of the IS elements in reducing downstream production are probably due to the presence of a terminator sequence that interrupts the process of transcription by the RNA polymerase.

Figure 17-3. Diagrammatic representation of the appearance of a heteroduplex DNA molecule formed by annealing corresponding strands of *λdgal*ᵐ DNA from two specific mutants caused by insertion sequences. This unexpected hybridization between corresponding strands (normally having the same rather than complementary base sequences) can be explained by the model shown in Figure 17-4.

Transposons

A frightening ability of pathogenic bacteria was discovered in Japanese hospitals in the 1950s. Bacterial dysentery is caused by bacteria of the genus *Shigella*. This bacterium proved sensitive to a wide array of antibiotics that were used originally to control the disease. In the Japanese hospitals, however, *Shigella* isolated from patients with dysentery proved to be simultaneously resistant to many of these drugs, including penicillin, tetracycline, sulfanilamide, streptomycin, and chloramphenicol. This multiple-drug-resistance phenotype was inherited as a single genetic package, and it could be transmitted in an infectious manner — not only to other sensitive *Shigella* strains, but also to other related species of bacteria! This talent is an extraordinarily useful one for the pathogenic bacterium, and its implications for medical science were terrifying. From the point of view of the geneticist, however, the situation is very interesting. The vector carrying these resistances from one cell to another proved to be a plasmid similar to the F factor. These **R plasmids** (for *r*esistance) are transferred rapidly upon cell conjugation, much like the F particle in *E. coli* (Chapter 13).

In fact, these R plasmids proved to be just the first of many similar F-like plasmids to be discovered. These plasmids have been found to carry many different kinds of genes in bacteria. Table 17-2 shows just some of the characteristics that can be borne by plasmids. What is the mode of action of these plasmids? How do they acquire their new genetic abilities? How do they carry them from cell to cell? Some answers to these questions can now be given.

If the DNA of a plasmid (carrying the genes for kanamycin resistance, for example) is denatured to single-stranded forms and then allowed to renature slowly, some of the strands form an unusual shape under the electron microscope — a large circular DNA ring is attached to a lollipop-shaped structure (Figure 17-5). The "stick" of the lollipop is double-stranded DNA, which has formed

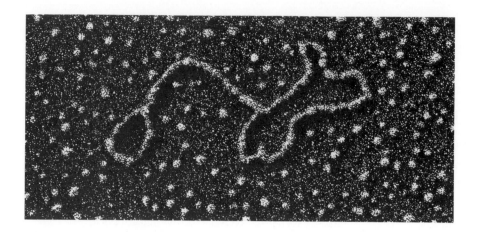

Figure 17-5. Peculiar structure formed when denatured plasmid DNA is reannealed. The double-stranded IR region separates a large circular loop from the small "lollipop" loop. (From S. N. Cohen.)

through the annealing of two **inverted repeat (IR) sequences** in the plasmid (Figure 17-6). Subsequent studies have shown that the IR sequences are a pair of IS elements in many cases. For instance, IS10 is present at the ends of the region carrying the genes for tetracycline resistance (Figure 17-7). In some cases, however, the IR sequences are much smaller.

The genes for drug resistance or other genetic abilities carried by the plasmid are located between the IR sequences, on the "lollipop head." The IR sequences together with their contained genes have been collectively called a **transposon (Tn)**. The remainder of the plasmid, bearing the genes coding for resistance-transfer functions (RTF), is called the **RTF region** (Figure 17-8). Table 17-3 lists some of the known transposons.

A transposon can jump from one plasmid to another plasmid or from a plasmid to a bacterial chromosome. Let us consider an example of this transposition. A transposon (Tn3) containing an ampicillin-resistance gene (Ap^R) is carried in a large *E. coli* plasmid R64-1. This Tn3 was then transferred to a small plasmid RSF1010, which carried the genes for sulfonamide resistance (Su^R) and streptomycin resistance (Sm^R) in another transposon (Tn4):

$$R64\text{-}1\ (Ap^R\ \text{in}\ Tn3) \longrightarrow RSF1010\ (Su^R Sm^R\ \text{in}\ Tn4)$$

The following procedure was used to carry out this transposition. First, R64-1 DNA was isolated and added as transforming DNA to a strain carrying RSF1010 that had been treated with $CaCl_2$ (a treatment that enhances the probability of uptake of the donor DNA). The Ap^R transformants were selected by plating on ampicillin medium. These transformants proved to be of several genotypes:

$$Ap^R Su^R Sm^R \quad Ap^R Su^R Sm^S \quad Ap^R Su^S Sm^R \quad Ap^R Su^S Sm^S$$

Apparently, the Ap^R transposon, once it had entered the recipient cell, could insert itself into the recipient's genome either outside the $Su^R Sm^R$ transposon or within it. If it inserted within the recipient's original Tn4 transposon, then it knocked out either one or both of the resistance functions originally possessed, depending on the precise point of insertion. New "lollipop" structures were observed in the transformed genotypes, corresponding to the acquisition of the new transposon. Figure 17-9 shows a composite diagram of an R plasmid, indicating the various places where transposons can be located, including the transposons just described. Techniques similar to those used in this experiment can also be used to demonstrate transposition from plasmid to bacterial DNA.

Insertion sequences also are commonly observed in the F factor. Figure 17-10 shows an example in an F *lac* plasmid.

Apparently, the IS regions are genetic elements that can mobilize themselves and can carry with them the genes conferring various traits. Thus, multiple-drug-resistant plasmids are generated. Even the F plasmid, judging from the strategically located pair of inverted IS elements, seems to owe its mobilization powers to this same process. As can be seen in Table 17-1, even a single IS element itself has a pair of short terminal repeats ranging from 20 to 50 base pairs long.

Phage Mu

Phage *mu* is a normal-appearing phage. We consider it here because, although it is a true virus, it has many features in common with IS elements. The DNA double helix of this phage is 36,000 nucleotides long — much larger than an IS element. However, it does appear to be able to insert itself anywhere in a bacterial (or plasmid) genome, in either orientation. Once inserted (again, like an IS), it causes mutation at the locus of insertion. (The phage was named for this ability: *mu* stands for *mutator*.) Normally, these mutations

■ **TABLE 17-2.** Genetic determinants borne by plasmids

Characteristic	Plasmid examples
Fertility	F, R1, Col
Bacteriocin production	Col E1
Heavy-metal resistance	R6
Enterotoxin production	Ent
Metabolism of camphor	Cam
Tumorigenicity in plants	T1 (in *Agrobacterium tumifaciens*)

(a)

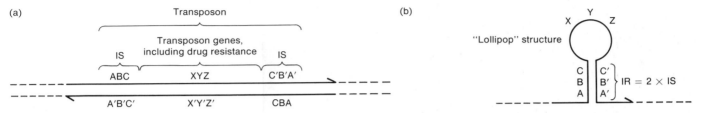

Transposon

Transposon genes, including drug resistance

IS   IS

ABC   XYZ   C'B'A'

A'B'C'   X'Y'Z'   CBA

Figure 17-6. An explanation at the nucleotide level for the "lollipop" structure seen in Figure 17-5. The structure is called a transposon. (a) The transposon in its double-stranded form before denaturing. Note the presence of oppositely oriented copies of an

(b)

"Lollipop" structure

X   Y   Z

C B A   C' B' A' IR = 2 × IS

insertion sequence (IS). (b) The lollipop structure formed by intrastrand annealing after denaturing. The two IS regions anneal to form the IR of the transposon; the transposon genes are carried in the lollipop loop.

■ **TABLE 17-3.** Transposons

Transposon	(1) Marker	(2) Length (bp)	(3) Inverted repeat
Tn1	Ampicillin	4957	38
Tn2	Ampicillin		
Tn3	Ampicillin		
Tn4	Ampicillin, streptomycin, sulfonamide	20,500	Short
Tn5	Kanamycin	5400	1500
Tn6	Kanamycin	4200	Not detectable with electron microscopy
Tn7	Trimethoprim, streptomycin	14,000	Not detectable with electron microscopy
Tn9	Chloramphenicol	2638	18/23
Tn10	Tetracycline	9300	1400
Tn204	Chloramphenicol, fusidic acid	2457	18/23
Tn402	Trimethoprim	7500	Not detectable by electron microscopy
Tn501	Mercuric ions	7800	38
Tn551	Erythromycin	5200	35
Tn554	Erythromycin, spectinomycin	6200	Not determined
Tn732	Gentamicin, tobramycin	11,000	Not determined
Tn903	Kanamycin	3100	1050
Tn917	Erythromycin	5100	Short
Tn951	*lac*	16,600	Short
Tn1681	Heat-stable enterotoxin	2088	768 (IS1)
Tn1721	Tetracycline	10,900	Short

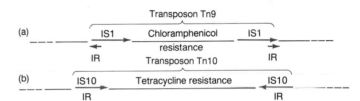

(a)

Transposon Tn9

IS1   Chloramphenicol resistance   IS1

IR   Transposon Tn10   IR

(b)

IS10   Tetracycline resistance   IS10

IR   IR

Figure 17-7. Two different transposons having different IR regions and carrying different drug-resistance genes. Tn9 has a short IR region, since the two IS1 elements are in the same orientation, and each element has a short inverted repeat, whereas Tn10 has a large IR region because the two IS10 components are in opposite orientation.

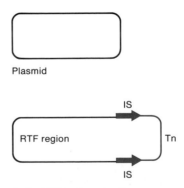

Plasmid

IS

RTF region   Tn

IS

R plasmid bearing a transposon

Figure 17-8. The insertion of a transposon (Tn) into a plasmid. RTF = the resistance-transfer functional genes of the plasmid. The Tn includes both the IS elements and the drug-resistance genes.

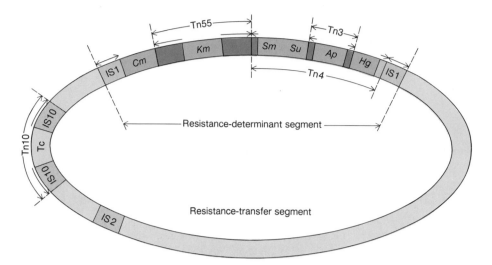

Figure 17-9. Role of transposable elements in the evolution of antibiotic-resistance plasmids is illustrated by a schematic map of a plasmid carrying many resistance genes. The plasmid appears to have been formed by the joining of a resistance-determinant segment and a resistance-transfer segment; there are insertion elements (IS1) at the junctions, where the two segments sometimes dissociate reversibly. Genes encoding resistance to the antibiotics chloramphenicol (*Cm*), kanamycin (*Km*), streptomycin (*Sm*), sulfonamide (*Su*), and ampicillin (*Ap*) and to mercury (*Hg*) are clustered on the resistance-determinant segment, which consists of multiple transposable elements; inverted-repeat termini are designated by arrows pointing outward from the element. A transposon encoding resistance to tetracycline (*Tc*) is on the resistance-transfer segment. Transposon Tn3 is within Tn4. Each transposon can be transferred independently. (Figures 17-9 and 17-15 from S. M. Cohen and J. A. Shapiro, "Transposable Genetic Elements. Copyright © 1980 by Scientific American, Inc. All rights reserved.)

cannot be reverted, but reversion can be produced by certain kinds of genetic trickery. When this reversion is produced, the phages that can be recovered show no deletion, proving that excision is exact and that the insertion of the phage therefore does not involve any loss of phage material either.

Each mature phage particle has a piece of flanking host DNA on each end (Figure 17-11). However, this DNA is not inserted anew into the next host. Its function is unclear. Phage *mu* also has an IR pair, but they are not terminal.

Mu can also act like a genetic snap fastener, mobilizing any kind of DNA and transposing it anywhere in the genome. For example, it can perform this trick on another phage (such as λ) or on the F factor. In such situations, the inserted DNA is flanked by two *mu* genomes (Figure 17-12). It can also transfer bacterial markers onto a plasmid; here again, the transferred region is flanked by a pair of *mu* genomes (Figure 17-13). Finally, the phage *mu* can mediate various kinds of structural chromosome rearrangements (Figure 17-14).

Mechanism of Transposition

Several recent findings have suggested models of transposition in bacteria in which a new copy of the transposable element is generated during the transposition event.

One important finding is that transposition to a new position is *not* accompanied by loss of the transposable element from its original position. In other words, when transposition occurs from one locus to a second locus, a copy of the transposable element is left behind at the first locus. This was nicely demonstrated by Elisabeth Ljungquist and Ahmad Bukhari, who used restriction-enzyme-digestion

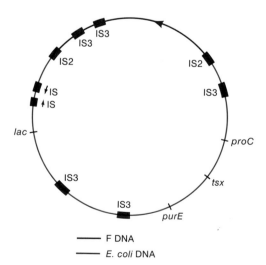

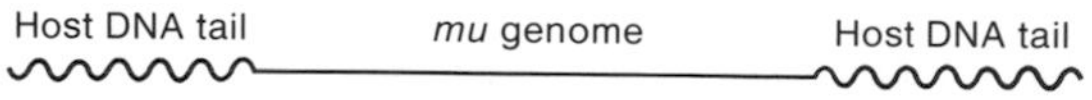

Figure 17-10. A map of an F *lac* plasmid showing positions of IS elements; *proC*, *tsx*, *purE*, and *lac* are bacterial markers. (From H. Ohtsubo and E. Ohtsubo, in *DNA Insertion Elements, Plasmids, and Episomes.* Edited by A. I. Bukhari, J. A. Shapiro, and S. L. Adhya. New York, Cold Spring Harbor Laboratory, 1977.)

Host DNA tail ~~~~~~~ *mu* genome ——————— Host DNA tail ~~~~~~~

Figure 17-11. The DNA of a free *mu* phage has tails derived from its previous host.

Host   *mu* genome   λ genome   *mu* genome   Host

Figure 17-12. Phage *mu* can mediate the insertion of phage λ into the bacterial chromosome, resulting in a structure like the one shown here.

patterns (see Chapter 19) to show that when phage *mu* transposes, segments of *mu* phage remain at the original location in the chromosome of *E. coli* while newly synthesized DNA appears at new locations in the chromosome. Therefore, at least in prokaryotes, transposable elements do not strictly "jump" from one location to another by first excising and migrating through the cytoplasm; instead, they "replicate" into a new location, leaving one copy behind.

Furthermore, the rare loss of inserted elements (a process termed "precise excision," discussed in the following section) has been shown to be unrelated to transposition. This was first indicated by the general finding that the frequency of transposition is several orders of magnitude greater than the frequency of precise excision. Moreover, elements with sharply reduced transposition frequencies due to induced mutations have normal rates of precise excision.

The molecular consequences of transposition reveal a second piece of new evidence: upon integration into a new target site, transposable elements generate a repeated sequence of target DNA. Figure 17-15 depicts the integration of IS1 into a gene. In the example shown, the integration event results in the repetition of a nine-base-pair target sequence. Analysis of many integration events reveals that the repeated sequence does not result from reciprocal site-specific recombination (as is the case with λ-phage integration, page 362) but rather is generated during the process

of integration itself. The number of base pairs repeated is a characteristic of each element. In bacteria, nine- and five-base-pair repeats are most common.

A third discovery that has influenced transposition models is the presence of **cointegrate** structures (a combined circle resulting from the fusion of two circular elements) as intermediates in the transposition process, as shown in Figure 17-16. For instance, certain mutations in the transposon Tn3 result in stable cointegrates during transposition. These mutations delete a region at which a recombination event takes place that resolves cointegrates into two smaller circles. This region is called the **internal resolution site.** Figure 17-17 shows the genetic organization of Tn3.

The preceding observations have been incorporated into current models of transposition, one of which is diagrammed in Figure 17-18. This model postulates that **staggered cuts** (cleavage at staggered sites, as illustrated in Figure 17-15) are made at the target site and at the ends of the transposable element by a transposase enzyme that is encoded by the transposable element (Figure 17-18a). One end of the transposable element is then attached by a single strand to each protruding end of the staggered cut (Figure 17-18b). This is followed by DNA replication beginning at the end of the element (Figure 17-18b). The resulting intermediate structure is a cointegrate (Figure 17-18c) that is subsequently resolved by site-specific recombination at the internal resolution site (Figure 17-18d).

Rearrangements Mediated by Transposable Elements

Transposable elements generate a high incidence of deletions in their vicinity, which emanate from one end of the

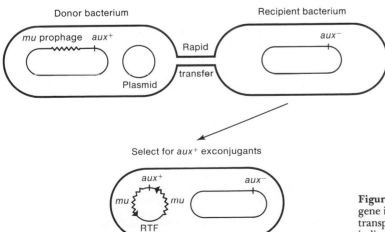

Donor bacterium   Recipient bacterium

mu prophage   *aux*⁺

Rapid

transfer

Plasmid

aux⁻

Select for *aux*⁺ exconjugants

aux⁺   *aux*⁻

mu   *mu*

RTF

Figure 17-13. Phage *mu* can mediate the transposition of a bacterial gene into a plasmid. The selection procedure for detecting the transposition is indicated here. An auxotrophic mutant gene is indicated by *aux*⁻.

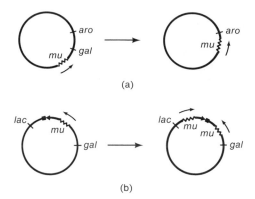

Figure 17-14. Phage *mu* can cause deletion or inversion of adjacent bacterial segments. (a) The *gal* region is deleted by transposition of phage *mu*. (b) The F-factor region of an *Hfr* strain is inverted by transposition of phage *mu*.

element into the surrounding DNA, as can be seen in Figure 17-19. Such events, as well as element-induced inversions, can be viewed as aberrant transposition events. Transposons also give rise to readily detectable deletions in which part of the element is deleted together with varying lengths of the surrounding DNA. Such **imprecise excision** events are now recognized as deletions or inversions emanating from the internal ends of the IR segments of the transposon. The process of **precise excision,** the loss of the transposable element and restoration of the gene that was disrupted by the insertion, also occurs, although at sharply reduced rates compared with the events just described.

Message   Some DNA sequences in bacteria and phage act as mobile genetic elements. They are capable of joining different pieces of DNA and thus are capable of splicing DNA fragments into or out of the middle of a DNA molecule. Some naturally occurring mobile or transposable elements carry antibiotic-resistance genes.

Transposable Genetic Elements in Eukaryotes

Transposable elements have been found in eukaryotes and have close similarities to those observed in bacteria. Several examples follow.

Ty Elements in Yeast

Figure 17-20 shows the structure of one of the **Ty elements** in yeast: the Ty1 sequence, which is present in approximately 35 copies in the yeast genome. The termini (terminal sequences), 338 base pairs long, are called δ (delta) sequences and are present in about 100 copies in the genome. Yeast δ sequences, as well as Ty elements, show significant sequence divergence. The terminal δ sequences are present in direct repeat, in contrast to transposable elements in bacteria, which carry inverted repeat (IR) sequences. However, like prokaryotic transposons, Ty elements generate a repeated sequence of target DNA (in this case, five base pairs) during transposition. Also, Ty elements cause muta-

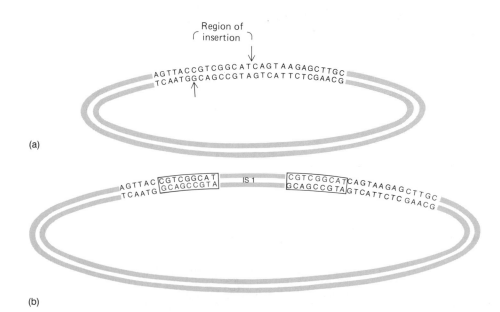

Figure 17-15. Duplication of a short sequence of nucleotides in the recipient DNA is associated with the insertion of a transposable element; the two copies bracket the inserted element. Here the duplication that attends the insertion of IS1 is illustrated in a way that indicates how the duplication may come about. IS1 insertion causes a nine-nucleotide duplication. If the two strands of the recipient DNA are cleaved (arrows) at staggered sites that are nine nucleotides apart, as shown in (a), then the subsequent filling in of single strands on each side of the newly inserted element, seen in (b), with the right complementary nucleotides could account for the duplicated sequences (colored boxes).

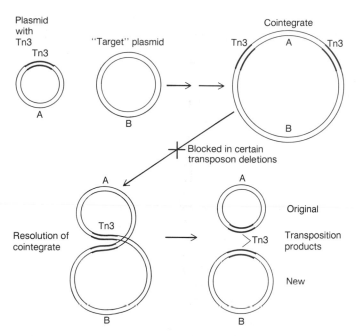

Figure 17-16. Transposition of Tn3 takes place via a cointegrate intermediate. Cointegrates in Tn3 transposition are observed for some internal deletions in the transposon. The correct explanation for this observation is that the cointegrates are intermediates in Tn3 transposition and that their resolution is blocked because the internal deletion removed an internal resolution site (IRS), where recombination occurs. (From F. Heffron, in *Mobile Genetic Elements*, pp. 223–260. Edited by J. A. Shapiro. Academic Press, 1983.)

tions by insertion into different genes in the yeast chromosome. It is now known that Ty elements transpose through an RNA intermediate (see the following section on retroviruses).

Transposable Elements in Drosophila

It is now estimated that most spontaneous mutations and chromosomal rearrangements in *Drosophila* are caused by transposable elements. As much as 10 percent of the *Drosophila* chromosome may be composed of families of dispersed, repetitive DNA sequences, which move as discrete elements! Three types of transposable elements have been characterized: the *copia*-like elements, the fold-back, or *FB*, elements, and the *P* elements. Their structures are summarized in Figure 17-21.

Copia-like Elements.   The **copia**-like elements compose at least seven families that range in size from 5 to 8.5 kb (kilobases). Members of each family appear at from 10 to 100 positions in the *Drosophila* chromosome. Each carries a long, direct terminal repeat and a short, imperfect inverted repeat (Figure 17-21), and is structurally similar to a yeast

Ty element (Figure 17-20). Also, *copia*-like elements repeat a characteristic number of base pairs of *Drosophila* DNA upon insertion. Certain classic *Drosophila* mutations result from the insertion of *copia*-like and other elements. For instance, the white-apricot (w^a) mutation, for eye color, is caused by the insertion of an element from the *copia* family (from which these elements derive their name) into the white locus. Some *copia*-like families have interesting properties. For instance, all of the insertion mutations detected so far that result from the *gypsy* family of *copia*-like elements are suppressible by a specific allele at one particular outside locus. In other words, the phenotypes resulting from the *gypsy* insertions are affected by unlinked genes. The mechanism of this effect is unknown.

FB Elements.   The **FB elements** range in size from a few hundred to a few thousand base pairs. The elements have sequence homologies, but different elements have sequence differences also. Each carries long inverted repeats at its termini (see Figure 17-21). Sometimes the entire element consists of inverted repeats, but in other elements a central sequence separates the inverted repeats. In either case, *FB* elements could literally fold back upon themselves owing to the inverted repeats — hence their name. Several unstable mutations in *Drosophila* have been shown to be caused by the insertion of *FB* elements. Mutations can result either from the interruption of a gene-coding sequence by *FB*-element insertion or from effects on gene expression due to *FB*-element insertion in or near a control region. The properties of some of the *FB*-insertion mutations suggest that *FB* elements can excise from the genome and promote chromosomal rearrangements at a high frequency.

P Elements.   Of all the transposable elements in *Drosophila*, the most intriguing and useful to the geneticist are the **P elements.** These *P* elements were discovered as a result of studying **hybrid dysgenesis,** a phenomenon that occurs when females from laboratory strains of *Drosophila melanogaster* are mated to males derived from natural populations. In such crosses, the laboratory stocks are desig-

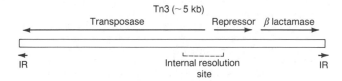

Figure 17-17. The structure of Tn3. Tn3 contains 4957 base pairs and codes for three polypeptides: the transposase is required for transposition, the repressor is a protein that regulates (see Chapter 18) the transposase gene, and β lactamase confers ampicillin resistance. Tn3 is flanked by inverted repeats (IR) of 38 base pairs and contains a site within the area designated internal resolution site, which is necessary for resolution of Tn3 cointegrates.

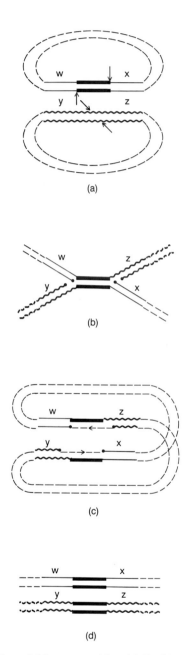

(a)

(b)

(c)

(d)

Figure 17-18. A model for transposition. (a) Single-stranded cuts are made at the ends of the transposable element, and a staggered cut of opposite polarity is made in the target DNA. (b) One end of the transposable element is attached by a single strand to each protruding end of the staggered cut. Two replication forks are thus created, and replication may proceed to copy the transposable element. (c) Semiconservative replication has generated two new transposable element and short direct repeat strands. If *wx* and *yz* were circles, *w*, *x*, *y*, and *z* would now be covalently connected and transposable elements would form the joint regions of a fused replicon. (d) A site-specific crossover between the transposable elements would resolve the cointegrate into the starting replicon *wx* and the target replicon *yz*, which now has a copy of the transposable element flanked by a short direct repeat. (After J. A. Shapiro, *Proc. Natl. Acad. Sci. USA* 76:1933–1937, 1979.)

nated as possessing **M cytotype** (cell type), and the natural stocks as having **P cytotype.** In a cross of M ♀ × P ♂, the progeny show a range of surprising phenotypes that are manifested in the germline. These include sterility, high mutation rate, and a high frequency of chromosomal aberrations and nondisjunction. These hybrid progeny are said to be **dysgenic** (hence the expression "hybrid dysgenesis"). Interestingly, the reciprocal cross P ♀ × M ♂ produces no dysgenic offspring. An important observation is that a large proportion of the dysgenically induced mutations are unstable — that is, they revert to wild-type, or to other mutant alleles, at very high frequencies. This instability is generally restricted to the germline of individuals possessing an M cytotype.

These findings led to the hypothesis that the mutations were caused by the insertion of foreign DNA within specific genes, thereby rendering them inactive. According to this hypothesis, reversion usually would result from spontaneous excision of these inserted sequences. This hypothesis was critically tested by isolating dysgenically derived unstable mutants at the eye color locus *white*. A plasmid was constructed carrying the white locus; this was used as a probe to recover the dysgenesis-mutated *white* genes. (This type of experiment is explained in Chapter 14.) The majority of these mutations were found to be caused by the insertion of a genetic element into the middle of the *white*⁺ gene. The element was called the *P* element and was found to be present in 30 to 50 copies per genome in P strains, but completely absent in M strains. The *P* elements vary in size, ranging from 0.5 to 2.9 kb in length (this size difference reflecting partially deleted elements derived from a single complete *P* element), but there is always a 31-base-pair perfect inverted repeat at their ends. There can be as many as three open reading frames in the central area of the *P* element, suggesting that the largest elements have the coding potential for three protein products.

The current explanation of hybrid dysgenesis is based on the proposal that *P* elements encode both transposase product and P-repressor products. According to this model, which is depicted in Figure 17-22, the transposase is responsible for mobilization of the *P* elements, whereas the repressor prevents transposase production, thereby blocking transposition of the element. (We consider repressor proteins in general in Chapter 18.) In the P cytotype, the high copy number of *P* elements leads to the abundant production of repressor, so that the *P* elements are immobilized. For some reason, most laboratory strains have no *P* elements, and consequently there is no repressor in the cytoplasm. In hybrids from the cross M ♀ × P ♂, the *P* elements are in a repressor-free environment and can transpose throughout the genome causing a variety of damage expressed as the various manifestations of hybrid dysgenesis.

Quite apart from their interest as a genetic phenomenon, the *P* elements have become major tools of the mod-

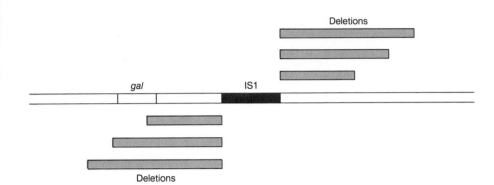

Figure 17-19. Deletion formation mediated by a transposable element. In this example, the transposable element IS1 is shown at a point in the *E. coli* chromosome near the *gal* genes. Deletions can be generated from each respective end of the IS1 element, extending into the neighboring DNA sequences. In cases where the deletions extend into the *gal* regions, they can be detected as a result of the Gal⁻ phenotype.

ern *Drosophila* geneticist. Two main analytical techniques are possible. In one technique, *P* elements are used to isolate physically any *Drosophila* gene of interest. First, the investigator simply looks for mutants of that gene in progeny of dysgenic crosses. Then a vector is constructed with a *P* element inserted. This vector is used as a probe to identify and isolate DNA segments containing *P* elements (see Chapter 14 for more details of these types of experiments); in a subset of these, *P* elements are found inserted into the gene of interest. These genes can then be cloned (Chapter 14) and studied.

The second major analytical technique stems from the discovery by Gerald Rubin and Allan Spradling that *P*-element DNA can be used as an effective vehicle for transferring donor genes into the germline of a recipient fly. Rubin and Spradling devised the following experimental procedure (see Figure 17-23). The recipient genotype was homozygous for the *rosy* (*ry⁻*) mutation, which confers a characteristic eye color, and was of M cytotype. From this strain embryos were collected at the completion of about nine nuclear divisions. At this stage, the embryo is one multinucleate cell, and the nuclei destined to form the germ cells are clustered at one end. Into embryos of this type were injected two types of DNA. The first was a bacterial plasmid carrying a deleted *P* element into which the *ry⁺* gene had been spliced. This deleted element is not able to transpose because of the deletion, so a helper plasmid bearing a complete element was also injected. Flies developing from these embryos were phenotypically still *rosy* mutants, but their

offspring contained a large proportion of *ry⁺* individuals. These *ry⁺* descendants showed Mendelian inheritance of the newly acquired *ry⁺* gene, suggesting that it was located on a chromosome. This was confirmed by in situ hybridization, which showed that the *ry⁺* gene, together with the deleted *P* element, had been inserted into one of several distinct chromosomal locations. None was exactly at the normal locus of the *rosy* gene. These new *ry⁺* genes were found to be inherited in a stable fashion.

Message *P* elements in *Drosophila* are a type of transposon that causes hybrid dysgenesis, and are very useful in two ways to the genetic analyst. First, they can be used through transposon mutagenesis to recover selectively any gene with a recognizable mutant phenotype. Marking a specific gene by transposon mutagenesis is termed transposon tagging. Second, they can be used as efficient vehicles for the transfer of a specific gene to a given recipient genotype.

Retroviruses

Retroviruses are single-stranded animal viruses that employ a double-stranded DNA intermediate for replication. Some retroviruses, such as mouse mammary tumor virus (MMTV) and Rous sarcoma virus (RSV), are responsible for the induction of cancerous tumors. When integrated into host chromosomes as double-stranded DNA they are

Figure 17-20. The structure of a yeast transposable element. The Ty1 sequence occurs approximately 35 times in the yeast genome. It contains two copies of delta (*δ*) sequence in direct orientation at each end. Delta occurs approximately 100 times in the yeast genome.

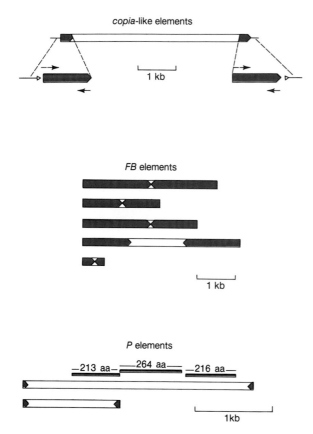

copia-like elements

1 kb

FB elements

1 kb

P elements

—213 aa— —264 aa— —216 aa—

1kb

Figure 17-21. Summary of the structures of three classes of *Drosophila* transposable elements. The *copia*-like elements carry long direct terminal repeats. Each repeat makes up about 5 percent of the length of the element. These repeats are shown on an expanded scale below the element to illustrate the presence of short, imperfect inverted repeats at the ends of each long direct repeat (-→ ←-) and the presence of a few base pairs of duplicate target sequence (▷) flanking the element that were present in one copy before insertion. The different genomic copies of the elements of one family are very similar in structure to one another.

The *FB* elements comprise a family of heterogeneous but cross-homologous sequences ranging in size from a few hundred base pairs to several kilobases. Each *FB* element carries long terminal inverted repeats. In some cases, the entire element consists of these inverted repeats. In other cases, a central sequence is located between the inverted repeats. The inverted repeat sequences themselves are internally repetitious, having a substructure made up primarily of 31-base-pair tandem repeats. The number of these 31-base-pair tandem repeats can differ not only between *FB* elements but also between the termini of a single *FB* element.

The *P* elements have a structure very different from that of both the *copia*-like and *FB* elements. *P* elements carry perfect terminal inverted repeats of 31 base pairs. A fraction of the *P* elements (about one-third in the one strain examined) are very similar in sequence to one another and are 2.9 kb in length. The remainder of the *P* elements are more heterogeneous, but all appear to have structures that are consistent with their having been derived from the 2.9-kb element by one or more internal deletions. DNA sequence analysis of the 2.9-kb element revealed three long, open translational reading frames, which are indicated. (From G. Robin, in *Mobile Genetic Elements*, pp. 329–361. Edited by J. A. Shapiro. Academic Press, 1983.)

termed **proviruses.** Proviruses, like *mu* phage in bacteria, can be considered as transposable elements, since they can in effect transpose from one location to another. Retroviruses have structural similarities to some transposable elements from bacteria and other organisms. In particular, the ends of the proviruses have long terminal repeats (LTRs), reminiscent of the δ sequences of yeast Ty1 elements and of the long terminal repeats of the *copia*-like elements from *Drosophila*. Also, integration results in the duplication of a short target sequence in the host chromosome. For example, in the case of MMTV, a six-base-pair sequence is duplicated on each side of the integrated provirus. These simi-

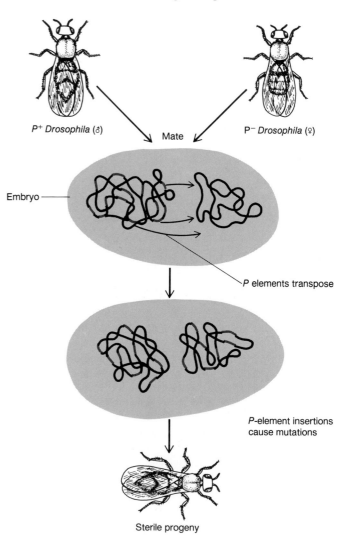

P+ *Drosophila* (♂) Mate P− *Drosophila* (♀)

Embryo

P elements transpose

P-element insertions cause mutations

Sterile progeny

Figure 17-22. The phenomenon known as hybrid dysgenesis results from the mobilization of DNA sequences called *P* elements in *Drosophila* embryos. When a sperm from a *P*-carrying strain fertilizes an egg from a non-*P*-carrying strain, the *P* elements transpose throughout the genome, usually disrupting vital genes. (After J. D. Watson, J. Tooze, and D. T. Kurtz, *Recombinant DNA: A Short Course.* Copyright © 1983 by W. H. Freeman and Co.)

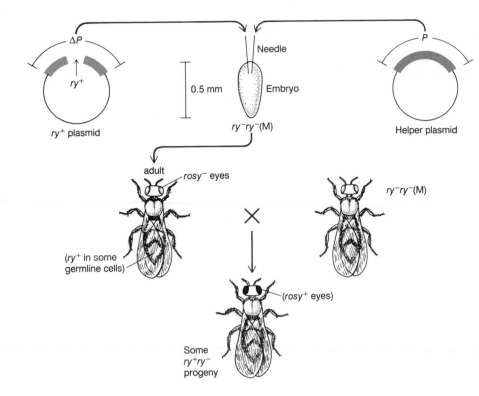

Figure 17-23. *P*-element-mediated gene transfer in *Drosophila*. The *rosy*⁺ (*ry*⁺) eye-color gene is inserted into a deleted *P* element (Δ*P*) carried on a bacterial plasmid. At the same time a helper plasmid bearing an intact *P* element is used. Both are injected into a *ry*⁻ embryo, where *ry*⁺ transposes with the Δ*P* element into the chromosomes of the germline cells.

larities have led to the idea that elements such as Ty1 in yeast and *copia*-like elements in *Drosophila* might also be integrated forms of retrovirus-like elements. This has been nicely confirmed in 1985 by Gerald Fink and his coworkers, who followed the pattern of sequence inheritance in Ty insertions in yeast. Comparison of marked Ty elements before and after transposition demonstrated that a portion of the sequence added to Ty is removed from an RNA intermediate during transposition.

Controlling Elements in Maize

In 1938, Marcus Rhoades analyzed an ear of Mexican black corn. The ear came from a selfing of a pure-breeding pigmented genotype, but it surprisingly showed a modified Mendelian dihybrid segregation ratio of $12:3:1$ among pigmented, dotted, and colorless kernels. Analysis showed that two events had occurred at unlinked loci. At one locus, a pigment gene A_1 had mutated to a_1; at another locus, a dominant allele Dt (*Dotted*) had appeared. The effect of Dt was to produce pigmented dots in the otherwise colorless phenotype of a_1a_1 (Figure 17-24). That is, the original line was very probably $A_1A_1\ dtdt$, and the mutations generated an $A_1a_1\ Dtdt$ plant, which upon selfing gave the observed ratio of progeny.

What was causing the dotted phenotype? A reverse mutation of $a_1 \rightarrow A_1$ in somatic cells would be an obvious possibility, but the large numbers of dots in the *Dotted* kernels would require extremely high reversion rates. Using special stocks, Rhoades was able to find anthers in the flowers of $a_1a_1\ Dt-$ plants that showed patches of pigment (Figure 17-25). He reasoned that these anthers might contain pollen grains bearing the reverted pigment genotype, and he used the pollen from these anthers to fertilize a_1a_1 tester females. Sure enough, some of the progeny were completely pigmented, showing that each dot in the parental plants was in fact the phenotypic manifestation of a genetic reversion event. Thus, a_1 was one of the first known examples of an **unstable mutant allele**—an allele for which reverse mutation occurs at a very high rate. The instability, however, is dependent on the presence of the unlinked Dt gene. Once the reverse mutations have occurred, they are stable; the Dt gene can be crossed out of the line with no loss of the A_1 character.

In the 1950s, Barbara McClintock demonstrated an analogous situation in another study of corn. She found a genetic factor Ds that causes a high tendency toward chromosome breakage at the location where it appears. These breaks could be located either cytologically (Figure 17-26a) or by the uncovering of recessive genes (Figure 17-26b). As you will appreciate, this action of Ds is another kind of instability. Once again, this instability proved to be depen-

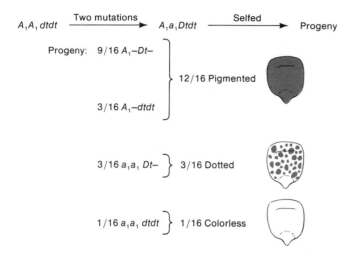

Figure 17-24. A formal genetic explanation of the appearance of the dotted phenotype in corn. The $A_1 a_1 Dtdt$ genotype is created by simultaneous mutations of $A_1 \rightarrow a_1$ and $dt \rightarrow Dt$. Upon selfing, this genotype yields the observed 12:3:1 ratio of kernel phenotypes.

dent on the presence of an unlinked gene Ac (*Activator*), in the same way that the instability of a_1 is dependent on Dt.

McClintock tried to map Ac, but she found it impossible to map! In some plants it mapped to one position, and in other plants of the same line it mapped to different positions. As if this were not enough of a curiosity, the Ds locus itself was constantly changing position on the chromosome arm, as indicated by the differing phenotypes of the variegated sections (as different recessive gene combinations

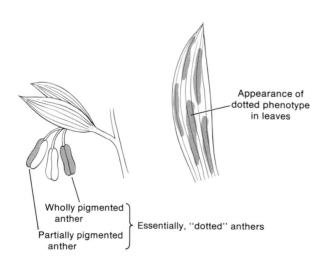

Figure 17-25. Rhoades used special stocks of $a_1 a_1 Dt-$ corn plants carrying certain genes that allow pigmented sectors to be detected in tissue other than the kernels. (After M. M. Rhoades, *Genetics* 23:382, 1938.)

were uncovered in a system such as that illustrated in Figure 17-26b).

The wanderings of the Ds element take on new meaning for us in the context of this chapter when we consider the results of the following cross:

$$\male\ CC\,DsDs\,AcAc^+ \times \female\ cc\,Ds^+Ds^+\,Ac^+Ac^+$$

where C allows color expression and Ds^+ and Ac^+ indicate the lack of the element. Most of the kernels from this cross were of the expected types (Figure 17-27), but one exceptional kernel was very interesting. In this individual, the Ds element seems to have wandered into the middle of the C gene and inactivated it, producing the colorless phenotype. Although the presence of Ac is still necessary to cause this instability, it now seems to take on the function of rendering the c mutation unstable (c^u), and patches of revertant color appear in the kernel. When Ac is crossed out of this line, the c^u becomes a stable mutant.

The analogy of this system with the $a_1 Dt$ system is obvious. Perhaps the earlier situation also was due to the insertion of a Ds-like element into the A_1 gene. It is natural to ask whether a_1 will respond to Ac, or c^u to Dt. The answer is no; there is some kind of specificity involved that prevents this cross-activation of mutational instability.

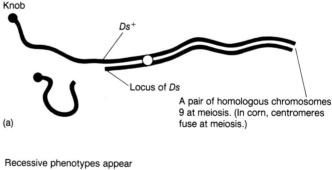

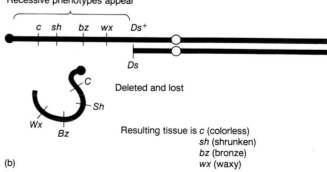

Figure 17-26. Detection of chromosomal breakage (instability) due to action of the Ds element in corn. (a) Cytological detection of the breakage. (Ds^+ indicates a lack of Ds.) (b) Genetic detection of the breakage.

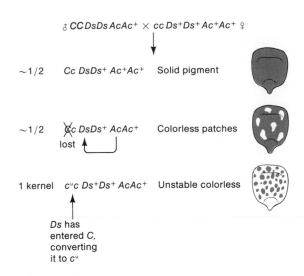

δ $CC\,DsDs\,AcAc^+ \times cc\,Ds^+Ds^+\,Ac^+Ac^+$ φ

~1/2 $Cc\ DsDs^+\ Ac^+Ac^+$ Solid pigment

~1/2 $\cancel{C}c\ DsDs^+\ AcAc^+$ Colorless patches

lost

1 kernel $c^uc\ Ds^+Ds^+\ AcAc^+$ Unstable colorless

Ds has
entered *C*,
converting
it to c^u

Figure 17-27. Results that indicate the transposition of *Ds* into the *C* gene in corn. (*C* allows color expression; *c* does not. *Ac* = activator.) The action of *Ds* is dependent on the presence of the unlinked gene, *Ac*.

The *Ds* element can wander not only into the middle of the *C* gene but also into other genes, rendering them also unstable mutants dependent on *Ac*. One such locus, *wx* (*waxy*), has been the subject of an intense study on the effects of the *Ds* element. Oliver Nelson has paired many unstable *waxy* alleles in the absence of the *Ac* mutation. In such $wx^{m\text{-}1}/wx^{m\text{-}2}$ heterozygotes, he has looked for rare wild-type *Wx* recombinants by staining the pollen with KI-I$_2$ reagent, which stains *Wx* pollen black and *wx* pollen

red. By counting the frequency of *Wx* pollen grains in each kind of heterozygote, Nelson was able to do fine-structure recombination mapping of the *waxy* gene. He showed that the different "mutable *waxy*" mutant alleles are in fact due to the insertion of the *Ds* element in different positions of the gene. In a subsequent experiment, he allowed *Wx*-bearing pollen to fertilize *wx* plants and produce rare *waxy* kernels, which could be detected by staining sliced-off slivers. The *waxy* kernels were then raised into plants, and Nelson was able to show that the *Wx* pollen grains arose from chromosome exchange, which also involved exchange of flanking markers.

Several systems like $a_1\,Dt$ and $Ds\,Ac$ have now been found in corn. Each shows similar action, having a **target gene** that is inactivated, presumably by the insertion of some **receptor element** into it, and a distant **regulator gene** that maintains the mutational instability of the locus, presumably through its ability to "unhook" the receptor element out of the target locus and thus return the locus to normal function. The receptor and the regulator are called **controlling elements.**

In the examples discussed so far, the unstable allele is said to be **nonautonomous.** It can revert only in the presence of the regulator. Sometimes, however, a system such as *Ac/Ds* can produce an unstable allele that is **autonomous.** Such mutants are recognized because they show Mendelian ratios (such as 3:1 for pigmented to dotted) apparently independent of any other element. In fact, such alleles appear to be caused by the insertion of *Ac* itself into the target gene. An allele of this type can subsequently be transformed into a nonautonomous allele. In such cases, the nonautonomy seems to result from the spontaneous generation of a *Ds* element from the inserted *Ac* element. In

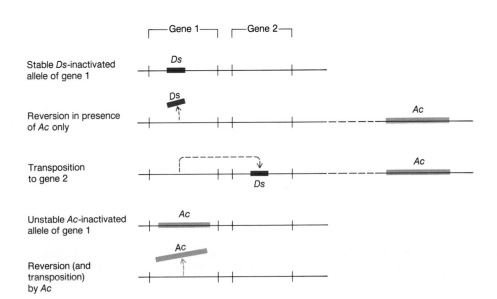

Figure 17-28. Summary of the main effects of controlling elements in corn. *Ac* and *Ds* are used as examples, acting on two hypothetical genes 1 and 2.

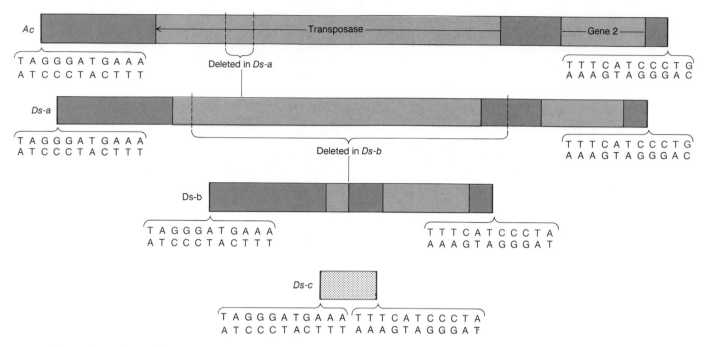

Figure 17-29. The structure of the *Ac* element of maize and several *Ds* elements. (From N. V. Federoff, "Transposable Genetic Elements in Maize." Copyright © 1984 by Scientific American, Inc. All rights reserved.)

other words, *Ds* is in all likelihood a partially incomplete version of *Ac* itself.

Figure 17-28 summarizes the overall behavior of the corn controlling elements as inferred from genetic data. Note that the mutation events that gave rise to Rhoades' original ratio are nicely explained by this model. A nonautonomous *Ds*-like element was generated from an *Ac*-like progenitor. Transposition of the *Ds*-like element into the A_1 gene produced an inactive but mutationally unstable allele a_1.

Molecular studies in the last few years on *Ac* and *Ds* and on other controlling elements in corn have confirmed McClintock's genetic model in a very satisfying way. One such study focused on *Ac*- or *Ds*-containing unstable alleles of the *Waxy* locus. First, the wild-type *Wx* gene had to be cloned so that it could be used as a probe to retrieve the unstable alleles. *Waxy* mRNA was identified as the endosperm mRNA which, on translation, produced a protein which was almost certainly the Waxy structural protein (as judged from the absence of this protein in *wx* mutants). A cDNA clone was made from this mRNA and was used to fish out, from total genomic DNA, a *Wx* gene, a *wx* gene containing either *Ds* or *Ac* inserted, and also *Wx* revertant alleles derived from unstable alleles. In all cases the DNA was sequenced, and some of the results are summarized in Figure 17-29. An *Ac* element is about 4500 base pairs long and has 11-base-pair imperfect inverted terminal repeats. It has two open reading frames, one of which seemed like a good candidate for a transposase. *Ds* elements proved to be deleted *Ac* elements, and the deletion could be small, within the transposase, as in *Ds-a*, or large, as in *Ds-b* and *Ds-c*.

Flanking the inserted transposons were found eight-

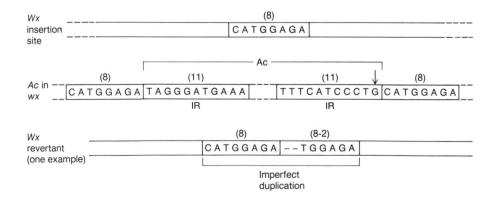

Figure 17-30. Target-insertion-site duplication produced by the transposon *Ac* at the *Wx* gene in maize.

base-pair-long duplications of the *Wx* gene DNA. Commonly, the duplication was imperfect. In the revertants, the eight-base-pair duplication remained, although often with a slight modification that would seem to be necessary to retain the proper reading frame of the gene. These duplications are shown in Figure 17-30.

Message Controlling elements in corn can inactivate a gene in which they reside, cause chromosomal breaks, and transpose to new locations within the genome. Complete elements can perform these functions unaided; other forms with partial deletions can transpose only with the help of a complete element elsewhere in the genome.

Summary

■ Nature has devised many different ways of changing the genetic architecture of organisms. We are now beginning to understand the molecular processes behind some of these processes. Gene mutation, recombination between chromosomes (discussed in the preceding two chapters), and transposition can all be reasonably explained at the DNA level. Far from merely producing genetic waste, these processes undoubtedly all have important roles in evolution. This idea is strengthened through the knowledge that the processes themselves are to a large extent under genetic control: there are genes that affect the efficiency of mutation, recombination, and transposition.

The analogies among the transposons of phage, bacteria, and eukaryotes are striking. At present it is not known whether transposons are elements that normally play a role in the day-to-day transactions of the genome, as originally proposed by Barbara McClintock in the 1950s, or whether they are pieces of "selfish DNA" that exist for no purpose other than their own survival. Whatever the truth of this matter is, transposons certainly represent a completely unexpected element of chaos in the genome, which geneticists have already harnessed into their team of analytical procedures. At the evolutionary level, transposons may be important in the sudden leaps that characterize the fossil record.

Problems

1. Describe the generation of multiple-drug-resistance plasmids.

2. What evidence indicates that transposable elements in prokaryotes do not strictly "jump" from one location to another?

3. Explain how the properties of *P* elements in *Drosophila* make possible gene-transfer experiments in this organism.

4. Figure 17-10 reveals that the F factor (Chapter 13) carries a number of transposable elements (in this case, IS elements). In light of the discovery of cointegrates as intermediates in the transposition process (Figures 17-16 and 17-18), diagram the formation of Hfr strains. Assume that they are generated by a transposition of the F factor into the chromosome, mediated by the resident IS elements.

5. When Rhoades took pollen from wholly pigmented anthers on plants of genotype $a_1a_1 DtDt$ and used this pollen to pollinate $a_1a_1 dtdt$ tester females, he found wholly pigmented kernels and, in addition, some dotted kernels. Explain the origin of *both* phenotypes.

6. In yeast, the *his4* region has three cistrons, A, B, and C, in that order, each mediating an enzymatic step of histidine synthesis. A certain spontaneous mutation is mapped in the cistron A, but these mutants are defective for all three functions (A, B, and C). The mutation is not suppressible by nonsense or frame-shift suppressors. Spontaneous reversion occurs quite frequently, but this rate is not enhanced by any mutagen. Discuss the possible nature of the mutation.

7. In *Drosophila*, M. Green found a *singed* allele *sn77-27* with some unusual characteristics. Females homozygous for this X-linked allele have singed bristles, but they have numerous patches of sn^+ (wild-type) bristles on their heads, thoraxes, and abdomens. When these flies are bred to *sn* males, some females give only singed progeny, but others give both singed and wild-type progeny, in variable proportions. Explain these results.

8. Crown-gall tumors are found in many dicotyledonous plants infected by the bacterium *Agrobacterium tumifaciens*. The tumors are caused by the insertion of DNA into the plant DNA from a large plasmid carried by the bacterium. A tobacco plant of type A (there are many types of tobacco plants) is infected, and it produces tumors. You remove tumor tissue and grow it on synthetic medium. Some of these tumor cultures produce aerial "shoots," and you graft one of these shoots onto a normal tobacco plant of type B. The graft grows to an apparently normal A-type shoot and flowers.

   a. You remove cells from the graft and place them in synthetic medium, where they grow like tumor cells. Explain why the graft appears normal.

   b. When seeds are produced by the graft, the resulting progeny are normal A-type plants. No trace of the inserted plasmid DNA remains. Propose a possible explanation for this "reversal."

9. Consider two corn plants:

   a. Genotype C/c^m $Ac/+$, where c^m is an unstable allele caused by Ds insertion

   b. Genotype C/c^m, where c^m is an unstable allele caused by Ac insertion.

What phenotypes and in what proportions would be produced when (1) each plant is crossed to a base pair substitution mutant c/c? (2) Plant (a) is crossed with plant (b)?

Assume that Ac and c are unlinked, and that chromosome breakage frequency is negligible; also that mutant c/c is Ac^+.

CHAPTER 18

Genetic Control Mechanisms in Prokaryotes

■ We saw in Chapter 12 how genes are transcribed into RNA molecules, many of which are translated into proteins. But how does the cell control the expression of all of its genes? What mechanism is used to "turn on genes" when the respective gene product is needed, and to "turn off genes" when the product is no longer needed? It would be a tremendous waste of the cell's energy to synthesize, at maximal rates, all the possible proteins encoded by an entire genome. In fact, the number of genes in even single-cell bacteria is so large that uncontrolled synthesis of all possible proteins would deplete the energy supply of the cell. Bacterial enzymes involved in sugar metabolism provide an example. Clearly, it is advantageous for the bacterial cell to have the potential to metabolize a variety of carbon sources. For instance, *E. coli* can synthesize enzymes that can break down many different sugars. However, it costs energy to synthesize each enzyme. If a cell were to produce at maximal rates the enzymes that could metabolize arabinose, melibiose, maltose, raffinose, lactose, galactose, and salicin (to mention a few), it would expend far more energy than it could recover from the metabolism of any of these sugars. Therefore, the cell must be able to recognize and react to situations in which the production of specific enzymes is desirable.

The first major breakthrough in understanding gene control came in the 1950s with the detailed genetic analysis, by François Jacob and Jacques Monod, of the enzymes concerned with lactose metabolism in *E. coli* and of phage-λ immunity.

The *lac* System: Negative Control

Jacob and Monod used the lactose-metabolism system of *E. coli* (see Figure 18-1) to attack the problem of enzyme **adaptation**—that is, the appearance of a specific enzyme only in the presence of its substrates. This phenomenon had been observed in bacteria for many years. How could a cell possibly "know" precisely which enzymes to synthesize? How could a particular substrate induce the appearance of a specific enzyme?

For the *lac* system, such an **induction** phenomenon could be illustrated by the fact that in the presence of certain galactosides, termed **inducers,** cells produce over 1000 times more of the enzyme beta (β)-galactosidase, which cleaves β-galactosides, than when grown in the absence of such sugars. What role did the inducer play in the induction phenomenon? One idea was that the inducer was simply activating a pre-β-galactosidase intermediate that had accumulated in the cell. However, when Jacob and Monod followed the fate of radioactively labeled amino acids added to growing cells either before or after the addition of inducer, they could show that induction represented the synthesis of new enzyme molecules. Kinetic studies es-

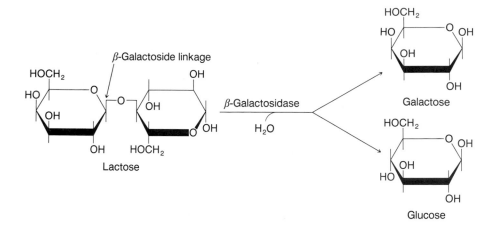

Figure 18-1 The metabolism of lactose. The enzyme β-galactosidase catalyzes a reaction in which water is added to the β-galactoside linkage to break lactose into separate molecules of galactose and glucose. The enzyme lactose permease is required to transport lactose into the cell.

tablished that these molecules could be detected as early as three minutes after addition of inducer! Also, withdrawal of inducer brought about an abrupt halt in the synthesis of new enzyme. Therefore, it became clear that the cell possessed a mechanism for turning on and off gene expression in response to environmental signals. What could this mechanism be?

A detailed examination of the substrate specificity of induction provided further important clues about the nature of the induction process. Next, Jacob and Monod wanted to determine the correlation between the catalytic center on the enzyme being induced and the molecular structure of the inducer. At that time, the notion was prevalent that the inducer (the small β-galactoside molecule) could instruct the formation of the catalytic center, in some way serving as a mold for the active site of the enzyme. It was found that although only galactosides serve as inducers, there is no correlation between the inducing capacity of a compound and its affinity for β-galactosidase. Some strong inducers, such as the synthetically prepared isopropyl-β,D-thiogalactoside (IPTG; see Figure 18-2), are not even substrates for the enzyme. The different stereospecificities for induction of β-galactosidase and for binding to β-galactosidase were clues that the element involved in con-

trolling β-galactosidase synthesis was distinct from β-galactosidase itself.

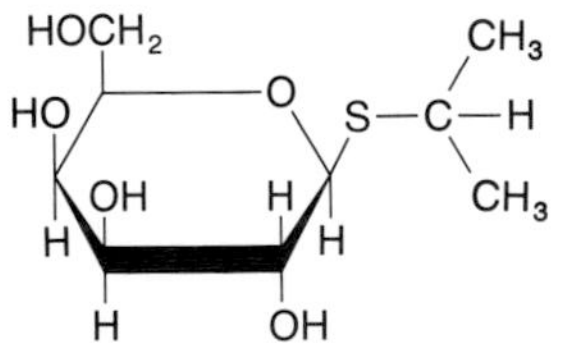

A permease activity involved in lactose metabolism was induced together with β-galactosidase. The analysis of mutants indicated that each enzyme was encoded by a different gene. The permease was required to transport lactose into the cell. A third enzyme, termed transacetylase (with a dispensable and as-yet unknown function), also was characterized and later shown to be encoded by a separate gene. Therefore, Jacob and Monod could identify three **coordinately controlled genes:** the Z gene encoding β-galactosidase, the Y gene encoding permease, and the A gene encoding transacetylase. Mapping defined the Z, Y, and A genes as being closely linked on the chromosome. Later studies of these and other coordinately controlled genes led to the realization that in many cases a single mRNA molecule, termed a **polycistronic** mRNA, was produced by a contiguous set of genes. Transcription of this mRNA and its translation into protein proceeded in the same direction (see also Chapter 12). This enables us to understand the basis of an additional class of mutation referred to as polar mutations. As we saw in Chapter 17, polar mutations not only affect the gene within which they map but also reduce or eliminate expression of all genes farther down the line — that is, "distal" to the gene containing the mutation. Polar mutations exert their effects by interfering with either continued transcription or translation of the polycistronic mRNA. The first type of polar mutations characterized were chain-terminating nonsense mutations located early in the Z gene, which lowered expression of permease and acetylase. Other polar mutations turned out to result from the insertion of DNA into the middle of genes (see page 368).

isopropyl-β,D-thiogalactoside
(IPTG)

Figure 18-2. Structure of the inducer of the *lac* operon, IPTG. The β,D-thiogalactoside linkage is not cleaved by β-galactosidase, allowing manipulation of the intracellular concentration of this inducer.

The I Gene

Further genetic analysis shed more light on the control circuit. Jacob and Monod characterized a new class of mu-

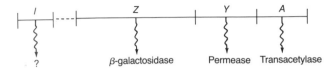

Figure 18-3. The *I* locus: the region controlling the inducibility of the *lac* enzymes.

tant, which synthesized all three enzymes at full levels even in the absence of inducer. For the first time a mutant was detected that was altered not in the *activity* of an enzyme but in the *control* of enzyme production. These **constitutive** mutants were found to have mutations mapping close to but distinct from the *Z*, *Y*, and *A* genes, permitting the definition of the *I* **locus** as the region controlling the inducibility of the *lac* enzymes. *I*+ cells synthesized full levels of the *lac* enzymes only in the presence of inducer, whereas *I*− cells synthesized full levels in the presence or absence of inducer. Figure 18-3 depicts the *lac* region defined by these experiments.

The discovery of F′ factors (see Chapter 13) carrying the *lac* region allowed complementation tests that established *I*, *Z*, and *Y* as independent cistrons. These experiments showed that *I*+ is dominant over *I*− in the trans position. Table 18-1 shows these results in schematic form. (Recall the complementation tests performed by Benzer, page 223, in which complementation occurring in the trans position implies the action of a diffusible product.) Therefore, Jacob and Monod formulated the hypothesis that the *I* **gene** determines the synthesis of a **repressor** molecule that blocks activation of the *lac* gene.

A piece of evidence in support of the repressor model was the characterization of *I*s mutations. Although mapping within the *I* gene, these mutations prevented the in-

duction of the *lac* enzymes by lactose or by the synthetic inducer IPTG (Figure 18-2). Moreover, they were dominant in trans to both an *I*+ and an *I*− allele (Table 18-2). The *I*s mutation eliminated response to inducer, presumably by altering the stereospecific binding site and destroying inducer binding. Therefore, even in the presence of IPTG, these molecules can still block *lac* enzyme synthesis. This would also explain their dominance, since the *I*s repressor would be unaffected by wild-type repressor that was inactivated by inducer. The *I*s mutations clearly pointed to a direct interaction between the *I* gene product and the inducer.

The Operator and the Operon

The specificity of interaction of the repressor with the *lac* system, which resulted in turning off enzyme synthesis, suggested a stereospecific complex with an element that Jacob and Monod termed the **operator.** They sought mutations in this recognition element that would allow synthesis of the *lac* enzymes even in the presence of active repressor. These mutations should be dominant in the cis position. Whereas trans dominance reflects a diffusible product, cis dominance reflects the action of an element that affects only the genes directly adjacent to it. There is no diffusible product that is altered by the mutation. By selecting for constitutivity (unrepressed synthesis) in cells with two copies of the *lac* region, such mutants were found and labeled *O*c, for operator constitutive. As Table 18-3 indicates, strains carrying these mutations are capable of synthesizing maximal amounts of enzyme in the presence of IPTG, and such mutant strains synthesize 10 to 20 percent of these levels in the absence of inducer. The *O*c mutations are indeed dominant in the cis position, as shown in Table 18-3. Mapping experiments pinpointed the operator locus between *I* and *Z*.

■ **TABLE 18-1.** Synthesis of β-galactosidase and permease in haploid and heterozygous diploid strains

Strain	Genotype	β-galactosidase		Permease	
		Noninduced	Induced	Noninduced	Induced
1	$I^+Z^+Y^+$	−	+	−	+
2	$I^-Z^+Y^+$	+	+	+	+
3	$I^+Z^-Y^+/F\,I^-Z^+Y^+$	−	+	−	+
4	$I^-Z^-Y^+/F\,I^+Z^+Y^-$	−	+	−	+
5	$I^-Z^-Y^+/F\,I^-Z^+Y^+$	+	+	+	+
6	$\nabla(I,Z,Y)/F\,I^-Z^+Y^+$	+	+	+	+

NOTE: bacteria were grown in glycerol as a carbon source and induced by IPTG. The presence of the maximal level of the enzyme is indicated by +; the absence or very low level of an enzyme is indicated by −; ∇ indicates deletion.

■ **TABLE 18-2.** Synthesis of β-galactosidase and permease by the wild-type and by strains carrying different alleles of the I gene

Genotype	Inducer	β-galactosidase	Permease
$I^+Z^+Y^+$	None	−	−
	IPTG	+	+
$I^sZ^+Y^+$	None	−	−
	IPTG	−	−
$I^sZ^+Y^+/FI^+$	None	−	−
	IPTG	−	−
$I^sZ^+Y^+/FI^-$	None	−	−
	IPTG	−	−

NOTE: bacteria were grown in glycerol with and without the inducer IPTG. Presence of the indicated enzyme is represented by +; absence or low levels, by −.

The $O-Z-Y-A$ segment constitutes a genetic unit of coordinate expression that Jacob and Monod termed the **operon.** Figure 18-4 depicts a simplified operon model for the *lac* system. The *lac* operon is said to be under the **negative control** of the *lac* repressor, since the repressor normally blocks expression of the *lac* enzymes.

Let us summarize the model in Figure 18-4. The Z and Y genes code for the structure of two enzymes required for the metabolism of the sugar lactose, β-galactosidase and permease, respectively. The A gene codes for transacetylase. All three genes are linked together on the chromosome. Their transcription into a single polycistronic mRNA provides the basis for coordinate control at the level of mRNA synthesis. The synthesis of the polycistronic *lac* mRNA can be blocked by the action of a repressor protein molecule, which binds to an operator region near the start point for transcription. The repressor is the product of the I gene. Therefore, mutations in the I gene that prevent the

synthesis of functional repressor result in unrepressed or constitutive synthesis of the *lac* enzymes. Repression can also be overcome by certain galactosides, termed inducers, which inactivate the repressor by binding to it and altering the affinity for the operator. In this manner the inducer can pull the repressor off the DNA. Mutations in the I gene have been characterized that alter the inducer binding site so that the repressor no longer binds to the inducer. These I^s mutations result in repression even in the presence of inducer. Also, mutations in the operator have been found that impair repressor recognition of this short DNA segment. Such O^c mutations allow moderate synthesis of the *lac* enzymes even in the presence of active repressor molecules.

We can see that the model in Figure 18-4 accounts for the observed phenotypes of different mutants. The model has as its central feature the recognition by a protein repressor of two different entities: the inducer molecule and the specific operator sequence at the beginning of the *lac* operon.

Characterization of the lac Repressor and lac Operator

Several genetic experiments argued strongly that the repressor was a protein, the most compelling of which was the discovery of suppressible nonsense mutations in the I gene, since the resulting nonsense codons exert their effect by provoking polypeptide chain termination during translation. The decisive experiment, however, was provided by Walter Gilbert and Benno Müller-Hill, who in 1966 isolated and purified the repressor by monitoring the binding of the radioactively labeled inducer IPTG. They demonstrated that the repressor is a protein consisting of four identical subunits, each with a molecular weight of approxi-

■ **TABLE 18-3.** Synthesis of β-galactosidase and permease by haploid and heterozygous diploid operator mutants

Genotype	β-galactosidase		Permease	
	Noninduced	Induced	Noninduced	Induced
$O^+Z^+Y^+$	−	+	−	+
$O^+Z^+Y^+/FO^+Z^-Y^+$	−	+	−	+
$O^cZ^+Y^+$	+	+	+	+
$O^+Z^+Y^-/FO^cZ^+Y^+$	+	+	+	+
$O^+Z^+Y^+/FO^cZ^-Y^+$	−	+	+	+
$O^+Z^-Y^+/FO^cZ^+Y^-$	+	+	−	+
$I^sO^+Z^+Y^+/FI^+O^cZ^+Y^+$	+	+	+	+

NOTE: bacteria were grown in glycerol with and without the inducer IPTG. Presence and absence of enzyme are indicated by + and − symbols, respectively.

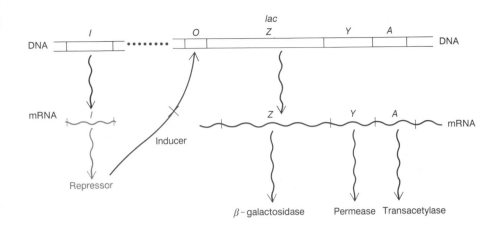

Figure 18-4 A simplified *lac* operon model. The three genes *Z*, *Y*, and *A* are coordinately expressed. The product of the *I* gene, the repressor, blocks the expression of the *Z*, *Y*, and *A* genes by interacting with the operator, *O*. The inducer can inactivate the repressor, thus preventing interaction with the operator. When this happens, the operon is fully expressed. Mutations in *I* or *O* can also result in expression of the three *lac* enzymes, even in the absence of inducer.

mately 38,000. Each molecule contains four IPTG-binding sites. (A more detailed description of the repressor is given later in the chapter.) In vitro, repressor binds to DNA containing the operator (see Figure 18-5) and comes off the DNA in the presence of IPTG. Gilbert and coworkers have shown that the repressor can protect specific bases in the operator from chemical reagents. These experiments provided crucial proofs of the mechanism of repressor action formulated by Jacob and Monod.

Gilbert used the enzyme DNase to break apart DNA bound to repressor, and he was able to recover short DNA strands shielded from the enzyme activity by the repressor

molecule and hence presumed to represent the operator sequence. This sequence was determined, and each operator mutation was shown to involve a change in the sequence (Figure 18-6). These results confirm the identity of the operator locus as a specific sequence of 17 to 25 nucleotides situated just before the structural *Z* gene. They also show the incredible specificity of the repressor-operator recognition, which is disrupted by a single base substitution. When the sequence of bases in the *lac* mRNA (transcribed from the *lac* operon) was determined, the first 21 bases on the 5′ initiation end proved to be complementary to the operator sequence Gilbert had determined.

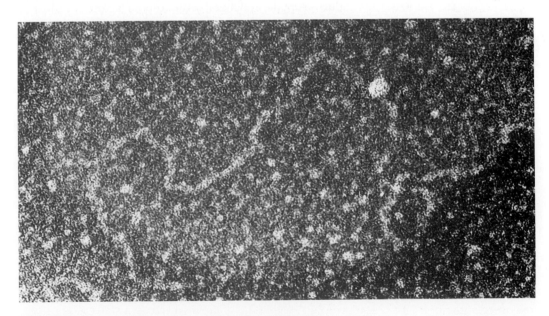

Figure 18-5. The *lac* repressor (large whitish sphere) bound to DNA at the promoter region of the operon. (From Jack D. Griffith.)

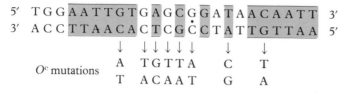

```
5′  T G G A A T T G T G A G C G G A T A A C A A T T  3′
3′  A C C T T A A C A C T C G C C T A T T G T T A A  5′
              ↓  ↓↓↓↓↓      ↓        ↓
Oᶜ mutations  A   TGTTA     C        T
              T   ACAAT     G        A
```

Figure 18-6. The DNA base sequence of the lactose operator and the base changes associated with eight O^c mutations. Regions of twofold rotational symmetry are indicated by horizontal lines above and below the symmetric base pairs and by a dot at their axis of symmetry. (From W. Gilbert, A. Maxam, and A. Mirzabekov, in N. O. Kjeldgaard and O. Malløe, eds., *Control of Ribosome Synthesis.* Academic Press, © 1976. By permission of Munksgaard International Publishers Ltd., Copenhagen.)

Allostery

The *lac* repressor is a protein with two different binding sites. One site recognizes the inducer molecule, and the second site recognizes the *lac* operator sequence on the DNA. Interaction of the repressor with the inducer lowers the affinity of the repressor for the operator. This change in affinity for operator, in response to the binding of inducer at a distant site, is mediated by a conformational change in the repressor protein. In one conformation the repressor binds operator well, whereas in a second conformation it does not. Proteins that function this way are termed **allosteric** proteins. Allosteric transitions, the change from one conformation to another, occur in many different proteins.

The lac Promoter

Genetic experiments suggested that an element essential for *lac* transcription was located between *I* and *O*. This element was termed the **promoter, *P***, and was postulated to serve as an initiation site for transcription. Promoter mutations affect in a similar manner the transcription of all of the genes in the operon. Promoter mutations are cis-dominant, as expected for a site on the DNA that serves as a recognition element for transcription initiation, since each promoter governs transcription only for those genes in the operon adjacent to it on the *same* DNA molecule. In vitro experiments demonstrated that RNA polymerase binds to the promoter region, and that repressor binding to the operator can block RNA polymerase from binding to the promoter. Mutant analysis, physical experiments, and comparison with other promoters identified two binding regions for RNA polymerase in a typical prokaryotic promoter. Figure 18-7 summarizes this body of information.

Message   The *lac* operon is a cluster of structural genes that specify enzymes involved in lactose metabolism. These genes are controlled by the coordinated actions of cis-dominant promoter and operator regions. The activity of these regions is in turn determined by a repressor molecule that is specified by a separate regulator gene. Figure 18-8 integrates all this information into a single picture.

Catabolite Repression of the *lac* Operon: Positive Control

There is an additional control system superimposed on the repressor-operator system described previously. This system exists because cells have specific enzymes that favor glucose uptake and metabolism. If both lactose *and* glucose are present, synthesis of β-galactosidase is not induced until all of the glucose has been utilized. Thus the cell conserves its metabolic machinery by utilizing any existing glucose before going through the steps of creating new machinery to exploit the lactose. The operon model outlined pre-

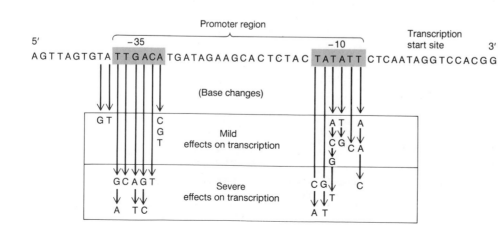

Figure 18-7 Specific DNA sequences are important for efficient transcription of *E. coli* genes by RNA polymerase. The boxed sequences at approximately −35 and −10 are highly conserved in all *E. coli* promoters. Point mutations in these regions have noticeable effects upon transcription efficiency. (From J. D. Watson, J. Tooze, and D. T. Kurtz, *Recombinant DNA: A Short Course.* Copyright © 1983 by W. H. Freeman and Co.)

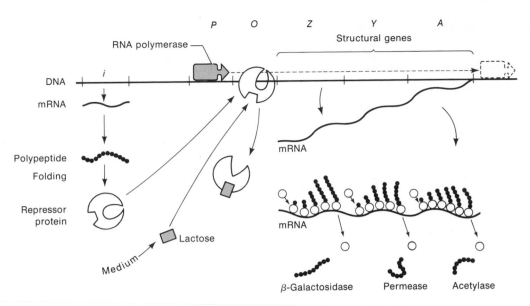

Figure 18-8. Regulations of the *lactose* operon. The *I* gene continually makes repressor. The repressor binds to the *O* (operator) region, blocking the RNA polymerase bound to *P* from transcribing the adjacent structural genes. When lactose is present, it binds to the repressor and changes its shape so that the repressor no longer binds to *O*. The RNA polymerase is then able to transcribe the *Z*, *Y*, and *A* structural genes, so the three enzymes are produced.

viously will not account for the suppression of induction by glucose, so we must modify it.

Studies indicate that in fact it is some catabolic breakdown product of glucose (whose exact identity is not yet known) that prevents activation of the *lac* operon by lactose, so this effect was originally called **catabolite repression**. The effect of the glucose catabolite is exerted on an important cellular constituent called cyclic adenosine monophosphate (cAMP). When glucose is present at high concentration, the cAMP concentration is low; as the glucose concentration decreases, the concentration of cAMP correspondingly increases. The high concentration of cAMP is necessary for activation of the *lac* operon. Mutants that cannot convert ATP to cAMP cannot be induced to produce β-galactosidase because the concentration of cAMP is

not great enough to activate the *lac* operon. In addition, there are other mutants that do make cAMP but cannot activate the *lac* enzymes, because they lack yet another protein called CAP (catabolite activator protein) made by the *crp* gene. The CAP protein forms a complex with cAMP, and it is this complex that activates the *lac* operon (Figure 18-9).

How does catabolite repression fit into our model for the structure and regulation of the *lac* operon? Recall the technique that Gilbert used to identify the operator base sequence. In a similar experiment, the CAP-cAMP complex was added to DNA, and the DNA then subjected to digestion by the enzyme DNase. The surviving strands are presumably those shielded from digestion by an attached CAP-cAMP complex, and the sequence of these strands is that shown in Figure 18-10. This sequence clearly is different from the operator sequence (Figure 18-6), but it also has a rotational twofold symmetry.

The entire *lac* operon can be inserted into λ phage in such a way that the initiation of transcription is prompted by the phage gene adjacent to *lac*. In this case, the transcribed product carries a complementary copy of the base sequence from the *lac* control regions (sequences not tran-

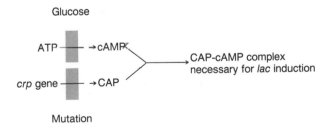

Figure 18-9. Catabolite control of the *lac* operon. The operon is inducible by lactose to the maximal levels when cAMP and CAP form a complex. The *lac* operon cannot be expressed at full levels if formation of cAMP is blocked by excess glucose or if formation of CAP is blocked by a mutation of the *crp* gene. (CAP = catabolic activator protein; cAMP = cyclic adenosine monophosphate; *crp* = structural gene responsible for synthesizing CAP.)

$$\text{GTGAGTTAGCTCAC}$$
$$\text{CACTCAATCGAGTG}$$

Figure 18-10. The DNA base sequence to which the CAP-cAMP complex binds. Regions of twofold rotational symmetry are indicated by horizontal lines above and below the symmetric base pairs and by a dot at their axis of symmetry.

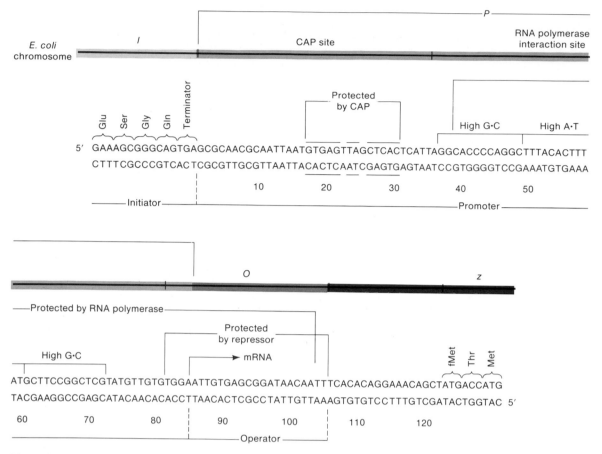

Figure 18-11. The base sequence and the genetic boundaries of the control region of the *lac* operon, with partial sequences for the structural genes. (After R. C. Dickson, J. Abelson, W. M. Barnes, and W. S. Reznikoff, "Genetic Regulation: The *Lac* Control Region." *Science* 187:27, 1975. Copyright 1975 by the American Association for the Advancement of Science.)

scribed in the *lac* mRNA). We already know the amino acid sequences for the repressor and β-galactosidase, so these sequences can be identified, and the remaining sequences can be assigned to the control regions (Figure 18-11). We can also fit the known repressor, CAP-cAMP, and RNA polymerase binding sites into the detailed model.

The knowledge about the *lac* operon provides insight into the elegance of gene regulation. The *E. coli* cell normally processes glucose as a source of energy and carbon. It possesses an "emergency" capability to process lactose, but it does not waste energy or materials in preparing the mechanism for that processing so long as glucose is available, even if lactose is also present. This control is accomplished because a glucose-breakdown product inhibits formation of the CAP-cAMP complex that is required for attachment of RNA polymerase at the *lac* promoter site. Even when there is a shortage of glucose catabolites and CAP-cAMP forms, the mechanism for lactose metabolism will be created only if lactose is present. This control is accomplished because lactose must bind to the repressor protein to remove it from the operator site and permit transcription of the *lac* operon. Thus, the cell conserves its energy and resources by pro-

ducing the lactose-metabolizing enzymes only when they are both needed and useful.

Whereas inducer-repressor control of the *lac* operon is an example of *negative* control, the CAP-cAMP system is an example of **positive control,** since expression requires the presence of an activating signal—in this case, the interaction of the CAP-cAMP complex with the CAP region. Figure 18-12 distinguishes between these two basic types of control systems.

Message The *lac* operon has an added level of control so that the operon remains inactive in the presence of glucose even if lactose is also present. A high concentration of glucose catabolites produces low concentrations of cyclic AMP, which must form a complex with CAP to permit induction of the *lac* operon.

By using different combinations of controlling elements, bacteria have evolved numerous strategies for regulating gene expression. Some examples follow.

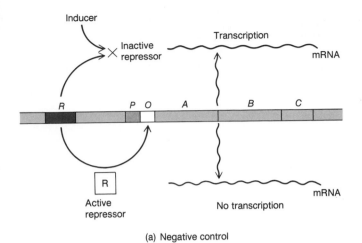

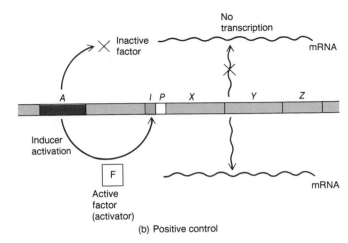

(a) Negative control

(b) Positive control

Figure 18-12. Comparison of positive and negative control. The basic aspects of negative and positive control are depicted. (a) In negative control, an active repressor (encoded by the *R* gene in the example shown here) blocks gene expression of the *A,B,C* operon by binding to an operator site (*O*). An inactive repressor allows gene expression. The repressor can be inactivated either by an inducer or by mutation. (b) In positive control, an active factor is required for gene expression, as shown for the *X,Y,Z* operon here. Small molecules can convert an inactive factor into an active one, as in the case of cyclic AMP and the CAP protein. An inactive positive control factor results in no gene expression. The activator binds to the control region of the operon, termed *I* in this case. (The position of both *O* and *I* with respect to the promoter, *P*, in the two examples is arbitrarily drawn.)

Dual Positive and Negative Control: The Arabinose Operon

The metabolism of the sugar arabinose is catalyzed by three enzymes encoded by the *araB*, *araA*, and *araD* genes. Figure 18-13 depicts the control circuits for this operon. Expression is activated at the adjacent **initiator** region, *araI*. Within this region, the product of the *araC* gene, when bound to arabinose, can activate transcription, perhaps by directly affecting RNA polymerase binding in the *araI* region. This represents positive control, since the product of the regulatory gene (*araC*) must be active in order for the operon to be expressed. An additional positive control is mediated by the same CAP-cAMP system that regulates *lac* expression. In the absence of arabinose, the *araC* product assumes a different conformation and actually represses the *ara* operon by binding to an operator region, *araO*! Therefore, the *araC* protein has two conformations that promote two opposing functions at two alternative binding sites. The conformation is dependent on whether the inducer, arabinase, is bound to the protein.

Metabolic Pathways

Coordinate control of genes in bacteria is widespread. In the early 1960s, when Milislav Demerec studied the distribution of loci affecting a common biosynthetic pathway, he found that the genes controlling steps in the synthesis of the amino acid tryptophan in *Salmonella typhimurium* are clustered together in a restricted part of the genome. In 1964, Demerec then looked at the distribution of genes involved in a number of different metabolic pathways. Analyzing auxotrophic mutations representing 87 different cistrons, he found that 63 could be located in 17 functionally similar clusters. A cluster is defined as two or more loci that control related functions, where the loci are carried on a single transducing fragment and are not separated by an unrelated gene. Furthermore, in cases where the sequence of catalytic activity is known, there is a remarkable congruence between the sequence of genes on the chromosome and the sequence in which their products act in the metabolic pathway. This congruence is strikingly illustrated by the histidine cluster in *Salmonella* that was extensively studied in the early 1960s by Philip Hartman and Bruce Ames (Figure 18-14), and by the tryptophan cluster in *E. coli* (see Figure 18-15 and later in the text) that was characterized during the same period by Charles Yanofsky.

Message   Genes involved in the same metabolic pathway are frequently tightly clustered on prokaryotic chromosomes, often in the same sequence as the reactions that they control. Furthermore, the genes within a cluster often are expressed at the same time.

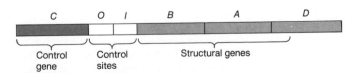

Figure 18-13. Map of the *ara* region. The *DAB* genes together with the *I* and *O* sites constitute the *ara* operon.

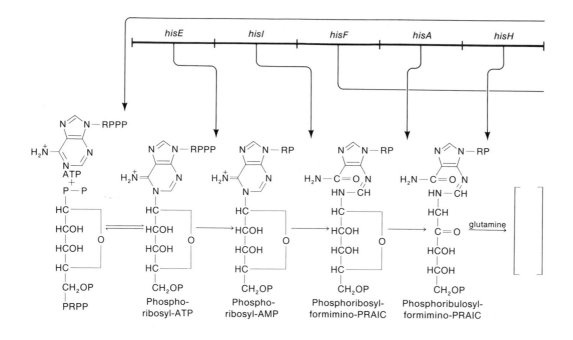

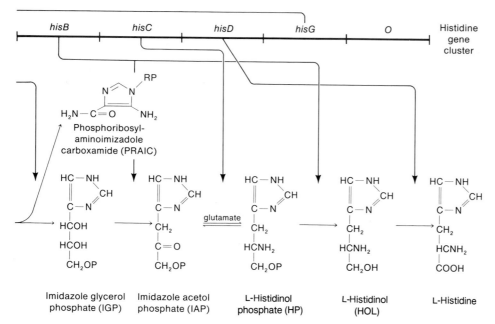

Figure 18-14 The *histidine* (*his*) gene cluster and the metabolic pathway that it controls. Note that the sequence of genes in the cluster generally corresponds to the sequence of steps that each gene catalyzes in the pathway for synthesis of histidine. The fact that the final gene in the sequence (*hisG*) catalyzes the first step in the reaction sequence is probably not a coincidence; this pattern is commonly found.

The *Tryptophan* Genes: Negative Control with Superimposed Attenuation

The *lac* operon is an example of an inducible system, in the sense that synthesis of an enzyme is induced by the presence of its substrate. Repressible systems also exist, in which an excess of product leads to a shutdown of the production of enzymes involved in synthesizing that product. Such a control system has been identified for a cluster of genes controlling enzymes in the pathway for tryptophan production. Synthesis of tryptophan is shut off when there is an excess of tryptophan in the medium. Jacob and Monod suggested that the cluster of five *trp* cistrons in *E. coli* forms

another operon, differing from the *lac* operon in that the tryptophan repressor will bind to the *trp* operator only when it *is* bound to tryptophan (Figure 18-15). (Recall that the *lac* repressor binds to the operator except when it is bound to lactose.) A second control pathway also modulates tryptophan biosynthesis at the level of enzyme activity. This is termed **feedback inhibition.** Here, the first enzyme in the pathway, encoded by the *trpE* and *trpD* genes, is inhibited by tryptophan itself.

As with the *lac* operon, further analysis of the *trp* operon revealed yet another level of control superimposed on the basic repressor-operator mechanism. Charles Yanofsky was studying constitutive mutant strains (carrying a mutation in *trpR*, the repressor locus) that continue to produce *trp* mRNA in the presence of tryptophan. Yanofsky

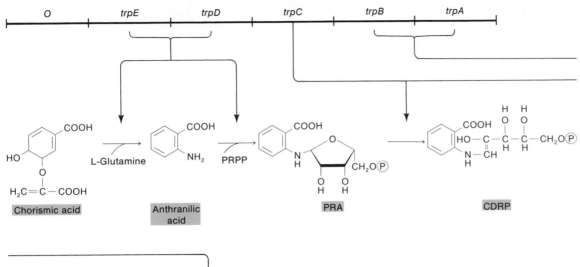

Figure 18-15. The genetic sequence of cistrons in the *trp* operon of *E. coli* and the sequence of reactions catalyzed by the enzyme products of the *trp* structural genes. The products of genes *trpD* and *trpE* form a complex that catalyzes specific steps, as do the products of genes *trpB* and *trpA*. (After S. Tanemura and R. H. Bauerle, *Genetics* 95:545–559, 1980.)

found that removal of tryptophan from the medium leads to almost a tenfold increase in *trp* mRNA production in these constitutive mutant strains. Furthermore, Yanofsky isolated a constitutive mutant strain that produces *trp* mRNA at the maximal level even in the presence of tryptophan, and he showed that this mutation has a deletion located between the operator and the *trpE* cistron.

Yanofsky was able to isolate the polycistronic *trp* operon mRNA. Upon sequencing it, he found a long sequence, termed the **leader sequence,** of 160 bases at the 5′ end before the first triplet in the *trpE* gene. The deletion

mutant that always produces *trp* mRNA at maximal levels has a deletion extending from base 130 to base 160 (Figure 18-16). Yanofsky called this the **attenuator** region, because its presence apparently leads to a reduction of the rate of mRNA transcription when tryptophan is present. But what is the role of the leader sequence from bases 1 through 130? A surprising observation provided the key to solving this problem.

When studying the mRNAs transcribed from the *trp* operon, Yanofsky discovered that the original constitutive mutant strains continue to produce the first 141 bases of

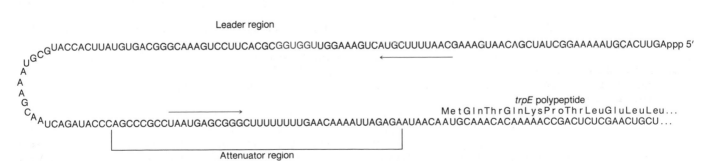

Figure 18-16. The leader sequence and attenuator sequence of the *trp* operon, with the beginning of the *trpE* structural sequence (showing the amino acid sequence of the *trpE* polypeptide). (From

G. S. Stent and R. Calendar, *Molecular Genetics*, 2d ed. Copyright © 1978 by W. H. Freeman and Co. Based on unpublished data provided by C. Yanofsky.)

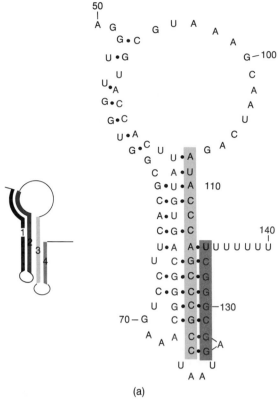

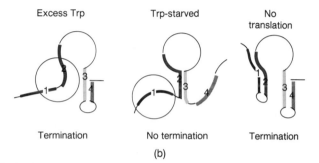

(a)

(b)

Figure 18-17. (a) Proposed secondary structures in *E. coli* terminated *trp* leader RNA. Four regions can base-pair to form three stem-and-loop structures. (b) Model for attenuation in the *E. coli trp* operon. Under conditions of excess tryptophan the ribosome (closed circles) translating the newly transcribed leader RNA will synthesize the complete leader peptide. During this synthesis the ribosome will mask regions 1 and 2 of the RNA and prevent the formation of stem-and-loop 1·2 or 2·3. Stem-and-loop 3·4 will be free to form and signal the RNA polymerase molecule (not shown) transcribing the leader region to terminate transcription. Under conditions of tryptophan starvation, charged tRNA^{Trp} will be limiting and the ribosome will stall at the adjacent *trp* codons in the leader peptide-coding region. Because only region 1 is masked, stem-and-loop 2·3 will be free to form as regions 2 and 3 are synthesized. Formation of stem-and-loop 2·3 will exclude the formation of stem-and-loop 3·4, which is required as the signal for transcription termination. (From D. L. Oxender, G. Zurawski and C. Yanofsky, *Proc. Nat. Acad. Sci. USA* 76:5524, 1979.)

the mRNA at maximal rate, even in the presence of tryptophan. In other words, the segment from base 141 through base 160 apparently normally acts as a chain terminator to halt transcription of about nine in every 10 mRNAs if tryptophan is present. When tryptophan is absent, every transcription is carried through this attenuator region and on to completion. In the deletion mutants, the attenuator region is missing, so transcription is carried through in every case regardless of the presence or absence of tryptophan.

What causes the interference with termination at the attenuator in the absence of tryptophan? Figure 18-17 presents a model based on alternate secondary structures formed by the mRNA in the leader region. The model proposes that one of the two conformations favors transcription termination and that the other favors elongation. Translation of part of the leader sequence would promote the conformation that favors termination.

It is known that the leader sequence can be translated to yield a short peptide of 11 amino acids. There are two tryptophan codons in the translated stretch of the leader mRNA (Figure 18-18). When excess tryptophan is present, there is a sufficient supply of charged tRNA to allow efficient translation through the relevant portion of the leader mRNA, which results in transcription termination. However, in the absence of tryptophan, charged *trp* tRNA is limiting, and translation stalls in the leader, thus allowing the secondary structure of the mRNA to form that is favorable to the continuation transcription. In this manner, an

Met - Lys - Ala - Ile - Phe - Val - Leu - Lys - Gly - Trp - Trp - Arg - Thr - Ser -

〜〜AUG AAA GCA AUU UUC GUA CUG AAA GGU UGG UGG CGC ACU UCC UGA〜〜

Figure 18-18. Translated portion of the *trp* leader region, shown with the corresponding sequence of the leader mRNA.

(a)

Met - Lys - His - Ile - Pro - Phe - Phe - Phe - Ala - Phe - Phe - Phe - Thr - Phe - Pro -Stop

5′ AUG AAA CAC AUA CCG UUU UUC UUC GCA UUC UUU UUU ACC UCC CCC UGA 3′

(b)

Met - Thr - Arg - Val - Gln - Phe - Lys - His - His - His - His - His - His - His - Pro - Asp -

5′ AUG ACA CGC GUU CAA UUU AAA CAC CAC CAU CAU CAC CAU CAU CCU GAC 3′

Figure 18-19. Amino acid sequence of the leader peptide and base sequence of the corresponding portion of mRNA from (a) the phenylalanine operon and (b) the histidine operon. Note that seven of the 15 residues in the phenylalanine operon leader are phenylalanine and that seven consecutive residues from the histidine operon leader peptide are histidine. (From L. Stryer, *Biochemistry.* Copyright © 1981 by W. H. Freeman and Co.)

additional 10-fold range of tryptophan biosynthetic enzymes is superimposed on the normal range that is achieved by repressor-operator interaction. The analysis of numerous point mutations in the *trp* leader sequence that favor or disfavor the respective secondary structures lends strong support to the Yanofsky model for attenuation.

Several operons for enzymes in biosynthetic pathways have attenuation controls similar to that described for tryptophan (as shown in Figure 18-19). For instance, the leader region of the *his* operon, which encodes the enzymes of the histidine biosynthetic pathway, contains a translated region with seven consecutive histidine codons. Mutations at outside loci that result in lowered levels of normal charged *his* tRNA result in partially constitutive levels of the enzymes encoded by the *his* operon.

Message   The *trp* operon is regulated by a negative repressor-operator control system that represses synthesis of tryptophan enzymes when tryptophan is present in the medium. A second level of control involves an attenuator region where termination of transcription is induced by the presence of tryptophan.

The λ Phage: A Complex of Operons

At the time they proposed the operon model, Jacob and Monod suggested that the genetic activity of temperate phages might be controlled by a system analogous to the *lac* operon. In the lysogenic state, the prophage genome is inactive—that is, repressed. In the lytic phase, the phage genes for reproduction are active—that is, induced. Since Jacob and Monod proposed the idea of operon control for phages, the λ phage has become one of the organisms whose genetic system is best understood. This phage does indeed have an operon-type system controlling its two functional

states. By now, you should not be surprised to learn that this system proved to be more complex than initially suggested.

Alan Campbell induced and mapped many conditionally lethal mutations in the λ phage, as shown in Figure 18-20). There is clear evidence for the clustering of genes with related functions. Furthermore, mutations in the *N*, *O*, and *P* genes prevent most of the genome from being expressed after phage infection, with only those loci lying between *N* and *O* being active. We shall soon see the significance of this observation.

When normal bacteria are infected by wild-type λ phage, two possible sequences may follow: (1) a phage may be integrated into the bacterial chromosome as an inert prophage (thus lysogenizing the bacterial cell), or (2) the phage may produce the necessary enzymes to guide production of products needed for phage maturation and cell lysis. When wild-type phage particles are placed on a lawn of sensitive bacteria, clearings (plaques) appear where bacterial cells are infected and lysed, but these plaques are turbid because lysogenized bacteria (which are resistant to phage superinfection) grow within the plaques.

Mutant phages that form clear plaques can be selected as a source of phages that are unable to lysogenize cells. Such *clear* (*c*) mutants prove to be analogous to *I* and *O* mutants in *E. coli*. For example, conditional mutants for a site called *cI* are unable to establish a lysogenic state under restrictive conditions, but they fail to induce lysis in a cell that has been lysogenized by a wild-type prophage. Apparently, the *cI* mutation produces a defective repressor in the phage control system.

Virulent mutants were isolated that do not lysogenize cells but will grow in a lysogenized cell, thus providing defects that are insensitive to the λ repressor. Genetic mapping revealed *two* operators, designated O_L and O_R and located on the left and right of *cI*, respectively. Furthermore, each operator has a promoter; the promoters are called P_L and P_R. Figure 18-21 shows a simplification of the genetic map of the phage control regions. Because transcription

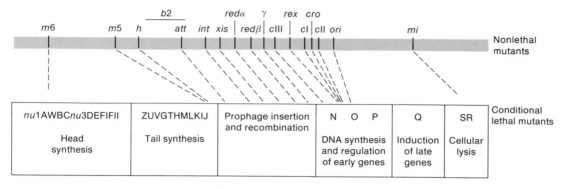

Figure 18-20. The genetic map of the λ phage. The positions of nonlethal and conditionally lethal mutations are indicated, and the characteristic clusters of genes with related functions are shown. (From A. Campbell, *The Episomes*, Harper & Row, 1969.)

extends from the *O* regions away from *cI*, the transcripts must be read from different strands of the DNA.

Mark Ptashne was able to purify the λ repressor. He showed that each λ genome binds six repressor molecules, three at each operator. Furthermore, the repressor-binding sites of O_R overlap with the promoter for the *cI* gene itself (Figure 18-22). Different affinities of the repressor for each of the three operator sites allow the repressor to regulate its own synthesis. When there is an excess of repressor, binding to the low-affinity third O_R site occurs, reducing further repressor synthesis. This keeps repressor concentrations from accumulating to the point where eventual induction would be difficult.

When a phage infects a cell, there is no repressor present. A host-cell enzyme (RNA polymerase) initiates transcription, beginning at O_L and extending through the *N* gene, and beginning at O_R and extending through the *cro* gene.

Now we see why the *N* gene is important: its product interacts with the RNA polymerase to modify it in such a way that transcription will not terminate in an attenuator region at the ends of *N* and *cro*. Instead, transcription proceeds through to genes that are involved in phage DNA replication, recombination, and lysogeny. The name of the *cro* gene is derived from the expression "*c*ontrol of *r*epressor and *o*ther things." The *cro* protein acts to inhibit production of the repressor by binding to a promoter region adjacent to the *cI* locus. Thus, the *cro* product appears to be a repressor of a repressor, and it must act during the lytic phage of λ growth. On the other hand, λ repressor binds to O_R, thus shutting off transcription of the *cro* gene. Thus, *cro* and *cI* activity must be mutually exclusive, with *cro* activity

required for lysis and *cI* activity required for lysogeny.

The complexity of the λ cycle only increases with further study. The description given here is an abbreviated version of a well-characterized process that provides further modifications of the operon model.

Message The regulation of the lytic and lysogenic states of the λ phage provides a model for interacting control systems that may be useful for interpreting gene regulation in eukaryotes.

Multioperon Repression

Repressors can simultaneously control several or even a large number of operons. For instance, the trp repressor simultaneously regulates the *trp* operon, the *aroH* gene, and the *trp* repressor gene itself. The three respective operators show important sequence homologies. Another multicomponent system subject to the same repressor is the set of functions that constitute the SOS repair pathway (discussed in conjunction with mutagenesis in Chapter 15). A repressor, encoded by the *lexA* gene, reduces expression of numerous genes involved in DNA repair, including the *recA*, *uvrA*, *uvrB*, and *umuC* genes (see Chapter 15). The LexA repressor also regulates its own synthesis. Some of these LexA-repressed genes still maintain a residual level of expression in the presence of the LexA repressor. In response to an inducing signal, somehow triggered by damaged DNA that blocks replication, a protease activity of the protein encoded by *recA* is activated. This results in the cleavage of the LexA repressor, allowing high levels of synthesis of the SOS functions. UV light and other agents that damage DNA induce the SOS functions. Figure 18-23 outlines this sequence of events. Interestingly, the RecA protease also cleaves the λ repressor (the product of the λ*cI* gene), as well as the repressors of several other phages related to λ. This is the physical basis for the classical UV-light induction of λ lysogens.

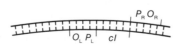

Figure 18-21. Genetic map of the control elements of λ reproduction on the double-stranded phage DNA. Each symbol is placed next to the strand that is transcribed for the corresponding gene.

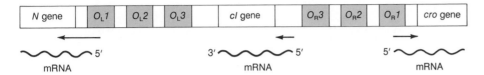

Figure 18-22. The *cI* control region for λ. (After L. Stryer, *Biochemistry.* Copyright © 1983 by W. H. Freeman and Co.)

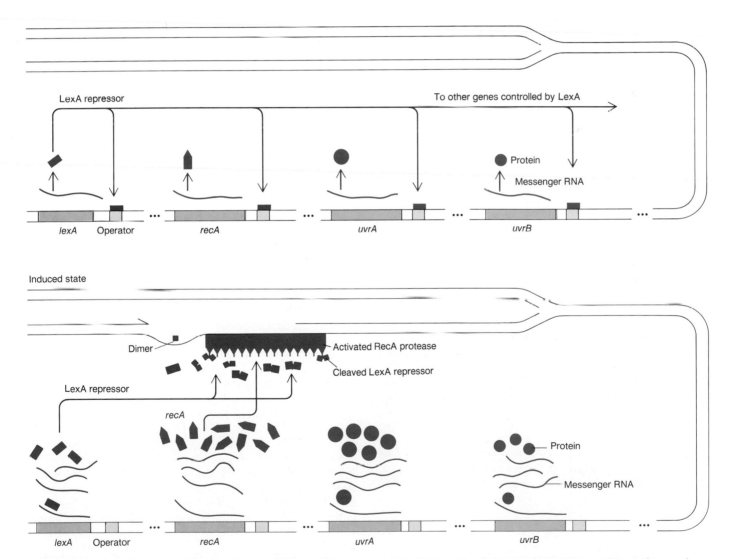

Figure 18-23. Regulatory system based on LexA and RecA. This system is quiescent during normal growth in the absence of damage to DNA (top). LexA repressor binds to the operators of *lexA, recA, uvrA, uvrB* and some other genes, keeping the synthesis of messenger RNA and protein at the low level characteristic of uninduced cells. Damage to DNA sufficient to produce a postreplication gap activates the *SOS* response (bottom). RecA protein binds to the single-stranded DNA opposite gap; its protein-cleaving activity is thereby activated and LexA repressor is cleaved. In the absence of functional repressor the LexA-controlled genes are switched on and protein is synthesized at an increased rate. (From P. Howard-Flanders, "Inducible Repair of DNA." Copyright © 1981 by Scientific American, Inc.)

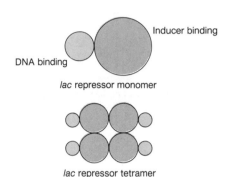

Figure 18-24. Schematic diagram showing arrangement of domains in *lac* repressor. All mutations affecting DNA and operator binding result in alterations in the amino-terminal end of the protein, whereas mutants defective in inducer binding or aggregation have alteration in the remaining portion of the protein.

Structure of Regulatory Proteins

Protein-sequence analyses and structural comparisons indicate that a number of DNA-binding regulatory proteins share important features. All consist of a DNA-binding domain, located at the amino-terminal end of the protein, which protrudes from the main "core" of the protein. In certain cases, the core protein contains the inducer binding site. Figure 18-24 shows this arrangement, which holds for the Lac, λcI, and λCro repressors, as well as for the CAP protein. It has been postulated that protruding α-(alpha)

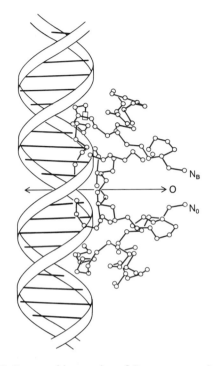

Figure 18-26. Presumed interaction of Cro repressor with DNA. Two monomers of Cro interact with the DNA. The respective amino termini of the two Cro molecules are labeled N_0 and N_B. A pair of twofold-related α-helices occupy successive major grooves of the DNA. (From W. F. Anderson et al. *Nature* 290:754–758, 1981.)

helices fit into the major groove of the DNA. The three-dimensional structure of the λCro repressor suggests how such an operator-repressor complex might look (Figure 18-25). A favored detailed model is shown in Figure 18-26. Here, two α-helices from the repressor protein interact with two consecutive major grooves of the DNA of the operator site.

The striking partial-sequence homologies of the DNA-binding domains of several regulatory proteins (Figure 18-27) suggest that they bind to other respective operator sites in a similar fashion. It is hoped that the determination of the three-dimensional structure of a repressor-operator complex by X-ray crystallography will allow the elucidation of the rules for DNA sequence recognition by regulatory proteins.

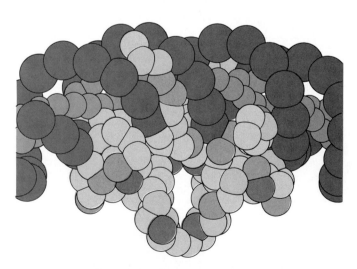

Figure 18-25. Schematic drawing of the proposed sequence-specific complex of Cro with DNA. For the stylized DNA (dark and medium gray) the large circles indicate the positions of the phosphate groups and the smaller circles follow the bottom of the major and minor grooves. For the Cro dimer (color and light gray) one circle is drawn for each amino acid. (From D. H. Ohlendorf et al. *Nature* 298:718–723, 1982.)

Summary

■ The operon model explains how prokaryotic genes are controlled through a mechanism that coordinates the activ-

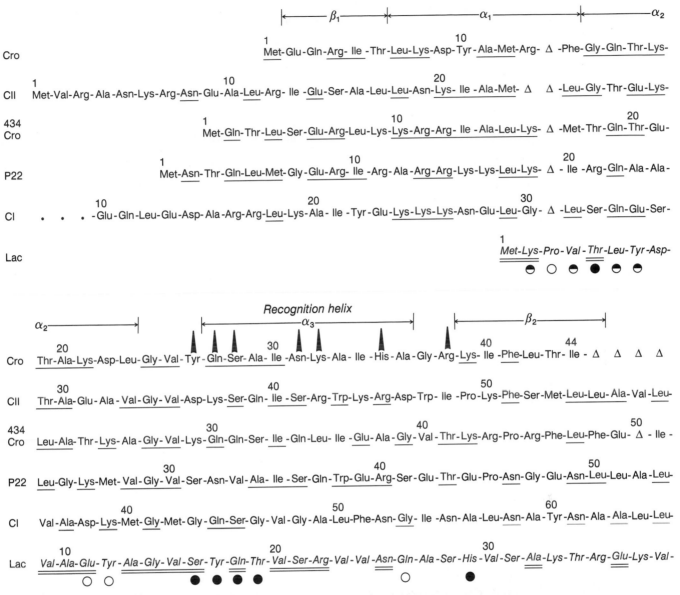

Figure 18-27. Comparison of the amino-terminal amino acid sequence of *lac* repressor with five other DNA-binding proteins. Residues that are homologous within the five DNA-binding proteins are indicated by color and a single underline. Residues of *lac* repressor that are common to one or more of the five proteins are colored and have a double underline. The letters α and β show the locations of the α-helices and β-sheet strands of *cro* protein. Residues of *cro* that are presumed from model building to interact with DNA are capped by an arrowhead. Δ indicates an assumed deletion. The solid circles underneath the *lac* sequence indicate those locations where known mutations dramatically reduce DNA-binding ability but do not interfere with inducer binding (i.e., they do not simply destabilize the whole protein). The half-filled circles indicate locations where amino acid substitutions may reduce DNA-binding affinity or where the reduction in binding is weak. Open circles indicate sites where substitution does not interfere with DNA binding. (Data compiled by B. W. Matthews et al., *Proc. Nat. Acad. Sci. USA* 79:1428–1432, 1982.)

ity of a number of related genes. In negative control, the initiation of transcription is controlled at the operator by a repressor whose binding affinities to the operator may be altered by inducer molecules. The inactivation of the repressor, the negative control element, is required for active transcription. In positive control, transcription initiation requires the activation of a factor. Sometimes one control system is superimposed on another. For instance, superimposed on the repressor-operator system for the *lac* operon is the cAMP-CAP positive control system. Modulation of transcription by an attenuator sequence supplements the repressor-operator control in the *trp* operon. In phage λ multiple binding sites for repressors, as well as repressors of repressors, add additional levels of control.

Problems

1. The genes shown in Table 18-4 are from the *lac* operon system of *E. coli.* The symbols *a*, *b*, and *c* represent the repressor (*I*) gene, the operator (*O*) region, and the structural gene (*Z*) for β-galactosidase, although not necessarily in that order. Furthermore, the order in which the symbols are written in the genotypes is not necessarily the actual sequence in the *lac* operon.

   a. State which symbol (*a*, *b*, or *c*) represents each of the *lac* genes *I*, *O*, and *Z*.

   b. In Table 18-4, a superscript minus on a gene symbol merely indicates a mutant, but you know there are some special mutant behaviors in this system that are given special mutant designations. For each of the genotypes in the table, indicate the genotype using the conventional gene symbols for the *lac* operon.

   (Problem 1 is from J. Kuspira and G. W. Walker, *Genetics: Questions and Problems*, McGraw-Hill, 1973.)

2. The map of the *lac* operon is

   $$I \quad P\,O\,Z\,Y$$

■ **TABLE 18-4.**

Genotype	Activity (+) or inactivity (−) of *z* gene	
	Inducer absent	Inducer present
$a^-b^+c^+$	+	+
$a^+b^+c^-$	+	+
$a^+b^-c^-$	−	−
$a^+b^-c^+/a^-b^+c^-$	+	+
$a^+b^+c^+/a^-b^-c^-$	−	+
$a^+b^+c^-/a^-b^-c^+$	−	+
$a^-b^+c^+/a^+b^-c^-$	+	+

■ **TABLE 18-5.**

Part	Genotype	β-galactosidase		Permease	
		No lactose	Lactose	No lactose	Lactose
Example	$i^+p^+O^+z^+y^+/i^+p^+O^+z^+y^+$	−	+	−	+
(a)	$i^cp^-O^cz^+y^+/i^+p^+O^+z^-y^-$				
(b)	$i^+p^-O^+z^+y^+/i^cp^+O^+z^+y^-$				
(c)	$i^+p^+O^oz^-y^+/i^+p^-O^+z^+y^-$				
(d)	$i^sp^+O^+z^+y^+/i^cp^+O^+z^+y^+$				
(e)	$i^cp^+O^oz^+y^+/i^cp^+O^+z^-y^+$				
(f)	$i^cp^-O^+z^+y^+/i^cp^+O^cz^+y^-$				
(g)	$i^+p^+O^+z^-y^+/i^cp^+O^+z^+y^-$				

The promoter (*P*) region is the site of initiation of transcription through the binding of the RNA polymerase molecule before actual mRNA production. Mutants of the promoter (*P*⁻) apparently cannot bind the RNA polymerase molecule. Certain predictions can be made about the effect of *P*⁻ mutations. Use your predictions and your knowledge of the lactose system to complete Table 18-5. Insert a plus where enzyme is produced and a minus where no enzyme is produced.

3. In a haploid eukaryotic organism, you are studying two enzymes that perform sequential conversions of a nutrient A supplied in the medium:

$$A \xrightarrow[E_1]{} B \xrightarrow[E_2]{} C$$

Treatment of cells with mutagen produces three different mutant types with respect to these functions. Mutants of type 1 show no E_1 function; all type 1 mutations map to a single locus on linkage group II. Mutants of type 2 show no E_2 function; all type 2 mutations map to a single locus on linkage group VIII. Mutants of type 3 show no E_1 or E_2 function; all type 3 mutants map to a single locus on linkage group I.

   a. Compare this system with the *lac* operon of *E. coli,* pointing out the similarities and the differences. (Be sure to account for each mutant type at the molecular level.)

   b. If you were to intensify the mutant hunt, would there be any other mutant types you would expect to find on the basis of your model? Explain.

4. In *Neurospora,* all mutants affecting the enzymes carbamyl phosphate synthetase and aspartate transcarbamylase map at the *pyr-3* locus. If you induce *pyr-3* mutations by ICR-170 (a chemical mutagen), you find that either both enzyme functions are lacking or only the transcarbamylase function is lacking; in no case is the synthetase activity lacking when the transcarbamylase activity is present.

(ICR-170 is assumed to induce frame-shifts.) Interpret these results in terms of a possible operon.

5. In 1972, Suzanne Bourgeois and Alan Jobe showed that a derivative of lactose, allolactose, is the true natural inducer of the *lac* operon, rather than lactose itself. Lactose is converted to allolactose by the enzyme β-galactosidase. How does this result explain the early finding that many Z^- mutations, which are not polar, still do not allow induction of *lac* permease and transacetylase by lactose?

6. Certain *lacI* mutations eliminate operator binding by the *lac* repressor but do not affect the aggregation of subunits to make a tetramer, the active form of the repressor. These mutations are partially dominant to wild-type. Can you explain the partially I^- phenotype of the I^-/I^+ heterodiploids?

7. Explain the fundamental differences between negative control and positive control.

CHAPTER 19

The Chromosome and Genetic Control Mechanisms in Eukaryotes

■ Unraveling the mysteries of the eukaryotic genome is far more difficult and challenging than understanding gene control in prokaryotes. The genome in eukaryotes is much larger, and the chromosome structures are more complex, than in prokaryotes. In order to get a clearer picture of eukaryotic genetic systems we shall consider four aspects of the genome:

1. The structure of chromosomes. Is the chromosome simply a structural framework that assembles the genes for proper partition during cell division? Or does the structure of the chromosome play some role in determining the functions of the genes within it?

2. The activity of chromosomes

3. The sequence organization of chromosomes

4. The regulation of eukaryotic genes

In this chapter we encounter many phenomena and observations for which there is as yet no explanation in terms of molecular biology; these pose the problems to be tackled with the growing arsenal of techniques and ideas. We begin with classical cytological and genetic observations that await reexamination in molecular terms.

The Structure and Activity of Chromosomes

By cytological examination, we can distinguish eukaryotic chromosome segments of varying staining intensity. Recall that heterochromatic elements — that is, heterochromatin — are densely stained; these regions generally are assumed to reflect a state of genetic inactivity. Euchromatic regions — that is, euchromatin — are less densely stained and typically less compact than the heterochromatin; these regions are assumed to represent the locations of active genes. The heterochromatic elements can be divided into two classes. First, there are entire chromosomes or specific chromosome segments that stain densely in every preparation from a given species; such elements are called **constitutive heterochromatin.** Second, there are chromosomes or chromosome segments that appear as euchromatin in some preparations and as heterochromatin in others; heterochromatin of this type is called **facultative heterochromatin.** We shall consider these two types of heterochromatin separately.

Constitutive Heterochromatin

In many species, there are heterochromatic chromosomes that have very minor biological roles (if they have any role at all). For example, corn may possess small heterochromatic elements called B chromosomes. However, no obvious phenotypic difference can be detected between lines having one, many, or no B chromosomes. Such apparently extraneous chromosomes were long ago named **satellite** or **accessory chromosomes.** They are found in many insect species that infect plants and in some vertebrate species (such as salamanders). In the fly *Sciara*, large metacentric heterochromatic chromosomes are found in the gonadal (germ) cells, but these satellite chromosomes do not appear in the somatic cells. What distinguishes satellite chromosomes from the functionally important ones? Why are such apparently useless chromosomes retained? We do not yet know the answers to these questions.

Not all heterochromatic chromosomes appear to be functionally useless. The Y chromosome in *Drosophila* and other organisms is composed of heterochromatin, but it does have a genetic function. In *Drosophila melanogaster*, the Y chromosome carries six distinguishable loci (all of them sites whose wild-type allele is necessary for male fertility). However, this chromosome is almost as long as the X, which carries a large number of genes.

Of even greater interest are the segments of heterochromatin that occur consistently within chromosomes such as those in Diptera (two-winged flies). In *Drosophila*, for example, these heterochromatic regions contain between one-fourth and one-third of all the chromosomal DNA. All of these regions are found in the **proximal** parts of the chromosomes near the centromere (Figure 19-1). These proximal regions make up a large part of the chromosomal complement, but they contain very few genetically detectable loci, which are concentrated in the **distal** (end) parts of the chromosomes. Furthermore, crossing-over occurs rarely (if ever) between loci that closely flank large blocks of this proximal heterochromatin. Since the 1930s, geneticists working with *Drosophila* have assumed that these regions of proximal heterochromatin are genetically inert — that is, virtually devoid of genes that are detectable by mutant alleles.

Does the paucity of detectable mutations in proximal heterochromatin truly reflect the absence of any biological function? The answer is not clear. On the one hand, molecular analyses have revealed that heterochromatin consists mainly of repetitive DNA. In regions of high redundancy, a single point mutation has no noticeable effect. On the other hand, much of the repetitive DNA may have no function. Also, some heterochromatin is composed of nonrepetitive DNA that probably does not encode proteins.

We saw in Chapter 8 (Figure 8-4) the polytene (giant) chromosomes formed in certain dipteran cells by multiple replication of the DNA strands. In these chromosomes, the heterochromatic segments are replicated to a drastically lesser extent than the euchromatic segments. Hybridization in situ reveals that the satellite DNAs are located in the proximal heterochromatic regions. It is clear that the cytological distinctions between heterochromatin and euchromatin reflect profound functional differences, but the nature of these differences remains a mystery.

Message Heterochromatin is distinguished cytologically from euchromatin by differences in structure and activity.

The Nucleolus Organizer. In early cytological studies, certain discrete structures of the nucleus were found to be unaffected by the stains that dye chromatin; each such structure was called a **nucleolus.** The nucleolus forms at a specific chromosomal site called the **nucleolus organizer** (NO), identified cytologically as a pinched region (secondary constriction) of the chromosome.

In amphibians, a mutation called *anucleolate(an)* is produced by deletion of the NO. The wild-type phenotype of two nucleoli per cell corresponds to the genotype an^+/an^+. The genotype an^+/an has the phenotype of one nucleolus per cell; the an/an homozygotes have no nucleoli and die. Thus, genetic studies confirm that the NO is the site of nucleolus production. What is the function and the structure of the nucleolus? And what is the relationship between the nucleolus and the chromosomal DNA of the NO?

Detailed studies reveal structures similar to ribosomes within the nucleolus. In the 1960s, it was suggested that the nucleolus is an assembly point for ribosomes, which then are distributed to daughter cells during mitosis. The NO region then might code for ribosomal RNAs. Ferruccio Ritossa and Sol Spiegelman tested this hypothesis by constructing *Drosophila* strains having different numbers of NO regions per cell. In *Drosophila melanogaster*, the NO is located in the proximal heterochromatin of the X chromosome and in the short arm of the Y chromosome. (In *Drosophila*, the X chromosome is always depicted with the distal

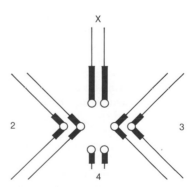

Figure 19-1. The mitotic chromosomes of a *Drosophila melanogaster* female. The X chromosomes are the sex chromosomes; the autosomes are labeled 2, 3, and 4. Open circles represent the centromeres; the thicker and darker regions of the chromosomes represent heterochromatin.

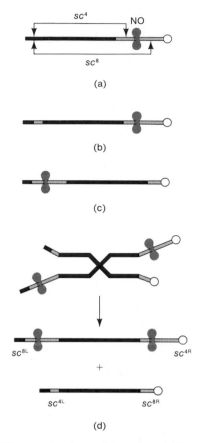

Figure 19-2. The *scute-4* and *scute-8* inversions. (a) Breakpoints for the two inversions on the *Drosophila* X chromosome. (b) The result of the sc^4 inversion. (c) The result of the sc^8 inversion. (d) A crossover between sc^4 and sc^8 in a heterozygous female yields one crossover product with two nucleolar organizers and another product with no nucleolar organizer. These products are identified as $sc^{8L}sc^{4R}$ and $sc^{4L}sc^{8R}$, respectively. The notation $sc^{8L}sc^{4R}$ indicates a chromosome whose left part is derived from the sc^8 chromosome and whose right part is derived from the sc^4 chromosome.

region on the left and the proximal region and centromere on the right. We assume this orientation of the chromosome in discussing positions on it.) Several mutant strains of *Drosophila* exist with inversions of the X chromosome in which the left breakpoint is near the *scute* locus and the right breakpoint is in the proximal region; these inversion mutants are named for the recessive **scute** phenotype they confer. The inversion *scute-8* (sc^8) has its right breakpoint between NO and the centromere; the inversion *scute-4* (sc^4) has its right breakpoint on the distal side of NO (Figure 19-2). From females heterozygous for sc^4 and sc^8, crossover products can be recovered carrying either two or zero NO regions. Different numbers of NO regions per cell can then be obtained by appropriate genetic combinations (Table 19-1).

By annealing radioactive ribosomal RNA to known amounts of DNA, Ritossa and Spiegelman measured the amount of DNA that hybridized to ribosomal RNA. They found a linear relationship between the number of NO regions per cell and the amount of 18S and 28S rRNA that hybridized (Figure 19-3). This result demonstrates that the

rRNA loci are located in the NO region. (Subsequently, hybridization in situ has confirmed the NO location of the DNA corresponding to rRNA.) Furthermore, we know the size of the 18S and the 28S rRNAs, and we know the percentage of the total DNA that hybridizes to them. Therefore, we can estimate the number of genes that code for ribosomal RNA, about 200 genes per chromosome. Obviously, such redundancy is one way of ensuring a large amount of rRNA per cell. However, this knowledge leads to a new question: how does the cell maintain the genetic equivalence of the multiple copies of each gene? It is likely that unequal crossing-over and gene conversion, described in Chapter 15, serve to maintain gene copy number and to eliminate from the genome point mutations affecting single copies.

Message The nucleolus organizer (NO) is a region that can be defined cytologically in heterochromatin. It proves to be associated with the DNA segments that code for ribosomal RNA.

Variegated Position Effects. Some clues about the nature of constitutive heterochromatin come from the study of puzzling **mosaic** phenotypes that sometimes result from chromosome rearrangements. For example, the *white* locus affecting eye color in *Drosophila* is normally found near the left (distal) tip of the X chromosome. The mutant allele *w* (white eyes) is recessive to the wild-type allele w^+ (red eyes), so that the heterozygote w^+/w has the wild-type phenotype. Let's use the symbol $R(w^+)$ to represent a chromosome rearrangement (an inversion or translocation) that moves the w^+ allele to a position near the proximal heterochromatin (Figure 19-4a). In some cases, an $R(w^+)/w$ heterozygote shows the expected wild-type phenotype, but many such individuals are **variegated** (with eyes that are mosaics of wild-type and white patches). Some kind of position effect

■ **TABLE 19-1.** Genotypes with varying numbers of NOs per cell

Genotype	Number of NOs per cell
$sc^{4L}sc^{8R}/Y$ ♂	1
$sc^{4L}sc^{8R}/X$ ♀	1
X/Y ♂	2
X/X ♀	2
$sc^{8L}sc^{4R}/X$ ♀	3
$sc^{8L}sc^{4R}/sc^{8L}sc^{4R}$ ♀	4

NOTE: here, the symbol X indicates a wild-type X chromosome with respect to the *scute* inversions.

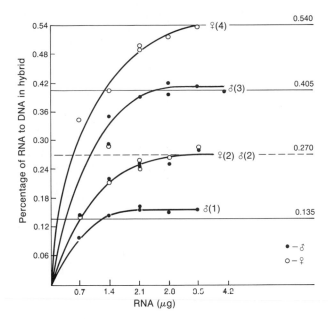

Figure 19-3. The amount of ribosomal RNA (rRNA) that hybridizes to a constant amount of DNA. The plateau is reached when all DNA complementary to the rRNA is hybridized. Each curve is obtained using DNA samples isolated from individuals with a particular number of NO regions per cell (in parentheses). (From F. M. Ritossa and S. Spiegelman, *Proc. Natl. Acad. Sci. USA* 53:737, 1965.)

must be involved. Apparently, the heterochromatin causes the inactivation of the wild-type allele in some (but not in all) somatic cells.

How far does this effect of the heterochromatin extend into the euchromatin? Let's include a second locus near *white* in our study. The *roughest (rst)* locus affects the surface texture of eye facets. Now we consider the heterozygote $R(w^+ rst^+)/w\,rst$ (Figure 19-4b). Many such heterozygotes do have variegated eyes, but the mosaic patches in the eyes do not exhibit all of the possible phenotypes. Some patches are smooth and red (wild-type), some are roughest and red, and some are roughest and white, but no sectors are ever found to be smooth and white. It would appear that the heterochromatin has a **spreading effect** that moves outward progressively across the adjacent euchromatin. The effect cannot inactivate the w^+ allele without first inactivating the rst^+ allele. The effect can extend quite far from the heterochromatin—to genes that are as much as 60 bands away from the heterochromatin in maps made from the giant (polytene) salivary chromosomes.

Message Position-effect variegation results when heterochromatin inactivates adjacent euchromatic loci in some somatic cells. This inactivation is a spreading effect that moves linearly outward from the heterochromatin through the sequence of genes in the adjacent euchromatin.

In some instances, the mutant tissues in the variegated phenotype appear in patches rather than in a "salt-and-pep-per" mixture of individual cells with differing phenotypes. Apparently, all of the cells in a given patch are related by some common event. It is now known that the inactivating effect of the heterochromatin occurs at some early stage in development, so that all daughter cells derived from the affected cell are inactivated.

What effect does the heterochromatin have on the wild-type allele? What determines the stage of development when this effect will be exercised? Why is the effect "permanent" through the divisional cycles of somatic cells, although no fixing of the activity of the allele occurs from generation to generation? These fascinating puzzles about constitutive heterochromatin await molecular explanations.

Message A rearranged chromosome has the potential in each generation to express or not to express its variegating loci. In the somatic cells of an individual, at a specific developmental stage, the potential activity of the loci is determined. After that determination, all daughter cells inherit the loci with their fixed functional states, even if the actual expression of the genetic activity does not occur until days later.

Facultative Heterochromatin

The problems posed by facultative heterochromatin are just as intriguing as those posed by the constitutive heterochromatin. We consider here examples drawn from two types of organisms: mealybugs and mammals.

Mealybugs. The insects classified as "true bugs" provide a classic example of the effects of facultative heterochroma-

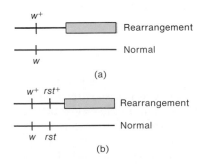

Figure 19-4. Chromosome rearrangements that lead to variegated position effects. (a) In the rearranged chromosome, the allele w^+ is moved to a position near the heterochromatin (colored block). A heterozygote carrying this $R(w^+)$ chromosome and a structurally normal chromosome with the w allele may exhibit the variegated phenotype. (b) The $R(w^+ rst^+)$ rearrangement shown at the top can also produce a variegated phenotype when heterozygous with a normal chromosome carrying the $w\,rst$ alleles.

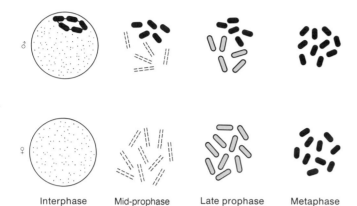

Interphase   Mid-prophase   Late prophase   Metaphase

Figure 19-5. Mitosis in male and female mealybugs (coccids) with a diploid chromosome number of $2n = 10$. In males, five of the chromosomes remain visible during interphase as densely staining heterochromatic elements. During prophase, the other five chromosomes appear less densely stained at first but eventually become heterochromatic. In contrast, none of the chromosomes in the female is visible during interphase; all ten chromosomes in the female behave like the euchromatic set in males. (From S. W. Brown and U. Nur, "Heterochromatic Chromosomes in the Coccids." *Science* 145:130–136, 1964. Copyright 1964 by the American Association for the Advancement of Science.)

tin. It has long been known that there is a striking sex difference in chromosome behavior in the scale insects called coccids, or mealybugs. In many coccid species, the diploid ($2n$) number is 10 chromosomes. In females, the chromosomes behave normally, disappearing during interphase and condensing for cell division. In contrast, early in the embryonic development of males, one chromosome of each pair becomes heterochromatic, and these chromosomes remain visible as a clumped chromocentral mass through interphase (Figure 19-5). After that point in the developmental process, the same chromosomes appear to remain heterochromatic throughout subsequent mitoses.

Chromosome behavior in meiosis also differs between the two sexes. In female coccids, meiosis is normal. However, in spermatogenesis, the first division is the equational one, in which the centromere splits to allow sister chromatids to separate, and the second division is reductional, with the homologous chromosomes separating (Figure 19-6). This pattern of meiosis in the mealybug males is, of course, the opposite of the normal meiotic sequence of divisions. At the second meiotic division in the males, the movement of chromosomes is nonrandom—all of the heterochromatic chromosomes go to one pole, and all of the euchromatic ones go to the other pole. Only the nuclei containing euchromatic elements form functional sperm. What determines which chromosomes become heterochromatic?

In the 1920s, Franz Schrader and Sally Hughes-Schrader described this strange behavior of chromosomes in coccids and suggested that the heterochromatic chromo-

somes (1) are those coming from the male parent and (2) are genetically inert. Both hypotheses were confirmed in 1957 by Spencer Brown and Walter Nelson-Rees through irradiation studies. In the male offspring of X-irradiated males, radiation-induced chromosome aberrations were found only in the heterochromatic chromosomes. In the male offspring of X-irradiated females, radiation-induced chromosome aberrations were found only in the euchromatic chromosomes. This observation confirmed the paternal origin of the heterochromatic chromosomes.

If the heterochromatic chromosomes are inert, then males are functionally haploid, because only the euchromatic chromosomes are genetically active. Brown and Nelson-Rees applied increasing doses of X rays to male coccids and studied the survival of their offspring. As the dosage was increased, the survival of daughters declined because of the induction of dominant lethal mutations. However, the survival of the sons remained constant, thus supporting the notion that any mutations induced in the father are not expressed in the active chromosomes of the sons.

This unusual genetic system poses some interesting puzzles. The differing functional states of the chromosomes cannot be determined by genetic differences between chromosomes. A male's euchromatic chromosomes came from his mother, but they in turn will become the heterochromatic chromosomes of his sons. What then controls the heterochromatization of certain chromosomes? Once the male or female origin of chromosomes (and therefore their functional fate in males) is set, each chromosome retains that imprint through subsequent cell generations in the somatic cells of the individual. What event establishes this functional state, and how is it retained through somatic cell divisions? Once again, a well-documented phenomenon awaits a molecular explanation.

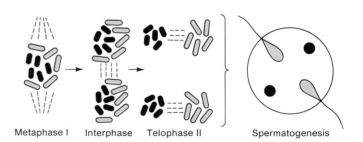

Metaphase I   Interphase   Telophase II   Spermatogenesis

Figure 19-6. Spermatogenesis in the mealybug (coccid). The first division is equational and the second is reductional in the male, the reverse of the usual meiotic process. In the second meiotic division, all heterochromatic chromosomes go to one pole. Only the euchromatic products form sperm; the heterochromatic products appear as deep-staining residues that slowly degenerate. (From S. W. Brown and U. Nur, "Heterochromatic Chromosomes in the Coccids." *Science* 145:130, 1964. Copyright 1964 by the American Association for the Advancement of Science.)

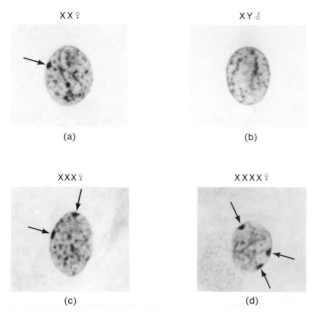

XX ♀   XY ♂

(a)   (b)

XXX ♀   XXXX ♀

(c)   (d)

Figure 19-7. Nuclei obtained from cells in the mucous membrane of the human mouth. (a) Nucleus from a female, showing one Barr body (arrow). (b) Nucleus from a male, with no Barr body. (c) Nucleus from an XXX female, showing two Barr bodies. (d) Nucleus from an XXXX female, showing three Barr bodies. (Parts a and b from M. M. Grumbach and M. L. Barr, *Rec. Progr. Hormone Res.* 14:26, 1958. Parts c and d courtesy of Dr. M. L. Barr.)

Message   In the male coccid, paternally derived chromosomes remain inactive and heterochromatic in the somatic cells and segregate together into nonfunctional nuclei during spermatogenesis. No molecular explanation is yet known for this pattern of facultative heterochromatin.

Mammals.   Another striking example of facultative heterochromatin is found in mammals. In many of the cells from a mammalian female, the nucleus is characterized by a densely staining heterochromatic element called a **Barr body** (named after its discoverer, Murray Barr). The Barr body contains DNA and is not found in males, so it was suggested that it may represent an X chromosome. Indeed, the number of Barr bodies is always one less than the number of X chromosomes in the genome (Figure 19-7). Another name commonly applied to the Barr body is **sex chromatin.**

In coccids, we found that the heterochromatic elements are genetically inert. Does the presence of the Barr body indicate that all but one of the female's X chromosomes are inactivated in somatic cells? Such a mechanism would provide an answer to the puzzling problem of how mammals adjust to the presence of twice as many X-linked genes in females as in males, because the X chromosome is known to carry many loci that are necessary for viability. Measurements of enzymes produced by sex-linked genes (glucose 6-phosphate dehydrogenase, for example; see below) show little quantitative difference in enzyme production between the sexes. There must be some **dosage compensation mechanism** to overcome the differences in gene numbers between sexes for X-linked genes, and inactivation of all but one of the female's X chromosomes would provide just such a mechanism.

VARIEGATION DUE TO DOSAGE COMPENSATION.   In the late 1950s, Liane Russell obtained a genetic clue to the mode of dosage compensation in mice through studies on mutations after radiation. She irradiated wild-type male mice and mated them to females homozygous for several recessive autosomal coat-color mutations. Any F_1 individual exhibiting a mutant coat color would be presumed to carry a radiation-induced mutant allele of one of the loci. Among the F_1 progeny, she recovered several females that exhibited a variegated phenotype, with patches of mutant and wild-type fur. She testcrossed these variegated females and recovered two types of male progeny: completely mutant or completely wild-type. Testcrossing the wild-type male progeny she obtained completely mutant males and variegated females. Figure 19-8 outlines the crosses and their outcomes. The last testcross shows that the phenotype is sex-linked in males. What is going on?

Russell and Jean Bangham found that variegation results from a translocation between the chromosome carrying the wild-type color-coat allele and the X chromosome. Apparently, in some cells of females heterozygous for the translocation, the translocated wild-type allele does not function in the production of pigment in fur (so that the cells are mutant). In other cells, the X-autosome part does produce wild-type gene product. In males, on the other hand, the translocated wild-type allele always functions to produce normal fur color in all cells (Figure 19-9). Again it appears that some mechanism is inactivating genes on one X chromosome in the female. The variegation suggests that inactivation occurs during development and that it may involve random selection of one of the X chromosomes, so that different patches show inactivation of different X chromosomes.

X-CHROMOSOME INACTIVATION.   In 1961, Liane Russell and Mary Lyon independently noted that, in addition to variegating chromosome rearrangements, many sex-linked point mutations in mice and humans exhibit a variegated phenotype in heterozygous females. They therefore suggested that dosage compensation in mammals may occur by the inactivation of one of the female's two X chromosomes—thus producing a functional equivalence of X-chromosome genes between males and females.

This hypothesis can be tested in humans by examining cells from females heterozygous for + and − alleles of the **glucose 6-phosphate dehydrogenase** (G-6-PD) locus that produce normal and inactive enzymes, respectively. When isolated cells from hair follicles are examined, each cell contains either the normal amount of G-6-PD or no enzyme at all. Also, two alleles that produce electrophoretically dis-

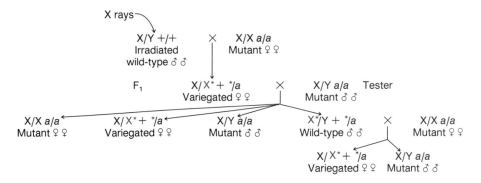

Figure 19-8. Induction of variegating chromosomes in mice. After irradiation, wild-type males are mated to females homozygous for a recessive autosomal marker (*a*). Some F_1 females carrying the irradiated chromosomes (indicated by asterisks) are variegated for the autosomal recessive. Such females are testcrossed, and the offspring show segregation for the mutant and variegating phenotypes in females and for the mutant and wild-type phenotypes in males. Testcrosses of the F_2 wild-type males show that they still transmit the variegating gene, which behaves like a sex-linked locus. These experiments indicate that the radiation must have induced a translocation linking the X chromosome to the autosomal locus *a*.

tinct enzymes, F and S, can be monitored. When isolated cells, often taken from a skin biopsy, are cloned, each clone contains either the F or the S form, but never both forms. These observations tell us a number of things.

1. The *G-6-PD* locus and, by inference, most or all of the loci on *one* of the female's X chromosomes are inactive.

2. Either the X chromosome received from the mother or that from the father can be the one inactivated.

3. Samples taken from a single follicle are mosaic, containing phenotypes. Therefore, the inactivation occurred at a stage when there were several prospective hair follicle cells. (It is now estimated that X-chromosome inactivation occurs at about the 20-cell stage.)

Figure 19-10 outlines mosaicism observed in hair-follicle cells.

4. Once the inactivation occurs, the state is inherited somatically, because a clone of cells is uniform in the expression of the same allele.

___

Message In a mammalian female at some stage in development, either of the X chromosomes in a somatic cell is inactivated by heterochromatization, and the process is normally irreversible. After that, all subsequent daughter cells inherit the same inactive X chromosome.

___

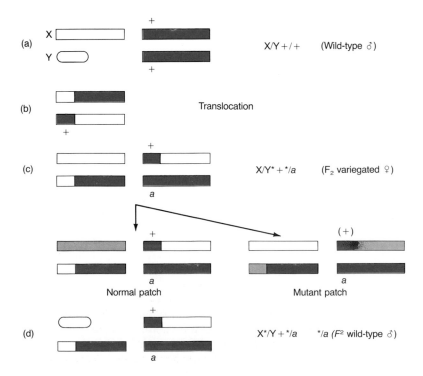

Figure 19-9. A model to explain variegation through an X-autosome translocation. (a) The $X/Y+/+$ genotype of the parental wild-type males before irradiation. (b) The translocation between X and the autosome induced by irradiation. (c) The $X/X*+*/a$ genotype in some F_1 females can produce variegation if one or the other X chromosome is inactivated randomly in various somatic cell lines during development. In cells where the X chromosome is inactivated *(gray)* the daughter cells will produce a normal patch because the $+/a$ genotype yields a wild phenotype. In cells where the X* translocation is inactivated, the + allele may be inactivated because of its proximity to the inactivated X heterochromatin; the daughter cells of this cell will have an *a* genotype and will exhibit the mutant phenotype. If the inactivation occurs once at some stage of development and then is inherited through all following somatic cell divisions, variegated patches will develop. (d) In the $X*/Y+*/a$ males of the F_2 generation, there is no X inactivation, so the $+/a$ genotype leads to a wild phenotype.

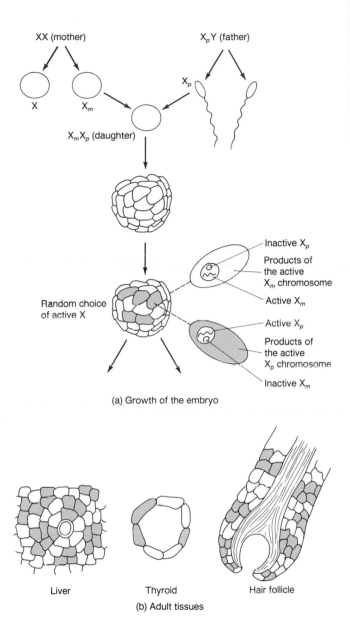

Figure 19-11. Tortoise-shell cat. An example of a genetic mosaic caused by dosage compensation. Lighter areas are orange; darker areas black. These cats are virtually always female and heterozygotes for a pair of X-linked alleles, a dominant black (say, o) and a recessive orange (say, O). Originally an $X^O X^o$ female, in such cats one chromosome is inactivated in each cell.

Figure 19-10. (a) Female mosaicism arising from X-chromosome inactivation. A female child has two X chromosomes. This child is the result of the fusion of an egg, which bears one of her mother's two X chromosomes, with a sperm bearing her father's X chromosome (a male child has an X and a Y chromosome and results from the fusion of the X-bearing egg with a sperm bearing his father's Y chromosome). Early in the development of the female embryo, when the fertilized egg has multiplied to give probably about 20 fetal cells (the precise moment is not known exactly), the process of X inactivation occurs. Each cell selects one of its two X chromosomes for inactivation: the choice is apparently made at random. As a result some of the cells are left with an active paternal X chromosome (X_p) and the others with an active maternal chromosome (X_m). Because the choice is never reversed, each female is therefore a mosaic of two kinds of cell. This mosaicism can be demonstrated whenever there happens to be some abnormality (i.e., mutation) of one of the two X chromosomes that leads to the presence of some detectably abnormal gene product in all the cells in which the abnormal X is active. (b) Demonstration of the female mosaicism in certain adult tissues. (From J. Cairns, *Cancer: Science and Society*. Copyright © 1978 by W. H. Freeman and Co.)

A good illustration of X inactivation is seen with tortoise-shell cats, which are mosaics with different-colored patches of fur. Because the clonal descendants of cells tend to adhere to one another, the fur in certain mammals (as well as the skin in humans) will be constituted of patches of cells, each derived from a single cell. Because of X inactivation, female cats heterozygous for black-coat and yellow-coat traits (C^Y/C^B) will have patched coats, as seen in Figure 19-11.

Another very dramatic demonstration of X inactivation is seen in human females who are heterozygous for an abnormality termed X-linked anhidrotic ectodermal dysplasia. The mutant allele causes the absence of sweat glands, and mutant sectors can be detected by altered electrical resistance of the skin or by effects of various sprays. Figure 19-12 shows the phenotypic effects in three generations of women.

SEX DETERMINATION. What activates the dosage compensation in mammalian females? Is it the femaleness (two X chromosomes) or the lack of maleness (absence of a Y chromosome)? To answer this question, we must first understand how sex is determined.

In 1959, William Welshons and William Russell reported a study of a dominant X-linked mutation, *Tabby* (*Ta*), that produces a dark coat color in mice. The *Ta/Ta* females have the same dark-furred Ta phenotype as the *Ta/Y* males, but the *Ta/+* females have patches of light and dark fur. Wild-type $+/+$ females and $+/Y$ males are a uniform light color. Mating *Ta/+* females with $+/Y$ males, Welshons and Russell recovered female progeny that were phenotypically similar to *Ta/Ta* females. (You can see that, if disjunction is normal, all females should be *Ta/+* or $+/+$.) If sex determination is like that in *Drosophila*, these exceptions probably are *Ta/Ta/Y* nondisjunctional females. Welshons and Russell then mated these Ta exceptions with $+/Y$ males. The progeny phenotypes were wild-type females, patched females, and Ta males in a 1:1:1 ratio. If the females were indeed *Ta/Ta/Y*, this

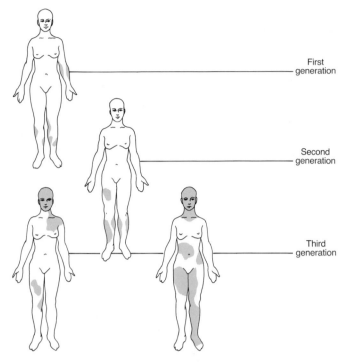

First generation

Second generation

Third generation

Figure 19-12. Somatic mosaicism in three generations of females heterozygous for sex-linked anhidrotic dysplasia. This abnormality in sweat-gland secretion can be demonstrated with a harmless dye. The location of the mutant tissue is determined by chance, but each female does exhibit the characteristic mosaic expression of a single X chromosome.

cross should have produced the progeny genotypes shown in Table 19-2.

The presence of wild-type females and the absence of Ta females among the progeny obviously show that the assumption of $Ta/Ta/Y$ for the parental female is wrong. Welshons suggested that the exceptional Ta female might have only a single X chromosome and no Y; we write the genotype as Ta/O. Such a female would produce Ta and O eggs, which would result in $Ta/+$ and $+/O$ female offspring in the cross. Welshons concluded that, in mice, the Y chromosome determines maleness, and its absence determines femaleness. This hypothesis was confirmed cytologi-

■ **TABLE 19-2.** Progeny expected if the exceptional Ta females are XXY

			Sperms	
			+	Y
Eggs	Normal	Ta	$Ta/+♀$	$Ta/Y♂$
		Ta/Y	$Ta/+/Y♀$	$Ta/Y/Y♂$
	Nondisjunctional	Ta/Ta	?	$Ta/Ta/Y♀$
		Y	$+/Y♂$	Y/Y lethal

■ **TABLE 19-3.** Correlation between numbers of sex chromosomes and Barr bodies

Sex-chromosome constitution		Number of Barr bodies
Males	Females	
XY, XYY	XO	0
XXY, XXYY, XXYYY	XX	1
XXXY	XXX	2
XXXXY	XXXX	3
XXXXXY	XXXXX	4

cally by the finding that the exceptional Ta females had only a single X chromosome, and it was confirmed genetically by the discovery of X/X/Y males.

In humans also, XO and XXY individuals are now recognized. Females who are XO are not completely normal, indicating that some activity of the second X is required at some time or in some tissues during female development. In fact, the short end of the X chromosome is not inactive in Barr bodies. The XO phenotype is called **Turner's syndrome** and includes underdeveloped sex organs, webbing of the neck, and short stature. Cells from females with Turner's syndrome lack the Barr body. An abnormal male genotype is XXY, which produces a recognizable phenotype called **Klinefelter's syndrome,** including long legs, small testes, and development of breasts. A Barr body is present in cells from males with Klinefelter's syndrome. The activity of the short end of the X chromosome in the Barr body is responsible for the observed phenotype. Obviously, phenotypic sex is not the factor that determines the formation of a heterochromatic X chromosome (a Barr body). Rather, it is the *number* of X chromosomes that determines whether facultative heterochromatization will occur. This is confirmed through the recognition of individuals carrying several sex chromosomes (many of these individuals are mosaics for different numbers of sex chromosomes), as shown in Table 19-3.

Message X-chromosome inactivation in mammals is determined by the number of X chromosomes per nucleus, not by the phenotypic sex of the individual. Phenotypic sex is determined by the presence or absence of a Y chromosome.

Here is another fascinating phenomenon for which we have no molecular explanation as yet: how does a cell recognize the presence of multiple X chromosomes and ensure that only one X functions?

Eukaryote Gene Function and Organization

Many fascinating phenomena and problems exist in the study of the way that genes function in eukaryotes. How are the genes organized so that their functions are coordinated in the developmental and biochemical cycles of the organism? How are specific genes activated under certain conditions or at certain times in the life cycle of the organism? What is the physical nature of the chromosome and of the organism? What is the physical nature of the chromosome and of the gene placement along it? We look now at some of these problems.

Dosage Compensation in Drosophila

Heterochromatization inactivates a large genetic segment, but this is a rather crude method for control of gene expression. Are there modulations of gene expression within a more restricted portion of a chromosome? In fact, dosage compensation was originally defined in regard to the observation in *Drosophila* that some alleles of the *white* locus produce the same eye phenotype in males and females, whereas other alleles produce more eye pigment in females than in males. The former alleles are said to be dosage-compensated; the excess dosage of X-linked genes in the female is not reflected in the phenotype. The deletion of the *Notch* gene on the X chromosome produces a mutant phenotype of nicked wings in females heterozygous for the deletion and a normal chromosome, thus proving that both X chromosomes do function in a normal *Drosophila* female.

In 1965, Ed Grell demonstrated the compensatory capabilities of sex-linked loci, using two loci that affect the enzyme xanthine dehydrogenase (XDH). He constructed strains carrying different numbers of the wild-type alleles of the sex-linked locus *maroon-like (ma-l)* and the chromosome-3 gene *rosy(ry)*. Upon measuring the relative amounts of enzyme activity in these *Drosophila* individuals, he obtained the results summarized in Table 19-4. Obviously, there is a dosage-compensation for the activity of *ma-l*+, whereas the number of *ry*+ genes is directly reflected in enzyme activity.

In a single cell, is only one allele active or do both alleles function? In *Drosophila*, various alleles of a single gene produce different electrophoretic mobilities of the enzyme 6-phosphogluconate dehydrogenase (6-PGD). Electrophoresis of the enzyme from heterozygous females reveals a hybrid band between the two parental bands. The hybrid band can be explained by assuming simultaneous activity of both alleles, with dimer formation by polypeptides from the two loci. Thus, unlike mammals, in *Drosophila* females, both X chromosomes function in all cells.

Measurement of enzymes controlled by X-linked loci shows that each dosage-compensated locus in a male produces twice as much product as each locus in a female. In different X-autosome translocations, the loci lying in the X portions remain compensated, whereas the autosomal loci are not compensated. These results suggest that no single region or small number of regions control X activity. Rather, each locus or small region apparently has information about the number of gene copies present and is able to control its own activity accordingly. No satisfactory molecular explanation of this method of gene regulation yet exists.

DNA Molecules in Chromosomes of Eukaryotes

Now we turn to the molecular analysis of chromosomes, which may eventually provide explanations for the genetic and cytological phenomena described in the preceding subsections. By staining chromosomes with dyes that bind to specific macromolecules, we can demonstrate that the visible chromosome contains DNA, RNA, and protein. But how is that material organized during interphase or during cell division? When cells are disrupted mechanically (by squeezing them under high pressure) or osmotically (by exploding them in hypotonic solutions), their contents can be mounted for electron microscopic examination. Such study reveals that the chromosome resembles a mass of spaghetti-like fibrils with diameters of about 230 Å, each composed of DNA with associated protein (Figure 19-13). Ernest DuPraw showed that few if any ends protrude from the fibrillar mass, as if there is a single long fiber that is coiled up in a compact mass.

Could it be that each chromosome contains a small number of DNA molecules? In 1973, Ruth Kavenoff and Bruno Zimm resolved this question using a **viscoelastic recoil technique** that essentially measures the size of the largest DNA molecules by their elastic properties in solution. Very simply, if DNA is stretched to an extended state (for example, by spinning a paddle in a DNA solution) and then allowed to recoil toward a random relaxed state (Figure 19-14), the recoil requires a time that is proportional to molecular size. This technique provides a sensitive indicator of the *largest molecules in the solution,* even when they represent a small fraction of the total number of molecules.

Kavenoff and Zimm studied the DNA molecules of *Drosophila melanogaster* (which has four pairs of chromo-

■ **TABLE 19-4.** Relative enzyme activities and numbers of gene copies

Number of gene copies	Relative enzyme activity for	
	ma-l+	*ry*+
1	1.0	0.5
2	1.0	1.0
3	1.0	1.5

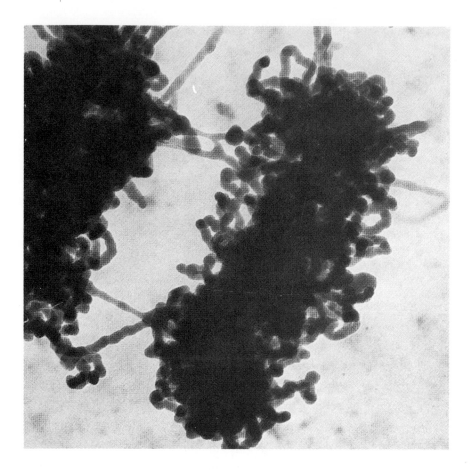

Figure 19-13. Electron micrograph of a metaphase chromatid from an embryonic honeybee cell. It appears to be a tangle of one continuous strand made up of a DNA core complexed with nuclear protein. (From E. J. DuPraw, *Cell and Molecular Biology*, p. 531, Fig. 18-4, 1968, Academic Press, Inc.)

somes; Figure 19-15). They extracted DNA gently (to avoid shear) from wild-type nuclei and obtained a value of 41×10^9 daltons ($\pm 3 \times 10^9$) from the viscoelastic measurements for the largest DNA molecule in solution. This value is remarkably close to George Rudkin's measurement.

Using DNA molecules from a mutant having an X-autosome translocation that increases the length of the autosomal portion by one-third (Figure 19-15), Kavenoff and Zimm obtained a viscoelastic value of 58×10^9 daltons for the largest DNA molecule. Rudkin's measurement for the translocated autosome was 59×10^9 daltons.

Finally, they studied DNA molecules from mutants with a pericentric inversion (Figure 19-16) that increased the length of one chromosome arm without affecting the total DNA content of the chromosome. In this case, they obtained a value of 42×10^9 daltons ($\pm 4 \times 10^9$), not significantly different from the wild-type value. In studies of other *Drosophila* species, Kavenoff and Zimm obtained values for the largest DNA molecules that were propor-

tional to the cytological lengths observed for the largest chromosomes. Therefore, they concluded that each chromosome is composed of a single DNA molecule that extends from one end of the chromosome through the centromere to the other end.

Message The eukaryotic chromosome is a single continuous molecule of DNA.

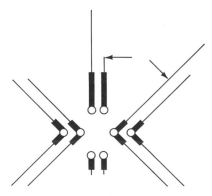

Figure 19-15. Karyotype of a *Drosophila* female heterozygous for an X-autosome translocation. Breakpoints are indicated by arrows. About 60 percent of the mitotic chromosome length of the X is attached to the tip of chromosome 3, thereby increasing the length of chromosome 3 by 37 percent.

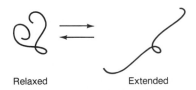

Relaxed   Extended

Figure 19-14. The relaxed and extended states of DNA.

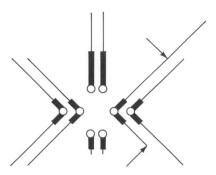

Figure 19-16. Karyotype of a *Drosophila* female heterozygous for a pericentric inversion of chromosome 3. Breakpoints are indicated by arrows. The inversion changes the ratio of the lengths of the two arms of chromosome 3 from 1:1 to about 7:1, but it causes no change in the total length of the chromosome.

DNA Packaging in Chromosomes of Eukaryotes

Each chromosome that becomes visible under the light microscope at division contains one remarkably long molecule of DNA. The typical bacterial or viral chromosome also is a single DNA molecule, but it is a relatively short molecule with a single site at which bidirectional replication begins. As we have seen in earlier chapters, the eukaryotic DNA contains multiple sites for initiation of replication.

But how are such long molecules packed into the compact entities we recognize as chromosomes? In terms of end-to-end lengths, the DNA molecule contained in a chromosome may be more than 100,000 times longer than the chromosome itself. How can this compact packaging be achieved in a way that permits orderly replication?

An important insight into the packaging problem came with the recovery from nuclease-digested chromatin of a histone-DNA complex called a **nucleosome.** About 140 base pairs of DNA are wrapped around a core of pairs of four histones called H2A, H2B, H3, and H4. Viewed under the electron microscope after special treatment, chromatin appears to be composed of a chain of granules (nucleosomes) that is about 100 Å in diameter (Figure 19-17). From additional experiments, the DNA appears to be coiled around the protein octamer in two twists (Figure 19-18). One model that can account for this structure is shown in Figure 19-19.

There is evidence (Figure 19-20) that the nucleosomes in turn are thrown into a coil that has been called a **solenoid structure** (resembling a solenoid coil in an automobile engine). The solenoid structure has a diameter of 200 Å to 300 Å (Figure 19-21). Obviously, the DNA can be compacted extensively by superimposing coils on coiled structures during cell division (Figure 19-22). An incredible cycle of coiling and supercoiling at the level visible in the light microscope appears during mitosis of gut parasites of termites (Figure 19-23). How are additional layers of coiling superimposed on the nucleosome-solenoid level seen in the interphase cell? That problem remains unsolved.

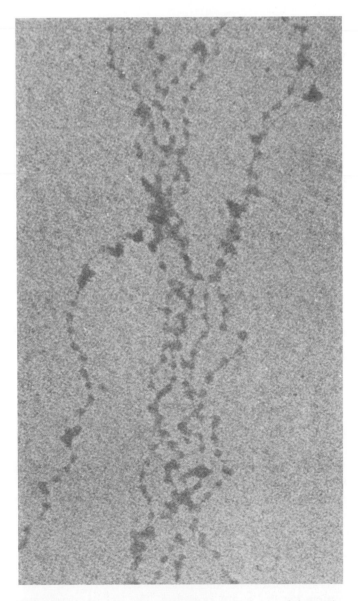

Figure 19-17. Electron micrograph of the central core of chromatin isolated from the eukaryote *Physarum.* The individual granules that form the chains presumably are nucleosomes.

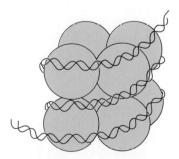

Figure 19-18. A diagrammatic representation of the four parts of histone molecules around which DNA is wound to form a nucleosome.

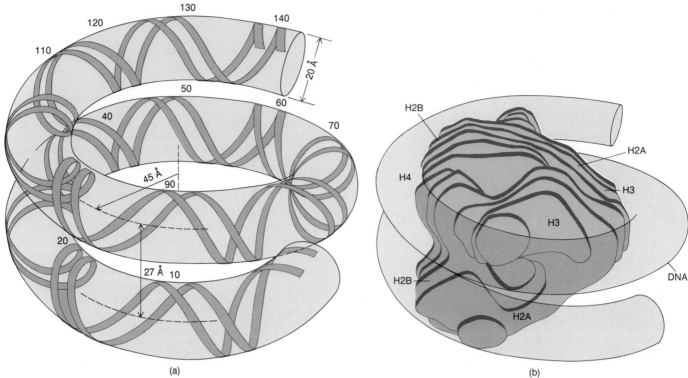

(a)

(b)

Figure 19-19. (a) Path of DNA around the histone octamer that can account for the bipartite structure of the nucleosome core is a superhelix with an external diameter of 110 Å and a pitch of 27 Å; the turns of the 20 Å-wide DNA helix are nearly in contact. There are about 80 nucleotide pairs of DNA per turn; the nucleosome core, an enzymatically reduced form of the nucleosome consisting of some 140 nucleotide pairs, has about one and three-quarter turns wrapped on it. (b) Model of nucleosome core was made by winding a tube simulating the DNA superhelix on a model of the histone octamer, which was built from a three-dimensional map derived from electron micrographs of the histone octamer. The ridges on the periphery of the octamer form a more or less continuous helical ramp on which a 146-nucleotide-pair length of DNA can be wound. The locations of individual histone molecules (whose boundaries are not defined at this resolution) are proposed here on the basis of chemical cross-linking data. (Figures 19-19, 19-20, and 19-22 from R. D. Kornberg and A. Klug, "The Nucleosome." Copyright © 1981 by Scientific American, Inc. All rights reserved.)

Message DNA in the eukaryotic chromosome is shortened more than 100,000-fold by superimposing different levels of coiling. At the core of this structure, the DNA is wrapped around a cluster of histone proteins; the fundamental histone-DNA complex thus formed is called the nucleosome.

Inspection of the chromosome with a scanning electron microscope fails to reveal how the tightly coiled strand is held together, but such study does show a mat of fibers that do not appear to have a free end (Figure 19-24). Ulrich Laemmli and his associates developed a method for gentle removal of histones from chromosomes, which can then be inspected under the electron microscope. This inspection reveals that sister chromatids remain paired and that each has a central structure surrounded by a halo of DNA. The chromosome appears to have a central "scaffold" of protein to which the DNA is anchored. Close inspection reveals the incredible density of DNA packaging (Figure 19-25). The ends of each loop of DNA that extend from the scaffold are attached near the same point, suggesting that the packaging process is regular and precise.

Message The DNA in the eukaryotic chromosome is organized about a central core from which segments may extend to form loops. The highly condensed metaphase chromosome that is seen under the light microscope results from many different orders of chromatin packing, as summarized in Figure 19-26.

Sequence Organization

Measurements of DNA in different organisms have revealed that, perhaps as expected, eukaryotic genomes consist of much more DNA than prokaryotic or viral genomes. Although, for the most part, higher eukaryotes contain more DNA than lower eukaryotes, there is considerable variation in the amounts of DNA even among similar species. Certain less complex species have significantly more DNA than other species higher on the evolutionary scale; in fact, amphibians and lilies usually have the highest DNA content per cell of any organism. The lack of correlation between amount of DNA and complexity of an organism is puzzling. Why do eukaryotes have so much extra DNA?

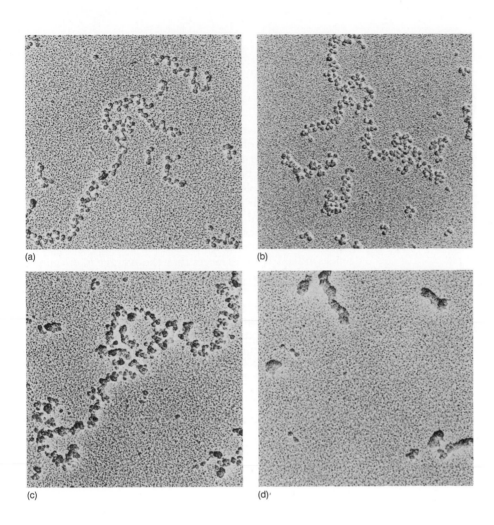

(a)   (b)

(c)   (d)

Figure 19-20. Condensation of chromatin with increasing salt concentration is demonstrated in electron micrographs made by Fritz Thoma and Theo Koller of the Swiss Federal Institute of Technology. At a very low salt concentration, as in (a), chromatin forms a loose fiber about 100 Å thick: nucleosomes connected by short stretches of DNA. At a concentration with an ionic strength closer to that of normal physiological conditions as in (d), chromatin forms a thick fiber some 250 to 300 Å thick. The origin of this "solenoid" can be deduced by examination of chromatin at increasing intermediate ionic strengths, as in (b) and (c). It arises from a shallow coiling of the nucleosome filament. The chromatin is enlarged here about 80,000 diameters.

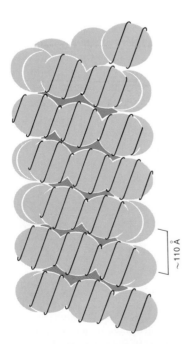

~110 Å

Figure 19-21. A higher level of packing is achieved in DNA when nucleosomes are wound into a solenoid structure. (From J. T. Finch and A. Klug, *Proc. Natl. Acad. Sci. USA* 71:1897, 1976.)

Does all of the extra DNA code for protein? Is the extra DNA essential? Scientists are beginning to resolve some of these questions, although there are still many areas of uncertainty. Estimates of proteins in higher cells suggest that as much as 90 percent of the DNA does *not* code for proteins. Molecular analyses of eukaryotic genomes have revealed several sources of untranslated DNA. These include **repetitive DNA sequences** (see Figure 19-27), **intervening sequences** that interrupt the coding sequences of genes, and **spacers** between genes.

Number of Genes in Drosophila

Measurements of DNA show that a haploid nucleus from *Drosophila* contains about 1.5×10^8 base pairs, one genome of *E. coli* contains about 4.56×10^6 base pairs, and a human haploid nucleus contains about 3.1×10^9 base pairs. In *Drosophila*, unique sequences (nonrepetitive DNA) make up about 70 percent of the total nuclear DNA, with the remaining 30 percent consisting of middle or highly repetitive sequences. A typical *E. coli* protein is encoded by about 1000 base pairs, so the unique sequences of *Drosophila* could code for around 100,000 such proteins. Looking at the arrangement of DNA in the giant salivary gland chromosomes, we see that most of the DNA is located in about 5000 to 6000 densely staining bands, the chromomeres.

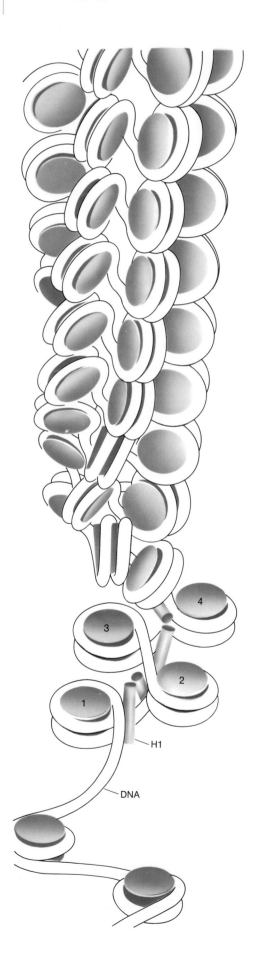

Cytogeneticists have long assumed that each chrommomere represents the cytological position of a gene locus. In the haploid nucleus, each chromomere is equivalent to from 5000 to 100,000 base pairs, with an average of 30,000. How can this 30-fold excess over the size of a typical *E. coli* gene be explained?

Perhaps the initial assumption of one gene per band is erroneous, and each chromomere in fact represents many genes. Another possibility is that the average *Drosophila* gene is indeed 30 times larger than the average *E. coli* gene, and certainly the existence of large introns (see page 422) can account for a lot of the excess. Most of the basic metabolic processes exist both in *E. coli* and in multicellular eukaryotes, so the major differences in the size of the genome could represent codings involved in regulation of gene activity rather than codings for new gene functions. Much of the eukaryotic DNA may be involved in regulating the gene activity in relation to developmental time, the nature of the tissue, and the extent of activity required. In order to distinguish between these alternative explanations, Burke Judd and Thomas Kaufman set out in the late 1960s to detect all of the genes within a limited region of the *Drosophila* X chromosome by inducing and recovering enough mutations to ensure that every locus was represented by at least one mutant.

They chose the interval from *zeste* to *white*, a span of 10 or 12 bands, for which several overlapping duplications and deficiencies exist with which to map new mutations (Figure 19-28). They selected newly induced mutations in the $z-w$ interval using the method for detection and recovery shown in Figure 19-29. Each mutagen-treated X chromosome was initially recovered in an F_1 female and then tested for its survival or phenotype when heterozygous with a $z-w$ deficiency. All mutant chromosomes were "captured" in males carrying a duplication. Each mutant was tested with the duplications and deficiencies to localize it, and all mutations falling within the same segment were tested for complementation and map position by crossing-over. In 1972, Judd and Kaufman reported that 121 point mutations had been assigned to 16 complementation

Figure 19-22. Helical superstructures might be formed with increasing salt concentration (bottom to top) with the participation of the histone protein H1, as is suggested here. The zigzag pattern of nucleosomes (1, 2, 3, 4) closes up, eventually to form a solenoid, a helix with about six nucleosomes per turn. (The helix is probably more irregular than it is in this drawing.) Cross-linking data indicate that H1 molecules on adjacent nucleosomes make contact. Extrapolation from the zigzag form to the solenoid suggests (but does not prove) that the aggregation of H1 at higher ionic strengths gives rise to a helical H1 polymer (not shown) running down the center of the solenoid. In the absence of H1 (bottom) no ordered structures are formed. The details of H1 associations are not known at this time; the drawing is meant to indicate only that H1 molecules contract one another and "linker" DNA.

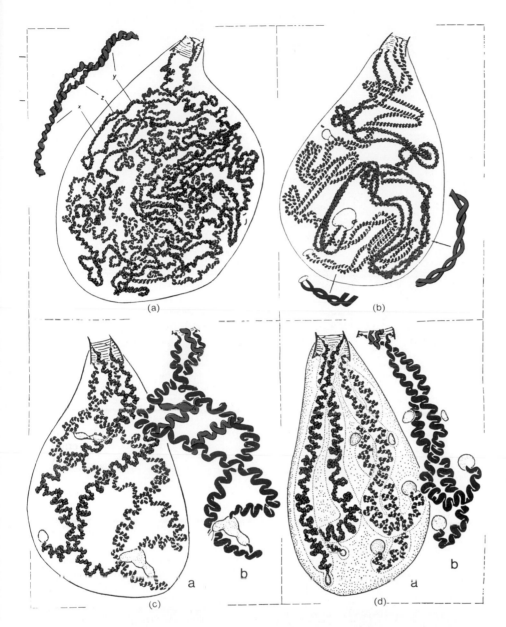

Figure 19-23. Drawings of chromosomes in meiotic prophase in a protozoan, demonstrating different degrees of coiling and supercoiling visible with the light microscope. Two large chromosomes are shown, one colored and the other black; (a) through (d) are a progression. (a) Coiling is seen though duplication becomes apparent. (b) Duplication is well advanced. (c) Supercoiling is beginning. (d) Supercoiling is well advanced. (From L. R. Cleveland, "The Whole Life Cycle of Chromosomes and Their Coiling Systems." *Transactions of the American Philosophical Society* 39, 1, 1949.)

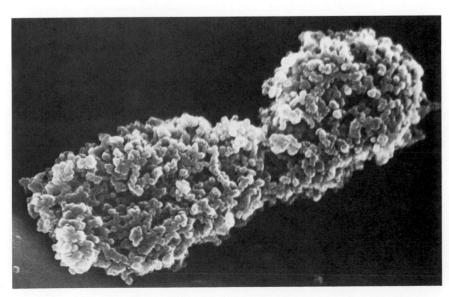

Figure 19-24. A scanning electron micrograph of a mitotic chromosome, showing the compact folding of the strand. (Wayne Wray.)

Figure 19-25. Electron micrograph of a metaphase chromosome from a cultured human cell. Note the central core, or scaffold, from which the DNA strands extend outward. No free ends are visible at the outer edge. At even higher magnification, it is clear that each loop begins and ends near the same region of the scaffold. (From W. R. Baumbach and K. W. Adolph, *CSHSQB,* Cold Spring Harbor Laboratory, 1977.)

groups that could be mapped by crossing-over (Figure 19-30). The position of each complementation group could be assigned to a single-band, thus leading to the conclusion that *each gene corresponds to one chromomere.* It is now known that there exist nontranslated spacers between genes, large introns that are excised from mRNA, and sequences that are removed during mRNA maturation. There are also a few cases in which some bands contain several genes — for instance, the chorion protein genes, which come in pairs. Whether these factors account for the 30-fold excess of DNA per chromomere has not yet been determined.

Message   In *Drosophila,* each polytene-chromosome chromomere apparently corresponds to one gene detect-

able by mutation and complementation. This means that there are 5000 to 6000 genes in *Drosophila.*

Intervening Sequences

In order to consider intervening sequences we must first understand several aspects of RNA synthesis and processing in eukaryotes.

RNA Synthesis.   Whereas a single RNA polymerase species synthesizes all RNAs in prokaryotes, there are three different RNA polymerases in eukaryotic systems.

1. RNA polymerase I synthesizes ribosomal RNA (rRNA).

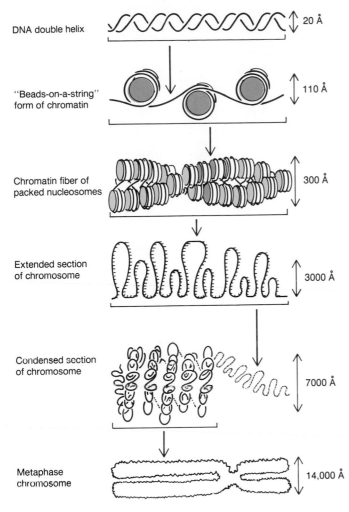

DNA double helix — 20 Å

"Beads-on-a-string" form of chromatin — 110 Å

Chromatin fiber of packed nucleosomes — 300 Å

Extended section of chromosome — 3000 Å

Condensed section of chromosome — 7000 Å

Metaphase chromosome — 14,000 Å

Figure 19-26. Schematic illustration of the many different orders of chromatin packing postulated to give rise to the highly condensed metaphase chromosome. (From B. Alberts et al., *Molecular Biology of the Cell.* Garland, 1983.)

2. RNA polymerase II synthesizes mRNA. The mRNA molecules are **monocistronic,** whereas many mRNAs are **polycistronic** in prokaryotes.

3. RNA polymerase III synthesizes tRNAs and also small nuclear and cellular RNA molecules.

RNA Processing. The primary RNA transcript produced in the nucleus usually is processed in several ways prior to its transport to the cytoplasm, where it is used to program the translation machinery, as schematized in Figure 19-31. Figure 19-32 depicts these events in detail. First a "cap" consisting of a 7-methylguanosine residue linked to the 5′ end of the transcript by a triphosphate bond is added during transcription. Then, stretches of adenosine residues are added at the 3′ ends. These "poly-A tails" are 150 to 200 residues long. Following these modifications, a crucial "splicing" step removes internal portions of the RNA transcript. The uncovering of this process, and the corresponding realization that genes are "split," with coding regions interrupted by "intervening sequences," constitutes one of the most important discoveries in molecular genetics in the last decade.

Split Genes. Studies of mammalian viral DNA transcripts first suggested a lack of correspondence between the genetic map and specific mRNA molecules. As recombinant-DNA techniques (see Chapter 14) facilitated the physical analysis of eukaryotic genes, it became apparent that primary RNA transcripts were being shortened by the elimination of internal segments before transport into the cytoplasm. In most higher eukaryotes studied, this was found to be true not only for mRNA but also for rRNA, and even for tRNA in some cases.

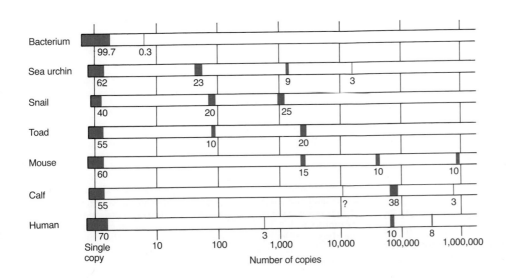

Figure 19-27. Abundance of repeated sequences in the DNA of seven organisms. The width of each band represents the percentage (also given below the band) of the total DNA that appears with a given degree of repetition. (From R. J. Britten and D. E. Kohne, "Repeated Segments of DNA." Copyright © 1970 by Scientific American, Inc. All rights reserved.)

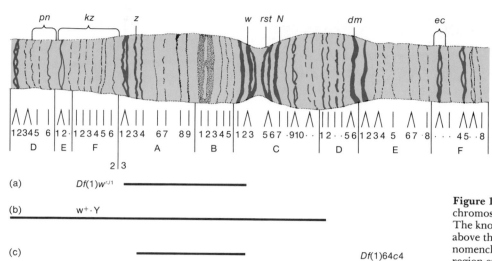

(a) $Df(1)w^{rJ1}$

(b) $w^+ \cdot Y$

(c)

Df(1)62g18
Df(1)65j26
Df(1)w^{258-42}
Df(1)K95
Df(1)w-N^{71a}
Df(1)64j4

Df(1)64c4
Df(1)w^{258-11}
Df(1)X12
Df(1)w^{rJ2}
Df(1)62d18
Df(1)w^{264-58a}
Dp(1;3)w^{264-58a}

Df(1)w^{258-45}
Df(1)64f1

Df(1)w^{-64d}

Figure 19-28. The segment of the polytene X chromosome within which the $z-w$ region lies. The known positions of mutations are shown above the chromosome, and the numbering nomenclature is indicated underneath (the $z-w$ region extends from 3A3 to 3C3). The deficiencies and duplications covering this region are indicated at the bottom, with the extent of each deficiency or duplication shown by the horizontal line. Mutations were (a) detected by their mutant phenotype when heterozygous with $Df(1)w^{rJ1}$, (b) maintained in males with $w^+ \cdot Y$, and (c) localized by their phenotypes when heterozygous with different deficiencies. (Figures 19-28, 19-29, and 19-30 from B. Judd, M. Shen, and T. Kaufman, *Genetics* 71:139, 1972.)

Figure 19-33 shows the organization of the gene for chicken ovalbumin, a 386-amino-acid polypeptide. The DNA segments that code for the structure of the protein are interrupted by intervening sequences, termed **introns.** In Figure 19-33, these segments are designated with the letters A, B, C . . . G. The primary transcript is processed by a series of "splicing" reactions, much in the same way that a tape-recorded message can be cut and pasted back together. Splicing removes the introns and brings together the coding regions, termed **exons,** to form an mRNA, which now consists of a sequence that is completely colinear with the ovalbumin protein. The exons are numbered 1, 2, 3 . . . 7 in Figure 19-33. In different genes introns have been detected that are as large as 2000 base pairs in length. Some genes have as many as 16 introns.

It is clear that splicing occurs after transcription, and in several steps, since RNA transcripts (previously termed "heterogeneous nuclear RNA," or HnRNA) can be isolated that correspond to the entire genetic region (introns + exons), as well as transcripts intermediate in length. In these intermediate-length RNA molecules, certain introns have already been removed, but others are retained. The entire sequence of events for RNA processing and splicing is summarized in Figure 19-34.

There are some interesting examples of the *same* primary transcript generating different mRNAs by using a different splicing route. Figure 19-35 shows how two protein hormones, calcitonin and the related CGRP, are produced from the same transcript. Other examples include mouse amylase and the t-antigen of SV40, each of which is synthesized in different forms by alternate splicing pathways operating on the same primary transcript.

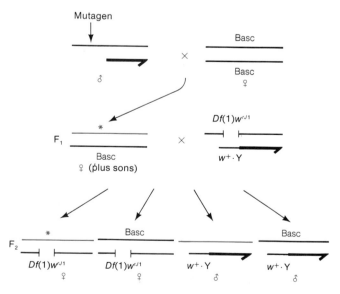

Figure 19-29. The mating scheme used to recover mutations in the $z-w$ region. Wild-type males were treated with a mutagen and then crossed to females carrying Basc, a multiply inverted chromosome marked with B and w^a. Then F_1 females carrying the mutagen-treated chromosome (indicated by an asterisk) were selected and individually mated to males carrying a deficiency on the X chromosome, $Df(1)w^{rJ1}$, and a duplication for this region on the Y chromosome, $w^+ \cdot Y$. A mutation in the $z-w$ region is indicated by the absence (if lethal) of the mutant phenotype of the non-Bar-eyed females. The chromosome is not lost because the mutation is covered by the duplication in non-Basc males.

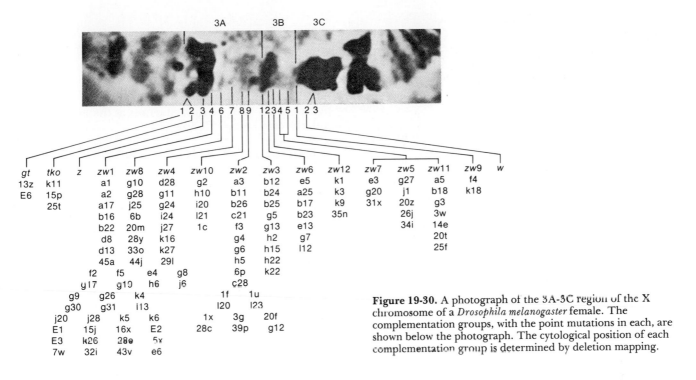

| | | | | 3A | | | 3B | 3C | | | | | | | | |

gt	tko	z	zw1	zw8	zw4	zw10	zw2	zw3	zw6	zw12	zw7	zw5	zw11	zw9	w	
13z	k11		a1	g10	d28	g2	a3	b12	e5	k1	e3	g27	a5	f4	k18	
E6	15p		a2	g28	g11	h10	b11	b24	a25	k3	g20	j1	b18	k18		
	25t		a17	j25	g24	i20	b26	b25	b17	k9	31x	20z	g3			
			b16	6b	i24	l21	c21	g5	b23	35n		26j	3w			
			b22	20m	j27	1c	f3	g13	e13			34i	14e			
			d8	28y	k16		g4	h2	g7				20t			
			d13	33o	k27		g6	h15	l12				25f			
			45a	44j	29l		h5	h22								
		f2	f5	e4	g8		6p	k22								
		yl7	g19	h6	j6		c28									
	g9	g26	k4				1f	1u								
	g30	g31	l13				l20	l23								
j20	j28	k5	k6		1x	3g	20f									
E1	15j	16x	E2		28c	39p	g12									
E3	k26	28e	5x													
7w	32i	43v	e6													

Figure 19-30. A photograph of the 3A–3C region of the X chromosome of a *Drosophila melanogaster* female. The complementation groups, with the point mutations in each, are shown below the photograph. The cytological position of each complementation group is determined by deletion mapping.

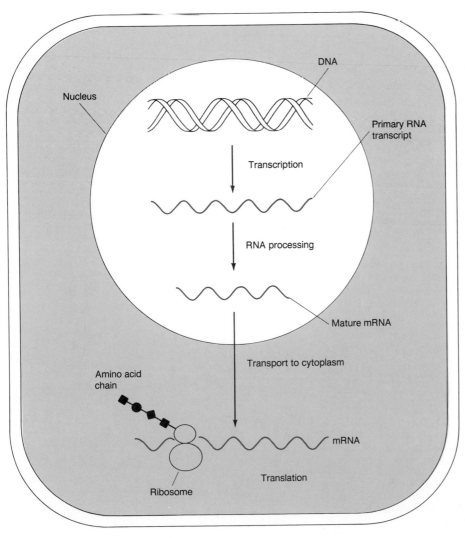

Figure 19-31. Gene expression in eukaryotes. The mRNA is processed in the nucleus prior to transport to the cytoplasm. (Figures 19-31 and 19-32 from J. E. Darnell, Jr., "The Processing of RNA." Copyright © 1983 by Scientific American, Inc. All rights reserved.)

Mechanism of Splicing

There are some sequence homologies at the exon-intron junctures of mRNAs. For instance, there is a –G–U– at the 5′ splice site and an –A–G– at the 3′ splice site of introns in virtually all mRNAs examined. It is thought that splicing enzymes recognize some common configuration of the mRNA and, perhaps with the help of certain small nuclear RNAs, catalyze the cutting and splicing reactions. The small RNA molecules may help to align the splice sites by hydrogen bonding to the sequences at the exon-intron boundaries (see Figure 19-36).

Implications of Split Genes

The finding that many eukaryotic genes are interrupted by DNA sequences that are not translated into protein shatters the concept of the gene that we had developed through the end of Chapter 12. Until now we had considered a gene as an uninterrupted sequence of nucleic acid coding for a

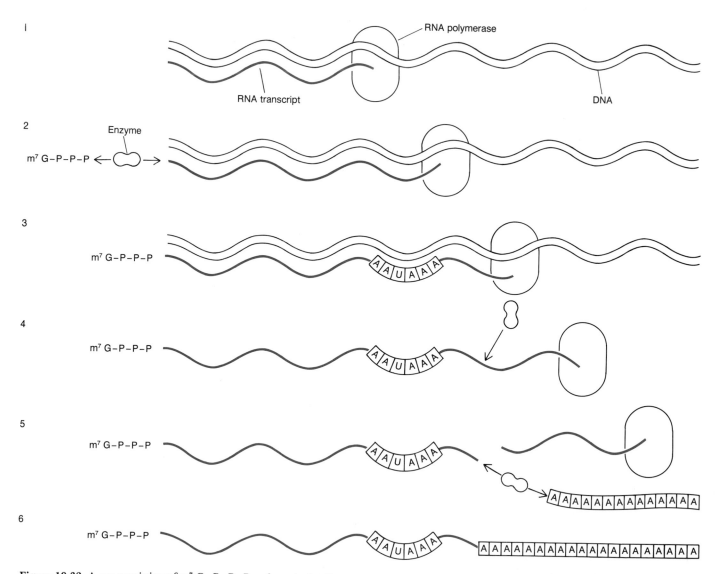

Figure 19-32. A cap consisting of m⁷ G–P–P–P and a poly-A tail are added to the RNA transcript in the first stages of mRNA processing. The sequence AAUAAA helps signal a cleavage event about 20 bases downstream. Then, 150 to 200 A residues are added to the 3′ end of the mRNA.

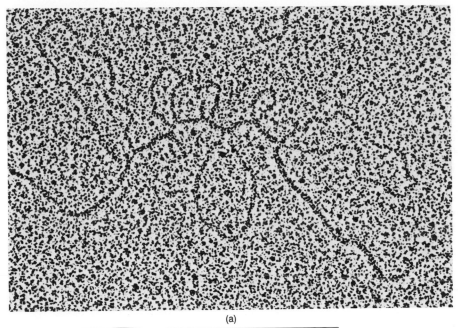

(a)

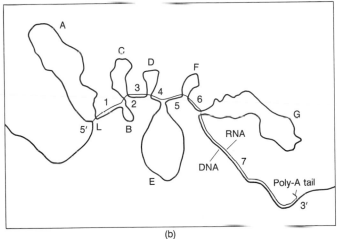

(b)

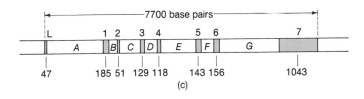

(c)

Figure 19-33. Split-gene organization of the gene for the protein ovalbumin. (a) The electron micrograph and (b) its map show the result of an experiment in which a single strand of the DNA incorporating the gene for the egg-white protein ovalbumin was allowed to hybridize with ovalbumin messenger RNA, the molecule from which the protein is translated. (c) The looped-out single-stranded segments represent the introns. The schematic representation of the gene shows the seven introns (white) and eight exons (color) and the number of base pairs in each of the exons; the size of the introns ranges from 251 base pairs (for *B*) to about 1600 (for *G*). (Figures 19-33 and 19-34 from P. Chambon, "Split Genes." Copyright © 1981 by Scientific American, Inc. All rights reserved.)

functional macromolecule (RNA or protein). The gene was colinear with the protein it encoded. Clearly, this definition of the gene must now be modified, because it no longer holds in all cases. In prokaryotes, and to a large extent in lower eukaryotes, genes do represent an uninterrupted coding sequence. For many eukaryotic genes, however, the presence of introns interrupts the coding sequence, and the initial RNA transcript must be processed by splicing reactions in order to generate the finished RNA molecule (either mRNA, tRNA, or rRNA).

Why Split Genes and Splicing?

It is not clear why introns and exons have evolved as such. Although in some cases mutations introduced into introns have no noticeable effect on gene expression, in other examples (e.g., SV40) the removal of an intron interferes with gene expression. Walter Gilbert has suggested that, in many cases, exons encode discrete domains of proteins, and that the shuffling of exons allowed a more rapid evolution

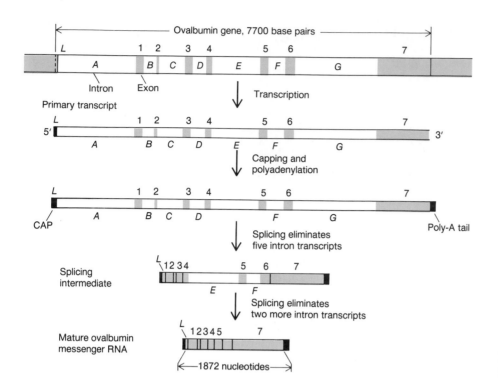

Figure 19-34. Mature messenger RNA is produced in a number of steps.

of proteins. The introns remain as a vestige of this process, according to this idea.

Protein Processing

Proteins that are secreted from the cell are synthesized with a short leader peptide, called a **signal sequence,** at the amino-terminal (N-terminal) end. This is a stretch of 15 to 25 amino acids, most of which are hydrophobic. The signal sequence allows for transport through the cell membrane, during which the signal sequence is cleaved by a peptidase (Figure 19-37). (A similar phenomenon exists for certain bacterial proteins that are secreted.) Moreover, several small peptide hormones, such as corticotropin (ACTH),

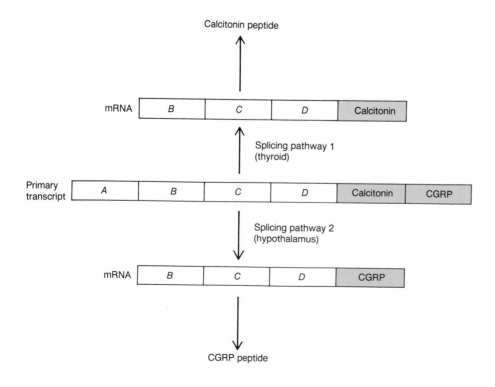

Figure 19-35. Alternate splicing pathways in two different organs generate different translation products from the same primary transcript.

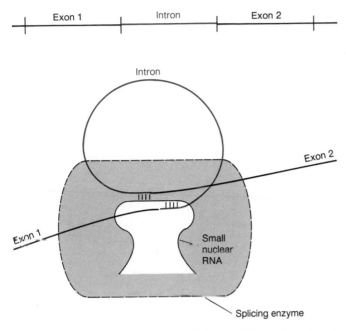

| Exon 1 | Intron | Exon 2 |

Figure 19-36. Schematic diagram depicting possible participation of small nuclear RNA in splicing reaction.

result from the specific cleavage of a single large polypeptide precursor.

Gene Families

The detailed analysis of parts of the eukaryotic chromosome by recombinant DNA techniques (described in Chap-

ter 14) has revealed that many genes are present in multiple copies in the genome. Sometimes the gene copies are virtually identical and serve to provide a source of increased gene products, as in the case of *Xenopus* 5S rRNA genes and sea-urchin histone genes (discussed on page 429). In other cases, the sequences are related but have diverged during evolution to the point where there are significant differences. Occasionally, chromosomal analysis reveals nonfunctional copies of genes, which are termed **pseudogenes,** that are remnants of the evolutionary process.

Genes that are derived from a common ancestral gene constitute a **gene family.** Often the members of gene families are clustered together on the chromosome, although in other cases they are widely dispersed throughout the genome. An interesting example of a clustered gene family is the globin gene family.

Hemoglobin consists of a tetrameric protein in association with its heme group (recall the analysis of altered hemoglobin molecules in Chapter 11). In adult mammals the tetramer consists of two α (alpha) and two β (beta) protein chains. However, mammalian embryos have hemoglobin molecules with different constituent chains. Instead of α and β chains, related proteins termed **α-like** and **β-like,** respectively, are found in embryonic hemoglobin. As the embryo develops, yet other α-like and β-like proteins appear to replace those originally present. Finally, after birth, the α and β chains emerge to replace the second set of related polypeptide chains. How the cell programs the production of the different globin proteins during development is a fascinating problem.

Table 19-4 details the specific globin polypeptides in the case of humans. The α-like chain found in embryonic and fetal hemoglobin is termed ζ (zeta). The β-like chain

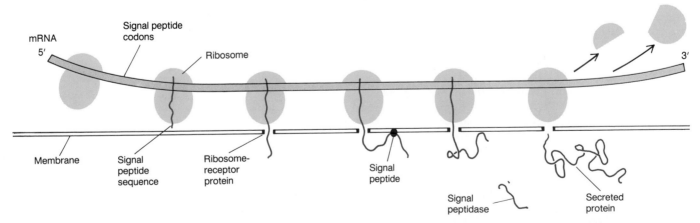

Figure 19-37. Signal sequences. Proteins destined to be secreted from the cell have an amino-terminal sequence that is rich in hydrophobic residues. This "signal sequence" binds to the membrane and draws the remainder of the protein through the lipid bilayer. The signal sequence is cleaved off the protein during this process by an enzyme called signal peptidase. (After J. D. Watson, J. Tooze, and D. T. Kurtz, *Recombinant DNA: A Short Course.* Copyright © 1983 by W. H. Freeman and Co.)

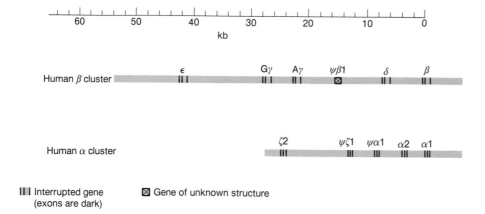

Figure 19-38. The human α-like and β-like globin gene families each are organized into a single cluster that includes functional genes and pseudogenes; the latter are denoted here by ψ (psi). (After B. Lewin, *Genes*. John Wiley & Sons, 1983.)

detected in embryonic hemoglobin is the $\boldsymbol{\epsilon}$ (epsilon) protein, whereas two forms of γ (gamma)—the G_γ and A_γ forms, which differ by only a single amino acid—predominate in fetal hemoglobin. These are replaced by the β chain in adults and, in a small percentage of the molecules, by another β-like chain termed δ (delta).

Figure 19-38 shows the two gene clusters that have been found for the globin genes in humans. The α and β clusters are found on different chromosomes. Here we can see the genetic organization of a 50-kb region of the chromosome, in the case of the β cluster. Note how the exons—the coding portions of the genes—occupy only a fraction of the region! Some pseudogenes (nonfunctional counterparts) were also discovered in these clusters; these are indicated in the figure according to the related functional gene.

Gene Regulation in Eukaryotes

We have already seen that there are several levels of control of gene expression in eukaryotes. Clearly, chromosome structure can profoundly influence gene activity. The inactivation of the X chromosome (see page 409) is an example of control at the level of the chromosome. Processing of the primary gene transcript (see Figures 19-31 and 19-32) is an example of control at a different level (posttranscriptional). What about control of the rate of transcription? What is known about the control signals for eukaryotic genes, and about their specific regulation at the level of transcription?

Sequence studies have revealed several features common to many eukaryotic genes, as summarized in Figure 19-39. Like their prokaryotic counterparts (see Figure 18-7), eukaryotic genes appear to have promoters with regions of conserved-sequence homology. Two such regions are the **TATA box** and the **CAT box,** which are probably involved in normal initiation of transcription.

As yet, there is no comprehensive understanding of regulatory circuits in eukaryotes, as there is in prokaryotes

(see Chapter 18). Molecular geneticists are only just beginning to understand the mechanism of activation of specific genes in higher cells. One model for regulatory systems, derived from studies of steroid hormones, is described in the following section.

Steroid Hormones

In a number of cases, the transcription of specific genes is activated by **steroid hormones,** which are formally analogous to inducers in certain bacterial systems. One example involves the female sex hormone estrogen. In chicken oviducts the egg-white protein ovalbumin is specifically synthesized in response to estrogen. Studies have shown that this is due to an increased transcription of the ovalbumin gene. The estrogen molecule activates transcription by binding to the chromatin together with a protein receptor molecule in the cytoplasm, which first recognizes the estrogen molecule and transports it to the nucleus. The detailed mechanism of specific binding of the steroid hormone-receptor complex to chromatin and the subsequent activation of transcription is not yet clear.

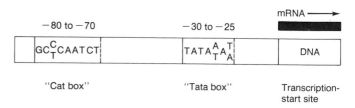

Figure 19-39. Two base sequences, dubbed the "CAT box" and the "TATA box," appear upstream of the transcription-start sites on many eukaryotic genes. These regions are probably control sequences for transcription. (After J. D. Watson, J. Tooze, and D. T. Kurtz, *Recombinant DNA: A Short Course*. Copyright © 1983, W. H. Freeman and Co.)

Control of Ubiquitous Molecules in Eukaryotic Cells

Several classes of molecules are found in abundance in every eukaryotic cell: histones, the translational apparatus, membrane components, and so on. Several strategies have evolved to maintain a sufficient amount of these products in the eukaryotic cell. These strategies include continuous and repeated transcription throughout the cell cycle, repetition of genes, and extrachromosomal amplification of specific gene sequences.

Genetic Redundancy. Genes coding for rRNA and tRNA have been extensively analyzed because the availability of purified gene products provides a probe with which to recover complementary DNA. Simple DNA/RNA hybridization shows that each *Xenopus* chromosome carrying a nucleolus organizer has 450 copies of the DNA coding for 18S and 28S rRNA. In contrast, there are 20,000 copies in each nucleus of the genes coding for 5S rRNA, and these genes are not located in the NO region. Donald Brown and his collaborators during the 1970s analyzed the NO DNA extensively and showed that it carries tandem duplications of a large (40S) transcription unit separated from its neighbors by nontranscribed **spacers.** The initial transcript is then processed to release smaller rRNAs finally found in the ribosome.

As we saw in Chapter 14, Max Birnstiel and his associates have shown that the five histone genes in sea urchins also are found as a tightly linked unit (Figure 14-2). There are several hundred copies of a repeating unit with the genes in the sequence *H4–H2B–H3–H2A H1.* Transcription begins at *H4* and ends at *H1*; each gene is transcribed as a single message. As we have seen in earlier chapters, tandem duplications can pair asymmetrically between homologous chromosomes or within the same chromosome; exchanges then increase or reduce the number of copies. It remains to be seen how (or whether) the number of tandem repeats is kept constant in a particular species.

Gene Amplification. Specific gene amplification has been studied extensively in the case of the rRNA genes in amphibian oocytes. As noted, each chromosome of *Xenopus* carries about 450 copies of the DNA coding for 18S and 28S rRNA. However, the oocyte contains up to 1000 times this number of copies of these genes. The oocyte is a very specialized cell that is loaded with the nutritive material needed to maintain the embryo until the tadpole stage without any ingestion of food. The cytoplasm also is prepared with the translational apparatus needed to carry out the complex program of differentiation in the many cells of the developing embryo.

During oogenesis, the maturing oocyte increases greatly in size as material is poured in from adjacent nurse cells. (Amazingly, so many ribosomes are present in the egg at fertilization that an *an/an* homozygotes carrying no genes for 18S and 28S rRNA will develop and differentiate to the twitching tadpole stage before death.) The oocyte nucleus also contributes material as the cell proceeds to the first meiotic prophase, where further development is arrested. The amphibian meiotic chromosomes are enormous, with numerous lateral loops representing regions of intense genetic activity (Figure 19-40). In the oocyte nucleus, there are hundreds of extrachromosomal nucleoli of varying size. Each nucleolus contains a ring of rDNA of different size that has been replicated and released from the chromosome. The steps involved in this process of DNA amplification are completely unknown. The DNA rings actively produce rRNA that is assembled into ribosomes, which are stored in the nucleolus until their release during meiosis.

Other examples of genetic amplification are known. Specific puffs of the polytene chromosomes in dipterans

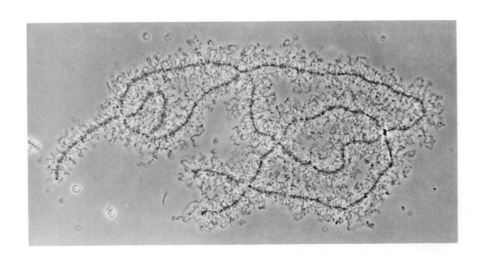

Figure 19-40. The "lampbrush" chromosomes of an amphibian oocyte. (Photograph courtesy of J. Gall.)

are found to produce excess DNA rather than mRNA. Also, George Rudkin showed in the early 1960s that the polytene chromosomes from *Drosophila* salivary glands themselves may represent specific amplification of euchromatic DNA about a thousandfold, whereas the proximal heterochromatic regions may be replicated only a few times. Thus, in addition to the mechanism for replicating chromosomal DNA normally for cell division, there exists a means for amplifying specific loci and not others.

Message   Cellular mechanisms exist to ensure an adequate supply of gene products that are vital to all cells. These mechanisms include increasing the number of gene copies per chromosome (redundancy) and increasing the number of gene copies in the cell (amplification).

Summary

■ Each eukaryotic chromosome apparently represents a single continuous DNA molecule extending from one end through the centromere to the other end. The molecule of DNA may be 10^5 times as long as the chromosome itself, and it is apparently packaged in a very regular and complex fashion within the chromosome. The packaging begins with the nucleosome, an aggregate of four pairs of histones around which the DNA is coiled twice. Chains of nucleosomes are then coiled, the coils in turn are coiled, and so on.

In eukaryotic chromosomes, differences in gene activity can be recognized by the degree of compaction (which is indicated by staining intensity). Densely staining heterochromatin represents nonactive material. Within a chromosome, heterochromatic regions are typically found at the tips, around the centromere, and around the nucleolus organizer. Such constitutive heterochromatin is generally highly redundant and relatively devoid of sequences for which RNA transcripts may be found, and it contains sequences of satellite DNA.

In some cases, a chromosome may exist in one of two states: functionally active or functionally inactive. Constitutive heterochromatin represents entire chromosomes or specific segments that are predictably heterochromatized and inactive during the cell cycle. In other cases, a chromosome or segment may or may not become heterochromatin —when it does, it is referred to as facultative heterochromatin. Once the functional state of the chromosome is determined, that state is replicated from cell to cell in further reproduction. Early in the development of a mammalian female, one of the two X chromosomes in each cell is inactivated (becoming a heterochromatic Barr body), thereby rendering the cell functionally equivalent to a male cell (which contains only one X chromosome). In contrast, organisms like *Drosophila* compensate for the double dose of sex-linked genes in females (compared to males) by a 50 percent reduction in gene activity on the female X chromosome.

In eukaryotes, specific DNA segments may be present as tandem duplications within the chromosome or as amplifications that represent extra copies transcribed and then released from the chromosome. RNA is processed in eukaryotes prior to transport to the cytoplasm. Caps and tails are added, and internal portions of the primary transcript are removed. Many genes are therefore "split" in eukaryotes, and the coding segments of a gene are not colinear with the processed mRNA. Table 19-5 summarizes some of the differences between prokaryotes and eukaryotes regarding RNA synthesis.

■ **TABLE 19-5.** Differences in gene expression between prokaryotes and eukaryotes

Prokaryotes	Eukaryotes
1. All RNA species are synthesized by a single RNA polymerase.	1. Three different RNA polymerases are responsible for the different classes of RNA molecules.
2. mRNA is translated during transcription.	2. mRNA is processed before transport to the cytoplasm, where it is translated. Caps and tails are added, and internal portions of the transcript are removed.
3. Genes are contiguous segments of DNA that are colinear with the mRNA that is translated into a protein.	3. Genes are often split. They are not contiguous segments of coding sequences; rather, the coding sequences are interrupted by intervening sequences (introns).
4. mRNAs are often polycistronic.	4. mRNAs are monocistronic.

Problems

1. Which of the following is *not* an advantage from having genes arranged in chromosomes rather than floating free?

   a. Favorable combinations of genes can be inherited more or less as a unit.

   b. Functionally related genes can be controlled in a coordinated fashion.

   c. DNA can pass through the nuclear pore into the cytoplasm.

   d. Orderly separation of genetic information can occur at cell division.

e. Replication of DNA can occur in orderly fashion.

2. The mealybug, *Planococcus citri,* has a diploid number of 10. The meiotic divisions in *P. citri* are thought to be reversed—that is, an equational division is followed by a reductional division. In the tetrads formed at meiosis I, it is difficult to distinguish sister chromatids from their paired homologs because they form a tightly paired unit. Sharat Chandra obtained a triploid strain of *P. citri.* What would you expect to observe at the end of meiosis I and II in this strain if: a. the division sequence is conventional? b. the division sequence is reversed?

3. Considering the length of each DNA molecule in a eukaryote and the levels of complexity in its packaged form in a chromosome, the mechanism of pairing between homologous sequences becomes staggering. How could pairing between chromosomes possibly take place so that specific base pairs are properly aligned?

4. In 1917, Alfred Sturtevant noted that crossing-over in any chromosome pair in a *Drosophila* female is increased if the female is heterozygous for an inversion in some different pair. This is called the "interchromosomal effect" on crossing-over. It has since been shown that an inversion of one chromosome always increases crossing-over in the others. Devise a hypothesis to explain this effect. Design an experimental test of your hypothesis.

5. In 1956, R. Alexander Brink noted some aberrant results from crosses with corn involving alleles of the *R* locus, which affects the color pattern in seeds. The alleles studied (and their corresponding phenotypes) were r^r (colorless seed), R^r (dark purple seed), and R^{st} (stippled seed, having irregular spots on a light background). In the cross $R^r r^r \times r^r r^r$, Brink obtained 50 percent dark and 50 percent colorless seeds. In the cross $R^{st} r^r \times r^r r^r$, he obtained 50 percent stippled and 50 percent colorless seeds. In the cross $R^r R^{st} \times r^r r^r$, he obtained 50 percent stippled and 50 percent "weakly colored" seeds. Apparently, in the $R^r R^{st}$ heterozygote, the R^r alleles change to a new and stable allelic state labeled R'. This effect is called **paramutation.** How does paramutation differ from mutation? Devise a hypothesis to explain the results. Design an experimental test of your hypothesis.

6. In embryos of the fungus gnat, *Sciara,* after the seventh cell division, the paternally inherited X chromosomes in all somatic cells migrate through the nuclear membrane and disintegrate in the cytoplasm. Helen Crouse studied the properties of a series of X-autosome translocations with the following X-chromosome breakpoints:

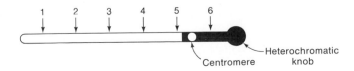

She found that, when males contributed the translocations to the offspring, the translocated portion carrying the X centromere in rearrangements 1 through 5 was lost during embryonic development. However, with translocation 6, the autosomal centromere carrying the right arm of the X was lost. Suggest an interpretation of these results.

7. Erich Wolff has studied the polytene chromosomes of two strains of a European midge, *Phryne cincta.* One strain (Berlin) has no heterochromatic elements on the X chromosome, whereas another strain (alpine) has two heterochromatic sites at which large amounts of DNA are produced and released into a nucleolus-like structure.

   a. Design experiments to study the nature of the DNA in the heterochromatic sites. (NOTE: the strains will mate with each other, and fertile F_1 progeny are obtained.)

   b. Wolff also has observed that some *Phryne* strains carry up to seven supernumary chromosomes that are not present in the normal genome. How would you study the DNA in these supernumary chromosomes?

8. When DNA from *Drosophila* is isolated from salivary-gland nuclei and from testes and spun in a CsCl gradient, the following distributions are obtained. What does this result suggest?

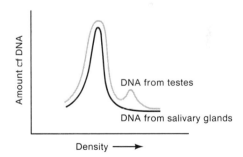

9. Joseph Gall and Mary Lou Pardue recognized that polytene chromosomes are like columns of DNA laid out in proper sequence. They developed a method for denaturing the DNA in these chromosomes without disrupting the spatial organization of the chromosomes. By incubating radioactive RNA on the denatured chromosomes and then removing the unbound RNA, they were able to localize the RNA/DNA hybrids by autoradiography. (This technique was described in Chapter 14.)

   a. What parameters would affect the resolving power of this technique—that is, the accuracy with which two adjacent sites can be distinguished?

   b. How would you demonstrate that such RNA binding does indeed reflect complementary sequences of DNA?

c. What do you infer when a certain RNA binds to a certain locus?

10. Highly redundant DNA sequences in *Drosophila* are concentrated in heterochromatin around all of the centromeres. However, in relation to their DNA content, these same regions have a disproportionately small number of loci that can be detected genetically. For that reason, Painter and Müller suggested that this proximal heterochromatin is "inert." Furthermore, very little crossing-over occurs within the heterochromatin. What biological function might be filled by these redundant sequences? Your hypothesis should explain the absence of detectable loci and the nonrandom distribution of the heterochromatin. (NOTE: this is an unsolved problem; no one knows the correct answer, although there are many hypotheses.)

11. When tandemly duplicated DNA is sequenced, the duplicate segments are identical. Suggest a mechanism that might preserve the exact duplication of these segments over time against the effects of random mutations.

12. You are a molecular biologist on a field trip in the jungles of Surinam, where you discover a purple tree frog with yellow stripes. Struck by its beauty, you capture several dozen males and females and smuggle them back to your laboratory. They breed easily and profusely, and you decide to use them in an investigation of the organization of the ribosomal RNA genes. Design experiments to carry out this investigation without the need for genetic crosses.

13. In *Neurospora*, all mutants affecting the enzymes carbamyl phosphate synthetase or aspartate transcarbamylase map at the *pyr-3* locus. If you induce *pyr-3* mutations in ICR-170 (a chemical mutagen), you find that either both enzyme functions are lacking or only the transcarbamylase function is lacking; in no case is the synthetase activity lacking when the transcarbamylase activity is present. (ICR-170 is assumed to induce frame-shifts.) Interpret these results in terms of a possible operon.

14. In *Drosophila*, an autosomal locus Adh^+ codes for alcohol dehydrogenase, an enzyme that converts alcohols into aldehydes. Wild-type flies, when fed pentenol, convert that alcohol into a toxic compound and die, whereas Adh^- mutants survive. Conversely, ethanol-fed flies die if they are Adh^- but survive if they are Adh^+ because they can convert the ethanol to a harmless aldehyde. Describe methods for the selection of mutants regulating the production and the amino acid sequence of alcohol dehydrogenase. How would you distinguish operationally among various mutant types?

15. There is a class of mutations in *Drosophila* that includes loci on all four chromosomes. These mutants are called *Minute,* and they are characterized by similar properties: recessive lethality, a dominant effect on bristles (which become slender and short) and development time (which is delayed by several days), and a *Minute* phenotype in the presence of a deficiency for any of the loci. There are at least 50 to 60 *Minute* loci. Speculate on the possible biological function of *Minute* genes. How would you study a *Minute* gene from a genetic point of view and from a molecular point of view?

CHAPTER 20

The Extranuclear Genome

■ In the analysis of eukaryotic organisms, the notion that genes reside in the nucleus has become a firm part of the general dogma of genetics. Indeed, there is no need to question the fundamental truth of this notion. The mechanics of the nuclear processes of meiosis and mitosis, together with the understanding that genes are located on nuclear chromosomes, provide the basic set of operational rules for genetics. In fact, the great successes of genetics in this century have been in large part due to the success of these operational rules in predicting inheritance patterns—from simple eukaryotes to human beings.

However, like most fundamental truths, this one does have exceptions, and these exceptions are the subject of this chapter. In eukaryotes, the special inheritance patterns of some genes reveal that these genes must be located outside the nucleus. Such **extranuclear genes** ("extra-" means "outside") have been found in a variety of eukaryotes. At first, the very idea of such genes seemed heretical, but their existence has gradually been accepted over the years as more and more results have turned up to confirm their reality. The inheritance patterns shown by extranuclear genes are less commonly encountered than those of nuclear genes, and indeed, there are fewer extranuclear genes than normal chromosomal genes. However, although they are exceptional in this sense, it is becoming increasingly clear that extranuclear genes play normal (but highly specialized) roles in the control of eukaryote phenotypes.

In the past decade or so, intense research activity has been directed toward study of extranuclear inheritance. This activity resulted from the discovery (and subsequent general availability) of new genetic and technological approaches. The great success of these analyses has led to a vastly improved understanding of the nature and function of extranuclear genes. We see in this chapter that the operational approaches in such research are often quite different from those used in studying nuclear genes (although there are similarities also). These unique analytical methods alone would merit special treatment, but their results also have revealed fascinating genetic systems that are novel and distinct enough in themselves to warrant major coverage in such a text as this.

A word of caution is in order here. A large proportion of the material presented in this chapter is based on frontier research. Although the experimental approaches to extranuclear inheritance are now well established, and a wealth of indisputable information has been accumulated, there are still many unanswered questions. For one thing, only a rather small number of species has proved suitable for the specialized techniques thus far developed. Even in the case of the well-studied organisms, we must await further research in cell biology to fill in many details not yet understood.

Conventionally, the eukaryotic cell is divided into two domains: the nucleus and the cytoplasm. The cytoplasm itself is a highly organized heterogeneous array of organ-

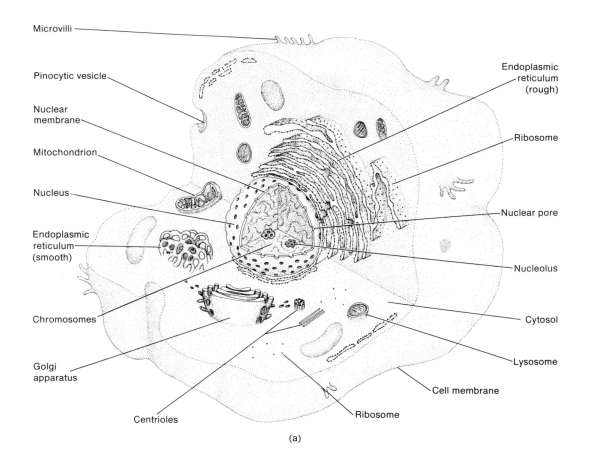

Microvilli

Pinocytic vesicle

Nuclear membrane

Mitochondrion

Nucleus

Endoplasmic reticulum (smooth)

Chromosomes

Golgi apparatus

Centrioles

Endoplasmic reticulum (rough)

Ribosome

Nuclear pore

Nucleolus

Cytosol

Lysosome

Cell membrane

Ribosome

(a)

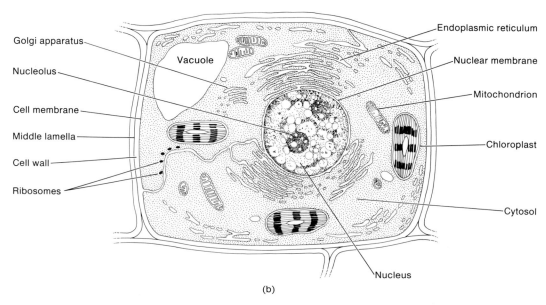

Golgi apparatus

Nucleolus

Cell membrane

Middle lamella

Cell wall

Ribosomes

Vacuole

Endoplasmic reticulum

Nuclear membrane

Mitochondrion

Chloroplast

Cytosol

Nucleus

(b)

Figure 20-1. The heterogeneity of the cytoplasm. The area called the cytoplasm (everything between the nuclear membrane and the cell membrane) embraces the cytosol (liquid phase) plus a rich assortment of organelles, membranes, and other structures. Extranuclear genes are found in the mitochondria and in the chloroplasts of green plants. (a) An animal cell. (b) A plant cell. (Part a from S. Singer and H. R. Hilgard, *The Biology of People*. Copyright © 1978 by W. H. Freeman and Co.; part b from J. Janick et al., *Plant Science*. Copyright © 1974 by W. H. Freeman and Co.)

elles, membranes, and various molecules in solution (Figure 20-1). Extranuclear genes are found in the mitochondria, and in the chloroplasts of green plants. These organelles serve the major functions of ATP synthesis and photosynthesis, respectively. Each organelle contains its own set of unique and autonomous genes, linked together in an organellar chromosome. Extranuclear genes often are called extrachromosomal genes—a term that is potentially confusing because the genes found in the mitochondria and chloroplasts do in fact comprise extranuclear chromosomes. Nevertheless, it must be emphasized that the organellar chromosomes show inheritance patterns and organization quite different from those of the nuclear chromosomes.

A great deal is now known about the genetics and biochemistry of organelle genes. This chapter outlines some of the major steps in the evolution of our present understanding. It is a beautiful example of the power of genetic analysis when combined with molecular biology.

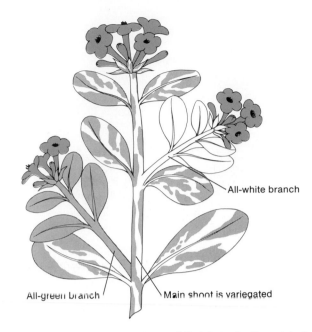

Figure 20-2. Leaf variegation in *Mirabilis jalapa,* the four-o'clock plant. Flowers may form on any branch (variegated, green, or white), and these flowers may be used in crosses.

Message   The genes that have been called cytoplasmic genes, extrachromosomal genes, or extranuclear genes are in fact located on a unique kind of chromosome inside cytoplasmic organelles.

Variegation in Leaves of Higher Plants

One of the first convincing examples of extranuclear inheritance was found in higher plants. In 1909, Carl Correns reported some surprising results from his studies on four-o'clock plants *(Mirabilis jalapa).* The blotchy leaves of these variegated plants showed patches of green and white tissue, but some branches carried only green leaves and others carried only white leaves (Figure 20-2).

Flowers appear on all types of branches. They may be intercrossed in a variety of different combinations by transferring pollen from one flower to another. Table 20-1 shows the results of such crosses. Two features of these results are surprising. First, there is a difference between reciprocal crosses: for example, white ♀ × green ♂ gives a different result from green ♀ × white ♂. Recall that Mendel never observed differences between reciprocal crosses. In fact, in conventional genetics, differences between reciprocal crosses are normally encountered only in the case of sex-linked genes. However, the results of the four-o'clock crosses cannot be explained by sex linkage.

The second surprising feature is that the phenotype of the maternal parent is solely responsible for determining the phenotype of all progeny. The phenotype of the male parent appears to be irrelevant, and its contribution to the progeny appears to be zero! This phenomenon is known as **maternal inheritance.** Although the white progeny plants

do not live for long because they lack chlorophyll, the other progeny types do survive and can be used in further generations of crosses. In these subsequent generations, maternal inheritance always appears in the same patterns as those observed in the original crosses.

How can such curious results be explained? The differences in leaf color were known to be due to the presence of either green or colorless chloroplasts. The inheritance patterns might be explained if these cytoplasmic organelles are somehow genetically autonomous and furthermore are never transmitted via the pollen parent. For an organelle to be genetically autonomous, it must have its own genetic determinants that are responsible for its phenotype. In this case, the chloroplasts would carry their own genetic deter-

■ **TABLE 20-1.** Results of crosses of variegated four-o'clock plants

Phenotype of branch bearing egg parent (♀)	Phenotype of branch bearing pollen parent (♂)	Phenotype of progeny
White	White	White
White	Green	White
White	Variegated	White
Green	White	Green
Green	Green	Green
Green	Variegated	Green
Variegated	White	Variegated, green, or white
Variegated	Green	Variegated, green, or white
Variegated	Variegated	Variegated, green, or white

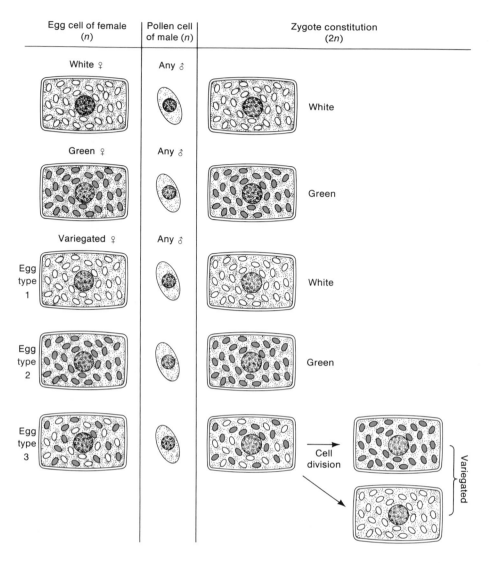

Egg cell of female (*n*)	Pollen cell of male (*n*)	Zygote constitution (2*n*)

Figure 20-3. A model explaining the results of the *Mirabilis jalapa* crosses in terms of autonomous chloroplast inheritance. The large, dark spheres are nuclei. The smaller bodies are chloroplasts, either green (color) or white. Each egg cell is assumed to contain many chloroplasts, and each pollen cell is assumed to contain no chloroplasts. The first two crosses exhibit strict maternal inheritance. If the maternal branch is variegated, three types of zygotes can result, depending on whether the egg cell contains only white, only green, or both green and white chloroplasts. In the latter case, the resulting zygote can produce both green and white tissue, so a variegated plant results.

minants responsible for chloroplast color. Thus, the suggestion arises that this organelle has its own genome. The failure to be transmitted via the pollen parent is reasonable because the bulk of the cytoplasm of the zygote is known to come from the maternal parent via the cytoplasm of the egg. Figure 20-3 diagrams a model that formally accounts for all the inheritance patterns in Table 20-1.

Variegated branches apparently produce three kinds of eggs: some contain only white chloroplasts, some contain only green chloroplasts, and some contain both kinds of chloroplasts. The egg type containing both green and white chloroplasts produces a zygote that also contains both kinds of chloroplasts. In the subsequent mitotic divisions, some form of cytoplasmic segregation occurs that segregates the chloroplast types into pure cell lines, thus producing the variegated phenotype in that progeny individual (Figure 20-4).

This process of sorting might be described as "mitotic segregation." However, this is an *extranuclear* phenomenon, not to be confused with mitotic segregation of nuclear genes, so a new term has been invented. This term — representing a hypothetical "black box" in which the segre-

gation and (as we shall see) recombination of organelle genotypes occur — is **cytoplasmic segregation and recombination,** referred to in this book by the convenient acronym CSAR. Throughout this chapter, CSAR crops up quite often; it appears to be a common behavior of extranuclear genomes. In one sense, CSAR is the cytoplasmic equivalent of meiosis, because meiosis is the process whereby segregation and recombination of nuclear genes regularly occur. However, CSAR is purely hypothetical — no physical counterpart is known for this process.

We might suspect that random chloroplast assortment could explain the green/white segregation in variegated plants, but this hypothesis has not been proved. Furthermore, the large numbers of chloroplasts in cells make this an unlikely possibility. In a cell with, let's say, 40 chloroplasts, consisting of 20 green and 20 colorless chloroplasts, the production by random assortment of one daughter cell containing only green and one daughter cell containing only colorless chloroplasts would be at best a very rare event. To be on the safe side, we shall treat the CSAR process as hypothetical. This hypothetical CSAR process is diagrammed in Figure 20-5.

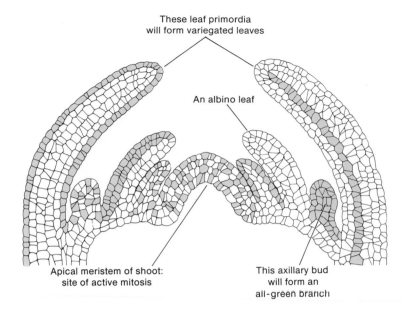

These leaf primordia
will form variegated leaves

An albino leaf

Apical meristem of shoot:
site of active mitosis

This axillary bud
will form an
all-green branch

Figure 20-4. In a plant containing both green and white chloroplasts, different green or white cell lines are established in the meristem (growing point). The egg from which such a plant is derived contains both types of chloroplasts; after fertilization and subsequent mitotic divisions, cytoplasmic segregation occurs, segregating the chloroplast types into pure cell lines. The color of any part of the plant thus depends on the particular cell types that happened to form the relevant leaf or shoot primordia.

Poky *Neurospora*

In 1952, Mary Mitchell isolated a mutant strain of *Neurospora* that she called poky. This mutant differs from the wild-type in a number of ways: it is slow growing, it shows maternal inheritance, and it has abnormal amounts of cytochromes. Cytochromes are mitochondrial electron-transport proteins necessary for the proper oxidation of foodstuffs to generate ATP energy. There are three main types: cytochromes *a*, *b*, and *c*. In poky, there is no cytochrome *a* or *b*, and there is an excess of cytochrome *c*.

How can maternal inheritance be expressed in a haploid organism? It is possible to cross some fungi in such a way that one parent contributes the bulk of cytoplasm to the progeny, and this cytoplasm-contributing parent is called the female parent, even though no true sex is involved. Maternal inheritance for the poky phenotype was demonstrated in the following crosses:

poky ♀ × wild-type ♂ ⟶ all poky

wild-type ♀ × poky ♂ ⟶ all wild-type

However, in such crosses, any nuclear genes that differ between the parental strains are observed to segregate in the normal Mendelian manner and to produce 1 : 1 ratios in the progeny (Figure 20-6). All poky progeny behave like the original poky strain, transmitting the poky phenotype down through many generations when crossed as females. Because poky does not behave like a nuclear mutation, it was termed an **extranuclear mutation.** To hammer the point home, it also has been called a **cytoplasmic mutation** because it seems to be carried in the cytoplasm of the female parent.

But where in the cytoplasm is the mutation carried? The important clue is that several aspects of the mutant phenotype seem to involve mitochondria. For instance, the cells' slow growth suggests lack of ATP energy, which is normally produced by mitochondria. There are abnormal amounts of cytochromes in the mutants, and cytochromes are known to be located in the mitochondrial membranes. These clues led to the conclusion that mitochondria are involved and inspired several interesting experiments designed to investigate mitochondrial autonomy.

David Luck labeled mitochondria with radioactive choline, a membrane component, and he then followed their division autoradiographically in unlabeled medium. He found that even after several doublings of mass, the mitochondria were still evenly labeled. Luck concluded that mitochondria can grow and divide in a fashion that

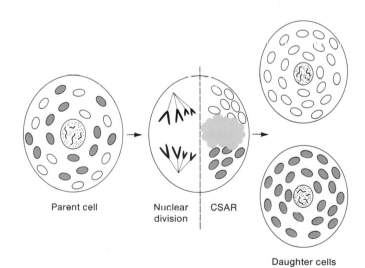

Parent cell

Nuclear   CSAR
division

Daughter cells

Figure 20-5. Two processes may be distinguished at cell division. Nuclear division (mitosis) is an observed physical process that parcels the genes on the nuclear chromosomes. The hypothetical CSAR process in the cytoplasm (for which no physical counterpart has been observed) would account for segregation and recombination of organelle genes, producing the new organelle sets of the daughter cells. The diagrams show how CSAR can generate two different organelle sets from a mixed parental cell.

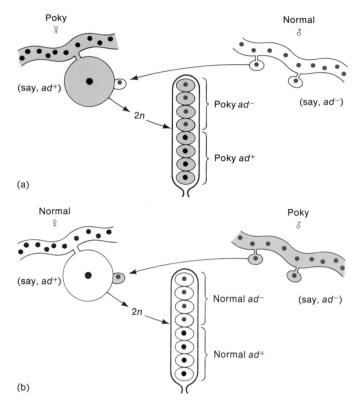

Figure 20-6. Explanation of the different results from reciprocal crosses of poky and normal *Neurospora*. Most of the cytoplasm of the progeny cells comes from the parent called female. Shading represents cytoplasm with the poky determinants. The nuclear gene ad^+/ad^- is used to illustrate the segregation of the nuclear genes in the expected 1:1 Mendelian ratio.

seems to be autonomous rather than nucleus directed. If mitochondria were synthesized anew, or de novo, some of the resulting population of mitochondria should be unlabeled, whereas the original ones would remain heavily labeled.

In 1965, a research group led by Edward Tatum extracted purified mitochondria from a mutant similar to poky, a mutant called *abnormal*. With an ultrafine needle and syringe, the experimenters injected the mitochondria into wild-type recipient cells, using appropriate controls. The recipient cells were cultured. After several of these subcultures, the abnormal phenotype appeared! In transferring the mitochondria, the experimenters had transferred the hereditary determinants of the abnormal phenotype. Presumably, then, the extranuclear genes involved in this phenotype are located in the mitochondria. These inferences gained credibility with the discovery of DNA in the mitochondria of *Neurospora* and other species (but more of that story later).

The Heterokaryon Test

Maternal inheritance is one criterion for recognizing organelle-based inheritance. Another test has been applied in filamentous fungi such as *Neurospora* and *Aspergillus*. In principle, this test could be applied to other systems involving heterokaryons. A heterokaryon is made between the prospective extranuclear mutant (say, a slow-growth mutant) and a strain carrying a known nuclear mutation. If the phenotype of the nuclear mutation can be recovered from the heterokaryon in combination with the phenotype of the slow-growth mutant being tested, then the growth mutant is a good candidate for an organelle-based mutation. This is because no diploidy occurs in a heterokaryon, so that there is no genetic exchange between nuclei. The slow-growth phenotype must have been transferred solely by cytoplasmic contact. The segregation of the pure extranuclear type from the mixed cytoplasm of the heterokaryon presumably involves the CSAR process (Figure 20-7).

Message Extranuclear inheritance can be recognized by uniparental (usually maternal) transmission through a cross, or by transmission via cytoplasmic contact.

Shell Coiling in Snails: A Red Herring

Does maternal inheritance always indicate extranuclear inheritance? Usually, but not always. It is possible for a maternal-inheritance pattern of reciprocal crosses to be generated by nuclear genes. In 1923, Alfred Sturtevant (who

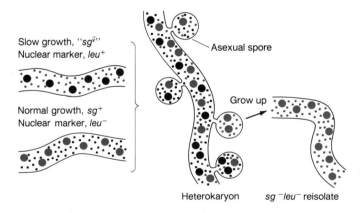

Figure 20-7. The heterokaryon test is used to detect extranuclear inheritance in filamentous (threadlike) fungi. A possible extranuclear mutation (here, sg^-, causing slow growth) is combined with a nuclear mutation (leu^-) to form a heterokaryon. Cultures of leu^- can be derived from the heterokaryon. If some of these cultures also are sg^- in phenotype, then sg is very likely an extranuclear gene, borne in an organelle. Since no nuclear recombination occurs in a heterokaryon, the sg^- phenotype must have been acquired by cytoplasmic contact.

studied crossing-over in *Drosophila*) found a good example in the water snail *Limnaea*. Sturtevant analyzed the results of crosses between snails that differed in the direction of their shell coiling. On looking into the opening of the shell, it is seen that some snails coil to the right — that is, the coiling direction is dextral — and that others coil to the left — that is, sinistral coiling. All of the F_1 progeny of the cross dextral♀ × sinistral♂ are dextral, but all of the F_1 progeny of the cross sinistral♀ × dextral♂ are sinistral. Thus far, the situation seems similar to that observed with poky or with chloroplast inheritance. However, the F_2 generation is all dextral from both pedigrees!

The F_3 generation in this case revealed that the inheritance of coiling direction involves nuclear genes rather than extranuclear genes. The F_3 is produced by individually selfing the F_2 snails. (This is possible because snails are hermaphroditic.) Three-fourths of the F_3 snails were found to be dextral, and one-fourth were found to be sinistral (Figure 20-8). This ratio reveals a Mendelian segregation in the F_2 generation. Apparently, dextral ($+^s$) is dominant to sinistral (*s*), but Sturtevant concluded that, strangely enough, the shell-coiling phenotype of any individual animal is determined by the genotype (not the phenotype) of its mother! We now know that this happens because the genotype of the mother's body determines the initial cleavage pattern of the developing embryo. Note that the segregation ratios shown in Figure 20-8 would never appear in the phenotypes of true organelle genes. This example

shows that one generation of crosses is not enough to provide certain evidence that maternal inheritance is due to organelle-based inheritance. The term **maternal effect** can be used for cases like the shell-coiling example in order to distinguish them from organelle-based inheritance.

Extranuclear Genes in *Chlamydomonas*

If an investigator could somehow design an ideal experimental organism with a simple life cycle, the result would be something like the unicellular freshwater alga *Chlamydomonas*. Like fungi, algae rarely have different sexes, but they do have mating types. In many algal and fungal species, there are two mating types that are determined by alleles at one locus. A cross can occur only if the parents are of different mating types. The mating types are physically identical but physiologically different. Such species are called **heterothallic** (literally, "different-bodied"). In *Chlamydomonas*, the mating-type alleles are called mt^+ and mt^- (in *Neurospora* they are *A* and *a*; in yeast, *a* and α). Figure 20-9 diagrams the *Chlamydomonas* life cycle. As you might guess, tetrad analysis (see Chapter 6) is possible and in fact is routinely performed.

In 1954, Ruth Sager isolated a streptomycin-sensitive mutant of *Chlamydomonas* with a peculiar inheritance pattern. In the following crosses, *sm-r* and *sm-s* indicate strep-

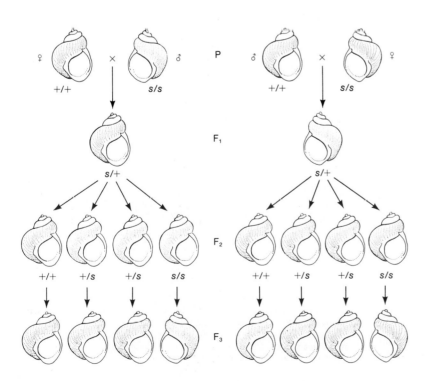

Figure 20-8. The inheritance of dextral (+) and sinistral (*s*) nuclear genes for shell coiling in a species of water snail. The direction of coiling is determined by the nuclear genotype of the mother, not the genotype of the individual involved. This explanation accounts for the initial difference between reciprocal crosses as well as the phenotypes of later generations. No organelle inheritance is involved (such a hypothesis would not explain the phenotypes of later generations).

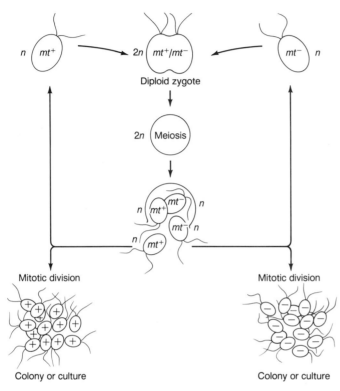

Figure 20-9. Diagrammatic representation of the life cycle of *Chlamydomonas*, a unicellular green alga. This organism has played a central role in research on organelle genetics. The nuclear mating-type alleles mt^+ and mt^- must be heterozygous in order for the sexual cycle to occur.

tomycin resistance and sensitivity, respectively, and *mt* is the mating-type gene discussed earlier:

$$sm\text{-}r\,mt^+ \times sm\text{-}s\,mt^- \longrightarrow \text{progeny all } sm\text{-}r$$

$$sm\text{-}s\,mt^+ \times sm\text{-}r\,mt^- \longrightarrow \text{progeny all } sm\text{-}s$$

Here we see a difference in reciprocal crosses; all progeny cells show the streptomycin phenotype of the mt^+ parent. Like the maternal inheritance discussed earlier, this is a case of **uniparental inheritance.** In fact, Sager now refers to the mt^+ mating type as the female, using this analogy. However, there is no observable physical distinction between the mating types as there would be if true sex were involved, nor is there a difference in the contribution of cytoplasm as seen in *Neurospora*. In these crosses, the conventional nuclear marker genes (such as *mt* itself) all behave normally and give 1 : 1 progeny ratios. For example, one-half of the progeny of the cross $sm\text{-}r\,mt^+ \times sm\text{-}s\,mt^-$ are $sm\text{-}r\,mt^+$, and one-half are $sm\text{-}r\,mt^-$.

To determine the sm-s or sm-r phenotypes of progeny, the cells are plated onto medium containing streptomycin. While performing these experiments, Sager observed that

the drug streptomycin itself acts as a mutagen. If a pure strain of *sm-s* cells is plated onto streptomycin, quite a significant proportion of streptomycin-resistant colonies will appear. In fact, treatment with streptomycin will produce a whole crop of different kinds of mutant phenotypes, all of them showing uniparental inheritance (and hence presumably extranuclear). Furthermore, streptomycin treatment does not produce nuclear mutants. Most of the mutants produced by streptomycin treatment show either (1) resistance to one of several different drugs or (2) defective photosynthesis. The photosynthetic mutants are unable to make use of CO_2 from the air as a source of carbon, so they survive only if soluble carbon (in some form such as acetate) is added to their medium. (How would you go about selecting such mutants?) Table 20-2 lists several different extra-

■ **TABLE 20-2.** Some of the *Chlamydomonas* mutants showing uniparental inheritance

Gene	Mutant phenotype
ac1 through *ac4*	Requires acetate
tm1, tm3 through *tm9*	Cannot grow at 35°C
tm2	Conditional: grows at 35°C only in presence of streptomycin
ti1 through *ti5*	Forms tiny colonies on all media
ery1	Resistant to erythromycin at concentration of 50 μg/ml
kan1	Resistant to kanamycin at concentration of 100 μg/ml
spc1	Resistant to spectinomycin at concentration of 50 μg/ml
spi1 through *spi5*	Resistant to spiramycin at concentration of 100 μg/ml
ole1 through *ole3*	Resistant to oleandomycin at concentration of 50 μg/ml
car1	Resistant to carbamycin at concentration of 50 μg/ml
ele1	Resistant to eleosine at concentration of 50 μg/ml
ery3 and *ery11*	Resistant to erythromycin, carbamycin, oleandomycin, and spiramycin (at concentrations listed above for individual drugs)
sm2 and *sm5*	Resistant to streptomycin at concentration of 500 μg/ml
sm3	Resistant to streptomycin at concentration of 50 μg/ml
sm4	Requires streptomycin for survival

NOTE: all of these mutants were produced by treatment with streptomycin except for the *ti* mutants, which were produced by treatment with nitrosoguanidine.
SOURCE: R. Sager, *Cytoplasmic Genes and Organelles*, Academic Press.

nuclear mutant types produced by the streptomycin treatment.

These experiments reveal the existence of a mysterious "uniparental genome" in *Chlamydomonas*—that is, a group of genes that all show uniparental transmission in crosses. Where is this uniparental genome located? What is the mechanism of the uniparental transmission? When there seems to be no physical difference between mating types, why are these genes transmitted only by the mt^+ parent?

There is evidence to suggest that the uniparental genome in this case is in fact chloroplast DNA (cpDNA). About 15 percent of the DNA of a *Chlamydomonas* cell in rapidly growing culture is found in the single chloroplast of the cell. This DNA forms a band in a CsCl gradient that is distinct from the band of nuclear DNA (Figure 20-10). Furthermore, the precise position of the cpDNA band can be altered by adding the heavy isotope of nitrogen, ^{15}N, to the growth medium. The position of the band can be calibrated in terms of the buoyant density of the cpDNA. With this technique, the cpDNA of the two parents in a cross can be labeled differently, one light (^{14}N) and one heavy (^{15}N).

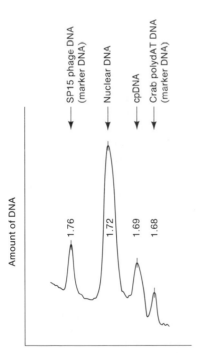

Figure 20-10. The chloroplast DNA (cpDNA) of *Chlamydomonas* can be detected in a CsCl density gradient as a band of DNA distinct from the nuclear DNA. In this particular experiment, two other DNA types were sedimented along with the *Chlamydomonas* DNA to act as known reference points in the gradient. The numbers represent buoyant densities (g/cm³) of the various DNA types. (Figures 20-10 and 20-11 after R. Sager, "Genetic Analysis of Chloroplast DNA in *Chlomydomonas*," in *Cytoplasmic Genes and Organelles*, Academic Press.)

■ **TABLE 20-3.** Buoyant densities of cpDNA in progeny from various *Chlamydomonas* crosses

Cross	Buoyant density of zygote cpDNA
^{14}N mt^+ × ^{14}N mt^-	1.69
^{15}N mt^+ × ^{15}N mt^-	1.70
^{15}N mt^+ × ^{14}N mt^-	1.70
^{14}N mt^+ × ^{15}N mt^-	1.69

SOURCE: R. Sager, *Cytoplasmic Genes and Organelles*, Academic Press.

The buoyant densities of the cpDNA from these parental cells are 1.69 and 1.70, respectively. Although this difference seems small, it provides appreciably different band positions in a CsCl gradient. With differently labeled parents, the zygote DNA can be examined to see how it compares with the parents (Table 20-3). The results indicate that the cpDNA of the mt^- parent is in fact lost, inactivated, or destroyed in some way. This loss of cpDNA from the mt^- parent, of course, parallels the loss of uniparental genes (such as the *sm* genes) borne by the mt^- parent.

Other experiments have been performed using similar logic. For example, crosses can be made between *Chlamydomonas* strains having cpDNAs with distinctly different restriction-enzyme-digest patterns on electrophoretic gels. Again, the specific cpDNA digest pattern passed on to the progeny is that of the mt^+ parent only.

Message The cpDNA of *Chlamydomonas* is inherited uniparentally. Because the behavior of this DNA parallels the behavior of the uniparentally transmitted genes, it appears that these genes are located in the cpDNA.

Mapping Chloroplast Genes in Chlamydomonas

We have seen (Table 20-2) that *Chlamydomonas* has a large number of uniparentally inherited genes. Is there linkage among these genes? Are they all in one linkage group (chromosome), or are they arranged in several linkage groups? Or does each gene assort independently as though on its own separate piece of DNA? Of course, the way to approach this question in the true tradition of classical genetics is to perform a recombination analysis. But here we run into a problem. Both sets of parental DNA must be present if there is to be an opportunity for recombination, and we have seen that the mt^- parent's cpDNA is eliminated in the zygote cell. Luckily, there is a way out of this dilemma.

In crosses of $mt^+ sm\text{-}r \times mt^- sm\text{-}s$, about 0.1 percent of the progeny zygotes were found to contain both $sm\text{-}r$ and $sm\text{-}s$. The presence of both alleles was inferred from the fact that the products of meiosis of such cells show both sm-r and sm-s phenotypes among their number. Segregation of the two alleles presumably arises from a CSAR process in the zygote or at a later stage of division. Such zygotes are called **biparental zygotes,** for obvious reasons, and their genetic condition is described as a **cytohet** (standing for "*cyto*plasmically *het*erozygous"). It appears as though the inactivation of the mt^- parent's cpDNA fails in these rare zygotes. However, whether this is what happens or not, the cytohets provide just the opportunity we need to study recombination: they are cells containing *both* sets of parental cpDNA. The rarity of cytohet zygotes does pose a problem for research, but their frequency can be increased by treatment of the mt^+ parent with ultraviolet light before mating. After such treatment, from 40 to 100 percent of the progeny zygotes are cytohets. (Note in passing that this observation implies a normal role of the mt^+ cell in actively eliminating the mt^- cell's cpDNA. The ultraviolet irradiation of the mt^+ cell must inactivate such a function.)

Message   In *Chlamydomonas,* biparental zygotes (or cytohets) must be the starting point for all studies on the segregation and recombination of chloroplast genes.

A good map of the cpDNA has been obtained using the cytohets. One of the most profitable ways of studying linkage relations was through the cosegregation patterns of two separate extrachromosomal genes in the same cross. For example, in a cross of the type $mt^+ sm\text{-}sac^+ \times mt^- sm\text{-}rac^-$, biparental zygotes are first obtained. Cytoplasmic segregation can be detected in the two daughter cells arising from each product of meiosis, or in the daughter cells arising from the subsequent few mitotic divisions. It is reasonable to assume that if the two genes are closely linked, then when one gene undergoes cytoplasmic segregation, the other probably will too. More distantly linked genes would show proportionately lower frequencies of cosegregation.

Sager was able to quantify these procedures by using standard cell populations. She showed that a consistent additive-linkage map of the genes in the "uniparental genome" could be obtained. However, the map had one major inconsistency—which could be resolved only by assigning the shape of a circle to the cpDNA molecule! The map resulting from this and other mapping techniques is shown in Figure 20-11. Circular cpDNA has now been demonstrated in several plant species. It is worth recalling the history of classical genetic analysis. The genetic maps for nuclear chromosomes were derived also before their physical counterparts were demonstrated to exist. A great deal more detail is now available on the cpDNA maps in

several organisms; we shall take another look at such maps after we have considered the extranuclear genome of yeast.

Mitochondrial Genes in Yeast

Possibly the greatest success story in the clarification of extranuclear inheritance has been the development of the current view of the mitochondrial genome in bakers' yeast (*Saccharomyces cerevisiae*). This achievement provides a classic example of the power of genetic analysis in combination with modern molecular techniques. Let us start with the contributions of genetic analysis.

Three kinds of mutants have been of particular importance: the petite, ant^R, and mit^- mutants. In the 1940s, Boris Ephrussi and his colleagues first described some curious mutants in yeast. The wild-type cells of yeast form relatively large colonies on the surface of solidified culture medium. Among these large, or "grande," colonies was found an occasional small, or "petite," colony. When isolated, the **petite mutants** proved to be of three types on the basis of their inheritance patterns. The first type was called **segregational petites** because on crossing to a grande strain, half the ascospores gave rise to grande colonies, and the other half gave rise to petite colonies. This 1 : 1 Mendelian segregation obviously indicates that the petite phenotype is due to a nuclear mutation in these cases. The second type was the **neutral petites,** which in crosses to a grande strain gave ascospores that all grew into grande colonies—a clear case of uniparental inheritance. The third type of petite mutants was the **suppressive petites,** which gave some ascospores that grew into grande colonies and some that grew into petite colonies. The ratio of grandes to petites was variable but strain-specific: some suppressive pe-

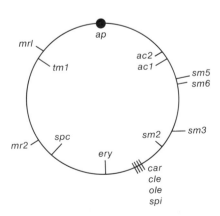

Figure 20-11. Circular map of *Chlamydomonas* cpDNA derived from genetic analysis. The map must be circular to accommodate all the linkage data.

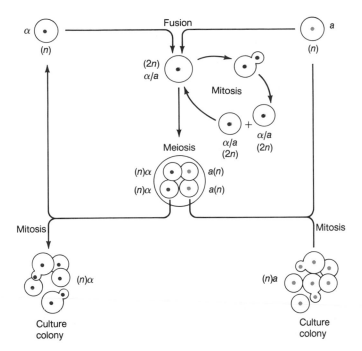

Figure 20-12. The life cycle of bakers' yeast *(Saccharomyces cerevisiae)*. The alleles *a* and α determine mating type and are nuclear alleles. Cell fusion between haploid *a* and α cells produces a diploid cell. Normally, the cell then goes through a diploid mitotic cycle (budding). However, the cell can be induced (by plating on a special medium) to undergo meiosis (sporulation), producing haploid products. Note that budding involves formation of a small growth on the side of the parent cell; this bud eventually enlarges and separates to become one of the daughter cells.

tites gave exclusively petite offspring in such crosses. The suppressive petites obviously show non-Mendelian inheritance, with some also showing uniparental inheritance.

In a yeast cross, the two parental cells fuse and apparently contribute equally to the cytoplasm of the resulting diploid cell (Figure 20-12). Furthermore, the inheritance of the neutral and suppressive petites is independent of mating type. In this sense, then, yeast is clearly quite different from *Neurospora*, and from *Chlamydomonas*. Nevertheless, since their inheritance is obviously extranuclear, the neutral and suppressive types became known as the **cytoplasmic petites.**

Several properties of the cytoplasmic petites pointed to the involvement of mitochondria in their phenotype.

1. In cytoplasmic petites, the mitochondrial electron-transport chain is defective. Since this chain is responsible for ATP synthesis, petites must rely on the less efficient process of fermentation to provide their ATP, and if placed in a medium containing a nonfermentable energy source such as glycerol, they will not grow.

2. These petites show no mitochondrial protein synthesis. Mitochondria normally possess their own unique protein-synthesizing apparatus, consisting of a unique set of tRNA molecules, and unique ribosomes, all quite different from those operating outside the mitochon-

drion in the nonorganellar phase of the cytoplasm, the **cytosol.**

3. Petites have massively altered **mitochondrial DNA (mtDNA).** Mitochondria in all organisms have their own unique mtDNA that, although smaller in amount, is quite different from nuclear DNA. Neutral petites were found to be totally lacking mtDNA, whereas suppressive petites showed altered base ratios compared with the grandes from which they sprang.

The second major class of yeast mutants, the **ant^R mutants,** were initially recognized at the phenotypic level by their resistance to antibiotics supplied in the medium. For example, strains were obtained that were resistant to chloramphenicol (cap^R), to erythromycin (ery^R), to spiromycin (spi^R), to paramomycin (par^R), or to oligomycin (oli^R). These mutations each showed non-Mendelian inheritance, similar to that in the suppressive petites. That is, in a cross such as ery^R × ery^S, a strain-specific non-Mendelian ratio was seen among the random ascospore progeny. However, examination of specific meioses by tetrad analysis revealed several now-familiar phenomena. Let us trace the cross through its sequential stages, as shown in Figure 20-13. When the parental cells fuse, the fusion product, as

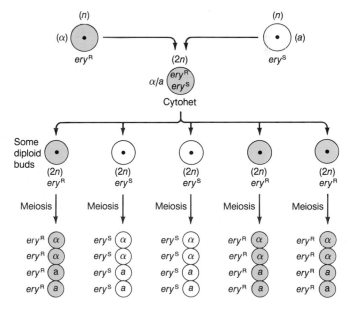

Figure 20-13. The special inheritance pattern shown by certain drug-resistant phenotypes in yeast. When diploid buds are induced to sporulate (undergo meiosis), the products of each meiosis show uniparental inheritance. (Only a representative sample of the diploid buds is shown here.) Note that the nuclear genes, represented here by the mating-type alleles *a* and α, segregate in a strictly Mendelian pattern. The alleles ery^R and ery^S determine erythromycin resistance and sensitivity, respectively.

well as being diploid, is a cytohet. The diploid cells can then be allowed to bud mitotically. During this mitotic division, the CSAR process occurs, and the daughter cells become either ery^R or ery^S. Therefore, when meiosis is induced by shifting the cells onto a special medium, all the haploid products of any single meiosis are identical with respect to erythromycin sensitivity or resistance. At the level of single meioses, then, we see uniparental inheritance at work. Note that the nuclear mating-type alleles a and α always segregate in a 1 : 1 ratio. Similar results were shown by all the ant^R mutations, pointing once again to their location in an "extrachromosomal genome."

The third important class of mutants was the **mit⁻ mutants.** These were last to be discovered and required the development of special selective techniques. These mutants are similar to petite mutants in having small colony size and abnormal electron-transport-chain functions, but they differ in having normal protein synthesis and in being able to revert. In a way, mit^- mutants are like point-mutation petites. The inheritance of mit^- mutants is comparable to the patterns shown by ant^R types—that is, they show cytoplasmic segregation and also uniparental inheritance at meiosis.

Mapping the Mitochondrial Genome in Yeast

The demonstration of genetic determinants constituting an extranuclear genome immediately raises the question of the physical interrelationship of these determinants. Are they all linked together on one mitochondrial "chromosome," or are they on separate structural units? Mapping the yeast mitochondrial genome has proceeded using many different approaches. A few representative analytical methods follow.

Recombination Mapping. We can set out to look for recombinants by using a cross between parents differing in two extranuclear gene pairs (a kind of "dihybrid cross"). For example, we can carry out the cross $ery^R spi^R \times ery^S spi^S$, allow the resulting diploid cell to bud through several cell generations, and then induce the resulting cells to sporulate. We can then identify the genotype of each bud cell by observing the phenotype common to all its ascospores.

Four genotypes could result from such a cross (Figure 20-14), and all were in fact observed. An early cross yielded the following results:

$ery^R spi^R$	63 tetrads
$ery^S spi^S$	48 tetrads
$ery^S spi^R$	7 tetrads
$ery^R spi^S$	1 tetrad

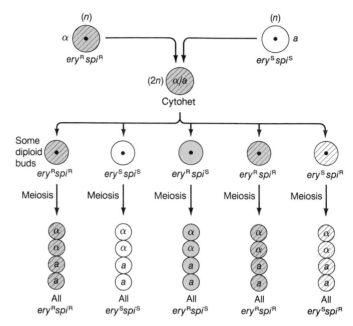

Figure 20-14. The study of inheritance in a cross between yeast cells differing with respect to two different drug-resistance alleles (ery^R = erythromycin resistance; spi^R = spiramycin resistance). Each diploid bud can be classified as parental or recombinant on the basis of these results. Note that the identity of the extranuclear genotype for all four products of meiosis confirms that the CSAR process must occur during the production of the diploid buds.

The genotypes $ery^S spi^R$ and $ery^R spi^S$, of course, represent recombinants that have been produced in the CSAR process during formation of diploid buds. (Note that these recombinants cannot have been produced by meiosis because the products of any given meiosis are identical with respect to the drug-resistance phenotypes.)

Message In yeast, extranuclear segregation and recombination (CSAR) are achieved during bud formation in diploid cytohets. The segregation and/or recombination may be detected directly in cultures of the diploid buds or may be detected by observing the products of meiosis that result when the buds are induced to sporulate.

We now seem to be just a short step away from the development of a complete map of all the drug-resistance genes in yeast. Unfortunately, the technique of recombination mapping proved to be of only limited usefulness. For one thing, recombination involving mitochondria proved to be a population phenomenon, rather like phage recombination. That is to say, there were so many rounds of recombination occurring that most genes appeared to be unlinked. Linkage was detectable only for genes that were very close together. Furthermore, the process of recombination was shown to be strongly influenced by a specific genetic factor, ω (omega), that was present in some mitochondrial genomes and not in others. The most useful mapping developments were to come from less conventional analyses, examples of which are described in the following subsections.

Mapping by Petite Analysis. The petite mutations, the drug-resistance (ant^R) mutations, and the mit^- mutations are apparently inherited on the mitochondrial genome of yeast. Some very effective techniques for mapping that genome have been developed through the combined study of these classes of mutants. Most of these approaches are based on the fact that petites represent deletions of the mtDNA. This fact opens up a new and different kind of genetic analysis that has been combined with new techniques of DNA manipulation to produce a rather complete genetic map of the mtDNA.

The pivotal observation came in studies where drug-resistant grande strains (such as ery^R) were used as the starting material for induction of petite mutants. We have seen that petite mutants form spontaneously, but they can also be induced at high frequencies by use of various specific mutagens, notably ethidium bromide. When petite cultures were obtained from grande ery^R strains, it was of interest to determine their drug resistance. Are they still ery^R, or has the petite mutation caused them to become ery^S? Unfortunately, the answer cannot be determined directly because drug resistance cannot be tested in petite cells!

However, genetic trickery comes to the rescue. The induced petites are combined with grande ery^S cells (which, of course, lack resistance to erythromycin) to form diploids, and the diploids are allowed to form diploid buds. Depending on the type of petite used, varying amounts of petite and grande diploid buds are formed. It is the grande diploid buds that are of interest here because they *can* be tested for drug resistance. If the original petites retain the drug resistance, then some of these diploid grande cells might be expected to have acquired that resistance through recombination during the CSAR process. In fact, for some petites, the derived grande diploid buds did prove to be of two phenotypes: ery^S (derived from the grande ery^S haploid) and ery^R (which must have been derived from the petite haploid). This result indicates that only the genetic determinants for the grande phenotype are lost in the original mutation event that generates these particular petite mutants; the genetic determinants for the drug resistance were not affected by the petite mutation.

Of particular interest, however, were those petites whose derived grande diploids were all ery^S. In this case, the original mutation event apparently inactivated or destroyed both the determinant for the grande phenotype *and* the determinant for drug resistance (Figure 20-15). The coincidental loss of several genetic determinants is

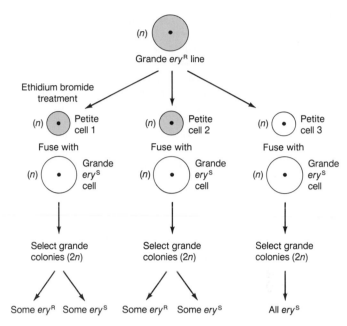

Figure 20-15. The retention or loss of drug resistance (ery^R) when petite mutants are induced from a drug-resistant grande culture. The petite cannot be tested directly for drug resistance, so any remaining drug resistance must be "rescued" through the mating of petite cells with drug-sensitive grande cells. Diploid buds can then be tested for drug resistance. In the examples shown here, the drug resistance was apparently retained in petite cells 1 and 2, but the drug resistance was apparently lost, together with the determinant for the grande phenotype, during the induction of the petite mutation in petite cell 3.

characteristic of deletion mutations in general genetic analysis. In fact, it is now known that the petite phenotype is produced by large deletions of the mtDNA.

The discovery of marker loss in petites is interesting for two main reasons. First, because the petite mutation alters the mtDNA and causes loss of a particular marker gene, the location of that marker can be assigned to the mtDNA beyond any reasonable doubt. This procedure can be used as a routine test to detect a mitochondrial mutation.

Message   Marker loss during petite induction is a good operational test for a gene located in mtDNA.

Second, the phenomenon of marker loss in petites gave rise to several mapping techniques, as follows. With one technique, it is possible to obtain a grande cell line that is resistant to several drugs; such a line might have the genotype $ery^R cap^R oli^R spi^R$. Petites can be induced in this line and then tested to see which of the resistance markers are retained in the petite lines. (Of course, this test must be performed by "rescuing" the markers in a cross with a drug-sensitive grande cell, as we have seen.) It then becomes a relatively simple matter to compare the frequencies with which various pairs of resistance genes are either retained or lost together, thus obtaining a good idea of which genes are closely linked. This idea can be extended in another mapping technique, which combines genetic analysis with physical techniques. Two different petite strains are derived from a grande line that shows multiple drug resistance. For example, suppose that strain A has retained cap^R, ery^R, and par^R, whereas strain B has retained cap^R, ery^R, oli^R, and ana^R. DNA is extracted from each strain and denatured. This DNA then is hybridized to a standard sample of grande DNA, both in individual experiments for DNA from each strain and with a mixture of DNA from A and B. Suppose that the amounts hybridized are a units in the case of A alone, b units in the case of B alone, and t units for the mixture of A and B.

Anthony Linnane has recently used these values to measure the degree of overlap (h) of the petite deletions. From Figure 20-16, we see that, if the retained (nondeleted) DNA in the two petites has a region in common, then the amount of DNA hybridized from the mixture will be less than the sum of the amounts bound when the petite DNAs are hybridized individually. In fact, study of the diagram should convince you that this difference equals the amount of overlap, so that $h = a + b - t$. Because cap^R and ery^R are the only two alleles retained in both of these petites, we know that these genes must be located in the overlap region. Therefore, the value h is proportional to the maxi-

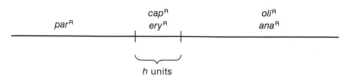

Figure 20-17. Genetic markers retained by specific petites can be correlated with regions of petite homology. Since petite induction causes the deletion of a part of the mitochondrial DNA, different petites will retain different genes. In the example, one petite retains cap^R, ery^R, and par^R, and another retains cap^R, ery^R, oli^R, and ana^R. The cap and ery loci must be within the overlap region of size h, as determined by DNA hybridization techniques. The loci par, oli, and ana must lie somewhere outside this region, and their relative positions can be assigned through study of other pairs of petites. In this manner, a map of genetic markers can be built up.

mum possible distance between cap and ery. Thus, we can insert genetic markers into map segments of defined size, and we have begun a comprehensive mapping process (Figure 20-17). This kind of mapping has been extended to many petites, and a "library" of petites with well-defined retained regions has been established. These results have been combined with the results of the marker-retention analysis to produce a complete genetic map of the mtDNA. Like the physically observed mtDNA, this map is a circle.

We have stated that the petite mtDNA is a small retained piece from the grande mtDNA. However, we must reconcile this view with the fact that a typical petite cell contains more or less the same amount of mtDNA as does a typical grande cell, and petite mtDNA circles can be the same as grande mtDNA circles. The answer to this puzzle is that the retained piece in the petite is present in as many tandem copies as it requires to make up an mtDNA of about the same length as the grande mtDNA (Figure 20-18). This model does not require any change in the interpretation of the petite-overlap experiments.

Once a defined set of petite deletions has been worked out, they can be very useful in subsequent mapping. For example, many mit^- mutants were mapped by fusing mit^- with several specific petites. If the mit^- mutation is in the region of mtDNA retained by the petite, then recombination can substitute petite DNA in place of the mit^- DNA, and the recombinant cell will be able to grow on a nonfermentable energy source.

Message   Marker loss or retention during petite induction and overlap of petite deletions are novel genetic techniques used in mapping mitochondrial genomes.

Mapping by Restriction-Enzyme Analysis.   As we saw in Chapter 14, the availability of restriction enzymes has provided a powerful new tool for the genetic analyst. This tool

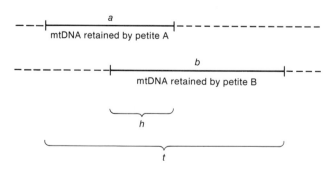

Figure 20-16. Measuring the extent of overlap between any two petite mtDNAs by hybridizing to a sample of grande mtDNA. In the case of petite A, a units of petite mtDNA hybridize to the grande mtDNA; in the case of petite B, b units hybridize. We assume that there is some overlap (homology) between the mtDNAs retained by the two petites. In that case, the total amount (t units) of a mixture of the petite mtDNAs that hybridizes to the grande mtDNA must be less than the sum of the individual totals by an amount h, and $h = a + b - t$. This value h is proportional to the amount of overlap. When many pairs of different petites are studied in this way, the relative sizes and positions of these different mtDNAs can be fitted together with information about the genes retained in common by each pair to produce a map of the mitochondrial genome.

has been particularly useful in the analysis of mtDNA, not only in yeast (which is discussed here) but also in the analysis of any mtDNA or cpDNA that can be extracted in pure form from any organism.

A restriction enzyme attacks DNA and cuts it at a specific base sequence. These specific target sequences of the enzymes may, in a sense, be considered as genetic markers. The positions of these target sequences may be mapped (Figure 20-19). Although this map is not particularly interesting in itself, it is an essential tool for the precise pinpointing of other genetic markers (such as drug-resistance genes) on the mtDNA.

One obvious way of using restriction analysis to map genes on mtDNA is in the case of the various unique mitochondrial RNAs, tRNAs, and rRNAs. A radioactively labeled RNA can be used as a probe in a Southern hybridization (see page 312) to a restriction-enzyme digest. The band that "lights up" on autoradiography represents the approximate location of the RNA. Further similar experiments using different restriction enzymes will narrow the region of hybridization down to a precise locus on the mtDNA.

What about the *ant*[R] and *mit*[-] genes? One approach is to correlate the retained restriction fragments in a number of different petites with (say) the antibiotic-resistance markers also retained in those strains. In this way, specific markers may be associated with specific regions of the mtDNA, as defined by the restriction-enzyme target sites. Another approach is to take a petite that retains only a single drug-resistance gene—say, *ery*[R]. The mtDNA is extracted from the petite and put into an *E. coli* transcription

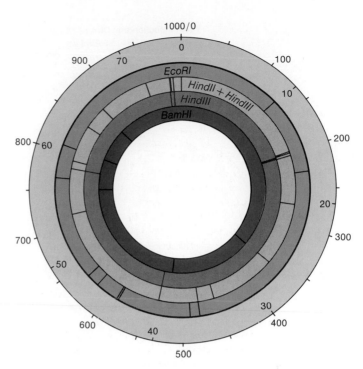

Figure 20-19. Map showing the target sites of various restriction enzymes on the yeast mtDNA. An arbitrary scale from 0 to 1000 is indicated on the outside of the outer circle; a scale in terms of thousands of DNA base pairs is indicated on the inside of the outer circle. The inner four bands show the fragments produced by treatment with particular restriction enzymes: *EcoRI, HindII + HindIII, HindIII,* and *BamHI.* The position for the zero point of this map is arbitrary. (After J. P. M. Sanders et al., "The Organization of Genes in Yeast Mitochondrial DNA, III." *Molec. Gen. Genet.* 157, 1977.)

system in vitro that makes RNA from DNA templates. The resulting RNA is complementary to the DNA being studied, so it is called complementary RNA (cRNA). This cRNA can be labeled through the use of radioactive uracil and then used as a probe. Its hybridization with the various restriction fragments can be tested, thus locating the portion of the mtDNA that is retained by this particular petite, and hence the locus of the *ery* gene. For example, if the cRNA from the *ery*[R] petite hybridizes with fragment X from one restriction enzyme and with fragment Y from another enzyme, then the *ery* locus must be located within the overlap region of these two fragments.

An Overview of the Mitochondrial Genome

Many specific areas of the yeast map have been subjected to more detailed dissection, such as sequencing and intron analysis. The present state of the yeast mtDNA map, based on the types of techniques we have considered, is shown in Figure 20-20, together with the human mtDNA map for comparison. The various genes in yeast discussed in this chapter are shown together with their protein products. We see that *cap*[R], *ery*[R], and *spi*[R] are in fact alterations of the

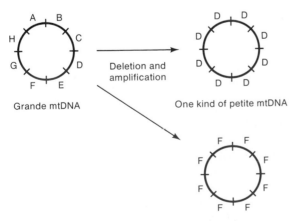

Figure 20-18. When a petite is produced from a grande cell, a large region of mtDNA may be deleted. Apparently, the DNA region retained by the petite (D or F in these examples) is amplified through tandem duplication to provide a chromosome of approximately the normal length.

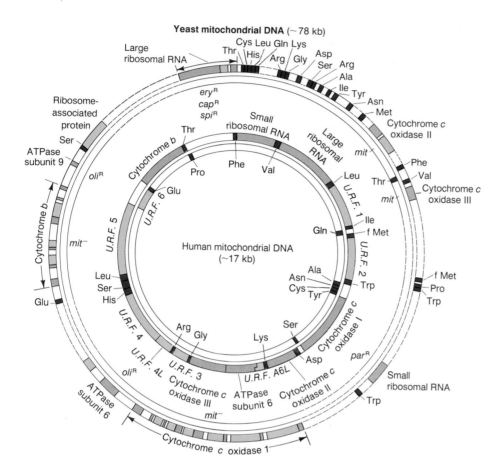

Figure 20-20. Maps of yeast and human mtDNAs. Each map is shown as two concentric circles corresponding to the two strands of the DNA helix. The human map has been produced exclusively by physical techniques. The yeast map has been produced by a combination of genetic and physical techniques as discussed in the text. Note that the mutants used in the yeast genetic analysis are shown opposite their corresponding structural genes. Gray =exons and uninterrupted genes, red =tRNA genes, and pink = U.R.F. (unassigned reading frame); tRNA genes are shown by their amino acid abbreviations. (NOTE: the human map is not drawn to the same scale as the yeast map.)

large mitochondrial rRNA genes, and that *par*[R] is associated with changes in the small rRNA gene. Other *ant*[R] mutations such as *oli*[R] are associated with alterations in various subunits of the enzyme ATPase. On the other hand, *mit*⁻ mutations are in fact lesions in either of several subunits of cytochrome oxidase (I through III), or in the cytochrome-*b* gene. In addition, several other genes are indicated, such as those for the mitochondrial tRNAs and a gene for a ribosome-associated protein.

The map contains some surprises too. Most prominent is the occurrence of introns in several genes. Subunit I of cytochrome oxidase contains nine introns! The discovery of introns in the mitochondrial genes is particularly surprising because in yeast nuclear genes, they are relatively rare. Another surprise is the occurrence of long **unassigned reading frames (URFs)**. These are sequences that have correct initiation codons and are uninterrupted by stop codons. These "genes in search of a function" are the subject of intense current research. Some URFs occurring within introns appear to be involved in specifying proteins important in the splicing out of the introns themselves at the RNA level. Notice that the human mtDNA is by comparison much smaller and more compact. There seems to be much less spacer DNA between the genes and URFs.

The overall view of the mitochondrial genome shows it to have two main functions: it codes for some proteins actually in or associated with the electron transport chain, and it

codes for some proteins, all the tRNAs, and both rRNAs necessary for mitochondrial protein synthesis. But in both of these processes, it is striking that the remaining necessary components are encoded by nuclear genes whose mRNA is translated on cytosolic ribosomes, and that their products are transported to the mitochondrion (see Figure 20-21). Why there should be this peculiar division of labor between nuclear and mitochondrial DNA is not known. Another curiosity is that some specific subunits are encoded by mtDNA in one organism but by nuclear DNA in another. Evidently there has been transposition of information between these organelles. There is also evidence of transposition between mitochondria and chloroplasts. Furthermore, inactive "pseudogenes" are detectable in the nucleus, showing homology with mitochondrial genes.

Altogether, 25 yeast and 22 human mitochondrial tRNAs are shown on the maps in Figure 20-20. These carry out all the translation that occurs in mitochondria. This is far less than the minimum of 32 required to translate nucleus-derived mRNA. The economy is achieved by a "more wobbly" wobble pairing (see page 251) of tRNA anticodons. The tRNA specificities in human mtDNA are shown in Figure 20-22. Notice that the codon assignments are in some cases different from the nuclear code. It is also known that there is variation between the mitochondria of different species. Hence, the genetic code is obviously not universal, as had been supposed for many years.

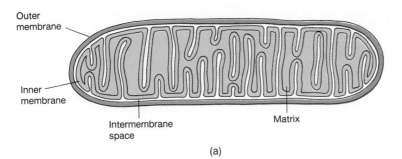

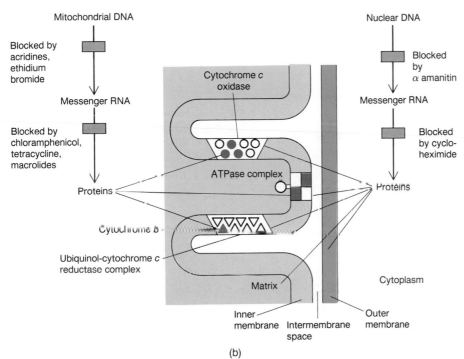

Figure 20-21. Cooperation of yeast mtDNA and nuclear DNA in coding for protein components of the inner mitochondrial membrane. (a) Overview of mitochondrial structure. (b) Details of membrane constitution. Three functional units are involved in the cooperation. The mtDNA supplies six proteins, three subunits of cytochrome-*c* oxidase, two subunits of ATPase, and cytochrome *b*.

First letter	Second letter				Third letter
	U	C	A	G	
U	Phe	Ser	Tyr	Cys	U
	Phe	Ser	Tyr	Cys	C
	Leu	Ser	*Stop*	*(Stop)* Trp	A
	Leu	Ser	*Stop*	Trp	G
C	Leu	Pro	His	Arg	U
	Leu	Pro	His	Arg	C
	Leu	Pro	Gln	Arg	A
	Leu	Pro	Gln	Arg	G
A	Ile (Met)	Thr	Asn	Ser	U
	Ile	Thr	Asn	Ser	C
	(Ile) Met	Thr	Lys	(Arg) *Stop*	A
	Met	Thr	Lys	(Arg) *Stop*	G
G	Val	Ala	Asp	Gly	U
	Val	Ala	Asp	Gly	C
	Val	Ala	Glu	Gly	A
	Val	Ala	Glu	Gly	G

Figure 20-22. The genetic code of the human mitochondrion. The functions of the 22 tRNA types are shown by the 22 non-*stop* codon boxes.

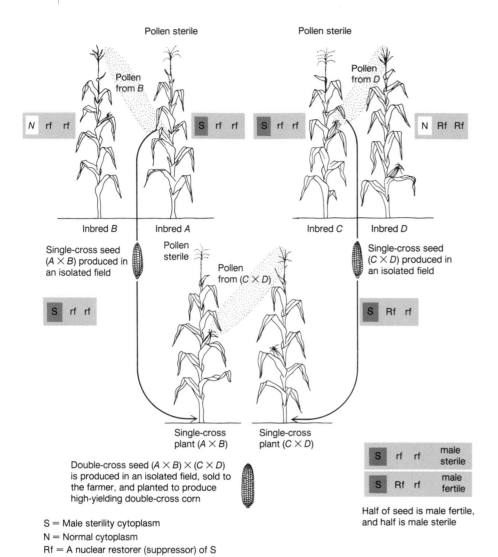

Pollen sterile   Pollen sterile

Pollen from *B*

Pollen from *D*

| N | rf | rf |

| S | rf | rf | | S | rf | rf |

| N | Rf | Rf |

Inbred *B*   Inbred *A*   Inbred *C*   Inbred *D*

Single-cross seed (*A* × *B*) produced in an isolated field

Pollen sterile

Pollen from (*C* × *D*)

Single-cross seed (*C* × *D*) produced in an isolated field

| S | rf | rf | | S | Rf | rf |

Single-cross plant (*A* × *B*)   Single-cross plant (*C* × *D*)

Double-cross seed (*A* × *B*) × (*C* × *D*) is produced in an isolated field, sold to the farmer, and planted to produce high-yielding double-cross corn

| S | rf | rf | male sterile |
| S | Rf | rf | male fertile |

Half of seed is male fertile, and half is male sterile

S = Male sterility cytoplasm
N = Normal cytoplasm
Rf = A nuclear restorer (suppressor) of S

Figure 20-23. The use of cytoplasmic male sterility to facilitate the production of hybrid corn. In this scheme, the hybrid corn is generated from four pure parental lines, *A*, *B*, *C*, and *D*. Such hybrids are called double-cross hybrids. At each step, selfing is prevented by appropriate combinations of cytoplasmic genes and nuclear restorer genes to ensure that the female parents will be pollen sterile (male sterile). (From J. Janick et al., *Plant Science*. Copyright © 1974 by W. H. Freeman and Co.)

Message Mitochondrial DNA has genes for mitochondrial translation components (mainly rRNAs and tRNAs) and for some subunits of the proteins associated with mitochondrial ATP production. Less understood regions include the introns, unassigned reading frames, and spacer DNA.

How Many Copies?

For the genetic and the biochemical approaches to the study of organelle genomes that we have examined, it does not matter much how many copies of organelle genome are present per cell. (Even in the case of the nuclear genome, the number of genomes present per chromosome was in doubt until very recently, and many uncertainties still exist in that area.) However, it is interesting to ask how many copies of the organelle genome do exist, and an answer can be given.

The number of copies turns out to vary among species.

More surprisingly, it also can vary within a single species. The leaf cells of the garden beet have about 40 chloroplasts per cell. The chloroplasts themselves contain specific areas that stain heavily with DNA stains; these areas are called **nucleoids,** and they are a feature commonly found in many organelles. Each beet chloroplast contains from four to 18 nucleoids, and each nucleoid can contain from four to eight cpDNA molecules. Thus, cells of a single beet leaf can contain as many as $40 \times 18 \times 8 = 5760$ copies of the chloroplast genome! Although *Chlamydomonas* has only one chloroplast per cell, the chloroplast contains from 500 to 1500 cpDNA molecules, commonly observed to be packed in nucleoids.

A "typical" haploid yeast cell can contain from one to 45 mitochondria, each having 10 to 30 nucleoids, with 4 or 5 molecules in each nucleoid.

How does this genome duplication relate to the CSAR process? How many genomes are present at the beginning of CSAR? Do all copies of the genome actually become involved in the CSAR process? Does CSAR occur when organelles fuse, and must the nucleoids fuse also? It seems that the number of organelles in a cell generally is too large to permit cytoplasmic segregation by random assortment of organelles. How can the CSAR process segregate the many copies of the genome scattered through the cell? Few answers to such questions are available at present. The situation is rather like that of early geneticists who knew about genes and linkage groups but knew nothing about their relation to the process of meiosis. As we have seen, such problems pose few limitations to progress in genetic research—they are problems for the cell biologist.

Other Examples of Extranuclear Inheritance

This discussion has concentrated on a few extranuclear systems that are relatively well understood. However, quite a few other examples of extranuclear inheritance have been encountered in the history of genetic analysis. They are detected experimentally as differences between reciprocal crosses, and many diverse phenotypes are affected.

One such phenotype of great importance in agriculture is that of male sterility in plants. Sterile male plants produce no functional pollen, but the trait of male sterility itself is inherited (rather obtusely) only via the female parent. This situation has been put to profitable use in the production of hybrid corn and other seeds. The hybrid corn seeds that we can buy from a seed supplier are produced from crosses between two specific parental strains. These parents, however, must be prevented from selfing (which would not produce hybrid kernels). The selfing is conveniently prevented by incorporating cytoplasmic male sterility into one parent (Figure 20-23). Surprisingly, examples of cytoplasmic male sterility have been found in natural populations.

Another interesting cytoplasmically inherited phenotype is the phenomenon of senescence in certain fungi. The best-studied example is in the filamentous fungus *Podospora anserina*. All wild-types of this species senesce and die, in contrast to other species that are immortal and show continuous vegetative propagation. In *Podospora*, each natural "race" has a specific life span measurable by the specific distance it will grow down a long growth tube before the hyphal front stops growing and death of the apical cells occurs. When a senescent culture is crossed as female to a "juvenile" male, some senescent and some juvenile offspring are produced, whereas in the reciprocal cross, all progeny are juvenile. Furthermore, when senescent cells are fused with juvenile cells in a kind of heterokaryon test, it can be shown that the juvenile cells quickly become senescent in the absence of nuclear exchange from the senescent cell. It has been demonstrated that senescence in this fungus is associated with degenerative changes in the mtDNA. Any one of five regions of the mtDNA, called senDNAs α through θ, become amplified to form circular multimers of the senDNA region, as shown in Figure 20-24. This process continues until, at death, only senDNA is found in the mitochondria. Another peculiar finding is that during senescence, senDNA turns up inserted into the DNA of the nucleus! Still another is that α senDNA corresponds exactly to an intron of the gene for subunit I of cytochrome oxidase! The causative trigger of senescence is still not clear, but presumably it involves some inherent instability of the mtDNA.

Let us now return to cpDNA at the molecular level. The cpDNA is more complex than mtDNA, in size, in the genes encoded, and in the structural organization. Figure 20-25 shows the map for spinach cpDNA. Some of the mapped features are tRNA genes, a large inverted repeat

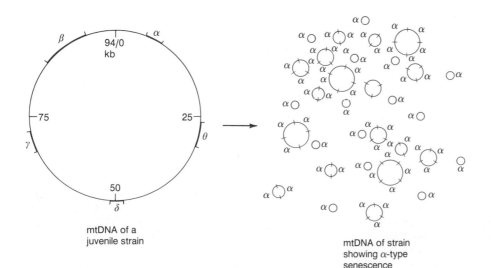

Figure 20-24. Degeneration of mtDNA during senescence in the fungus *Podospora*. Any of five specific regions of the juvenile mtDNA—α, β, γ, δ, or θ—becomes amplified into plasmid-like multimers at the expense of the rest of the mtDNA. An α senescent event is illustrated.

mtDNA of a juvenile strain

mtDNA of strain showing α-type senescence

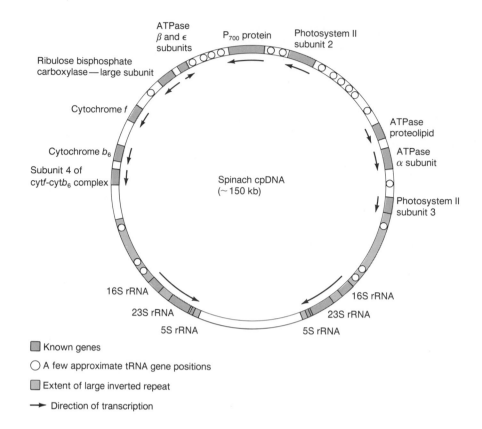

Figure 20-25. Map of spinach cpDNA. Most of the genes shown code for components involved in photosynthesis or chloroplast protein synthesis. Note the large inverted repeat spanning the rRNA operon; this is a feature of cpDNA from several different species.

involving rRNA genes, and several proteins of the thyla-koid membrane of the chloroplast. It has been shown recently that these large cpDNA molecules can be unstable, resulting in smaller circles by intramolecular recombination.

The organelle genes have been fully investigated in only a few organisms, but these studies have produced general analytical techniques that should have widespread application in the study of extranuclear genomes in many other organisms.

Summary

■ The extranuclear genome supplements the nuclear genome of eukaryotic organisms discussed in earlier chapters. The existence of the extranuclear genome is recognized at the genetic level chiefly by uniparental transmission of the relevant mutant phenotypes. At the cellular level, a combination of genetic and biochemical techniques has demonstrated that the extracellular genome is organelle DNA—either mitochondrial (mtDNA) or chloroplast (cpDNA).

The mtDNA of yeast is the best-understood organelle DNA. This DNA codes for unique mitochondrial translational components, and it also codes for some components of the respiratory enzymes normally found in the mitochondrial membranes. Mutations in the translational-component genes typically produce drug-resistant phenotypes; mutations in the respiratory-enzyme genes typically produce phenotypes involving respiratory insufficiency.

The chloroplast DNA is larger (about 2.5 times greater in diameter) and more complex than the yeast mtDNA. Mutations in cpDNA typically produce photosynthetic defects or drug resistance.

Problems

1. In the genus *Antirrhinum*, a yellowish leaf phenotype called prazinizans (pr) is inherited as follows:

   normal × pr ⟶ 41,203 normal + 13 variegated

   pr × normal ⟶ 42,235 pr + 8 variegated

   Explain these results with a hypothesis involving cytoplasmic inheritance. (Explain both the majority *and* the minority classes of progeny.)

2. You are studying a plant whose tissue includes green sectors and white sectors. You wish to decide whether this phenomenon is due to (1) a chloroplast mutation of the type discussed in this chapter or (2) a dominant nuclear mutation that inhibits chlorophyll production and is present only in certain tissue layers of the plant as a mosaic. Outline the experimental approach you would use to resolve this problem.

3. A dwarf variant of tomato appears in a research line. The dwarf is crossed as female to normal plants, and all the F_1 progeny are dwarf. These F_1 individuals are selfed, and the F_2 progeny are all normal. Each of the F_2 individuals is selfed, and the resulting F_3 generation is $3/4$ normal and $1/4$ dwarf. Can these results be explained by: a. cytoplasmic inheritance? b. cytoplasmic inheritance plus nuclear suppressor gene(s)? c. maternal effect on the zygotes? Explain your answers.

4. Assume that diploid plant A has a cytoplasm genetically different from that of plant B. To study nuclear-cytoplasmic relations, you wish to obtain a plant with the cytoplasm of plant A and the nuclear genome predominantly of plant B. How would you go about producing such a plant?

5. Two species of *Epilobium* (fireweed) are intercrossed reciprocally as follows:

$$♀ \textit{E. luteum} \times ♂ \textit{E. hirsutum} \longrightarrow \text{all very tall}$$

$$♀ \textit{E. hirsutum} \times ♂ \textit{E. luteum} \longrightarrow \text{all very short}$$

The progeny from the first cross were backcrossed as females to *E. hirsutum* for 24 successive generations. At the end of this crossing program, the progeny still were all tall, like the initial hybrids. a. Interpret the reciprocal crosses. b. Explain why the program of backcrosses was performed.

6. One form of male sterility in maize is maternally transmitted. Plants of a male-sterile line crossed with normal pollen give male-sterile plants. In addition, some lines of maize are known to carry a dominant nuclear restorer gene (*Rf*) that restores pollen fertility in male-sterile lines.

a. Research shows that introduction of restorer genes into male-sterile lines does not alter or affect the maintenance of the cytoplasmic factors for male sterility. What kind of research results would lead to such a conclusion?

b. A male-sterile plant is crossed with pollen from a plant homozygous for gene *Rf*. What is the genotype of the F_1? What is its phenotype?

c. The F_1 plants from part b are used as females in a testcross with pollen from a normal plant (*rfrf*). What would be the result of this testcross? Give genotypes and phenotypes, and designate the kind of cytoplasm.

d. The restorer gene already described can be called *Rf-1*. Another dominant restorer, *Rf-2,* has been found; it is located in a different chromosome from that of *Rf-1*. Either or both of the restorer alleles will give pollen fertility. Using a male-sterile plant as a tester, what would be the result of a cross where the male parent was (i) heterozygous at both restorer loci? (ii) homozygous dominant at one restorer locus and homozygous recessive at the other? (iii) heterozygous at one restorer locus and homozygous recessive at the other? (iv) heterozygous at one restorer locus and homozygous dominant at the other?

7. Treatment with streptomycin induces the formation of streptomycin-resistant mutant cells in *Chlamydomonas*. In the course of subsequent mitotic divisions, some of the daughter cells produced from some of these mutant cells show the normal phenotype. Suggest a possible explanation of this phenomenon.

8. Cosegregation mapping is performed in *Chlamydomonas* on four chloroplast markers, *m1*, *m2*, *m3*, and *m4*. The markers are considered pairwise in heterozygous condition, and cosegregation frequencies are obtained as follows:

	m1	*m2*	*m3*	*m4*
m1	———	29.0	18.0	18.4
m2		———	10.9	26.2
m3			———	8.8
m4				———

(For example, *m1* and *m2* cosegregate in 29 percent of the cell divisions followed.) Draw a rough genetic map based on these results.

9. In *Aspergillus*, a "red" mycelium arises in a haploid strain. You make a heterokaryon with a nonred haploid that requires *para*-aminobenzoic acid (PABA). From this heterokaryon, you obtain some PABA-requiring progeny cultures that are red, along with several other phenotypes. What does this information tell you about the gene determining the red phenotype?

10. On page 438, an experiment is described in which abnormal mitochondria are injected into normal *Neurospora*. The text mentions that "appropriate controls" are used. What controls would you use?

11. Adrian Srb crossed two closely related species, *Neurospora crassa* and *N. sitophila*. In the progeny of some of these crosses, there appeared a phenotype called aconidial (ac) that involves a lack of conidia (asexual spores). The observed inheritance was

$$♀ \textit{N. sitophila} \times ♂ \textit{N. crassa} \longrightarrow 1/2 \text{ ac, } 1/2 \text{ normal}$$

$$♀ \textit{N. crassa} \times ♂ \textit{N. sitophila} \longrightarrow \text{all normal}$$

a. What is the explanation of this result? Explain all components of your model with symbols.

b. From which parent(s) did the genetic determinants for the ac phenotype originate?

c. Why were neither of the parental types ac?

12. Several crosses involving poky or nonpoky strains A, B, C, D, and E were made in *Neurospora*. Explain the results of the following crosses, and assign genetic symbols for each of the strains involved. (NOTE: poky strain D behaves just like poky strain A in all crosses.)

Cross	Progeny
a. nonpoky B ♀ × poky A ♂	all nonpoky
b. nonpoky C ♀ × poky A ♂	all nonpoky
c. poky A ♀ × nonpoky B ♂	all poky
d. poky A ♀ × nonpoky C ♂	1/2 poky, all identical (e.g., D) 1/2 nonpoky, all identical (e.g., E)
e. nonpoky E ♀ × nonpoky C ♂	all nonpoky
f. nonpoky E ♀ × nonpoky B ♂	1/2 poky 1/2 nonpoky

13. In yeast, an antibiotic-resistant haploid strain ant^R arises spontaneously. It is combined with a normal ant^S strain of opposite mating type to form a diploid culture that is then allowed to go through meiosis. Three tetrads are isolated:

tetrad 1	tetrad 2	tetrad 3
$\alpha\ ant^R$	$\alpha\ ant^R$	$a\ ant^S$
$\alpha\ ant^R$	$a\ ant^R$	$a\ ant^S$
$a\ ant^R$	$a\ ant^R$	$\alpha\ ant^S$
$a\ ant^R$	$\alpha\ ant^R$	$\alpha\ ant^S$

a. Interpret these results.

b. Explain the origin of each ascus.

c. If an ant^R grande strain were used to generate petites, would you expect some of the petites to be ant^S? Explain.

14. In yeast, two haploid strains are obtained that are both defective in their cytochromes; the mutants are named $cyt1$ and $cyt2$. The following crosses are made:

$$cyt1^- \times cyt1^+$$
$$cyt2^- \times cyt2^+$$

One tetrad is isolated from each cross; they are the following:

$cyt1^-$	$cyt2^-$
$cyt1^-$	$cyt2^-$
$cyt1^+$	$cyt2^-$
$cyt1^+$	$cyt2^-$

a. Explain the difference in the natures of these two mutants.

b. What other ascus types might be expected from each cross?

c. How might the two genes involved in these mutants interact at the functional level?

15. In a marker-retention analysis in yeast, a multiply resistant strain $apt^R bar^R cob^R$ is used to induce 500 petites. Table 20-4 shows, for different pairs of markers, the number of petites in which only one marker of the pair was lost. (For example, 87 petites were $apt^S bar^R$, and 120 were $apt^R bar^S$.) Use these results to draw a rough map of these mitochondrial genes.

■ **TABLE 20-4.**

Gene pair	Petites in which first marker is lost	Petites in which second marker is lost
$apt\ bar$	87	120
$apt\ cob$	27	18
$bar\ cob$	48	69

16. A grande yeast culture of genotype $cap^R ery^R oli^R par^R$ is used to obtain petites by treatment with ethidium bromide. The petites are tested for (1) their drug resistance and (2) the ability of their mtDNA to hybridize with various specific mtRNA types. In all, 12 petites are tested, and Table 20-5 shows the results. Using this information, plot a map of the mtDNA showing the sequence of the 11 genetic loci involved in these phenotypes. Be sure to state your assumptions and draw a complete map.

17. The mtDNA is compared from two haploid strains of bakers' yeast. Strain 1 (mating type α) is from North America, and strain 2 (mating type a) is from Europe. A single restriction enzyme is used to fragment the DNAs, and the fragments are separated on an electrophoretic gel. The sample from strain 1 produces two bands, corresponding to one very large and one very small fragment. Strain 2 also produces two bands, but they are of more intermediate sizes. If a standard diploid budding analysis is performed, what results do you expect to observe in the resulting cells and in the tetrads derived from them? In other words, what kinds of restriction-fragment patterns do you expect?

18. In yeast, some strains are found to have in their cytoplasm circular DNA molecules that are 2 micrometers (μm) in circumference. In some strains, this 2-μm DNA has a single EcoRI restriction site; in other strains, there are two such sites. A strain with one site is mated to a strain with two sites. All of the resulting diploid buds are found to contain both kinds of 2-μm DNA.

a. Is the 2-μm DNA inherited in the same fashion as mtDNA?

■ **TABLE 20-5.**

Petite culture	Drug resistance (R) or sensitivity (S)				Ability (+ or −) of petite mtDNA to hybridize with mtRNAs						
	cap	ery	oli	par	rRNA$_{large}$	rRNA$_{small}$	tRNA$_1$	tRNA$_2$	tRNA$_3$	tRNA$_4$	tRNA$_5$
1	R	S	S	S	+	−	−	−	−	−	−
2	S	S	S	S	−	−	−	−	−	+	−
3	S	S	S	S	−	−	−	+	−	−	+
4	S	S	R	S	−	−	+	−	−	−	−
5	S	R	S	S	+	+	−	−	−	−	−
6	R	S	S	S	−	−	−	−	+	−	−
7	S	S	R	R	−	−	−	+	−	−	−
8	S	S	S	S	−	+	−	−	−	+	+
9	S	R	S	S	+	−	−	−	−	−	−
10	S	S	S	S	−	−	+	−	+	−	−
11	R	S	R	R	−	+	+	+	+	+	+
12	S	R	S	S	+	+	−	−	−	−	−

b. What do you think the 2-μm DNA is likely to represent functionally?

19. Circular mitochondrial DNA is cut with two restriction enzymes A and B, with the following results:

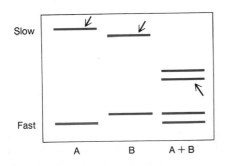

(The arrows indicate the bands that bound a radioactive mtrRNA-derived cDNA probe in a Southern blot. Draw a rough map of the positions of the restriction site(s) of A and B, and also show approximately where the mtrRNA gene is located.

20. You are interested in the mitochondrial genome of a fungal species for which genetic analysis is very difficult, but in which mtDNA can be extracted easily. How would you go about finding the positions of the major mitochondrially coded genes in this species? (Assume some evolutionary conservation for such genes.)

21. Rare senescent cultures of *Neurospora* have been found.

a. When these cultures are crossed as male with nonsenescent partners, no senescent progeny are obtained, but when they are crossed as female, some but not all progeny senesce, and some senescent progeny die sooner than others and either sooner or later than the parental strain. Explain these findings.

b. When mtDNA from senescent cultures is cut with EcoRI, the large normal fragment 1 is missing, and in its place are four new fragments B, C, E, and G, totaling 10 kb more than fragment 1. A map of the normal fragment 1 is as follows, where *Eco* represents *EcoRI* sites and *Hi* represents *HindIII* sites, and two segments cloned as probes are also shown.

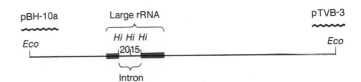

Probe pBH-10a binds to B but not C, and probe pTVB-3 binds to C but not B; neither probe binds to E or G. A *HindIII* digest shows absence of fragment 20 and the appearance of two new large fragments, K1 and K2. K1 hybridizes to C, E, and G, and K2 hybridizes to B and E. Fragment C also hybridizes to *HindIII* fragment 15. What can you deduce from these data?

CHAPTER 21

Developmental Genetics

■ The fine structure of a single cell or the anatomical complexity of a multicellular organism offers an incredible challenge to the geneticist interested in how genes affect phenotype. For just as hair or eye color is a reflection of genotype, the proper location, size, function, and fine structure of an organ within a whole organism are also determined by genes. In humans, a single egg combined with a single spermatozoon constitutes the sole cellular legacy passed from parent to child; the resulting single-celled zygote will increase to about 10^{14} cells in an adult. As that seemingly nondescript cell proliferates, an anteroposterior, ventral-dorsal distinction will arise. From the original egg alone will be derived the amazing array of cell types present in a mature individual. The determination of those types is so precise that two adjacent cells may have very different phenotypes and functions. Furthermore, in contrast to a new car, for example, which works only when all of its basic parts have been properly assembled, a developing zygote is, at every moment, a vibrant, functioning entity of integrated components. Each step of development is dependent on and builds from the preceding stage. Any disruption in the normal sequence of events results in an abnormal phenotype: from these we can learn about the normal sequence.

We have come to understand the remarkable fidelity with which the genetic material is replicated and distributed at each cell division. Every complete normal genome contains the blueprint for accurate reproduction of an organism in a given species. But how is the genetic program read to confer the complexity evident in a multicellular organism or even within a single cell? It is clear from previous chapters that different genes are not all present in equal numbers, nor transcribed all at once or at the same rate. Development and differentiation, therefore, must reflect the coordinated regulation of genetic activity over time. Genetic analysis offers a way of probing the mechanisms of control involved.

As we shall see, genetic analysis has yielded answers to basic questions about the events of development. What are the relative roles of nucleus and cytoplasm in differentiation? Does the genetic material remain completely intact after cellular differentiation has occurred? What is the evidence for differential gene activity as a basis for differentiation? How can mutations be used to probe developmental phenomena? What role does cellular regulation play in special phenomena such as sex determination? This chapter explores how genetic analysis has been used to answer these questions.

Nuclear and Cytoplasmic Factors in Development

For decades, classical embryologists argued that the nucleus plays a relatively passive role in directing the primary events determining the developmental fates of cells and

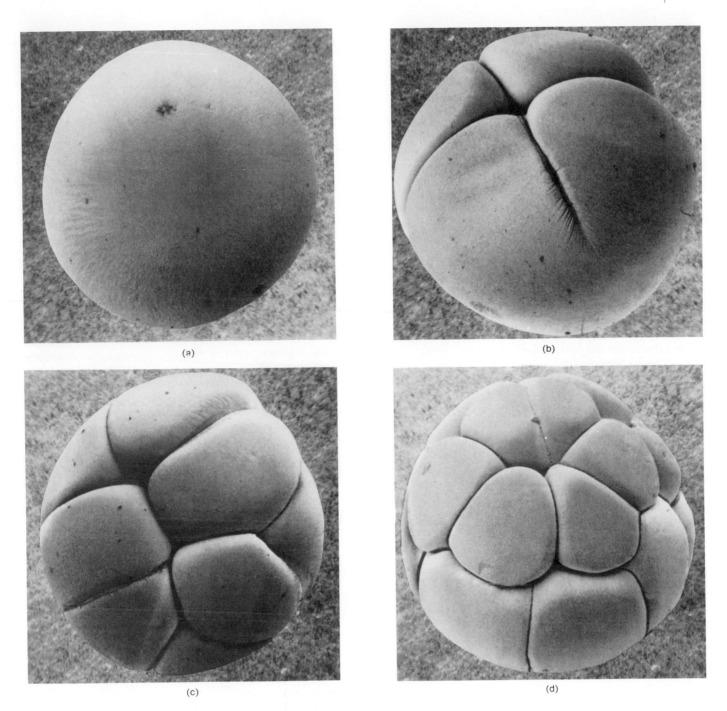

Figure 21-1. Early cleavages of an amphibian egg. It can be seen that asymmetries soon develop owing to the presence of yolk at the lower (vegetal) pole of the zygote cell. (a) Undivided egg. (b) Second cleavage. (c) Eight-cell stage. (d) 16-cell stage. (Lloyd M. Beidler, Florida State University.)

tissues. Different cells develop in different ways within the embryo, but each cell seems to inherit an identical set of nuclear genetic material. On the other hand, asymmetries are known to exist in the distribution of cytoplasmic material during cell divisions. Thus it seems reasonable that the varying developmental patterns in different cells are under cytoplasmic rather than nuclear control.

Mitochondria and yolk, for example, are not evenly distributed through the egg. The planes of division in early cleavages after fertilization result in the inclusion of different amounts of yolk and mitochondria in different daughter cells (Figure 21-1). Within a few divisions, differences in division rates and size become apparent among the cells of the embryo; such differences mean that environmental factors (oxygen, waste materials, temperature, and so on) impinge on the various parts in different ways.

The importance of the cytoplasm can be demonstrated experimentally. A part of a cell cortex (outer layer) without nuclei is removed from the embryo and grafted onto another, as shown in Figure 21-2. The resulting embryo may develop an extra set of some structure (twinned spinal cords in the example illustrated), showing that the cytoplasm (without the nucleus) can exert a major influence on development.

Environmental Effects

Environmental effects are also important in determining the course of development. In the 1940s, Richard Goldschmidt showed that a variety of environmental factors can produce phenotypic abnormalities in *Drosophila* that resemble the abnormal phenotypes of known genetic mutations. This environmentally induced phenotype is called a **phenocopy.** Phenocopies have subsequently been produced in a number of organisms, by a variety of agents, including heat (or cold), radiation, and an array of chemical compounds. Goldschmidt showed that the agent must be applied at a specific critical period in development in order to obtain each particular phenocopy. In 1945, Walter Landauer demonstrated such **phenocritical periods** in the embryonic response of chickens to such compounds as insulin, boric acid, and pilocarpin. These studies revealed the existence of a nongenetic process that can produce abnormalities—a process called **teratogenesis.** A variety of teratogenic agents (for example, the German measles virus and various drugs) have been proved to produce abnormalities in the human fetus.

Message   The egg cytoplasm is not homogeneous, and regional differences in the cytoplasm play a role in development. Furthermore, environmental agents can provoke specific defects during development.

Maternal Effects

While embryologists were searching in the cytoplasm for the key factors controlling development, geneticists were seeking evidence of nuclear control. There is no doubt that the egg cytoplasm does regulate the early events in embryonic development—for example, an enucleated frog egg will still go through the early cleavages. However, the architecture and molecular composition of the oocyte cytoplasm are themselves under rigid control by the nuclear genome of the mother! We have already considered an example: the *anucleolate (an)* mutation in *Xenopus.* The cross *an/+ × an/+* forms some *an/an* homozygotes that are incapable of forming ribosomes. Nonetheless, these embryos develop to twitching tadpoles before dying. Their survival is a result of the prefertilization amplification of ribosomal genes and the consequent store of ribosomes (which must reflect the maternal genotype). The most striking illustration of maternal genotypic influences on the phenotype of the offspring is seen in the coiling of snail shells (Chapter 20).

Another dramatic illustration of maternal genotype on the oocyte is found in *Drosophila* eggs. In the *Drosophila* egg, the anterior end can be distinguished from the posterior end, where a special region of the cortex can be seen to have densely staining **polar granules.** The granules define a region containing pole cytoplasm, from which the cytoplasm of all gonadal cells is derived. An autosomal recessive mutation discovered in *D. pseudoobscura* is called *grandchildless (gs)* for reasons that will become apparent. In the cross *gs/+ × gs/+*, some *gs/gs* homozygotes are formed. These homozygotes are fertile, but all eggs produced by *gs/gs* females lack polar granules. Regardless of the genotype of their mates, *gs/gs* females produce only offspring that lack gonads (and thus are sterile and fail to produce grandchildren of the *gs/gs* females). Obviously, in this case the maternal genotype plays a major role in determining the cytoplasmic makeup of eggs, thus affecting the phenotype of the offspring.

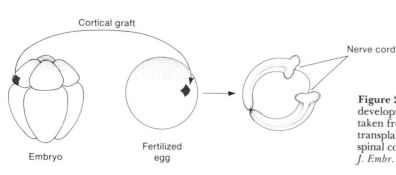

Figure 21-2. Experimental demonstration of extranuclear control of development. A graft of cell membrane and underlying cytoplasm is taken from the smaller cells of an embryo at the eight-cell stage and transplanted to the equatorial region of a fertilized egg. A second spinal cord develops in the resulting embryo. (From A. S. G. Curtis, *J. Embr. Exp. Morphol.* 10:416, 1972.)

Figure 21-3. Identical quadruplets. (Photograph courtesy of Erika Stone, © Peter Arnold, Inc.)

Message   Maternal genotype affects the architecture and composition of the egg cytoplasm and thus can affect the phenotype of the offspring.

Is the cytoplasm or the nucleus the site for control of the developmental process? It should be obvious by now that this is rather like asking whether the chicken or the egg came first! In the context of development, the nucleus in isolation from the cytoplasm is as useless as a cell without its nucleus. Much of the immediate control of developmental processes seems to come from the cytoplasm, but nuclear genetic factors play a major role in determining the nature of the cytoplasm. Are the detectable changes during development a reflection of directed alterations of the genetic material of the nucleus, or does it remain unchanged from its state at fertilization?

Are Nuclei of Differentiated Cells Totipotent?

Classical studies of embryology of organisms, such as worms and insects, revealed that not all somatic cells carried the same number or amount of chromosomal elements. It was suggested, therefore, that a mechanism for controlling the developmental sequence could be by a specified order of genetic elimination. Mitosis maintains a constant chromosome number—but does each cell of a highly differentiated embryo contain all of the genetic material necessary for complete development? One way to confirm this would be to show that each cell's nucleus remains

totipotent, that is, still capable of supporting complete development from egg to adult. Note that the answer may differ from species to species; throughout this chapter, each aspect of development will be considered in several systems —particularly mammalian, amphibian, and *Drosophila*.

Cloning

There are cases of multiple births in which "identical" siblings are derived from a single fertilized human egg (Figure 21-3). The Dionne quintuplets were genetically identical. Thus we conclude that the genetic information is faithfully reproduced through at least the first three cleavages after fertilization (two cleavages produce only four cells). But it is known that early embryonic development is controlled primarily by maternal genotype. What of the nuclei in cells resulting from later divisions? Do they remain totipotent?

Many highly differentiated organisms can regenerate new organs and tissues. For example, a starfish can regrow a lost "arm" (Figure 21-4), and a reptile can re-form a lost tail; in humans, the body can repair a damaged liver. However, such regeneration is possible only in certain tissues. Regeneration of a complete organism from a single somatic cell is not observed among animals in nature.

Plants.   In the 1950s, Frederick Steward demonstrated that highly differentiated phloem cells in the root of a carrot plant are totipotent. He was able to obtain an entire carrot plant from a single phloem cell (Figure 21-5). Using this method, he obtained a number of genetically identical plants from the somatic cells of a single plant. This asexual method of reproduction is now called **cloning** (in fact, the

Figure 21-4. Two "arms" (rays) of this starfish *(Asterias)* were severed. New rays have begun to form, and they will eventually grow into normal-sized rays. (Photograph courtesy of Grant Heilman.)

word clone is derived from a Greek word referring to a plant cutting). This work has important implications because of the economic potential for obtaining duplicates of any individual plant with a particularly useful phenotype. Almost all commercially available orchids are produced by cloning. One of the problems in breeding any organism that reproduces sexually is the constant disruption of useful gene combinations by random assortment and crossing-over. Cloning retains genetic combinations intact, and this process is now used commercially to maintain lines of trees. Of course, gardeners and farmers have long used asexual reproduction in the grafting of a branch from one geno-type onto another or in the generation of new plants from cuttings.

Message   Cloning of plants shows that differentiated cells remain totipotent.

Individual cells of multicellular organisms can be treated and analyzed like microorganisms when grown in cell cultures. Mutations can be induced and selected from these cells for such qualities as increased content of certain amino acids. If such mutant cells can be stimulated to differentiate into mature plants, then the process of plant breeding is tremendously simplified and accelerated. Such a procedure seems quite possible in plants, because the toti-

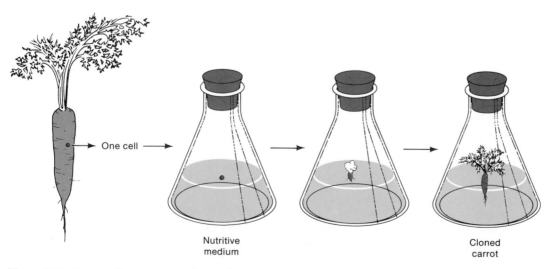

One cell →

Nutritive
medium

Cloned
carrot

Figure 21-5. Cloning of a carrot plant from a single cell taken from the phloem tissue of a mature root. The nutritive media in the different flasks must contain appropriate plant hormones.

potency of at least some kinds of differentiated plant cells has been demonstrated. However, are differentiated animal cells similarly totipotent?

Nuclear Transplantation in Amphibians. In the early 1950s, Robert Briggs and Thomas King developed techniques for manipulating nuclei in amphibian cells. They created **enucleated** frog eggs (eggs lacking nuclei) by inserting fine glass pipettes into unfertilized eggs and sucking the nuclei out. Such manipulation made possible the study of totipotency in animal cells. In order to test the developmental capacity of the nucleus from a differentiated cell within the cytoplasmic environment of an unfertilized egg, Briggs and King removed nuclei from differentiated cells and injected them into enucleated eggs (Figure 21-6). They found that an enucleated egg will divide when provided with a somatic nucleus. Furthermore, they found that a nucleus removed from a cell of the **blastula** (a stage when the embryo is still a hollow ball of cells) is totipotent. When the nucleus from a blastula cell is inserted into an enucleated egg, the egg divides normally and develops into an adult.

However, different results were obtained when the nucleus was taken from a cell at the **gastrula** stage of development (when infolding of the layers of cells begins). A nucleus from a gastrula cell will not support normal development when inserted into an enucleated egg. It appears that some process of nuclear differentiation begins at gastrulation, destroying the totipotency of the nucleus from a frog somatic cell.

Even if each cell does not retain a complete complement of DNA, it is obvious that some regulation process must activate and inactivate specific parts of the genome as development occurs. Perhaps a certain amount of time is required for such activation and inactivation to take place. Then, the renucleated egg may divide before the transplanted nucleus can return to a condition appropriate to the first division. Such an effect could lead to abnormal development even though the transplanted nucleus was in theory totipotent. To eliminate this possibility, Briggs and King performed another group of experiments. They kept nuclei in the cytoplasmic environment that encourages totipotency (cytoplasm from pre-gastrulation cells) by serially transplanting nuclei from gastrula embryos into enucleated eggs (Figure 21-7). Even after many serial transplantations, the nuclei remained incapable of supporting normal development.

These experiments show that somatic nuclei of the frog *Rana* differentiate irreversibly after gastrulation—at least under the conditions of the nucleus-transplantation experiments. However, John Gurdon repeated these experiments in 1964 with a different amphibian, the African clawed toad, *Xenopus laevis.* He took nuclei from highly differentiated cells of the gut of tadpoles and inserted them

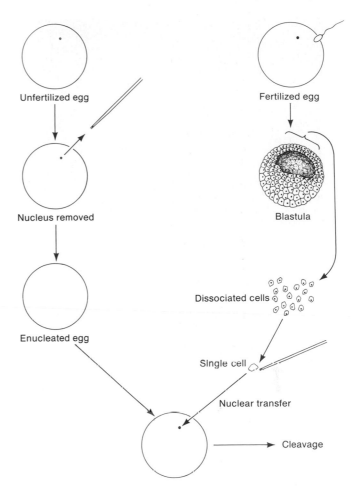

Figure 21-6. Transplantation of a nucleus from an embryonic amphibian cell into an enucleated egg. The nucleus of an unfertilized egg is removed mechanically by micropipette (left). Cells of a fertilized egg that has developed to the blastula stage are dissociated (right) so that the nucleus of a single cell can be removed and inserted into the enucleated egg (bottom).

into eggs whose nuclei had been destroyed by a beam of ultraviolet light (Figure 21-8). Although many of the eggs failed to develop or produced abnormal growth, a significant number did develop normally into adults whose genetic markers showed them to be identical clones of the nucleus-donor tadpole (not of the toad from which the unfertilized egg was taken). The results with *Xenopus* clearly differ from those obtained with the frog *Rana*. Obviously, a nucleus can remain totipotent at a highly differentiated stage in at least one vertebrate organism.

It is not yet known why the nuclei of the frog *Rana* cease to be totipotent at gastrulation, whereas those of the toad *Xenopus* can remain totipotent in the tadpole stage. Therefore, we must be very cautious about extrapolating from one species to another in this kind of research. Of course, the implications of techniques for cloning humans have received extensive popular discussion. Aldous Huxley's *Brave New World* develops one classic scenario based on this possibility. But is there any reason to believe that nuclei remain totipotent in animals other than *Xenopus*?

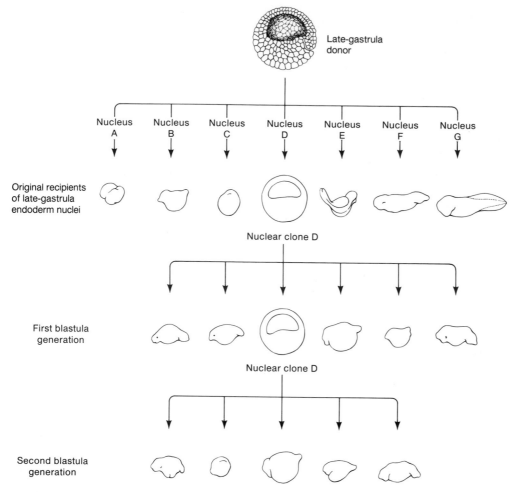

Figure 21-7. Serial transplants of gastrula nuclei in the frog *Rana*. All eggs except D are allowed to proceed to the end of their development (all develop abnormally). The D clone is allowed to proceed to the blastula stage. Then, nuclei from the blastula cells are transplanted to enucleated eggs, and the same procedure is repeated. Normal development of any renucleated cells was never observed, even after many repetitions of this procedure. (From R. Briggs, *Cold Spring Harbor Symp. Quant. Biol.* 21:277, 1956.)

Totipotency in Drosophila and Mammals. Karl Illmensee has obtained evidence to support the idea of totipotency in differentiated cells from both mice and *Drosophila*. In one set of experiments, Illmensee took cells from a teratocarcinoma, a type of tumor of the gonads, and injected them into the peritoneal cavity in normal mice. The ability of such cells to retain their phenotype is notable: injection of a single cell results in the growth of a teratocarcinoma in the mouse. Single cells from one genetically marked line were then injected into an embryo from another line (Figure 21-9). Next, the mosaic embryo was implanted into the uterus of a "pseudopregnant" female—a female whose uterus is receptive to embryo implantation following her mating to a sterile male (Figure 21-10). The embryo developed normally, but the newborn mouse proved to be a **chimera** (or mosaic) containing a clone of cells derived from the injected tumor cell. This clone had been com-

pletely integrated into the organ or organs in which it developed. Illmensee found that if the clone of injected cells is included in the gonadal region, the animals can be mated and normal offspring derived from gametes formed from cells of the clone. Hence, the nuclei from the teratocarcinoma are indistinguishable from normal cells in their totipotency. Using a similar microinjection technique, Illmensee introduced single marked cells of *Drosophila* embryos into unfertilized eggs, which then developed into adult fruit flies. Again, the differentiated embryonic cells proved to be totipotent.

These results show that differentiated cells in many different organisms can be totipotent under certain experimental conditions. It seems reasonable to conclude that every cell in a highly differentiated organism may contain a complete copy of the DNA from the original zygote. In many such cells, the expression of parts of the genome is

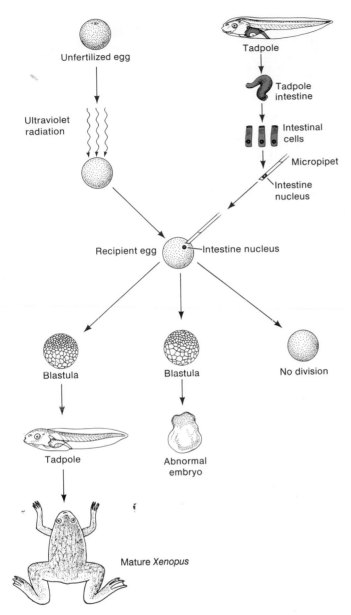

Figure 21-8. Cloning of the toad *Xenopus* by nuclear transplantation. The nucleus of an unfertilized egg is destroyed by a beam of ultraviolet light (upper left), which specifically damages DNA. A nucleus taken from a gut cell of a tadpole (upper right) is transplanted into the enucleated egg (center). Many of the resulting zygotes develop abnormally or fail to divide, but a few of the zygotes develop into mature individuals (bottom left). (From J. B. Gurdon, "Transplanted Nuclei and Cell Differentiation." Copyright © 1968 by Scientific American, Inc. All rights reserved.)

blocked in such a way that the nucleus from the differentiated cell cannot direct normal development when transplanted to an unfertilized egg. The nature of this blockage then becomes the subject for further research. How is the expression of DNA regulated during development?

Message Mitosis accurately duplicates and distributes DNA sequences among the daughter cells at each division during development. Hence, each somatic cell contains the

same genetic information as the newly fertilized egg from which the organism developed.

Turning Genes On and Off

We have seen that many cells carry a complete nuclear genome, but we know that certain genes exert their effects only at specific stages of development. A hypothesis involving differential activation of various genes at different stages of development seems very attractive. Can such differential gene activation be demonstrated?

Early Embryonic Gene Regulation

We have seen that cell divisions just after fertilization are relatively rapid and are controlled by maternally derived information in the cytoplasm, with little genetic control from the zygotic nuclei. At what point in development do the embryonic nuclei begin to play a major role? (We know that they must play such a role because the zygote genotype does have a major effect on the phenotype.)

Nineteenth-century embryologists devised ingenious experimental approaches to answer this question. For example, Theodor Boveri studied species of sea urchin in which the embryos differ in morphology. He enucleated an egg from one species and fertilized it with sperm from another species. The sperm nucleus can promote development in such situations. He showed that development of the embryo follows the pattern dictated by the genotype of the sperm, and he determined the point in the developmental sequence at which this paternal influence becomes obvious. A similar approach can now be used to measure the time of appearance of some gene product (either RNA or protein) encoded by the paternal genes. Drugs such as actinomycin D that inhibit RNA synthesis can be tested to determine the time in development when they have lethal effects — thus showing when the products of the embryonic nuclei are required for survival. Such studies show that zygotic genes probably begin to act at approximately the time of gastrulation in amphibians. However, lethal effects of actinomycin D on mouse embryos begin to appear at around the eight-cell or 16-cell stage of development.

As we shall see, most studies of gene activation in development have concentrated on loci coding for specific cell products found in large quantities in highly differentiated cells. However, those genes acting early in development, before differentiated tissues have appeared, can have a more profound effect on the organism as a whole. A method for cataloging them has been developed by Thomas Sargent and Igor Dawid. They studied *Xenopus* embryos in which there are a lot of maternally deposited mRNAs but in which no activity of new genes occurs until the gastrula stage. The gastrula is the first stage at which

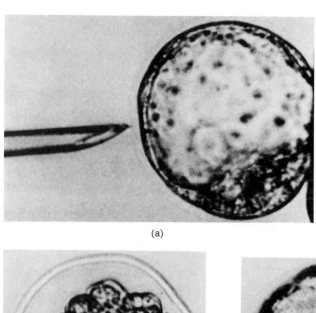

(a)

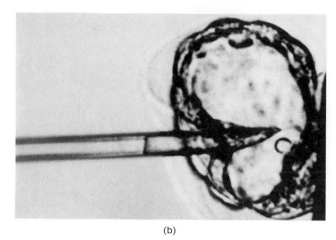

(b)

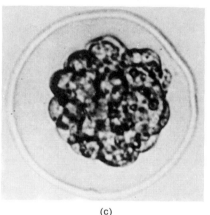

(c)

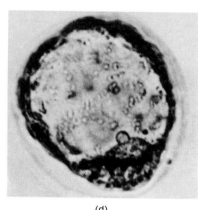

(d)

Figure 21-9. Formation of a mosaic embryo. (a) A mouse embryo is held on the end of a pipette while a teratocarcinoma cell is brought up to it. (b) The teratocarcinoma cell is injected into the center of the embryo. (c) The teratocarcinoma cell becomes integrated into the embryo. (d) All of the cells of the embryo (including that from the teratocarcinoma) multiply as development proceeds. The descendants of the injected cell will be integrated into tissues of the embryo; which tissues will depend on the location of the injection. (From K. Illmensee, in *Genetic Mosaics and Chimeras in Mammals.* Edited by Liane B. Russell. Plenum Publishing Corp., 1978.)

differentiation of the three primitive cell layers occurs. From gastrulae, they isolated poly-A-containing RNA on poly-dT columns. From this gastrula mRNA (which contains all of the maternally inherited mRNA as well), cDNA was made. The cDNA was hybridized with mRNA taken from unfertilized eggs. All cDNA complementary to the maternally inherited transcripts form double strands, while the gastrula-activated cDNA remains unpaired. The double strands were separated from the single strands. From the single strands, large cDNA molecules (400 to 2000 bases in length) were isolated and then inserted into plasmids, until a library of 150,000 clones was derived. What these investigators had obtained, in essence, was a large array of DNAs complementary to mRNAs transcribed at gastrulation. Of course, many of the sequences obtained in such procedures will be repeats of the same mRNAs, so the number of clones coding for a particular mRNA will reflect the abundance of those transcripts at gastrulation.

Taking 84 randomly selected clones, Sargent and Dawid bound their DNA to filters and then exposed them to radioactive mRNA from different stages. Autoradiographs (Figure 21-11) showed that the cDNAs represent genes that are activated in gastrulation and that the level of transcription varies from gene to gene. Most of these gastrula mRNAs declined in abundance in later stages, even though RNA was increased by six- to 10-fold in relative mass. One mRNA represented in the clones increased in the tadpole stage. Apparently, beginning with gastrulation,

a specific group of genes is activated, with each gene being expressed in varying amounts; most are subsequently shut off by the tadpole stage. It is reasonable to assume that development proceeds by controlled activation and inactivation of specific genes.

Message   Analysis of poly-A-containing transcripts shows that genes in amphibians are activated at gastrulation, to produce varying numbers of mRNA molecules. Most are shut off by the tadpole stage, at which time many new loci are activated. Development must proceed by a sequence of turning genes on and off.

Visible Differentiation of Gene Activity

If differential gene activation is a mechanism of differentiation, is it possible to "see" this phenomenon occur? Let's take another look at the giant polytene chromosomes of Diptera (Chapter 8). Recall that certain stains show that these chromosomes contain regions that are rich in RNA, suggesting that these regions may be cytologically visible sites of RNA synthesis. This has been verified by experiments in which polytene chromosomes were incubated in ^{3}H-labeled uracil (which is incorporated into RNA, thereby identifying it). Autoradiographs of the chromosomes were

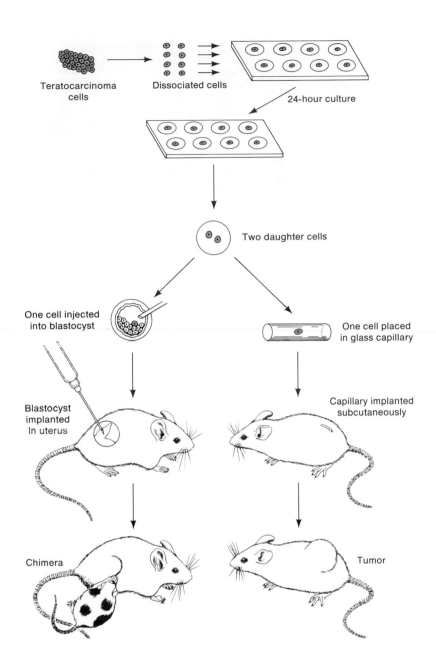

Teratocarcinoma cells

Dissociated cells

24-hour culture

Two daughter cells

One cell injected into blastocyst

One cell placed in glass capillary

Blastocyst implanted In uterus

Capillary implanted subcutaneously

Chimera

Tumor

Figure 21-10. Experimental analysis of teratocarcinoma cells. Individual cells are allowed to divide once, and one of the daughter cells is injected into an embryo of the blastocyst stage (left). The resulting mosaic embryo is then inserted into the uterus of a recipient female, where it develops normally. The other cell is placed in a glass capillary tube that is placed under the skin of another mouse, where it develops into a tumor (right). Material from the tumor can be used for comparison with cells from the chimera. (From K. Illmensee and L. C. Stevens, "Teratomas and Chimeras." Copyright © 1979 by Scientific American, Inc. All rights reserved.)

then prepared, which revealed that certain parts of the chromosome do indeed incorporate the RNA precursor, especially in the swollen **puffs** and **Balbiani rings** (Figure 21-12).

In *Drosophila*, studies have shown that in a given polytene-chromosome-containing gland, puffing patterns do change predictably during larval development. Heat shock can also induce changes in puffing patterns that can be correlated with the appearance of specific mRNAs and proteins (Figure 21-13). Synthesis of a steroid hormone, ecdysone, near the end of larval life is accompanied by a major change in the pattern of puffing, which can be mimicked earlier in larval life by injection of the compound. These studies provide no evidence on whether the different patterns of puff formation are the cause or the result of tissue differentiation. However, they do provide a very graphic demonstration of genes being turned on and turned off.

Message RNA-rich regions of polytene chromosomes, recognized as cytologically visible puffs and Balbiani rings, correspond to RNA transcribed from chromosomal DNA. The puffing pattern is tissue- and developmental-stage-specific and provides a model for gene activation and inactivation in response to factors in the cytoplasm.

Turning Genes On and Off in Microorganisms

Development appears to reflect a coordinated sequence of gene activation and inactivation. What is the mechanism of control? It already appears that there are many mechanisms that have evolved. However, the study of gene regulation in prokaryotes has provided the operon as a model for control in eukaryotes. By linking different operons, more complex control circuits develop. In the phage λ, for example, there are very different alternate states of lysis and lyso-

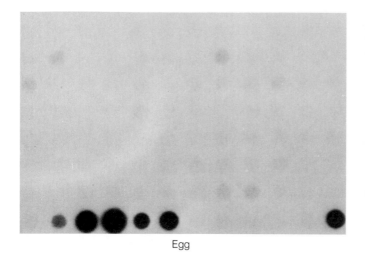

Egg

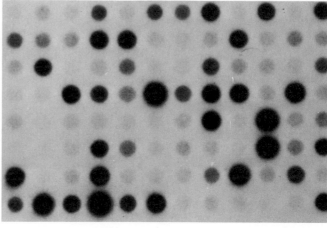

Gastrula

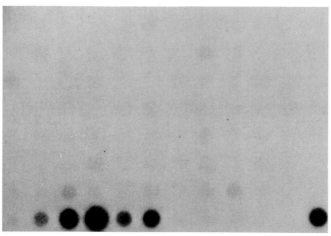

Blastula

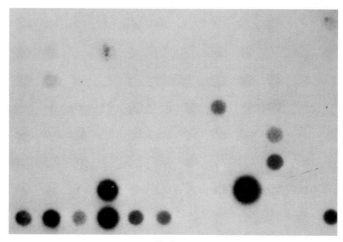

Tadpole

Figure 21-11. Autoradiographs of DNA clones with radioactive mRNA taken from different developmental stages of *Xenopus*. The four panels contain an identical arrangement of the same set of 84 different clones. The bottom rows are reference DNAs. Radioactive mRNA obtained from egg, blastula, gastrula, and tadpole was hybridized to the filters; after the unbound material was removed, an autoradiograph was made. Note that none of the 84 DNAs is represented by pre-gastrula mRNAs and that the quantity of each mRNA can be measured by spot intensity. Finally, most of the "gastrula genes" are repressed in later stages, although the expression of one such gene is enhanced.

geny determined by two different repressors. The production of λ repressor shuts off the *cro* gene without which phage multiplication cannot proceed. Alternatively, production of *cro* product shuts off λ repressor. Similarly, the multiple activity of a single gene product as a repressor and an activator of different genes provides a cascading hierarchy of specific changes, as seen in Figure 21-14. Obviously, gene 1 at the apex of the pyramid has a major effect, in contrast to the next levels of loci, whose effects will be progressively restricted. This type of sequence, referred to as **combinatorial** gene regulation, serves to illustrate why differentiation is so often irreversible, requiring a very specific sequence of reversals. However, it is from yeast that a striking example of regulation at the DNA level is shown.

Message In microorganisms, a variety of mechanisms

exist for turning genes on and off. The operon is the most refined mechanism and by linking different operons together, a combinatorial sequence of gene control provides enormous variability.

Mating-Type Transposition in Homothallic Yeast

In the yeast *Saccharomyces cerevisiae*, transposition has been demonstrated as a normal part of the sexual cycle. Strains of *S. cerevisiae* can be either heterothallic or homothallic. A heterothallic strain is stable as either mating type, α or a, and the successful completion of the sexual cycle depends on the union of α and a strains. We have already seen that in such cases, the two phenotypes segregate 1 : 1 in the progeny, showing their determination by two nuclear alleles. The alleles are now called *MATα* and *MATa*. Homothallic strains, on the other hand, start out as either α or a mating type; however, any culture can go through the sexual cycle

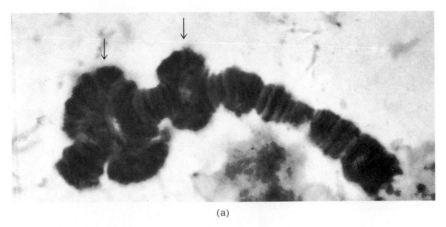

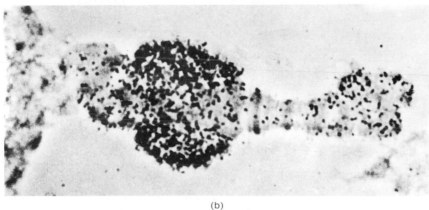

Figure 21-12. Balbiani rings in salivary gland chromosomes from the midge *Chironomus*. (a) Electron micrograph showing visible Balbiani rings (arrows). (b) Autoradiograph after incubation in medium containing ^{3}H-labeled uracil. The incorporation of the ^{3}H-labeled uracyl shows that heavy RNA synthesis is occurring in the Balbiani ring. (Part a by Ulrich Clever; part b by Claus Pelling, Max Planck Institute for Biology.)

by itself without being paired with a strain of opposite mating type. In such cases, the products of meiosis (starting with, say, an α cell) are of two types: one half is α and (surprisingly) one half is a! Careful studies in which cell lineages were followed have shown that the way this remarkable process is achieved is through the switching of mating type by some cells, usually within two or three cell generations. Hence, a cell that starts out as, say, α quickly develops into a culture that is a mixture of α and a cells; these types then pair and go through the sexual cycle.

It became clear from genetic analyses that the process was under genetic control. Four important loci were initially shown to be involved. First, of course, there was the *MAT* locus itself. Second, an unlinked gene *HO* was essential for any kind of mating-type switching to occur, and its allele *ho* was inactive in this regard. Third and fourth, two loci both designated *HM* had to carry the appropriate alleles for switches of a specific mating type to occur. Linked 57 map units to the right of *MAT* was the locus initially designated *HMα*. Apparently, in order for α cells to switch to a, under the influence of *HO*, the allele *HMα* was essential, and *hmα* was not adequate. Linked 65 map units to the left of *MAT* was the locus originally designated *HMa*. It appeared that in order for a cell to switch to α, the allele *HMa* was a prerequisite, and *hma* would not work. However, there was a major paradox: the genotype *hmα hma*, supposedly containing the inactive forms of both loci, would allow switching of either α or a cells!

Another important advance in the elucidation of transposition mechanics came from the observation that the *HMa/HMα* genotype will promote sequential switching, such as from *MATα* to *MATa* and then back to *MATα* again. This was not particularly surprising because the *HM* genes for both kinds of switching are present. What was surprising, however, was that if the culture was initially carrying a defective allele at the *MAT* locus, such as a defective *MATα*, then switching was first to *MATa* and then back, not to the

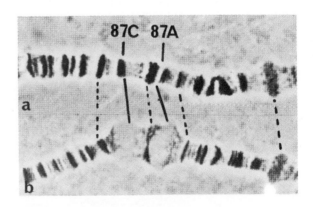

Figure 21-13. Induction of puffs in chromosome 3 of *Drosophila* by a 40-minute exposure to 37°C. (a) Control experiment with no heat shock. (b) Puffs formed after heat shock. (From Ashburner and Bonner, *Cell* 17:241, 1979. Copyright MIT Press.)

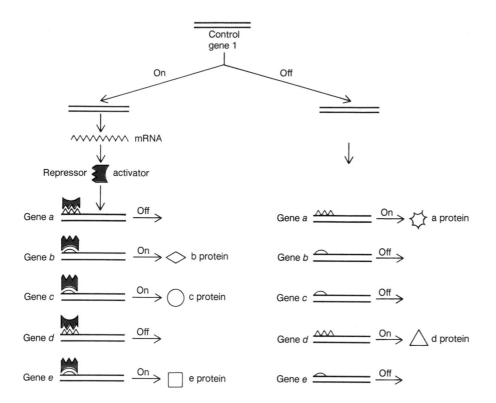

Figure 21-14. A cascade effect produced by a hypothetical gene 1, which behaves as a repressor or an activator for a series of five other operons. Enormous variability from cell to cell is possible.

defective *MATα*, but to a perfectly functional *MATα*. The defective *MATα* allele seemed to have been removed and lost!

The model that was designed to explain all these results led to an exciting series of genetic and molecular tests that revealed a fascinating transposition system. The model, called the **cassette model**, was based on the idea that the *HM* loci were depots of "silent" *MAT* information that could be "played" like cassettes after their physical transposition to the *MAT* locus. At the *MAT* locus itself, the cassette that was inserted by transposition replaced the original cassette residing there, which was lost. However, at the silent *HM* depots, the cassettes that were transposed had to be copies of the cassettes residing there, because the *HM* genotype of the cells remained constant. According to the model, the *HMα* and *hmα* alleles were renamed *HMRa* and *HMRα*, respectively (the R in HMR stands for right). Thus, either silent a (*HMRa*) or silent α (*HMRα*) information can reside at this locus. To the left, *HMa* became *HMLα* and *hma* became *HMLa*, showing that either silent α (*HMLα*) or silent a (*HMLa*) information could reside there too. The *hma hmα* paradox was explained because its new designation was *HMLa HMRα* and as such it was viewed as containing silent information of both mating types and hence could switch either α to a or a to α. Note that *HMLα HMRa* is a comparable genotype, whereas *HMLα HMRα* is capable only of switching a to α but not the reverse, and likewise, *HMLa HMRa* can only switch α to a. The model is graphically depicted in Figure 21-15.

The cassette model was confirmed by a Southern blot analysis using a probe derived from a yeast plasmid carrying the *MAT* locus. The probe bound to three DNA fragments, which were shown to be *HML*, *MAT*, and *HMR*. The three regions have now been sequenced; summary diagrams are shown in Figure 21-16. All three regions show similar sequences, but it turns out that only the Y region is

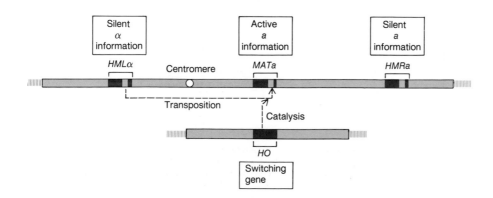

Figure 21-15. Mating-type switching in a yeast cell of genotype *HMLα MATa HMRa*. A silent copy of *MATα* information is present at the *HML* locus, designated *HMLα*, and a silent copy of *MATa* information is present at the *HMR* locus, designated *HMRa*. Under the influence of an unlinked gene *HO*, *HMLα* material is physically transposed to *MAT* with the exclusion of the a information residing there. At this point, the mating type of the cell switches from a to α.

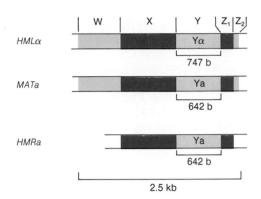

Figure 21-16. The structure of the *HML, MAT,* and *HMR* loci. *HML* and *MAT* always have W and Z_2, but *HMR* never does. Either Ya or Yα can exist at any of the three loci. Only the Y region is transposed.

unique to one mating type, and this is the part that is transposed.

How does transposition occur? One clue came from showing that homothallic cells regularly contained a double-stranded DNA break at the Y–Z junction of the *MAT* locus only. The break is produced there at a specific DNA target sequence by the product of the *HO* gene, which is a restriction-enzyme-like endonuclease. Either the *HML* or the *HMR* gene bends over the *MAT* gene, the *MAT* Y region is degraded, and Y information is inserted from *HMR* or *HML* by a gene conversion-like process (Figure 21-17). The precise involvement of the single strand break is currently under study.

Message The ability of yeast to switch mating types is determined by the activation of either alternate state through the appropriate insertion into the site responsible for its expression.

Differentiated Tissue Reflects Different Gene Activity

In multicellular organisms, can a difference in genetic activity be demonstrated as a characteristic of differentiated cells? James Darnell and his group isolated a spectrum of moderately abundant mRNAs from mouse liver and then performed experiments to see whether these mRNAs were also present in mouse brain cells. These investigators separated mRNA from total RNA by using the ability of poly-A sequences to bind to poly-dT sequences attached to a cellulose matrix. The liver mRNA was then used as a template for reverse transcriptase to make double-stranded cDNA. The cDNA molecules were then inserted into plasmids, which were cloned in *E. coli*. Each cloned liver cDNA was

tested for hybridization with labeled mRNA from mouse liver, brain, and hepatoma (a liver tumor). In this way, DNA complementary to mRNA only in liver or in all three cells was identified. These DNAs could be used to assay specific mRNAs from different tissues quantitatively. Darnell's group found no detectable liver-specific mRNA in brain or hepatoma cells. Even if an undetectable but low level of liver mRNA is made in brain cells, the maximum rate would be 1/10 to 1/50 of the rate in liver cells. Thus, at the molecular level, the differentiated phenotypes of specialized cells do indeed mirror altered expression of genomic sequences, although it must be pointed out that all of the cells tested express a common set of genes as well.

Message Isolation of mRNA from differentiated tissues shows that each tissue has its own set of expressed genes.

Inducible Systems in Multicellular Organisms

Mechanisms exist for altering gene activity in populations of individual microorganisms. But are there indications of how gene activity is controlled in different cells of the same individual?

Drosophila *Puffs.* Puffs are visible in highly specialized secretory glands of Diptera, and both the pattern and size of specific puffs are determined by levels of the molting hormone, ecdysone. In principle, it should be possible to correlate a puff with a specific function in the gland. Such evidence has come from studies on *Drosophila* salivary glands. These glands' main function is the production and extrusion of a thick saliva, which acts to "glue" the late third-instar larva to a solid surface when it pupates. The saliva begins to be found in the lumen of the gland in the middle of the third instar and is extruded about three hours before pupation. Günter Korge showed that the salivary secretion contains at least five proteins, one of which was

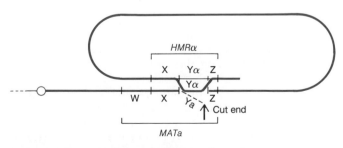

Figure 21-17. Transposition is effected by one of the *HM* genes (here, *HMR*) pairing with *MAT*, followed by an HO-enzyme-mediated cut at the Yα-Z boundary, degradation of Ya, and replacement with a copy of Yα DNA.

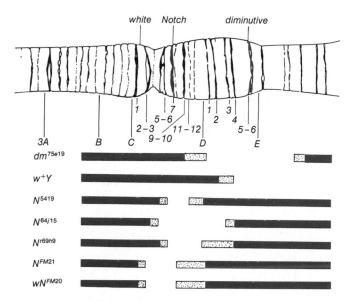

Figure 21-18. The 3A–D region near the tip of the X chromosome of a *Drosophila* salivary gland. The regions missing in the deficiencies are left as open spaces, while the uncertain borders of the breakpoints are indicated by stippling. *w*⁺Y is a duplication of a large segment of the X carried by a Y chromosome. The top three chromosomes carry *Sgs-4*; the rest do not.

called sgs-4 (salivary gland secretion protein-4). He localized the *Sgs-4* locus to region 3C8–3D1 near the tip of the X chromosome where a puff appears 5 to 6 hours before detectable levels of sgs-4. Steven Beckendorf and his group then more accurately localized *Sgs-4* by a series of overlapping deletions (Figure 21-18). DNA of the *Sgs-4* locus was recovered in two ways. Beckendorf's group used clones from a library of *Drosophila* known to hybridize in situ to the 3C region. Other workers—Marc Muskavitch and David Hogness—isolated poly-A-containing RNAs (presumed to be mRNA) of the glands at different developmental stages. From these types of mRNA, the experimenters made cDNAs to use as probes for mRNAs made at specific developmental stages. In this way, they recovered sequences that hybridize in the region 3C7–3D1 of the X. Once the DNA around the *Sgs-4* locus was identified, restriction maps were made in both laboratories, and nucleotide sequences flanking the ends of the part coding for RNA were determined. Muskavitch and Hogness then screened *Drosophila* strains of different geographical origin and found those that underproduced or overproduced sgs-4. Three underproducers from Japan carried a 52-base-pair (bp) deletion at a site 305 bp upstream from the 5' end of *Sgs-4;* a strain that produced no detectable sgs-4 had a 95-bp deletion 392 bp upstream. In contrast, Beckendorf's group found two other types of underproducers of sgs-4. In one type, two mutants with single base changes

300 to 500 bp upstream from the *Sgs-4* structural gene made 50 percent less sgs-4 RNA. The other type was recovered when anomalous-sized DNA fragments, after restriction-enzyme treatment of a low-producing strain, were noted. A 1.3-kb insert 150 bp upstream from the *Sgs-4* structural gene was found. The insert, called hobo, reduces expression of *Sgs-4* by 50- to 100-fold, and of the transcripts produced, *four* different types (two starting in the hobo element), instead of one, are found. The ability to analyze the DNA of genetic variants of an inducible locus will provide a great deal of information about how gene expression is regulated.

Message   DNA in a specific puff on the *Drosophila* X chromosome codes for the production of the glue protein, sgs-4. Strains of genetic variants that underproduce sgs-4 are found to carry deletions or insertions upstream from the 5' end of the structural gene. Thus, the regulatory controls of the structural gene are built into the DNA sequence ahead of it.

Chick Oviducts.   Can a normal developmental process that can be manipulated by the experimenter be examined to determine the factors responsible for the control? This was the question posed by Bert O'Malley in the 1960s and led him to investigate the egg-producing system of female chickens. This complex system passes an egg through a series of chambers in the oviduct where it is elaborated, first with the nutrients necessary to sustain a developing chick and finally enclosed in a protective shell (Figure 21-19). In newborn chicks, the oviduct is undeveloped, and its walls are not yet differentiated for their egg-processing roles (Figure 21-20). Injection of newborn or older chicks with estrogen or with the synthetic steroid hormone diethylstilbestrol (DES) stimulates oviduct growth and the differentiation and production of various components of a mature

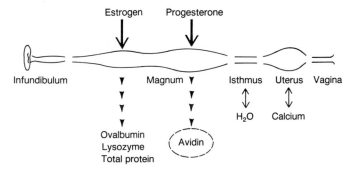

Figure 21-19. The functional segments of the chick oviduct. Eggs released by the ovary pass into the infundibulum and accumulate various components before being enclosed within a shell inside the uterus and extruded from the vagina.

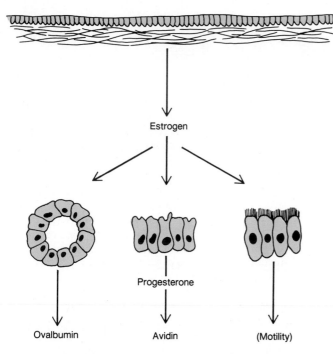

Figure 21-20. Effect of steroid hormones on the mucosal lining of the chick oviduct. Different cell types specialized for specific functions appear.

egg. In the first six days of hormone treatment, the cells lining the oviduct undergo visible changes, while little ovalbumin, one of the main protein components of egg white, is detectable (Figure 21-21). In six to 15 days, ovalbumin synthesis reaches high levels. The increase in ovalbumin in the tubular cells is paralleled by a large increase in mRNA, which permitted O'Malley to purify the ovalbumin message. Ovalbumin mRNA is essentially undetectable before administration of estrogen, but 18 days after, the amount increases until there are 48,000 molecules per cell, making up about half of all mRNAs in the cell. From ovalbumin mRNA, cDNA was made and used as a probe to isolate the ovalbumin gene. The cDNA:DNA hybrids revealed the existence of introns in the structural gene.

But how is the ovalbumin gene activated? O'Malley showed that the steroid hormone alone does not act as an inducer. Upon entering the cell, the steroid is bound to two specific protein receptors, called A and B, to form an active complex. The hormone-receptor complex is then translocated to the nucleus, where it binds to DNA flanking the ovalbumin gene. By attaching the hormone-receptor complex to a column and passing DNA fragments through it, O'Malley was able to recover specifically bound sequences. He showed that a 114-bp segment, starting 135 bp upstream from the oviduct structural gene, is probably the binding site. Interestingly, within this segment is the very AT-rich sequence—AATTAAAAACTAATATTT—that may be the actual binding site.

Other proteins of specific loci that are activated in specialized cells have been analyzed. These include hemoglobin in red blood cells, yolk proteins in amphibian eggs, and silk proteins in moths. The ability to isolate cloned DNA

sequences of specific structural genes and flanking sequences provides a powerful method for determining the importance of DNA sequence, and ultimately structure, in gene regulation. The interesting question then becomes the following: how does the regulating sequence actually affect transcription?

Message   Inducible genes in eukaryotic multicellular organisms can provide information about the specific sequences necessary for activity. In the case of a chick oviduct protein, steroid hormones induce the synthesis of specific mRNAs by forming a hormone-receptor protein complex, which then binds to a region flanking the structural gene.

Mutations as Developmental Markers

In order to probe development, we need a great deal of descriptive biology of the developmental process so that we can formulate a question or develop an experimental procedure. If you have ever watched time-lapse movies of embryogenesis, you know that cell and tissue movements are extremely complex. In the dynamic process of embryogenesis, folding or migration can bring a group of cells to an area of the embryo very far from its original positions in the blastula. How can we trace these cell movements during embryogenesis? The classical approach was physical: to label specific cells of amphibian embryos with visible carbon particles, so that movements of the marked cells (or their descendants) could be traced during development.

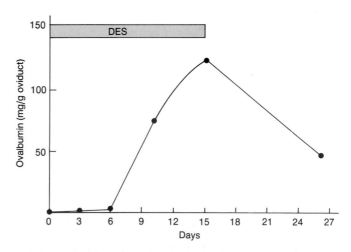

Figure 21-21. Effect of diethylstilbestrol (DES) on ovalbumin levels in immature chick oviducts. Chicks received 5 mg of DES daily for 15 days.

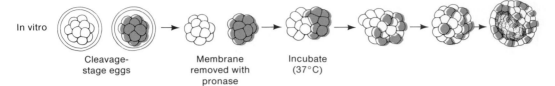

In vitro

Cleavage-stage eggs → Membrane removed with pronase → Incubate (37°C)

Figure 21-22. Formation of a genetic chimera by fusion of two mouse embryos of different genotypes. The embryos (at the eight-cell or 16-cell stage) are stripped of their surrounding membranes by treatment with the enzyme pronase, which breaks down proteins. The two cell clusters are placed together and incubated at 37°C. The cells adhere and mix together to form a single mosaic embryo. (From B. Mintz, *Proc. Natl. Acad. Sci. USA* 58:345, 1967.)

With this marking technique, researchers constructed **fate maps** showing the destinies of the descendants of particular cells in early stages of embryogenesis.

An alternative method is to mark cells *genetically* so that they and their descendants can be distinguished phenotypically. This approach is possible using genetic mosaics, individuals composed of several genetically distinct cell populations. Such mosaics do occur naturally. For example, the exchange of blood cells in the placentas of twin cattle can produce chimeras that carry two blood types. As discussed in Chapter 9, somatic nondisjunction in humans can produce a person whose cells carry different numbers of X and Y chromosomes. Furthermore, every female mammal is a mosaic in terms of the functional states of her two X chromosomes.

Tetraparental Mice

Recall Illmensee's experimental generation of mosaics by injection of single cells into embryos of *Drosophila* and mice (Figure 21-9). Beatrice Mintz has developed a very elegant technique for fusing the developing embryos of two different mouse genotypes (Figure 21-22). When implanted in a host female, such a **tetraparental** embryo develops as a single mosaic individual.

The sex of the embryos being fused is not known at the time of fusion; by chance, about half of the fusions will be between a male embryo and a female embryo. Under the influence of the male hormones, most of these sexual chimeras differentiate as males even though the presence of the XX cells can be demonstrated. All the daughter cells of those introduced at the time of embryo fusion represent genetic clones, so the recovery of a genotypically identical cluster of cells indicates their common origin through division. Mintz fused embryos from a mouse strain having black fur with embryos from a stock having white fur. If cells from either genotype can become precursors of skin, then the pattern of fur color should reflect the clonal origins of the skin cells. She found that the fur pattern of such mice always involves bands of black or white fur that circle the body to form a stripe from the stomach (ventral surface) to the back (dorsal surface) on each side (Figure 21-23). This information indicates that the cells whose descendants will produce fur pigment line up randomly in pairs along the midline of the embryo and that then each divides to form a clonal sheet extending halfway around the body to meet the other. Clearly, mutations producing easily identified phenotypic features such as fur color are extremely useful as genetic markers in tracing cell lineage during development. As we shall see later in this chapter, such genetic dissection of development has been honed to a fine edge in *Drosophila*.

Using tetraparental mice, Mintz set out to obtain a definitive solution to the problem of the origin of the multiple nuclei in a striated muscle cell. A muscle cell differentiates from precursor cells called **myoblasts,** each of which has a single nucleus. Does a muscle cell arise through successive fusion of different myoblasts, or does a mononucleate

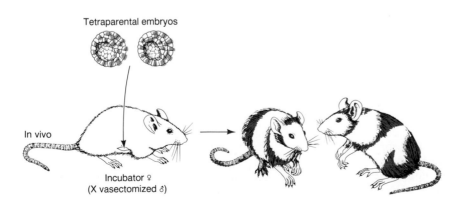

Tetraparental embryos

In vivo

Incubator ♀
(X vasectomized ♂)

Figure 21-23. Tetraparental mouse embryos are transplanted into a female whose womb is receptive for implantation after mating with a sterile male. The resulting offspring are mosaics for the fur genotypes of the two strains from which they are derived. The patterning of the fur phenotypes in dorsal-to-ventral stripes indicates the regions of skin that have been derived from a single embryonic cell. (From B. Mintz, *Proc. Natl. Acad. Sci. USA* 58:345, 1967.)

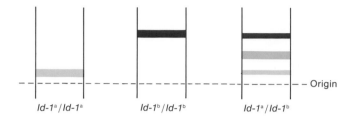

Figure 21-24. Electrophoretic mobility of isocitrate dehydrogenase-1 of different genotypes. Each homozygote shows a single isocitrate dehydrogenase-1 band with a specific mobility in the electrical field. However, the heterozygote *(Id-1ᵃ/Id-1ᵇ)* shows three bands, one each with the mobility of the parental strain and a band of intermediate mobility. The intermediate band stains approximately twice as intensely as either parental band. This pattern indicates that isocitrate dehydrogenase-1 is a dimer, and the intermediate band contains one polypeptide from each of the parental alleles.

myoblast undergo a series of nuclear divisions without division of the cytoplasm? To distinguish between these two models, Mintz produced tetraparental mice from two lines that differ in the electrophoretic mobility of the enzyme isocitrate dehydrogenase-1. Electrophoretically distinct enzymes are produced by *Id-1ᵃ* and *Id-1ᵇ* homozygotes, whereas the *Id-1ᵃ/Id-1ᵇ* heterozygotes also exhibit an intermediate hybrid band indicative of a dimer containing one polypeptide unit from each phenotype (Figure 21-24). Formation of the hybrid dimer can occur only if both polypeptides are synthesized in the same cell, as shown by the fact that only the parental enzyme types are derived from the livers of mice that are chimeric for uninucleate cells of both homozygous lines.

The pattern of enzyme phenotypes in tetraparental mice permits a test between the two hypotheses for the origin of the muscle-cell nuclei (Figure 21-25). The division model predicts that a single muscle cell will contain nuclei of only a single genotype, so enzyme derived from muscle cells of a tetraparental mouse should show only the parental patterns. The fusion model predicts that a single cell in a tetraparental mouse may contain nuclei of both genotypes, so that the hybrid dimer can be formed. Therefore, Mintz's results (the formation of the hybrid dimer in muscle cells of tetraparental mice) provided definitive proof that a striated muscle cell is formed by myoblast fusion.

Tetraparental mice have been used to provide precise solutions to other problems in developmental biology. For

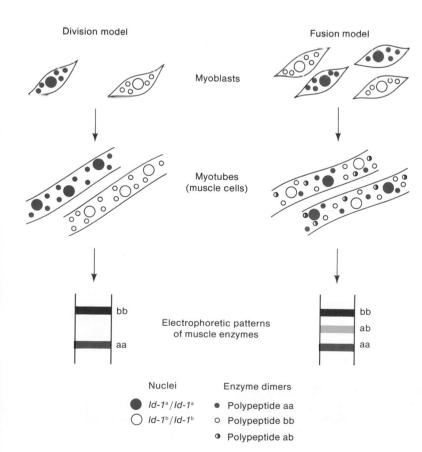

Figure 21-25. Predictions of differing results for electrophoresis of enzymes based on two different models for the origin of multinucleate muscle cells, or myotubes. If a myotube is formed by successive divisions of the nucleus in a single myoblast, the electrophoretic pattern should show only the parental enzyme bands. If a myotube is formed by fusion of numerous myoblasts, a third band should appear as a result of the formation of hybrid enzyme dimers within the cell that has nuclei of both genotypes. The experimental results support the fusion model.

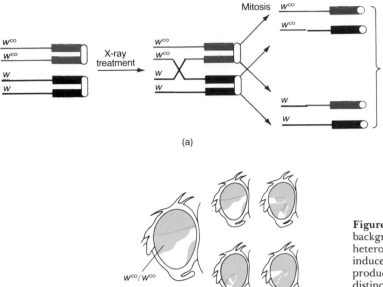

(a)

(b)

w^{co}/w^{co}

Figure 21-26. Production of twin spots of mutant tissue in a background of cells of a different phenotype. (a) Larvae heterozygous for the sex-linked alleles w and w^{co} are irradiated to induce a mitotic crossover in prospective eye cells. This crossover produces cells homozygous for w and w^{co} that are phenotypically distinct from the surrounding w/w^{co} tissue. (b) Some representative mosaic eyes. (Part b is after H. J. Becker, *Verhandl. deutsch. zool. Ges.*, 1956.)

example, in humans the sex-linked condition called Duchenne's muscular dystrophy involves a muscular degeneration that develops progressively. It is difficult to determine biologically whether this degeneration of muscle tissues is a direct result of the mutation or is a secondary effect due to genetically controlled changes in other tissues (such as nerve cells). A comparable hereditary condition exists in mice. Alan Peterson created tetraparental mice from normal lines and from lines carrying the gene for muscular dystrophy. These two lines also produce distinct forms of an enzyme. Peterson used the enzyme as a marker to determine the genetic origin of muscle cells in tetraparental mice showing the dystrophic phenotype. He found that such a mouse may have muscle cells derived from the normal line but that the nerve cells enervating the deteriorating muscles are always derived from the mutant line. Thus, it appears that the mutation has its direct effect on the nerve tissue, with the muscular deterioration appearing as a secondary effect due to the changes in nerve cells.

Message Genetic mosaics can be generated in a variety of ways. Such mosaics provide an extremely useful tool for following the destinies of cells and their daughters through development.

Genetic Mosaics in Drosophila

We have already seen the value of genetic mosaicism as an analytical tool. However, the chance detection or tedious experimental production of such mosaics makes any systematic use of this approach very difficult in many organisms. In *Drosophila*, a variety of procedures have been developed to make the production of numerous mosaics a relatively simple matter. Two general mechanisms are in-

volved in the formation of the mosaics: mitotic crossing-over and chromosome loss.

Mitotic Crossing-Over. We have already seen (Chapter 6) how mitotic pairing and crossing-over in *Drosophila* heterozygotes can produce "twin spots" of homozygous tissue. This provides a way of marking clonally related cells that can be presumed to come from a single crossover event. In 1957 Hans Becker used this method of marking in larvae heterozygous for w^{co} and w (different alleles of the *white* locus). He chose these genotypes because the phenotypes of w^{co}/w^{co}, w/w, and w^{co}/w can be distinguished from one another. Becker irradiated young larvae to induce mitotic crossovers. Such crossovers in w^{co}/w genotype lead to twin spots of homozygous w/w and w^{co}/w^{co} tissue (Figure 21-26). If the mitotic crossover is induced at an early stage of eye development, a large segment of the adult eye will derive from the daughter cells of the mitosis at which the crossover occurred, so the twin spot will cover a large part of the eye. If the crossover is induced late in eye development, then the twin spot will involve relatively few facets of the adult eye. Studying many such crossovers and mapping the twin spots, Becker was able to trace the **cell lineage** of the lower half of the eye to eight early larval cells. The daughter cells of each larval cell occupy one of the eight sectors shown in Figure 21-27. You can see how cell lineages are inferred from genetic mosaics.

In 1971, Antonio Garcia-Bellido and John Merriam used somatic crossing-over in an attempt to determine the time when a particular gene ceases to be active. They induced crossovers by irradiating females with the genotype $yHw+/++sn^3$ at different developmental stages. (Hw is a dominant mutation that causes the growth of extra bristles along wing veins and is closely linked to y, the mutation for yellow body color; sn^3 produces short, gnarled bristles and is more distantly linked.) Induced crossovers between the

sn^3 locus and the centromere produce twin spots, with one spot of the genotype $yHw+/yHw+$ and the other $++sn^3/++sn^3$. Garcia-Bellido and Merriam found that y Hw and sn^3 mutant patches can be induced by irradiation at any time during the third-instar larval stage or during the first 24 hours of the pupal stage. However, if the irradiation occurs during the last 12 hours of the third-instar stage or the first 24 hours of the pupal stage, the sn^3 patches also show the Hw phenotype. In other words, one spot of the twin spot is y Hw, and the other spot is Hw sn^3. No crossover pattern can explain this observation; the Hw alleles cannot be present in the sn^3 spot cells. Garcia-Bellido and Merriam concluded that the Hw allele somehow acts before the last 12 hours of larval life to imprint its phenotype irreversibly on the cell committed to form wing.

Chromosome Loss.   In 1929, Sturtevant observed that eggs from females of *Drosophila simulans* homozygous for the autosomal recessive mutation ca^{nd} (claret-nondisjunction) commonly lose a chromosome during the first and second divisions after fertilization. If the lost chromosome was an X, then a mosaic of XX (♀) and XO (♂) cells is formed. If the original fertilized egg was heterozygous (say, $++/wm$), then loss of the wild-type chromosome permits expression of the recessive phenotype in the hemizygous tissue (Figure 21-28). The resulting mosaic flies do *not* show a "salt-and-pepper" phenotype with male and female cells randomly arranged. The mosaic patterns observed indicate that nuclei more closely related by cell division tend to stay together. This observation led Sturtevant to the realization that the distribution of mutant and nonmutant tissue in a mosaic can provide information about the spatial relationships *in the embryo* of prospective adult nuclei.

Since Sturtevant's time, several different mutants that cause chromosome loss have been studied. The most useful, described by Claude Hinton in 1955, is a ring X chromosome called $In(1)w^{vC}$ (we'll call it w^{vC} for short) that has the completely mysterious property of great instability in the newly formed zygote nucleus. Thus, w^{vC} is lost at a very

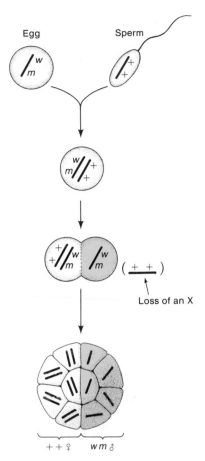

Figure 21-28. Production of a mosaic by the loss of an X chromosome shortly after fertilization in *Drosophila*. If the XO cells of the gynandromorph carry recessive markers on the X, then the mutant phenotype is visible. Loss of the X can be induced in a number of ways, including the presence of certain mutations or by irradiation. (From A. M. Srb, R. D. Owen, and R. S. Edgar, *General Genetics*, 2d ed. Copyright © 1965 by W. H. Freeman and Co.)

high frequency, and, if the egg was initially w^{vC}/m, gynandromorphs of w^{vC}/m (wild-type ♀) and m/O (mutant ♂) cells are created. This is an extremely useful aberration.

Using data originally obtained by Sturtevant in the 1930s, Garcia-Bellido and Merriam in 1969 set out to determine whether the pattern of mosaicism in adult flies can be used to infer relationships between cells in the embryo. But first we must understand the special nature of early embryonic development in *Drosophila*.

Early Embryonic Development.   After fertilization the zygotic nucleus undergoes a rapid series of divisions without separation into cells. Thus, the newly fertilized egg develops as a syncytium (a single multinucleated cell). In the posterior part of the egg is a region characterized by cytoplasmic inclusions called polar granules; as we have seen, these are maternally deposited elements that determine differentiation of the gonadal tissue. The nuclei divide synchronously. After the ninth division, when about 512 nuclei are present, they migrate to the periphery of the egg

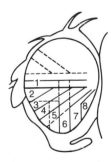

Figure 21-27. All of the cells in each sector of the lower eye of *Drosophila* are derived from one of eight original larval cells. (After H. J. Becker, *Verhandl. deutsch. zool. Ges.*, 1956.)

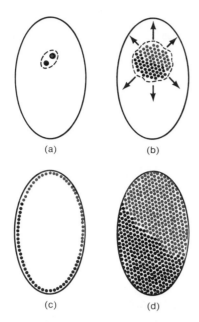

Figure 21-29. Early divisions leading to blastoderm formation in *Drosophila.* (a) The first division of the nucleus occurs shortly after fertilization. No division of the cytoplasm occurs. (b) After nine synchronous nuclear divisions without cell cleavage, the embryo is a syncitium with about 500 nuclei. The nuclei now begin to migrate to the periphery of the egg cytoplasm. (c) After a few more nuclear divisions, the cell has some 4000 to 8000 nuclei in a layer near its surface. (d) Cell membranes form to enclose each nucleus in a separate cell, thus forming the blastoderm stage of the embryo. (From S. Benzer, "Genetic Dissection of Behavior." Copyright © 1973 by Scientific American, Inc. All rights reserved.)

cytoplasm. After four more synchronous divisions, when there are 4000 to 8000 nuclei, cell membranes enclose them to form the mononucleated cells of the **blastoderm,** which is essentially a cell monolayer enclosing the yolk (Figure 21-29). All of these events occur within three hours after fertilization. An important feature of blastoderm for-

mation is that the pattern of nuclear migration is very ordered. Those nuclei most recently related by nuclear division remain nearer to one another than do more distantly related nuclei.

After the blastoderm stage, cell movements and folding of sheets of cells create the cell layers from which tissues will differentiate. Up to the blastoderm stage, the nuclei are totipotent, as Illmensee demonstrated by recovering adults after transplantation of blastoderm nuclei into enucleated eggs. However, after the blastoderm stage, each nucleus is restricted to a limited potential fate. Prospective cells for both various adult structures and larval structures are present in the surface of the blastoderm.

Fate Mapping. Now let us return to the Garcia-Bellido–Merriam analysis of Sturtevant's data. Such an analysis should be possible since the related nuclei are arranged in close proximity in the blastoderm. It appears that the orientation of the division plane for the first nuclear division is tilted randomly with respect to the anteroposterior and dorsoventral axes of the egg, because all kinds of mosaic patterns are formed in the adult (Figure 21-30). We can also assume that prospective cells for imaginal disks and for larval structures are distributed throughout the surface of the blastoderm.

If cells destined to form two structures are located close to each other within the blastoderm (and hence are probably closely related), then the chance that they are genetically *different* in a mosaic is small. (This is because the dividing line between mutant and nonmutant cells determined at first cleavage is randomly distributed on the blastoderm.) The farther apart the positions of the cells in the blastoderm, the greater is the probability that the dividing line will fall between them so that they will develop into

First cleavage

Mosaic produced

Figure 21-30. Orientation of the plane of the first nuclear division after fertilization. The spindle fibers can be tilted within the egg in any orientation with respect to the anterior-posterior poles of the cytoplasm. Because daughter nuclei tend to remain together and migrate to nearby locations at the egg surface, the orientation of the division plane determines the mosaic pattern observed in the adult (if the two nuclei produced from the first division are genetically different). (From S. Benzer, "Genetic Dissection of Behavior." Copyright © 1973 by Scientific American, Inc. All rights reserved.)

Figure 21-31. A hypothetical cut through the blastoderm to separate the right and left halves. The blastoderm fate maps are representations of the surface of one such half.

genetically different adult structures. Thus, the "distance" between blastoderm cells destined to become different adult structures can be quantified as the percentage of mosaics in which the two adult structures are genotypically different:

$$\frac{\text{distance between}}{\text{blastoderm cells}} = \frac{\text{number of mosaics in which structures differ} \times 100}{\text{total number of mosaics scored}}$$

What these "distances" mean in real physical terms is not yet known, but the same situation applied when linkage maps were first constructed. In this case, we can develop a two-dimensional map because the spatial distribution is over the surface of a hollow spheroid. We can standardize the surface as that seen when the spheroid is cut along the axis of symmetry, as shown in Figure 21-31. Suppose that we map structures A and B as 10 units apart. We can introduce a second dimension by measuring their distances from a third structure, C. If A is 8 units from C and B is 4 units from C, then we obtain the map shown in Figure 21-32. This point to which an adult structure maps on the blastoderm surface can be regarded as a **focus** from which the growth and movement of the structure proceeds during development and differentiation.

Using this map distance between embryonic foci for adult structures, Garcia-Bellido and Merriam were able to construct an embryonic "fate map" like that shown in Figure 21-33. These maps can be made as refined as we desire by studying ever more detailed features of the adult structures. Such maps are assumed to have some congruence with the actual spatial distribution of determined cells in the blastoderm.

In 1972, Yoshiki Hotta and Seymour Benzer took this analysis one step further by analyzing the foci pertinent to a mutant behavioral phenotype. Consider a recessive mutation that causes the legs of a fly to twitch when the fly is anesthetized; we can map the cells responsible for the twitch in relation to the external markers. Let's call the behavioral mutant *kic* (for *kicker*) and make a cross to generate *y kic/++* flies. A female that has no yellow tissue but exhibits leg kicking must have internal cells that are *y kic/O*.

We can calculate the distance from the focus for *kic* to the focus for the right front leg, for example, as

$$\frac{\begin{array}{c}\text{number of } y \text{ nonkicking legs} \\ + \text{ number of } y^+ \text{ kicking legs}\end{array}}{\text{total mosaics}} \times 100$$

where only the right front legs of mosaic flies are counted. Again, by triangulation with another focus, such as that for a thoracic bristle, we can map the focus for kicking.

Hotta and Benzer found that the mutants with presumed defects in leg muscles and nerves mapped near each other and near the foci of external leg structures. Their positions correspond very well with cytological studies of the neural and muscular tissues developing from blastoderm cells. Such cytological studies provide the reference points for orientation of the fate map to the poles of the blastoderm. With all of this evidence, we can construct a hypothetical map of the locations in the blastoderm of the ancestors of the imaginal disks (described in detail later in the chapter). Figure 21-34 presents a revised fate map. Of course, the mapping procedure becomes much more complex in the cases of the many neurological mutants that involve simultaneous defects in several anatomical positions.

Message The locations of cells destined to form particular adult structures can be mapped in relation to one another in the embryo by the use of mosaics.

The Genetics of Development

Once a developmental phenomenon has been described, how can we begin to probe it? In classical studies of development, embryologists disrupted the normal sequences me-

Figure 21-32. Embryonic map of cells destined to form adult structures A, B, and C. The map positions presumably represent the relative positions in the blastoderm of the cells from which these adult structures will eventually develop. The "distance" between blastoderm cells determined for different adult structures can be quantified as the percentage of mosaics in which two adult structures are genotypically different:

$$\frac{\text{number of mosaics in which structures are different}}{\text{total number of mosaics recorded}} \times 100$$

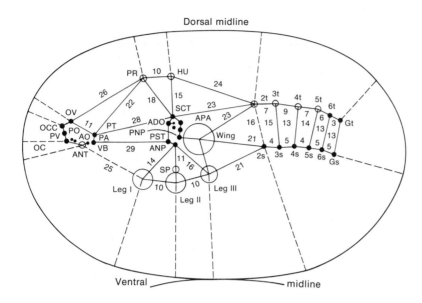

Figure 21-33. The embryonic fate map of adult structures. The map shows the foci for various structures and individual bristles. The distances between them are indicated in map units called **sturts.** (From S. Benzer, "Genetic Dissection of Behavior." Copyright © 1973 by Scientific American, Inc. All rights reserved.)

chanically. Parts of an embryo were destroyed, removed, replaced, or shifted to determine the consequences and to infer from such results the normal process. What tools can a geneticist bring to the problem? A mutation is comparable to the embryologist's scalpel, providing a method of disrupting developmental sequences to produce a mutant phenotype. In a sense, every mutant phenotype reflects an alteration in development.

Mutations Affecting Developmental Processes

Lethals. Some examples of hereditary abnormalities in domesticated animals have economic importance, as well as potential usefulness for the study of the developmental defect. Figure 21-35 shows fetuses with extreme contraction of muscles in the legs and neck that probably is a result of a muscular or neurological defect. The mutations pictured are lethal in that the affected animal fails to survive to adult-

hood. There are many examples of lethal mutations in laboratory animals. Ernst Hadorn studied a number in *Drosophila* and defined the **effective lethal phase** (LP) as the developmental period during which death occurs. In surveying many lethals, he showed that the bulk of the LPs fell in the embryonic or pupal stages, the two periods of great change in a fly's life. Many of the mutations exhibit very specific patterns of the abnormality that is the ultimate cause of death. For example, the strain lethal giant larva (*lgl*) has a phenotype of a prolonged larval life and continued growth prior to death. This results from a defect in production of hormones necessary for pupation. But can this phenotype be related to the primary action of the gene? The difficulty with as broad a phenotype as lethality, as with mutants with visible defects, is the pleiotrophy of a gene. In Chapter 4 (Figure 4-9), we saw how a primary defect in cartilage formation in rats resulted in a number of characteristic anomalies, such as problems in breathing, eating,

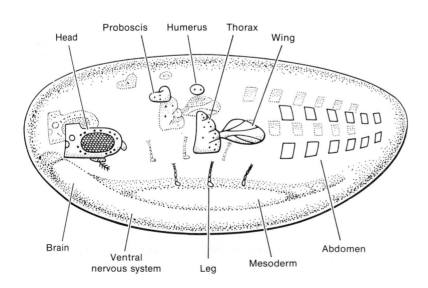

Figure 21-34. A redrawn version of the fate map in Figure 21-33, showing the adult fate of the cells that occupy specific regions of the embryo. Note that the anterior-posterior arrangement of adult structures is approximately retained in the arrangement of blastoderm cells. (From S. Benzer, "Genetic Dissection of Behavior." Copyright © 1973 by Scientific American, Inc. All rights reserved.)

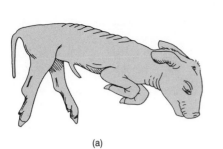
(a)

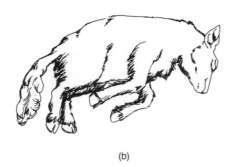
(b)

(c)

Figure 21-35. Lethal mutations with a similar phenotype in different domestic-animal species. Affected animals are born with muscles tightly flexed and often with the head pulled to one side. (a) Pig; (b) sheep; (c) cow.

and heart beat, which were a secondary consequence of the cartilage lesion. So it is often difficult to determine the primary gene effect.

The Bithorax Complex. The best example of the value of mutations in the study of development is a complex locus called the *bithorax* complex (BX-C) in *Drosophila*. Calvin Bridges discovered the first mutant in the BX-C, bx^1, but it was Ed Lewis who analyzed the many additional mutants in the locus and has doggedly persisted in its genetic analysis since 1948. Now Lewis is participating in the molecular corroboration of all of his genetic inferences. The evolutionary history of the Diptera—the two-winged flies—suggests that they came from four-winged flies. All that remains of the second pair of wings are vestigial balancing organs, called halteres (Figure 21-36). In turn, the ancestral four-winged insects probably evolved from arthropod forms with multiple legs, perhaps a millipede-like creature. Lewis reasoned that the evolutionary sequence must have occurred by an ancient mutation that suppressed leg formation in the abdominal segments and a later one that suppressed wing formation in one thoracic segment. Such changes do appear to have occurred and to have become the wild-type in the primordial dipteran and are now clustered in the BX-C. Recent mutations within the locus can

cause a loss of the suppressing function with a consequent reversal to a four-winged or multilegged insect.

The adult fly consists of a series of segments; the cells in each segment come from a small number of adjacent founding cells in the embryo. Each segment has a unique set of external markers that permit its unambiguous identification. Thus, the head is followed by three thoracic segments (prothorax, mesothorax, and metathorax, which are referred to as T1, T2, T3) and eight abdominals (labeled A1 to A8), as shown in Figure 21-37. Interestingly, the segments visible in the adult are mirrored in those recognizable in larvae, seen to the left in the figure. Mutations in the BX-C belong to a class called **homeotic,** which are mutations that convert one part of a body segment into another part of the same or a different body segment. Thus, for example, a strong *bx* mutation causes the anterior part of T3 to develop as the anterior part of T2. This is interpreted as showing that bx^+ must act in a specific part of the fly to direct those cells to differentiate to anterior T3. The inactivation of bx^+ by mutation leads to the automatic expression of those cells as anterior T2. We can conclude that bx^+ does not act in the cells that normally form anterior T2, since T2 is unaffected by a *bx* mutation. So, it is assumed that bx^+ acts like a binary switch—turned on in anterior T3 and turned off in anterior T2. Flies homozygous for a dele-

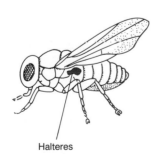

Halteres

Figure 21-36. The haltere of *Drosophila*. It is a vestigial wing that has evolved to serve as an organ of balance.

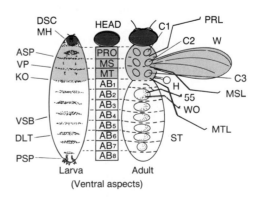

Figure 21-37. Ventral view of body segments of *Drosophila* larva and adult stages. In the larva (left), each of the 12 segments can be identified. The larval segments correspond to those in the adult (right).

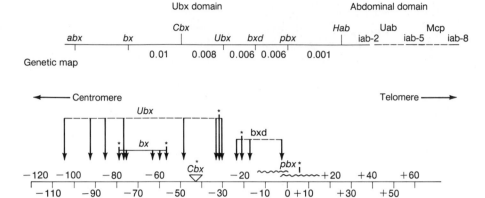

Genetic map

DNA map

Figure 21-38. The genetic and DNA maps of the *bithorax* complex. The mutants appear to be located in two domains, the Ubx and Abdominal, which affect thoracic and abdominal development, respectively. In the DNA map, each arrow points to the position of an alteration. Those arrows marked with an asterisk represent mutants also mapped genetically and show complete congruence with the genetic map.

tion of the entire *bx* locus die as late embryos. Inspection of those embryos at death reveals that T3, as well as each abdominal segment, resembles T2 (which carries the wing and second leg). Thus, T2 can be considered to be the "developmental ground state" in the absence of BX-C activity. Components of the BX-C are required to direct differentiation of the posterior segments along specialized lines. Recessive mutations that affect a specific segment transform it to a more anterior segment, that is, toward the ground state, and *can* be considered to be inactive alleles. There are also dominant mutations which transform structures away from the ground state.

The genetic map has also been correlated with DNA sequences that are known to overlap the BX-C locus (Figure 21-39). All the genetic data have been corroborated by sequence analysis. Lewis concludes, then, that there are spheres or domains of control by elements within the BX-C (Figure 21-39). In this model, Lewis proposes that each successive segment, proceeding from front to back, requires additional wild-type activity. We can now see how loss of a function results in reversion toward the ground state—toward the more anterior segment. This model leads to predictions about which segments each of the genes in the BX-C will function in (for example, *bx*⁺ should act in the anterior part of T3 but not T2). Remarkably, the use of labeled probes for the gene products from different parts of the BX-C permits these predictions to be tested, and they have been confirmed by in situ hybridization (Figure 21-40). The BX-C story is a wonderful example of how genetic analysis, when coupled with molecular tools, can provide profound insights into development.

Message Visible mutations in the *bithorax* complex reveal the genetic control over normal differentiation of *Drosophila* body segments.

Temperature-Sensitive Mutations. Can mutations that give other clues to their mode of actions be recovered? Lethal mutations whose expression is conditionally expressed provide an extra dimension for analysis in a variety of organisms from viruses to mammals. We've already seen how

the metabolic step affected by auxotrophic mutants can be inferred from the supplements necessary for survival. Another useful class is sensitive to temperature. Recall that temperature sensitivity reflects the thermolability of mutant proteins. Studies of temperature-sensitive (ts) mutations, under restrictive conditions, reveal their mutant phenotype; the actual time of sensitivity can be inferred from "shift" studies. Let us look at an example involving a tumor virus called Rous sarcoma virus. Normally, mammalian connective-tissue cells grow in culture as a flat sheet (Figure 21-41); upon infection with the virus, the cells become round and form clumps. This "transformation" is an in vitro indication of the changes associated with tumor formation in vivo. A Rous sarcoma virus gene, *src*, codes for an enzyme that phosphorylates proteins. A ts allele of *src* per-

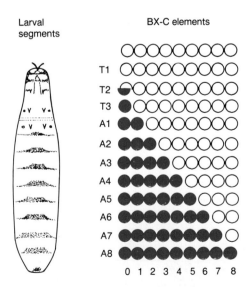

Figure 21-39. Model of function of the *bithorax* complex with larval segments. The BX-C is divided into nine elements (0 and 1 in the Ubx domain, the rest in the Abdominal). Active elements are filled in; inactive are open. The half-filled circle represents *Ubx*⁺ in the posterior compartment of T2. Note that in each progressively posterior segment, one more element is active.

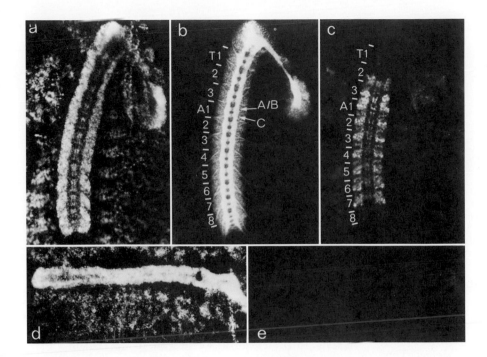

Figure 21-40. Visualization of *Ubx* gene product in the embryonic *Drosophila* nervous system by immunofluorescence. A bacterial clone containing the 5′ *Ubx* exon was used to synthesize a partial *Ubx* protein sequence and antibodies to this were prepared. The antibodies were joined to a fluorescent dye and added to the embryo, where they were bound to the *Ubx* protein in situ. Fluorescence is seen from the posterior T2 through A8 segments as predicted by Lewis' model. (a) Wild-type embryo. (b) The same preparation as in (a) stained for neural tissue. (c) The same preparation as in (a) tagged with fluorescent antibodies for the *Ubx* protein. Note the total absence of product in T1 and the posterior localization in other segments. (d) An embryo, *Df bxd*[100], carrying a deletion for the *Ubx* region. (e) The same preparation as in (d) stained with fluorescent antibodies to the *Ubx* protein.

mits the shifting of cultures between restrictive and permissive temperatures (Figure 21-42). This reveals that transformation is not irreversibly determined at a specific time but rather is maintained by the continued presence of wild-type enzymes.

The utility of imposing "pulses" of restrictive temperatures on a ts strain was strikingly shown in the analysis of a mutation in *Drosophila* discovered by Thomas Grigliatti. The allele, *shibire* temperature-sensitive 1 (*shi*[ts1]), was named after the Japanese word for paralysis. Flies with the *shi*[ts1] gene develop normally at 22°C but when adults are transferred to a container at 29°C, they become paralyzed within minutes and eventually die. However, if shifted back to 22°C, the flies recover mobility within minutes. Cultures shifted from 22° to 29°C at different developmental stages revealed a succession of different lethal phases (LPs); it was found that larvae can also be paralyzed. When cultures were exposed to short "pulses" of 29°C and the surviving adults inspected, a range of phenotypic defects in bristles, hairs, and eyes was found to be induced at different times (Figure 21-43). These pleiotropic effects of the *shi* locus were detectable only by the property of temperature sensitivity. The gene specifies a product involved in nerve transmission of impulses.

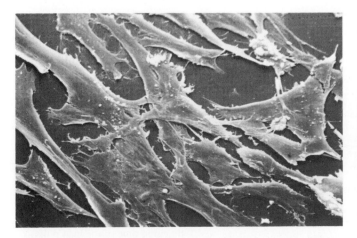

Figure 21-41. Scanning electron micrographs of connective tissue cells (fibroblasts) before (left) and after (right) infection with Rous sarcoma virus. The normal cells form a flat, extended sheet; transformed cells become round and clump together. (Courtesy G. Steven Martin.)

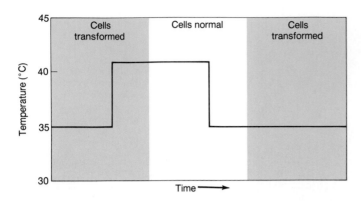

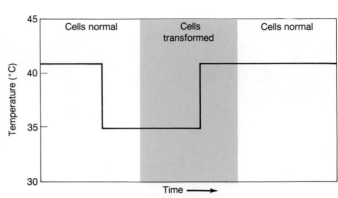

Figure 21-42. Shift studies of cells infected by Rous sarcoma virus carrying a temperature-sensitive allele of *src*. At 35°C, cells are transformed (i.e., *src* is active), but a few hours after a shift to 41°C, the cells revert to normal. Upon return to 35°C, the cells again become transformed after a few hours. Reciprocal shifts give reciprocal results. These tests show that the *src* gene must be continuously active for the transformation phenotype and that its product turns over in a few hours.

Message The conditional expression of a mutant phenotype permits a more precise determination of the time of gene activity and the nature of the primary defect. Temperature sensitivity is a particularly useful property.

Drosophila Development

In contrast to development in vertebrates, many organisms like insects go through two very distinct life forms. The mosquito and dragonfly, for example, live their early lives as nymphs underwater and emerge into the air as flying insects. In *Drosophila*, as we've seen, nuclei remain totipotent during the early stages of embryogenesis. But at some point they change and as the nuclei differentiate, they fall into two classes with very different prospects. One set of cells must develop into a larva that tunnels into its food and, although lacking vision, responds to temperature, gravity, light, and odors while crawling, eating, and excreting; it is a sophisticated organism with a central nervous system that coordinates its behavior in response to environmental stim-

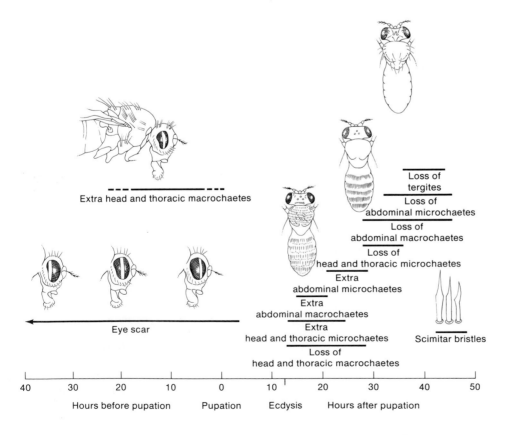

Figure 21-43. Temporal relationships of the temperature-sensitive periods for the various visible abnormalities of *shi*^ts1 flies, with diagrammatic representations of some of these abnormalities. The horizontal lines indicate the time during development when a heat pulse can produce the various abnormalities. Note the change in position of the eye scar with the changing time of the heat pulse (29°C). This corresponds to the location of mitotically active cells. (From Poodry et al., *Dev. Biol.* 32:381, 1973.)

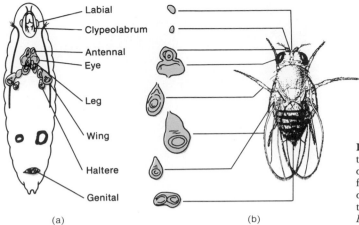

Labial
Clypeolabrum
Antennal
Eye
Leg
Wing
Haltere
Genital

(a)   (b)

Figure 21-44. The imaginal disks of *Drosophila*. (a) The larva in the third-instar stage of development, showing the positions of the disks. The larva is significantly larger than the adult. (b) The adult fly, showing the part that is derived from each disk. Note that the disks can be identified by their differing sizes and shapes as well as by their positions in the larva. (From J. W. Fristrom, in *Problems in Biology*, University of Utah Press, 1969.)

uli. The other set of cells will shape a second organism that will emerge from the larval carcass as an adult fly bearing no resemblance to its larval predecessor and capable of seeing, walking, flying, and mating. This remarkable transformation is anticipated in the larva by the presence of packets of cells programmed to differentiate into external adult tissue upon exposure to the proper hormonal cues. These packets of cells are called **imaginal disks** (often known simply as disks). They can be recognized by their sizes, shapes, and locations in the larva (Figure 21-44).

How do we know that the disks are already programmed (determined) for an adult fate? An eye disk, for example, can be removed and implanted in another larval host, which then pupates and emerges as an adult. This adult will have, somewhere within its body, extra adult eye structures derived from the implanted disk! Similar results are obtained with each of the other disk types. The stimulus for the differentiation of the already determined disk is the molting hormone ecdysone, which is released in the late third-instar stage of the larva. This effect can be demonstrated by isolating disks from late third-instar larvae and exposing them to ecdysone; they will then begin to differentiate.

On pupation, the larval carcass begins to break down. Its residues act as a thick medium nourishing and embedding each of the disks. The disks now begin to differentiate into their specific adult structures, so that each part of the adult forms as a separate element. The separate elements then fuse with the correct neighbors to form a complete adult.

The imaginal disks play no functional role in the larva. A series of mutants has been recovered lacking all imaginal disks or specific sets of disks. These mutant larvae are completely viable until after much of pupation, when they die. The incredibly intricate and precise program whereby the disks are activated and differentiate into adult structures is acted out each time a fly is "born." You can see that mutations blocking various parts of this complex developmental process provide a great deal of information about the process itself. They also provide evidence about the genetic system controlling the process.

Time of Disk Determination

Let's now go back and examine a few parts of the *Drosophila* development process in more detail. At what point in development are the nuclei of the embryo committed to become parts of specific imaginal disks? The answer was provided by using techniques for culturing cells in vivo. Larval cells can be transplanted into an adult host (by injection). The cells escape exposure to ecdysone, which triggers metamorphosis, so they simply proliferate as larval cells in the adult host. The clone of larval cells can then be removed from the adult host and used for experimentation. For example, the cell mass can be implanted in a larval host about to undergo metamorphosis, so that the differentiation of the cells upon ecdysone stimulation can be studied. (Recall Illmensee's experiments, in which blastoderm nuclei were shown to be totipotent because they developed normally when transplanted into enucleated eggs.)

In 1971, Lilian Chan and Walter Gehring performed an experiment with a *Drosophila* genotype distinct from the wild-type. They took a blastoderm and bisected it into anterior and posterior halves. They then dissociated the cells from each half, compacted them into pellets by centrifugation, and injected the pellets into adult hosts for culturing (Figure 21-45). Next they removed the cultures of larval cells from the adult host and injected them into wild-type larval hosts, where their differentiation could be observed after metamorphosis. (The distinctive genotype of the experimental cells distinguished them from the cells of the host.) Chan and Gehring found that the cells from the anterior half of the blastoderm developed into anterior adult structures (head and thorax), whereas the cells from the posterior half of the blastoderm developed into posterior adult structures (thorax and abdomen). These results indicate that the developmental fate of the blastoderm cells was already determined; the cells retained their determined status even through repeated rounds of division in the adult host.

Further evidence of early determination comes from studies on damaged embryos. If the blastoderm is punctured, burned, or subjected to ultraviolet irradiation in spe-

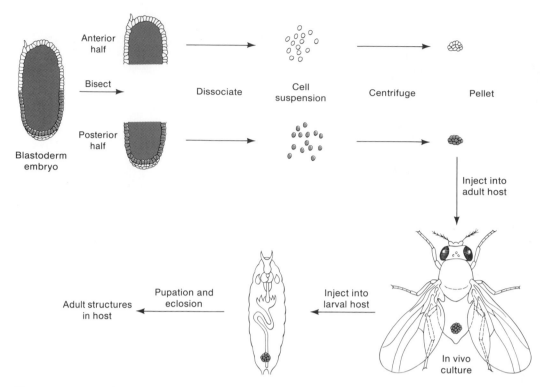

Figure 21-45. Experimental technique for testing the developmental fate of blastoderm cells. The cells multiply by mitotic division in the adult host but do not undergo differentiation. After a larger mass of cells is obtained from in vivo culture in the adult, their determination state is tested by implanting them into a larval host. These cells will now undergo differentiation just as will the imaginal structures of the host larva. When an adult fly emerges, it can be dissected, and the adult fate of the donor cells can be observed.

cific regions of the embryo, then the adult fly that develops from the embryo shows damage in specific structures corresponding to the damaged part of the blastoderm. Illmensee showed that the cell nuclei remain totipotent until after the blastoderm stage. Therefore, we can conclude that the early determination is an effect of the cytoplasm. Further experiments indicate that this early determination occurs at roughly the time when the nuclei are enclosed by membranes to form the blastoderm cells.

As we have seen in the example of snail-shell coiling (Chapter 20), the egg cytoplasm contains developmental cues dictated by the genotype of the mother. Therefore, we would expect to find mutations that are expressed in females as an abnormal phenotype *in their offspring*. The *grandchildless* mutation of *Drosophila* mentioned earlier in this chapter is an example of just such a mutation.

Message The pattern of determination of embryonic cells is apparently established in the cytoplasm of the multinucleate egg, and it is under the control of the maternal genotype.

Disk Development

In the embryo, the imaginal disk originates as a small number of cells that are programmed to form specific parts of adult structures. The number of founding cells of a disk can be estimated by inducing genetic mosaics by chromosome loss or mitotic crossing-over, as already described. Suppose that we obtain XO/XX mosaics formed by a chromosome loss. If a disk originates from a single determined cell, no mosaic adult could have both male and female tissue in the adult derivative of that disk. On the other hand, if two cells begin a disk, then the adult structure they form could be a mosaic of 50 percent male and 50 percent female cells. It could, of course, be entirely male or female, depending on the location of the boundary between X/O and X/X nuclei. Thus, the smallest proportion occupied by mutant tissue in a mosaic structure provides an estimate of the number of founding cells, and among disks this number ranges from eight to 40. Determination must occur progressively as the cell number increases, since there are far more structures derived from a mature disk than there are cells in the founding group. It should be obvious that another way to derive a fate map of the cells within a disk is by cutting the disk into different fragments and implanting the fragments into larval hosts to see what adult structures they form.

Homeotic Mutations. Two exceptions have been encountered to the normal process of disk development. One exception occurs in homeotic mutations. Recall that the BX-C mutations are one example of these. As another example, the mutation *ophthalmoptera* causes wing structures to develop from an eye disk, whereas the mutation *aristapedia* causes the feathery arista of the antennal complex to develop as a leg instead (Figure 21-46). In the 1940s, many of

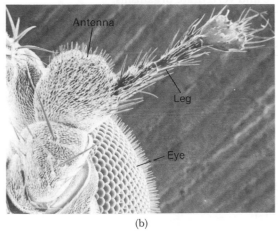

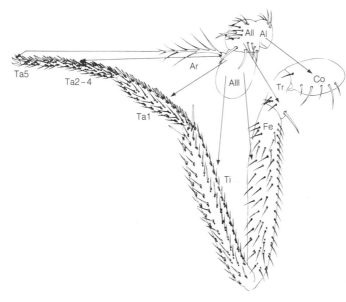

Figure 21-47. The correspondence between antennal and leg structures in *Drosophila,* based on position-specific transformations in homeotic antennae of *Antennapedia.* The symbols identify various corresponding parts of the structures. (From J. Postlethwait and H. Schneiderman, *Developmental Biology* 25:606, 1971.)

Figure 21-46. Scanning electron micrographs of the antennal complex of *Drosophila,* showing the effects of a homeotic mutation. (a) A wild-type fly. (b) A mutant fly in which the feathery arista is replaced by the distal part of a leg. This mutation is called *aristapedia.* (c) Four-winged *Drosophila* produced by combining three homeotic mutations of the *bithorax* gene complex. The haltere-bearing (3rd) thoracic segment closely resembles the wing-bearing (2nd) thoracic segment, as a result of reduction in function of three genes of the complex: *abx, bx³,* and *pbx.* (Part c provided by E. B. Lewis.)

the homeotic mutations were found to be temperature sensitive. Temperature-shift experiments were performed to determine the developmental stage at which the homeotic transitions occur. Almost all of these studies indicate that the temperature-sensitive periods occur during the third-instar stage of larval development. After that stage, the fate of each disk seems to be firmly determined in a way that cannot be affected by these mutations.

In 1969, John Postlethwait and Howard Schneiderman studied the dominant mutation *Antennapedia,* which converts part of the antenna into leg structures. By inducing mitotic crossovers in a heterozygote, they were able to generate a mosaic of wild-type cells in an *Antennapedia* background. They showed that the replacement of parts is position-specific — that is, a given antennal segment is always replaced by a specific part of the leg (Figure 21-47). These observations suggest that there is some overall developmental plan on which the specific details of leg or antennal development are overlaid.

Most of the homeotic mutations fall in two clusters on the right arm of chromosome 3: the *Antennapedia* complex (ANT-C) and *bithorax* complex (BX-C) discussed previously. While BX-C controls the posterior thoracic and abdominal segments, genes in the ANT-C affect head and thorax. In three different homeotic strains affecting segmentation, Walter Gehring's group discovered a small shared region in the 3′ exon of each gene. These shared sequences are 180 base pairs long and are called **homeo boxes.** They have subsequently been found associated with

BX-C

ANT

Fig
con
be
to
abc
will

produce YY males. Treatment of a YY egg with estrogen also leads to development of an individual with female phenotype. A cross of YY females with YY males obviously must produce only male progeny. It is clear that the X and Y chromosomes in this species must be very similar in their genetic content; otherwise, the YY genotype would produce an abnormal phenotype because of a lack of genes carried on the X chromosome. Analogous results have been obtained in frogs, which have a W-Z sex-determining mechanism. A WZ female tadpole that is fed male hormones (androgens) will develop into an adult with a male phenotype. A cross of such WZ males with WZ females produces some WW females, and these also can be modified by hormones to produce a male phenotype.

Ploidy.   In hymenopteran species (bees, wasps, and so on), sex is typically determined by the ploidy (or number of sets of chromosomes) of the egg, which is controlled by the mother. For example, a honeybee queen (whose diploid number is 32) can lay two types of eggs. By controlling the sphincter of her sperm receptacle (which holds sperm previously obtained in matings with males), she produces a fertilized egg (a zygote having 32 chromosomes and developing into a female) or an unfertilized egg (a zygote having 16 chromosomes and developing into a male). The diploid (female) zygotes can differentiate into either workers or queens, depending on the diet they consume during development. This is a striking example of chromosomal control of basic sexual constitution with environmental factors controlling subsequent differentiation.

Balance Theory.   Recall C. B. Bridges' studies of nondisjunction in *Drosophila* (Chapter 3). He showed that an XXY sex constitution forms phenotypically normal female flies and that an XO constitution forms sterile male flies. Obviously, the Y chromosome is necessary for male fertility but not for development of the male phenotype. What does determine sex in *Drosophila?* Triploid flies carrying three X chromosomes and three sets of autosomes are normal females. Let us represent a complete set of autosomes as A, so we can write this genotype as 3X:3A. When triploid females are crossed with normal males, some offspring having different combinations of X chromosomes and autosomes can survive. Bridges found that flies carrying two X chromosomes and three sets of autosomes (2X:3A) are **intersexes,** having phenotypic characteristics intermediate between those of the two sexes. He concluded that sex-determining genes are present on both the X chromosome and the autosomes and that the *balance* between these two kinds of chromosomes determines the phenotypic sex.

For example, suppose that the male-determining genes are on the autosomes and that the female-determining genes are on the X chromosome. In the normal flies, the XX genotype (with an X:A ratio of 2X:2A = 1.0) is female, and the XY genotype (1X:2A = 0.5) is male. If the

X:A ratio in fact determines the sex, it is not surprising to find that 3X:3A flies (ratio = 1.0) are female and that XO flies (1X:2A = 0.5) are male. The 2X:3A flies have an intermediate ratio of 0.67, and the corresponding phenotype is intermediate. This model is confirmed by the observation of 1X:3A (=0.33) individuals that have an extreme male phenotype and 3X:2A (=1.5) individuals that have an extreme female phenotype. (Both of these abnormal genotypes produce very weak individuals that would have poor chances of survival in normal environments.) This **balance model** for sex determination in *Drosophila* seems to explain the observations very well.

Message   In *Drosophila,* sex is determined by the balance between male-determining genes on the autosomes and female-determining genes on the X chromosome.

The notion of a "balance" between sex chromosome and autosomal segments implies a weighing of blocks of chromatin. But are there specific loci involved? The existence of major sex-influencing genes was suggested when Sturtevant discovered an autosomal gene called *transformer (tra).* Both *tra* and *transformer-2 (tra-2),* another locus on a different autosome, have no effect on XY males, but XX zygotes homozygous for either gene become phenotypic males. These transformed "males" are sterile, but have all of the external features of males, internal male genital duct systems, and male courtship behavior. An autosomal mutant makes both XX and XY zygotes intersexes, whereas yet another mutation, *intersex,* has no effect on XY males but makes XX flies intersexes. Clearly, there are important loci whose normal alleles initiate the major events to drive a zygote to differentiate as one sex or the other.

Cancer

As we've seen, the study of abnormalities in mutants often provides insights into the normal process of development. In the case of cancer, there is a double payoff: knowledge about normal differentiation and control of cell division gained by studying this abnormal process and, as a bonus, the potential to cure the disease. Tumors are aggregates of cells derived from an initial aberrant founder cell that, although surrounded by normal tissue, is no longer integrated into that environment. Cancer cells often differ from their neighbors by a host of specific phenotypic changes, such as rapid division, invasion of new cellular territories, high metabolic rate, new membrane antigens, altered shapes, and so on. Clearly, the factors regulating normal cell differentiation have been altered, and the interest is in the primary causes of alterations. Is the multiplicity of changes a reflection of several defects within the tumor

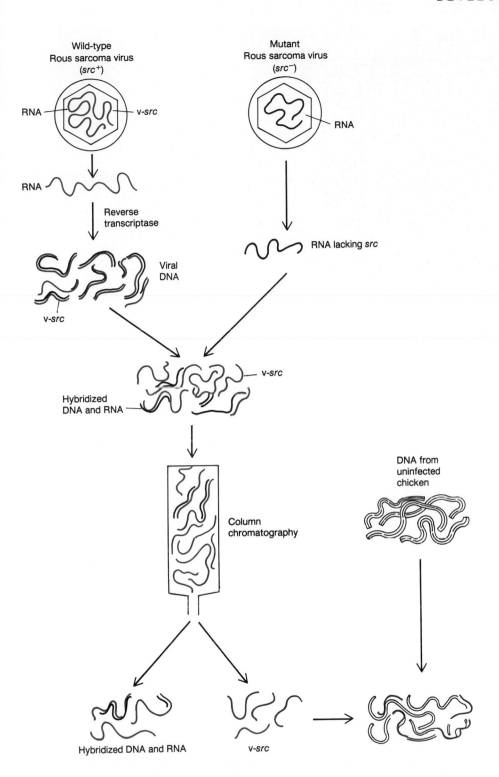

Figure 21-54. Demonstration that proto-oncogenes exist in normal cells. The oncogenic virus RNA is used to make DNA, which is hybridized to mutant viral RNA lacking the oncogene. The viral oncogene can be separated by column chromatography as unhybridized material, which in turn can be used as a probe to hybridize with complementary sequences in normal chicken DNA.

cells, or a pleiotropic result of a single lesion? Recently, dramatic new insights have been gained that provide knowledge of normal cell functions and directions for treatment.

Environment versus Heredity. Is there an underlying basis for tumor induction common to all cancers? For decades, scientists have searched for such a mechanism. The observations that radiation and certain chemicals are carcino-

genic pointed to one or more "targets" of such agents in cells. The known mutagenicity of many of the carcinogens also suggested that DNA might be one of the targets. Well-documented inherited types of cancer such as retinoblastoma and xeroderma pigmentosum do occur, but such types make up a small proportion of all known cancers. Indeed, it is now agreed by most cancer experts that up to 80 percent of all tumors are induced by environmental factors.

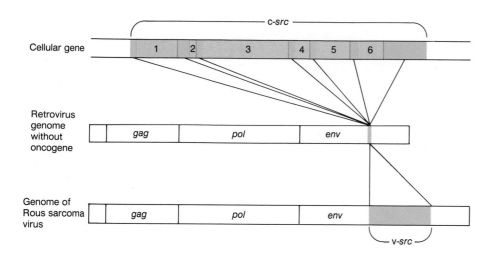

Figure 21-55. A comparison between the viral oncogene and cellular proto-oncogene *(c-src)*. The proto-oncogene consists of both exons and introns. Somehow a retrovirus (center) was able to pick up the RNA without the introns and attach it at the end of the virus genome.

Tumor Viruses. How can researchers approach the question of the cause of tumor formation? This field of study is known as oncology. Back in 1910, Peyton Rous showed evidence for a "filterable agent" (which was how viruses were defined then) that induced the kind of tumor called sarcoma in chickens. For years, his colleagues didn't believe his claims, but eventually, the Rous sarcoma virus became an important tool in the study of tumors. A number of oncogenic (cancer-causing) viruses have been demonstrated in experimental animals, but in spite of an intensive search, they have proved elusive in humans. Nevertheless, the study of oncogenic viruses has led to concepts relevant to human disease.

In the early 1960s, Marguerite Vogt and Renato Dulbecco showed that hamster embryonic fibroblasts grown in vitro underwent a profound cellular transformation when infected with polyoma virus. As we've already seen, the transformed phenotype is a reflection of the cancerous state, since transformed cells form tumors upon injection into an animal. (Most, but not all, oncogenic viruses induce transformation in vitro.) Vogt and Dulbecco demonstrated that transformation was a consequence of specific genes brought in by the virus. Mutation or deletion of those genes prevented transformation and tumor-forming capability. Thus, with oncogenic viruses at least, the tumor phenotype is the product of a limited number of genes.

Oncogenes. The Rous sarcoma virus belongs to a group called **retroviruses,** so named because, unlike polyoma, which has a DNA genome, their RNA is transcribed "backward" (retro) by reverse transcriptase to make DNA. Transformation of cells by Rous sarcoma virus is found to result from the action of a single gene, called *src,* at one end of the RNA molecule. Here, then, is a single gene that causes cancer. Such a gene is called an **oncogene.** What is the function of the *src* oncogene? The virus can multiply with no difficulty even when the *src* locus is deleted, so the oncogene is obviously not necessary for survival. By comparing proteins made by Rous sarcoma virus with and without *src,* Raymond Erikson and his colleagues identified a protein product: an enzyme, called a protein kinase, that phosphorylates (attaches phosphate groups) the amino acid

tyrosine. Phosphorylation affects the activity of a protein. Thus, the src protein alters protein activity and can be considered to be regulatory; it is found concentrated in cell membranes and appears to alter the adhesive properties of membrane proteins.

Origin of src. But where did *src* come from if it plays no role in viral growth? Using radioactive *src* RNA (Figure 21-54), Michael Bishop's group found that in uninfected chicken cells, complementary DNA exists. This shows that *src* DNA is a normal part of the chicken genome. A comparison of viral DNA coding for the viral src protein with the homologous chicken DNA revealed an interesting difference (Figure 21-55). The chicken *src* DNA is typical of eukaryotes with a number of introns, whereas the virally made DNA lacks the introns—suggesting that the virus had somehow picked up processed mRNA from which the introns were cleaved. Nor is the existence of DNA related to *src* in normal cells unique. Almost every (15 out of 16) retrovirus oncogene tested so far has one or more closely related DNA sequences in uninfected host cells.

Is attachment of an oncogene to the viral genome necessary for its oncogenic activity? George Vande Wonde and Edward Scolnick attached isolated cellular oncogenes (one from a mouse, two from rats) to a viral promotor. This engineered DNA was found to transform cells in vitro, thereby suggesting that cancer-causing ability reflects the rate of transcription of the DNA.

Message Mammalian cell transformation provides an in vitro assay for cancer induction. Viral induction of tumors is due to oncogenes that are not necessary for viral reproduction and appear to be derived from the normal genome of uninfected cells. Tumor induction, therefore, is a reflection of abnormal regulation of gene activity.

The hope that oncogenic viruses would be the primary cause of cancer in humans has not been realized; yet studies of viral oncogenes have converged with an exciting new approach.

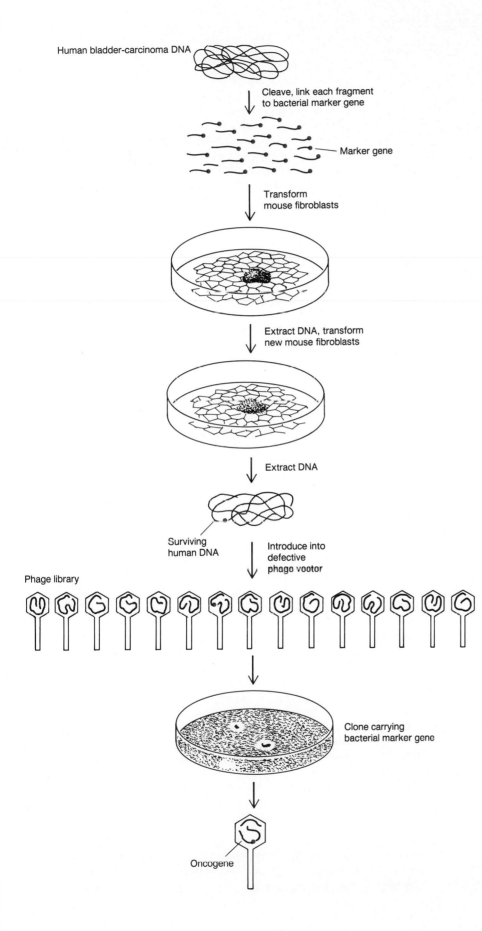

Human bladder-carcinoma DNA

Cleave, link each fragment
to bacterial marker gene

Marker gene

Transform
mouse fibroblasts

Extract DNA, transform
new mouse fibroblasts

Extract DNA

Surviving
human DNA

Introduce into
defective
phage vector

Phage library

Clone carrying
bacterial marker gene

Oncogene

Figure 21-56. Method for identifying the DNA clone carrying a human oncogene. DNA from a human bladder tumor was extracted and cleaved; each fragment was attached to a bacterial marker gene and then used to transform mouse cells. DNA from transformed cells is then cleaved and cloned in a defective phage that can only grow in the presence of the bacterial gene to which the human DNA was originally linked. Upon plating onto bacteria, the presence of the bacterial gene is indicated by phage plaques, which are then tested for the oncogene.

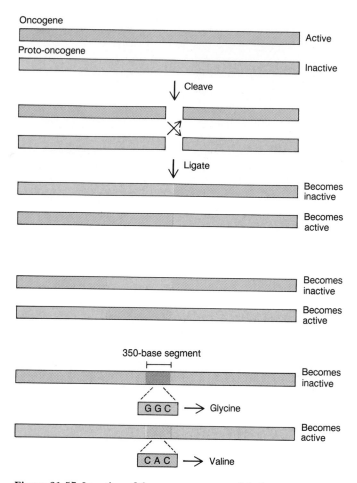

Figure 21-57. Location of the sequence responsible for oncogenicity. With restriction enzymes, the proto-oncogene and oncogene are cleaved at the same site, the fragments recombined, and the recombinants tested for transforming activity. In this way, the exact position was narrowed to a 350-base-pair region, which was sequenced. The cause of oncogenic activity was a single-base change (G → A) that results in a valine substitution for glycine.

Cell Transformation with DNA. How could investigators test the involvement of DNA in tumor formation? In 1978, Chiaho Shih and Robert Weinberg devised a direct test based on the original method of Avery and his coworkers (Chapter 13) to prove that DNA is the genetic material. They took DNA from tumors and used it as "transforming principle" to induce the cellular phenotypic changes that (unfortunately) are also called transformation. In other words, they were asking whether the DNA of tumor viruses was oncogenic. They found that it is! Since DNA of tumor cells is oncogenic, cell transformation is a phenotypic indication of the uptake and incorporation of DNA oncogenes. Then the question was whether a large number of different genes present in the high concentration of DNA, to which the cells were exposed, was responsible. Shih and Weinberg ruled out this possibility by extracting DNA from transformed cells and retransforming normal cells. This could be repeated through three or four cycles. Since extraction of DNA is accompanied by its fragmentation into numerous pieces, only a few of which are actually taken up by the

transformed cells, the factor(s) responsible for transformation must remain intact in a single molecule. This conclusion is based on the observation that mammalian DNA transfection results *not* in homologous recombination, as in bacteria or yeast, but in insertion at any of a number of nonhomologous sites. We can conclude, as was the case with oncogenic viruses, that the multiple phenotypic changes signaling cell transformation are pleiotropic effects of a small number (perhaps even one) of lesions.

Message DNA from tumor cells transforms cells in vitro; therefore, the basis for cancer formation rests in the DNA itself.

Recovery of Oncogenes from Normal Cells. The retrovirus genome, being RNA, provides a convenient probe to search for complementary sequences in the host DNA. But without such a probe, how can an oncogene be recovered from the vast number of sequences in a normal cell? Three different approaches have been successful. First, DNA is fragmented into pieces and attached to a vector, such as the phage λ, for cloning. In this way, a library of cloned sequences is constructed. Geoffrey Cooper searched for the oncogene of chicken lymphoma by screening ever smaller subsets of the several hundred thousand cloned sequences. Thus, initially, he divided the total genome into ten groups and tested each for its transforming ability. He then subdivided the portion that was oncogenic into ten samples and tested them; each successive test group represented a tenfold decrease in DNA quantity. He eventually identified the cloned sequence carrying the oncogene.

Shih and Weinberg applied a different principle in the search for a human bladder oncogene. Mouse cells were transformed with DNA from the human tumor. DNA from the transformed mouse cells was used to transform another set of mouse cells. Since only fragments of transforming DNA are actually taken up, the second round of transformed mouse cells must contain the human oncogene and very little other human DNA. As we've already seen, human-specific repeat sequences belonging to the *Alu* family are found widely distributed throughout the genome. Shih and Weinberg used the *Alu*-specific probe to identify clones carrying human DNA. Fortunately, the human bladder oncogene did carry an *Alu* sequence and was found.

Michael Wigler developed a technique that obviated the search through subsets and the requirement for *Alu* sequences. He, too, took DNA from a human bladder carcinoma and fragmented it. Before using the fragments as transforming principle, he attached a bacterial marker to each fragment (Figure 21-56). Cells were then transformed, and DNA from transformed cells was extracted and cloned. Each clone was tested for the presence of the

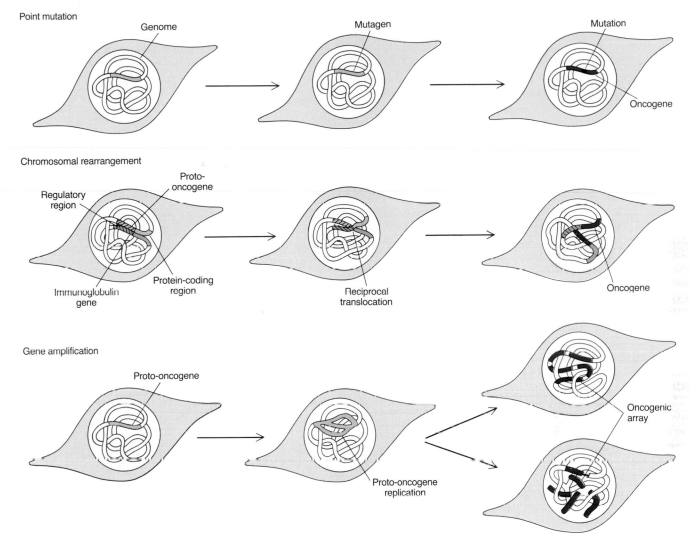

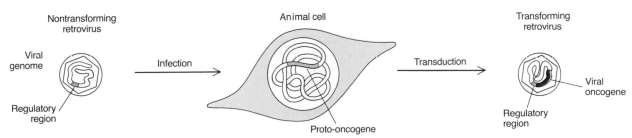

Figure 21-58. Proposed mechanisms of activation of proto-oncogenes. From top down: A point mutation induced by a chemical or radiation carcinogen can cause a change in the protein, thereby initiating cancerous growth. Another possibility is the induction of a chromosomal rearrangement that places the proto-oncogene next to the regulatory regions of an immunoglobulin gene. This will lead to the expression of the proto-oncogene inappropriately. If the proto-oncogene is amplified either as repeat segments within the chromosome or extrachromosomally, the gene product will be overproduced. The final possibility is the retrovirus transfer of a proto-oncogene picked up in another animal cell.

bacterial gene by infecting bacterial cells in which the phage vector was unable to grow unless it carried the bacterial marker. In this way, the bladder oncogene was readily detected.

Message   It is possible to isolate oncogenes from tumor cell DNA using a variety of techniques. The identified oncogenes show that tumor formation results from a change in a small segment of the total genome.

This is just one of the current views. There are others about the number (≥ 2) and type of genes that must mutate to change from normal to malignant. The cell line used in Shih and Weinberg's experiments is already one step from normal; other cell lines give different results. Once oncogene DNA is isolated, it in turn can be used as a probe to hybridize with any complementary sequences that might exist in a normal genome. Such sequences have been found. Obviously, they cannot be identical to the oncogene sequences or tumors would develop, but they are sufficiently closely related to form hybrids with the probe. The sequences found in normal cells are called **proto-oncogenes.** Such oncogene-related sequences have been found in other mammals, in chickens, and even in *Drosophila*, thereby showing that they must have existed more than 600,000,000 million years ago before these diverse groups separated.

Oncogene Fine Structure.   Identification of a specific oncogene and a proto-oncogene allows the determination of the part of the oncogene DNA responsible for tumorigenicity. Weinberg's group found the answer using a classic method of genetic analysis, recombination. With restriction enzymes, oncogenes and proto-oncogenes were cleaved at identical points, and the segments recombined (Figure 21-57). Each recombinant molecule was tested for its ability to transform cells. In this way, the active site was precisely pinpointed to a segment of 350 nucleotide pairs, which was then sequenced. Astonishingly, the difference between oncogene and proto-oncogene was in a single base pair of a 5000-bp sequence! As a result of a single amino acid substitution, a normal protein apparently is sufficiently changed to produce an aberrant phenotype of cancer. There are still many questions to be answered, but the identification and manipulation of oncogenes provides a powerful means of resolving the basic features of tumor formation. From such an understanding should emerge a clearer picture of the normal regulation of cell differentiation, as well as strategies for treating cancer.

Message   Oncogenes may differ from related proto-oncogenes in normal cells by a single base change. The identi-

fication of and ability to manipulate oncogenic sequences provides a powerful tool for the study of cancer.

The current model of how a proto-oncogene may be activated to produce a tumor is shown in Figure 21-58.

Immunogenetics

All aspects of a complex organism's phenotype are ultimately traced to the differential expression of genes, so all eventually come under the umbrella of genetic regulation. Thus, the blood-producing system, liver, brain, and other organs and structures all represent specific examples of how differentiation occurs. In this sense, the immune system may also be seen as another example of specialized gene regulation. However, there exist unique uses of the genetic material that set this particular system apart from others. Immunogenetics has grown explosively in the past decade and is often taught today as an entire course. We shall concentrate here on only one special aspect relating to the production of a specific molecule, the antibody.

The immune system of a vertebrate organism provides the body's main line of defense against invasion by such disease-causing organisms as bacteria, viruses, and fungi. The system also attacks cancer cells produced by the organism itself. It is a complex system made up of several components produced by various differentiation processes; antibody production, however, seems to involve an exceptional method of generating genetic diversity.

Antibodies.   When the body is invaded by a foreign agent, whether microbial, a chemical substance, or a larger structure such as dust or a pollen grain, one of the most powerful mechanisms for eliminating it is in the production of an **antibody.** The antibody is a protein that recognizes a specific steriochemical shape determined by the invading **antigen.** The antigenic portion may be an entire molecule or a part of a molecule or structure.

Humans seem to be able to make an unlimited variety of antibodies against millions of potential antigens. The antibodies have been shown to be proteins belonging to a class called **immunoglobulins.** The genetic dilemma is that antibody specificity reflects its primary amino acid sequence—yet the human genome has only perhaps a million genes. Furthermore, only a small number of genes actually code for the immunoglobulins. The paradox of generating a large number of different products from a small number of genes is now being resolved at the molecular level.

Antibody Structure.   Antibodies are made up of two pairs of identical subunits, light and heavy polypeptide chains bound together by disulfide bridges. Amino-acid-sequence analysis and comparison of different antibodies reveal that

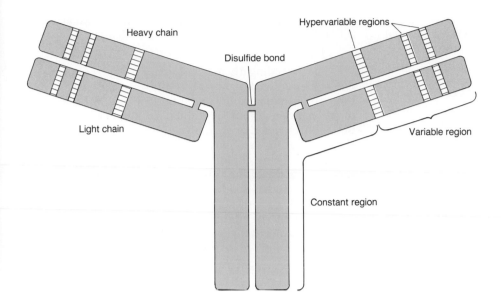

Figure 21-59. A diagrammatic representation of an antibody. It is made up of two pairs of identical polypeptides, each of which contains a light chain and a heavy chain linked by disulfide bridges. The constant regions are located in the stem region, while the variable and hypervariable areas are in the region of the branches.

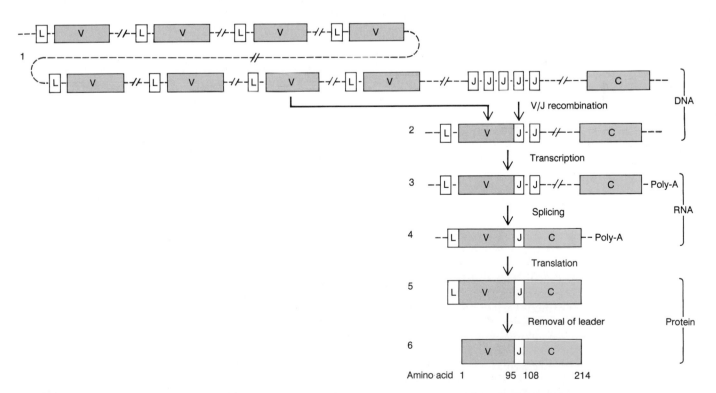

Figure 21-60. The formation of an active light chain of an antibody. The DNA is organized into families of related elements: one copy of the gene for the constant region, five repeats of a joiner (J) sequence, and up to 150 related but different variable (V) sequences, each separated by a leader (L) sequence. By recombination, one of the V elements with its L sequence is inserted into the J segment. This entire complex is transcribed into RNA from which excess J and linking sequences to C are excised. The mature RNA is translated, and the amino acids coded by the L portion are removed from the protein.

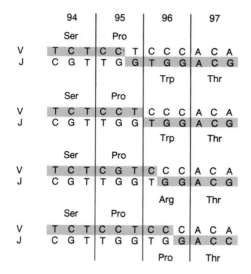

Figure 21-61. Recombination at certain points between V and J sequences can generate new codons. Amino acids 95 and 96 of an active light chain are at the position of exchanges between V and J. Exchanges in the codon for amino acid 96 can lead to arginine or proline instead of tryptophan.

there are large areas that are similar in all antibodies (Figure 21-59); such areas are called **constant.** Within the **variable** domain, in which amino acid differences do occur from antibody to antibody, a large proportion of amino acids is nevertheless similar except for short **hypervariable** segments, but in these there is extreme variation responsible for antibody specificity. How does the variability come about? The ability to clone DNA coding for light and heavy chains has revealed a surprising mechanism. Separate DNA segments code for the constant and variable parts of the chains. In embryonic DNA, the constant and variable parts are not closely linked, but in somatic cells, the two parts are brought into closer juxtaposition by some kind of somatic recombination event. There are families of variable sequences that, in spite of differences, share certain amino acids that always differ between families. The kind of picture that emerges shows perhaps 100 to 200 different copies of the variable portion linked via a series of short joining sequences to a single constant region (Figure 21-60). Somatic recombination links a specific variable segment to the constant gene, while gene splicing maturation of RNA and protein removes excess coding portions. From our standpoint, the important fact is that recombination between segments of homologous DNA molecules is the mechanism whereby enormous variety can be generated by shuffling linked sequences. Note that, just as Yanofsky showed (Chapter 11), recombination between two different triplets can also generate yet other, new triplets in the hypervariable region (Figure 21-61).

Message The enormous variability of antigens derives from a small number of genes. Two groups, variable and constant genes, can be linked together by somatic recombi-

nation. This provides a means of generating a vast array of different gene products.

The preceding discussion presented an extremely brief description of what is obviously a fascinating system. The tools of molecular biology are rapidly exposing the secrets of the immune system. The ability to combine the properties of unrestricted growth of cancer with the specific antibody-producing capability of single lymphocytes by cell fusion is now being exploited to produce large amounts of single antibodies. The fused cells are called **hybridomas,** and the antibodies produced are termed **monoclonal.** It is not clear whether the DNA shuffling that occurs between the components of immunoglobulin genes is used uniquely by the immune system or has broader implications for gene regulation.

Summary

■ Developmental biologists seek an understanding of the mechanisms whereby a fertilized egg differentiates into the many cell types of a multicellular organism. In the early stages of development, each somatic cell receives a complete complement of DNA and, therefore, should be totipotent; this has been demonstrated in some plants and a few vertebrates and invertebrates. The cytoplasmic architecture and content of an egg is determined by the maternal genotype and controls the early developmental sequences. Many complex molecules and cell organelles possess the capacity to self-aggregate and assemble. But the bulk of differentiation proceeds by differential gene activation and inactivation.

Molecular models of regulated genes are best exemplified by the operon. By connecting products of an operon to other operons, as repressors or activators, a multitude of phenotypic fates is readily determined. From gastrulation onward, transcription sequences are stage-specific and reflect regulated gene activity. Specific phenotypes in highly differentiated cells, such as chick oviduct or *Drosophila* salivary glands, provide diagnostic criteria for molecular probes into the regulation of activity and recovery of gene products. Mutations reveal that a great deal of regulation is effective in sequences upstream from the 5′ end of the structural gene.

For the geneticist, mutations are the key to studying development. Mutations disrupt normal events, and the aberrant phenotype may enable us to trace its primary basis or to examine a process of interest. The study of mutations in the *bithorax* locus of *Drosophila* reveals the power of mutation as an analytical tool.

In addition, mutations can be used as markers to distinguish different populations of cells in a single individual.

Thus, fusion of mouse embryos of different genotypes permits the construction of fate maps or deduction of the cellular origin of certain organs. In *Drosophila*, genetic mosaics produced by chromosome loss or somatic crossing-over have revealed the existence of developmental compartments within which cells are clonally related. During development, the cells within compartments undergo progressive restrictions in their potential fates.

All differentiated cells and tissues are the products of regulated gene activity, but certain in vivo systems are of special interest for different reasons: sex determination, cancer, and the immune system. Sex determination in *Drosophila* reflects a balance between male- and female-determining factors scattered through the genome. Nevertheless, there are major sex-determining elements whose mutation can drastically affect sex differentiation.

Cancer represents unregulated cell growth. Convergent studies with oncogenic viruses and DNA of tumors reveal the existence of oncogenes, which are capable of inducing tumors. They, in turn, appear to be derivatives of DNA normally found in all cells.

The immune system defends the body against invasion by foreign elements. The mechanism of destruction of foreign antigens is by antibodies, proteins called immunoglobulins. The enormous variety of antigens is determined by somatic recombination of different genetic elements.

Problems

1. Review preceding chapters and prepare a list of all the ways in which variegation (sectoring) of biological tissue can occur.

2. a. Of what significance are phenocopies in medical genetics?

   b. How could phenocopies be used to study gene action?

   c. How can an investigator determine whether an altered phenotype is due to a phenocopy or to a mutation?

3. Throughout history and mythology, there are stories of the birth of children to virgin mothers. Such parthenogenesis definitely does occur in many organisms. In theory, it could occur in mammals, including humans. Describe the mechanism that might be involved if any of the claims of virgin birth of a son are true.

4. Cells of organisms that are phylogenetically distantly related can be fused to form single mononucleate hybrids. For example, human-mouse, human-fish, human-bird, human-insect, and human-plant hybrid cells have been created. These hybrids even grow and divide.

   a. What conclusions can be drawn from these observations?

   b. When a chicken erythrocyte (which has a nucleus and actively synthesizes hemoglobin) is fused to a mouse fibroblast, some of the inactive chicken DNA becomes transcriptionally active, but hemoglobin synthesis is shut off. What conclusions can you draw from this observation?

5. In his book *In His Image: The Cloning of a Man,* David Rorvik claimed that a baby had been cloned from the cells of an elderly man. Few (if any) geneticists believe this story, but many scientists do feel that human cloning is a definite possibility in the future. Naturally occurring human clones (identical twins) do exist. How would the ability to produce human clones in the laboratory be useful in studying the relative importance of heredity and environment in determining the final phenotype of a human individual?

6. The accompanying figure illustrates an experiment performed by Hämmerling in 1943 on two species of the unicellular alga *Acetabularia*. *A. mediterranea* has an intact, umbrella-like "hat," whereas the hat of *A. crenulata* is deeply indented. The nucleus is embedded in the base of the single cell in both species, and the hat is borne on a long cytoplasmic stem.

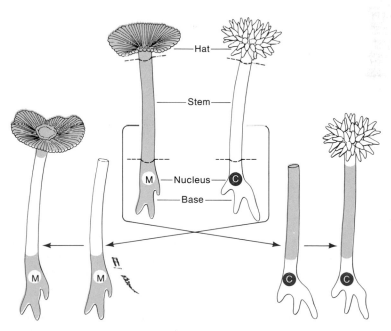

See Problem 6. Grafting experiments in *Acetabularia* have provided important information about the control of patterns of regeneration. When a cut stem from *A. crenulata* (C) is grafted to a base from *A. mediterranea* (M), the stem regenerates a hat of the *A. mediterranea* type (left). In the reciprocal experiment, the regenerated hat again matches the phenotype of the base (right). (After J. Hämmerling, *Z. Abstg. Vererb.* 81:114, 1943.)

a. The stem of an *A. mediterranea* individual is cut off just at the base, and the hat is removed by a cut at the top of the stem. The cut stem is grafted to the base of an *A. crenulata* individual, and a new hat forms (regenerates) on the top of the stem, as shown in the right side of the figure. A reciprocal transplant of an *A. crenulata* stem to an *A. mediterranea* base also leads to regeneration of a new hat, as shown in the left side of the figure. In each case, the phenotype of the new hat is consistent with that normal for the base to which the stem is transplanted rather than that normal for the stem from which the hat grows. On the basis of these results, discuss the cytoplasmic versus nuclear control of regeneration in *Acetabularia*.

b. If the nucleus of an *Acetabularia* cell is removed and the hat is then cut off, the enucleated cell immediately regenerates a new hat. However, if the upper part of the stem is removed along with the hat, the enucleated cell does not regenerate a new hat. Assume that some "hat-forming substance" is responsible for regeneration. Discuss the origin, qualitative control, and distribution of this substance in the intact cell.

c. If a stem with intact hat is transplanted from one species of *Acetabularia* to the base of another species, the hat retains its original character. How does this observation modify your answer to part b?

7. Boris Ephrussi and George Beadle have developed (and applied to good advantage) a technique for the study of genetic effects on hormone-like materials in *Drosophila*. The accompanying figure diagrams this technique and some of the results of its application. A piece of the larval disk that would later produce an adult eye is transplanted to a genetically different larva. The developmental interactions between host and transplant are then observed, particularly in terms of the color of pigment developed by the transplanted eye disk as the host larva matures.

a. The reciprocal transplants shown in part (a) of the figure are typical of a large majority of *Drosophila* transplantation experiments. The larval disk from a wild-type fly develops the pigment color characteristic of its own genotype, even when its differentiation and pigment development occur in a white-eyed host. Similarly, an eye disk from a white-eyed larva develops according to its own genotype and is not influenced in any noticeable fashion by a wild-type host environment. Would you conclude that the white-eyed gene affects production of a circulating (hormone-like) material or that it acts directly in the developing eye tissue itself?

b. The experiment shown in part (b) of the figure represents the kind of exception from which a good deal of information has been derived. Again, when wild-type eye disks are transplanted to either vermilion *(v)* or cinnabar *(cn)* host larvae, the transplants develop autonomously into wild-type eyes. However, when vermilion or cinnabar disks are transplanted to wild-type larvae, the disks do not develop according to their own genotypes but rather produce wild-type eyes! Provide a detailed explanation of these experimental results, assuming that the body of the wild-type host is capable of providing the developing eye tissue with circulating or diffusing materials that compensate for the genetic blocks in vermilion and cinnabar flies.

c. Part (c) shows the results of reciprocal transplants between vermilion and cinnabar larvae. Cinnabar disks

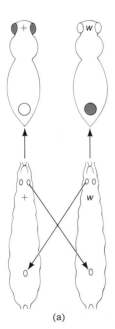
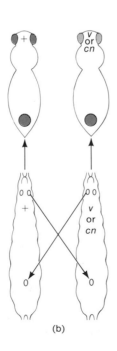
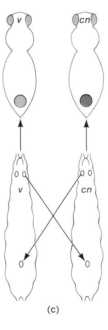

(a)   (b)   (c)

See Problem 7. Transplants of larval tissue have elucidated some aspects of gene action in *Drosophila*. (After B. Ephrussi, *Quart. Rev. Biol.* 17:329, 1942.)

developing in vermilion hosts maintain their cinnabar phenotype, but vermilion disks develop as wild-type in cinnabar hosts. These genes are now known to be involved in control of sequential steps in a biochemical synthesis of hormone-like materials directly involved in production of eye pigment:

$$\text{tryptophane} \xrightarrow{v^+} \underset{\substack{(\text{``}v^+ \\ \text{substance})}}{\text{kynurenine}} \xrightarrow{cn^+} \underset{(\text{``}cn^+ \text{ substance})}{\text{hydroxykynurenine}}$$

$$\downarrow$$

$$\text{pigment}$$

Using this information, give a detailed explanation of *all* the transplantation results shown in the figure.

8. One theory of aging (senescence) assumes that randomly occurring somatic mutations accumulate over time in different cells within an individual, gradually disrupting the normal cellular processes necessary for life. Another theory suggests that lifespan is a genetically determined character and that aging and death are simply the final stages of development and differentiation. These hypotheses are sufficiently specific to permit design of direct tests. Design experiments to test each of these theories. (NOTE: choose your organism and the kinds of tests carefully.)

9. You observe that, during larval development of *Drosophila,* an enzyme specifically found in the salivary glands appears, increases, and disappears in exactly the same pattern as a specific puff on the polytene X chromosome.

   a. Does this observation prove that the enzyme is specified by the puff? Explain.

   b. Design experiments to test the hypothesis that the puff specifies the enzyme.

10. The following diagram shows a hypothetical operon circuit in which the structural genes *(G)* adjacent to the operators *(O)* of two operons specify enzymes (E) that act by converting substrates (S) into products (P). Each product

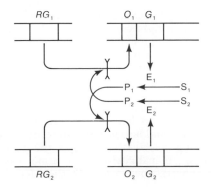

interacts with the repressor produced by the repressor gene *(RG)* to shut off the operator of the *other* operon. What would be the reaction of this system to variations in supplies of the substrates S_1 and S_2?

11. Different molecules in many complex structures (such as ribosomes and phage particles) can assemble spontaneously in a specific sequence. Design experiments to determine whether nucleosomal elements possess this capacity and whether the histones distinguish between DNAs.

12. The X-linked allele for glucose 6-phosphate deficiency (Gd^-) also confers resistance to malaria. You make a microscopic examination of the blood of a woman suffering from malaria. You observe that about one half of the cells contain parasites, whereas one-half of the cells are unaffected. Explain this result.

13. Women who are XO have a distinctive phenotype that includes short stature, webbed necks, and sterility. Men who are XXY can also be recognized phenotypically by reduced axillary hair, enlarged breasts, and sterility. However, XYY males seem to be fertile and phenotypically normal. What does this observation indicate about sex-chromosome function?

14. Through some aberrant circumstance, chromosome doubling occurs in certain somatic cells in a triploid *Drosophila* female. Will these clones of hexaploid cells differentiate as "male" or as "female" tissue?

15. The addition of duplication fragments of X chromosomes into nuclei from *Drosophila* intersexes (2X : 3A) shifts the balance of sexuality. Will this shift be in the direction of maleness or femaleness?

16. In *Drosophila,* an autosomal recessive *tra* acts only in females and transforms them into sterile males. What ratio of males and females would you expect among the progeny of a $+/tra \,♀ \times +/tra \,♂$ cross?

17. There is a sex-linked gene in mice that causes muscular dystrophy. Alan Peterson fused embryos from the muscular dystrophic strain with wild-type embryos. Because the two strains also differ in enzyme patterns, he could determine the parental origin of particular cells in the tetraparental mice. He found that animals with muscle cells from the wild-type and enervated by nerve cells from the dystrophic strain always have muscular dystrophy. However, in parabiosis studies (in which two animals are surgically bound together), attaching nerves from a dystrophic animal to the muscles of a wild-type mouse did not induce dystrophy in the muscles. Explain the significance of these results.

18. Jonathan Jarvik and David Botstein developed the following genetic method for determining the order of activity of different genes. Suppose that you obtain two different phage mutations, *A* and *B*, with an identical phenotype of

incomplete head assembly. You recover a heat-sensitive mutation of A (the mutant dies at 40°C) and a cold-sensitive mutation of B (the mutant dies at 25°C); both mutants survive at 35°C. You construct a phage carrying both mutations ($A^{hs} B^{cs}$) and infect bacteria with it. You keep one culture of infected bacteria at 25°C for 10 minutes and then shift it to 40°C (call this the lo → hi culture). You keep another culture (hi → lo) at 40°C for 10 minutes and then shift it to 25°C. Interpret each of the following possible results of this experiment.

a. Phages are released only in the hi → lo culture.

b. Phages are released only in the lo → hi culture.

c. No phages are released in either culture.

d. Some phages are released in both cultures.

19. In many forms of cancer, immunologically detectable changes occur at the surface of cancer cells. In many cases, the new antigens made by a cancer cell are identical to those found on normal embryonic cells. Propose an explanation for these observations.

20. Methylcholanthrene is a potent tumor-causing chemical in mice. It is also a potent mutagen. If a methylcholanthrene-induced tumor (T_A) is removed from mouse A, the mouse is "cured." The T_A cells can be kept alive in another mouse. If the T_A cells are reintroduced into the cured mouse, the mouse is seen to be immune (no tumors develop), although tumors can be induced by injection of T_A cells into mouse B, which has not previously been exposed to T_A cells. However, the mice surgically cured of tumor T_A are not immune to T_C cells removed from a methylcholanthrene-induced tumor in mouse C; such an injection induces a T_C-type tumor in mouse A. Propose an explanation for these observations in terms of gene-protein relations, bearing in mind that cell-surface proteins can act as immunological antigens.

21. After massive whole-body irradiation for cancer, blood-forming capacity of the spleen is usually destroyed. If nonirradiated cells are injected into the blood system, they lodge in the spleen, form colonies, and repopulate it. How could you determine whether each focus of blood-producing cells develops from a single cell or a cluster of cells?

22. You have two separate homothallic cultures of *Saccharomyces cerevisiae* with genotypes

MAT αHO HMLa HMRa
MAT αHO HMLα HMRa

Each culture is allowed to sporulate and one tetrad is isolated from each. What mating behavior is expected for the individual ascospores? (For each tetrad indicate the mating behavior of each of the four ascospores as either α, a, or homothallic. The order within the ascus is unimportant; also, ignore recombination.)

23. In mice, the *little* mutation *(lit)* results in dwarfism. Even though the growth hormone (GH) gene is present and normal, no GH mRNA is detectable. Homozygous *lit/lit* fertilized eggs were injected with about 500 copies of a 5-kb linear DNA fragment containing the rat GH structural gene adjacent to the mouse metallothionin gene's regulator/promoter sequence, which responds to heavy metals as inducers. These eggs were implanted into pseudopregnant female mice and baby mice were reared. About 1 percent of these offspring were transgenic, showing increased size if induced. One such transgenic mouse was crossed to a *lit/lit* female, and the next two generations are shown in the pedigree. The numbers under the symbols show the ratio of body weight to that of dwarf littermates at 6 weeks of age. Explain all these results and show how you would test your explanation. What portions of this technology could be applied to the correction of human gene defects, and what might be some of the problems?

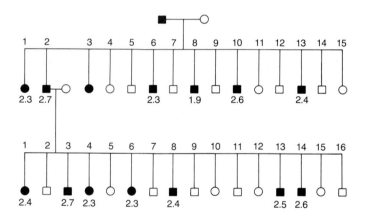

24. In *Drosophila,* heterozygotes for dominant temperature-sensitive lethal mutations are viable and fertile at the permissive temperature, but they die at the restrictive temperature. What could be the molecular basis for such dominant lethality?

25. Let us assign numbers to each leg of *Drosophila* as follows: legs 1, 2, and 3 are the front, mid, and hind legs on the left side, respectively, and legs 4, 5, 6 are the front, mid, and hind legs on the right side. A fly normally walks by moving legs 1, 3, and 5 together and then moving legs 2, 4, and 6 together. A mutation called *wobbly* causes the fly to get its mid legs tangled with its front or its hind legs. What could be wrong with the mutant, and how would you study it?

26. Mutations in *Drosophila* that affect behavior have been very useful in the analysis of the nervous system. Describe methods that could be developed to recover mutants with the following defects originating in the nervous system: a. blindness; b. inability to fly; c. abnormal feeding responses. (NOTE: flies taste with their feet. When they

detect edible molecules, such as sugar, their proboscis is automatically lowered to feed.)

27. You are a molecular biologist studying the properties of muscle proteins in *Drosophila*. Design an experimental procedure for the detection and recovery of appropriate mutants. (This experiment has not been attempted, so you may be able to propose a clever scheme that is worth trying. NOTE: what would be the phenotype of a muscle mutant? Wouldn't it be lethal?)

28. The sex-linked dominant mutation *Hyperkinetic-1* (Hk^1) causes shaking of a fly's legs while the fly is etherized. Seymour Benzer and Yoshiki Hotta generated mosaic flies with the tissue genotypes $yHk^1/++$ and yHk^1/O. They scored 600 fly sides for leg shaking and mutant cuticle tissue. Table 21-1 summarizes their results. Draw a fate map of the foci for Hk^1-caused shaking, the three legs, the antenna, and the humeral bristle.

■ **TABLE 21-1.**

Structure	Color of cuticle tissue	Shaking of leg 1	
		Normal	Mutant
Leg 1	Wild-type	277	50.5
	Yellow	33	223.5
Leg 2	Wild-type	261.5	69
	Yellow	44	215.5
Leg 3	Wild-type	250.5	82.5
	Yellow	46.5	215.5
Antenna	Wild-type	253	82
	Yellow	84.5	179.5
Humeral bristle	Wild-type	241	94
	Yellow	66.5	197.5

29. The *Notch* locus near the tip of the X chromosome of *Drosophila* has been extensively studied genetically. Deletions of the entire locus produce a dominant visible phenotype of nicked wings and recessive lethality. As well, several point mutations mapping throughout the locus have a similar phenotype. There are also alleles with recessive visible phenotypes affecting eyes, bristles, and wings. Design experiments to recover DNA spanning the *Notch* locus.

30. Competition studies of nucleic acid hybridization provide a means of comparing sequences from different sources. In order to study mRNA in mice, suppose we attach a fixed amount of cold, single-stranded mouse DNA to nitrocellulose filters and, in the presence of a fixed amount of hot mRNA from liver, mix different amounts of cold mRNA from either lung or liver. We get the results shown in the following graph.

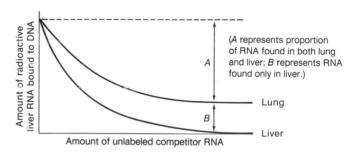

a. What conclusions can we draw about differentiation?

b. How would we determine the mRNA sequences found only in liver and in no other body tissues?

31. Eukaryotic cells can be lysed without breaking down the nuclear membrane. This technique permits separation of cytoplasmic from nuclear material. In competition studies, unlabeled nuclear RNA is found to compete with the binding of labeled cytoplasmic RNA to the DNA. However, unlabeled cytoplasmic RNA fails to interfere with the binding of a considerable amount of labeled nuclear RNA to the DNA. What do these studies show? Can you suggest a possible biological interpretation of these observations?

CHAPTER 22

Quantitative Genetics

■ The possibility of working out the laws of transmission genetics and of the molecular genetics underlying them has depended critically on the existence of a special kind of phenotypic trait. These are the traits that allow classification of individuals into discrete and unambiguous phenotypic classes. They may be the tall and short plants or purple and white flowers of Mendel's peas, or the lactose fermenters and nonfermenters of modern microbial genetics. In all such cases, the phenotypic effect of an allelic substitution at some locus is sufficiently drastic that the substitution produces a clear effect. There is a uniquely distinguishable phenotype for each such genotype, and there is only a single genotype for each phenotype. At most, because of dominance, two genotypes may produce the same phenotype, but this confusion can be sorted out by a simple genetic cross. Such a one-to-one relation between genotype and phenotype is necessary for basic genetic experiments, because usually we can identify (and therefore study) the genotype only through the phenotype. For the most part, then, the study of genetics presented in the previous chapters is the study of allelic substitutions causing *qualitative* differences in phenotype.

However, most of the actual variation among organisms is not qualitative but quantitative. Wheat plants in a cultivated field or wild asters at the side of the road do not sort themselves neatly into two categories, "tall" and "short," any more than humans are neatly sorted into "black" and "white." Height, weight, shape, color, metabolic activity, reproductive rate, and behavior are characteristics that vary more or less continuously over a range. Even when the character is intrinsically countable (such as eye-facet or bristle number in *Drosophila*), the number of countable classes may be so large that the variation is nearly continuous. Even if we consider extreme individuals—say, a corn plant eight feet tall and one three feet tall—a cross between them will not reproduce Mendel's result. Such a cross will produce plants about six feet tall, with some clear variation among sibs. The F_2 from selfing the F_1 will not fall into two or three discrete height classes in ratios of 3 : 1 or 1 : 2 : 1. Instead, the F_2 will be continuously distributed in height from one parental extreme to the other. It is important to realize that, when we depart from the level of primary gene products, this behavior of crosses is not an exception but is the rule for most characters in most species. In general, size, shape, color, physiological activity, and behavior do not assort in a simple way in crosses.

The fact that most phenotypic characters vary continuously does not mean that their variation is the result of some genetic mechanisms different from the Mendelian genes we have been dealing with. The continuity of phenotype is a result of two phenomena. First, each genotype does not have a single phenotypic expression but a norm of reaction (see Chapter 1) that covers a wide phenotypic range. As a result, the phenotypic differences between genotypic classes become blurred, and we are not able to assign a particular phenotype unambiguously to a particular genotype. Second, there may be many segregating loci whose alleles make a difference to the phenotype being observed. Suppose, for example, that there are five equally important loci affecting some trait and that each has two alleles—call them + and −. For simplicity, suppose that there is no dominance and that a + allele adds 1 unit to the trait whereas a − allele adds nothing. There are $3^5 = 243$ different possible genotypes, ranging from $\frac{+++++}{+++++}$ through $\frac{+++++}{-----}$ to $\frac{-----}{-----}$, but there will only be 11 phenotypic classes (10, 9, 8, . . . , 0), because many of the genotypes will have the same numbers of + and − alleles. For example, although there is only one genotype with 10 + alleles and therefore an average phenotypic value of 10, there are 51 different genotypes with 5 + alleles and 5 − alleles. These include a single pentuple heterozygote $\frac{+++++}{-----}$, 20 different triple heterozygotes, such as $\frac{+++-+}{---+-}$ and $\frac{++-++}{+-----}$, and 30 different single heterozygotes, such as $\frac{++-+-}{++---}$ and $\frac{+++--}{-+++--}$. Thus, many different genotypes may have the same average phenotype. At the same time, because of environmental variation, two individuals of the same genotype may not have the same phenotype. This lack of a one-to-one correspondence between genotype and phenotype obscures the underlying Mendelian mechanism. If we cannot study directly the behavior of the Mendelian factors controlling such traits, what then can we learn about their genetics? The following questions that can be asked about the genetics of quantitative variation are those for which some kind of experimental answers can be given with current experimental techniques.

1. Is the observed variation in the character influenced *at all* by genetic variation? Are there alleles segregating in the population that produce some differential effect on the character, or is all the variation simply the result of environmental variation and developmental noise (see Chapter 1)?

2. If there is genetic variation, what are the norms of reaction of the various genotypes?

3. How important is genetic variation as a source of total phenotypic variation? Are the norms of reaction and the environments such that nearly all the variation is a consequence of environmental difference and developmental instabilities, or does genetic variation predominate?

4. Are many loci (or only a few) varying with respect to the character? How are they distributed over the genome?

5. How do the different loci interact with each other in influencing the character? Is there dominance or epistasis?

6. Is there any nonnuclear inheritance—for example, any maternal effect?

The precision with which these questions can be framed and answered varies greatly. On the one hand, it is relatively simple in experimental organisms to determine whether there is any genetic influence at all, but extremely laborious experiments are required to localize the genes, even approximately. On the other hand, in humans it is extremely difficult to answer even the question of the presence of genetic influence for most traits because of the near-impossibility of separating environmental from genetic effects in an organism that cannot be manipulated experimentally. As a consequence, we know a relatively large amount about the genetics of bristle number in *Drosophila* but essentially nothing about the genetics of any complex human trait, except that some (such as skin color) are influenced by genes whereas others (such as the specific language spoken) are not.

Some Basic Statistical Notions

In order to consider the answers to these questions about the most common kinds of genetic variation, we must first examine a number of statistical tools that are essential in the study of quantitative genetics.

Distributions

The outcome of a cross for a Mendelian character is described in terms of the proportion of the offspring falling in each of several distinct phenotypic classes, or often simply by the presence or absence of a class. For example, a cross between a red-flowered and a white-flowered plant might be expected to yield all red-flowered plants, or, if it were a backcross, 1/2 red-flowered and 1/2 white-flowered plants. However, we require a different mode of description for quantitative characters. The basic concept is that of the **statistical distribution.** If the heights of a large number of male undergraduates are measured to the nearest 5 cm, they will vary (say, between 145 and 195 cm), but many more individuals will fall in the middle categories (say, between 170 and 180 cm) than at the extremes.

Representing each measurement class as a bar, with its height proportional to the number of individuals in each class, we can graph the result as in Figure 22-1a. Such a

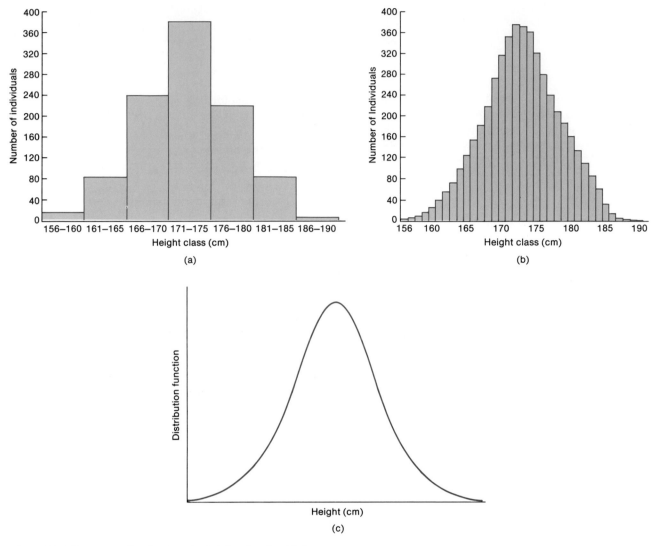

Figure 22-1. Frequency distributions for height of males. (a) A histogram with 5-cm class intervals. (b) A histogram with 1-cm class intervals. (c) The limiting continuous distribution.

graph of numbers of individuals observed against measurement class is a **frequency histogram.** Suppose now that the number of individuals measured is multiplied by five and that each individual is measured to the nearest centimeter. The classes in Figure 22-1a are now subdivided to produce a histogram like that in Figure 22-1b. If we continue this process, refining the measurement but proportionately increasing the number of individuals measured, the histogram eventually takes on the continuous appearance of Figure 22-1c, which is the **distribution function** of heights in the population.

Of course, this continuous curve is an idealization because no measurement can be taken with infinite accuracy or on an unlimited number of individuals. Moreover, the measured variate itself may be intrinsically discontinuous because it is the count of some number of discrete objects, such as eye facets or bristles. It is sometimes convenient, however, to develop concepts using this slightly idealized

picture as a shorthand for the more cumbersome observed frequency histogram of Figure 22-1a. We should not forget, however, that the distribution function is indeed an idealization.

The Mode. Most distributions of phenotypes look roughly like that of Figure 22-1. There is a single most frequent class, the **mode,** near the middle of the distribution, with frequencies decreasing on either side. There are exceptions to this pattern, however. Figure 22-2a shows the very asymmetric distribution of seed weights in the plant *Crinum longifolium.* Figure 22-2b shows a **bimodal** (two-mode) distribution of larval survival probabilities for different second-chromosome homozygotes in *Drosophila willistoni.*

A bimodal distribution may indicate that the population being studied could better be considered as a mixture of two populations, each with its own mode. For example, suppose we sample 100 undergraduates and measure their

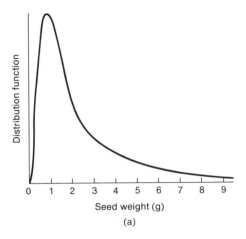

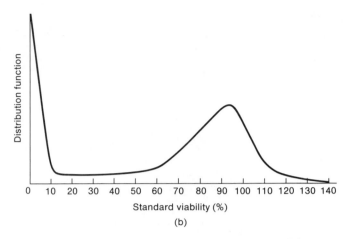

Figure 22-2. Asymmetric distribution functions. (a) Asymmetric distribution of seed weight in *Crinum longifolium*. (b) Bimodal distribution of survival of *Drosophila* expressed as percentage of standard survival. (Adapted from S. Wright, *Evolution and the Genetics of Populations*, Vol. I, University of Chicago Press, 1968.)

heights. These 100 individuals will include some males and some females. Thus, our sample is really a mixture of a sample from the population of male undergraduates and one from the population of female undergraduates, even though we have chosen the group in a single operation of sampling. In Figure 22-2b, the left-hand mode probably represents severe one-locus mutations that are extremely deleterious when homozygous, whereas the right-hand mode is part of the distribution of "normal" viability. If the heights of both male and female undergraduates had been plotted in Figure 22-1, the distribution would have been bimodal, because the heights of females are distributed around a mode at a value considerably smaller than the mode of the males' heights.

The Mean. Complete information about the distribution of a phenotype in a population can be given only by specifying the frequency of each measured class, but a great deal of information can be summarized in two statistics. First, we need some measure of location of the distribution along the axis of measurement—for example, do the individuals' measurements tend to cluster around 100 cm or 200 cm? One possibility is to give the measurement of the most common class, the mode. In Figure 22-1b, the mode is 172 cm. For females, the mode would be about 6 cm less. A more common measure of location is the arithmetic average, or **mean.** The mean of the measurement, $\bar{x}$, is simply the sum of all the measurements, x_i, divided by the number (N) of measurements in the sample:

$$\bar{x} = \frac{x_1 + x_2 + x_3 + \cdots + x_N}{N} = \frac{1}{N} \sum x_i$$

where Σ represents summation, and x_i is the ith measurement.

In a typical large sample, the same measured value will appear more than once, because several individuals will have the same value within the accuracy of the measuring instrument. For example, many individuals will be 170 cm tall. In such a case, $\bar{x}$ can be rewritten as the sum of all the measurement values, each weighted by how frequently it occurs in the population. From a total of N individuals measured, suppose that n_1 fall in the class with value x_1, that n_2 fall in the class with value x_2, and so on, so that $\Sigma n_i = N$. Then

$$\bar{x} = \frac{n_1}{N} x_1 + \frac{n_2}{N} x_2 + \cdots + \frac{n_k}{N} x_k$$

If we let f_i, be the *relative frequency* of the ith measurement class, so that

$$f_i = \frac{n_i}{N}$$

then we can rewrite the mean as

$$\bar{x} = f_1 x_1 + f_2 x_2 + \cdots + f_k x_k = \Sigma f_i x_i$$

where x_i equals the value of the ith measurement class. For the heights of male undergraduates in Figure 22-1, $\bar{x} = 173.5$ cm.

The Variance. A second characteristic of a distribution is the width of its spread around the central class. Two distributions with the same mean might differ very much in how closely the measurements are concentrated around the mean. The most common measure of variation around the center is the **variance,** defined as the *average squared deviation of the observations from the mean.* That is,

$$\text{variance} = s^2 = \frac{(x_1 - \bar{x})^2 + (x_2 - \bar{x})^2 + \cdots + (x_N - \bar{x})^2}{N}$$

$$= \frac{1}{N} \sum (x_i - \bar{x})^2$$

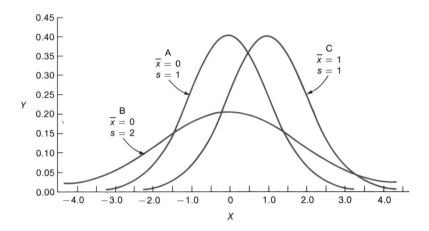

Figure 22-3. Three distribution functions with different means and standard deviations.

In the case where more than one individual has the same measured value, this may be written as

$$\text{variance} = s^2$$
$$= f_1(x_1 - \bar{x})^2 + f_2(x_2 - \bar{x})^2 + \cdots + f_k(x_k - \bar{x})^2$$
$$= \Sigma f_i(x_i - \bar{x})^2$$

To avoid subtracting every value of x separately from the mean, we can use an alternative computing formula, algebraically identical to the preceding equation:

$$s^2 = \frac{1}{N} \sum x_i^2 - \bar{x}^2$$

Because the variance has squared units (square centimeters, for example), it is common to take the square root of variance, which then has the same units as the measurement itself. This square-root measure of variation is called the **standard deviation** of the distribution:

$$\text{standard deviation} = s = \sqrt{\text{variance}} = \sqrt{s^2}$$

Figure 22-3 shows two distributions having the same mean but different standard deviations (curves A and B) and two distributions having the same standard deviation but different means (curves A and C).

The mean and variance of a distribution do not describe it completely, of course. They will not distinguish a symmetric distribution from an asymmetric one, for example. We can even construct symmetric distributions that have the same mean and variance but still have somewhat different shapes. Nevertheless, for the purposes of dealing with most quantitative genetic problems, the mean and variance suffice to characterize a distribution.

Correlation

Another statistical notion that we need is that of association or **correlation** between variables. Because of complex paths of causation, many variables in nature vary together but in an imperfect or approximate way. Figure 22-4a is an example, showing the lengths of two particular teeth in several individual specimens of a fossil mammal, *Phena-*

codus primaevis. The longer an individual's first lower molar is, the longer its second molar is, but the relation is imprecise. Figure 22-4b shows that the total length and tail length in individual snakes *(Lampropeltis polyzona)* are quite closely related to each other, whereas Figure 22-4c shows that length and the number of caudal (tail) scales seem to have no relation at all.

The usual measure of the precision of a relationship between two variables x and y is the **correlation coefficient,** r_{xy}. It is calculated from the product of the deviation of each observation of x from the mean of the x values and the deviation of each observation of y from the mean of the y values, a quantity called the **covariance** of x and y:

$$\text{cov } xy =$$
$$\frac{(x_1 - \bar{x})(y_1 - \bar{y}) + (x_2 - \bar{x})(y_2 - \bar{y}) + \cdots}{N}$$
$$+ \frac{(x_N - \bar{x})(y_N - \bar{y})}{N}$$
$$= \frac{1}{N} \sum (x_i - \bar{x})(y_i - \bar{y})$$

$$\text{correlation} = r_{xy} = \frac{\text{cov } xy}{s_x \times s_y}$$

This formula for the covariance is rather awkward for computation because it requires subtracting every value of x and y from the respective means, $\bar{x}$ and $\bar{y}$. A formula that is exactly algebraically equivalent, but makes computation easier, is

$$\text{cov } xy = \frac{1}{N} \sum x_i y_i - \bar{x}\bar{y}$$

In the formula for correlation, the products of the deviations are divided by the product of the standard deviations of x and y (s_x and s_y). This normalization by the standard deviations has the effect of making r_{xy} a dimensionless number, independent of the units in which x and y are measured. So defined, r_{xy} will vary from -1, signifying a perfectly linear negative relation between x and y, to $+1$ for

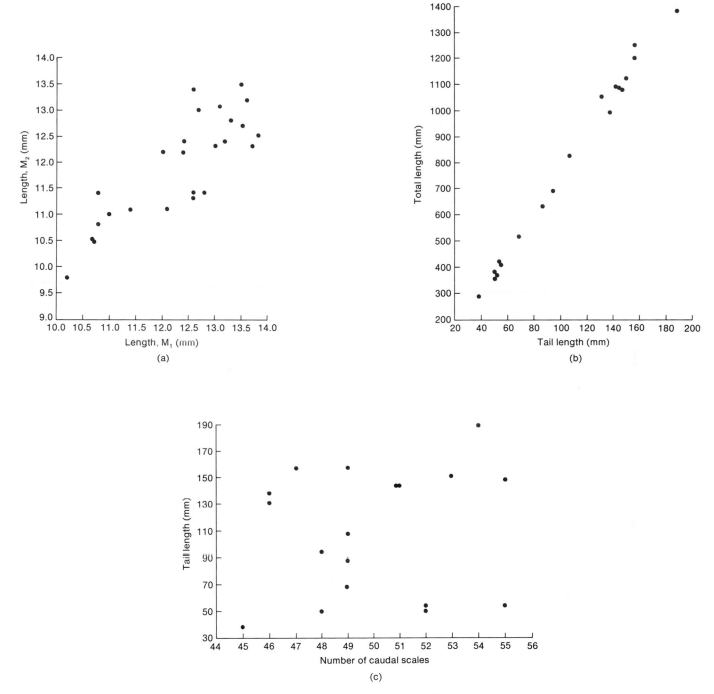

Figure 22-4. Scatter diagrams of relationships between pairs of variables. (a) Relationship between the lengths of the first and second lower molars, M_1 and M_2, in the extinct mammal *Phenacodus*. Each point gives the two measurements, M_1 and M_2, for one individual. (b) Tail length and body length of 19 individuals of a snake, *Lampropeltis polyzona*. (c) Number of caudal scales and tail length related in the same 19 snakes as in (b).

a perfectly linear positive relation. If $r_{xy} = 0$, there is no linear relation between the variables. It is important to notice, however, that sometimes when there is no *linear* relation between two variables, if there is a regular *nonlinear* relationship between them, one variable may be perfectly predicted from the other. Consider, for example, the pa-

rabola shown in Figure 22-5. The values of y are perfectly predictable from the values of x; yet $r_{xy} = 0$, because, on the average over the whole range of x values, larger x values are not associated with either larger or smaller y values. The data in parts (a), (b), and (c) in Figure 22-4 have r_{xy} values of 0.82, 0.99, and 0.10, respectively.

In these examples, correlations have been described as the relation between a pair of measurements taken on the same individual, but a single measurement taken on pairs of individuals is also a subject for correlation analysis. Thus we can determine the correlation between the height of a parent (x) and that of an offspring (y), or the heights of an older sib (x) and a younger sib (y). This use of correlation is directly relevant to the problems of quantitative genetics. Figure 22-6 is an example showing the relation between the wing length of an offspring and the average wing length of its two parents (midparent value) in *Drosophila*.

Correlation and Identity. It is important to notice that correlation is not the same thing as identity. Values can be perfectly correlated without being equal. The variables x and y in the pairs

x	y
1	22
2	24
3	26

are perfectly correlated ($r = +1.0$), although each value of y is about 20 units greater than the corresponding value of x. Two variables are perfectly correlated if, for a unit increase in one, there is a constant increase in the other (or decrease if r is negative). The importance of the difference between correlation and identity arises when we consider the effect of environment on heritable characters. Parents and offspring could be perfectly correlated in some trait such as height; yet, because of an environmental difference between generations, every child could be taller than its parents. This phenomenon appears in adoption studies, where children may be correlated with their biological parents yet because of a change in social situation, may be on the average quite different from the parents.

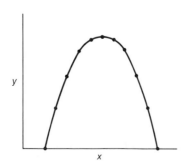

Figure 22-5. A parabola. Each value of y is perfectly predictable from the value of x, but there is no linear correlation.

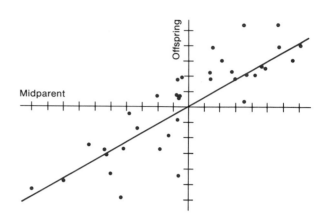

Figure 22-6. Relation between the wing lengths of individual *Drosophila* and the mean wing lengths of their two parents. (From D. Falconer, *Quantitative Genetics*, Longman Group Limited. Copyright © 1981.)

Regression

The measurement of correlation provides us only with an estimate of the *precision* of relationship between two variables. A related problem is that of predicting the value of one variable given the value of the other. If x increases by two units, how much will y increase? If the two variables are linearly related, then that relationship can be expressed as

$$y = bx + a$$

where b is the slope of the line relating y with x and a is the y-intercept of the line.

Figure 22-7 shows a scatter diagram of points for two variables, y and x, together with a straight line expressing the general linear trend of y with increasing x. This line, called the **regression line of y on x**, has been chosen to have the property that the deviations of the points from the line are as small as possible. Specifically, if Δy is the distance of any point from the line in the y direction, then the line has been chosen so that

$$\Sigma (\Delta y)^2 = \text{a minimum}$$

Any other straight line passed through the points on the scatter diagram will have a larger total squared deviation of the points from it.

Obviously, we cannot find this "least squares" line by trial and error. It turns out, however, that if the slope b is calculated by

$$b = \frac{\text{cov } xy}{s_x^2}$$

and if a is then calculated from

$$a = \bar{y} - b\bar{x}$$

so that the line passes through the point $\bar{x}, \bar{y}$, then these values of b and a give the least-squares prediction equation.

Note that the prediction equation cannot predict y exactly for a given x, because there is scatter around the line. What the equation does is to predict the *average* y for a given x, if large samples are taken.

Samples and Populations

The preceding sections have described the distributions and some statistics of particular assemblages of individuals that have been collected in some experiments or sets of observations. For some purposes, however, we are not really interested in the particular 100 undergraduates or 27 snakes that have been measured. We are interested rather in a wider world of phenomena, of which those particular individuals are representative. Thus, we might want to know the average height of undergraduates *in general,* or the average seed weight *in general* of plants of the species *Crinum longifolium.* That is, we are interested in the characteristics of a **universe,** of which our small collection of observations is only a **sample.** The characteristics of any particular sample are, of course, not identical with those of the universe but will vary from sample to sample. Two samples of undergraduates drawn from the universe of all undergraduates will not have exactly the same mean, $\bar{x}$, or variance, s^2, nor will these values for a sample typically be exactly equal to the mean and variance in the universe. We distinguish between statistics of a sample and the values in the universe by using Roman letters, such as $\bar{x}$, s^2, and r, for sample values and Greek letters μ (for the mean), σ^2 (for the variance), and ρ (for the correlation) for the values in the universe.

The sample mean $\bar{x}$ is an approximation to the true mean μ of the universe. It is a statistical *estimate* of that true mean. So, too, s^2, s, and r are estimates of σ^2, σ, and ρ in the universe from which a sample has been taken.

If we are interested in a particular collection of individuals not for its own sake, but as a way of getting information about a universe, then we want the sample statistics such as $\bar{x}$ and s^2 to be good estimates of the true values of μ, σ^2, and so on. There are many criteria of what a "good" estimate is, but one that seems clearly desirable is that, if we take a very large number of samples, then the average value of the estimate over these samples should be the true value in the universe. That is, the estimate should be **unbiased.** It turns out that $\bar{x}$ is indeed an unbiased estimate of μ. If a very large number of samples are taken and $\bar{x}$ is calculated in each one, then the average of these $\bar{x}$ values will be μ. Unfortunately, s^2, as we have defined it, is not an unbiased estimate of σ^2. It tends to be a little too small, so that the average of many s^2 values is less than σ^2. The amount of bias is precisely related to the size N of each sample, and it can be shown that $[N/(N-1)]s^2$ is an unbiased estimate of σ^2. Thus, whenever one is interested in the variance of a set of measurements, not as a characteristic of the particular collection but as an estimate of a universe from which the sample has been taken, then the appropriate quantity to use is $[N/(N-1)]s^2$ rather than s^2 itself. You may note that this new quantity is equivalent to dividing the sum of squared deviations by $N-1$ instead of N in the first place. That is,

$$\left(\frac{N}{N-1}\right)s^2 = \left(\frac{N}{N-1}\right)\frac{1}{N}\sum(x_i - \bar{x})^2$$

$$= \frac{1}{N-1}\sum(x_i - \bar{x})^2$$

It is this latter quantity that is often called the "sample variance," but that term is really not correct. The sample variance is s^2, whereas $[N/(N-1)]s^2$ is an adjustment to the sample variance to make it an unbiased estimate of σ^2. Which of the two quantities is to be used depends on whether one is interested primarily in the sample or in the universe.

All of these considerations about bias also apply to the sample covariance. In the formula for the correlation coefficient, however, the factor $N/(N-1)$ appears in both the numerator and denominator and cancels out, so we can ignore it for purposes of computation.

Genotypes and Phenotypic Distribution

Using the concepts of distribution, mean, and variance, we can understand the difference between quantitative and Mendelian genetic traits. Suppose that a population of plants contains three genotypes, each of which has some

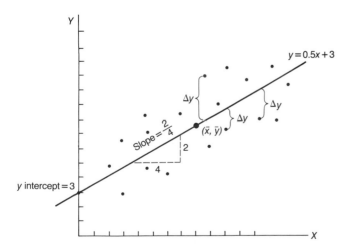

Figure 22-7. A scatter diagram showing the relation between two variables, x and y, with the regression line of y on x. This line, with a slope of 2/4, minimizes the squares of the deviations, Δy.

differential effect on growth rate. Further, suppose that there is some environmental variation from plant to plant because of inhomogeneity in the soil in which the population is growing and that there is some developmental noise (see Chapter 1). For each genotype separately, there will be a distribution of phenotypes whose mean and standard deviation depend on the genotype and the set of environments. Suppose that they look like the three height distributions in Figure 22-8a. Suppose, finally, that the population consists of a mixture of the three genotypes but in unequal proportions, 1 : 2 : 3. Then the phenotypic distribution of individuals in the population as a whole will look like the black line in Figure 22-8b, which is the result of summing the three underlying separate genotypic distributions, weighted by their frequencies in the population. The mean of this total distribution is the average of the three genotypic means, weighted by the frequencies of the genotypes in the population. The variance of the total distribution is produced partly by the environmental variation within each genotype and partly by the slightly different means of the three genotypes.

Two features of the total distribution are noteworthy. First, there is only a single mode. Despite the existence of three separate genotypic distributions underlying it, the population distribution as a whole does not reveal the separate modes. Second, any individual whose height lies between the two arrows could have come from any one of the three genotypes, because they overlap so much. The result is that we cannot carry out any simple Mendelian analysis. For example, suppose the three genotypes are in fact the two homozygotes and the heterozygote for a pair of alleles at a locus. Let *aa* be the short homozygote and *AA* the tall one, with the heterozygote being intermediate in height. Because there is so much overlap of the phenotypic distributions, we cannot know to which genotype a given individual belongs. Conversely, if we cross two individuals that happen to be a homozygote *aa* and a heterozygote *Aa*, the offspring will not fall into two discrete classes in a 1 : 1 ratio but will cover almost the entire range of phenotypes smoothly. Thus, we could not know that the cross had in fact been *aa* × *Aa* and not *aa* × *AA* or *Aa* × *Aa*.

If the hypothetical plants of Figure 22-8 are grown in a stress environment, but care is taken that each plant has the same environment, then the picture changes. The phenotypic variance of each separate genotype is reduced because all the plants are grown under identical conditions, but at the same time the differences between genotypes may become greater because the small differences in physiology may be exaggerated under stress. The result (Figure 22-9) is a separation of the population as a whole into three non-overlapping phenotypic distributions, each characteristic of one genotype. We could now carry out a perfectly conventional Mendelian analysis of plant height. A "quantitative" character has been converted into a "qualitative" one! This conversion has been accomplished by making the differences between the means of the genotypes large as compared with the variation within genotypes.

Message A **quantitative** character is one for which the average phenotypic differences between genotypes are small as compared with the variation between individuals within genotypes.

It is sometimes said that continuous variation in a character is a consequence of a large number of segregating genes that influence the measurement, so that continuous variation is to be taken as prima facie evidence for control by many genes. But, as we have just shown, that is not

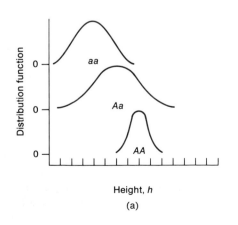

(a)

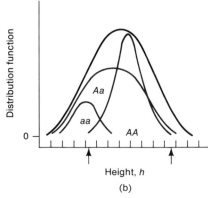

(b)

Figure 22-8. (a) Phenotypic distributions of three genotypes. (b) A population phenotypic distribution results from mixing individuals of the three genotypes in proportions 1 : 2 : 3.

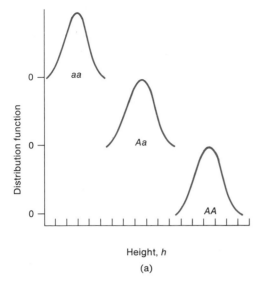

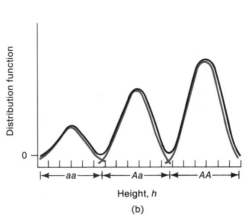

Figure 22-9. When the same genotypes as those in Figure 22-8 are grown in carefully controlled stress environments, the result is a smaller phenotypic variation in each genotype and greater difference between genotypes.

necessarily true. If the difference between genotype means is small compared to the environmental variance, then the simple one-gene–two-allele case results in continuous variation.

Of course, if the range of a character is limited, and if there are many segregating loci influencing it, then we expect the character to show continuous variation, because each allelic substitution must account for only a small difference in the trait. This **multiple-factor hypothesis** (that large numbers of genes, each with a small effect, are segregating to produce quantitative variation) has long been the basic model of quantitative genetics. A special name, **polygenes**, has been coined for these factors of small-but-equal effect as opposed to the genes of simple Mendelian analysis.

It is important to remember, however, that the *number* of segregating loci that influence a trait is not what separates quantitative and qualitative characters.

Even in the absence of large environmental variation, a very few genetically varying loci will produce variation that is indistinguishable from the effect of many loci of small effect. As an example, we can consider one of the earliest experiments in quantitative genetics, that of Wilhelm Johannsen on pure lines. Johannsen produced, by inbreeding, 19 homozygous lines of bean plants from an originally genetically heterogeneous population. Each line had a characteristic average seed weight ranging from 0.64 g per seed for the heaviest line down to 0.35 g per seed for the lightest. It is by no means clear that all these lines were genetically different. For example, five of the lines had seed weights of 0.450, 0.453, 0.454, 0.454, and 0.455 g, but let us take the most extreme position—that they *were* all different. Obviously these observations would be incompatible with a simple one-locus–two-allele model of gene action. In that case, if the original population were segregating for the two alleles, A and a, all inbred lines derived from that population would have to fall into one of two classes: AA or aa. If, in contrast, there were, say, 100

loci, each of small effect, that were segregating in the original population, then there would be a vast number of different inbred lines that could be produced, each with a different combination of homozygotes at different loci. One line might be

$$\frac{A}{A} \frac{B}{B} \frac{c}{c} \frac{D}{D} \cdots \frac{Z}{Z} \cdots$$

and another might be

$$\frac{a}{a} \frac{b}{b} \frac{c}{c} \frac{D}{D} \cdots \frac{z}{z} \cdots$$

and so on.

However, we do not need such a large number of loci to get the result observed by Johannsen. Suppose there were only five loci, each with three alleles. There would then be $3^5 = 243$ different kinds of homozygotes that could be produced from the inbreeding process. If we make 19 inbred lines at random there is a good chance, about 50 percent, that all nineteen will belong to a different one of the 243 classes. So Johannsen's experimental results could easily be explained by a relatively small number of genes. Thus, there is no real dividing line between polygenic traits and others. It is safe to say that no phenotypic trait above the level of the amino acid sequence in a polypeptide is influenced by only one gene. Moreover, traits influenced by many genes are not equally influenced by them all. Some genes will have major effects on the trait, and some, minor effects.

Message The critical difference between Mendelian and quantitative traits is not the number of segregating loci but

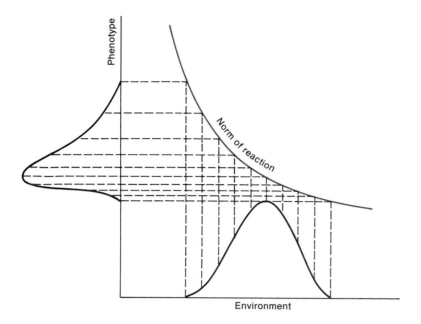

Figure 22-10. The distribution of environments on the horizontal axis is converted to the distribution of phenotypes on the vertical axis by the norm of reaction of a genotype.

the size of phenotypic differences between genotypes as compared with the individual variation within genotypic classes.

Norm of Reaction and Phenotypic Distribution

The phenotypic distribution of a trait, as we have seen, is a function of the average differences between genotypes and of the variation between genotypically identical individuals. But both of these are in turn functions of the environments in which the organisms develop and live. For a given genotype, each environment will result in a given phenotype (for the moment, ignoring developmental noise). Then a **distribution of environments** will be reflected biologically as a **distribution of phenotypes.** The way in which the environmental distribution is transformed into the phenotypic distribution is determined by the norm of reaction, as shown in Figure 22-10. The horizontal axis is environment (say, temperature) and the vertical axis is phenotype. The distribution on the horizontal axis represents the relative frequency of different environments. For example, most of these individuals developed at a temperature of 20°C, fewer at 18°C and 22°C, and so on. The norm of reaction for the genotype falls steeply at lower temperatures but flattens at high temperatures. Because each temperature produces a corresponding phenotype, as shown by the dotted lines, the distribution of temperatures results in the phenotypic distribution on the vertical axis. The norm of reaction is like a distorting mirror that reflects the environmental distribution onto the phenotypic axis.

By means of the same analysis, Figure 22-11 shows how a population consisting of two genotypes with different norms of reaction has a phenotype distribution that depends on the distribution of environments. If the environments are distributed as in the black curve, then the result-

ing population of plants will have a unimodal distribution, because the difference between genotypes is very small in this range of environments as compared with the sensitivity of the norms of reaction to small changes in temperature. If the distribution of environments is shifted to the right, however, as shown by the colored curve, a bimodal distribution of phenotypes results, because the norms of reaction are nearly flat in this environmental range but very different from each other.

Message A distribution of environments is reflected biologically as a distribution of phenotypes. The transformation of environmental distribution into phenotypic distribution is determined by the norm of reaction.

The Heritability of a Trait

The most basic question to be asked about a quantitative trait is whether the observed variation in the character is influenced by genes at all. It is important to note that this is not the same question as whether genes play any role in the character's development. Gene-mediated developmental processes lie at the base of every character, but *variation* from individual to individual is not necessarily the result of *genetic variation*. Thus, the possibility of speaking any language at all depends critically on the structure of the central nervous system as well as that of vocal cords, tongue, mouth, and ears, which in turn depend on the nature of the human genome. There is no environment in which cows will speak. But although the particular language that is spoken by humans varies from nation to nation, that variation is totally nongenetic.

Message The question of whether a trait is heritable is a

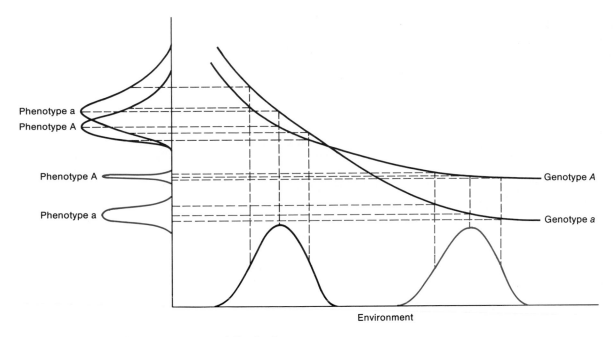

Figure 22-11. Two different environmental distributions are converted into different phenotype distributions by two different genotypes.

question about the role that differences in genes play in the phenotypic *differences* between individuals or groups.

Familiality and Heritability

In principle, it is easy to determine whether there is any genetic variation. If genes are involved, then (on the average) biological relatives should resemble each other more than unrelated individuals do. This resemblance would be reflected as a positive correlation between parents and offspring or between sibs (offspring of the same parents). Parents larger than the average should have offspring larger than the average; the more seeds a plant produces, the more seeds its sib should produce. Such correlations between relatives, however, are evidence for genetic variation *only if the relatives do not share common environments more than do nonrelatives.* It is absolutely fundamental to distinguish *familiality* from *heritability*.

Message Traits are **familial** if members of the same family share them, for whatever reason. Traits are **heritable**, however, only if the similarity arises from shared genotypes.

In experimental organisms, there is no problem in separating environmental from genetic similarities. The offspring of a cow producing milk at a high rate and the offspring of a cow producing milk at a low rate can be raised together in the same environment to see whether, despite the environmental similarity, each resembles its own parent. In natural populations, and especially in humans, the

problem is difficult. Because of the nature of human societies, members of the same family not only share genes but also have similar environments. Thus, the observation of simple familiality of a trait is uninterpretable genetically. In general, people who speak Hungarian have Hungarian-speaking parents, whereas Japanese speakers have Japanese-speaking parents. Yet the massive experience of immigration to North America has demonstrated that these linguistic differences, although familial, are nongenetic. The highest correlation between parents and offspring for any social traits in the United States are those for political party and religious sect. But they are not heritable. The distinction between familiality and heredity is not always so obvious. The Public Health Commission that originally studied the vitamin-deficiency disease pellagra in the southern United States came to the conclusion that it was genetic because it ran in families!

To determine whether a trait is heritable in human populations, we must use adoption studies to avoid the usual environmental similarity between biological relatives. The ideal experimental subject is the case of identical twins raised apart, because they are genetically identical but environmentally different. Such adoption studies must be so contrived that there is no correlation between the social environment of the adopting family and that of the biological family. These requirements are exceedingly difficult to meet, so that in practice we know very little about whether human quantitative traits that are familial are also heritable. Skin color is clearly heritable, as is adult height —but even here we must be very careful. We know that skin color is affected by genes because of the result of crossracial adoptions and because the offspring of black African slaves were black even when born and raised in

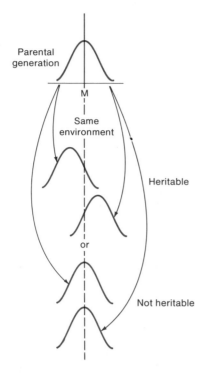

Figure 22-12. Standard method for testing heritability in experimental organisms. Crosses are performed within two populations of individuals selected from the extremes of the phenotypic distribution in the parental generation. If the phenotypic distributions of the two groups of offspring are significantly different from each other, then the trait is heritable. If the offspring distributions both resemble the distribution for the parental generation, then the trait is not heritable.

Canada. But are the differences in height between Japanese and Europeans affected by genes? The children of Japanese immigrants to North America, born and raised in North America, are taller than their parents but shorter than the North American average, so we might conclude that there is some influence of genetic difference. However, the second generation of Japanese-Americans are even taller than their American-born parents! It appears that some environmental-cultural influence, or perhaps a maternal effect, was still felt in the first generation of births in North America. We cannot yet say whether genetic differences in height distinguish North Americans of Japanese and Swedish ancestry.

Personality traits, temperament, and cognitive performance (such as IQ scores) are all familial, but there are no well-designed adoption studies to show whether they are heritable. The only large-sample studies of human IQ performance that claimed to involve randomized environments (Cyril Burt's reports on identical twins raised apart) have recently been shown to be completely fraudulent.

Figure 22-12 summarizes the usual method for testing heritability in experimental organisms. Individuals from both extremes of the distribution are mated with their own kind, and the offspring are raised in a common controlled environment. If there is an average difference between the two offspring groups, the trait is heritable. Most morphological traits in *Drosophila,* for example, turn out to be

heritable—but not all. If flies whose right wings are slightly longer than their left wings are mated together, their offspring have no greater tendency to be "right-winged" than do offspring of "left-winged" flies. As we shall see later (page 528), this method can also be used to get quantitative information about heritability.

Message In experimental organisms, environmental similarity may be readily distinguished from genetic similarity (or heritability). In humans, however, it is very difficult to determine whether a particular trait is heritable.

Determining Norms of Reaction

Remarkably little is known about the norms of reaction for any quantitative traits in any species. This is partly because it is difficult, in most sexually reproducing species, to replicate a genotype so that it can be tested in different environments. It is for this reason, for example, that we do not have a norm of reaction for any genotype for any human quantitative trait.

A few norm-of-reaction studies have been carried out with plants that can be clonally propagated. The results of one of these experiments are discussed in Chapter 1. It is possible to replicate genotypes in sexually reproducing organisms by the technique of mating of close relatives, or **inbreeding.** By selfing (where that is possible) or by mating brother and sister repeatedly generation after generation, an originally **segregating line** (that is, one that contains both homozygotes and heterozygotes at a locus) can be made homozygous.

In corn (which can be self-pollinated), for example, a single individual is chosen and self-pollinated. Then, in the next generation, a single one of its offspring is chosen and self-pollinated. In the third generation, a single one of *its* offspring is chosen and self-pollinated, and so on. Suppose the original individual in the first generation was already a homozygote at some locus. Then all of its offspring from self-pollination will also be homozygous and identical at the locus. Future generations of self-pollination will simply preserve the homozygosity. If, on the other hand, the original individual was a heterozygote, then the selfing $Aa \times Aa$ will produce $1/4$ AA homozygotes and $1/4$ aa homozygotes. If a single offspring is chosen in this subsequent generation to propagate the line, there is then a 50 percent chance that it is now a homozygote. If, by bad luck, the chosen individual should be still a heterozygote, there is another 50 percent chance of the selected individual in the third generation being homozygous, and so on. Of the ensemble of all heterozygous loci, then, after one generation of selfing, only $1/2$ will still be heterozygous; after two generations, $1/4$; after three, $1/8$. In the nth generation,

$$\text{Het}_n = \frac{1}{2^n} \text{Het}_0$$

where Het_n is the proportion of heterozygous loci in the nth generation and Het_0 is the proportion in the 0th generation. When selfing is not possible, brother-sister mating will accomplish the same end, although more slowly. Table 22-1 is a comparison of the amounts of heterozygosity left after n generations of selfing and brother-sister mating.

To carry out a norm-of-reaction study of a natural population, a large number of lines are sampled from the population and inbred for a sufficient number of generations to guarantee that each line is virtually homozygous at all its loci. Each line is then homozygous at each locus for a randomly selected allele present in the original population. The inbred lines themselves cannot be used to characterize norms of reaction in the natural population, because such totally homozygous genotypes do not exist in the original population. Each line can be crossed to each other line to produce heterozygotes that reconstitute the original population, and an arbitrary number of individuals from each cross can be produced. If inbred line 1 has the genetic constitution $AA\,BB\,cc\,dd\,EE \cdots$ and line 2 is $aa\,BB\,CC\,dd\,ee \cdots$, then a cross between them would produce a large number of offspring, all of whom are identically $Aa\,BB\,Cc\,dd\,Ee \cdots$, and these can be raised in different environments.

Inbreeding by mating of close relatives results in total homozygosity for the entire genome. In genetically well-marked species, particularly *Drosophila*, it is possible to produce lines that are homozygous for only a single chromosome, rather than the whole set, by an application of Müller's ClB technique (Chapter 7). The scheme as applied

to an autosome is shown in Figure 22-13. A single male from the population to be sampled is crossed to a female carrying a chromosome with a crossover suppressor C (usually a complex inversion), a recessive lethal l, and a dominant visible marker M_1 heterozygous with a second dominant visible M_2. In the F_1 a *single* male carrying the ClM_2 chromosome is chosen. This male, which is also carrying a wild-type chromosome from the population, is again crossed to the marker stock. In the F_2 all flies showing the M_1 trait but not M_2 are necessarily all heterozygotes for copies of the original wild-type chromosome because ClM_1/ClM_1 is lethal, and no crossovers have taken place. In the F_3 all wild-type flies are identically homozygous for the wild-type chromosome and are now available to make a stock for norm-of-reaction studies and for crosses.

Figure 22-14 shows the norms of reaction of abdominal bristle number as a function of temperature for second-chromosome homozygotes of *Drosophila pseudoobscura*. Like the growth-rate norms of *Achillea* (Chapter 1), the norms cross each other, with different genotypes having different temperature maxima. The heterozygotes (which are the natural genotypes) are more similar to each other than are the chromosomal homozygotes (which seldom if ever occur in a natural population).

Results of Norm-of-Reaction Studies

Very few norm-of-reaction studies have been carried out for quantitative characters for the normally heterozygous genotypes found in natural populations. Only easily inbred species, such as maize or *Drosophila*, and clonal species, such as strawberries, have been studied to any degree. Whenever such studies have been made, the outcomes resemble Figure 22-14. That is, no genotype is consistently above or below other genotypes; there are rather small differences among genotypes, and the direction of these differences is not consistent over a wide range of environments.

These facts have two important consequences. First, the selection of "superior" genotypes in domesticated animals and cultivated plants will result in very specifically adapted varieties that may not show their superior properties in other environments. To some extent, this problem is overcome by deliberately testing genotypes in a range of environments—for example, over several years and in several locations. It would be even better, however, if plant breeders could test their selections in a variety of controlled environments in which different environmental factors could be separately manipulated. The consequences of actual plant-breeding practices can be seen in Figure 22-15. The yields of two varieties of corn are shown as a function of different farm environments. Variety 1 is an older variety of hybrid corn, whereas variety 2 is a later "improved" hybrid. These performances are compared at a low planting density, which prevailed when variety 1 was developed, and at a high density characteristic of farming practice

■ **TABLE 22-1.** Heterozygosity remaining after various generations of inbreeding for two systems of mating

Generation	Remaining heterozygosity	
	Selfing	Brother-sister mating
0	1.000	1.000
1	0.500	0.750
2	0.250	0.625
3	0.125	0.500
4	0.0625	0.406
5	0.03125	0.338
10	0.000977	0.114
20	1.05×10^{-6}	0.014
n	$\text{Het}_n = \frac{1}{2}\text{Het}_{n-1}$	$\text{Het}_n = \frac{1}{2}\text{Het}_{n-1} + \frac{1}{4}\text{Het}_{n-2}$

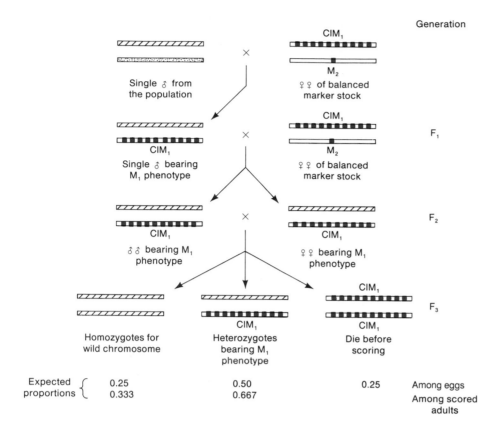

Generation

Single ♂ from the population

CIM₁
♀♀ of balanced marker stock

Single ♂ bearing M₁ phenotype

CIM₁
♀♀ of balanced marker stock

F₁

♂♂ bearing M₁ phenotype

♀♀ bearing M₁ phenotype

F₂

Homozygotes for wild chromosome

Heterozygotes bearing M₁ phenotype

Die before scoring

F₃

| Expected proportions | 0.25 | 0.50 | 0.25 | Among eggs |
| | 0.333 | 0.667 | | Among scored adults |

Figure 22-13. Adaptation of Müller's ClB method for autosomes to make homozygotes.

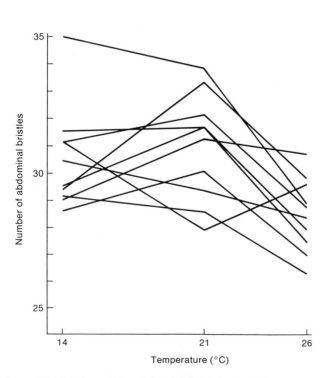

Figure 22-14. The number of abdominal bristles in different homozygous genotypes of *Drosophila pseudoobscura* at three different temperatures. (Data courtesy of A. P. Gupta.)

when hybrid 2 was selected. At the high density, the new variety is clearly superior to the old variety in all environments as shown in Figure 22-15a. At the low density, however, the situation is quite different. First, note that the new variety is less sensitive to environment than the older hybrid, as evidenced by its flatter norm of reaction. Second, the new "improved" variety is actually poorer under the best farm conditions. Third, the yield improvement of the new variety is not apparent under the low densities characteristic of the earlier agricultural practice.

The second consequence of the nature of reaction norms is that, in the human species, even if it should turn out that there is genetic variation for various mental and emotional traits (which is by no means clear), this variation is unlikely to favor one genotype over another across a range of environments. We must beware of hypothetical norms of reaction for human cognitive traits that show one genotype unconditionally superior to another. Even putting aside all questions of moral and political judgment, there is simply no basis for describing different human genotypes as "better" or "worse" on any scale, unless the investigator is able to make a very exact specification of environment.

Message Norm-of-reaction studies show only small differences among natural genotypes, and these differences are not consistent over a wide range of environments. Thus, "superior" genotypes in domesticated animals and cultivated plants may be superior only in certain environments. If it should turn out that humans exhibit genetic

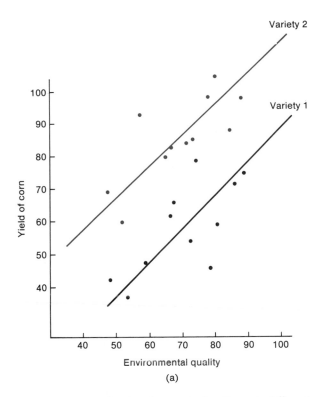

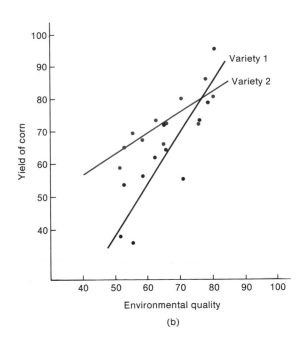

Figure 22-15. Yields of grain of two varieties of corn in different environments: (a) at a high planting density; (b) at a low planting density. (Data of W. A. Russell, *Proc. 29th Annual Corn and Sorghum Research Conference,* 1974.)

variation for various mental and emotional traits, this variation is unlikely to favor one genotype over another across a range of environments.

Quantifying Heritability

If a trait is shown to have some heritability in a population, then it is possible to quantify the degree of heritability. In Figure 22-8, we see that the variation among phenotypes in a population arises from two sources. First, there are average differences between the genotypes, and second, each genotype has phenotypic variance because of environmental variation. The total phenotypic variance of the population (s_p^2) can then be broken into two portions, the variance among genotypic means (s_g^2) and the remaining variance (s_e^2). The former is called the **genetic variance** and the latter is called the **environmental variance,** although, as we shall see, these names are quite misleading. The degree of heritability can then be defined as the proportion of the total variance that is due to the genetic variance:

$$H^2 = \frac{s_g^2}{s_p^2} = \frac{s_g^2}{s_g^2 + s_e^2}$$

H^2, so defined, is called the **broad heritability** of the character.

It must be stressed that this measure of "genetic influence" tells what proportion of the population's *variation* in phenotype is assignable to *variation* in genotype. It does not tell what proportion of an *individual's* phenotype can be ascribed to its heredity and what proportion to its environment. This latter distinction is not a reasonable one. An individual's phenotype is a consequence of the interaction between its genes and its sequence of environments. It clearly would be silly to say that you owe 60 inches of your height to genes and 10 inches to environment. All measures of the "importance" of genes are framed in terms of the proportion of variance ascribable to their variation. This approach is a special application of the more general technique of the **analysis of variance** for apportioning relative weight to contributing causes. The method was, in fact, invented originally to deal with experiments in which different environmental and genetic factors were influencing the growth of plants. (For a sophisticated but accessible treatment of the analysis of variance written for biologists, see R. Sokal and J. Rohlf, *Biometry,* 2d ed., W. H. Freeman and Company, 1980.)

Methods of Estimating H^2

The genetic variance and the heritability can be estimated in several ways. Most directly, one could obtain an estimate of s_e^2 by making a number of homozygous lines from the population, crossing them in pairs to reconstitute individual heterozygotes, and measuring the phenotypic variance *within* each heterozygous genotype. Because there is no genetic variance within a genotypic class, these variances would (when averaged) provide an estimate of s_e^2. This value can then be subtracted from the value of s_p^2 in the original population to give s_g^2.

Other estimates of genetic variance can be obtained by considering the genetic similarity between relatives. Using simple Mendelian principles, we can see that full sibs will (on the average) be identical for one-half of their genes. For identification purposes, we can label the alleles at a locus carried by the parents differently—so that they are, say, A_1A_2 and A_3A_4. Now the older sib has a probability of $1/2$ of getting A_1 from its father, and so does the younger sib, so they have a chance of $1/2 \times 1/2 = 1/4$ of both carrying A_1. On the other hand, they might both have received an A_2 from their father, so again, with probability $1/4$ they will carry a gene in common that they inherited from their father. Thus, the chance is $1/4 + 1/4 = 1/2$ that both sibs will carry an A_1 or that both sibs will carry an A_2. The other half of the time, one will have inherited an A_1 and the other an A_2. So, as far as paternally inherited genes are concerned, full sibs have a 50 percent chance of carrying the same allele. But the same reasoning applies to their maternally inherited gene. Averaging over their paternally and maternally inherited genes, half the genes of full sibs are identical between them. Their **genetic correlation** is $1/2$.

If we apply this reasoning to half-sibs—say, with a common father but different mothers—we get a different result. Again, the two sibs have a 50 percent chance of inheriting an identical gene from their father, but this time they have no way of inheriting the same gene from their mothers, since they have two different mothers. Averaging the maternally inherited and the paternally inherited genes thus gives a probability of $(1/2 + 0)/2 = 1/4$ that these half-sibs carry the same gene.

The result is that the difference in genetic correlation between full sibs and half-sibs is $1/2 - 1/4 = 1/4$. Let us contrast this with their **phenotypic correlations.** If the environmental similarity is the same for half-sibs and full sibs, a very important condition of estimating heritability, then environmental similarities will cancel out if we take the difference in correlation between the two kinds of sibs. This difference in phenotypic correlation will then be proportional to how much of the variance is genetic. Thus

$$\begin{array}{l} \text{genetic correlation} \\ \text{of full sibs} \end{array} - \begin{array}{l} \text{genetic correlation} \\ \text{of half-sibs} \end{array} = 1/4$$

but

$$\begin{array}{l} \text{phenotypic} \\ \text{correlation} \\ \text{of full sibs} \end{array} - \begin{array}{l} \text{phenotypic} \\ \text{correlation} \\ \text{of half-sibs} \end{array} = H^2 \times 1/4$$

so an estimate of H^2 is

$$H^2 = 4\left(\begin{array}{l}\text{correlation} \\ \text{of full sibs}\end{array} - \begin{array}{l}\text{correlation} \\ \text{of half-sibs}\end{array}\right)$$

where the correlation here is the *phenotypic* correlation.

We can use similar arguments about genetic similarity between parents and offspring and between twins to obtain two other estimates of H^2:

$$H^2 = 4\left(\begin{array}{l}\text{correlation} \\ \text{of full sibs}\end{array}\right) - 2\left(\begin{array}{l}\text{parent-offspring} \\ \text{correlation}\end{array}\right)$$

or

$$H^2 = 2\left(\begin{array}{l}\text{correlation of} \\ \text{monozygotic twins}\end{array}\right) - \left(\begin{array}{l}\text{correlation} \\ \text{of dizygotic twins}\end{array}\right)$$

These formulas come from considering the genetic similarity between relatives. They are only approximate and depend on assumptions about the way genes act. The first two formulas, for example, assume that genes at different loci add together in their effect on the character. The last formula is particularly inaccurate, because it also assumes that the alleles at each locus show no dominance. (See the discussion of components of variance on page 525.) If we ignore these problems of gene interaction, the genetic correlation between full sibs is $1/2$ and between half-sibs is $1/4$. Substituting the values in the first formula gives $H^2 = 1$, which would be the case if all the variation were genetic. If there is nongenetic variation, it will be common to both half-sibs and full sibs, and this will make their correlations more similar and reduce the value of H^2. A similar argument applies, for example, to the twin formula, since monozygotic twins have a genetic correlation of 1, while dizygotic twins are just full sibs and have a genetic correlation of $1/2$.

All of these estimates, as well as others based on correlations between relatives, depend critically on the assumption that environmental correlations between individuals are the same for all degrees of relationship. If closer relatives have more similar environments, as they do in humans, the estimates of heritability are biased. It is reasonable that most environmental correlations between relatives are positive, in which case the heritabilities would be overestimated. Negative environmental correlations can also exist. For example, if the members of a litter must compete for food in short supply, negative correlations in growth rate between sibs could occur.

In general, the presence of greater environmental correlation between close relatives makes heritability estimates uninterpretable. It is for this reason that there are no legitimate estimates of heritability for human quantitative traits. Despite their widespread use in human genetics, parent-offspring correlations are estimates of *familiality,* but not of heritability. Even the difference between identical and fraternal twin correlations will not do, because there is the implicit assumption that identical twins are treated no more alike than fraternal twins—an assumption that is unwarranted by the facts. Volumes have been written on the heritability of human IQ, for example, and many modern textbooks of genetics treat the numerical estimates of the heritability of IQ seriously (0.8 is the usual figure given). The absence of studies that treat the environmental correlations between relatives, however, make all the numbers meaningless.

The Meaning of H^2

Attention to the problems of estimating broad heritability distracts from the deeper questions of the meaning of the ratio when it can be estimated. Despite its widespread use as a measure of how "important" genes are in influencing a trait, H^2 actually has a special and limited meaning.

First, H^2 is not a fixed characteristic of a trait but depends on the population in which it is measured and the set of environments in which the population has developed. In one population, alleles segregating at many loci may influence a trait. In another population, these loci may be homozygous. In such a homozygous population, the trait will show no heritability because $s_g^2 = 0$. That value does not mean that genes have no role in influencing the trait's development, but only that none of the variation between individuals within that population can be ascribed to genetic variation. Similarly, a population developing in a very homogeneous environment will have a smaller s_e^2 for a trait than one in a varying environment. The lack of environmental heterogeneity will result in a high value of H^2, but that value does not mean that the trait is insensitive to all environments.

Message In general, the heritability of a trait is different in each population and each set of environments, and it cannot be extrapolated from one population and set of environments to another.

Second, the separation of variance into genetic and environmental components, s_g^2 and s_e^2, does not really separate the genetic and environmental causes of variation. Consider Figure 22-16, which shows two genotypes in a population, with their two norms of reaction. In Figure 22-16a, the population is assumed to consist of the two genotypes in equal frequency, and the distribution of environments (shown on the horizontal axis) is centered toward the right. The phenotypic distribution (shown on the vertical axis) is composed of two underlying distributions that are very different in their means and have rather little envi-

ronmental variation. H^2 has a high value. In Figure 22-16b, the environmental distribution has been shifted to the left. As a result, the average difference between genotypes is very much less. The important point is that the so-called *genetic variance* has been changed by shifting the *environment.* In Figure 22-16c, we suppose that the environments are the same as in Figure 22-16b, but now genotype II has become extremely common in the population and genotype I is rare. Then the phenotypic distribution is almost entirely a reflection of norm of reaction II. The population has a smaller environmental variance, s_e^2, than does the population of Figure 22-16b because it has become enriched for the more developmentally stable genotype. In this case, the *environmental variance* has been changed by a change in *genotypes.* In general, genetic variance depends on the environments to which the population is exposed, and environmental variance depends upon the frequencies of the genotypes.

Message Because genotype and environment interact to produce phenotype, no partition of variation can actually separate causes of variation.

Third, as a consequence of the argument just given, knowledge of the heritability of a trait does not permit prediction of how the distribution of the trait will change if either genotypic frequencies or environment are changed markedly.

Message A high heritability does not mean that a trait is unchangeable by environment.

Compare parts (a) and (b) in Figure 22-16, for example. All that high heritability means is that, for the particular population developing in the particular distribution of environments in which the heritability was measured, average differences between genotypes are large compared to environmental variation within genotypes. If the environment is changed, immense differences in phenotype may occur.

How Useful Is H^2?

If we cannot predict the changeability of a trait due to environmental or genetic manipulation from knowing the trait's broad heritability, of what use is a measure of H^2? This concept has been introduced as a *pedagogical step* toward understanding a related concept (narrow heritability) that is of considerable importance in plant and animal breeding. In fact, plant and animal breeders never use H^2, and the British statistician and geneticist R. A. Fisher, who

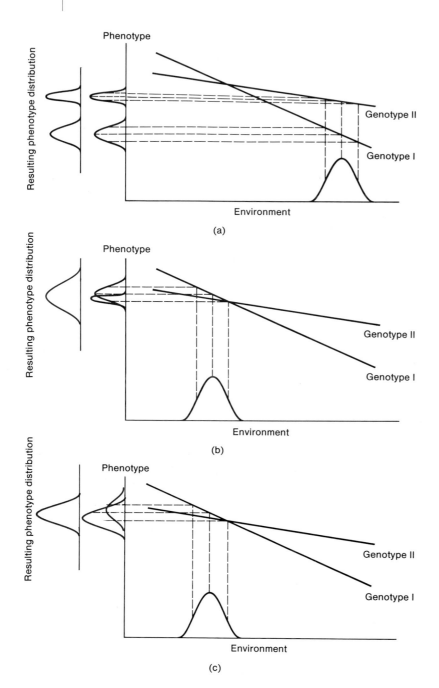

Figure 22-16. Genetic variance can be changed by changing the environment, and environmental variance can be changed by changing the relative frequencies of genotypes.

invented the analysis of variance into genetic and environmental fractions, did not use the concept at all. Unfortunately, the actual history of teaching and research in genetics has led to a widespread but erroneous use of H^2 in characterizing traits. Instead of remaining an intermediate step in pedagogy, H^2 has taken on a life of its own. As important as it is to understand what can be done by the genetic analysis of quantitative variation, it is equally important to understand its limitations, especially when it is widely misused.

Despite its limited meaning, H^2 has been used over and over again, especially by human geneticists and psychologists. They have done so in the erroneous belief that they can estimate H^2 without strict adoption studies and that, if

they could estimate H^2, it would tell them something important about clinical or social policy. Students should not suppose that a practice is justified just because many professionals adhere to it. Sometimes scientists simply do not know what else to do, so they continue to pursue useless and even incorrect lines. Sometimes they literally do not understand the basic structure of assumptions that underlie this practice. Sometimes they use incorrect methods and concepts in an attempt to justify an ideological or social prejudice (as is clearly the case for some of the studies of the heritability of human temperamental and cognitive functions, such as IQ performance).

Since early in the nineteenth century, there has been a form of biological determinism that has attempted to ex-

plain human social differentiation as the direct consequence of biological differences. For example, in 1905,
E. L. Thorndike (the most influential founder of modern
American psychology) wrote that "in the actual race of life,
which is not to get ahead, but to get ahead of somebody, the
chief determining factor is heredity." This dictum, which
appeared in a paper in a scientific journal, could only have
been pure prejudice in 1905 — only five years after the
rediscovery of Mendel's paper, but five years *before* the
chromosome theory of inheritance, ten years *before* the development of the theory of correlation, and 13 years *before*
Fisher's foundations of the theory of quantitative genetics.
Much of the history of human psychological genetics since
that time describes the vain attempt to justify Thorndike's
claim.

If the investigator were seriously interested in knowing
how the genes might constrain or influence the course of
development of any trait in any organism, it would be necessary to study directly the norms of reaction of the various
genotypes in the population over the range of projected
environments. No less detailed information will do. Summary measures such as H^2 are not first steps toward a more
complete analysis and therefore are not valuable in themselves.

Message   Because H^2 characterizes present populations
in present environments, it cannot predict the consequences of changing the environment or genotype.

Counting and Locating the Genes

It is not possible with purely genetic techniques to identify
all genes that influence the development of a given trait.
That is true even for simple qualitative traits — for example, the genes involved in determining the total antigenic
configuration of the membrane of the human red blood
cell. About 40 loci determining human blood groups are
known at present, each having been discovered by finding
at least one person with an immunological specificity different from those of other people. There may be many other
loci determining red-cell membrane structure that remain
undiscovered because all individuals studied are genetically
identical. That is, *genetic analysis* detects genes only when
there is some allelic variation. In contrast, of course, *molecular analysis*, by dealing directly with DNA and its translated
information, can identify genes even when they do not
vary — provided the gene products can be identified.

Moreover, the power of classical genetic analysis to detect loci depends on the amount of genetic variation. Even
in the case of qualitative human blood groups, only five
were discovered in the first 40 years of research on the
subject, these five being genetically variable in human pop-

ulations. Then, during World War II, vast numbers of individuals were blood-typed in connection with the treatment
of burns and other war-related injuries, so that loci for
which most individuals are identically homozygous were
discovered from the rare genetic variants.

The Method of Artificial Selection

The standard method of finding the loci that are segregating with respect to a given quantitative trait in a genetically
well-marked species such as *Drosophila melanogaster* is to
begin with two populations that are very divergent for the
character. These may be two natural populations, but more
frequently they are two subpopulations that have been created by artificial selection. For example, in one subpopulation the largest individuals are chosen as parents each generation, while in the other subpopulation the smallest
individuals are chosen. As generations pass, the upwardly
selected line will become enriched for alleles that lead to
larger size, while in the downwardly selected line the alternative alleles will accumulate. If selection is carried on for a
long enough time, the two populations will become virtually homozygous for "high" and "low" alleles. Alternatively, many inbred lines could have been made from the
original population, and the most divergent lines chosen as
the "high" and "low" populations. Whichever method is
used, the two divergent populations will probably differ
only for those loci that were somewhat heterozygous in the
original population.

Once the divergent lines have been established, each
chromosome in one line can be separately substituted into
the other line using dominant marker stocks with crossover
suppressors. An idealization of the method is shown in Figure 22-17, where A_I, A_{II}, A_{III}, B_I, . . . are dominant
marker systems for chromosomes I, II, and III. Lines homozygous and heterozygous for various combinations of
"+" and "−" chromosomes are measured for the trait, and
in this way the contribution of each chromosome to the
genetic differences between the lines is determined. An
example of the application of this technique by J. Crow to
the study of DDT resistance in *Drosophila melanogaster* is
shown in Figure 22-18. Crow did not manufacture lines
that were homozygous for introduced chromosomes, so we
see only the effect of chromosomes when heterozygous.
The figure shows that every chromosome seems to have
some genes that differ between the resistant and the susceptible line.

Linkage Analysis

The experiment of Figure 22-17 must be elaborated to find
individual genes. A more detailed analysis can be carried
out with recessive marker stocks that allow recombination.
A cross between a multiply marked susceptible chromo-

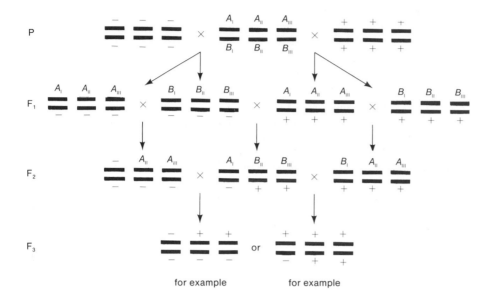

Figure 22-17. Scheme of mating to produce individuals with different combinations of chromosomes from a high selection line (+) and a low selection line (−). A_I, B_I, . . . are dominant marker crossover suppressors.

some and a resistant chromosome, followed by a backcross to the marker stock, will result in a large number of recombinant types of varying resistance. In the simplest situation, all recombinants carrying a given short region will be resistant, while those not carrying the region will be susceptible. This would be strong evidence for a single locus of major effect in the region. In the worst case, all the recombinants will show partial resistance, so that no localization has been accomplished.

Where localization experiments have been carried out, as for example for the sternopleural bristles on the side of the thorax of *Drosophila melanogaster*, most of the difference between selected lines has been localized to two or three genes with major effects, plus a residue of "genes with small effects."

The possibility exists that many quantitative characters (perhaps even most) will turn out to vary not as a consequence of the segregation of alleles at large numbers of loci with small effects (as the multiple-genes hypothesis supposes), but rather as a consequence of segregation of very few loci with major effects. This study of the "genetic architecture" of quantitative traits is a leading problem of quantitative genetics. It can be solved by straightforward but excessively tedious experiments in well-marked species, such as *Drosophila melanogaster*. In *Homo sapiens*, such experiments cannot be done, and we have no information on the number or localization of loci contributing to quantitative traits. Even for a character with obvious genetic influence and with a relatively simple biochemical and developmental basis (such as skin color), we do not know the number of loci (except to say that there must be several) or their distribution over the human chromosome set.

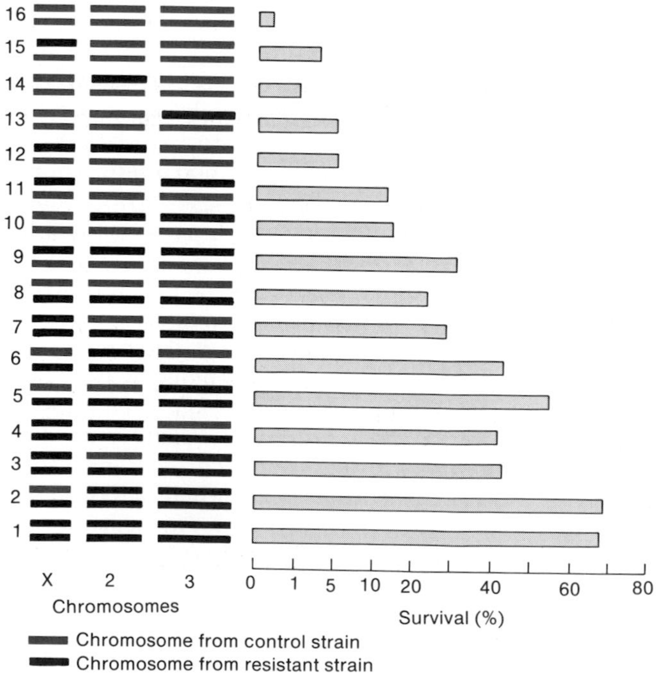

Gene Action

The question of gene action is closely tied to the problem of detecting the loci. The methods described in the preceding section are biased toward detection of loci where allelic differences are of large effect. The process of selection by which the contrasting populations are established is relatively efficient only for allelic substitutions of large effect.

Even without being able to localize the genes, we can obtain some information about their actions and interactions. We can judge average dominance at the chromosomal level by comparing homozygotes and heterozygotes

Figure 22-18. Survival of *Drosophila melanogaster* genotypes with different combinations of chromosomes from a selected line (black chromosomes) and a nonselected line (colored chromosomes). Black chromosomes are from strains that have been selected for resistance to DDT. (From J. Crow, *Ann. Rev. Entomology* 2:228, 1957.)

in chromosomal substitution experiments. In Figure 22-18, a comparison of lines 1 and 2 shows that the X chromosomes do not differ, whereas lines 15 and 16 show that they do. An explanation of this discrepancy would be the complete dominance of resistance alleles over susceptibility alleles. A comparison of lines 7, 9, and 10 supports the hypothesis of dominance because 7 and 9 are equally resistant, whereas 10 is much less so.

There is also evidence of specific epistatic interactions. Line 5 in the figure has both the substitutions of lines 2 and 3 and so should be at least as susceptible as line 3; yet it is intermediate between 2 and 3. It would seem that heterozygosity for a susceptible X chromosome actually decreases the susceptibility when in combination with a susceptible second-chromosome heterozygote. Such evidences of dominance and epistasis of whole chromosomes throw only indirect light on individual gene action because a single gene of major effect with dominance or strong epistasis would hide the effects of several other genes of small effect.

Evidence for non-nuclear effects can also be deduced from the chromosomal substitution experiments. For example, in Figure 22-18, lines 8 and 9 have the same chromosomal constitution but are the result of reciprocal crosses and so have different cytoplasm. There clearly is a maternal effect.

More on Analyzing Variance

Knowledge of the broad heritability (H^2) of a trait in a population is not very useful in itself, but a finer subdivision of phenotypic variance can provide important information for plant and animal breeders. The genetic variation and the environmental variation can themselves be subdivided in a way that can provide information about gene action and the possibility of shaping the genetic composition of a population.

Additive and Dominance Variance

Our previous consideration of gene action suggests that the phenotypes of homozygotes and heterozygotes ought to have a simple relation. If one of the alleles codes for a less active gene product or one with no activity at all, and if one unit of gene product is sufficient to allow full physiological activity of the organism, then we expect complete dominance of one allele over the other, as Mendel observed for flower color in peas. If, on the other hand, physiological activity is proportional to the amount of active gene product, we would expect the heterozygote's phenotype to be exactly intermediate between the homozygotes (no dominance). For many quantitative traits, however, neither of these simple cases is the rule. In general, heterozygotes are not exactly intermediate between the two homozygotes but are closer to one of the homozygotes (partial dominance).

The complexity of biochemical and developmental pathways is such that intermediate activity of primary gene product is not exactly scaled as intermediate phenotype. Indeed, in some cases the heterozygote may lie outside the phenotypic range of the homozygotes altogether—a feature termed **overdominance**. For example, newborn babies who are intermediate in size have a higher chance of survival than very large or very small newborns. Thus, if survival were the phenotype of interest, heterozygotes for genes influencing growth rate would show overdominance.

Suppose there are two alleles, a and A, segregating at a locus influencing height. In the environments encountered by the population, the mean phenotypes (heights) and frequencies of the three genotypes might be

	aa	Aa	AA
Phenotype	10	18	20
Frequency	0.36	0.48	0.16

There is genetic variance in the population; the phenotypic means of the three genotypic classes are different. Some of the variance arises because there is an average effect on phenotype of substituting an allele A for an allele a. That is, the average height of all individuals with A alleles is greater than that of all individuals with a alleles. By defining the average effect of an allele as the average phenotype of all individuals that carry it, we necessarily make the average effect of the allele depend on the frequencies of the genotypes. If nearly all the a alleles are in homozygotes, then each added a allele is worth 10 units; if most a alleles are in heterozygotes, then each added a is worth 18 units.

The average effect is easily calculated by simply counting the a and A alleles and multiplying them by the height of the individuals in which they appear. So, 0.36 of all the individuals are homozygous aa, each aa individual has two a alleles, and the average height of aa individuals is 10 cm. Heterozygotes make up 0.48 of the population, each has only one a allele, and the average phenotypic measurement of Aa individuals is 18 cm. The total "number" of a alleles is $2(0.36) + 1(0.48)$. Thus, the average effect of all the a alleles is

$$\bar{a} = \text{average effect of } a = \frac{2(0.36)(10) + 1(0.48)(18)}{2(0.36) + 1(0.48)}$$
$$= 13.20 \text{ cm}$$

and, by a similar argument,

$$\bar{A} = \text{average effect of } A = \frac{2(0.16)(20) + 1(0.48)(18)}{2(0.16) + 1(0.48)}$$
$$= 18.80 \text{ cm}$$

This average difference in effect between A and a alleles of 5.60 cm accounts for some of the variance in phenotype, but not for all, because the heterozygote is not exactly intermediate between the homozygotes. There is some dominance. The total genetic variance associated with this locus can then be partitioned between the **additive genetic variance** (s_a^2) associated with the average effect of substituting A for a, and the **dominance variance** (s_d^2) resulting from the partial dominance of A over a in heterozygotes. Thus, $s_g^2 = s_a^2 + s_d^2$.

The components of variance in this example can be calculated using the definitions of mean and variance that were developed earlier in this chapter. Remembering that a mean is the sum of the values of a variable, each weighted by the frequency with which that value occurs (see page 507), we can calculate the mean phenotype to be

$$\bar{x} = \Sigma f_i x_i = (0.36)(10) + (0.48)(18) + (0.16)(20)$$
$$= 15.44 \text{ cm}$$

The total genetic variance that arises from the variation among the mean phenotypes of the three genotypes is

$$s_g^2 = \Sigma f_i(x_i - \bar{x})^2 = (0.36)(10 - 15.44)^2$$
$$+ (0.48)(18 - 15.44)^2$$
$$+ (0.16)(20 - 15.44)^2$$
$$= 17.13 \text{ cm}^2$$

The additive variance is calculated from the squared deviation of the average a effect from the mean, weighted by its frequency, plus the squared deviation of the average A effect from the mean, weighted by its frequency. The frequency of the a allele is

$$f_a = \frac{2(0.36) + 1(0.48)}{2} = 0.60$$

and the frequency of the A allele is

$$f_A = \frac{2(0.16) + 1(0.48)}{2} = 0.40$$

Thus, since there are two alleles present in diploid individuals,

$$s_a^2 = 2[f_a(\bar{a} - \bar{x})^2 + f_A(\bar{A} - \bar{x})^2]$$
$$= 2[(0.60)(13.20 - 15.44)^2$$
$$+ (0.40)(18.80 - 15.44)^2]$$
$$= 15.05 \text{ cm}^2$$

and

$$s_d^2 = s_g^2 - s_a^2 = 17.13 - 15.05 = 2.08 \text{ cm}^2$$

The usefulness of this subdivision of genetic variance is in the prediction that can be made about the effect of selective breeding. This use becomes clear in an extreme case. Suppose that there is overdominance and the phenotypic means and frequencies of three genotypes are

	$\dfrac{AA}{10}$	$\dfrac{Aa}{12}$	$\dfrac{aa}{10}$
Phenotype	10	12	10
Frequency	0.25	0.50	0.25

It is apparent (and a calculation like the preceding one will confirm it) that there is no average difference between a and A alleles, because each has an effect of 11 units. So there is no *additive genetic variance*, although there is dominance variance. The largest individuals are heterozygotes. If a breeder attempts to increase height in this population by selective breeding, mating these heterozygotes together will simply reconstitute the original population. Selection will be totally ineffective. This illustrates the general law that the effect of selection depends on the additive genetic variance and *not* on genetic variance in general.

The total phenotypic variance can now be written as

$$s_p^2 = s_g^2 + s_e^2 = s_a^2 + s_d^2 + s_e^2$$

We define a heritability, h^2, the **heritability in the narrow sense,** as

$$h^2 = \frac{s_a^2}{s_p^2} = \frac{s_a^2}{s_a^2 + s_d^2 + s_e^2}$$

It is this heritability, not to be confused with H^2, that is useful in determining whether a program of selective breeding will succeed in changing the population. The greater the h^2, the more of the difference between selected parents and the population as a whole will be preserved in the next generation.

What has been described as the "dominance" variance is really more complicated. It is all the genetic variation that cannot be explained by the average effect of substituting A for a. If there is more than one locus affecting the character, then any epistatic interactions between loci will appear as variance not associated with the average effect of substituting alleles at the A locus. In principle we can separate this interaction variance s_i^2 from the dominant variance s_d^2, but in practice this cannot be done with any semblance of accuracy, so all the nonadditive variance appears as "dominance" variance.

Estimating Genetic Variance Components

Genetic components of variance are estimated from covariance between relatives. Ignoring the epistatic contributions to variance that are contained to some degree in all covariances between relatives, Table 22-2 shows some of the components of variance contained in the covariances between relatives. These relations can be used, together with the total phenotypic variance, to estimate h^2. For example, we see from Table 22-2 that the covariance between parent and offspring contains half the additive variance. That is,

$$\text{cov (parent-offspring)} = s_a^2/2$$

Therefore,

$$2 \text{ cov (parent-offspring)} = s_a^2$$

By the definition of correlation, and taking into account that the phenotypic variance is the same in the parental and offspring generation so that $s_o = s_p$, we see that

$$\frac{2 \text{ cov (parent-offspring)}}{s_p^2} = 2 \text{ correlation (parent-offspring)}$$

$$= \frac{s_a^2}{s_p^2} = h^2$$

Thus, twice the parent-offspring correlation is an estimate of h^2.

There is yet another way to estimate h^2 that provides an insight into its real meaning. Suppose we plot the phenotypes of offspring against the average phenotypes of their two parents, the so-called **midparent value.** We may observe a relationship like that in Figure 22-19. The regression line will pass through the mean of all the parents and the mean of all the offspring, which will be equal to each other because no change has occurred in the population between generations. Moreover, taller parents have taller children, and shorter parents, shorter children; the slope of the line is positive. But the slope is not unity. That is, very short parents have children somewhat taller than they themselves are, and very tall parents have children somewhat shorter than they themselves. This slope of less than

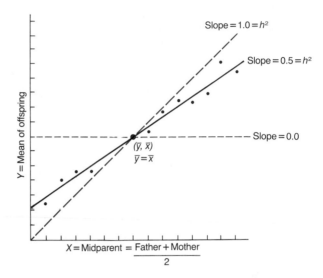

Figure 22-19. The regression (black line) of offspring measurements (y) on midparents (x) for a trait with narrow heritability (h^2) of 0.5. The colored line shows the regression slope if the trait were perfectly heritable.

unity for the regression line arises because heritability is less than perfect. If the phenotype were additively inherited with complete fidelity, then height of the offspring would be identical to the midparent value, and the slope of the line would be 1. On the other hand, if offspring have no heritable similarity to their parents, all parents would have offspring of the same average height, and the slope of the line would be 0. This suggests that the slope of the regression line of offspring on midparent is an estimate of additive heritability. In fact, the relationship is precise. By definition (see page 508), the regression of offspring value, y, on midparent value, x, is

$$b = \frac{\text{cov } xy}{s_x^2}$$

But from Table 22-2,

$$\text{cov (parent-offspring)} = \frac{s_g^2}{2}$$

and this covariance is not changed if we consider the covariance of offspring with the average of their two parents. On the other hand, the variance of midparental values is the variance of an average of two measurements and is thus only one-half the variance of the measurements themselves. Obviously, average values vary less than their component numbers. So, letting s_p^2 = phenotypic variance of the parents (which is the same as the phenotypic variance of the offspring generation),

■ **TABLE 22-2.** Proportion of the additive variance (s_a^2) and the dominance variance (s_d^2) contained in the genetic covariance between various related individuals

Relatives	Estimated proportion of	
	s_a^2	s_d^2
Cov (identical twins)	1	1
Cov (parent-offspring)	1/2	0
Cov (half-sibs)	1/4	0
Cov (full sibs)	1/2	1/4

$$b = \frac{s_g^2/2}{s_p^2/2} = \frac{s_g^2}{s_p^2} = h^2$$

The fact that the slope equals the additive heritability now allows us to use h^2 to predict the effects of artificial selection. Suppose we select parents for the next generation who are on the average 2 units above the general mean of the population from which they were chosen. If h^2 is 0.5, then their offspring, who form the next, selected, generation will lie $0.5(2.0) = 1.0$ unit above the mean of the present population, since the regression coefficient predicts how much increase in y will result from a unit increase in x. We can define the **selection differential** as the difference between the selected parents and the unselected mean, and the **selection response** as the difference between their offspring and the previous generation. Then

selection response $= h^2 \times$ selection differential

or

$$h^2 = \frac{\text{selection response}}{\text{selection differential}}$$

This last expression provides us with yet another way to estimate h^2: by selecting for one generation and comparing the response with the selection differential. Usually this is carried out for several generations, and the average response is used.

Remember that any estimate of h^2, like H^2, depends on the assumption of no greater environmental correlation between closer relatives. Moreover, h^2 in one population in one set of environments will not be the same as that in a different population at a different time. Figure 22-20 shows the range of heritabilities reported for a number of traits in chickens. The very small ranges are generally close

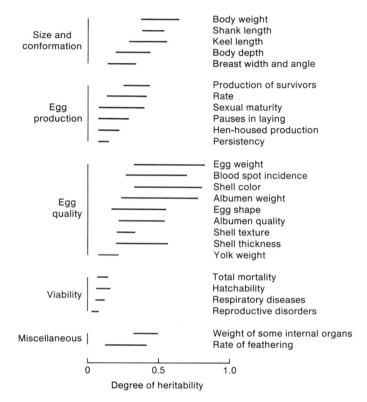

Figure 22-20. Ranges of heritabilities (h^2) reported for a variety of characters in chickens. (From I. M. Lerner.)

to zero. For most traits for which a substantial heritability has been reported in some population, there are big differences from study to study.

Partitioning Environmental Variance

Environmental variance, like genetic variance, can also be further subdivided. In particular, developmental noise is usually confounded with environmental variance, but when a character can be measured on left and right sides of an organism, or over repeated body segments, it is possible to separate noise from environment. Table 22-3 shows the complete partitioning of variation for two characters in a population of *Drosophila melanogaster* raised in standard laboratory conditions. For each character there is a substantial h^2, so we might expect that selective breeding could increase or decrease bristle number and ovary size. Moreover, nearly all the nongenetic variation is due to developmental noise. These values, however, are a consequence of the relatively rigorously controlled environment of the laboratory. Presumably s_e^2 in nature would be considerably larger, with a consequent diminution in the relative size of h^2 and of s_a^2. As always, such studies of variation are applica-

■ **TABLE 22-3.** Partition of the total phenotypic variance for two characters in a population of *Drosophila melanogaster*

Source of variation			Percentage of variance	
			Number of abdominal bristles	Ovary size
Additive genetic	s_a^2	s_g^2	52	30
Dominance + epistatic variance	s_d^2		9	40
Environmental variance	s_e^2	s_e^2	1	3
Developmental noise	s_n^2		38	27
Total		s_p^2	100	100

SOURCE: D. Falconer, *Quantitative Genetics*, Longman Group Limited. Copyright © 1981.

Figure 22-21. Quantitative genetic theory has been extensively applied to poultry breeding. (Photograph courtesy of Welp, Inc., Bancroft, Iowa.)

ble only to a particular population in a given distribution of environments.

The Use of h^2 in Breeding

Even though h^2 is a number that applies to a particular population and a given set of environments, it is still of great practical importance to breeders (Figure 22-21). A poultry geneticist interested in increasing, say, growth rate, is not concerned with the genetic variance over all possible flocks and all environmental distributions. The question is, given a particular flock (or a choice between a few particular flocks) under the environmental conditions approximating present husbandry practice, can a selection scheme be used to increase growth rate and, if so, how fast? If one flock has a lot of genetic variance and another only a little, the breeder will choose the former to carry out selection. If the heritability in the best flock is very high, then the mean of the population will respond quickly to the selection imposed, because most of the superiority of the selected parents will appear in the offspring. The higher the h^2, the higher is the parent-offspring correlation. If, on the other hand, h^2 is low, then only a small fraction of the increased growth rate of the selected parents will be reflected in the next generation.

If h^2 is very low, some alternative breeding scheme may be needed. It is this case where H^2 together with h^2 can be of use to the breeder. Suppose that h^2 and H^2 are both low. This means that there is a lot of environmental variance as compared to genetic variance. Some scheme of reducing s_e^2 must be used. One method is to change the husbandry conditions so that environmental variance is lowered. Another is to use **family selection.** Rather than choosing the best individuals, the breeder allows pairs to produce several progeny, and the *mating* is selected on the basis of the average performance of the progeny. By averaging over prog-

eny, uncontrolled environmental and developmental-noise variation is cancelled out, and a better estimate of the genotypic difference between pairs can be made.

If, on the other hand, h^2 is low but H^2 is high, then there is not much environmental variance. The low h^2 is the result of a small amount of additive genetic variance as compared to dominance and interaction variance. Such a situation calls for special breeding schemes that make use of nonadditive variance. One widely used scheme is the **hybrid-inbred method** used almost universally for maize. A large number of inbred lines are created by selfing. These are then crossed in many different combinations (all possible combinations, if that is economically feasible), and the cross that gives the best hybrid is chosen. Then new inbred lines are developed from this best hybrid, and again crosses are made to find the best second-cycle hybrid. This scheme selects for dominance effects, because it takes the best heterozygotes, and it has been the basis of major genetic advances in hybrid maize yield in North America since 1930. However, it is debatable whether this technique *ultimately* produces higher-yielding varieties than those that would have resulted from years of simple selection techniques based on additive variance.

The hybrid method has been introduced into the breeding of all kinds of plants and animals. Tomatoes and chickens, for example, are now almost exclusively hybrids. Attempts have also been made to breed hybrid wheat, but thus far the wheat hybrids obtained do not yield consistently better than the nonhybrid varieties now used.

Message   The subdivision of genetic variation and environmental variation provides important information about gene action that can be used in plant and animal breeding.

Summary

■ Many—perhaps most—of the phenotypic traits we observe in organisms vary continuously. In many cases, the variation of the trait is determined by more than a single segregating locus. Each of these loci may contribute equally to a particular phenotype, but it is more likely that they contribute unequally. Measurement of these phenotypes and the determination of the contribution of specific alleles to the distribution must be done, in these cases, on a statistical basis. Some of these variations of phenotype, such as height in some plants, may show a normal distribution around a mean value; others, such as seed weight in some plants, will illustrate a skewed distribution around a mean value.

In other characters, the variation of one phenotype may be correlated with the variation in another. A correlation coefficient may be calculated for these two variables.

A quantitative character is one for which the average phenotypic differences between genotypes are small as compared with the variation between individuals within genotypes. This situation may be true even for characters that are influenced by alleles at one locus. The distribution of environments is reflected biologically as a distribution of phenotypes. The transformation of environmental distribution into phenotypic distribution is determined by the norm of reaction. Norms of reaction can be characterized in organisms where large numbers of genetically identical individuals can be produced.

By the use of genetically marked chromosomes, it is possible to determine the relative contributions of different chromosomes to variation in a quantitative trait, to observe dominance and epistasis from whole chromosomes, and, in some cases, to map genes that are segregating for a trait.

Traits are familial if members of the same family share them, for whatever reason. Traits are heritable, however, only if the similarity arises from shared genotypes. In experimental organisms, environmental similarities may be readily distinguished from genetic similarities, or heritability. In humans, however, it is very difficult to determine whether a particular trait is heritable. Norm-of-reaction studies show only small differences among genotypes, and these differences are not consistent over a wide range of environments. Thus, "superior" genotypes in domesticated animals and cultivated plants may be superior only in certain environments. If it should turn out that humans exhibit genetic variation for various mental and emotional traits, this variation is unlikely to favor one genotype over another across a range of environments.

The attempt to quantify the influence of genes on a particular trait has led to the determination of heritability in the broad sense (H^2). In general, the heritability of a trait is different in each population and each set of environments and cannot be extrapolated from one population and set of environments to another. Because H^2 characterizes present populations in present environments only, it is fundamentally flawed as a predictive device. Heritability in the narrow sense, h^2, measures the proportion of phenotypic variation that results from substituting one allele for another. This quantity, if large, predicts that selection for a trait will succeed rapidly. If h^2 is small, special forms of selection are required.

Problems

1. Suppose that two triple heterozygotes $Aa\,Bb\,Cc$ are crossed. Assume that the three loci are in different chromosomes.

   a. What proportions of the offspring are homozygous at one, two, and three loci, respectively?

   b. What proportions of the offspring carry 0, 1, 2, 3, 4, 5, and 6 alleles represented by capital letters, respectively?

2. In Problem 1, suppose that at the A locus the average phenotypic effect of the three genotypes is $AA = 4$, $Aa = 3$, $aa = 1$, and similar effects exist for the B and C loci. Moreover, suppose that the effects of loci add to each other. Calculate and graph the distribution of phenotypes in the population (assuming no environmental variance).

3. In Problem 2, suppose that there is a threshold in the phenotypic character so that when the phenotypic value is above 9, the individual has three bristles; when it is between 5 and 9, the individual has two bristles; and when the value is 4 or less, the individual has one bristle. Discuss the outcome of crosses within and between bristle classes. Given the result, could you infer the underlying genetic situation?

4. Suppose the general form of a distribution of a trait for a given genotype is

$$f = 1 - \frac{(x - \bar{x})^2}{s_e^2}$$

   over the range of x where f is positive.

   a. Plot on the same scale the distributions for three genotypes whose means and environmental variances are as follows:

Genotype	$\bar{x}$	s_e^2	Approximate range of phenotype
1	0.20	0.3	$x = 0.03$ to $x = 0.37$
2	0.22	0.1	$x = 0.12$ to $x = 0.24$
3	0.24	0.2	$x = 0.10$ to $x = 0.38$

b. Plot the phenotypic distribution that would result if the three genotypes were equally frequent in a population. Can you see distinct modes?

5. The following table shows a distribution of bristle number in *Drosophila*. Calculate the mean, variance, and standard deviation of the distribution.

Bristle number	Number of individuals
1	1
2	4
3	7
4	31
5	56
6	17
7	4

6. The following sets of hypothetical data represent paired observations on two variables (x, y). Plot each set of data pairs as a scatter diagram. Looking at the plot of the points, make an intuitive guess at the correlation between x and y. Then calculate the correlation coefficient for each set of data pairs and compare this value with your estimate.

   a. (1, 1); (2, 2); (3, 3); (4, 4); (5, 5); (6, 6).

   b. (1, 2); (2, 1); (3, 4); (4, 3); (5, 6); (6, 5).

   c. (1, 3); (2, 1); (3, 2); (4, 6); (5, 4); (6, 5).

   d. (1, 5); (2, 3); (3, 1); (4, 6); (5, 4); (6, 2).

7. A recent book on the problem of heritability of IQ makes the following three statements. Discuss the validity of each statement and its implications about the *authors' understanding of* h^2 and H^2.

   a. "The interesting question then is . . . 'How heritable'? The answer [0.01] has a very different theoretical and practical application from the answer [0.99]." [The authors are talking about H^2.]

   b. "As a rule of thumb, when education is at issue, H^2 is usually the more relevant coefficient, and when eugenics and dysgenics are being discussed, h^2 is ordinarily what is called for."

   c. "But whether the different ability patterns derive from differences in genes . . . is not relevant to assessing discrimination in hiring. Where it could be relevant is in deciding what, in the long run, might be done to change the situation."

8. Using the concepts of norms of reaction, environmental distribution, genotypic distribution, and phenotypic distribution, try to restate in terms that are more exact the statement that "80% of the difference in IQ performance

between the two groups is genetic." What would it mean to talk about the heritability of a difference between two groups?

9. Describe an experimental protocol involving studies of relatives that could estimate the broad heritability of alcoholism. Remember that you must make an adequate observational definition of the trait itself!

10. A line selected for high bristle number in *Drosophila* has a mean of 25 sternopleural bristles, whereas a low selected line has a mean of only 2. Marker stocks involving the two large autosomes II and III were used to create stocks with various mixtures of chromosomes from the high (h) and low (l) lines. The mean number of bristles for each chromosomal combination is as follows:

$$\frac{h\ h}{h\ h}\ 25.1 \qquad \frac{h\ h}{l\ h}\ 22.2 \qquad \frac{l\ h}{l\ h}\ 19.0$$

$$\frac{h\ h}{h\ l}\ 23.0 \qquad \frac{h\ h}{l\ l}\ 19.9 \qquad \frac{l\ h}{l\ l}\ 14.7$$

$$\frac{h\ l}{h\ l}\ 11.8 \qquad \frac{h\ l}{l\ l}\ 9.1 \qquad \frac{l\ l}{l\ l}\ 2.3$$

What conclusions can you reach about the distribution of genetic factors and their action from these data?

11. Suppose that number of eye facets is measured in a population of *Drosophila* under various conditions of temperature. Further suppose that it is possible to estimate total genetic variance s_g^2 as well as the phenotypic distribution. Finally, suppose that there are only two genotypes in the population. Draw pairs of reaction norms that would lead to the following results:

   a. An increase in mean temperature decreases the phenotypic variance.

   b. An increase in mean temperature increases H^2.

   c. An increase in mean temperature increases s_g^2 but decreases H^2.

   d. An increase in temperature *variance* changes a unimodal into a bimodal phenotype distribution (one reaction norm is sufficient here).

12. The following variances and covariances between relatives have been found for egg weight in poultry: $s_p^2 = 14.8$; cov (mother-daughter) $= 1.7$; cov (sisters) $= 2.7$; cov (half-sisters) $= 0.8$. Calculate the broad and narrow heritabilities, H^2 and h^2.

13. Francis Galton compared the heights of male undergraduates to the heights of their fathers, with the results shown in the following graph. The average height of all fathers is the same as the average of all sons, but the individual height classes are not equal across generations. The very tallest fathers had sons somewhat shorter than the fathers,

whereas very short fathers had sons somewhat taller than the fathers. As a result, the best line that can be drawn through the points on the scatter diagram has a slope of about 0.67 *(solid line)* rather than 1.00 *(dashed line)*. Galton used the term regression to describe this tendency for the phenotype of the sons to be closer to the population mean than was the phenotype of their fathers.

a. Propose an explanation for regression.

b. How are regression and heritability related?

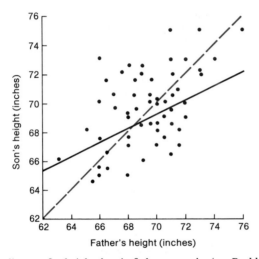

Scatter diagram for height data in father-son pairs (see Problem 13). The best line that can be drawn through the scatter points (black line) has a slope less than the line of identity (colored line). (After W. F. Bodmer and L. L. Cavalli-Sforza, *Genetics, Evolution, and Man.* Copyright © 1976 by W. H. Freeman and Co.)

CHAPTER 23

Population Genetics

■ Mendel's investigations of heredity—and indeed all of the interest in heredity in the nineteenth century—arose from two related problems: how to breed improved crops and how to understand the nature and origin of species. What is common to these problems (and what differentiates them from the problems of transmission and gene action) is that they are concerned with *populations* rather than with *individuals*. Studies of gene replication, of protein synthesis, of development, and of chromosome movement are all concerned with processes that go on within the cells of individual organisms. But the transformation of a species, either in the natural course of evolution or by the deliberate intervention of human beings, is a change in the properties of a collectivity—of an entire population or a set of populations.

Message The problem of population genetics is to relate the heritable changes in populations of organisms to the underlying individual processes of inheritance and development.

Darwin's Revolution

Many people think that the concept of organic evolution was first proposed by Charles Darwin, but that is certainly not the case. Most scholars had abandoned the notion of fixed species (unchanged since their origin in a grand creation of life) long before publication of Darwin's *The Origin of Species* in 1859. Most biologists agreed that new species arise through some process of evolution from older ones; the problem was to explain *how* this evolution can occur. The theories preceding Darwin's were *transformational theories,* which postulated the same transformation of quality for each individual organism within a species, much as every individual in its lifetime changes from an infant to an adult. Jean-Baptiste Lamarck (1744–1829), for example, claimed that each individual changes slightly because of an inner striving or will to adapt itself to its environment. These small individual changes are passed on to the offspring, who in turn continue the process of change by their own strivings to adapt.

Darwin broke fundamentally with these transformational hypotheses by creating a *variational theory.* In this theory, variation exists among organisms within a species. Individuals of one generation are qualitatively different from one another. Evolution of the species as a whole results from the differential rates of reproduction of the various types, so that the relative frequencies of the types change over time. Evolution, in this view, is a sorting process rather than a transformational one. For Lamarck, evolution was the sum of individual changes, with each individual changing itself slightly and passing that change along to its offspring. For Darwin, evolution was the sum of population changes, with each generation having offspring that survived in a slightly altered proportion of various types.

Message Darwin proposed a new explanation to account for the accepted phenomenon of evolution. He argued that the population of a given species at a given time includes individuals of varying characteristics. The population of the next generation will contain a higher frequency of those types that most successfully survive and reproduce under the existing environmental conditions. Thus the frequencies of various types within the species will change over time.

There is an obvious similarity between the process of evolution as Darwin described it and the process by which the plant or animal breeder improves a domestic stock. The plant breeder selects the highest-yielding plants from the current population and (as far as possible) uses them as the parents of the next generation. If the characteristics causing the higher yield are heritable, then the next generation should produce a higher yield. It was no accident that Darwin chose the term **natural selection** to describe his model of evolution through differential rates of reproduction of different variants in the population. He had in mind as a model for this evolutionary process the selection that the breeder exercises on successive generations of domestic plants and animals.

We can summarize Darwin's theory of evolution through natural selection in three principles.

1. **The principle of variation.** Among individuals within any population, there is variation in morphology, physiology, and behavior.

2. **The principle of heredity.** Offspring resemble their parents more than they resemble unrelated individuals.

3. **The principle of selection.** Some forms are more successful at surviving and reproducing than are others in a given environment.

Clearly, a selective process can produce change in the population composition only if there are some variations to select among. If all individuals are identical, no amount of differential reproduction of individuals can affect the composition of the population. Furthermore, the variation must be in some part heritable if differential reproduction is to alter the population's genetic composition. If large animals have more offspring than small ones, but if their offspring are no larger on the average than those of small animals, no change from one generation to another in population composition can occur. Finally, if all variant types

leave, on the average, the same number of offspring, then we expect the population to remain unchanged.

Message Darwin's principles of variation, heredity, and selection must hold true if there is to be evolution by a variational mechanism.

Variation and Its Modulation

Population genetics is the translation of Darwin's three principles into precise genetic terms. Thus, it deals with the following problems.

1. The description of the genetic variation within and between populations.

2. The study of the introduction of new variation into populations by mutation, recombination, and the migration of individuals.

3. The study of the patterns of differential reproduction of genotypes as a result of variation in mating patterns, fertility, and survival of individuals of different genotypes.

4. The creation of a formal machinery of deduction (theoretical population genetics) that allows prediction of the effects of the introduction of variation and of the differential rate of reproduction of variants on the genetic composition of a population.

5. The observation of actual changes in the composition of populations over time, either in nature or in controlled culture, and the comparison of these changes with those predicted from the theory, in order to check the adequacy of the entire theoretical structure.

6. The application of the theory to the controlled evolution of domesticated plants and animals, pests, pathogens, and other organisms relevant to human welfare.

Message Population genetics is the study of inherited variation and its modulation in time and space.

Observations of Variation

Population genetics necessarily deals with genotypic variation, but only phenotypic variation can be observed. Some of this phenotypic variation has a simple one-to-one correspondence to genotype—for example, the phenotypic variation in amino-acid sequence of a protein, coded by allelic substitutions at a structural-gene locus. For reasons of experimental convenience, most population genetics of nondomesticated species has concentrated on such pheno-types. For plant and animal breeding, however, the charac-ters of interest (such as yield, growth rate, or body shape) typically are quantitative and have a complex relation to genotype. As a consequence, the study of such variation is a two-step process involving (1) the description of the pheno-typic variation, and (2) a genetic analysis of that variation by the methods of Chapter 22.

The simplest description of Mendelian variation is the frequency distribution of genotypes in a population. Table 23-1 shows the frequency distribution of the three geno-types at the MN blood-group locus in several human popu-lations. There is variation both within and between popula-tions. More typically, instead of the frequencies of the diploid genotypes, the frequencies of the alternative alleles are used. If f_{AA}, f_{Aa}, and f_{aa} are the proportions of the three genotypes at a locus with two alleles, then the frequencies $p(A)$ and $q(a)$ of the alleles are obtained by counting alleles.

$$p = f_{AA} + \tfrac{1}{2} f_{Aa} = \text{frequency of } A$$

$$q = f_{aa} + \tfrac{1}{2} f_{Aa} = \text{frequency of } a$$

$$p + q = f_{AA} + f_{aa} + f_{Aa} = 1.00$$

If there are multiple alleles, then the frequency for each allele is simply the frequency of its homozygote plus one-half the sum of the frequencies for all the heterozygotes in which it appears. Table 23-1 shows the values of p and q for each of the populations.

As an extension of p, which represents the **gene fre-quency** or **allele frequency,** we can describe variation at more than one locus simultaneously by the **gametic fre-quencies.** There is a locus S (the secretor factor) closely linked to the MN locus in humans. Table 23-2 shows the gametic frequencies of the four gametic types (MS, Ms, NS, and Ns) in various populations.

A *measure* of genetic variation (as opposed to its *descrip-tion* by gene frequencies) is the amount of **heterozygosity** at a locus in a population, which is given by the total frequency of heterozygotes at a locus. If one allele is in very high frequency and all others are near zero, then there will be very little heterozygosity because, by necessity, most indi-viduals will be homozygous for the common allele. We ex-pect heterozygosity to be greatest when there are many alleles at a locus, all at equal frequency. In Table 23-1, the heterozygosity is simply equal to the frequency of the MN genotype in each population. When more than one locus is considered, there are two possible ways of calculating he-terozygosity. First, we can average the frequency of hetero-zygotes at each locus separately. Alternatively, we can take the gametic frequencies, as in Table 23-2, and calculate the proportion of all individuals who carry two different game-tic forms. So, for example, an individual MS/Ms is a hetero-zygote, even though it is heterozygous only at one of the two loci. These two methods do not, in general, give the same value for heterozygosity. In Table 23-2, the results of both calculations are given.

Simple Mendelian variation can be observed within and between populations of any species at various levels of phenotype, from external morphology down to the amino-acid sequence of enzymes and other proteins. Indeed, with the new methods of DNA sequencing, variations in DNA sequence (such as third-position variants that are not differ-entially coded in amino-acid sequences, and even variations in nontranslated intervening sequences) have been ob-served. Every species of organism ever examined has re-vealed considerable genetic variation, or **polymorphism,** that is reflected at one or more levels of phenotype, either within populations or between populations or both. Ge-netic variation that might be the basis for evolutionary

■ **TABLE 23-1.** Frequencies of genotypes for alleles at the MN blood-group locus in various human populations

| Population | Genotype | | | Allele frequencies | |
	MM	MN	NN	$p(M)$	$q(N)$
Eskimos	0.835	0.156	0.009	0.913	0.087
Australian aborigines	0.024	0.304	0.672	0.176	0.824
Egyptians	0.278	0.489	0.233	0.523	0.477
Germans	0.297	0.507	0.196	0.550	0.450
Chinese	0.332	0.486	0.182	0.575	0.425
Nigerians	0.301	0.495	0.204	0.548	0.452

SOURCE: W. C. Boyd, *Genetics and the Races of Man.* Boston, D. C. Heath, 1950.

■ **TABLE 23-2.** Frequencies of gametic types for the MNS system in various human populations

| Population | Gametic type | | | | Heterozygosity (H) | |
	MS	Ms	NS	Ns	From gametes	From alleles
Ainus	0.024	0.381	0.247	0.348	0.672	0.438
Ugandans	0.134	0.357	0.071	0.438	0.658	0.412
Pakistanis	0.177	0.405	0.127	0.291	0.704	0.455
English	0.247	0.283	0.080	0.390	0.700	0.469
Navahos	0.185	0.702	0.062	0.051	0.467	0.286

SOURCE: A. E. Mourant, *The Distribution of the Human Blood Groups,* Blackwell Scientific Pub., 1954.

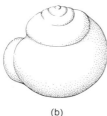

Figure 23-1. Shell patterns of the snail *Cepaea nemoralis.* (a) Banded. (b) Unbanded.

Figure 23-2. Dimorphism in the most common species of mussel found on the west coast of North America. Two morphological forms are found wherever the species occur: the blue form (right) and the brown form (left). Typically, the blue form is more frequent. The phenotypic difference is caused by an allelic difference at a single locus: B = brown and b = blue.

change is ubiquitous. The tasks for population genetics are to describe that ubiquitous variation quantitatively in terms that allow predictions of evolution and to build a theory of evolutionary change that can use the observations in prediction.

It is quite impossible in this book to provide an adequate picture of the immense richness of genetic variation that exists in species. We can consider only a few examples of the different kinds of Mendelian variation to gain a superficial sense of the genetic diversity within species. Each of these examples can be multiplied many times over in other species and with other traits.

Morphological Variation. The shell of the land snail *Cepaea nemoralis* may be pink or yellow, depending on two alleles at a single locus, with pink dominant to yellow. Also, the shell may be banded or unbanded (Figure 23-1) as a result of segregation at a second (unlinked) locus, with unbanded dominant to banded. Table 23-3 shows the variation of these two loci in several European colonies of the snail. The populations also show polymorphism for the number of bands and the height of the shells, but these characters have a complex genetic basis.

Figure 23-2 shows another example of a naturally occurring morphological genetic polymorphism (in this case, a dimorphism). The natural population of the illustrated mussel species includes two forms, one blue and the other brown. The difference is caused by an allelic difference at one locus.

Examples of naturally occurring morphological variation within plant species were discussed in Chapter 1 (*Plectritis*), Chapter 2 (*Collinsia*), and Chapter 4 (clover).

Chromosomal Polymorphism. Although the karyotype is often regarded as a distinctive characteristic of a species, in fact numerous species are polymorphic for chromosome number and morphology. Extra chromosomes (supernumeraries), reciprocal translocations, and inversions segregate in many populations of plants, insects, and even mam-

■ **TABLE 23-3.** Frequencies of snails (*Cepaea nemoralis*) with different shell colors and banding patterns in three French populations

Population	Yellow		Pink	
	Banded	Unbanded	Banded	Unbanded
Guyancourt	0.440	0.040	0.337	0.183
Lonchez	0.196	0.145	0.564	0.095
Peyresourde	0.175	0.662	0.100	0.062

SOURCE: Lamotte, *Bulletin Biologique de France et Belgique,* supplement 35: 1–238, 1951.

■ **TABLE 23-4.** Frequencies of third-chromosome inversions in *Drosophila pseudoobscura* from various North American populations

Population	Inversion				
	Standard	Arrowhead	Chiricahua	Pikes Peak	Others
Mount San Jacinto, CA	0.390	0.262	0.310	0.000	0.038
Prescott, AZ	0.110	0.790	0.090	0.010	0.000
South central Texas	0.002	0.117	0.000	0.703	0.178
Panamint Mountains, CA, 1937	0.138	0.674	0.184	0.000	0.004
1957	0.255	0.589	0.112	0.009	0.045
1963	0.243	0.409	0.053	0.129	0.166

SOURCE: T. Dobzhansky, W. W. Anderson, O. Pavlovsky, B. Spassky, and C. J. Wills, *Evolution* 18: 164–176, 1964.

mals. Table 23-4 gives the frequencies of various inversions in some populations of *Drosophila pseudoobscura* from western North America. Although one chromosomal arrangement is called "Standard," it is in fact impossible to say which of these types is "normal" and which a derived inversion. Indeed, in Mexico, there are no "Standard" chromosomes.

The variation within a population is not necessarily stable over time. Table 23-4 also shows the change in inversion frequencies in one population over a 25-year period.

Table 23-5 gives the frequency of supernumerary chromosomes and of translocation heterozygosis in a population of the plant *Clarkia elegans* from California.

Immunological Polymorphism. A number of loci in vertebrates code for antigenic specificities, such as the ABO blood types. Over 40 different specificities on human red cells are known, and several hundred are known in cattle. Another major polymorphism in humans is the HLA system of cellular antigens that are implicated in tissue graft compatibility (Chapter 18). Table 23-6 gives the allele frequencies for the ABO blood-group locus in some very different human populations. The polymorphism for the HLA system is vastly greater. There appear to be two main loci, each with five distinguishable alleles. Thus there are $5^2 = 25$ different possible gametic types, making 25 different homozygous forms and $(25)(24)/2 = 300$ different het-

erozygotes. All genotypes are not phenotypically distinguishable, however, so only 121 phenotypic classes can be seen. L. L. Cavalli-Sforza and W. F. Bodmer report that, in a sample of only 100 Europeans, 53 of the 121 possible phenotypes were actually observed!

Protein Polymorphism. In recent years, studies of genetic polymorphism have been carried down to the level of the polypeptides coded by the structural genes themselves. If there is a nonredundant codon change in a structural gene (say, GGU to GAU), this will result in an amino-acid substitution in the polypeptide produced at translation (in this case, glycine to aspartic acid). If a specific protein could be purified and sequenced from separate individuals, then it would be possible to detect genetic variation in a population at this level. In practice, this is tedious for large organisms and impossible for small ones unless a large mass of protein can be produced from a homozygous line.

There is, however, a practical substitute for sequencing that makes use of the change in physical properties of a protein when an amino acid is substituted. Five amino acids (glutamic acid, aspartic acid, arginine, lysine, and histidine) have ionizable side chains that give a protein a characteristic net charge, depending on the pH of the surrounding medium. Amino-acid substitutions may directly replace one of these charged amino acids, or a noncharged substitution near one of them in the polypeptide chain may affect

■ **TABLE 23-5.** Frequencies of plants with supernumerary chromosomes and of translocation heterozygotes in a population of *Clarkia elegans* from California

No supernumeraries or translocations	Supernumeraries	Translocations	Both translocations and supernumeraries
0.560	0.265	0.133	0.042

SOURCE: H. Lewis, *Evolution* 5: 142–157, 1951.

■ **TABLE 23-6.** Frequencies of the alleles I^A, I^B, and i at the ABO blood-group locus in various human populations

Population	I^A	I^B	i
Eskimos	0.333	0.026	0.641
Sioux	0.035	0.010	0.955
Belgians	0.257	0.058	0.684
Japanese	0.279	0.172	0.549
Pygmies	0.227	0.219	0.554

SOURCE: W. C. Boyd, *Genetics and the Races of Man.* Boston. D. C. Heath, 1950.

the degree of ionization of the charged amino acid, or a substitution at the joining between two α-helices may cause a slight shift in the three-dimensional packing of the folded polypeptide. In all of these cases, the net charge on the polypeptide will be altered.

To detect the change in net charge, protein can be subjected to the method of gel electrophoresis. Figure 23-3 shows the outcome of such an electrophoretic separation of variants of an esterase enzyme in *Drosophila pseudoobscura*. Each track is the protein from a different individual. Figure 23-4 shows a similar gel for different variant human hemoglobins. In this case, each individual is heterozygous for the variant and normal hemoglobin A. Table 23-7 shows the frequencies of different alleles for three enzyme-coding loci in *D. pseudoobscura* in several populations: a nearly monomorphic locus (malic dehydrogenase), a moderately

polymorphic locus (α-amylase), and a highly polymorphic one (xanthine dehydrogenase).

The technique of gel electrophoresis (or sequencing) differs fundamentally from other methods of genetic analysis in allowing the study of loci that are not segregating, because the presence of a polypeptide is prima facie evidence of a structural gene. Thus, it has been possible to ask what proportion of all structural genes in the genome of a species is polymorphic, and what the average heterozygosity is in a population. Very large numbers of species have been sampled by this method, including bacteria, fungi, higher plants, vertebrates, and invertebrates. The result is remarkably consistent over species. About one-third of structural gene loci are polymorphic, and the average heterozygosity in a population over all loci sampled is about 10 percent. This means that, if one scans the genome in virtually any species, about one in every ten loci is in heterozygous condition and that about one-third of all loci have two or more alleles segregating in any population. This represents an immense potential of variation for evolution. The disadvantage of the electrophoretic technique is that it detects variation only in structural genes. If most of the evolution of shape, physiology, and behavior rests on changes in regulatory elements, then the observed variation in structural genes would be beside the point.

Message Within species there exists great variation. The simplest *description* of variation is the frequency distribu-

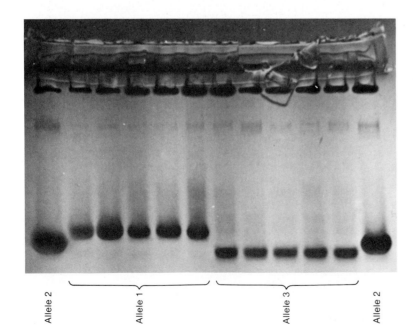

Allele 2   Allele 1   Allele 3   Allele 2

Figure 23-3. Electrophoretic gel showing homozygotes for three different alleles at the *esterase-5* locus in *Drosophila pseudoobscura*. Repeated samples of the same allele are identical, but there are repeatable differences between alleles.

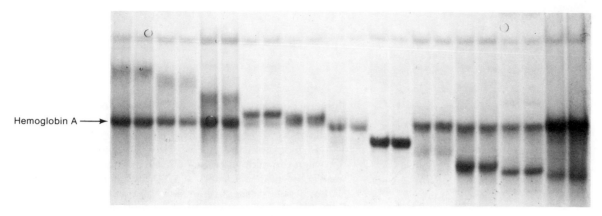

Hemoglobin A ⟶

Figure 23-4. Electrophoretic gel showing heterozygotes of normal hemoglobin A and a number of different variant hemoglobin alleles. One of the dark-staining bands is marked as hemoglobin A. There is a second dark-staining band in each track representing the second protein derived from the second allele of the heterozygote, each with a different electrophoretic mobility. (The dark-staining band with the same electrophoretic mobility in all tracks toward the top of the gel represents a protein other than hemoglobin.)

tion of genotypes in a population. A *measure* of variation is the amount of heterozygosity in a population.

Variation Within and Between Populations

The various examples just given show that there are genetic differences between individuals within a population and also that the allelic frequencies differ between populations. The relative amounts of variation within and between populations vary from species to species, depending on history and environment. In humans, some gene frequencies (for example, those for skin color or hair form) obviously are well differentiated among populations and major geographical groups (so-called geographical "races"). If we look at identifiable structural genes, however, rather than these outward phenotypic characters, the situation is rather

different. Table 23-8 gives the allele frequencies in a random sample of enzyme loci in a European and an African population. Except for phosphoglucomutase-3, where the allele frequencies are reversed between the populations, blacks and whites are very similar in their allelic distributions. In contrast to this random sample of loci, Table 23-9 shows three loci for which Caucasians, Negroids, and Mongoloids are known to be most different from each other (Duffy and Rhesus blood groups and the P antigen) compared with the three polymorphic loci for which the races are most similar (Auberger blood group and Xg and secretor factors). Even for the most divergent loci, no race is homozygous for one allele that is absent in other races.

In general, different human populations show rather similar gene frequencies for polymorphic genes. Figure 23-5 is a **triallelic diagram** for the three main allelic classes I^A, I^B, and i of the ABO blood group. Each point represents

■ **TABLE 23-7.** Frequencies of various alleles at three enzyme-coding loci in four populations of *Drosophila pseudoobscura*

Locus (enzyme encoded)	Allele	Population			
		Berkeley	Mesa Verde	Austin	Bogotá
Malic dehydrogenase	A	0.969	0.948	0.957	1.00
	B	0.031	0.052	0.043	0.00
α-Amylase	A	0.030	0.000	0.000	0.00
	B	0.290	0.211	0.125	1.00
	C	0.680	0.789	0.875	0.00
Xanthine dehydrogenase	A	0.053	0.016	0.018	0.00
	B	0.074	0.073	0.036	0.00
	C	0.263	0.300	0.232	0.00
	D	0.600	0.581	0.661	1.00
	E	0.010	0.030	0.053	0.00

SOURCE: R. C. Lewontin, *The Genetic Basis of Evolutionary Change*, Columbia University Press, 1974.

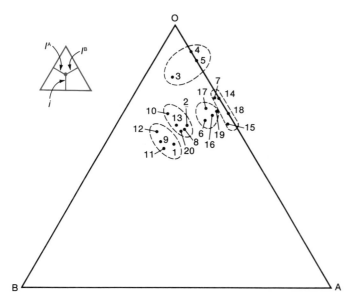

Figure 23-5. Triallelic diagram of the ABO blood-group allele frequencies for human populations. Each point represents a population; the perpendicular distances from the point to the sides represent the allele frequencies as indicated in the small triangle. Populations 1–3 are African, 4–7 are American Indian, 8–13 are Asian, 14–15 are Australian aborigine, and 16–20 are European. Dashed lines enclose arbitrary classes with similar gene frequencies, which do not correspond to the "racial" classes. (After A. Jacquard, 1970.)

the allelic composition of a population, where the three allelic frequencies can be read by taking the lengths of the perpendiculars from each side to the point. The diagram shows that all human populations are bunched together in the region of high i, intermediate I^A, and low I^B frequencies. Moreover, neighboring points (enclosed by dashed lines) do not correspond to geographical races, so that geographical races are not distinguished from each other by characteristic allele frequencies for this gene. The study of polymorphic blood groups and enzyme loci in a variety of

human populations has shown that about 85 percent of total human genetic diversity is found within local populations, about 8 percent between local populations within major geographical "races," and the remaining 7 percent between the major "races." Clearly, the genes influencing skin color, hair form, and facial form that are well differentiated between races are not a random sample of structural gene loci.

Message In general, the genetic difference between individuals within human races is much greater than the average difference between races.

Quantitative Variation

The variation in quantitative characters cannot be described in terms of allelic frequencies because individual loci and their alleles cannot be identified. Such variation can be characterized, however, by the amount of genetic variance (or the heritability of the trait) in the population. Figure 22-20 (page 528) shows that many morphological and physiological traits in poultry have genetic variance of different amounts in different populations. A simple technique for estimating the additive genetic variance (Chapter 22) of a character is to choose two groups of parents that are extremely different and then measure the difference between their offspring groups. The difference between offspring groups divided by the difference between parental groups is a measure of the heritability, h^2. Where this technique has been applied to morphological variation in *Drosophila*, for example, virtually every variable trait is found to have some genetic variance, so evolution of the trait can

---

■ **TABLE 23-8.** Allelic frequencies at seven polymorphic loci in Europeans and black Africans

Locus	Europeans			Africans		
	Allele 1	Allele 2	Allele 3	Allele 1	Allele 2	Allele 3
Red-cell acid phosphatase	0.36	0.60	0.04	0.17	0.83	0.00
Phosphoglucomutase-1	0.77	0.23	0.00	0.79	0.21	0.00
Phosphoglucomutase-3	0.74	0.26	0.00	0.37	0.63	0.00
Adenylate kinase	0.95	0.05	0.00	1.00	0.00	0.00
Peptidase A	0.76	0.00	0.24	0.90	0.10	0.00
Peptidase D	0.99	0.01	0.00	0.95	0.03	0.02
Adenosine deaminase	0.94	0.06	0.00	0.97	0.03	0.00

SOURCE: R. C. Lewontin, *The Genetic Basis of Evolutionary Change,* Columbia University Press, 1974.
Adapted from H. Harris, *The Principles of Human Biochemical Genetics.* North Holland, Amsterdam and London, 1970.

occur. Indeed, the method of estimating heritability just described is itself a kind of one-generation artificial-selection experiment.

It should not be supposed that all variable traits are heritable, however. Certain metabolic traits (such as resistance to high salt concentrations in *Drosophila*) show individual variation but no heritability. Left-right asymmetry is also nonheritable: "left-winged" flies (those with left wings slightly longer than their right wings) have no more left-winged offspring than do their right-winged companions. In general, behavioral traits have lower heritabilities than morphological ones, especially in organisms with more complex nervous systems, where there is immense individual flexibility in central nervous states. Before any judgment can be made about the evolution of a particular quantitative trait, it is essential to determine whether there is genetic variance for it in the population whose evolution is to be predicted. Thus, suggestions that, in the human species, such traits as performance on IQ tests, temperament, or social organization are in the process of evolving or have evolved at particular epochs in human history, depend critically on evidence about genetic variation for these traits. No such evidence is presently available.

One of the most important findings in evolutionary genetics has been the discovery of substantial genetic variation underlying characters that show no morphological variation! These are called **canalized characters,** because

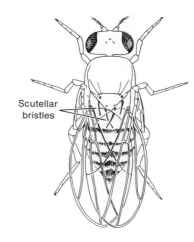

Figure 23-6. The scutellar bristles of the adult *Drosophila.* This is an example of a canalized character—all wild-type *Drosophila* will have four scutellar bristles in a very wide range of environments.

the final outcome of their development is held within narrow bounds despite disturbing forces. Development is such that, for canalized characters, all the different genotypes have the same constant phenotype over the range of environments that is usual for the species. The genetic differences are revealed if the organisms are put in a stress environment or if a severe mutation stresses the developmental system. For example, all wild-type *Drosophila* have exactly four scutellar bristles (Figure 23-6). If the recessive mutant *scute* is present, the number of bristles is reduced, but, in addition, there is variation from fly to fly. This variation is heritable, and lines with 0 or 1 bristles and lines with 3 or 4 bristles can be obtained in the presence of the *scute* mutation. When the mutation is removed, these lines now have 2 and 6 bristles, respectively. Similar experiments have been performed using extremely stressful environments in place of mutants.

Message Even characters with no apparent phenotypic variance may evolve when developmental conditions are changed drastically.

The Sources of Variation

The variational theory of evolution has a peculiar self-defeating property. If evolution occurs by the differential reproduction of different variants, we expect that the variant with the highest rate of reproduction will eventually take over the population, and all other genotypes will disappear. But then there is no longer any variation for further evolution. Genetic variation is the fuel for the evolutionary process, but differential reproduction consumes that fuel and so destroys the very condition necessary for further evolution. The possibility of continued evolution is critically dependent on renewed variation.

For a given population, there are three sources of such variation—mutation, recombination, and immigration of

■ **TABLE 23-9.** Examples of extreme differentiation and close similarity in blood-group allele frequencies in three racial groups

Gene	Allele	Population		
		Caucasoid	Negroid	Mongoloid
Duffy	Fy	0.0300	0.9393	0.0985
	Fy^a	0.4208	0.0607	0.9015
	Fy^b	0.5492	0.0000	0.0000
Rhesus	R_0	0.0186	0.7395	0.0409
	R_1	0.4036	0.0256	0.7591
	R_2	0.1670	0.0427	0.1951
	r	0.3820	0.1184	0.0049
	r'	0.0049	0.0707	0.0000
	Others	0.0239	0.0021	0.0000
P	P_1	0.5161	0.8911	0.1677
	P_2	0.4839	0.1089	0.8323
Auberger	Au^a	0.6213	0.6419	—
	Au	0.3787	0.3581	—
Xg	Xg^a	0.67	0.55	0.54
	Xg	0.33	0.45	0.46
Secretor	Se	0.5233	0.5727	—
	se	0.4767	0.4273	—

SOURCE: A summary provided in L. L. Cavalli-Sforza and W. F. Bodmer, *The Genetics of Human Populations,* W. H. Freeman and Company, 1971, pp. 724–731. See this source for information on other loci and for data sources.

■ TABLE 23-10. Some point-mutation rates in different organisms

Organism	Gene	Mutation rate per generation
Bacteriophage	Host range	2.5×10^{-9}
Escherichia coli	Phage resistance	2×10^{-8}
Zea mays (corn)	R (color factor)	2.9×10^{-4}
	Y (yellow seeds)	2×10^{-6}
Drosophila melanogaster	Average lethal	2.6×10^{-5}

Source: T. Dobzhansky, *Genetics and the Origin of Species,* 3d ed., revised. New York, Columbia University Press, 1951.

genes. However, recombination by itself does not produce variation unless there are already alleles segregating at different loci, because otherwise there is nothing to recombine, and immigration cannot provide variation if the entire species is homozygous for the same allele. Ultimately, the source of all variation must be mutation.

Variation from Mutations

Mutations are the *source* of variation, but the *process* of mutation does not itself drive evolution. The rate of gene-frequency change from the mutation process is very low because spontaneous mutation rates are low (Table 23-10). Let μ be the **mutation rate** from allele A to allele a (the probability that a gene copy A will become a during meiosis). If p_t is the frequency of the A allele in generation t, and $q_t = 1 - p_t$ is the frequency of the a allele, then change in allelic frequency in one generation is

$$\Delta p = p_t - p_{t-1} = -\mu p_{t-1}$$

That is, the frequency of A decreases (and the frequency of a increases) by an amount that is proportional to the muta-

tion rate μ and to the proportion p of all the genes that are still available to mutate. Thus, Δp gets smaller as the frequency of p itself decreases, because there are fewer and fewer A alleles to turn into a alleles.

If we rearrange the formula for a change in allele frequency, we find that

$$p_t = p_{t-1} - \mu p_{t-1} = (1 - \mu)p_{t-1}$$

That is, the value of p in the next generation is simply $(1 - \mu)$ times the value in the previous generation. Then, after yet another generation,

$$p_{t+1} = (1 - \mu)p_t = (1 - \mu)^2 \, p_{t-1}$$

and so on for as many generations as we please. After n generations of mutation, then, the value of p is

$$p_n = (1 - \mu)^n \, p_0$$

When a variable x is very small, the value of $(1 - x)^n$ is very close to e^{-nx}, where e is the base of the natural logarithms. So, we can make the approximation

$$p_n \cong p_0 e^{-n\mu}$$

which is shown in Figure 23-7. If μ is, for example, 10^{-5} (a rather high rate for mutations), then after 10,000 generations

$$p = p_0 e^{-(10^4)(10^{-5})} = p_0 e^{-0.1} = 0.904 p_0$$

So, if the population starts with only A alleles ($p_0 = 1.0$), it would still have only 10 percent a alleles after 10,000 generations, and it would require 60,000 additional generations to reduce p to 0.5. Even if mutation rates were doubled (say, by environmental mutagens), the rate of evolution would be very slow. Radiation of intensity suffi-

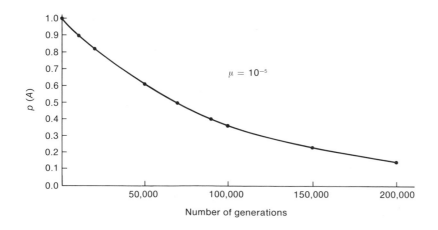

Figure 23-7. The change over generations in the frequency of a gene A because of mutation from A to a at a constant mutation rate (μ) of 10^{-5}.

cient to double the mutation rate over the reproductive lifetime of an individual human would be more than the amount necessary to cause death, so rapid genetic change in the species would not be one of the effects of increased radiation. Although we have many things to fear from environmental radiation pollution, turning into a species of monsters is not one of them.

If we look at the mutation process from the standpoint of the increase of a particular new allele rather than the decrease of the old form, the process is even slower. Most mutation rates that have been determined are the sum of all mutations of A to any mutant form with a detectable effect. Any *specific* base substitution is likely to be at least two orders of magnitude lower in frequency than the sum of all changes. So, precise back-mutations to the original allele A are unlikely, although many mutations may produce alleles that are *phenotypically* similar to the original.

Message Mutation rates are so low that they cannot account for rapid evolution of populations and species.

It is not possible to measure locus-specific mutation rates for continuously varying characters, but the rate of accumulation of genetic variance can be determined. Beginning with a completely homozygous line of *Drosophila* derived from a natural population, between 1/1000 and 1/500 of the genetic variance for bristle number in the original population is restored each generation by spontaneous mutation. On the other hand, for genetic variance in probability of survival, about 1/60 of the genetic variance present in a natural population is regenerated each generation in an inbred line.

Variation from Recombination

The creation of genetic variance by recombination can be a great deal faster than that due to mutation. When two chromosomes of *Drosophila* with "normal" survival are allowed to recombine for a single generation, they produce an array of chromosomes that have between 25 and 75 percent as much genetic variance in survival as does the original wild population from which the parent chromosomes were sampled. This is simply a consequence of the fact that a single homologous pair of chromosomes that is heterozygous at n loci (taking into account only single and double crossovers) can produce $n(n-1)/2$ new unique gametic types from one generation of recombination. If the heterozygous loci are well spread on the chromosomes, these new gametic types will be frequent, and a considerable variance will be generated. Asexual organisms, or those like bacteria that very seldom undergo sexual recombination, do not have this source of variation, so that new mutations are the only way in which a change in gene com-

binations can be achieved. As a result, asexual organisms may evolve more slowly under natural selection than sexual organisms.

Variation from Migration

A further source of variation is migration into a population from other populations with different gene frequencies. If p_t is the frequency of an allele in the recipient population in generation t, and P is the average allele frequency over all the donor populations, and m is the proportion of migrants, then in the next generation the gene frequency is the result of mixing $(1 - m)$ genes from the population with m genes from the donor populations. Thus,

$$p_{t+1} = (1 - m)\, p_t + mP = p_t + m(P - p_t)$$

and

$$\Delta p = p_{t+1} - p_t = m(P - p_t)$$

The change in gene frequency is proportional to the difference in frequency between the recipient population and the average of the donor populations. Unlike the mutation rate, the migration rate m can be large, so the change in frequency may be substantial.

We must understand *migration* as meaning any form of introduction of genes from one population into another. So, for example, genes from Europeans have "migrated" into the population of African origin in North America steadily since the Africans were introduced as slaves. We can use the frequency-change formula to determine the amount of this migration by looking at the frequency of an allele that is found only in Europeans and not in Africans and comparing the frequency among blacks in North America.

We can use the formula for the change in gene frequency from migration if we modify it slightly to take account of the fact that several generations of admixture have taken place. If the rate of admixture has not been too great, then (to a close order of approximation) the sum of the single-generation migration rates over several generations (let us call it M) will be related to the total change in the recipient population after these several generations by the same expression as that for changes due to migration. If, as before, P is the allele frequency in the donor population and p_0 the original frequency among the recipients,

$$\Delta p_{\text{Total}} = M(P - p_0)$$

so

$$M = \frac{\Delta p_{\text{Total}}}{P - p_0}$$

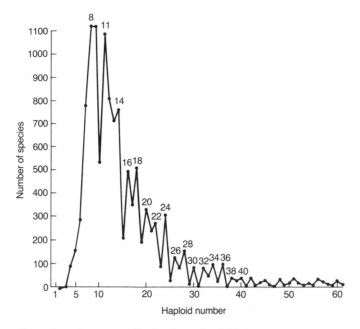

Figure 23-8. Frequency distribution of haploid chromosome numbers in dicotyledonous plants. (From Verne Grant, *The Origin of Adaptations,* Columbia University Press, 1963.)

Once an expansion in total DNA of the genome has occurred, it may require only a few base substitutions in a gene to provide it with a new function. For example, B. Hall has experimentally produced a gene with a new function in *E. coli.* In addition to the *lac Z* genes specifying the usual lactose-fermenting β-galactosidase activity in *E. coli,* there is another structural gene locus *ebg* that specifies another β-galactosidase that does not ferment lactose although it is induced by lactose. The natural function of this second enzyme is unknown. Hall was able to alter this gene into one specifying an enzyme that will ferment lactobionate. To do so, it was necessary to alter the regulatory element to a constitutive state and to produce three successive structural-gene mutations.

Message   Evolution would come to a stop by running out of variation if new genetic variation were not added to populations by mutation, recombination, and migration. Ultimately, all new variation derives from gene and chromosome mutations.

For example, the Duffy blood-group allele Fy^a is absent in Africa but has a frequency of 0.42 in whites from the state of Georgia. Among blacks from Georgia, the Fy^a frequency is 0.046. Therefore,

$$M = \frac{\Delta p_{\text{Total}}}{P - p} = \frac{0.046 - 0}{0.42 - 0} = 0.1095$$

When the same analysis is carried out on American blacks from Detroit or Oakland, M comes out to be 0.26 and 0.22, respectively, showing either (1) greater admixture rates in these cities than in Georgia or (2) differential movement into these cities by American blacks with more European ancestry. In any case the genetic variation at the Fy locus has been increased by this admixture.

The Origin of New Functions

Point mutations or chromosome rearrangements are themselves a limited source of variation for evolution because they can only alter a function or change one kind of function into another. To add quite new functions requires expansion in the total repertoire of genes through duplication and polyploidy, followed by a divergence between the duplicated genes, presumably by the usual process of mutation. Expansion of the genome by polyploidy has clearly been a frequent process, at least in plants. Figure 23-8 shows the frequency distribution of *haploid* chromosome numbers among dicotyledonous plant species. Even numbers are much more common than odd numbers, a consequence of frequent polyploidy.

The Effect of Sexual Reproduction on Variation

For the evolutionary theorists of the nineteenth century, there was a fundamental difficulty in Darwin's theory of evolution through natural selection. The possibility of continued evolution by natural selection is limited by the amount of genetic variation. But biologists of the nineteenth century, including Darwin, believed in one form or another of **blending inheritance,** a model postulating that the characteristics of each offspring are some intermediate mixture of the parental characters. Such a model of inheritance has fatal implications for a theory of evolution that depends on variation.

Suppose that some trait (say, height) has a distribution in the population and that individuals mate more or less at random. If intermediate individuals mate with each other, they will produce only intermediate offspring according to a blending model. But the mating of a tall with a short individual will also produce only intermediate offspring. Only the mating of tall with tall and short with short will preserve extreme types. The net result of all matings will be an increase in intermediate types and a decrease in the extremes. The variance of the distribution will shrink, simply as a result of sexual reproduction. In fact, it can be shown that the variance is *cut in half* each generation, so that before very many generations have passed the population will be essentially uniformly intermediate in height. There will then be no variation on which natural selection can operate. This was a very serious problem for the early

Darwinists, and it was necessary for Darwin to assume that new variation is generated at a very rapid rate by the inheritance of characters acquired by individuals during their lifetimes.

The rediscovery of Mendelism changed the picture completely. The discrete nature of the Mendelian genes and the segregation of alleles at meiosis have the result that a cross of intermediate with intermediate individuals does *not* result in all intermediate offspring. On the contrary, extreme types (homozygotes) segregate out of the cross. To see the consequence of Mendelian inheritance for genetic variation, consider a population in which males and females mate with each other at random with respect to some gene locus A,a. That is, individuals do not choose their mates preferentially with respect to the partial genotype at the locus. Such random mating is equivalent to mixing all the sperm in the population together and all the eggs, and then matching randomly drawn sperm with randomly drawn eggs.

If the frequency of the allele A is p in both sperm and eggs, and the frequency of a is $q = 1 - p$, then the consequences of random unions of sperms and eggs are those shown in Figure 23-9. The probability that both sperm and egg carry A is $p \times p = p^2$, so this will be the frequency of AA homozygotes in the next generation. In like manner, the chance of heterozygotes Aa will be $(p \times q) + (q \times p) = 2pq$, and that of homozygotes aa will be $q \times q = q^2$. The three genotypes, after a generation of random mating, will be in the frequencies $p^2:2pq:q^2$. As the figure shows, the allele frequency of A has not changed and is still p. Therefore, in the second generation, the frequencies of the three genotypes will again be $p^2:2pq:q^2$, and so on, forever.

Message Mendelian segregation has the property that random mating results, after only one generation, in an equilibrium distribution of genotypes.

The equilibrium distribution

AA	Aa	aa
p^2	$2pq$	q^2

is called the **Hardy-Weinberg** (or Hardy-Weinberg-Tschetverikov) **equilibrium** after those who independently discovered it.

The Hardy-Weinberg equilibrium means that sexual reproduction does not cause a constant reduction in genetic variation each generation; on the contrary, the amount of variation remains constant generation after generation, in the absence of other disturbing forces. The equilibrium is the direct consequence of the segregation of alleles at meiosis in heterozygotes.

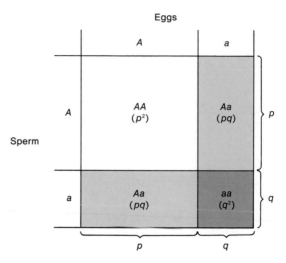

Eggs

Figure 23-9. The Hardy-Weinberg equilibrium frequencies that result from random mating. The frequencies of A and a among both eggs and sperms are p and q $(=1 - p)$, respectively. The total frequencies of the zygote genotypes are p^2 for AA, $2pq$ for Aa, and q^2 for aa. The frequency of the allele A in the zygotes is the frequency of AA plus one-half the frequency of Aa, or $p^2 + pq = p(p + q) = p$.

Numerically, the equilibrium shows that, irrespective of the particular mixture of genotypes in the parental generation, the genotypic distribution after one round of mating is completely specified by the allelic frequency p. For example, consider three hypothetical populations all having the same frequency of $A(p = 0.3)$:

	AA	Aa	aa
I	0.3	0.0	0.7
II	0.2	0.2	0.6
III	0.1	0.4	0.5

After one generation of random mating, each of the three populations will have the same genotypic frequencies,

AA	Aa	aa
$(0.3)^2 = 0.09$	$2(0.3)(0.7) = 0.42$	$(0.7)^2 = 0.49$

and they will remain so indefinitely.

One consequence of the Hardy-Weinberg proportions is that rare gene alleles are virtually never in homozygous condition. An allele whose frequency is 0.001 occurs in homozygotes at a frequency of only one in a million; most copies of such rare alleles are found in heterozygotes. In general, since two copies of an allele are in homozygotes, but only one copy of that allele in each heterozygote, the

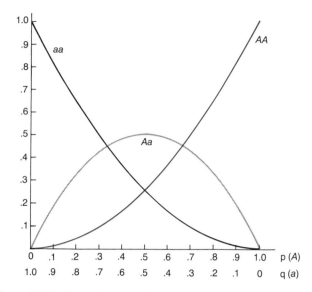

Figure 23-10. Curves showing the proportions of homozygotes AA (colored line), homozygotes aa (black line), and heterozygotes Aa (gray line) in populations of different allele frequencies if the populations are in Hardy-Weinberg equilibrium.

relative frequency of the allele in heterozygotes as opposed to homozygotes is

$$\frac{2pq}{2q^2} = \frac{p}{q}$$

which for $q = 0.001$ is a ratio of 999 : 1. Thus, frequency of heterozygous carriers of rare genes that are deleterious in homozygous condition is much greater than the frequency of the affected homozygotes.

The general relation between homozygote and heterozygote frequencies is shown in Figure 23-10.

In our derivation of the equilibrium, we assumed that the allele frequency p is the same in sperm and eggs. If, in the initial generation, p for males is not equal to p for females, then it takes one generation to equalize the frequencies between the sexes and then a *second* generation to reach the Hardy-Weinberg equilibrium. As an extension of this effect, the Hardy-Weinberg equilibrium theorem does not apply to sex-linked genes even after two generations if males and females start with unequal gene frequencies (see Problem 3).

Random mating with respect to particular genes is quite common. Human beings, for example, do not choose mates with respect to their blood groups. Table 23-11 shows the result of sampling MN blood groups in various populations. Clearly, the populations are mating at random with respect to this locus.

Inbreeding and Assortative Mating

Random mating with respect to a locus is common, but it is not universal. There are two kinds of deviation from random mating that must be distinguished. First, individuals may mate with each other nonrandomly because of their degree of common ancestry or degree of genetic relationship. If mating between relatives occurs more commonly than would occur by pure chance, the population is inbreeding. If mating between relatives is less common than chance, the population is undergoing **enforced outbreeding,** or negative inbreeding.

Second, individuals may choose each other as mates, not because of their degree of genetic relationship but because of their resemblance to each other at some locus. Mating of like with like is called **positive assortative mating.** Mating with unlike partners is called **negative assortative mating.**

Inbreeding levels in natural populations are a consequence of geographical distribution, of the mechanism of reproduction, and of behavioral characteristics. If close relatives occupy adjacent areas, then simple proximity may result in inbreeding. The seeds of many plants, for example, fall very close to the parental source, and pollen is not widely spread, so there will be a high frequency of sib mating. Some plants (such as corn) can be self-pollinated as well as cross-pollinated, so that wind pollination results in some very close inbreeding. Yet other plants, like the peanut, are obligatorily selfed. Many small mammals (such as house

■ **TABLE 23-11.** Comparison between observed frequencies of genotypes for the MN blood-group locus and the frequencies expected from random mating

Population	Observed			Expected		
	MM	*MN*	*NN*	*MM*	*MN*	*NN*
Eskimos	0.835	0.156	0.009	0.834	0.159	0.008
Egyptians	0.278	0.489	0.233	0.274	0.499	0.228
Chinese	0.332	0.486	0.182	0.331	0.488	0.181
Australian aborigines	0.024	0.304	0.672	0.031	0.290	0.679

NOTE: the expected frequencies are computed according to the Hardy-Weinberg equilibrium, using the values of p and q computed from the observed frequencies.

mice) live and mate in restricted family groups that persist generation after generation. Humans, on the other hand, generally have complex mating taboos and proscriptions that reduce inbreeding.

Assortative mating for some traits is common. In humans, there is positive assortative mating for skin color and height, for example. In plants and in many insects with one generation per year, there is positive assortative mating for time of development to sexual maturity. An important difference between assortative mating and inbreeding is that the former is specific to a trait whereas the latter applies to the entire genome. Individuals may mate assortatively with respect to height but at random with respect to blood group. Cousins, on the other hand, resemble each other genetically on the average to the same degree at all loci.

For both positive assortative mating and inbreeding, the consequence to population structure is the same: there is an increase in homozygosity above the level predicted by the Hardy-Weinberg equilibrium. If two individuals are related, they have at least one common ancestor. Thus there is some chance that an allele carried by one of them and an allele carried by the other are both descended from the identical DNA molecule. The result is that there is an extra chance of **homozygosity by descent,** to be added to the chance of homozygosity ($p^2 + q^2$) that arises from the random mating of unrelated individuals. The probability of homozygosity by descent is called the **inbreeding coefficient,** F. Figure 23-11 illustrates the calculation of this probability of homozygosity by descent. Individuals I and II are full sibs because they share both parents. We label

each allele in the parents uniquely to keep track of them. Individuals I and II mate to produce individual III. If individual I is A_1A_3 and the gamete that it contributes to III contains the allele A_1, then we would like to calculate the probability that the gamete produced by II is also A_1. The chance is $1/2$ that II will receive A_1 from its father, and if it does so, the chance is $1/2$ that II will pass A_1 to the gamete in question. Thus the probability that III receives an A_1 from II is $1/2 \times 1/2 = 1/4$, and this is the chance that III, the product of a full-sib mating, will be homozygous by descent.

To see one of the deleterious consequences of such close inbreeding, consider a rare deleterious allele a, which, when homozygous, causes a metabolic disorder. If the frequency of the allele in the population is p, then the probability of a random couple producing a homozygous offspring is only p^2. Thus if p is, say, $1/1000$, then the frequency of homozygotes will be 1 in 1,000,000. But suppose now that the couple are brother and sister. If one of their common parents was a heterozygote for the disease, they may both receive it and both pass it on to the offspring they produce. The probability of a homozygous aa offspring is

probability one or the other grandparent is Aa
$\times$ probability a is passed to male sib
$\times$ probability a is passed to female sib
$\times$ probability of a homozygous aa offspring from $Aa \times Aa$
$$= (2pq + 2pq) \times 1/2 \times 1/2 \times 1/4$$
$$= pq/4$$

We assume that the chance that both grandparents are Aa is negligible. If p is very small, then q is nearly 1.0, and the chance of an affected offspring is close to $p/4$. For $p = 1/1000$, there is 1 chance in 4000 of an affected child as compared to the one-in-a-million chance from a random mating. In general, for full sibs, the ratio of risks will be

$$\frac{p/4}{p^2} = \frac{1}{4p}$$

so the rarer the gene, the worse the *relative* risk of a defective offspring from inbreeding. For more distant relatives the chance of homozygosity by descent is, of course, less but still substantial. For first cousins, for example, the relative risk is $1/16p$ as compared to random mating.

The population consequences of inbreeding depend on its intensity and form. We next consider some examples.

Systematic Inbreeding. In experimental genetics (especially in plant and animal breeding), generation after generation of systematic selfing, full-sib, parent-offspring, or other form of mating between relatives may be used to increase homozygosity. Such systematic mating schemes, when they are between close relatives, lead eventually to

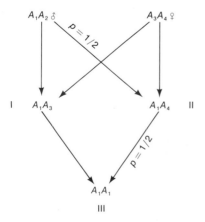

Figure 23-11. Calculation of homozygosity by descent for an offspring (III) of a brother-sister (I-II) mating. The probability that II will receive A_1 from its father is $1/2$, and, if it does, the probability that II will pass A_1 to the generation producing III is $1/2$. Thus, the probability that III receives an A_1 from II is $1/2 \times 1/2 = 1/4$.

complete homozygosity of the population, but at different rates. Refer back to Table 22-1 to see the amount of heterozygosity still left within lines after various numbers of generations of inbreeding. Which allele is fixed within a line is a matter of chance. If, in the original population from which the inbred lines are taken, allele A has frequency p and a has frequency $q = 1 - p$, then a proportion p of the homozygous lines established by inbreeding will be homozygous AA, and q of the lines will be aa. What inbreeding does is to take the genetic variation present *within* the original population and to convert it into variation *between* homozygous inbred lines sampled from the population (Figure 23-12).

Random Inbreeding.   In a natural population, there will be some fraction of mating between relatives (or even selfing if that is possible) because of spatial proximity. However, there is no continuity of inbreeding within any specific family. If some proportion of wind-pollinated plants are selfed in a particular generation, these are not necessarily the progeny of selfed plants in the previous generation, but they are distributed at random over selfed and outcrossed progeny. A consequence of such random inbreeding is that there is an equilibrium frequency of homozygotes and heterozygotes similar to the Hardy-Weinberg equilibrium but with more homozygotes. Thus, genetic variation is still preserved, in contrast to the result of systematic experimental inbreeding.

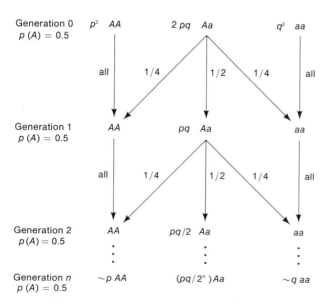

Figure 23-12. Repeated generations of self-fertilization (or inbreeding) will eventually split a heterozygous population into a series of completely homozygous lines. The frequency of AA lines among the homozygous lines will be equal to the frequency of the allele A in the original heterozygous population.

Small Populations.   Suppose that a population is founded by some small number of individuals who mate at random to produce the next generation but that no further immigration into the population ever occurs again. (For example, the rabbits now in Australia probably descend from a single introduction of a few animals in the nineteenth century.) Then, in later generations, everyone is related to everyone else, because if their family trees are traced back they will be found to have common ancestors here and there in their pedigrees. Such a population is then inbred, in the sense that there is some probability of a gene being homozygous by descent. As generations go on, F increases and finally reaches 1.00, so that the population is totally homozygous. The rate of loss of heterozygosity in such a closed, finite, randomly breeding population is inversely proportional to the total number ($2N$) of haploid genomes, where N is the number of diploid individuals in the population. In each generation $1/2N$ of the remaining heterozygosity is lost so that

$$H_1 = H_0 \left(1 - \frac{1}{2N} \right)^t \cong H_0 e^{-t/2N}$$

where H_t and H_0 are the proportions of heterozygotes in the tth and original generation, respectively. As the number t of generations becomes very large, H_t approaches zero.

Which of the original alleles becomes fixed at each locus is a chance matter. If allele A_i has frequency p_i in the original population, then the probability is p_i that eventually the population will become homozygous $A_i A_i$. Suppose that a number of isolated island populations are founded from some large, heterozygous mainland population. Eventually, if these island populations remain completely isolated from each other, each will become homozygous for one of the alleles at each locus. Some will be homozygous $A_1 A_1$, some $A_2 A_2$, and so on. Thus the result of this form of inbreeding is to cause genetic differentiation between populations.

Message   Once again we see that inbreeding is a process that converts genetic variation within a population into differences between populations by making each separate population homozygous for a randomly chosen allele.

Within each population, there is a change in allele frequency from the original p_i to either 1 or 0, depending on which allele is fixed, but the average allele frequency over all such populations remains p_i. Figure 23-13 shows the distribution of allelic frequencies among islands in successive generations, where $p(A_1) = 0.5$. In generation zero, all populations are identical. As time goes on, the gene frequencies among the populations diverge and some become fixed. After about $2N$ generations, every allelic frequency except the fixed classes ($p = 0$ and $p = 1$) is equally likely, and about one-half of the populations are totally homozygous. By the time $4N$ generations have gone by, 80 percent of the populations are fixed, one-half of them being homozygous AA and one-half homozygous aa.

The process of differentiation by inbreeding in island populations is slow, but not on an evolutionary or geological time scale. If an island can support, say, 10,000 individuals of a rodent species, then after 20,000 generations (about 7000 years, assuming three generations per year), the population will be homozygous for about one-half of all the loci that were initially at the maximum of heterozygosity. Moreover, the island will be differentiated from other similar islands in two ways. For the loci that are fixed, many of the other islands will still be segregating, whereas others will be fixed at a different allele. For the loci that are still segregating in all the islands, there will be a large variance

in gene frequency from island to island, as shown in Figure 23-13.

The Balance Between Inbreeding and New Variation

Any population of any species is finite in size, so all populations should eventually become homozygous and differentiated from one another because of inbreeding. Evolution would then cease. In nature, however, new variation is always being introduced into populations by mutation and by some migration between localities. The actual variation available for natural selection thus is a balance between the introduction of new variation and its loss through local inbreeding. The rate of loss of heterozygosity in a closed population is $1/2N$, so any effective differentiation between populations will be negated if the rate of introduction of new variation is at this rate or higher. If m is the migration rate into a given population and μ is the rate of mutation to new alleles, then roughly (to an order of magnitude) a population will retain most of its heterozygosity and will not differentiate much from other populations by local inbreeding if

$$m \geq \frac{1}{N} \quad \text{or} \quad \mu \geq \frac{1}{N}$$

or if

$$Nm \geq 1 \quad \text{or} \quad N\mu \geq 1$$

For populations of intermediate and even fairly large size, it is unlikely that $N\mu \geq 1$. For example, if the population size is 100,000, then the mutation rate must exceed 10^{-5}, which is somewhat on the high side for known mutation rates, although not unknown. On the other hand, a migration rate of 10^{-5} per generation is not unreasonably large. In fact,

$$m = \frac{\text{number of migrants}}{\text{total population size}} = \frac{\text{number of migrants}}{N}$$

Thus the requirement that $Nm \geq 1$ is equivalent to the requirement that

$$Nm = N \times \frac{\text{number of migrants}}{N} \geq 1$$

or

$$\text{number of migrant individuals} \geq 1$$

irrespective of population size! For many populations, more than a single migrant individual per generation is quite

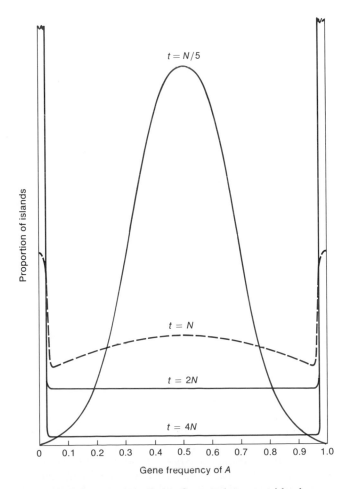

Figure 23-13. Distribution of gene frequencies among island populations after various numbers of generations of isolation.

likely. Human populations (even isolated tribal populations) have more migration than this minimal value and, as a result, show remarkably little gene-frequency differentiation among populations. There is, for example, no locus known in humans for which one allele is fixed in some populations and an alternative allele in others (see Table 23-9).

Selection

Fitness and the Struggle for Existence

Darwin recognized that evolution consists of two processes, both of which must be explained. One is the origin of the *diversity* of organisms, and the second is the origin of the *adaptation* of these same organisms. Evolution is not simply the origin and extinction of different organic forms; rather, it is also a process that creates some kind of match between the phenotypes of species and the environments in which they live. Darwin regarded "organs of extreme perfection" (such as the eye) as tests of his theory. His explanation of such organs was that there is a constant *struggle for existence.* Organisms with phenotypes better suited to the environment have a greater probability of surviving the struggle and will leave more offspring. Presumably, the better an organism can see, the better is its chance to find food, defend itself, find mates, and so on. The relative probability of survival and rate of reproduction of a phenotype or genotype is now called its **Darwinian fitness.**

Although geneticists sometimes speak loosely of the fitness of an individual, the concept of fitness really applies to classes of individuals and is a statement about the average survival and reproduction of the individuals in that class. Because of chance events in the life histories of individuals, even two organisms with identical genotypes and identical environments will differ in their survival and reproduction. No evolutionary prediction can be made from the unique life history of a single organism. It is the fitness of a genotype on the average over all its possessors that matters.

Fitness is a consequence of the relationship between the phenotype of the organism and the environment in which the organism lives, so the *same genotype will have different fitnesses in different environments.* In part this is because different environments during development will result in different phenotypes for the same genotypes. But even if the phenotype is the same, the success of the organism depends on the environment. Having webbed feet is fine for paddling in water but a positive disadvantage for walking on land, as a few moments of observation of a duck will reveal. No genotype is unconditionally superior in fitness to all others in all environments (see Figure 23-15).

Furthermore, the environment is not a fixed situation that is experienced passively by the organism. The environment of an organism is defined by the activities of the organism itself. Dry grass is part of the environment of a junco, so juncos that are more efficient at gathering it may waste less energy in nest building and thus have a higher reproductive fitness. But dry grass is part of a junco's environment *because juncos gather it to make nests.* The rocks among which the grass grows are not part of the junco's environment, although the rocks are physically present there. However, the rocks are part of the environment of thrushes, which use them to break snails against. Moreover, the environment that is defined by the life activities of an organism evolves as a result of those activities. The structure of the soil that is in part determinative of the kinds of plants that will grow is altered by the growth of those very plants. Organisms define and alter the environment. Thus, as they evolve in response to the present environment, they find themselves in new environments that are direct consequences of their own evolution. Environment is both the cause and the result of evolution of organisms. Organisms are both the cause and result of changes in the environment. The human hand is at the same time the organ of human labor and the evolutionary product of that labor.

Darwinian or reproductive fitness is not to be confused with "physical fitness" in the everyday sense, although they may be related. No matter how strong, healthy, and mentally alert the possessor of a genotype may be, that genotype has a fitness of zero if, for some reason, the possessor is sterile. Thus, such statements as "the unfit are outreproducing the fit so the species may become extinct" are meaningless. By definition, the unfit cannot outreproduce the fit, although some aspect of the phenotype of the more fit may be disadvantageous for some purpose. The fitness of a genotype is a consequence of all the phenotypic effects of the genes involved. Thus, an allele that doubles the fecundity of its carriers while at the same time reducing the average lifetime of its possessors by 10 percent will be more fit than its alternatives, despite its life-shortening property. The most common example is parental care. An adult bird that expends a great deal of its energy gathering food for its young will have a lower probability of survival than one that keeps all the food for itself. But a totally selfish bird will leave no offspring because its young cannot fend for themselves. As a consequence, parental care is favored by natural selection.

Two Forms of the Struggle for Existence

Darwin saw the "struggle for existence" as having two quite different forms, with different consequences for fitness. In one form, the organism "struggles" with the environment directly. Darwin's example was the plant that is struggling for water at the edge of a desert. The fitness of a genotype in such a case does not depend on whether it is frequent or rare in the population, because fitness is not mediated through interactions of individuals but is a direct

Figure 23-14. A blue jay eating a monarch butterfly, which induces vomiting in the jay. Because of this experience, the jay later will refuse to eat a viceroy butterfly that is similar in appearance to the monarch, although jays that have never tried monarchs will eat the viceroys with no ill effects. (Photographs courtesy of Lincoln Brower.)

consequence of the physical relation to the external environment. Fitness is then **frequency-independent.** Other examples are the differential probability of a seedling's surviving freezing temperatures, or the differential ability of ground squirrels to dig burrows for nesting.

The other form of struggle is between organisms competing for a resource in short supply or otherwise interacting so that their relative abundances determine fitness. If prey are in short supply but relatively easy to catch, then the faster of two predators will have the higher fitness. Suppose that the faster lion, F, always wins out when it competes directly with the slower lion, S. Then, as F types become more numerous, the S type will have to compete directly with more F lions and so will have fewer and fewer chances to acquire prey. Thus its fitness will decrease as compared with that of F. A more complex example is mimicry in butterflies. Some species of butterflies (such as the brightly colored orange and black monarchs) are distasteful to birds, who learn, after a few trials, to avoid attacking them (Figure 23-14). It is then advantageous for a palatable species (such as the viceroy butterfly) to evolve to look like the distasteful one, because birds will avoid the tasty mimics as well as the distasteful models. But as the frequency of the mimics increases, birds will increasingly have the experience that butterflies with this morphology are, in fact, good to eat. They will no longer avoid them, and the mimics will lose their fitness advantage. These are examples of **frequency-dependent** fitness.

For reasons of mathematical convenience, most models to explain mechanisms of natural selection have been constructed with frequency-independent fitness. In actual fact, however, a very large number of selective processes (perhaps most) are frequency-dependent. The ki-

netics of the evolutionary process depend on the exact form of frequency dependence, and, for that reason alone, it is difficult to make any generalizations. The result of positive frequency dependence (such as the competing predators, where fitness increases with increasing frequency) is quite different from the case of negative frequency dependence (such as the butterfly mimics, where fitness of a genotype declines with increasing frequency). For the sake of simplicity, and to illustrate the main qualitative features of selection, we deal only with models of frequency-independent selection in this chapter, but convenience should not be confused with reality.

Measuring Fitness Differences

For the most part, the differential fitness of different genotypes can be most easily measured when the genotypes differ at many loci. In very few cases (except for laboratory mutants, horticultural varieties, and major metabolic disorders) does the effect of an allelic substitution at a single locus make enough difference to the phenotype to be reflected in measurable fitness differences. Figure 23-15 shows the probability of survival from egg to adult—that is, the **viability**—of a number of second-chromosome homozygotes of *Drosophila pseudoobscura* at three different temperatures. As is generally the case, the fitness (in this case, a component of the total fitness, viability) is different in different environments. A few homozygotes are lethal or nearly so at all three temperatures, whereas a few have consistently high viability. Most genotypes, however, are not consistent in viability between temperatures, and no genotype is unconditionally the most fit at all temperatures. The fitness of these chromosomal homozygotes were not

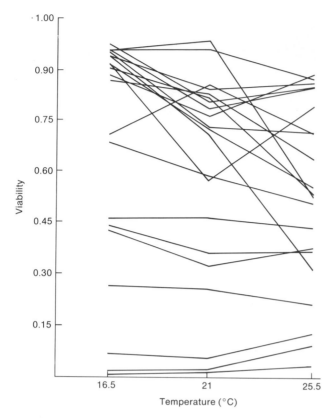

Figure 23-15. Viabilities of various chromosomal homozygotes of *Drosophila pseudoobscura* at three different temperatures.

measured in competition with each other, but all are measured against a common standard, so we do not know whether they are frequency-dependent. An example of frequency-dependent fitnesses is shown in the estimates for inversion homozygotes and heterozygotes of *Drosophila pseudoobscura* in Table 23-12.

Examples of clear-cut fitness differences associated with single gene substitutions are the many "inborn errors of metabolism," where a recessive allele interferes with a metabolic pathway and causes lethality of the homozygotes. Two examples in humans are phenylketonuria (where tissue degeneration is the result of the accumulation of a toxic intermediate in the pathway of tyrosine metabolism) and Wilson's disease (where death results from copper poisoning because the pathway of copper detoxification is blocked). A case that illustrates the relation of fitness to environment is sickle-cell anemia. An allelic substitution at the structural-gene locus for the β chain of hemoglobin results in substitution of valine for the normal glutamic acid at chain position 6. The abnormal hemoglobin crystallizes at low oxygen pressure, and the red cells deform and hemolyze. Homozygotes $Hb^S Hb^S$ have a severe anemia, and survivorship is low. Heterozygotes have a mild anemia and under ordinary circumstances have the same or only slightly lower fitness than normal homozygotes $Hb^A Hb^A$. However, in regions of Africa with a high incidence of falciparum malaria, heterozygotes ($Hb^A Hb^S$) have a *higher* fitness than normal homozygotes because the presence of

some sickling hemoglobin apparently protects them from the malaria. Where malaria is absent, as in North America, the fitness advantage of heterozygosity is lost.

In contrast to chromosomal homozygotes and metabolic diseases, it has not been possible to measure fitness differences for most single-locus polymorphisms. The evidence for differential net fitness for different ABO or MN blood types is shaky at best. The extensive enzyme polymorphism present in all sexually reproducing species is for the most part unconnected with measurable fitness differences, although in *Drosophila* clear-cut differences in fitness of different genotypes have been demonstrated in the laboratory for a few loci, such as α-amylase and alcohol dehydrogenase.

How Selection Works

Suppose that a population is mating at random with respect to a given locus with two alleles and that the population is so large that (for the moment) we can ignore inbreeding. Just after eggs have been fertilized, the eggs will be in Hardy-Weinberg equilibrium:

Genotype	AA	Aa	aa
Frequency	p^2	$2pq$	q^2

and $p^2 + 2pq + q^2 = (p + q)^2 = 1.0$, where p is the frequency of A.

Further suppose that the three genotypes have probabilities of survival to adulthood (viabilities) of $W_{AA} : W_{Aa} : W_{aa}$. Then, among the progeny when they have reached adulthood, the frequencies will be

Genotype	AA	Aa	aa
Frequency	$p^2 W_{AA}$	$2pq W_{Aa}$	$q^2 W_{aa}$

These adjusted frequencies do not add up to unity. However, we can readjust them so that they do, without changing their relation to each other, by dividing each frequency by the sum of the frequencies after selection, $\overline{W}$:

$$\overline{W} = p^2 W_{AA} + 2pq W_{Aa} + q^2 W_{aa}$$

So defined, $\overline{W}$ is called the **mean fitness** of the population because it is, indeed, the mean of the fitnesses of all individuals in the population. After this adjustment, we have

Genotype	AA	Aa	aa
Frequency	$p^2 \dfrac{W_{AA}}{\overline{W}}$	$2pq \dfrac{W_{Aa}}{\overline{W}}$	$q^2 \dfrac{W_{aa}}{\overline{W}}$

We can now determine the frequency p' of the allele A in the next generation by counting up genes:

■ **TABLE 23-12.** Comparison of fitnesses for inversion homozygotes and heterozygotes in laboratory populations of *Drosophila pseudoobscura* when measured in different competitive combinations

Experiment	Homozygotes			Heterozygotes		
	ST/ST	AR/AR	CH/CH	ST/AR	ST/CH	AR/CH
ST and AR alone	0.8	0.5	–	1.0	–	–
ST and CH alone	0.8	–	0.4	–	1.0	–
AR and CH alone	–	0.86	0.48	–	–	1.0
ST, AR, and CH together	0.83	0.15	0.36	1.0	0.77	0.62

$$p' = AA + (1/2)Aa = p^2 \frac{W_{AA}}{\overline{W}} + \frac{pqW_{Aa}}{\overline{W}} = p\frac{pW_{AA} + qW_{Aa}}{\overline{W}}$$

Finally, we note that the expression $pW_{AA} + qW_{Aa}$ is the mean fitness of A alleles, because A alleles occur with frequency p in homozygotes with another A and in that condition have a fitness of W_{AA}, whereas they occur with frequency q in heterozygotes with a and have a fitness of W_{Aa}. Using $\overline{W}_A$ to denote $pW_{AA} + qW_{Aa}$, we can give the final answer for the new gene frequency:

$$p' = p\frac{\overline{W}_A}{\overline{W}}$$

In other words, after one generation of selection, the new value of the frequency of A is equal to the old value (p) multiplied by the ratio of the average fitness of A alleles to the fitness of the whole population. If the fitness of A alleles is greater than the average fitness of all alleles, then $\overline{W}_A/\overline{W}$ is greater than unity, and p' is larger than p. The allele A increases in the population. Conversely, if $\overline{W}_A/\overline{W}$ is less than unity, A decreases. But the mean fitness of the population, $\overline{W}$, is the average fitness of the A alleles and of the a alleles. So if $\overline{W}_A$ is greater than the mean fitness of the population, it must be greater than $\overline{W}_a$, the mean fitness of a alleles.

Message   The allele with the higher average fitness increases in the population.

It should be noted that the fitnesses W_{AA}, W_{Aa}, and W_{aa} may be expressed as absolute probabilities of survival and absolute reproduction rates, or they may all be rescaled relative to one of the fitnesses, which is given the standard value 1.0. This rescaling has absolutely no effect on the formula for p' because it cancels out in numerator and denominator.

Message   The course of selection depends only on relative fitnesses.

An increase in the allele with the higher fitness means that the average fitness of the population as a whole increases, so that selection can also be described as a process that *increases mean fitness*. This rule is strictly true only for frequency-independent genotypic fitnesses, but it is close enough to a general rule to be used as a fruitful generalization. This maximization of fitness does not necessarily lead to any optimal property for the species as a whole because fitnesses are only defined relative to each other within a population. It is relative and not absolute fitness that is increased by selection. The population does not necessarily become larger, faster growing, or less likely to become extinct.

The Rate of Change of Gene Frequency

An alternative way to look at the process of selection is to solve for the *change* in allele frequency in one generation:

$$\Delta p = p' - p = \frac{p\overline{W}_A}{\overline{W}} - p = \frac{p(\overline{W}_A - \overline{W})}{\overline{W}}$$

But $\overline{W}$, the mean fitness of the population, is the average of the allelic fitnesses, $\overline{W}_A$ and $\overline{W}_a$. That is,

$$\overline{W} = p\overline{W}_A + q\overline{W}_a$$

Substituting this expression for $\overline{W}$ in the formula for Δp, we obtain (after some algebraic manipulation)

$$\boxed{\Delta p = \frac{pq(\overline{W}_A - \overline{W}_a)}{\overline{W}}}$$

which is the general expression for a change in allele frequency as a result of selection. This general expression is particularly illuminating. It says that Δp will be positive (A will increase) if the mean fitness of A alleles is greater than that of a alleles, as we saw before. But it also shows that the speed of the change depends not only on the difference in fitness between the alleles but also on the factor pq, which is proportional to the frequency of heterozygotes ($2pq$). For a given difference in fitness of alleles, gene frequency will change most rapidly when the alleles A and a are in intermediate frequency so that pq is large: If p is near zero or 1 (that is, if A or a is nearly fixed), then pq is nearly zero and selection will proceed very slowly. Figure 23-16 shows the S-shaped curve that represents the course of selection of a new favorable allele A that has recently entered a population of homozygotes aa. At first, the change in frequency is very small because p is still close to zero. Then it accelerates as A becomes more frequent, but it slows down again as A takes over and a becomes very rare. This is precisely what is expected from a *selection* process. When most of the population is of one type, there is nothing to select. For evolution by natural selection, there must be genetic variance, and the more variance, the faster the process.

An important consequence of the dependence of selection on genetic variance can be seen in a case of artificial selection. In the early part of this century, it became fashionable to advocate a program of **negative eugenics.** It was proposed that individuals with certain undesirable genetic traits (say, metabolic or nervous disorders) should be prevented from having any offspring. By this means, it was thought, the frequency of the trait in the population would be lowered, and the trait could eventually be eradicated. Suppose that such a program is completely efficient, so that every homozygote aa is prevented from reproducing. The fitnesses of the genotypes then are

Genotype	AA	Aa	aa
Fitness	1.0	1.0	0

If p is the frequency of A, and q is the frequency of a, then

$$\overline{W}_A = pW_{AA} + qW_{Aa} = p(1) + q(1) = 1.0$$
$$\overline{W}_a = pW_{Aa} + qW_{aa} = p(1) + q(0) = p$$
$$\overline{W} = p^2W_{AA} + 2pqW_{Aa} + q^2W_{aa} = p\overline{W}_A + q\overline{W}_a$$
$$= p(1) + q(p) = p(1 + q)$$

so

$$q' = q\frac{\overline{W}_a}{\overline{W}} = q\frac{p}{p(1 + q)} = \frac{q}{1 + q}$$

If we iterate this formula over generations, we get

$$q'' = \frac{q'}{1 + q'} = \frac{\dfrac{q}{1 + q}}{1 + \dfrac{q}{1 + q}} = \frac{q}{1 + 2q}$$
$$q''' = \frac{q}{1 + 3q}$$
$$q^{(n)} = \frac{q}{1 + nq} = \frac{1}{n + \dfrac{1}{q}}$$

From this sequence we can see what would be the fate of a negative eugenics program. A deleterious gene will already be rare in a population. Suppose that $q = 1/100$, for example. Then after one generation the frequency would be $1/101$, after two generations $1/102$, and so on. It would take 100 generations to reduce the frequency to $1/200$, and then another 200 generations again to cut it in half to $1/400$. But a human generation is 25 years, so it would require 2500 years (the time since the founding of the Roman republic) with perfectly efficient selection against the recessive just to reduce the frequency from $1/100$ to $1/200$. The negative eugenics plan clearly is impractical.

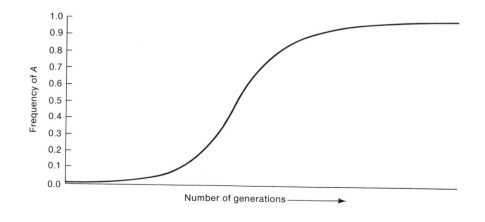

Figure 23-16. The time pattern of increasing frequency of a new favorable allele A that has entered a population of aa homozygotes.

Of course, if the *heterozygote* for the deleterious genes (as, for example, in sickle-cell anemia) could be detected, then in a single generation all copies of the gene could be removed from the population if the heterozygotes were all prevented from having offspring. The only trouble with this suggestion is that every human being is heterozygous for several different deleterious recessive genes, so no one would be allowed to breed. Negative eugenics is no longer seriously proposed by geneticists.

When alternative alleles are not rare, selection can cause quite rapid changes in allele frequency. Figure 23-17 shows the course of elimination of a malic dehydrogenase allele in a laboratory population of *Drosophila melanogaster*. The fitnesses in this case are

$$W_{AA} = 1.0 \qquad W_{Aa} = 0.75 \qquad W_{aa} = 0.40$$

Of course, the frequency of *a* was not reduced to zero, and further reduction in frequency will require longer and longer times, as was shown in the negative eugenics case.

Message Unless alternative alleles are present in intermediate frequencies, selection (especially against recessives) is quite slow. Selection depends on genetic variation.

Balanced Polymorphism

Reexamine the general formula for allele frequency change (page 553):

$$\Delta p = pq \frac{(\overline{W}_A - \overline{W}_a)}{\overline{W}}$$

Under what conditions will the process stop? When is $\Delta p = 0$? Two immediately obvious answers are when $p = 0$, or when $q = 0$ — that is, when either allele A or allele a has been eliminated from the population. One of these events will eventually occur if $\overline{W}_A - \overline{W}_a$ is consistently positive or negative so that Δp is always positive or negative irrespective of the value of p. The condition for such unidirectional selection is that the heterozygote fitness be somewhere between the fitnesses of the two homozygotes:

$(\overline{W}_A - \overline{W}_a)$ positive: $W_{AA} \geq W_{Aa} \geq W_{aa}$ so A is favored

$(\overline{W}_A - \overline{W}_a)$ negative: $W_{AA} \leq W_{Aa} \leq W_{aa}$ so a is favored

But there is another possibility for $\Delta p = 0$, even when p and q are not zero:

$$\overline{W}_A = \overline{W}_a$$

This can occur if the heterozygote is not intermediate between the homozygotes but has a fitness that is more extreme than either homozygote. Then $\overline{W}_A > \overline{W}_a$ for part of the range of values of p, whereas $\overline{W}_A < \overline{W}_a$ for the rest of the range. Just between these ranges is a value of p (denoted by $\hat{p}$) for which the mean fitnesses of the two alleles are just equal. A little algebraic manipulation of

$$\overline{W}_A - \overline{W}_a = 0 = (\hat{p}W_{AA} + \hat{q}W_{Aa}) - (\hat{p}W_{Aa} + \hat{q}W_{aa})$$

gives us the solution for $\hat{p}$:

$$\hat{p} = \frac{(W_{aa} - W_{Aa})}{(W_{aa} - W_{Aa}) + (W_{AA} - W_{Aa})}$$

The equilibrium value is a simple ratio of the differences in fitness between homozygotes and the heterozygote. For example, consider three cases:

	W_{AA}	W_{Aa}	W_{aa}
Case 1	0.9	1.0	0.8
Case 2	0.8	1.0	0.6
Case 3	0.99	1.0	0.98

The fitness values in all three cases have exactly the same equilibrium value of $\hat{p} = 2/3$, although the speed at which the population would reach the equilibrium differs very much in the three cases.

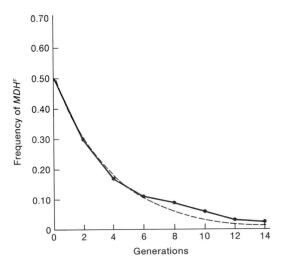

Figure 23-17. The loss of an allele of the malic dehydrogenase locus, MDH^F, due to selection in a laboratory population of *Drosophila melanogaster*. The colored line shows the theoretical curve of change computed for the fitnesses $W_{AA} = 1.0$, $W_{Aa} = 0.75$, and $W_{aa} = 0.4$. (From R. C. Lewontin, *The Genetic Basis of Evolutionary Change*, Columbia University Press, 1974.)

There are, in fact, two qualitatively different possibilities for $\hat{p}$. One possibility is that $\hat{p}$ is an *unstable* equilibrium so that there will be no change in frequency if the population has exactly this value of p, but the frequency will move *away* from the equilibrium (toward $p = 0$ or $p = 1$) if the slightest perturbation of frequency occurs. This unstable case will exist when the heterozygote is *lower* in fitness than either homozygote; such a condition is an example of **underdominance.** The alternative possibility is a *stable* equilibrium, or **balanced polymorphism,** in which slight perturbations from the value of $\hat{p}$ will result in a return to $\hat{p}$. The condition for this balance is that the heterozygote be *greater* in fitness than either homozygote—the condition termed **overdominance.**

In nature, the chance that a gene frequency would remain balanced on the knife edge of an unstable equilibrium is negligible, so we should not expect to find polymorphisms in natural populations with heterozygotes less fit than homozygotes. On the contrary, the observation of a long-lasting polymorphism in nature might be taken as prima facie evidence of a superior heterozygote.

Unfortunately, life confounds theory. The *Rh* locus (rhesus blood group) in humans has a widespread polymorphism, with Rh^+ and Rh^- alleles. In Europeans, the frequency of the Rh^- allele is about 0.4, whereas in Africans it is about 0.2. Thus this must be a very old human polymorphism, antedating the origin of modern geographical races. But this polymorphism causes a maternal fetal incompatibility when an Rh^- mother (homozygous Rh^-/Rh^-) produces an Rh^+ fetus (heterozygous Rh^-/Rh^+). Their incompatability results in hemolytic anemia (from a destruction of red blood cells) and the death of the fetus in a moderate proportion of cases. Thus, there is selection against heterozygotes. This polymorphism is unstable and should have disappeared from the species. Yet, it exists in most human populations. There have been many hypotheses proposed

to explain its apparent stability, but the mystery remains.

In contrast, there are many polymorphisms of blood groups (and the ubiquitous polymorphism of enzymes revealed by electrophoresis) for which no fitness difference at all can be demonstrated. It has been suggested that such polymorphisms are not under selection at all but that

$$W_{AA} = W_{Aa} = W_{aa}$$

This situation of **selective neutrality** would, of course, also satisfy the requirement that $\overline{W}_A = \overline{W}_a$, but instead of a stable equilibrium, it gives rise to a **passive** (or **neutral**) **equilibrium** such that any allele frequency p is as good as any other. This leaves unanswered the problem of how the populations became highly polymorphic in the first place. Nevertheless, it is clear that the presence of a widespread polymorphism is not necessarily evidence for superior heterozygotes. The best case of overdominance for fitness at a single locus remains that of sickle-cell anemia, where the two homozygotes are at a disadvantage relative to the heterozygote for quite different reasons.

The best-studied cases of balanced polymorphism in nature and in the laboratory are the inversion polymorphisms in several species of *Drosophila*. Figure 23-18 shows the course of frequency change for an inversion, *ST*, against an alternative arrangement, *CH*, in a laboratory population of *Drosophila pseudoobscura*. The inversions *ST* and *CH* are part of a chromosomal polymorphism in natural populations of this species. The fitnesses estimated for the three genotypes in the laboratory are

$$W_{ST/ST} = 0.89 \qquad W_{ST/CH} = 1.0 \qquad W_{CH/CH} = 0.41$$

Applying the formula for the equilibrium value $\hat{p}$ we obtain $\hat{p} = 0.85$, which agrees quite well with the observations in Figure 23-18.

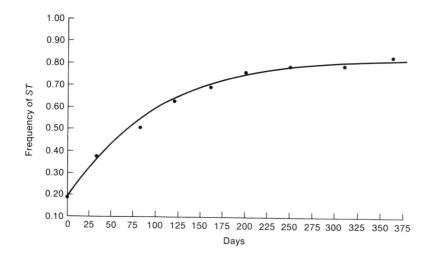

Figure 23-18. Changes in the frequency of the inversion *Standard* (*ST*) in competition with *Chiricahua* (*CH*) in a laboratory population of *Drosophila pseudoobscura.*

Multiple Adaptive Peaks

We must avoid taking an overly simplified view of the consequences of selection. At the level of the gene, or even at the level of partial phenotype, the outcome of selection for a trait in a given environment is not unique. Selection to alter a trait (say, to increase size) may be successful in a number of ways. When F. Robertson and E. Reeve (1952) selected to change wing size in *Drosophila* in two different populations, they succeeded in both—but in one case the *number* of cells in the wing had changed, whereas in the other the *size* of the cells had changed. Two different genotypes had been selected, both causing a change in wing size. Which of these selections occurred depended on the initial state of the population when selection was started.

The way in which the same selection can lead to different outcomes can most easily be illustrated by a simple hypothetical case. Suppose there are two loci (there will usually be many more) whose variation influences a character and that (in a particular environment) intermediate phenotypes have the highest fitness. (For example, newborn babies have a higher chance of surviving birth if they are neither too big nor too small.) If the alleles act in a simple way in influencing the phenotype, then there are three genetic constitutions that would give high fitness — *Aa Bb*, *AA bb*, and *aa BB* — because all would be intermediate in phenotype. On the other hand, very low fitness will

characterize the double homozygotes *AA BB* and *aa bb*. What will the result of selection be? We can predict the result by using the mean fitness $\overline{W}$ of a population. As previously discussed, selection acts in most simple cases to increase $\overline{W}$. Therefore, if we calculate $\overline{W}$ for every possible combination of gene frequencies at the two loci, we can find which combinations give high values of $\overline{W}$. Then we should be able to predict the course of selection, by following a curve of increasing $\overline{W}$. The surface of mean fitness for all possible combinations of allele frequency is called an **adaptive surface,** or an **adaptive landscape,** as shown in Figure 23-19. The figure is like a topographic map. The frequency of the allele *A* at one locus is plotted on one axis, and the frequency of allele *B* at the other locus is plotted on the other axis. The height above the plane (represented by topographic lines) is the value of $\overline{W}$ that the population would have for a particular combination of frequencies of *A* and *B*. According to the rule of increasing fitness, selection should carry the population from a low-fitness "valley" to a high-fitness "peak." However, Figure 23-19 shows that there are two adaptive peaks, corresponding to a fixed population of *AA bb* and a fixed population of *aa BB*, with an adaptive valley between them. Which peak the population will ascend, and therefore its final genetic composition, depends on whether the initial genetic composition of the population was on one side or the other of the "fall line" indicated by the dashed line.

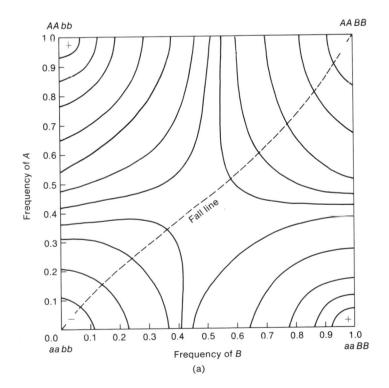

(a)

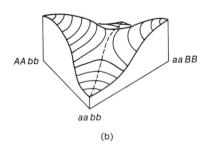

(b)

Figure 23-19. An adaptive landscape with two adaptive peaks (+), two adaptive valleys (−), and a topographic saddle in the center of the landscape. The topographic lines are lines of equal mean fitness. If the genetic composition of a population always changes in such a way as to move the population "uphill" in the landscape, the final composition will depend on where the population began with respect to the fall line (dashed line). (a) Topographic map of the adaptive landscape. (b) A perspective sketch of the surface shown in the map.

(a)

(b)

Figure 23-20. Differences in horn morphology in two geographically separated species of rhinoceroses. (a) The African rhinoceros. (b) The Indian rhinoceros. (Part a from Leonard Lee Rue, copyright © Tom Stack & Associates; part b copyright © Tom Stack & Associates.)

Message Under identical conditions of natural selection, two populations may arrive at two different genetic compositions as a direct result of natural selection.

The existence of multiple adaptive peaks for a selective process means that some differences between species are the result of history and not of environmental differences.

African rhinoceroses have two horns, and Indian rhinoceroses have one (Figure 23-20). We need not invent a special story to explain why it is better to have two horns on the African plains and one in India. It is much more plausible that the trait of having horns was selected, but that two long, slender horns and one short, stout horn are simply alternative adaptive features, and that historical accident differentiated the species. Explanations by natural selection do not require that every difference between species be differentially adaptive.

It is important to note that nothing in the theory of selection requires that the different adaptive peaks be of the same height. The kinetics of selection is such that $\overline{W}$ increases, not that it necessarily reaches the highest possible peak in the field of gene frequencies. Suppose, for example, that a population is near the peak $AA\,bb$ in Figure 23-19 and that this peak is lower than the $aa\,BB$ peak. Selection alone cannot carry the population to $aa\,BB$ because that would require a temporary decrease in $\overline{W}$ as the population descended the $AA\,bb$ slope, crossed the saddle, and ascended the other slope. Thus, the force of selection is myopic. It drives the population to a *local* maximum of $\overline{W}$ in the field of gene frequencies, not to a *global* one.

Artificial Selection

In contrast to the difficulties of finding simple, well-behaved cases in nature that will exemplify the simple formulas of natural selection, there is a vast record of the effectiveness of artificial selection in changing populations phenotypically. These changes have been produced by laboratory selection experiments and by selection of animals and plants in agriculture—for example, for increased milk production in cows or for rust resistance in wheat. No analysis of these experiments in terms of allelic frequencies is possible because individual loci have not been identified and followed. Nevertheless, it is clear that genetic changes have occurred in the populations and that some analysis of selected populations has been carried out by the methods of Chapter 22. Figure 23-21 shows, as an example, the large changes in average bristle number achieved in a selection experiment with *Drosophila melanogaster*. Figure 23-22 shows the change in the number of eggs laid per chicken as a consequence of 30 years of selection.

For characters of high heritability, the usual method of selection is **truncation selection.** The individuals in a given generation are pooled (irrespective of their families), a sample is measured, and only those individuals above (or below) a given phenotypic value (the truncation point) are chosen as parents for the next generation. This phenotypic value may be a fixed value over successive generations—that is, selection is by **constant truncation.** More commonly, the highest (or lowest) K percent of the population is chosen—that is, selection is by **proportional truncation.** With con-

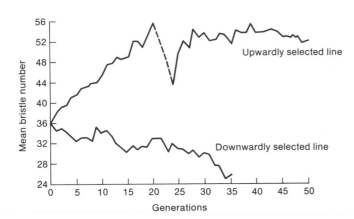

Figure 23-21. Changes in average bristle number obtained in two laboratory populations of *Drosophila melanogaster* through artificial selection for high bristle number in one population and for low bristle number in the other. The dashed segment in the curve for the upwardly selected line indicates a period of five generations during which no selection was performed. (From K. Mather and B. J. Harrison, "The Manifold Effects of Selection," *Heredity* 3:1–52, 1949.)

stant truncation, the intensity of selection decreases with time, as more and more of the population exceeds the fixed truncation point. With proportional truncation, the intensity of selection is constant, but the truncation point moves upward as the population distribution moves. Figure 23-23 shows these two schemes.

No matter which scheme of selection is used, narrow heritability will eventually decline as selected alleles go to fixation, so that further progress becomes more and more difficult and eventually ceases when h^2 goes to zero. For characters of initially low heritability, some scheme of family selection is used (see page 529).

A common experience in artificial selection programs is that, as the population becomes more and more extreme, the viability and fertility decrease. As a result, no further progress under selection is possible, despite the presence of genetic variance for the character, because the selected individuals do not reproduce. The loss of fitness may be a direct phenotypic effect of the genes for the selected character, in which case nothing much can be done to improve the population further. Often, however, the loss of fitness comes from linked sterility genes that are carried along with the selected loci. In such cases, a number of generations without selection allow recombinants to be formed, and selection can then be continued.

We must be very careful in the interpretation of long-term agricultural selection programs. In the real world of agriculture, changes in cultivation methods, machinery, fertilizer, insecticides, herbicides, and so on are occurring along with the production of genetically improved varieties. Increases in average yields are consequences of all

these changes. For example, the average yield of corn in the United States increased from 40 bushels to 80 bushels per acre between 1940 and 1970. But experiments with reconstruction of varieties and testing in common environments show that only about one-half of this increase is a direct result of new corn varieties, the other one-half being a result of improved farming techniques. Furthermore, the new varieties are most superior to the old ones at the high densities of modern planting for which they were selected.

Random Events

If a population is finite in size (as all populations are), and if a given pair of parents have only a small number of offspring, then, even in the absence of all selective forces, the frequency of a gene will not be exactly reproduced in the next generation. There is sampling error. If, in a population of 1000 individuals, the frequency of a is 0.5 in one generation, then in the next generation it may by chance be 0.493 or 0.505 because of the chance production of a few more or a few less progeny of each genotype. But in the second generation, there is again a sampling error based on the new gene frequency, so it may go from 0.505 to 0.511, or back to 0.498. This process of random fluctuation continues generation after generation, with no force pushing the frequency back to its initial state because the population has no "genetic memory" of its state many generations ago. Each generation is an independent event. The final result of this random change in allele frequency is that the population eventually drifts to $p = 1$ or $p = 0$, after which no further change is possible. It becomes homozygous. A different population, isolated from the first, also undergoes this **random genetic drift,** but it may become homozygous for allele A, whereas the first one drifted to homozygous a. As time goes on, isolated populations diverge from each other,

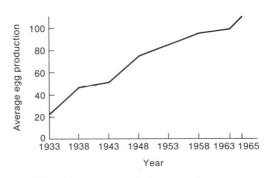

Figure 23-22. Changes in average egg production in a chicken population selected for increase in egg-laying rate over a period of 30 years. (From I. M. Lerner and W. J. Libby, *Heredity, Evolution, and Society,* 2d. ed. Copyright © 1976 by W. H. Freeman and Co. Data courtesy of D. C. Lowry.)

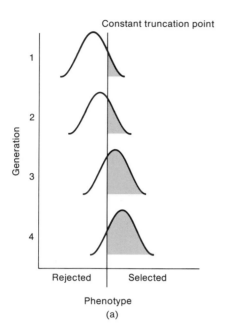
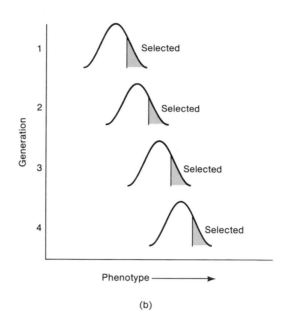

Figure 23-23. Two schemes of truncation selection for a continuously varying trait. (a) Constant truncation. (b) Proportional truncation.

each losing heterozygosity. The variation originally present *within* populations now appears as variation *between* populations.

One form of genetic drift occurs when a small group breaks off from a larger population to found a new colony. This "acute drift," called the **founder effect,** results from a single generation of sampling, followed by several generations during which the population remains small. Founder effect is probably responsible for the virtually complete lack of blood group B in American Indians, whose ancestors arrived in very small numbers across the Bering Strait during the end of the last Ice Age, about 10,000 years ago. More recent examples are seen in religious isolates like the Dunkers and Old Order Amish of North America. These sects were founded by small numbers of migrants from their much larger congregations in central Europe. They have since remained nearly completely closed to immigration from the surrounding American population. As a result, their blood-group gene frequencies are quite different from those in the surrounding populations, both in Europe and in North America.

The process of genetic drift should sound familiar. It is, in fact, another way of looking at the inbreeding effect in small populations discussed earlier. Whether regarded as inbreeding or as random sampling of genes, the effect is the same. Populations do not exactly reproduce their genetic constitutions; there is a random component of gene frequency change.

One result of random sampling is that most new mutations, even if they are not selected against, never succeed in entering the population. Suppose that a single individual is heterozygous for a new mutation. There is some chance that the individual in question will have no offspring at all. Even if it has one offspring, there is a chance of $1/2$ that the new mutation will not be transmitted. If it has two offspring, the chance that neither carries the new mutation is $1/4$, and so on. Suppose that the new mutation is success-

fully transmitted to an offspring. Then in the next generation the lottery is repeated, and again the allele may be lost. In fact, if a population is of size N, the chance that a new mutation is eventually lost by chance is $(2N-1)/2N$. But if the new mutation is not lost, then the only thing that can happen to it in a finite population is that eventually it will sweep through the population and become fixed! This event has the probability of $1/2N$. In the absence of selection, then, the history of a population looks like Figure 23-24. For some period of time, it is homozygous. Then a new mutation appears. The new mutant allele will be lost immediately or very soon in most cases. Occasionally, however, a new mutant allele drifts through the population,

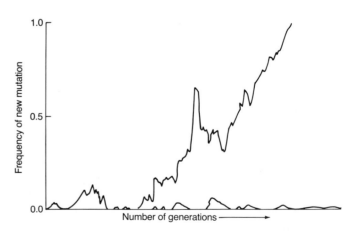

Figure 23-24. The appearance, loss, and eventual incorporation of new mutations during the life of a population. If random genetic drift does not cause the loss of a new mutation, then it must eventually cause the entire population to become homozygous for the mutation (in the absence of selection). (After J. Crow and M. Kimura, *An Introduction to the Population Genetics Theory,* Harper & Row, 1970.)

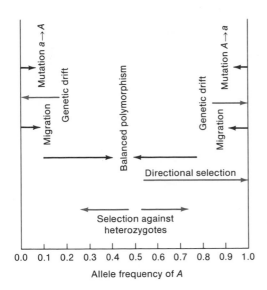

Figure 23-25. The effects on gene frequency of various forces of evolution.

and the population becomes homozygous for the new allele. The process then begins again.

Message New mutations can become established in a population even though they are not favored by natural selection simply by a process of random genetic drift.

A Synthesis of Forces

The genetic variation within and between populations is a result of the interplay of the various evolutionary forces (Figure 23-25). Generally, as Table 23-13 shows, those forces that increase or maintain variation within populations prevent the differentiation of populations from each other, whereas the divergence of populations is a result of forces that make each population homozygous. Thus random drift (inbreeding) produces homozygosity while causing different populations to diverge. This divergence and homozygosity are counteracted by the constant flux of mutation and the migration between localities, which introduce variation into the population again and tend to make them more like each other.

The effects of selection are more variable. Directional selection pushes a population toward homozygosity, rejecting most new mutations as they are introduced but occasionally (if the mutation is advantageous) spreading a new allele through the population to create a new homozygous state. Whether or not such directional selection promotes differentiation of populations depends on the environment and on chance events. Two populations living in very similar environments may be kept genetically similar by directional selection, but, if there are environmental differences, selection may drive the populations to different compositions. Advantageous new mutations are rare, so that a given mutation may occur in one population but not

(for a very long time) in others. Directional selection will then, temporarily, cause divergence of the population in which the mutation has appeared. Given enough time, of course, the mutation should be incorporated in all populations, especially if there is migration between them. But populations and species do not last forever, so directional selection operating on rare mutants may in fact be a cause of much divergence.

A particular case of interest, especially in human populations, is the interaction between mutation and directional selection in a very large population. New deleterious mutations are constantly arising spontaneously or as the result of the action of mutagens. These mutations may be completely recessive or partly dominant. Selection removes them from the population, but there will be an equilibrium between their appearance and removal. Let q be the frequency of the deleterious allele a, and let $p = 1 - q$ be the frequency of the normal allele. The change in allele frequency due to the mutation rate μ is

$$\Delta q_{mut} = \mu p$$

For a recessive deleterious gene, a simple way to express the fitnesses is $W_{AA} = W_{Aa} = 1.0$ and $W_{aa} = 1 - s$, where s is the loss of fitness in homozygotes. We can now substitute these fitnesses in our general expression for allelic frequency change, $\Delta p = pq(W_A - W_a)/\overline{W}$ as follows:

$$W_A = pW_{AA} + qW_{Aa} = p(1) + q(1) = 1$$
$$W_a = pW_{Aa} + qW_{aa} = p(1) + q(1 - s) = p + q - sq = 1 - sq$$

so

$$\overline{W} = pW_A + qW_a = p(1) + q(1 - sq)$$
$$= p + q - sq^2 = 1 - sq^2$$

Thus

$$\Delta p = \frac{pq(W_A - W_a)}{\overline{W}} = \frac{pq(sq)}{1 - sq^2}$$

■ **TABLE 23-13.** How the forces of evolution increase (+) or decrease (−) the variation within and between populations

Force	Variation within	Variation between
Inbreeding or genetic drift	−	+
Mutation	+	−
Migration	+	−
Selection		
directional	−	+/−
balancing	+	−
incompatibility	−	+

but the change in q, the frequency of the a allele, must be equal in magnitude and opposite in sign to the change in p, the frequency of the A allele:

$$\Delta q = -\Delta p$$

Thus, we finally obtain

$$\Delta q_{sel} = \frac{-pq(sq)}{1 - sq^2}$$

The requirement for equilibrium is that

$$\Delta \hat{q}_{mut} + \Delta \hat{q}_{sel} = 0$$

Remembering that $\hat{q}$ at equilibrium will be quite small, so that $1 - s\hat{q}^2 \cong 1$, we have

$$\mu\hat{p} - \frac{s\hat{p}\hat{q}^2}{1 - s\hat{q}^2} \cong \mu\hat{p} - s\hat{p}\hat{q}^2 = 0$$

or

$$\hat{q} = \sqrt{\frac{\mu}{s}}$$

So, for example, a recessive lethal ($s = 1$) mutating at the rate $\mu = 10^{-6}$ will have an equilibrium frequency of 10^{-3}. Indeed, if we knew that a gene was a recessive lethal and had no heterozygous effects, we could estimate its mutation rate as the square of the allele frequency. The basis for such calculations must be firm, however. Sickle-cell anemia was once thought to be a recessive lethal with no heterozygous effects, which led to an estimated mutation rate in Africa of 0.1 for this locus!

For a partly dominant deleterious gene, let the fitnesses be $W_{AA} = 1.0$, $W_{Aa} = 1 - hs$, and $W_{aa} = 1 - s$. Then a similar calculation gives

$$\hat{q} = \frac{\mu}{hs}$$

where h is the degree of dominance of the deleterious allele. So, if $\mu = 10^{-6}$, and the lethal is not totally recessive but has a 5 percent deleterious effect in heterozygotes ($s = 1.0$, $h = 0.05$), then

$$\hat{q} = \frac{10^{-6}}{5 \times 10^{-2}} = 2 \times 10^{-5}$$

which is smaller by two orders of magnitude than the equilibrium frequency for the purely recessive case.

Selection favoring heterozygotes (balancing selection) will, for the most part, maintain more or less similar poly-

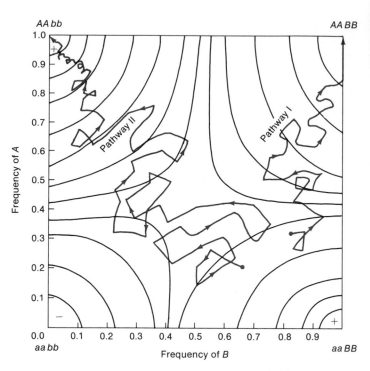

Figure 23-26. Selection and random drift can interact to produce different changes of gene frequency in an adaptive landscape. Without random drift, both populations would have moved toward *aa BB* as a result of selection alone.

morphisms in different populations. However, again, if environment is different enough between them, the populations will show some divergence. The opposite of balancing selection is selection against heterozygotes, which produces unstable equilibria. Such selection will cause homozygosity and divergence between populations.

The Exploration of Adaptive Peaks

Random and selective forces should not be thought of as simple antagonists. The outcome of the evolutionary process is a result of their simultaneous operation. Random drift may counteract the force of selection, but it may enhance it as well. Figure 23-26 illustrates these possibilities. There are multiple adaptive peaks. Because of random drift, a population under selection does not ascend an adaptive peak smoothly. Instead, it takes an erratic course in the field of gene frequencies, like a drunken mountain climber. Pathway I shows a population history where adaptation has failed. The random fluctuations of gene frequency were sufficiently great that the population by chance went to fixation at an unfit genotype. In any population, some proportion of loci are fixed at a selectively unfavorable allele because the intensity of selection is insufficient to overcome the random drift to fixation. Very great skepticism should be maintained toward naive theories about evolution that assume that populations always or nearly always reach an optimal constitution under selection. The existence of multiple adaptive peaks and the random fixation of less fit alleles are integral features of the evolutionary process. Natural selection cannot be relied upon to produce the best of all possible worlds.

Pathway II in Figure 23-26, on the other hand, shows how random drift may improve adaptation. The population was originally in the sphere of influence of the lower adaptive peak, but, by random fluctuation in gene frequency, its composition passed over the adaptive saddle, and the population was captured by the higher, steeper adaptive peak. This passage from a lower to a higher adaptive stable state could never have occurred by selection in an infinite population, because, by selection alone, $\overline{W}$ could never decrease temporarily in order to cross from one slope to another.

Message The interaction of selection and random drift makes possible the attainment of higher fitness states than those obtainable with natural selection operating alone.

The Origin of Species

By a species (at least in sexually reproducing organisms), we mean a group of individuals biologically capable of interbreeding yet isolated genetically from other groups. The origin of a new species—**speciation**—is the origin of a group of individuals capable of making a living in a new way and at the same time acquiring some barrier to genetic exchange with the species from which it arose. The genetic differentiation of a population by inbreeding, genetic drift, and differential selection is always threatened by the reintroduction of genes from other groups by migration. The reduction of gene migration to a very low value is thus a prerequisite for speciation.

Generally, this reduction is the result of geographical isolation of the population as a consequence of chance historical events. A few long-distance migrants may reach a new island; a part of the mainland may be cut off by a rise in sea level; an insect vector that formerly passed pollen from one population to another may become locally extinct; the grassy plain that connected the feeding grounds of two grazers may, by a slight change in rainfall pattern, become a desert. Once the population is isolated physically, the processes of genetic differentiation will go on unimpeded until the genetic constitution of the isolated population is so different from its parental group that there is real difficulty in interbreeding.

If migration is reestablished before this critical period, speciation will not occur and the divergent populations will once again converge. This has already happened in the human species, where genetic differentiation of geographical populations never proceeded beyond some superficial physical traits and a mixed differentiation of frequencies at polymorphic loci. On the other hand, if populations are very divergent before they come back in contact with each other, hybrid offspring will have genotypes with such low fitness that they do not survive or are sterile. At this stage of differentiation, there is a definite selective advantage for the newly forming species to avoid mating with each other and so avoid the wastage of gametes. New (secondary) barriers to interbreeding will then be selected, and the speciation process will be complete.

Beyond this generalized sketch of speciation, remarkably little can be said with certainty. Because species do not interbreed, it is difficult to analyze their differences genetically. A great deal must be made of the few cases where some hybrid offspring can be produced in the laboratory or garden. The methods of electrophoresis, immunology, and protein sequencing have made it possible to describe the differences in the proteins of species, but we have very few cases of species that have just recently separated. Thus, we do not know how much of the genome, and what part of it, is involved in the first divergence, nor do we know whether that divergence is often a consequence of diversifying selection or random drift. A detailed genetic analysis of the process of speciation remains one of the most important tasks for population genetics.

Summary

■ Charles Darwin revolutionized the study of biology when he constructed a theory of evolution based on the principles that variation existed within populations, that variation was heritable, and that the phenotype of the individuals in the population changed through generations because of natural selection. These basic tenets of evolution, put forward in *The Origin of Species* in 1859 prior to any knowledge of Mendelian genetics, have required only minor modification since that time. The study of changes within a population, or population genetics, relates the heritable changes in populations of organisms to the underlying individual processes of inheritance and development. Population genetics is the study of inherited variation and its modification in time and space.

Identifiable inherited variation within a population can be studied by observing morphological differences among individuals, or by examining the differences in specific amino-acid sequences of proteins, or even by examining, most recently, the differences in nucleotide sequences within the DNA. These kinds of observations have led to the conclusion that there is considerable polymorphism at many loci within a population. A measure of this variation is the amount of heterozygosity in a population. Population studies have shown that, in general, the genetic differences among individuals within human races is much greater than the average differences among races.

The ultimate source of all variation is mutation. However, within a population, the quantitative frequency of specific genotypes can be changed by recombination, immigration of genes, continued mutational events, and chance.

One property of Mendelian segregation is that, after one generation, random mating results in an equilibrium distribution of genotypes. However, inbreeding is one process that converts genetic variation within a population into differences between populations by making each separate population homozygous for a randomly chosen allele. On the other hand, for most populations, a balance is reached for any given environment between inbreeding, mutation from one allele to another, and immigration.

"Directed" changes of allele frequencies within a population occur through natural selection of a favored genotype. In many cases such changes lead to homozygosity at a particular locus. On the other hand, the heterozygote may be more suited to a given environment than either of the homozygotes, leading to a balanced polymorphism.

Environmental selection of specific genotypes is rarely this simple, however. More often than not, phenotypes are determined by several interacting genes, and alleles at these different loci will be selected for at different rates. Furthermore, closely linked loci, unrelated to the phenotype in question, may have specific alleles carried along during the selection process. In general, genetic variation is the result of the interaction of evolutionary forces. For instance, a recessive deleterious mutant will never be totally eliminated from a population, because mutation constantly resupplies it to the population. Immigration can also reintroduce the undesirable allele into the population. And, indeed, a deleterious allele may, under environmental conditions of which we are unaware (including the remaining genetic makeup of the individual), be selected for.

Unless alternative alleles are in intermediate frequencies, selection, especially against recessives, is very slow, requiring many generations. In many populations, especially those of small size, new mutations can become established even though they are not favored by natural selection, simply by a process of random genetic drift. Such slow changes in different allele frequencies throughout the genome can lead eventually to the formation of new races and new species.

Problems

1. You are studying protein polymorphism in a natural population of a certain species of a sexually reproducing haploid organism. You isolate many strains from various parts of the test area and run extracts from each strain on electrophoretic gels. You stain the gels with a reagent specific for enzyme "X" and find that in the population there is a total of, say, five electrophoretic variants of enzyme X.

You speculate that these variants represent various alleles of the structural gene for enzyme X.

a. How would you demonstrate that this is so, both genetically and biochemically? (You can make crosses, make diploids, run gels, test enzyme activities, test amino acid sequences, and so on.) Lay out the steps and conclusions precisely.

b. Name at least one other possible way of generating the different electrophoretic variants, and say how you would distinguish this possibility from the one described here.

2. A study made in 1958 in the mining town of Ashibetsu in Hokkaido province of Japan revealed the frequencies of MN blood-type genotypes shown in the following table (for individuals and for married couples).

Genotype	Number of individuals or couples
Individuals	
$L^M L^M$	406
$L^M L^N$	744
$L^N L^N$	332
Total	1482
Couples	
$L^M L^M \times L^M L^M$	58
$L^M L^M \times L^M L^N$	202
$L^M L^N \times L^M L^N$	190
$L^M L^M \times L^N L^N$	88
$L^M L^N \times L^N L^N$	162
$L^N L^N \times L^N L^N$	41
Total	741

a. Show whether the population is in Hardy-Weinberg equilibrium with respect to the MN blood types.

b. Show whether mating is random with respect to MN blood types.

(Problem 2 is from J. Kuspira and G. W. Walker, *Genetics, Questions and Problems*, McGraw-Hill, 1973.)

3. For a sex-linked character in a species where the male is the heterogametic sex, suppose that the allelic frequencies at a locus are different for males and females.

a. Let the frequency of A be 0.8 in males and 0.2 in females. Show what happens to the allelic frequencies in successive generations in the two sexes.

b. Try to develop a general expression for the difference of frequency in males (p) and in females (P) in the nth generation, given that the initial values were p_0 and P_0.

4. Consider the populations whose genotypes are shown in the following table.

Population	AA	Aa	aa
1	1.0	0.0	0.0
2	0.0	1.0	0.0
3	0.0	0.0	1.0
4	0.50	0.25	0.25
5	0.25	0.25	0.50
6	0.25	0.50	0.25
7	0.33	0.33	0.33
8	0.04	0.32	0.64
9	0.64	0.32	0.04
10	0.986049	0.013902	0.000049

a. Which of the populations are in Hardy-Weinberg equilibrium?

b. What are p and q in each population?

c. In population 10, it is discovered that the mutation rate from A to a is 5×10^{-6} and that reverse mutation is negligible. What must be the fitness of the aa phenotype?

d. In population 6, the a allele is detrimental, and furthermore the A allele is incompletely dominant so that AA is perfectly fit, Aa has a fitness of 0.8, and aa has a fitness of 0.6. If there is no mutation, what will p and q be in the next generation?

5. Color blindness is due to a sex-linked recessive allele. One male in ten is color-blind.

a. What proportion of women are color-blind?

b. By what factor is color blindness more common in men (or, how many color-blind men are there for each color-blind woman)?

c. In what proportion of marriages would color blindness affect one-half of the children of each sex?

d. In what proportion of marriages would all children be normal?

e. In a population that is not in equilibrium, the frequency of the allele for color blindness is 0.2 in women and 0.6 in men. After one generation of random mating, what proportion of the female progeny will be color-blind? what proportion of the male progeny?

f. What will the allele frequencies be in the male and in the female progeny in part e?

(Problem 5 courtesy of Clayton Person.)

6. In a wild population of beetles of species X, you notice that there is a 3 : 1 ratio of shiny to dull wing covers. Does this prove that *shiny* is dominant? (Assume that the two states

are caused by the alleles of one gene.) If not, what does it prove? How would you elucidate the situation?

7. It seems clear that most new mutations are deleterious. Why?

8. Most mutations are recessive to wild-type. Of those rare mutations that are dominant in *Drosophila*, for example, the majority turn out to be chromosomal aberrations or to be inseparable from chromosomal aberrations. Can you offer an explanation for why wild-type is usually dominant?

9. Ten percent of the males of a large and randomly mating population are color-blind. A representative group of 1000 from this population migrates to a South Pacific island, where there are already 1000 inhabitants, and where 30 percent of the males are color-blind. Assuming that Hardy-Weinberg conditions apply throughout (in the two original populations before emigration, and in the mixed population immediately following immigration), what fractions of males and females are expected to be color-blind in the generation immediately following the arrival of the immigrants?

10. Using pedigree diagrams, find the probability of homozygosity by descent of the offspring of: a. parent-offspring matings; b. first-cousin matings; c. aunt-nephew or uncle-niece matings.

11. In a survey of Indian tribes in Arizona and New Mexico, it was found that, in most groups, albinos were completely absent or very rare. (There is 1 albino per 20,000 North American Caucasians.) However, in three populations, albino frequencies were exceptionally high: 1 per 277 Indians in Arizona, 1 per 140 Jemez Indians in New Mexico, and 1 per 247 Zuni Indians in New Mexico. All three of these populations were culturally, but not linguistically, related. What possible factors might explain the high incidence of albinos in these three tribes?

12. In an animal population, 20 percent of the individuals are AA, 60 percent are Aa, and 20 percent are aa. What are the allele frequencies? In this population, mating is always with *like phenotype* but is random within phenotype. What genotype and allele frequencies will prevail in the next generation? Such *assortative mating* is common in animal populations. Another type of assortative mating is that which occurs only between *unlike* phenotypes: answer the above question with this restriction imposed. What will the end result be after many generations of mating of both types?

13. In *Drosophila*, a stock isolated from nature has an average of 36 abdominal bristles. By selectively breeding only those flies with more bristles, the mean is raised to 56 in twenty generations! What would be the source of this genetic flexibility? The 56-bristle stock is very infertile, so selection is relaxed for several generations and the bristle number drops to about 45. Why does it not drop to 36?

When selection is reapplied, 56 bristles are soon attained, but this time the stock is *not* sterile. How could this situation arise?

14. The fitnesses of three genotypes are $W_{AA} = 0.9$; $W_{Aa} = 1.0$; and $W_{aa} = 0.7$.

    a. If the population starts at allele frequency $p = 0.5$, what is the value of p in the next generation?

    b. What is the predicted equilibrium?

15. AA and Aa individuals are equally fertile. If 0.1 percent of the population is aa, what selection pressure exists against aa if the mutation rate $A \rightarrow a$ is 10^{-5}?

16. Gene B is a deleterious autosomal dominant. The frequency of affected individuals is 4.0×10^{-6}. Such individuals have a reproductive capacity about 30 percent that of normal individuals. Estimate μ, the rate at which b mutates to its deleterious allele B.

17. Of 31 children born of father-daughter matings, six died in infancy, 12 were very abnormal and died in childhood, and 13 were normal. From this information, calculate roughly how many recessive lethal genes we have in our human genomes on the average. For example, if the answer is 1, then a daughter would stand a 50 percent chance of having it, and the probability of the union producing a lethal combination would be $1/2 \times 1/4 = 1/8$. (So, obviously, 1 is not the answer.) Consider also the possibility of undetected fatalities in utero in such matings. How would they affect your result?

18. Let us define the **total selection cost** to a population of a deleterious recessive gene as the loss of fitness per individual affected, s, times the frequency of affected individuals, q^2. That is,

$$\text{genetic cost} = sq^2$$

    a. Suppose that a population is at equilibrium between mutation and selection for a deleterious recessive gene, where $s = 0.5$ and $\mu = 10^{-5}$. What is the equilibrium frequency of the gene? What is the genetic cost?

    b. Suppose that we now start irradiating people, so that the mutation rate doubles. What will be the new equilibrium frequency of the gene? What will be the genetic cost?

    c. Suppose that we do not change the mutation rate but instead lower the selection intensity to $s = 0.3$. What happens to the equilibrium frequency and genetic cost?

Further Reading

■ Students interested in pursuing genetics further should start reading original research articles in scientific journals. Some important journals are *Cell, Current Genetics, Evolution, Gene, Genetic Research, Genetics, Heredity, Human Genetics, Journal of Medical Genetics, Journal of Molecular Biology, Molecular and General Genetics, Mutation Research, Nature, Plasmid, Proceedings of the National Academy of Sciences of the United States of America,* and *Science.* Useful review articles may be found in *Annual Review of Genetics, Advances in Genetics,* and *Trends in Genetics.*

Some particularly useful references, mostly general reviews, are listed below under the chapters to which they relate.

Chapter 1

Clausen, J., D. D. Keck, and W. W. Hiesey. 1940. *Experimental Studies on the Nature of Species,* Vol. 1: *The Effect of Varied Environments on Western North American Plants.* Carnegie Institute of Washington, Publ. No. 520,1–452. This publication and the following one by the same authors are the classic studies of norms of reaction of plants from natural populations.

Clausen, J., D. D. Keck, and W. W. Hiesey. 1958. *Experimental Studies on the Nature of Species,* Vol. 3: *Environmental Responses of Climatic Races of* Achillea. Carnegie Institute of Washington, Publ. No. 581, 1–129.

Milunsky, A., and G. J. Annas, eds. 1975. *Genetics and the Law.* New York: Plenum Press. Interesting accounts of the ramifications of genetics in the lives of individuals.

Schmalhausen, I. I. 1949. *Factors of Evolution: The Theory of Stabilizing Selection.* Philadelphia: Blakiston. The most general discussion of the relation of genotype and environment in the formation of phenotypic variation.

Chapter 2

Carlson, E. A. 1966. *The Gene: A Critical History.* Philadelphia: W. B. Saunders. A readable history of genetics.

Grant, V. 1975. *Genetics of Flowering Plants.* New York: Columbia University Press. One of the few texts on this subject.

Harpstead, D. 1971. "High-Lysine Corn." *Scientific American* (August). An account of the breeding of lines with increased amounts of normally limiting amino acids.

Hutt, F. B. 1964. *Animal Genetics.* New York: Ronald Press. A standard text on the subject with many interesting examples.

Jennings, P. R. 1976. "The Amplification of Agricultural Production." *Scientific American* (September). A discussion of genetics and the green revolution.

Olby, R. C. 1966. *Origins of Mendelism.* London: Constable. An enjoyable account of Mendel's work and the intellectual climate of his time.

Singer, S. 1978. *Human Genetics.* New York: W. H. Freeman and Co. A short and readable treatment of the subject.

Stern, C., and E. R. Sherwood. 1966. *The Origin of Genetics. A Mendel Source Book.* New York: W. H. Freeman and Co. A short collection of important early papers, including Mendel's papers and correspondence.

Sturtevant, A. H. 1965. *A History of Genetics*. New York: Harper & Row. Another useful historical text.

Todd, N. B. 1977. "Cats and Commerce." *Scientific American* (November). Includes some genetics of domestic cat coat colors and the use of this information to study cat migration throughout history.

Chapter 3

McLeish, J., and B. Snoad. 1958. *Looking at Chromosomes*. New York: Macmillan. A short classic book consisting of many superb photos of mitosis and meiosis.

Rick, C. M. 1978. "The Tomato." *Scientific American* (August). Includes an account of tomato genes and chromosomes and their role in breeding.

Stern, C. 1973. *Principles of Human Genetics*, 3d ed. New York: W. H. Freeman and Co. A standard text including many examples of the inheritance of human traits.

von Wettstein, D., et al. 1984. "The Synaptonemal Complex in Genetic Segregation." *Annual Review of Genetics* 18: 331–414. An up-to-date review of the structure and function of the complex.

Chapter 4

Bodmer, W. F., and L. L. Cavalli-Sforza. 1976. *Genetics, Evolution and Man*. New York: W. H. Freeman and Co. A very readable, well-illustrated book, including a clear account of HLA genetics.

Carlson, E. A. 1984. *Human Genetics*. Lexington: Heath. A readable and up-to-date account of human inheritance.

Day, P. R. 1974. *Genetics of Host-Parasite Interaction*. New York: W. H. Freeman and Co. A short technical account of the subject, which is of great importance to agriculture. It includes good examples of gene interaction.

Griffiths, A. J. F., and F. R. Ganders. 1984. *Wildflower Genetics*. Vancouver: Flight Press. A field guide to plant variation in natural populations and its genetic basis, including examples relevant to this chapter.

Silvers, W. K. 1979. *The Coat Colors of Mice*. New York: Springer-Verlag. A standard handbook on the subject, including many examples of gene interaction.

Chapter 5

O'Brien, S. J., ed. 1984. *Genetic Maps*. Cold Spring Harbor Press. A recent compendium of the detailed maps of 80 well-analyzed organisms.

Peters, J. A., ed. 1959. *Classic Papers in Genetics*. Englewood Cliffs, N.J.: Prentice-Hall. A collection of important papers in the history of genetics.

White, R., et al. 1985. "Construction of Linkage Maps with DNA Markers for Human Chromosomes." *Nature* 313: 101–104. An extension of the techniques of this chapter to DNA markers.

Chapter 6

Evans, D. A., W. R. Sharp, P. V. Ammirato, and Y. Yamada, eds. 1983. *Handbook of Plant Cell Culture*, Vol. 1. New York: Macmillan. Practical details of the techniques of propagation and breeding plants by cell, tissue, and organ culture.

Finchman, J. R. S., P. R. Day, and A. Radford. 1979. *Fungal Genetics*, 3d ed. London: Blackwell. A large, standard technical work. Good for tetrad analysis.

Kemp, R. 1970. *Cell Division and Heredity*. London: Edward Arnold. A short, clear introduction to genetics. Good for map functions and tetrad analysis.

Murray, A. W., and J. W. Szostak. 1983. "Construction of Artificial Chromosomes in Yeast." *Nature* 305: 189–193. The first creation of new chromosomes by splicing together known telomere, centromere, replicator, and then DNA fragments by recombinant DNA technology. Includes tetrad analysis of markers on the new chromosomes.

Puck, T. T., and F-T. Kao. 1982. "Somatic Cell Genetics and Its Application to Medicine." *Annual Review of Genetics* 16: 225–272. A technical but readable review.

Ruddle, F. H., and R. S. Kucherlapati. 1974. "Hybrid Cells and Human Genes." *Scientific American* (July). A popular account of the use of cell hybridization in mapping human genes.

Stahl, F. W. 1969. *The Mechanics of Inheritance*, 2d ed. Englewood Cliffs, N.J.: Prentice-Hall. A short introduction to genetics, including some advanced material presented with a novel approach.

Chapter 7

Induced Mutations—A Tool in Plant Research. 1981. Vienna: International Atomic Energy Agency. A collection of papers by eminent workers in agricultural genetics illustrating the practical uses of mutations in plant breeding.

Lawrence, C. W. 1971. *Cellular Radiobiology*. London: Edward Arnold. A short standard text.

Neuffer, M. G., L. Jones, and M. S. Zuber. 1968. *The Mutants of Maize*. Madison: Crop Science Society of America. A color catalog of the many, and often bizarre, mutants used by corn geneticists.

Schull, W. J., et al. 1981. "Genetic Effect of the Atomic Bombs: A Reappraisal." *Science* 213: 1220–1227. A summary of all the indicators of potential genetic effects of the Hiroshima and Nagasaki explosions, concluding that "In no instance is there a statistically significant effect of parental exposure; but for all indicators the observed effect is in the direction suggested by the hypothesis that genetic damage resulted from the exposure."

Chapters 8 and 9

Epstein, C. J., et al. 1983. "Recent Developments in Prenatal Diagnosis of Genetic Diseases and Birth Defects." *Annual Review of Genetics* 17: 49–83. Includes amniocentesis.

Feldman, M. G., and E. R. Sears. 1981. "The Wild Gene Resources of Wheat." *Scientific American* (January). A general discussion of the genomes of wheat and its relatives, and how new genes can be introduced.

Friedmann, T. 1971. "Prenatal Diagnosis of Genetic Disease." *Scientific American* (November). An early article on amniocentesis and its uses.

Fuchs, F. 1980. "Genetic Amniocentesis." *Scientific American* (August).

German, J., ed. 1974. *Chromosomes and Cancer*. New York: Wiley. A large technical work, but readable, describing the relation of chromosome changes and cancer.

Hassold, T. J., and P. A. Jacobs. 1984. "Trisomy in Man." *Annual Review of Genetics* 18: 69–98. A comprehensive summary of trisomy, including a discussion of the maternal age effect.

Hulse, J. H., and D. Spurgeon. 1974. "Triticale." *Scientific American* (August). An account of the development and possible benefits of this wheat-rye amphidiploid.

Lawrence, W. J. C. 1968. *Plant Breeding*. London: Edward Arnold (*Studies in Biology*, No. 12). A short introduction to the subject.

Maniatis, T. E., et al. 1980. "The Molecular Genetics of Human Hemoglobins." *Annual Review of Genetics* 14: 145–178. A useful summary, which could be profitably read at this point in the course or after reading the material on molecular genetics.

Shepherd, J. F. 1982. "The Regeneration of Potato Plants from Protoplasts." *Scientific American* (May). A review by one of the leaders in this field.

Swanson, C. P., T. Mertz, and W. J. Young. 1967. *Cytogenetics*. Englewood Cliffs, N.J.: Prentice-Hall.

Chapter 10

Dickerson, R. E. 1983. "The DNA Helix and How It Is Read." *Scientific American* (December). An article with some beautiful color models of DNA structures.

Kornberg, A. 1980. *DNA Replication*. New York: W. H. Freeman and Co. The definitive technical treatment of the subject, based on genetic and chemical analysis.

Wang, J. C. 1982. "DNA Topoisomerases." *Scientific American* (July). Diagrams different topological forms of DNA.

Watson, J. D. 1968. *The Double Helix*. New York: Atheneum. An enjoyable personal account of Watson and Crick's discovery, including the human dramas involved.

Chapter 11

Benzer, S. 1962. "The Fine Structure of the Gene." *Scientific American* (January). A popular version of the author's pioneer experiments.

Watson, J. D. 1976. *The Molecular Biology of the Gene*, 3d ed. Menlo Park, Calif.: Benjamin/Cummings. A superb development of the subject, written in a highly readable style and well illustrated.

Yanofsky, C. 1967. "Gene Structure and Protein Structure." *Scientific American* (May). This article gives the details of colinearity at the molecular level.

Chapter 12

Crick, F. H. C. 1962. "The Genetic Code." *Scientific American* (October). This article and the following one are popular accounts of code-cracking experiments.

Crick, F. H. C. 1966. "The Genetic Code: III." *Scientific American* (October).

Lake, J. A. 1981. "The Ribosome." *Scientific American* (August). Three-dimensional model of the ribosome.

Lane, C. 1976. "Rabbit Haemoglobin from Frog Eggs." *Scientific American* (August). This article describes experiments illustrating the universality of the genetic system.

Miller, O. L. 1973. "The Visualization of Genes in Action." *Scientific American* (March). A discussion of electron microscopy of transcription and translation.

Moore, P. B. 1976. "Neutron-Scattering Studies of the Ribosome." *Scientific American* (October). This article gives the details of ribosome substructure.

Nirenberg, M. W. 1963. "The Genetic Code: II." *Scientific American* (March). Another account of early code-cracking experiments.

Rich, A., and S. H. Kim. 1978. "The Three-Dimensional Structure of Transfer RNA." *Scientific American* (January). A presentation of the experimental evidence behind the structure described in this chapter.

Chapter 13

Adelberg, E. A. 1966. *Papers on Bacterial Genetics*. Boston: Little, Brown.

Hayes, W. 1968. *The Genetics of Bacteria and Their Viruses*, 2d ed. New York: Wiley. The standard and classic text, written by a pioneer in the subject.

Lewin, B. 1977. *Gene Expression*, Vol. 1: *Bacterial Genomes*. New York: Wiley. An excellent set of volumes, all of which are relevant to various sections of this text.

Lewin, B. 1977. *Gene Expression*, Vol. 3: *Plasmids and Phages*. New York: Wiley.

Stent, G. S., and R. Calendar. 1978. *Molecular Genetics*, 2d ed. New York: W. H. Freeman and Co. A lucidly written account of the development of our present understanding of the subject, based mainly on experiments in bacteria and phage.

Chapter 14

Britten, R. J., and D. Kohne. 1968. "Repeated Sequences in DNA." *Science* 161: 529–540. One of the important summaries of the theoretical basis for distinguishing DNAs by renaturation.

Broda, P. 1979. *Plasmids*. New York: W. H. Freeman and Co. One of the few technical books on the subject.

Brown, D. D. 1973. "The Isolation of Genes." *Scientific American* (August). Illustrates the power of focusing molecular techniques on one specific locus with special properties.

Cohen, S. 1975. "The Manipulation of Genes." *Scientific American* (July). A summary of recombinant DNA techniques by one of the main innovators.

Fiddes, J. C. 1977. "The Nucleotide Sequence of a Viral DNA." *Scientific American* (December). This is a review of a landmark, the DNA sequence of an entire virus genome with an unexpected discovery.

Gilbert, W., and L. Villa-Komaroff. 1980. "Useful Proteins from Recombinant Bacteria." *Scientific American* (April). A description of the method of DNA sequencing used most extensively. Also discusses the potential application of recombinant DNA techniques.

Itakura, K., et al. 1977. "Expression in *E. coli* of a Chemically Synthesized Gene for the Hormone Somatostatin." *Science* 198. A technical paper well worth reading for its historical significance. It represents the start of bioengineering—using DNA manipulation to modify cells to produce a medically useful human protein.

Khorana, H. G., et al. 1972. "Studies on Polynucleotides. CIII. Total Synthesis of the Structural Gene for an Alanine Transfer Ribonucleic Acid from Yeast." *Journal of Molecular Biology* 72: 209–217. A classic technical paper.

Mertens, T. R. 1975. *Human Genetics: Readings on the Implications of Genetic Engineering*. New York: Wiley. A collection of popular articles.

Nathans, D., and H. O. Smith. 1975. "Restriction Endonucleases in the Analysis and Restructuring of DNA Molecules." *Annual Review of Biochemistry* 44: 273–293. A technical review of restriction enzymes by two pioneers in the field.

Sinsheimer, R. L. 1977. "Recombinant DNA." *Annual Review of Biochemistry* 46. A provocative article by a leading molecular biologist who has expressed concern about potential hazards of DNA manipulation.

Watson, J. D., J. Tooze, and D. T. Kurtz. 1983. *Recombinant DNA: A Short Course*. New York: W. H. Freeman and Co. An excellent introduction to the theory and applications of recombinant DNA.

Chapter 15

Auerbach, C. 1976. *Mutation Research*. London: Chapman & Hall. Standard text by a pioneer researcher.

Cairns, J. 1978. *Cancer: Science and Society*. New York: W. H. Freeman and Co. A fascinating discussion of the origins of human cancers, and of the role played by the environment.

Croce, C. M., and H. Koprowski. 1978. "The Genetics of Human Cancer." *Scientific American* (February). An excellent popular account.

Devoret, R. 1979. "Bacterial Tests for Potential Carcinogens." *Scientific American* (August). This article describes the use of mutation tests to screen for carcinogens and includes some details of DNA reactions.

Drake, J. W. 1970. *The Molecular Basis of Mutation*. San Francisco: Holden-Day. One of the few standard texts on the subject.

Miller, J. H. 1983. "Mutational Specificity in Bacteria." *Annual Review of Genetics* 17: 215–238. A discussion of the specificity of mutagens in bacteria.

Walker, G. C. 1984. "Mutagenesis and Inducible Responses to Deoxyribonucleic Acid Damage in *Escherichia coli*," *Microbiological Reviews* 48: 60–93. A review of mutagenesis and repair, with an excellent discussion of the SOS system.

Chapter 16

Alverts, B., D. Bray, J. Lewis, M. Raff, K. Roberts, and J. D. Watson. 1983. *Molecular Biology of the Cell*. New York: Garland. See pages 240 to 250 for an excellent description of recombination at the molecular level, with nice figures.

Stahl, F. W. 1979. *Genetic Recombination: Thinking About It in Phage and Fungi*. New York: W. H. Freeman and Co. A rather technical short book on recombination models.

Whitehouse, H. L. K. 1973. *Towards an Understanding of the Mechanism of Heredity*, 3d ed. London: Edward Arnold. An excellent general introduction to genetics stressing the historical approach and the pivotal experiments. It includes a good section on recombination models.

Chapter 17

Baltimore, D. 1985. "Retroviruses and Retrotransposons: The Role of Reverse Transcription in Shaping the Eukaryotic Genome." *Cell* 40: 481–482. A short review of recent work on RNA intermediates in transposition.

Bukhari, A. I., J. A. Shapiro, and S. L. Adhya, eds. 1977. *DNA Insertion Elements, Plasmids and Episomes*. Cold Spring Harbor Laboratory. An excellent large collection of short summary papers involving lower and higher life forms.

Cohen, S. N., and J. A. Shapiro. 1980. "Transposable Genetic Elements." *Scientific American* (February). A popular account stressing bacteria and phages.

Fedoroff, N. V. 1984. "Transposable Genetic Elements in Maize." *Scientific American* (June). An account of the early experiments in maize, with recent results on the molecular basis of transposition.

Shapiro, J. A., ed. 1983. *Mobile Genetic Elements*. New York: Academic Press. A comprehensive set of reviews covering the latest developments on transposition in later prokaryotes and eukaryotes.

Chapter 18

Herskowitz, I. 1973. "Control of Gene Expression in Bacteriophage Lambda." *Annual Review of Genetics* 7: 289–324. A technical review of the complex and well-analyzed regulation of lambda genes.

Jacob, F., and J. Monod. 1961. "Genetic Regulatory Mechanisms in the Synthesis of Proteins." *Journal of Molecular Biology* 3: 318–356. A classic paper setting forth the elements of an operon and the experimental evidence.

Maniatis, T., and M. Ptashne. 1976. "A DNA Operator-Repressor System." *Scientific American* (January). This article discusses the molecular structures of the components of the *lac* operon.

Miller, J. H., and W. S. Reznikoff, eds. 1978. *The Operon*. Cold Spring Harbor Laboratory. A valuable set of reviews on gene regulation in bacteria.

Ptashne, M., and W. Gilbert. 1970. "Genetic Repressors." *Scientific American* (June). The exciting story of how repressors were identified and purified, thereby confirming the predictions of Jacob and Monod.

Weber, I. T., D. B. McKay, and T. A. Steitz. 1982. Two Helix DNA Binding Motif of CAP Found in *lac* Repressor and *gal* Repressor. *Nucleic Acids Research* 10: 5085–5102. Discussion of models for repressor-operator recognition.

Chapter 19

Britten, R. J., and D. E. Kohne. 1970. "Repeated Segments of DNA." *Scientific American* (April).

Brown, S. W. 1966. "Heterochromatin." *Science* 151: 417–425. A nice review of the classic cytological observations.

Chambon, P. 1981. "Split Genes." *Scientific American* (May). The discovery of intervening sequences is described.

Davidson, E., and R. Britten. 1973. "Organization, Transcription and Regulation in the Animal Genome." *Quarterly Review of Biology* 48: 565–613. The analysis of renaturation kinetics of DNA fragments provides insights into chromosome structure.

Dupraw, E. J. 1970. *DNA and Chromosomes*. New York: Holt, Rinehart & Winston. A useful book on chromosome substructure, containing excellent photographs by the author.

Edgar, R. S., and R. H. Epstein. 1965. "The Genetics of a Bacterial Virus." *Scientific American* (February). In analyzing a large number of mutations, the clustering of functionally related genes became apparent.

Glover, D. M., et al. 1975. "Characterization of 6 Cloned DNAs from *Drosophila melanogaster* Including One That Contains the Genes for rRNA." *Cell* 5: 149–157. A technical paper showing how the isolation of random segments of *Drosophila* DNA in *E. coli* can be used to study chromosome structure.

Hayashi, S., et al. 1980. "Hybridization of tRNAs of *Drosophila melanogaster*." *Chromosoma* 76: 65–84. A technical report showing how specific genes can be located cytologically by hybridization of labeled RNA to chromosomes in situ.

Judd, B. H., et al. 1972. "The Anatomy and Function of a Segment of the X Chromosome of *Drosophila melanogaster*." *Genetics* 71: 139–156. A beautiful example of genetic analysis leading to a significant insight into chromosome structure.

Kavenoff, R., and B. H. Zimm. 1973. "Chromosome-Sized DNA Molecules from *Drosophila*." *Chromosoma* 41. An elegant experiment involving the study of chromosome aberrations with physicochemical techniques.

Kornberg, R. D. 1974. "Chromatin Structure: A Repeating Unit of Histones and DNA." *Science* 184: 868–871. A technical review of the evidence for nucleosomes.

Kornberg, R. D., and A. Klug. 1981. "The Nucleosome." *Scientific American* (February). Detailed analysis of chromosome structure.

Lewin, B. 1977. *Gene Expression*, Vol. 2: *Eucaryotic Chromosomes*. New York: Wiley.

Lucchesi, J. C. 1973. "Dosage Compensation in *Drosophila*." *Annual Review of Genetics* 7: 225–237. A technical survey of the phenomenon and its possible mechanisms.

Lyon, M. L. 1962. "Sex Chromatin and Gene Action in the Mammalian X Chromosome." *American Journal of Human Genetics* 14: 135–148. The first proposal that, in human females, one X is inactive, with supporting evidence of mosaic expression of sex-linked mutations.

Chapter 20

Borst, P., and L. A. Grivell. 1978. "The Mitochondrial Genome of Yeast." *Cell* 15: 705–723. A nontechnical review of the molecular biology of mtDNA.

Dujon, B. 1981. "Mitochondrial Genetics and Functions," in *The Molecular Biology of the Yeast* Saccharomyces. Edited by J. N. Strathern, E. W. Jones, and J. R. Broach. Cold Spring Harbor Laboratory. The most comprehensive review available. This book is useful for many other aspects of yeast genetics and molecular biology.

Gillham, N. W. 1978. *Organelle Heredity*. New York: Raven Press. A rather technical work on the subject, especially strong on genetic analysis.

Grivell, L. A. 1983. "Mitochondrial DNA." *Scientific American* (March). An excellent and up-to-date review including a discussion of the unique mitochondrial translation system and of splicing of mitochondrial introns.

Laughan, J. R., and S. Gabay-Laughan. 1983. "Cytoplasmic Male Sterility in Maize." *Annual Review of Genetics* 17: 27–48. A recent survey of the genetics and molecular biology of this phenotype.

Linnane, A. W., and P. Nagley. 1978. "Mitochondrial Genetics in Perspective: The Derivation of a Genetic and Physical Map of the Yeast Mitochondrial Genome." *Plasmid* 1: 324–345. An excellent review of the genetics and molecular biology of yeast mtDNA.

Osiewacz, H., and K. Esser. 1984. "The Mitochondrial Plasmid of *Podospora anserina*: A Mobile Intron of a Mitochondrial Gene." *Current Genetics* 8: 299–305. The paper that showed α senDNA is an intron.

Sager, R. 1965. "Genes Outside Chromosomes." *Scientific American* (January). A popular description of early *Chlamydomonas* experiments.

Sager, R. 1972. *Cytoplasmic Genes and Organelles*. New York: Academic Press.

Wright, R. M., et al. 1982. "Are Mitochondrial Structural Genes Selectively Amplified During Senescence in *Podospora anserina*?" *Cell* 29: 505–515. A key paper in the development of the fungal senescence story.

Chapter 21

Beerman, W., and U. Clever. 1964. "Chromosome Puffs." *Scientific American* (April). A description of the cytology of puffing.

Bender, W., et al. 1983. "Molecular Genetics of the Bithorax Complex in *Drosophila melanogaster*." *Science* 221: 23. This is not an easy article to read, but it is well worth the effort. It illustrates the power of combining good genetic analysis with biochemistry.

Benzer, S. 1973. "The Genetic Dissection of Behavior." *Scientific American* (December). A beautiful illustration of the power of genetic analysis to probe development and behavior. Includes focus mapping.

Bishop, J. M. 1982. "Oncogenes." *Scientific American* (March). An exciting look at the first clues of a gene basis for cancers.

DeRobertis, E. M., and J. B. Gurdon. 1979. "Gene Transplantation and the Analysis of Development." *Scientific American* (December).

Garcia-Bellido, A., et al. 1979. "Compartments in Animal Development." *Scientific American* (July). This article is not easy reading, but it points to an underlying principle in development that appears to be widespread.

Garcia-Bellido, A., and J. R. Merriam. 1969. "Cell Lineage of the Imaginal Discs of *Drosophila melanogaster*." *Journal of Experimental Zoology* 170: 61–76. A clever genetic experiment to determine the end of gene activity in development.

Gurdon, J. B. 1968. "Transplanted Nuclei and Cell Differentiation." *Scientific American* (December). A review of nuclear transplantation and the successful cloning of a vertebrate.

Hadorn, E. 1968. "Transdetermination in Cells." *Scientific American* (November). A fascinating look at a puzzling phenomenon.

Hayflick, L. 1980. "The Cell Biology of Human Aging." *Scientific American* (January). This intriguing report suggests that the aging process is a normal, regulated part of development—a point not treated in this textbook.

Hood, L. E., L. Weissman, and W. B. Wood. 1978. *Immunology*. Menlo Park, Calif.: Benjamin/Cummings. A fascinating and relatively easy reading introduction to immunology.

Illmensee, K., and L. C. Stevens. 1979. "Teratomas and Chimeras." *Scientific American* (April). A review of the use of genetic mosaics to analyze development in mammals.

Jonathan, P., et al. 1978. "The Assembly of a Virus." *Scientific American* (November). A study of the assembly of RNA and coat protein to form a functional tobacco mosaic virion.

Lake, J. A. 1981. "The Ribosome." *Scientific American* (August). An intriguing model of ribosome structure and function based on its physical properties.

Leder, P. 1982. "The Genetics of Antibody Diversity." *Scientific American* (May). An excellent review of a complex topic.

Markert, C. L., and H. Ursprung. 1971. *Developmental Genetics*. Englewood Cliffs, NJ: Prentice-Hall. A good short book on the subject.

Milstein, C. 1980. "Monoclonal Antibodies." *Scientific American* (October). This is a description of one of the most powerful techniques of cell biology by the Nobel-prize-winning originator.

Nomura, M. 1984. "The Control of Ribosome Synthesis." *Scientific American* (January).

Ptashne, M., et al. 1982. "Genetic Switch in a Bacterial Virus." *Scientific American* (November). This is the best-understood example of molecular control of gene activity.

Suzuki, D. T. 1970. "Temperature-Sensitive Mutations in *Drosophila melanogaster*." *Science* 170: 695–706. A review of the usefulness of conditional mutations.

Weinberg, R. A. 1983. "The Molecular Basis of Cancer." *Scientific American* (November). The discovery of oncogenes in normal human cells has signaled a radical new approach to cancer study.

Wood, W. B., and R. S. Edgar. 1967. "Building a Bacterial Virus." *Scientific American* (July). A fascinating review of the discovery that virus particles assemble in a specific sequence.

Chapter 22

Bodmer, W. F., and L. L. Cavalli-Sforza. 1970. "Intelligence and Race." *Scientific American* (October). A popular treatment, including a discussion of heritability.

Falconer, D. S. 1981. *Introduction to Quantitative Genetics*, 2d ed. New York: Ronald Press. A widely read text with a strong mathematical emphasis.

Feldman, M. W., and R. C. Lewontin. 1975. "The Heritability Hangup." *Science* 190: 1163–1168. A discussion of the meaning of heritability and its limitations, especially in relation to human intelligence.

Lewontin, R. C. 1974. "The Analysis of Variance and the Analysis of Causes." *American Journal of Human Genetics*. 26: 400–411. A discussion of the meaning of the analysis of variance in genetics as a method for determining the roles of heredity and environment in determining phenotype.

Lewontin, R. C. 1982. *Human Diversity*. New York: Scientific American Books. Includes a discussion of quantitative variation in human populations.

Chapter 23

Beadle, G. W. 1980. "The Ancestry of Corn." *Scientific American* (January). A popular account of the various clues that led to the modern version.

Bodmer, W. F., and L. L. Cavalli-Sforza. 1976. *Genetics, Evolution, and Man*. New York: W. H. Freeman and Co.

Clarke, B. 1975. "The Causes of Biological Diversity." *Scientific American* (August). A popular account emphasizing genetic polymorphism.

Crow, J. F. 1979. "Genes That Violate Mendel's Rules." *Scientific American* (February). An interesting article on a topic called segregation distortion (not treated in this text) and its effects in populations.

Dobzhansky, T. 1951. *Genetics and the Origin of Species*. New York: Columbia University Press. The classic synthesis of population genetics and the processes of evolution. The most influential book on evolution since Darwin's *Origin of Species*.

Ford, E. B. 1971. *Ecological Genetics*, 3d ed. London: Chapman & Hall. A nonmathematical treatment of the role of genetic variation in nature, stressing morphological variation.

Futuyma, D. J. 1979. *Evolutionary Biology*. Sunderland, Mass.: Sinauer Associates. The best modern discussion of population genetics, ecology, and evolution from both a theoretical and an experimental point of view.

Hartl, D. 1980. *Principles of Population Genetics*. Sunderland, Mass: Sinauer Associates.

Lerner, I. M., and W. J. Libby. 1976. *Heredity, Evolution and Society*, 2d ed. New York: W. H. Freeman and Co. A text meant for nonscience students.

Lewontin, R. C. 1974. *The Genetic Basis of Evolutionary Change*. New York: Columbia University Press. A discussion of the prevalence and role of genetic variation in natural populations. Both morphological and protein variations are considered.

Lewontin, R. C. 1982. *Human Diversity*. New York: Scientific American Books. Applies concepts of population genetics to human diversity and evolution.

Scientific American. September 1978. "Evolution." This volume contains several articles relevant to population genetics.

Glossary

A Adenine, or adenosine.

abortive transduction The failure of a transducing DNA segment to be incorporated into the recipient chromosome.

acentric chromosome A chromosome having no centromere.

acrocentric chromosome A chromosome having the centromere located slightly nearer one end than the other.

active site The part of a protein that must be maintained in a specific shape if the protein is to be functional—for example, in an enzyme, the part to which the substrate binds.

adaptation In the evolutionary sense, some heritable feature of an individual's phenotype that improves its chances of survival and reproduction in the existing environment.

adaptive landscape The surface plotted in a three-dimensional graph, with all possible combinations of allele frequencies for different loci plotted in the plane, and mean fitness for each combination plotted in the third dimension.

adaptive peak A high point (perhaps one of several) on an adaptive landscape; selection tends to drive the genotype composition of the population toward a combination corresponding to an adaptive peak.

adaptive surface *See* **adaptive landscape.**

additive genetic variance Genetic variance associated with the average effects of substituting one allele for another.

adenine A purine base that pairs with thymine in the DNA double helix.

adenosine The nucleoside containing adenine as its base.

adenosine triphosphate *See* **ATP.**

adjacent segregation In a reciprocal translocation, the passage of a translocated and a normal chromosome to each of the poles.

ADP Adenosine diphosphate.

Ala Alanine (an amino acid).

alkylating agent A chemical agent that can add alkyl groups (for example, ethyl or methyl groups) to another molecule; many mutagens act through alkylation.

allele One of two or more forms that can exist at a single gene locus, distinguished by their differing effects on the phenotype.

allele frequency A measure of the commonness of an allele in a population; the proportion of all alleles of that gene in the population that are of this specific type.

allopolyploid *See* **amphidiploid.**

allosteric transition A change from one conformation of a protein to another.

alternate segregation In a reciprocal translocation, the passage of both normal chromosomes to one pole and both translocated chromosomes to the other pole.

alternation of generations The alternation of gametophyte and sporophyte stages in the life cycle of a plant.

amber codon The codon UAG, a nonsense codon.

amber suppressor A mutant allele coding for tRNA whose anticodon is altered in such a way that the tRNA inserts an amino acid at an amber codon in translation.

Ames test A widely used test to detect possible chemical carcinogens; based on mutagenicity in the bacterium *Salmonella.*

amino acid A peptide; the basic building block of proteins (or polypeptides).

amniocentesis A technique for testing the genotype of an embryo or fetus in utero with minimal risk to the mother or the child.

AMP Adenosine monophosphate.

amphidiploid An allopolyploid; a polyploid formed from the union of two separate chromosome sets and their subsequent doubling.

amplification The production of many DNA copies from one master region of DNA.

anaphase An intermediate stage of nuclear division during which chromosomes are pulled to the poles of the cell.

aneuploid cell A cell having a chromosome number that differs from the normal chromosome number for the species by a small number of chromosomes.

angstrom (Å) A unit of length equal to 10^{-10} meter; many scientists now prefer to use the nanometer (1 nm = 10^{-9}m = 10 Å).

animal breeding The practical application of genetic analysis for development of pure-breeding lines of domestic animals suited to human purposes.

annealing Spontaneous alignment of two single DNA strands to form a double helix.

antibody A protein (immunoglobulin) molecule, produced by the immune system, that recognizes a particular foreign antigen and binds to it; if the antigen is on the surface of a cell, this binding leads to cell aggregation and subsequent destruction.

anticodon A nucleotide triplet in a tRNA molecule that aligns with a particular codon in mRNA under the influence of the ribosome, so that the peptide carried by the tRNA is inserted in a growing protein chain.

antigen A molecule (typically found in the surface of a cell) whose shape triggers the production of antibodies that will bind to the antigen.

antiparallel A term used to describe the opposite orientations of the two strands of a DNA double helix; the 5′ end of one strand aligns with the 3′ end of the other strand.

AP sites Apurinic or apyrimidinic sites resulting from the loss of a purine or pyrimidine residue from the DNA.

Arg Arginine (an amino acid).

ascospore A sexual spore from certain fungus species in which spores are found in a sac called an ascus.

ascus In fungi, a sac that encloses a tetrad or an octad of ascospores.

asexual spores *See* **spore.**

Asn Asparagine (an amino acid).

Asp Aspartate (an amino acid).

ATP (adenosine triphosphate) The "energy molecule" of cells, synthesized mainly in mitochondria and chloroplasts; energy from the breakdown of ATP drives many important reactions in the cell.

attached X A pair of *Drosophila* X chromosomes joined at one end and inherited as a single unit.

attenuator A region adjacent to the structural genes of the *trp* operon; this region acts in the presence of tryptophan to reduce the rate of transcription from the structural genes.

autonomous controlling element A controlling element that apparently has both regulator and receptor functions combined in the single unit, which enters a gene and causes an unstable mutation.

autopolyploid A polyploid formed from the doubling of a single genome.

autoradiography A process in which radioactive materials are incorporated into cell structures, which are then placed next to a film of photographic emulsion, thus forming a pattern on the film corresponding to the location of the radioactive compounds within the cell.

autosome Any chromosome that is not a sex chromosome.

auxotroph A strain of microorganisms that will proliferate only when the medium is supplemented with some specific substance not required by wild-type organisms.

B chromosomes Small plant chromosomes of variable number between individuals of a species, having no known phenotypic role.

bacteriophage (phage) A virus that infects bacteria.

balanced polymorphism Stable genetic polymorphism maintained by natural selection.

Balbiani ring A large chromosome puff.

Barr body A densely staining mass that represents an X chromosome inactivated by dosage compensation.

base analog A chemical whose molecular structure mimics that of a DNA base; because of the mimicry, the analog may act as a mutagen.

bead theory The disproved hypothesis that genes are arranged on the chromosome like beads on a necklace, indivisible into smaller units of mutation and recombination.

bimodal distribution A statistical distribution having two modes.

binary fission The process in which a parent cell splits into two daughter cells of approximately equal size.

biparental zygote A *Chlamydomonas* zygote that contains cpDNA from both parents; such cells generally are rare.

blastoderm In an insect embryo, the layer of cells that completely surrounds an internal mass of yolk.

blending inheritance A discredited model of inheritance suggesting that the characteristics of an individual result from the smooth blending of fluidlike influences from its parents.

branch migration The process by which a single "invading" DNA strand extends its partial pairing with its complementary strand as it displaces the resident strand.

bridging cross A cross made to transfer alleles between two sexually isolated species by first transferring the alleles to an intermediate species that is sexually compatible with both.

broad heritability (H^2) The proportion of total phenotypic variance at the population level that is contributed by genetic variance.

bud A daughter cell formed by mitosis in yeast; one daughter cell retains the cell wall of the parent, and the other (the bud) forms a new cell wall.

buoyant density A measure of the tendency of a substance to float in some other substance; large molecules are distinguished by their differing buoyant densities in some standard fluid. Measured by density-gradient ultracentrifugation.

C Cytosine, or cytidine.

cAMP (cyclic adenosine monophosphate) A molecule that plays a key role in the regulation of various processes within the cell.

canalized character A character whose phenotype is kept within narrow boundaries even in the presence of disturbing environments or mutations.

cancer A syndrome that involves the uncontrolled and abnormal division of eukaryotic cells.

CAP (catabolite activator protein) A protein whose presence is necessary for the activation of the *lac* operon.

carbon source A nutrient (such as sugar) that provides carbon "skeletons" needed in the organism's synthesis of organic molecules.

carcinogen A substance that causes cancer.

carrier An individual who possesses a mutant allele but does not express it in the phenotype because of a dominant allelic partner; thus, an individual of genotype *Aa* is a carrier of *a* if there is complete dominance of *A* over *a*.

cassette model A model to explain mating-type interconversion in yeast. Information for both *a* and *α* mating types is assumed to be present as silent "cassettes"; a copy of either type of cassette may be transposed to the mating-type locus, where it is "played" (transcribed).

catabolite activator protein *See* **CAP.**

catabolite repression The inactivation of an operon caused by the presence of large amounts of the metabolic end product of the operon.

cation A positively charged ion (such as K$^+$).

cDNA *See* **complementary DNA.**

cell division The process by which two cells are formed from one.

cell lineage A pedigree of cells related through asexual division.

centimorgan (cM) *See* **map unit.**

central dogma The hypothesis that information flows only from DNA to RNA to protein; although some exceptions are now known, the rule is generally valid.

centromere A kinetochore; the constricted region of a nuclear chromosome, to which the spindle fibers attach during division.

character Some attribute of individuals within a species for which various heritable differences can be defined.

character difference Alternative forms of the same attribute within a species.

chase *See* **pulse-chase experiment.**

chiasma (plural, **chiasmata**) A cross-shaped structure commonly observed between nonsister chromatids during meiosis; the site of crossing-over.

chimera *See* **mosaic.**

chi-square (χ^2) test A statistical procedure used to determine whether differences between two sets of values exceed those expected by chance if the two sets were randomly selected from a single large population.

chloroplast A chlorophyll-containing organelle in plants that is the site of photosynthesis.

chromatid One of the two side-by-side replicas produced by chromosome division.

chromatid conversion A type of gene conversion that is inferred from the existence of identical sister-spore pairs in a fungal octad that shows a non-Mendelian allele ratio.

chromatid inference A situation in which the occurrence of a crossover between any two nonsister chromatids can be shown to affect the probability of those chromatids being involved in other crossovers in the same meiosis.

chromatin The substance of chromosomes; now known to include DNA, chromosomal proteins, and chromosomal RNA.

chromocenter The point at which the polytene chromosomes appear to be attached together.

chromomere A small beadlike structure visible on a chromosome during prophase of meiosis and mitosis.

chromosome A linear end-to-end arrangement of genes and other DNA, sometimes with associated protein and RNA.

chromosome aberration Any type of change in the chromosome structure or number.

chromosome loss Failure of a chromosome to become incorporated into a daughter nucleus at cell division.

chromosome map *See* **linkage map.**

chromosome mutation *See* **chromosome aberration.**

chromosome puff A swelling at a site along the length of a polytene chromosome; the site of active transcription.

chromosome rearrangement A chromosome aberration involving new juxtapositions of chromosome parts.

chromosome set The group of different chromosomes that carries the basic set of genetic information for a particular species.

chromosome theory of inheritance The unifying theory stating that inheritance patterns may be generally explained by assuming that genes are located in specific sites on chromosomes.

cis conformation In a heterozygote involving two mutant sites within a gene or gene cluster, the arrangement $a_1a_2 / + +$.

cis dominance The ability of a gene to affect genes next to it on the same chromosome.

cis-trans test A test to determine whether two mutant sites of a gene are in the same functional unit or gene.

cistron Originally defined as a functional genetic unit within which two mutations cannot complement. Now equated with the term gene, as the region of DNA that encodes a single polypeptide (or functional RNA molecule such as tRNA or rRNA).

clone (1) A group of genetically identical cells or individuals derived by asexual division from a common ancestor. (2) *(colloquial)* An individual formed by some asexual process so that it is genetically identical to its "parent." (3) *See* **DNA clone.**

cM (centimorgan) *See* **map unit.**

code dictionary A listing of the 64 possible codons and their translational meanings (the corresponding amino acids).

codominance The situation in which a heterozygote shows the phenotypic effects of both alleles equally.

codon A section of DNA (three nucleotide pairs in length) that codes for a single amino acid.

coefficient of coincidence The ratio of the observed number of double recombinants to the expected number.

colinearity The correspondence between the location of a mutant site within a gene and the location of an amino-acid substitution within the polypeptide translated from that gene.

colony A visible clone of cells.

compartmentalization The existence of boundaries within the organism beyond which a specific clone of cells will never extend during development.

complementary DNA (cDNA) Synthetic DNA transcribed from a specific RNA through the action of the enzyme reverse transcriptase.

complementary gene action Intergenic complementation between mutant alleles at different loci to give wild-type phenotype.

complementary RNA (cRNA) Synthetic RNA produced by transcription from a specific DNA single-stranded template.

complementation The production of a wild-type phenotype when two different mutations are combined in a diploid or a heterokaryon.

complementation test *See* **cis-trans test.**

conditional mutation A mutation that has the wild-type phenotype under certain (permissive) environmental conditions and a mutant phenotype under other (restrictive) conditions.

conjugation The union of two bacterial cells, during which chromosomal material is transferred from the donor to the recipient cell.

conjugation tube *See* **pilus.**

conservative replication A disproved model of DNA synthesis suggesting that one-half of the daughter DNA molecules should have both strands composed of newly polymerized nucleotides.

constant region A region of an antibody molecule that is nearly identical with the corresponding regions of antibodies of different specificities.

constitutive heterochromatin Specific regions of heterochromatin always present and in both homologs of a chromosome.

controlling element A mobile genetic element capable of producing an unstable mutant target gene; two types exist, the regulator and the receptor elements.

copy-choice model A model of the mechanism for crossing-over, suggesting that crossing-over occurs during chromosome division and can occur only between two supposedly "new" nonsister chromatids; the experimental evidence does not support this model.

correction The production (possibly by excision and repair) of a properly paired nucleotide pair from a sequence of hybrid DNA that contains an illegitimate pair.

correlation coefficient A statistical measure of the extent to which variations in one variable are related to variations in another.

cosegregation In *Chlamydomonas*, parallel behavior of different chloroplast markers in a cross, due to their close linkage on cpDNA.

cotransduction The simultaneous transduction of two bacterial marker genes.

cotransformation The simultaneous transformation of two bacterial marker genes.

coupling conformation Linked heterozygous gene pairs in the arrangement *A B / a b.*

covariance A statistical measure used in computing the correlation coefficient between two variables; the covariance is the sum of $(x - \bar{x})(y - \bar{y})$ over all pairs of values for the variables x and y, where $\bar{x}$ is the mean of the x values and $\bar{y}$ is the mean of the y values.

cpDNA Chloroplast DNA.

cri-du-chat syndrome An abnormal human condition caused by deletion of part of one homolog of chromosome 5.

crisscross inheritance Transmission of a gene from male parent to female child to male grandchild—for example, X-linked inheritance.

cRNA *See* **complementary RNA.**

cross The deliberate mating of two parental types of organisms in genetic analysis.

crossing-over The exchange of corresponding chromosome parts between homologs by breakage and reunion.

crossover suppressor An inversion (usually complex) that makes pairing and crossing-over impossible.

cruciform configuration A region of DNA with palindromic sequences in both strands, so that each strand pairs with itself to form a helix extending sideways from the main helix.

CSAR (cytoplasmic segregation and recombination) An acronym used in this book to describe the process whereby organelle-based genes assort and recombine in a cytohet.

culture Tissue or cells multiplying by asexual division, grown for experimentation.

cyclic adenosine monophosphate *See* **cAMP.**

Cys Cysteine (an amino acid).

cytidine The nucleoside containing cytosine as its base.

cytochromes A class of proteins, found in mitochondrial membranes, whose main function is oxidative phosphorylation of ADP to form ATP.

cytogenetics The cytological approach to genetics, mainly involving microscopic studies of chromosomes.

cytohet A cell containing two genetically distinct types of a specific organelle.

cytoplasm The material between the nuclear and cell membranes; includes fluid (cytosol), organelles, and various membranes.

cytoplasmic inheritance Inheritance via genes found in cytoplasmic organelles.

cytosine A pyrimidine base that pairs with guanine.

cytosol The fluid portion of the cytoplasm, outside the organelles.

Darwinian fitness The relative probability of survival and reproduction for a genotype.

degenerate code A genetic code in which some amino acids may be encoded by more than one codon each.

deletion Removal of a chromosomal segment from a chromosome set.

denaturation The separation of the two strands of a DNA double helix, or the severe disruption of the structure of any complex molecule without breaking the major bonds of its chains.

denaturation map A map of a stretch of DNA showing the locations of local denaturation loops, which correspond to regions of high AT content.

deoxyribonuclease *See* **DNase.**

deoxyribonucleic acid *See* **DNA.**

development The process whereby a single cell becomes a differentiated organism.

developmental noise The influence of random molecular processes on development.

dicentric chromosome A chromosome with two centromeres.

dihybrid cross A cross between two individuals identically heterozygous at two loci—for example, *Aa Bb × Aa Bb.*

dimorphism A "polymorphism"involving only two forms.

dioecious plant A plant species in which male and female organs appear on separate individuals.

diploid A cell having two chromosome sets, or an individual having two chromosome sets in each of its cells.

directional selection Selection that changes the frequency of an allele in a constant direction, either toward or away from fixation for that allele.

dispersive replication Disproved model of DNA synthesis suggesting more-or-less random interspersion of parental and new segments in daughter DNA molecules.

distribution *See* **statistical distribution.**

distribution function A graph of some precise quantitative measure of a character against its frequency of occurrence.

DNA (deoxyribonucleic acid) A double chain of linked nucleotides (having deoxyribose as their sugars); the fundamental substance of which genes are composed.

DNA clone A section of DNA that has been inserted into a vector molecule, such as a plasmid or a phage chromosome, and then replicated to form many copies.

DNA polymerase An enzyme that can synthesize new DNA strands using a DNA template; several such enzymes exist.

DNase (deoxyribonuclease) An enzyme that degrades DNA to nucleotides.

dominance variance Genetic variance at a single locus attributable to dominance of one allele over another.

dominant allele An allele that expresses its phenotypic effect even when heterozygous with a recessive allele; thus if *A* is dominant over *a*, then *AA* and *Aa* have the same phenotype.

dominant phenotype The phenotype of a genotype containing the dominant allele; the parental phenotype that is expressed in a heterozygote.

dosage compensation (1) Inactivation of X chromosomes in mammals so that no cell has more than one functioning X chromosome. (2) Regulation at some autosomal loci so that homozygous dominants do not produce twice as much product as the heterozygote.

dose *See* **gene dose.**

double crossover Two crossovers occurring in a chromosomal region under study.

double helix The structure of DNA first proposed by Watson and Crick, with two interlocking helices joined by hydrogen bonds between paired bases.

double infection Infection of a bacterium with two genetically different phages.

Down's syndrome An abnormal human phenotype including mental retardation, due to a trisomy of chromosome 21; more common in babies born to older mothers.

drift *See* **random genetic drift.**

duplicate genes Two identical allele pairs in one diploid individual.

duplication More than one copy of a particular chromosomal segment in a chromosome set.

dyad A pair of sister chromatids joined at the centromere, as in the first division of meiosis.

ecdysone A molting hormone in insects.

electrophoresis A technique for separating the components of a mixture of molecules (proteins, DNAs, or RNAs) in an electric field within a gel.

endogenote *See* **merozygote.**

endonuclease An enzyme that cleaves the phosphodiester bond within a nucleotide chain.

endopolyploidy An increase in the number of chromosome sets caused by replication without cell division.

endosperm Triploid tissue in a seed, formed from fusion of two haploid female and one haploid male nucleus.

enforced outbreeding Deliberate avoidance of mating between relatives.

enucleate cell A cell having no nucleus.

environment The combination of all the conditions external to the genome that potentially affect its expression and its structure.

environmental variance The variance due to environmental variation.

enzyme A protein that functions as a catalyst.

episome A genetic element in bacteria that can replicate free in the cytoplasm or can be inserted into the main bacterial chromosome and replicate with the chromosome.

epistasis A situation in which an allele of one gene obliterates the phenotypic expression of all allelic alternatives of another gene.

equational division A nuclear division that maintains the same ploidy level of the cell.

ethidium A molecule that can intercalate into DNA double helices when the helix is under torsional stress.

euchromatin A chromosomal region that stains normally; thought to contain the normally functioning genes.

eugenics Controlled human breeding based on notions of desirable and undesirable genotypes.

eukaryote An organism having eukaryotic cells.

eukaryotic cell A cell containing a nucleus.

euploid A cell having any number of complete chromosome sets, or an individual composed of such cells.

excision repair The repair of a DNA lesion by removal of the faulty DNA segment and its replacement with a wild-type segment.

exconjugant A female bacterial cell that has just been in conjugation with a male and that contains a fragment of male DNA.

exogenote *See* **merozygote.**

exon Any non-intron section of the coding sequence of a

gene; together, the exons constitute the mRNA and are translated into protein.

exonuclease An enzyme that cleaves nucleotides one at a time from an end of a polynucleotide chain.

expressivity The degree to which a particular genotype is expressed in the phenotype.

F⁻ cell In *E. coli*, a cell having no fertility factor; a female cell.

F⁺ cell In *E. coli*, a cell having a free fertility factor; a male cell.

F factor *See* **fertility factor.**

F′ factor A fertility factor into which a portion of the bacterial chromosome has been incorporated.

F₁ generation The first filial generation, produced by crossing two parental lines.

F₂ generation The second filial generation, produced by selfing or intercrossing the F₁.

facultative heterochromatin Heterochromatin located in positions that are composed of euchromatin in other individuals of the same species, or even in the other homolog of a chromosome pair.

familial trait A trait shared by members of a family.

family selection A breeding technique of selecting a pair on the basis of the average performance of their progeny.

fate map A map of an embryo showing areas that are destined to develop into specific adult tissues and organs.

fertility factor (F factor) A bacterial episome whose presence confers donor ability (maleness).

filial generations Successive generations of progeny in a controlled series of crosses, starting with two specific parents (the P generation) and selfing or intercrossing the progeny of each new (F₁, F₂, . . .) generation.

filter enrichment A technique for recovering auxotrophic mutants in filamentous fungi.

fingerprint The characteristic spot pattern produced by electrophoresis of the polypeptide fragments obtained through denaturation of a particular protein with a proteolytic enzyme.

first-division segregation pattern A linear pattern of spore phenotypes within the ascus for a particular allele pair, produced when the alleles go into separate nuclei at the first meiotic division, showing that no crossover has occurred between that allele pair and the centromere.

fitness *See* **Darwinian fitness.**

fixed allele An allele for which all members of the population under study are homozygous, so that no other alleles for this locus exist in the population.

fixed breakage point According to the heteroduplex DNA recombination model, the point from which unwinding of the DNA double helices begins, as a prelude to formation of heteroduplex DNA.

fluctuation test A test used in microbes to establish the random nature of mutation, or to measure mutation rates.

fMet *See* **formylmethionine.**

focus map A fate map of areas of the *Drosophila* blastoderm destined to become specific adult structures, based on the frequencies of specific kinds of mosaics.

formylmethionine (fMet) A specialized amino acid that is the very first one incorporated into the polypeptide chain in the synthesis of proteins.

forward mutation A mutation that converts a wild-type allele to a mutant allele.

frame-shift mutation The insertion or deletion of a nucleotide pair or pairs, causing a disruption of the translational reading frame.

frequency-dependent fitness Fitness differences whose intensity changes with changes in the relative frequency of genotypes in the population.

frequency-dependent selection Selection that involves frequency-dependent fitness.

frequency histogram A "step curve" in which the frequencies of various arbitrarily bounded classes are graphed.

frequency-independent fitness Fitness that is not determined by interactions with other individuals of the same species.

frequency-independent selection Selection in which the fitnesses of genotypes are independent of their relative frequency in the population.

fruiting body In fungi, the organ in which meiosis occurs and sexual spores are produced.

G Guanine, or guanosine.

gamete A specialized haploid cell that fuses with a gamete from the opposite sex or mating type to form a diploid zygote; in mammals, an egg or a sperm.

gametophyte The haploid gamete-producing stage in the life cycle of plants; prominent and independent in some species but reduced or parasitic in others.

gene The fundamental physical and functional unit of heredity, which carries information from one generation to the next; a segment of DNA, composed of a transcribed region and a regulatory sequence, that makes possible transcription.

gene conversion A meiotic process of directed change in which one allele directs the conversion of a partner allele to its own form.

gene dose The number of copies of a particular gene present in the genome.

gene family A set of genes descended from the same ancestral gene.

gene frequency *See* **allele frequency.**

gene interaction The collaboration of several different genes in the production of one phenotypic character (or related group of characters).

gene locus The specific place on a chromosome where a gene is located.

gene map A linear designation of mutant sites within a gene, based upon the various frequencies of interallelic (intragenic) recombination.

gene mutation A point mutation that results from changes within the structure of a gene.

gene pair The two copies of a particular type of gene present in a diploid cell (one in each chromosome set).

generalized transduction The ability of certain phages to transduce any gene in the bacterial chromosome.

genetic code The set of correspondences between nucleotide pair triplets in DNA and amino acids in protein.

genetic dissection The use of recombination and mutation to piece together the various components of a given biological function.

genetic markers Alleles used as experimental probes to keep track of an individual, a tissue, a cell, a nucleus, a chromosome, or a gene.

genetic variance The phenotypic variance due to the presence of different genotypes in the population.

genetics (1) The study of genes through their variation. (2) The study of inheritance.

genome The entire complement of genetic material in a chromosome set.

genotype The specific allelic composition of a cell—either of the entire cell or, more commonly, for a certain gene or a set of genes.

germinal mutations Mutations occurring in the cells that are destined to develop into gametes.

Gln Glutamine (an amino acid).

Glu Glutamate (an amino acid).

Gly Glycine (an amino acid).

gradient A gradual change in some quantitative property over a specific distance.

guanine A purine base that pairs with cytosine.

guanosine The nucleoside having guanine as its base.

gynandromorph A sexual mosaic.

half-chromatid conversion A type of gene conversion that is inferred from the existence of nonidentical sister spores in a fungal octad showing a non-Mendelian allele ratio.

haploid A cell having one chromosome set, or an organism composed of such cells.

haploidization Production of a haploid from a diploid by progressive chromosome loss.

Hardy-Weinberg equilibrium The presence in a population of the three genotypes AA, Aa, and aa in the frequencies p^2, $2pq$, and q^2, respectively (where p and q are the frequencies of the alleles A and a). At these genotype frequencies, there is no change from one generation to the next.

harlequin chromosomes Sister chromatids that stain differently, so that one appears dark and the other light.

hemizygous gene A gene present in only one copy in a diploid organism—for example, X-linked genes in a male mammal.

hemoglobin (Hb) The oxygen-transporting blood protein in animals.

heredity The similarity among offspring and parents.

heritability in the broad sense *See* **broad heritability.**

heritability in the narrow sense (h²) The proportion of phenotypic variance that can be attributed to additive genetic variance.

hermaphrodite (1) A plant species in which male and female organs occur in the same flower of a single individual (*compare* **monoecious plant**). (2) An animal with both male and female sex organs.

heterochromatin Densely staining condensed chromosomal regions, believed to be for the most part genetically inert.

heteroduplex A DNA double helix formed by annealing single strands from different sources; if there is a structural difference between the strands, the heteroduplex may show such abnormalities as loops or buckles.

heteroduplex DNA model A model that explains both crossing-over and gene conversion by assuming the production of a short stretch of heteroduplex DNA (formed from both parental DNAs) in the vicinity of a chiasma.

heterogametic sex The sex that has heteromorphic sex chromosomes (for example, XY) and hence produces two different kinds of gametes with respect to the sex chromosomes.

heterogeneous nuclear RNA (HnRNA) A diverse assortment of RNA types found in the nucleus, including mRNA precursors and other types of RNA.

heterokaryon A culture of cells composed of two different nuclear types in a common cytoplasm.

heterokaryon test A test for cytoplasmic mutations, based on new associations of phenotypes in cells derived from specially marked heterokaryons.

heteromorphic chromosomes A chromosome pair with some homology but differing in size, shape, or staining properties.

heterothallic fungus A fungus species in which two different mating types must unite to complete the sexual cycle.

heterozygosity A measure of the genetic variation in a population; with respect to one locus, stated as the frequency of heterozygotes for that locus.

heterozygote An individual having a heterozygous gene pair.

heterozygous gene pair A gene pair having different alleles in the two chromosome sets of the diploid individual—for example, Aa or A^1A^2.

hexaploid A cell having six chromosome sets, or an organism composed of such cells.

high-frequency recombination (Hfr) cell In *E. coli*, a cell having its fertility factor integrated into the bacterial chromosome; a donor (male) cell.

His Histidine (an amino acid).

histocompatibility antigens Antigens that determine the acceptance or rejection of a tissue graft.

histocompatibility genes The genes that code for the histocompatibility antigens.

homeo box Short (~180 bp) homologous sequence found in the 3′ exon of homeotic genes in *Drosophila*. Similar sequences have been found in other organisms. Possibly involved in DNA binding during gene regulation.

homeologous chromosomes Partially homologous chromosomes, usually indicating some original ancestral homology.

homeotic mutations Mutations that can change the fate of an imaginal disk.

homogametic sex The sex with homologous sex chromosomes (for example, XX).

homolog A member of a pair of homologous chromosomes.

homologous chromosomes Chromosomes that are identical in shape, size, and function.

homothallic fungus A fungus species in which a single sexual spore can complete the entire sexual cycle (*compare* **heterothallic fungus**).

homozygote An individual having a homozygous gene pair.

homozygous gene pair A gene pair having identical alleles in both copies—for example, AA or A^1A^1.

host range The spectrum of strains of a given bacterial species that a given strain of phage can infect.

hot spot A part of a gene that shows a very high tendency to become a mutant site, either spontaneously or under the action of a particular mutagen.

hybrid (1) A heterozygote. (2) A progeny individual from any cross involving parents of differing genotypes.

hybrid dysgenesis A syndrome of effects including sterility, mutation, chromosome breakage, and male recombination in the hybrid progeny of crosses between certain laboratory and natural isolates of *Drosophila*.

hybridization in situ Finding the location of a gene by adding specific radioactive probes for the gene and detecting the location of the radioactivity on the chromosome after hybridization.

hybridize (1) To form a hybrid by performing a cross. (2) To anneal nucleic acid strands from different sources.

hydrogen bond A weak bond involving the sharing of an electron with a hydrogen atom; hydrogen bonds are important in the specificity of base pairing in nuclei acids and in determining protein shape.

hydroxyapatite A form of calcium phosphate that binds double-stranded DNA.

hyperploid Aneuploid containing a small number of extra chromosomes.

hypervariable region The part of a variable region that actually determines the specificity of an antibody.

hypha (plural, **hyphae**) A threadlike structure (composed of cells attached end to end) that forms the main tissue in many fungus species.

hypoploid Aneuploid with a small number of chromosomes missing.

Ig *See* **immunoglobulin.**

Ile Isoleucine (an amino acid).

imaginal disk A small group of cells in an insect larva that is destined to develop into an entire adult structure (for example, a leg).

immune system The animal cells and tissues involved in recognizing and attacking foreign substances within the body.

immunoglobulin (Ig) A general term for the kind of globular blood proteins that constitute antibodies.

in situ "In place"; *see* **hybridization in situ.**

in vitro In an experimental situation outside the organism (literally, "in glass").

in vivo In a living cell or organism.

inbreeding Mating between relatives more frequently than would be expected by chance.

inbreeding coefficient The probability of homozygosity that results because the zygote obtains copies of the *same* ancestral gene.

incomplete dominance The situation in which a heterozygote shows a phenotype quantitatively (but not exactly) intermediate between the corresponding homozygote phenotypes. (Exact intermediacy is no dominance.)

independent assortment *See* **Mendel's second law.**

inducer An environmental agent that triggers transcription from an operon.

infectious transfer The rapid transmission of free episomes (plus any chromosomal genes they may carry) from donor to recipient cells in a bacterial population.

inosine A rare base that is important at the wobble position of some tRNA anticodons.

insertion sequence (IS) A mobile piece of bacterial DNA (several hundred nucleotide pairs in length) that is capable of inactivating a gene into which it inserts.

insertional translocation The insertion of a segment from one chromosome into another nonhomologous one.

intercalating agent A chemical that can insert itself between the stacked bases at the center of the DNA double helix, possibly causing a frame-shift mutation.

interchromosomal recombination Recombination resulting from independent assortment.

interference A measure of the independence of crossovers from each other, calculated by subtracting the coefficient of coincidence from 1.

interphase The cell cycle stage between nuclear divisions, in which chromosomes are extended and functionally active.

interrupted mating A technique used to map bacterial genes by determining the sequence in which donor genes enter recipient cells.

interstitial region The chromosomal region between the centromere and the site of a rearrangement.

intervening sequence An intron; a segment of largely unknown function within a gene. This segment is initially transcribed, but it is not found in the functional mRNA.

intrachromosomal recombination Recombination resulting from crossing-over between two gene pairs.

intron *See* **intervening sequence.**

inversion A chromosomal mutation involving the removal of a chromosome segment, its rotation through 180 degrees, and its reinsertion in the same location.

inverted repeat (IR) sequence A sequence found in identical (but inverted) form, for example, at the opposite ends of a transposon.

IR *See* **inverted repeat sequence.**

IS *See* **insertion sequence.**

isoaccepting tRNAs The various types of tRNA molecules that carry a specific amino acid.

isotope One of several forms of an atom having the same atomic number but differing atomic masses.

karyotype The entire chromosome complement of an individual or cell, as seen during mitotic metaphase.

kinetochore *See* **centromere.**

Klinefelter's syndrome An abnormal human male phenotype involving an extra X chromosome (XXY).

λ (lambda) phage One kind ("species") of temperate bacteriophage.

λdgal A λ phage carrying a *gal* bacterial gene and defective *(d)* for some phage function.

lampbrush chromosomes Large chromosomes found in amphibian eggs, with lateral DNA loops that produce a brushlike appearance under the microscope.

lawn A continuous layer of bacteria on the surface of an agar medium.

leader sequence The sequence at the 5′ end of an mRNA that is not translated into protein.

leaky mutant A mutant (typically, an auxotroph) that results from a partial rather than a complete inactivation of the wild-type function.

lesion   A damaged area in a gene (a mutant site), a chromosome, or a protein.

lethal gene   A gene whose expression results in the death of the individual expressing it.

Leu   Leucine (an amino acid).

ligase   An enzyme that can rejoin a broken phosphodiester bond in a nucleic acid.

line   A group of identical pure-breeding diploid or polyploid organisms, distinguished from other individuals of the same species by some unique phenotype and genotype.

linear tetrad   A tetrad that results from the occurrence of the meiotic and postmeiotic nuclear divisions in such a way that sister products remain adjacent to one another (with no passing of nuclei).

linkage   The association of genes on the same chromosome.

linkage group   A group of genes known to be linked; a chromosome.

linkage map   A chromosome map; an abstract map of chromosomal loci, based on recombinant frequencies.

locus (plural, **loci**)   *See* **gene locus.**

Lys   Lysine (an amino acid).

lysis   The rupture and death of a bacterial cell upon the release of phage progeny.

lysogen   *See* **lysogenic bacterium.**

lysogenic bacterium   A bacterial cell capable of spontaneous lysis due, for example, to the uncoupling of a prophage from the bacterial chromosome.

macromolecule   A large polymer such as DNA, a protein, or a polysaccharide.

map unit (m.u.)   The "distance" between two linked gene pairs where 1 percent of the products of meiosis are recombinant; a unit of distance in a linkage map.

mapping function   A formula expressing the relationship between distance in a linkage map and recombinant frequency.

marker   *See* **genetic markers.**

marker retention   A technique used in yeast to test the degree of linkage between two mitochondrial mutations.

maternal effect   The environmental influence of the mother's tissues on the phenotype of the offspring.

maternal inheritance   A type of uniparental inheritance in which all progeny have the genotype and phenotype of the parent acting as the female.

mating types   The equivalent in lower organisms of the sexes in higher organisms; the mating types typically differ only physiologically and not in physical form.

matroclinous inheritance   Inheritance in which all offspring have the nucleus-determined phenotype of the mother.

mean   The arithmetic average.

medium   Any material on (or in) which experimental cultures are grown.

meiocyte   Cell in which meiosis occurs.

meiosis   Two successive nuclear divisions (with corresponding cell divisions) that produce gametes (in animals) or sexual spores (in plants and fungi) having one-half of the genetic material of the original cell.

meiospore   Cell that is one of the products of meiosis in plants.

melting   Denaturation of DNA.

Mendelian ratio   A ratio of progeny phenotypes reflecting the operation of Mendel's laws.

Mendel's first law   The two members of a gene pair segregate from each other during meiosis; each gamete has an equal probability of obtaining either member of the gene pair.

Mendel's second law   The law of independent assortment; unlinked or distantly linked segregating gene pairs behave independently.

merozygote   A partially diploid *E. coli* cell formed from a complete chromosome (the endogenote) plus a fragment (the exogenote).

messenger RNA   *See* **mRNA.**

Met   Methionine (an amino acid).

metabolism   The chemical reactions that occur in a living cell.

metacentric chromosome   A chromosome having its centromere in the middle.

metaphase   An intermediate stage of nuclear division when chromosomes align along the equatorial plane of the cell.

midparent value   The mean of the values of a quantitative phenotype for two specific parents.

minimal medium   A medium containing only inorganic salts, a carbon source, and water.

missense mutation   A mutation that alters a codon so that it encodes a different amino acid.

mitochondrion   A eukaryotic organelle that is the site of ATP synthesis and of the citric acid cycle.

mitosis   A type of nuclear division (occurring at cell division) that produces two daughter nuclei identical to the parent nucleus.

mitotic crossover   A crossover resulting from the pairing of homologs in a mitotic diploid.

mobile genetic element   *See* **transposable genetic element.**

mode   The single class in a statistical distribution having the greatest frequency.

modifier gene   A gene that affects the phenotypic expression of another gene.

molecular genetics   The study of the molecular processes underlying gene structure and function.

monocistronic mRNA   An mRNA that codes for one protein.

monoecious plant   A plant species in which male and female organs are found on the same plant but in different flowers (for example, corn).

monohybrid cross   A cross between two individuals identically heterozygous at one gene pair—for example, $Aa \times Aa$.

monoploid   A cell having only one chromosome set (usually as an aberration), or an organism composed of such cells.

monosomic   A cell or individual that is basically diploid but that has only one copy of one particular chromosome type and thus has chromosome number $2n - 1$.

mosaic   A chimera; a tissue containing two or more genetically distinct cell types, or an individual composed of such tissues.

mRNA (messenger RNA)   An RNA molecule transcribed from the DNA of a gene, and from which a protein is translated by the action of ribosomes.

mtDNA   Mitochondrial DNA.

m.u.   *See* **map unit.**

mu **phage**   A kind ("species") of phage with properties similar to those of insertion sequences, being able to insert, transpose, inactivate, and cause rearrangements.

multimeric structure   A structure composed of several identical or different subunits held together by weak bonds.

multiple allelism   The existence of several known alleles of a gene.

multiple-factor hypothesis   A hypothesis to explain quantitative variation by assuming the interaction of a large number of genes (polygenes), each with a small additive effect on the character.

multiplicity of infection   The average number of phage particles that infect a single bacterial cell in a specific experiment.

mutagen   An agent that is capable of increasing the mutation rate.

mutant   An organism or cell carrying a mutation.

mutant allele   An allele differing from the allele found in the standard, or wild-type.

mutant hunt   The process of accumulating different mutants showing abnormalities in a certain structure or function, as a preparation for mutational dissection of that function.

mutant site   The damaged or altered area within a mutated gene.

mutation   (1) The process that produces a gene or a chromosome set differing from the wild-type. (2) The gene or chromosome set that results from such a process.

mutation breeding   Use of mutagens to develop variants that can increase agricultural yield.

mutation event   The actual occurrence of a mutation in time and space.

mutation frequency   The frequency of mutants in a population.

mutation rate   The number of mutation events per gene per unit of time (for example, per cell generation).

mutational dissection   The study of the components of a biological function through a study of mutations affecting that function.

muton   The smallest part of a gene that can be involved in a mutation event; now known to be a nucleotide pair.

myeloma   A cancer of the bone marrow.

narrow heritability   *See* **heritability in the narrow sense.**

negative assortative mating   Preferential mating between phenotypically unlike partners.

negative control   Regulation mediated by factors that block or turn off transcription.

Neurospora   A pink mold, commonly found growing on old food.

neutral mutation   (1) A mutation that has no adaptive significance. (2) A mutation that has no phenotypic effect.

neutral petite   A petite that produces all wild-type progeny when crossed with wild-type.

neutrality   *See* **selective neutrality.**

nicking   Nuclease action to sever the sugar-phosphate backbone in one DNA strand at one specific site.

nitrocellulose filter   A type of filter used to hold DNA for hybridization.

nitrogen bases   Types of molecules that form important parts of nucleic acids, composed of nitrogen-containing ring structures; hydrogen bonds between bases link the two strands of a DNA double helix.

nondisjunction   The failure of homologs (at meiosis) or sister chromatids (at mitosis) to separate properly to opposite poles.

nonlinear tetrad   A tetrad in which the meiotic products are in no particular order.

non-Mendelian ratio   An unusual ratio of progeny phenotypes that does not reflect the simple operation of Mendel's laws; for example, mutant: wild ratios of 3:5, 5:3, 6:2, or 2:6 in tetrads indicate that gene conversion has occurred.

nonparental ditype (NPD)   A tetrad type containing two different genotypes, both of which are recombinant.

nonsense codon   A codon for which no normal tRNA molecule exists; the presence of a nonsense codon causes termination of translation (the end of the polypeptide chain). The three nonsense codons are called amber, ocher, and opal.

nonsense mutation   A mutation that alters a gene so as to produce a nonsense codon.

nonsense suppressor   A mutation that produces an altered tRNA that will insert an amino acid during translation in response to a nonsense codon.

norm of reaction   The pattern of phenotypes produced by a given genotype under different environmental conditions.

NPD   *See* **nonparental ditype.**

nu body   *See* **nucleosome.**

nuclease   An enzyme that can degrade DNA by breaking its phosphodiester bonds.

nucleoid   A DNA mass within a chloroplast or mitochondrion.

nucleolar organizer   A region (or regions) of the chromosome set physically associated with the nucleolus and containing rRNA genes.

nucleolus   An organelle found in the nucleus, containing rRNA and amplified multiple copies of the genes coding for rRNA.

nucleoside   A nitrogen base bound to a sugar molecule.

nucleosome   A nu body; the basic unit of eukaryotic chromosome structure; a ball of eight histone molecules wrapped about by two coils of DNA.

nucleotide   A molecule composed of a nitrogen base, a sugar, and a phosphate group; the basic building block of nucleic acids.

nucleotide pair   A pair of nucleotides (one in each strand of DNA) that are joined by hydrogen bonds.

nucleotide-pair substitution   The replacement of a specific nucleotide pair by a different pair; often mutagenic.

null allele   An allele whose effect is either an absence of normal gene product at the molecular level or an absence of normal function at the phenotypic level.

nullisomic   A cell or individual with one chromosomal type missing, with a chromosome number such as $n - 1$ or $2n - 2$.

ocher codon   The codon UAA, a nonsense codon.

octad   An ascus containing eight ascospores, produced in species in which the tetrad normally undergoes a postmeiotic mitotic division.

oncogene A gene that causes cancer.

opal codon The codon UGA, a nonsense codon.

open reading frame A nucleotide sequence with no stop codons, discovered by sequencing.

operator A DNA region at one end of an operon that acts as the binding site for repressor protein.

operon A set of adjacent structural genes whose mRNA is synthesized in one piece, plus the adjacent regulatory signals that affect transcription of the structural genes.

organelle A subcellular structure having a specialized function—for example, the mitochondrion, the chloroplast, or the spindle apparatus.

origin of replication The point or specific sequence at which DNA replication is initiated.

overdominance A phenotypic relation in which the phenotypic expression of the heterozygote is greater than that of either homozygote.

palindrome A sequence of DNA that is the same when each strand is read in the same direction.

paracentric inversion An inversion not involving the centromere.

parental ditype (PD) A tetrad type containing two different genotypes, both of which are parental.

partial diploid *See* **merozygote.**

particulate inheritance The model proposing that genetic information is transmitted from one generation to the next in discrete units ("particles"), so that the character of the offspring is not a smooth blend of essences from the parents (*compare* **blending inheritance**).

pathogen An organism that causes disease in another organism.

patroclinous inheritance Inheritance in which all offspring have the nucleus-based phenotype of the father.

PD *See* **parental ditype.**

pedigree A "family tree," drawn with standard genetic symbols, showing inheritance patterns for specific phenotypic characters.

penetrance The proportion of individuals with a specific genotype who manifest that genotype at the phenotype level.

peptide *See* **amino acid.**

peptide bond A bond joining two amino acids.

pericentric inversion An inversion that involves the centromere.

permissive conditions Those environmental conditions under which a conditional mutant shows the wild-type phenotype.

petite A yeast mutation producing small colonies and altered mitochondrial functions. In cytoplasmic petites (neutral and suppressive petites), the mutation is a deletion in mitochondrial DNA; in segregational petites, the mutation occurs in nuclear DNA.

phage *See* **bacteriophage.**

Phe Phenylalanine (an amino acid).

phenocopy An evironmentally induced phenotype that resembles the phenotype produced by a mutation.

phenotype (1) The form taken by some character (or group of characters) in a specific individual. (2) The detectable outward manifestations of a specific genotype.

phenotypic sex determination Sex determination by nongenetic means.

Philadelphia chromosome A translocation between the long arms of chromosomes 9 and 22, often found in the white blood cells of patients with chronic myeloid leukemia.

phosphodiester bond A bond between a sugar group and a phosphate group; such bonds form the sugar-phosphate backbone of DNA.

pilus (plural, **pili**) A conjugation tube; a hollow hairlike appendage of a donor *E. coli* cell that acts as a bridge for transmission of donor DNA to the recipient cell during conjugation.

plant breeding The application of genetic analysis to development of plant lines better suited for human purposes.

plaque A clear area on a bacterial lawn, left by lysis of the bacteria through progressive infections by a phage and its descendants.

plasmid Autonomously replicating extrachromosomal DNA molecule.

plate (1) A flat dish used to culture microbes. (2) To spread cells over the surface of solid medium in a plate.

pleiotropic mutation A mutation that has effects on several different characters.

point mutation A mutation that can be mapped to one specific locus.

Poisson distribution A statistical equation that describes the process of sampling in situations where the number of events per sample is potentially very large but in practice is very small.

poky A slow-growing mitochondrial mutant in *Neurospora*.

polar gene conversion A gradient of conversion frequency along the length of a gene.

polar granules Granules at the anterior end of the cytoplasm of a *Drosophila* egg.

polar mutation A mutation that affects the transcription or translation of the part of the gene or operon only on one side of the mutant site—for example, nonsense mutations, frame-shift mutations, and IS-induced mutations.

poly-A tail A string of adenine nucleotides added to mRNA after transcription.

polyacrilamide A material used to make electrophoretic gels for separation of mixtures of macromolecules.

polycistronic mRNA An mRNA that codes for more than one protein.

polygenes *See* **multiple-factor hypothesis.**

polymorphism The occurrence in a population (or among populations) of several phenotypic forms associated with alleles of one gene or homologs of one chromosome.

polypeptide A chain of linked amino acids; a protein.

polyploid A cell having three or more chromosome sets, or an organism composed of such cells.

polysaccharide A biological polymer composed of sugar subunits—for example, starch or cellulose.

polytene chromosome A giant chromosome produced by an endomitotic process in which the multiple DNA sets remain bound in a haploid number of chromosomes.

position effect Used to describe a situation where the phenotypic influence of a gene is altered by changes in the position of the gene within the genome.

position-effect variegation Variegation caused by the inactivation of a gene in some cells through its abnormal juxtaposition with heterochromatin.

positive assortative mating A situation in which like phenotypes mate more commonly than expected by chance.

positive control Regulation mediated by a protein that is required for the activation of a transcription unit.

primary structure of a protein The sequence of amino acids in the polypeptide chain.

Pro Proline (an amino acid).

probe Defined nucleic acid segment that can be used to identify specific DNA molecules bearing the complementary sequence, usually through autoradiography.

product of meiosis One of the (usually four) cells formed by the two meiotic divisions.

product rule The probability of two independent events occurring simultaneously is the product of the individual probabilities.

proflavin A mutagen that tends to produce frame-shift mutations.

prokaryote An organism composed of a prokaryotic cell, such as bacteria and blue-green algae.

prokaryotic cell A cell having no nuclear membrane and hence no separate nucleus.

promoter A regulatory region a short distance from the 5′ end of a gene that acts as the binding site for RNA polymerase.

prophage A phage "chromosome" inserted as part of the linear structure of the DNA chromosome of a bacterium.

prophase The early stage of nuclear division during which chromosomes condense and become visible.

propositus In a human pedigree, the individual who first came to the attention of the geneticist.

proto-oncogene A gene that, when mutated or otherwise affected, becomes an oncogene.

protoplast A plant cell whose wall has been removed.

prototroph A strain of organisms that will proliferate on minimal medium (*compare* **auxotroph**).

provirus A virus "chromosome" integrated into the DNA of the host cell.

pseudodominance The sudden appearance of a recessive phenotype in a pedigree, due to deletion of a masking dominant gene.

pseudogene An inactive gene derived from an ancestral active gene.

puff *See* **chromosome puff.**

pulse-chase experiment An experiment in which cells are grown in radioactive medium for a brief period (the pulse) and then transferred to nonradioactive medium for a longer period (the chase).

Punnett square A grid used as a graphic representation of the progeny zygotes resulting from different gamete fusions in a specific cross.

pure-breeding line or strain A group of identical individuals that always produce offspring of the same phenotype when intercrossed.

purine A type of nitrogen base; the purine bases in DNA are adenine and guanine.

pyrimidine A type of nitrogen base; the pyrimidine bases in DNA are cytosine and thymine.

quantitative variation The existence of a range of phenotypes for a specific character, differing by degree rather than by distinct qualitative differences.

quaternary structure of a protein The multimeric constitution of the protein.

R plasmid A plasmid containing one or several transposons that bear resistance genes.

random genetic drift Changes in allele frequency that result because the genes appearing in offspring do not represent a perfectly representative sampling of the parental genes.

random mating Mating between individuals where the choice of a partner is not influenced by their genotypes (with respect to specific genes under study).

reading frame The codon sequence that is determined by reading nucleotides in groups of three from some specific start codon.

realized heritability The ratio of the single-generation progress of selection to the selection differential of the parents.

reannealing Spontaneous realignment of two single DNA strands to re-form a DNA double helix that had been denatured.

receptor element A controlling element that can insert into a gene (making it a mutant) and can also exit (thus making the mutation unstable); both of these functions are nonautonomous, being under the influence of the regulator element.

recessive allele An allele whose phenotypic effect is not expressed in a heterozygote.

recessive phenotype The phenotype of a homozygote for the recessive allele; the parental phenotype that is not expressed in a heterozygote.

reciprocal crosses A pair of crosses of the type genotype A ♀ × genotype B ♂ and genotype B ♀ × genotype A ♂.

reciprocal translocation A translocation in which part of one chromosome is exchanged with a part of a separate nonhomologous chromosome.

recombinant An individual or cell with a genotype produced by recombination.

recombinant DNA A novel DNA sequence formed by the combination of two nonhomologous DNA molecules.

recombinant frequency (RF) The proportion (or percentage) of recombinant cells or individuals.

recombination (1) In general, any process in a diploid or partially diploid cell that generates new gene or chromosomal combinations not found in that cell or in its progenitors. (2) At meiosis, the process that generates a haploid product of meiosis whose genotype is different from either of the two haploid genotypes that constituted the meiotic diploid.

recombinational repair The repair of a DNA lesion through a process, similar to recombination, that uses recombination enzymes.

recon A region of a gene within which there can be no crossing-over; now known to be a nucleotide pair.

reduction division A nuclear division that produces daughter nuclei each having one-half as many centromeres as the parental nucleus.

redundant DNA *See* **repetitive DNA.**

regression A term coined by Galton for the tendency of the quantitative traits of offspring to be closer to the population mean than are their parents' traits. It arises from nongenetic influences on traits.

regression coefficient The slope of the straight line that most closely relates two correlated variables.

regulator element *See* **receptor element.**

regulatory genes Genes that are involved in turning on or off the transcription of structural genes.

repetitive DNA Redundant DNA; DNA sequences that are present in many copies per chromosome set.

replication DNA synthesis.

replication fork The point at which the two strands of DNA are separated to allow replication of each strand.

replicon A chromosomal region under the influence of one adjacent replication-initiation locus.

repressor protein A molecule that binds to the operator and prevents transcription of an operon.

repulsion conformation Two linked heterozygous gene pairs in the arrangement *A b / a B.*

resolving power The ability of an experimental technique to distinguish between two genetic conditions (typically discussed when one condition is rare and of particular interest).

restriction enzyme An endonuclease that will recognize specific target nucleotide sequences in DNA and break the DNA chain at those points; a variety of these enzymes are known, and they are extensively used in genetic engineering.

restrictive conditions Environmental conditions under which a conditional mutant shows the mutant phenotype.

retrovirus An RNA virus that replicates by first being converted into double-stranded DNA.

reverse transcriptase An enzyme that catalyzes the synthesis of a DNA strand from an RNA template.

reversion The production of a wild-type gene from a mutant gene.

RF *See* **recombinant frequency.**

ribonucleic acid *See* **RNA.**

ribosomal RNA *See* **rRNA.**

ribosome A complex organelle that catalyzes translation of messenger RNA into an amino-acid sequence. Composed of proteins plus rRNA.

RNA (ribonucleic acid) A single-stranded nucleic acid similar to DNA but having ribose sugar rather than deoxyribose sugar and uracil rather than thymine as one of the bases.

RNA polymerase An enzyme that catalyzes the synthesis of an RNA strand from a DNA template.

rRNA (ribosomal RNA) A class of RNA molecules, coded in the nucleolar organizer, that have an integral (but poorly understood) role in ribosome structure and function.

S (Svedberg unit) A unit of sedimentation velocity, commonly used to describe molecular units of various sizes (because sedimentation velocity is related to size).

satellite A terminal section of a chromosome, separated from the main body of the chromosome by a narrow constriction.

satellite chromosomes Chromosomes that seem to be additions to the normal genome.

satellite DNA DNA that forms a separate band in a density gradient because of its different nucleotide composition.

scaffold The central core of a eukaryotic nuclear chromosome, from which DNA loops extend.

SCE *See* **sister-chromatid exchange.**

secondary structure of a protein A spiral or zigzag arrangement of the polypeptide chain.

second-division segregation pattern A pattern of ascospore genotypes for a gene pair showing that the two alleles separate into different nuclei only at the second meiotic division, as a result of a crossover between that gene pair and its centromere; can only be detected in a linear ascus.

second-site mutation The second mutation of a double mutation within a gene; in many cases, the second-site mutation suppresses the first mutation, so that the double mutant has the wild-type phenotype.

sector An area of tissue whose phenotype is detectably different from the surrounding tissue phenotype.

sedimentation The sinking of a molecule under the opposing forces of gravitation and buoyancy.

segregation (1) Cytologically, the separation of homologous structures. (2) Genetically, the production of two separate phenotypes, corresponding to two alleles of a gene, either in different individuals (meiotic segregation) or in different tissues (mitotic segregation).

segregational petite A petite that in a cross with wild-type produces $1/2$ petite and $1/2$ wild-type progeny; caused by a nuclear mutation.

selection coefficient (s) The proportional excess or deficiency of fitness of one genotype in relation to another genotype.

selection differential The difference between the mean of a population and the mean of the individuals selected to be parents of the next generation.

selection progress The difference between the mean of a population and the mean of the offspring in the next generation born to selected parents.

selective neutrality A situation in which different alleles of a certain gene confer equal fitness.

selective system An experimental technique that enhances the recovery of specific (usually rare) genotypes.

self To fertilize eggs with sperms from the same individual.

self-assembly The ability of certain multimeric biological structures to assemble from their component parts through random movements of the molecules and formation of weak chemical bonds between surfaces with complementary shapes.

semiconservative replication The established model of DNA replication in which each double-stranded molecule is composed of one parental strand and one newly polymerized strand.

semisterility The phenotype of individuals heterozygotic for certain types of chromosome aberration; expressed as a reduced number of viable gametes and hence reduced fertility.

senDNA An amplified section of mtDNA found in senescent

Podospora cultures; circular and plasmid-like in nature.

Ser Serine (an amino acid).

sex chromosome A chromosome whose presence or absence is correlated with the sex of the bearer; a chromosome that plays a role in sex determination.

sex linkage The location of a gene on a sex chromosome.

sexduction Sexual transmission of donor *E. coli* chromosomal genes on the fertility factor.

sexual spore *See* **spore.**

shotgun technique Cloning a large number of different DNA fragments as a prelude to selecting one particular clone type for intensive study.

signal sequence The N-terminal sequence of a secreted protein, which is required for transport through the cell membrane.

silent mutation Mutation in which the function of the protein product of the gene is unaltered.

sister-chromatid exchange (SCE) An event similar to crossing-over that can occur between sister chromatids at mitosis or at meiosis; detected in harlequin chromosomes.

site-specific recombination Recombination occurring between two specific sequences that need not be homologous, and mediated by a specific recombination system.

S-9 mix A liver-derived supernatant used in the Ames test to activate or inactivate mutagens.

solenoid structure The supercoiled arrangement of DNA in eukaryotic nuclear chromosomes.

somatic cell A cell that is not destined to become a gamete; a "body cell," whose genes will not be passed on to future generations.

somatic mutation A mutation occurring in a somatic cell.

somatic-cell genetics Asexual genetics, involving study of somatic mutation, assortment, and crossing-over, and of cell fusion.

somatostatin A human growth hormone.

SOS repair The error-prone process whereby gross structural DNA damage is circumvented by allowing replication to proceed past the damage through imprecise polymerization.

spacer DNA Repetitive DNA found between genes; its function is unknown.

specialized (restricted) transduction The situation in which a particular phage will transduce only specific regions of the bacterial chromosome.

specific-locus test A system for detecting recessive mutations in diploids. Normal individuals treated with mutagen are mated to testers that are homozygous for the recessive alleles at a number of specific loci; the progeny are then screened for recessive phenotypes.

spindle The set of microtubular fibers that appear to move eukaryotic chromosomes during division.

splicing The reaction that removes introns and joins together exons in RNA.

spontaneous mutation A mutation occurring in the absence of mutagens, usually due to errors in the normal functioning of cellular enzymes.

spore (1) In plants and fungi, sexual spores are the haploid cells produced by meiosis. (2) In fungi, asexual spores are somatic cells that are cast off to act either as gametes or as the initial cells for new haploid individuals.

sporophyte The diploid sexual-spore-producing generation in the life cycle of plants—that is, the stage in which meiosis occurs.

stacking The packing of the flattish nitrogen bases at the center of the DNA double helix.

staggered cuts The cleavage of two opposite strands of duplex DNA at points near one another.

standard deviation The square root of the variance.

statistic A computed quantity characteristic of a population, such as the mean.

statistical distribution The array of frequencies of different quantitative or qualitative classes in a population.

strain A pure-breeding lineage, usually of haploid organisms, bacteria, or viruses.

structural gene A gene encoding the amino-acid sequence of a protein.

subvital gene A gene that causes the death of some proportion (but not all) of the individuals that express it.

sum rule The probability that one or the other of two mutually exclusive events will occur is the sum of their individual probabilities.

supercoil A closed double-stranded DNA molecule that is twisted on itself.

superinfection Phage infection of a cell that already harbors a prophage.

supersuppressor A mutation that can suppress a variety of other mutations; typically a nonsense suppressor.

suppressive petite A petite that in a cross with wild-type produces progeny of which variable non-Mendelian proportions are petite.

suppressor mutation A mutation that counteracts the effects of another mutation. A suppressor maps at a different site than the mutation it counteracts, either within the same gene or at a more distant locus. Different suppressors act in different ways.

synapsis Close pairing of homologs at meiosis.

synaptonemal complex A complex structure that unites homologs during the prophase of meiosis.

syncytium A single cell with many nuclei.

T (1) Thymine, or thymidine. (2) *See* **tetratype.**

tandem duplication Adjacent identical chromosome segments.

tautomeric shift The spontaneous isomerization of a nitrogen base to an alternative hydrogen-bonding condition, possibly resulting in a mutation.

telocentric chromosome A chromosome having the centromere at one end.

telomere The tip (or end) of a chromosome.

telophase The late stage of nuclear division when daughter nuclei re-form.

temperate phage A phage that can become a prophage.

temperature-sensitive mutation A conditional mutation that produces the mutant phenotype in one temperature range and the wild-type phenotype in another temperature range.

template A molecular "mold" that shapes the structure or sequence of another molecule; for example, the nucleotide sequence of DNA acts as a template to control the nucleotide sequence of RNA during transcription.

teratogen An agent that interferes with normal development.

teratoma A tumor composed of a chaotic array of different tissue types.

terminal redundancy In phage, a linear DNA molecule with single-stranded ends that are longer than is necessary to close the DNA circle.

tertiary structure of a protein The folding or coiling of the secondary structure to form a globular molecule.

testcross A cross of an individual of unknown genotype or a heterozygote (or a multiple heterozygote) to a tester individual.

tester An individual homozygous for one or more recessive alleles; used in a testcross.

testicular feminization The creation of an apparent female phenotype in an XY individual as a result of an X-linked mutation.

tetrad (1) Four homologous chromatids in a bundle in the first meiotic prophase and metaphase. (2) The four haploid product cells from a single meiosis.

tetrad analysis The use of tetrads (definition 2) to study the behavior of chromosomes and genes during meiosis.

tetraparental mouse A mouse that develops from an embryo created by the experimental fusion of two separate blastulas.

tetraploid A cell having four chromosome sets; an organism composed of such cells.

tetratype (T) A tetrad type containing four different genotypes, two parental and two recombinant.

Thr Threonine (an amino acid).

three-point testcross A testcross involving one parent with three heterozygous gene pairs.

thymidine The nucleoside having thymine as its base.

thymine A pyrimidine base that pairs with adenine.

thymine dimer A pair of chemically bonded adjacent thymine bases in DNA; the cellular processes that repair this lesion often make errors that create mutations.

totipotency The ability of a cell to proceed through all the stages of development and thus produce a normal adult.

trans conformation In a heterozygote involving two mutant sites within a gene or gene cluster, the arrangement $a_1 +/+ a_2$.

transcription The synthesis of RNA using a DNA template.

transdetermination A specific change in the fate of an imaginal disk that can occur when the disk is cultured.

transduction The movement of genes from a bacterial donor to a bacterial recipient using a phage as the vector.

transfer RNA *See* **tRNA.**

transformation (1) The directed modification of a genome by the external application of DNA from a cell of different genotype. (2) Conversion of normal higher eukaryotic cells in tissue culture to a cancer-like state of uncontrolled division.

transient diploid The stage of the life cycle of predominantly haploid fungi (and algae) during which meiosis occurs.

transition A type of nucleotide-pair substitution involving the replacement of a purine with another purine, or of a pyrimidine with another pyrimidine — for example, GC → AT.

translation The ribosome-mediated production of a polypeptide whose amino-acid sequence is derived from the codon sequence of an mRNA molecule.

translocation The relocation of a chromosomal segment in a different position in the genome.

transmission genetics The study of the mechanisms involved in the passage of a gene from one generation to the next.

transposable genetic element A general term for any genetic unit that can insert into a chromosome, exit, and relocate; includes insertion sequences, transposons, some phages, and controlling elements.

transposition *See* **translocation.**

transposon A mobile piece of DNA that is flanked by terminal repeat sequences and typically bears genes coding for transposition functions.

transversion A type of nucleotide-pair substitution involving the replacement of a purine with a pyrimidine, or vice versa — for example, GC → TA.

triplet The three nucleotide pairs that compose a codon.

triploid A cell having three chromosome sets, or an organism composed of such cells.

trisomic Basically a diploid with an extra chromosome of one type, producing a chromosome number of the form $2n + 1$.

tritium A radioactive isotope of hydrogen.

tRNA (transfer RNA) A class of small RNA molecules that bear specific amino acids to the ribosome during translation; the amino acid is inserted into the growing polypeptide chain when the anticodon of the tRNA pairs with a codon on the mRNA being translated.

Trp Tryptophan (an amino acid).

true-breeding line or strain *See* **pure-breeding line or strain.**

truncation selection A breeding technique in which individuals in whom quantitative expression of a phenotype is above or below a certain value (the truncation point) are selected as parents for the next generation.

Turner's syndrome An abnormal human female phenotype produced by the presence of only one X chromosome (XO).

twin spot A pair of mutant sectors within wild-type tissue, produced by a mitotic crossover in an individual of appropriate heterozygous genotype.

Tyr Tyrosine (an amino acid).

U Uracil, or uridine.

underdominance A phenotypic relation in which the phenotypic expression of the heterozygote is less than that of either homozygote.

unequal crossover A crossover between homologs that are not perfectly aligned.

uniparental inheritance The transmission of certain phenotypes from one parental type to all the progeny; such inheritance is generally produced by organelle genes.

unstable mutation A mutation that has a high frequency of reversion; a mutation caused by the insertion of a controlling element, whose subsequent exit produces a reversion.

uracil A pyrimidine base that appears in RNA in place of thymine found in DNA.

URF (unassigned reading frame)   A genelike nucleotide sequence with proper start and stop codons but with no known function.

uridine   The nucleoside having uracil as its base.

Val   Valine (an amino acid).

variable   A property that may have different values in various cases.

variable region   A region in an immunoglobin molecule that shows many sequence differences between antibodies of different specificities; the part of the antibody that binds to the antigen.

variance   A measure of the variation around the central class of a distribution; the average squared deviation of the observations from their mean value.

variant   An individual organism that is recognizably different from an arbitrary standard type in that species.

variate   A specific numerical value of a variable.

variation   The differences among parents and their offspring or among individuals in a population.

variegation   The occurrence within a tissue of sectors with differing phenotypes.

vector   In cloning, the plasmid or phage chromosome used to carry the cloned DNA segment.

viability   The probability that a fertilized egg will survive and develop into an adult organism.

virulent phage   A phage that cannot become a prophage; infection by such a phage always leads to lysis of the host cell.

wild-type   The genotype or phenotype that is found in nature or in the standard laboratory stock for a given organism.

wobble   The ability of certain bases at the third position of an anticodon in tRNA to form hydrogen bonds in various ways, causing alignment with several possible codons.

X linkage   The presence of a gene on the X chromosome but not on the Y.

X-and-Y linkage   The presence of a gene on both the X and Y chromosomes (rare).

X-ray crystallography   A technique for deducing molecular structure by aiming a beam of X rays at a crystal of the test compound and measuring the scatter of rays.

Y linkage   The presence of a gene on the Y chromosome but not on the X (rare).

zygote   The cell formed by the fusion of an egg and a sperm; the unique diploid cell that will divide mitotically to create a differentiated diploid organism.

zygotic induction   The sudden release of a lysogenic phage from an Hfr chromosome when the prophage enters the F^- cell, and the subsequent lysis of the recipient cell.

Answers to Selected Problems

Chapter 2

1. Charlie was not pure-breeding but heterozygous, Bb, where b is a recessive allele causing red and white coat. His mates were BB. Half of his progeny were Bb, and these, when interbred, gave $3/4 \, B-$ and $1/4 \, bb$.

2. Recessive.

6. Father probably Hh (disease is rare), so man has $1/2$ chance of getting H from father.   a. $1/2$;   b. $1/2 \times 1/2 = 1/4$.

7. a. Dominant;   b. Dd and Dd;   c. $1/4$ for normal, $3/4$ for dwarf.

9. 91 spotted-leafed plants and 28 unspotted, approximately a $3:1$ ratio.

   a. Spots $= S$, no spots $= s$. Parental plant Ss, gave $3/4$ $S-$ and $1/4 \, ss$.

   b. All unspotted plants should be pure-breeding, and $1/3$ of spotted plants should be pure-breeding.

14. (Pedigree 1 answer only.) Must be recessive condition. Genotypes: Line 1: $A-, aa$. Line 2: $Aa, Aa, Aa, A-, A-, Aa$. Line 3: Aa, Aa. Line 4: aa.

15. $1/4$

16. $1/32$

18. a. $CcSs \times CcSs$ c. $Ccss \times Ccss$

    b. $CCSs \times CCss$ f. $CCSs \times CCSs$

    c. $CcSS \times ccSS$ g. $CcSs \times Ccss$

    d. $ccSs \times ccSs$

20. a. 2

    b. Bow and knock are alleles of one; hairy and smooth are alleles of other.

    c. $B =$ bow, $b =$ knock
       $H =$ hairy, $h =$ smooth

    d. $\dfrac{Bb \, Hh,}{\text{(p)}} \dfrac{Bb \, HH,}{\text{(q)}} \dfrac{Bb \, hh,}{\text{(r)}} \dfrac{bb \, hh,}{\text{(s)}} \dfrac{BB \, Hh.}{\text{(t)}}$

       so that mating 1 is p $\times$ q or q $\times$ p; mating 2 is r $\times$ s; mating 3 is p $\times$ s; mating 4 is p $\times$ t or t $\times$ p.

21. *Phenotypically*

    a. $1/2 \times 3/4 \times 1/2 \times 3/4 \times 1/2 = 9/128$

    b. $1/2 \times 3/4 \times 1/2 \times 3/4 \times 1/2 = 9/128$

    c. $9/128 + 9/128 = 18/128$

    d. $1 - 18/128 = 110/128$

    Genotypically

    a. $1/2 \times 1/2 \times 1/2 \times 1/2 \times 1/2 = 1/32$

b. $1/2 \times 1/2 \times 1/2 \times 1/2 \times 1/2 = 1/32$

c. $1/32 + 1/32 = 2/32$

d. $1 - 2/32 = 30/32$

22. Parents must both be heterozygous. For two-child families, there are only four possibilities in regard to the trait. 1. First child has it and second doesn't: $p = 1/4 \times 3/4 = 3/16$ of families. 2. First child doesn't have it and second does: $p = 3/4 \times 1/4 = 3/16$ of families. 3. Both children have it: $p = 1/4 \times 1/4 = 1/16$ of families. 4. Neither child has it: $p = 3/4 \times 3/4 = 9/16$ of families. The last possibility can be ignored because we are told at least one child has the trait. Hence the total proportion of affected children is

$$[(1/2 \times 3/16) + (1/2 \times 3/16) + (1/16)] \div 7/16$$
$$= 4/16 \div 7/16 = 4/7$$

Chapter 3

2. a. 92;   b. 92;   c. 46;   d. 46;   e. 23.

4. a. 20;   b. 10.

5. For a child's karyotype to be the same as his, the man's sperm must contain a satellited 4, an abnormal 7, and a Y. The overall probability of this is $1/2 \times 1/2 \times 1/2 = 1/8$.

6. Probability $= 1 \times 1/2 \times 1/2 \times 1/2 \cdots 1/2 = (1/2)^{n-1}$

9. In schmoos, females are obviously the heterogametic sex. $G♀ \times gg♂$ gives Gg male and g female offspring where G = graceful, g = gruesome.

10. 4

13. a.   Her mother must have been Dd, so there is a $1/2$ chance that the woman got the d from her mother and is heterozygous herself. $1/2$ of her children will be sons, and $1/2$ of them will have muscular dystrophy. Overall probability $= 1/2 \times 1/2 \times 1/2 = 1/8$.

b.   One of the grandparents had the gene so there is a $1/2$ chance that your mother has, and a further $1/2$ chance that you have it, if you are a ♂ or ♀. Overall probability $= 1/2 \times 1/2 = 1/4$.

c.   Since your father does not have the disease, there is no way you can get it.

16. a.   Suppose the genes for black and yellow are alleles on the X chromosome; call them t^b and t^y, respectively. Then males are $X^{t^b}Y$ (black) and $X^{t^y}Y$ (yellow). Females could be $X^{t^b}X^{t^b}$ (black), $X^{t^y}X^{t^y}$ (yellow), and $X^{t^b}X^{t^y}$ (tortoise-shell). Females heterozygous for the two alleles have a phenotype different from either homozygote.

b.

$$X^{t^y}X^{t^y} \text{ (yellow)}♀ \times X^{t^b}Y \text{ (black)}♂$$
$$\downarrow$$
$$X^{t^y}X^{t^b} \text{ (tortoise-shell)}♀ \quad X^{t^y}Y \text{ (yellow)}♂$$

c.

$$X^{t^b}X^{t^b} \text{ (black)}♀ \times X^{t^y}Y \text{ (yellow)}♂$$
$$\downarrow$$
$$X^{t^b}X^{t^y} \text{ (tortoise-shell)}♀ \quad X^{t^b}Y\text{(black)}♂$$

d.   tortoise shell ♀♀ and black ♂♂.

e.   tortoise shell ♀♀ and yellow ♂♂.

17. 1/4

20. a. Excluded;   b. consistent;   c. excluded;   d. excluded;   e. excluded.

21. a.   Bent is dominant (bent × bent gives normals in 6).

b.   X-linked.

c.

1.	$bb \times B$	Bb	b
2.	$Bb \times b$	$1/2Bb$ $1/2bb$	$1/2B$ $1/2b$
3.	$BB \times b$	Bb	B
4.	$bb \times b$	bb	b
5.	$BB \times B$	BB	B
6.	$Bb \times B$	$1/2BB$ $1/2Bb$	$1/2B$ $1/2b$

Chapter 4

2. Erminette is a case of codominance — the phenotype is a heterozygote (Ee), where EE = black and ee = white. Thus Ee selfed gives a $1:2:1$ ratio. One possible test is to cross erminettes to white; a ratio of $1/2$ erminette to $1/2$ white is expected.

4. Progeny types: 12, 14, 23, 34. a. 1/4;   b. 1/4;   c. 1/2.

6. e.

8. Baby 1 is from cross 4, baby 2 is from cross 2, baby 3 is from cross 1, baby 4 is from cross 3.

10. Platinum phenotype due to an allele which is lethal when homozygous. Test by crossing platinum to normal; predict a $1:1$ ratio. Or examine aborted fetuses in platinum × platinum; expect $1/4$.

12. Short-bristled flies are always females. Only half as many males are produced as females. Suppose the allele for short bristles is dominant (call it S). Hence S/S^+ females have short bristles, but S is also a recessive lethal so that S Y males never live. The first cross is

SS^+(short bristle)♀ $\times$ S^+Y(long)♂

$\downarrow$

1 SS^+(short)♀ : 1 S^+S^+(long)♀ : 1 S^+Y(long)♂ : 1 SY ♂ dies

The second cross is

S^+S^+(long)♀ $\times$ S^+Y(long)♂

$\downarrow$

S^+S^+(long)♀ S^+Y(long)♂

The third cross is the same as the first.

16. Recessive albino alleles at two independent genes. Cross is $A_1A_1a_2a_2 \times a_1a_1A_2A_2$, which gives all $A_1a_1A_2a_2$ (normal).

17. c^{sr} = sun red, c^o = orange, c^p = pink; allelic series with dominance in the order shown.

Cross 1 $c^{sr}c^{sr} \times c^pc^p$ gives $F_1 c^{sr}c^p$, gives 3 : 1 in F_2.

Cross 2 $c^oc^o \times c^{sr}c^{sr}$ gives $F_1 c^oc^{sr}$, gives 3 : 1 in F_2.

Cross 3 $c^oc^o \times c^pc^p$ gives $F_1 c^oc^p$, gives 3 : 1 in F_2.

Scarlet is an allele of a separate independent gene s.

Cross 4 $c^oc^oSS \times CCss$ gives

F_1 Cc^oSs, normal (yellow)

F_2 $C-S-$, yellow 9

   $C-ss$, scarlet 3

   c^oc^oS-, orange 3

   c^oc^oss, orange 1 (epistasis)

20. The 9 : 3 : 3 : 1 indicates that 2 pairs of genes are involved. The alleles for scarlet and brown eyes must be recessive since the F_1 are normal. Let the allele for scarlet eyes be s and for brown eyes be b.

$ss\,b^+b^+$ (scarlet) $\times$ $s^+s^+\,bb$ (brown)

$s^+s\,b^+b$ (red) $\times$ $s^+s\,b^+b$ (red)

$\downarrow$

9 $s^+ - b^+ -$ red
3 $ss\ \ \ b^+ -$ scarlet
3 $s^+ - bb$ brown
1 $ss\ \ \ bb$ white

23. a. The genes causing scarlet eyes in strains A and B are different. They are recessive to their wild-type alleles. The gene for scarlet in strain B must be autosomal.

b. The gene for scarlet eyes in strain A is sex-linked.

c. Let the genes for scarlet in strain A be a and in strain B be b (the normal alleles are A and B, respectively).

$aY\,BB$ ♂ $\times$ $AA\,bb$ ♀

$\downarrow$

$Aa\,Bb$ ♀ $\times$ $AY\,Bb$ ♂

$$
\begin{array}{lll}
1/4\ AA \left\{ \begin{array}{l} 1/4\ BB \\ 1/2\ Bb \\ 1/4\ bb \end{array} \right. & \begin{array}{l} 1/16\ AA\ BB\ \text{normal ♀} \\ 1/8\ \ AA\ Bb\ \text{normal ♀} \\ 1/16\ AA\ bb\ \text{scarlet ♀} \end{array} & \Big\} 6/16 \\
1/4\ Aa \left\{ \begin{array}{l} 1/4\ BB \\ 1/2\ Bb \\ 1/4\ bb \end{array} \right. & \begin{array}{l} 1/16\ Aa\ BB\ \text{normal ♀} \\ 1/8\ \ Aa\ Bb\ \text{normal ♀} \\ 1/16\ Aa\ bb\ \text{scarlet ♀} \end{array} & \Big\} 2/16 \\
1/4\ AY \left\{ \begin{array}{l} 1/4\ BB \\ 1/2\ Bb \\ 1/4\ bb \end{array} \right. & \begin{array}{l} 1/16\ AY\ BB\ \text{normal ♂} \\ 1/8\ \ AY\ Bb\ \text{normal ♂} \\ 1/16\ AY\ bb\ \text{scarlet ♂} \end{array} & \Big\} 3/16 \\
1/4\ aY \left\{ \begin{array}{l} 1/4\ BB \\ 1/2\ Bb \\ 1/4\ bb \end{array} \right. & \begin{array}{l} 1/16\ aY\ BB\ \text{scarlet ♂} \\ 1/8\ \ aY\ Bb\ \text{scarlet ♂} \\ 1/16\ aY\ bb\ \text{scarlet ♂} \end{array} & \Big\} 5/16
\end{array}
$$

26. Cross 1 proves plant is either $Aa\ CC$ or $AA\ Cc$. Cross 2 proves plant is $Aa\ Rr$. Cross 3 confirms $Aa\ CC$ alternative from cross 1. Plant is $Aa\ CC\ Rr$.

27. a. $td + (1/4)$ b. $1/4 : 3/4$ or $1:3$
   $+ su\ (1/4)$
   $+ + \ (1/4)$
   $td\ su\ (1/4)$

28.

	Cross 1	Cross 2
white	32/48	16/24
solid black	9/48	3/24
spotted black	3/48	3/24
solid chestnut	3/48	1/24
spotted chestnut	1/48	1/24

30. *For host:*

F_2 $R_\alpha\_R_{\beta}-$ 9   no disease

   $R_\alpha\_r_\beta r_\beta$ 3 ⎫
   $r_\alpha r_\alpha R_\beta-$ 3 ⎬ disease
   $r_\alpha r_\alpha r_\beta r_\beta$ 1 ⎭

R_α and R_β are dominant host alleles at separate loci, conferring resistance to α and β, respectively. A is $r_\alpha r_\alpha R_\beta R_\beta$; B is $R_\alpha R_\alpha r_\beta r_\beta$; F_1 is $R_\alpha r_\alpha R_\beta r_\beta$.

For parasite:
Hypothesis 1. Virulence alleles (*) at separate loci, that is, α is $V_A^*V_B$, β is $V_AV_B^*$. Prediction: 4 genotypes from crossing $\alpha \times \beta$:

	A	B
V_A*V_B	+	−
$V_A V_B*$	−	+
V_A*V_B*	+	+
$V_A V_B$	−	−

Hypothesis 2. Different virulence alleles at one locus, that is, α is V_A, β is V_B. Prediction: 2 equally frequent genotypes from $\alpha \times \beta$:

	A	B
$1/2\ V_A$	+	−
$1/2\ V_B$	−	+

31. A must have had the gene but with very low (or zero) penetrance, due either to suppressor genes or to environmental suppression of gene action.

33. (i)

$$MM\,Dd\,ww \times mm\,dd\,ww$$

$$\downarrow$$

$1/2\ Mm\,Dd\,ww$

$1/2\ Mm\,dd\,ww$

(ii)

$$mm\,Dd\,Ww \times MM\,dd\,ww$$

$$\downarrow$$

$1/2\ Mm\,(Dd$ or $dd)Ww$

$1/4\ Mm\,Dd\,ww$

$1/4\ Mm\,dd\,ww$

Chapter 5

2. The H/h locus is closely linked to the I/i locus, so that crossovers are very rare.

3. Two genes are linked 10 map units apart. The female parent was of the type AB/ab.

5. b

6. a. $\dfrac{B \quad\ Ad \quad\ c}{b \quad\ aD \quad\ C}$

b. $AA\,BB\,cc\,dd \times aa\,bb\,CC\,DD$

c.

$$\overset{10\text{ m.u.}\qquad\quad 30\text{ m.u.}}{\underset{B/b \qquad A/a \qquad\qquad C/c}{\rule{0pt}{0pt}}}$$

$\qquad\qquad\qquad D/d$

d. $I = 1 - 15/(0.1 \times 0.3 \times 1000)$
  $= 1 - 15/30 = 0.5$

8. The results indicate linkage. The parents of the children must have been $P\ I^A$ (where P is the allele for nail-patella

$\overline{\overline{p\ i}}$

syndrome). If you make a grid of the combinations of parental and recombinant gametes, you will see that the $p\ i/p\ i$ (normal, O blood) is the only phenotypically unique class and is produced by two parentals. The frequency of $p\ i$ gametes must be the square root of the $p\ i/p\ i$ class $= \sqrt{0.16} = 0.4$. Assume the $P\ I$ gametes occur with the same frequency so the recombinants occur at a frequency of 0.2 and the distance between p and i is 20 map units.

	$0.4\ P\ I^A$	$0.4\ p\ i$	$0.1\ P\ i$	$0.1\ p\ I^A$
$0.4\ P\ I^A$	$0.16\,\dfrac{P\ I^A}{P\ I^A}$	$0.16\,\dfrac{p\ i}{P\ I^A}$	$0.04\,\dfrac{P\ i}{P\ I^A}$	$0.04\,\dfrac{p\ I^A}{P\ I^A}$
$0.4\ p\ i$	$0.16\,\dfrac{P\ I^A}{p\ i}$	$0.16\,\dfrac{p\ i}{p\ i}$	$0.04\,\dfrac{P\ i}{p\ i}$	$0.04\,\dfrac{p\ I^A}{p\ i}$
$0.1\ P\ i$	$0.04\,\dfrac{P\ I^A}{P\ i}$	$0.04\,\dfrac{p\ i}{P\ i}$	$0.01\,\dfrac{P\ i}{P\ i}$	$0.01\,\dfrac{P\ I^A}{P\ i}$
$0.1\ p\ I^A$	$0.04\,\dfrac{P\ I^A}{p\ I^A}$	$0.04\,\dfrac{p\ i}{p\ I^A}$	$0.01\,\dfrac{P\ i}{p\ I^A}$	$0.01\,\dfrac{p\ I^A}{p\ I^A}$

10. There were two linked genes, each with two alleles coding for an F and S allele. The conformation of the alleles was $ADH^F\ PGM^S/ADH^S\ PGM^F$ (repulsion). The $21 + 19$ individuals are recombinants; $RF = 40/237 = 0.17$.

12. a. The cross is $a\ b\ c/+++\,♀ \times a\ b\ c/+++\,♂$. Since there is no crossing-over in males, two types of sperm are produced, $a\ b\ c$ and $+++$. There should be as many $+++/a\ b\ c$ as $a\ b\ c/a\ b\ c$. The data then are

Parental ($a\ b\ c$ and $+++$)	730
Single recombinants between a and b ($a++$ and $+\,b\ c$)	91
Single recombinants between b and c ($a\ b+$ and $++c$)	171
Double recombinants ($+\,b+$ and $a+c$)	9
Total	1001

$a - b = [(91 + 9)/1001] \times 100 = 10$ map units

$b - c = [(171 + 9)/1001] \times 100 = 18$ map units

b. Expected number of double recombinants assuming no interference $= (0.1 \times 0.18)(1001) = 18$. Coefficient of coincidence $=$ observed/expected $= 9/18 = 0.5$.

14. Gene sequence is $lg - b - y$. Map distances are 28 m.u. (lg to b) and 18 m.u. (b to y). Coefficient of coincidence is about 0.8.

16. Cross $+++ \times fat^-\ tail^-\ flag^-$

Progeny: $+ + +$
$+ + flag^-$
$fat^- + +$
$fat^- + flag^-$
$fat^- tail^- flag^-$
$fat^- tail^- +$
$+ tail^- flag^-$
$+ tail^- +$

Linkage map:

$+ / fat^-$	$+ / tail^-$	$+ / flag^-$
9.3 m.u.	15.3 m.u.	

19. a. Yes; b. probably dominant; c. yes, mother would be RE/re. The single crossover-derived child $(Rr\ ee)$ provides a rough estimate of 10 m.u.

20. a. $PAR = (0.85 \times 0.80) \div 2 = 0.34$

b. $par = (0.85 \times 0.80) \div 2 = 0.34$

c. $PaR = (0.15 \times 0.20) \div 2 = 0.015$

d. $Par = (0.15 \times 0.80) \div 2 = 0.06$

22. Cross 1 χ^2 (3 df) = 2.12; p = >50%; unlinked.

Cross 2 χ^2 (3 df) = 6.6; p = >10%; unlinked.

Cross 3 χ^2 (3 df) = 66; p = <0.5%; linked.

Cross 4 χ^2 (3 df) = 11.6; p = ~1%; linked.

24. Father of x and y has c only, and mother of x and y must have c and h in coupling because two of her sons express both c and h. The derivation of the female sibship of x and y is therefore

$$\frac{c \qquad\qquad +}{\downarrow} \times \frac{+ \qquad\qquad +}{|\ \leftarrow 10 \rightarrow\ |}$$
$$ c \qquad\qquad h$$

Type 1 0.45 $++/c+$ normal

Type 2 0.45 $c\,h/c\,+$ ⎫
Type 3 0.05 $c+/c+$ ⎬ color-blind
⎭

Type 4 0.05 $+h/c\,+$ normal

x can be type 1 or 4, but only 4 can produce a hemophiliac son. Hence, answer is $0.05/(0.45 + 0.05) \times 1/2 = 1/10 \times 1/2 = 1/20$.

y can be type 2 or 3, but only 2 can produce a hemophiliac son. Hence answer is $0.45/(0.45 + 0.05) \times 1/2 = 9/10 \times 1/2 = 9/20$.

Chapter 6

1. a. ad and nic linked, leu and arg linked. Parents were

$$ad^-nic^+leu^+arg^- \times ad^+nic^-leu^-arg^+$$

b. Crossover between ad and nic (the reciprocal type not found in this small sample).

3. a. $0.2 = 1/2\ (1 - e^{-m})$; $m = 0.51 \equiv 0.51 \times 50 = 25.5$ m.u.

b. Hypothesis: no linkage. Prediction: $50:50:50:50$. $\chi^2 = 2.52$ (3 d.f.); $p = 30-50\%$. Therefore these data are a common deviation from a $1:1:1:1$ ratio, and there is no need to postulate linkage.

5. a. 0.704; b. 0; c. 0.176; d. 0.012; e. 0.096; f. 0; g. 0.012.

7.

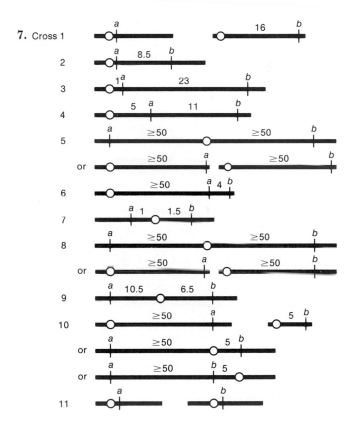

8.

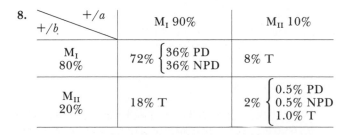

$+/a$ \ $+/b$	M_I 90%	M_{II} 10%
M_I 80%	72% ⎰ 36% PD ⎱ 36% NPD	8% T
M_{II} 20%	18% T	2% ⎰ 0.5% PD ⎸ 0.5% NPD ⎱ 1.0% T

a. 36.5%; b. 36.5%; c. 27.0%; d. 50.0%; e. 25.0%.

10. Cross 1, linked; Cross 2, unlinked; Cross 3, linked or unlinked; Cross 4, unlinked; Cross 5, unlinked; Cross 6, linked or unlinked.

12. *his-4*, because T requires exchange between centromere and either *ad-3* or *his-?*, and since *ad-3* is known to be close to its centromere, only *his-4* has the necessary distance to give 60 percent T.

13. First mutant *w*, second at separate locus *t*.
Crossed $w\,t^+ \times w^+\,t$:

Asci	$w\,t^+$ (white)	$w\,t^+$ (white)	$w\,t$ (white)
	$w\,t^+$ (white)	$w\,t$ (white)	$w\,t$ (white)
	$w^+\,t$ (tan)	$w^+\,t^+$ (black)	$w^+\,t^+$ (black)
	$w^+\,t$ (tan)	$w^+\,t$ (tan)	$w^+\,t^+$ (black)
	(PD)	(T)	(NPD)

Note that *w* is epistatic to *t*.

15. *Yy* (yellowish). Mitotic crossover produces a twin spot of genotype *YY* (normal) and *yy* (yellow).

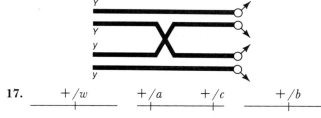

17.
$$\underline{\quad +/w \quad}\underset{+}{\quad\quad} \underline{\quad +/a \quad\quad +/c \quad}\underset{+}{\quad} \underline{\quad +/b \quad}$$

19. a. They indicate linkage of *pro* and *paba* to *fpa*, and their different frequencies reflect the sizes of linkage group intervals. The absence of a class requiring *pro* only means that *paba* is distal to *pro*.

	pro		*paba*		*fpa*
●—————+—————————————+——————————+
	6		71		23
	(=9/154)		(=110/154)		(=35/154)

   c. *pro, paba, fpa.*

21. α on 7, β on 1, γ on 5, δ on 6, ϵ not on these eight.

Chapter 7

2. Make master plate on medium with arginine; replicate plate onto arginineless medium and look for failure to duplicate a colony.

4. Strain 2 carried a recessive *mei* mutant and passed this on to strains 4, 6, 7, and 8. Only crosses homozygous for *mei* show meiotic abnormalities. Perhaps *mei* inhibits pairing.

5. $e^{-\mu \times 10^6} = 0.37$, and $\mu = -\ln 0.37 \times 10^{-6} = 1$ per 10^6 cell division.

7. We have to make the assumption that chromosomes are genetically inert when they are heterochromatic. The data then suggest that in males the heterochromatic chromosomes are all of paternal origin. Hence, irradiation of females produces lethal mutations that kill females (dominant) and males (recessive). Irradiation of males kills daughters but has no effect on sons because their irradiated chromosomes are inert.

9. Study pollen grains (which are haploid) and look for red grains under the microscope.

13. It is possible (although not certain) that the achondroplasia mutation arose in the germ line of the father as a result of radiation exposure. However, the hemophilia allele *must* have been transmitted from the mother (father contributes Y), and plant cannot be held responsible.

14. There are $10 - 2 = 8$ new mutant alleles per $94,075 \times 2$ alleles; this equals 4.25×10^{-5}, or about 1 in 24,000 alleles.

Chapter 8

2. Consider two hypotheses:

   i. Deletion of left arm in nucleus 2.

   ii. Mitotic crossover generates homozygosity of left arm of nucleus 1.

   Hypothesis (ii) is unlikely, since we should be able to recover nucleus 2 alleles in a cross. Although these alleles must be present in the HK to provide *ad-3A⁺* and *nic⁺* function, they cannot cross because their mating allele has been deleted.

4. Small deletions *within* the *ad-3B* gene.

5. a. Deletions spanning the loci whose mutant alleles are expressed.

   b. A deletion not spanning a mutant allele; or, alternatively, a dominant lethal point mutation.

8.

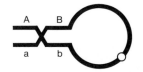

crossover

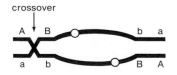

Another possible rare type

10. a. Inversion from close to *f* to close to *y*.

b. Double crossovers; or single crossovers in the noninverted end of the *f-b* region.

11. a. m = 0.22

    b. i. 0.8
        ii. 0.18
        iii. <u>0.02</u>
             1.00 (rounded off)

    c. i. 8:0 (dark:light)
        ii. 4:4
        iii. 8:0, 0:8, and 4:4 in a 1:1:2 ratio.

    d.
Number of crossovers	8:0	0:8	4:4
0 (0.8)	0.8	—	—
1 (0.18)	—	—	0.18
2 (0.02)	0.005	0.005	0.01
Totals	0.805	0.005	0.19

12. a. Classes 1 and 2 are parentals. Classes 3 to 10 are all double recombinants. We'd expect such results if one of the chromosomes carried a very large inversion spanning the entire marked region from *y* to *car*.

    b. Class 11 is patroclinous in that the flies carry a paternal X chromosome. This could result from nondisjunction or a four-strand double-exchange tetrad that produces nullo X eggs.

    c. If egg nuclei could be looked at cytologically, you'd expect to see double dicentric bridges if the four-strand doubles occur.

15. The wild-type from nature was a reciprocal translocation for the chromosomes carrying the marked loci.

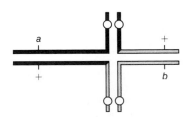

Alternate segregation guarantees *ab* and ++ genotypes (predominantly), with some *a*+ and +*b* resulting from exchange in the breakpoint to locus intervals.

18. Cross 1 Normal cross, recombination by independent assortment.

    Cross 2 Abnormal strain has reciprocal translocation between I (bearing *ad-3*) and VI (*pan-2*⁺), with the *ad-3* and *pan-2* genes close to the breakpoints.

    Cross 3 Half the black spores are N₁ + N₂ types, and half are T₁ + T₂ of genotype *ad-3 pan-2*⁺.

20. Treat the translocation point as a locus and calculate RF in the usual way. This gives the value of 18.2%, which = 18.2 m.u.

21.

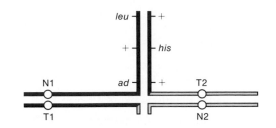

Since short arm nonessential, N1 + T2 is now a viable duplication and is the only P.O.M. that will grow on medium lacking leucine, histidine, and adenine. (Double recombinants will be much rarer.)

24. species B
    ↓
    species D — paracentric inversion of *x y* segment.
    ↓
    species E — translocation of *z x y* to *k l m*.
    ↓
    species A — translocation of *a b c* to *d e f*.
    ↓
    species C — pericentric inversion of *b c d e*.

Chapter 9

1. a. 6*x* × 4*x* gives 5*x* progeny.

   b. 4*x*(*aaaa*) × 2*x*(*AA*) gives *Aaa* progeny.

   c. *Aa** plus colchicine gives *AAa*a**.

   d. 6*x*(*aaaaaa*) × 2*x*(*AA*), or 4*x*(*aaaa*) × 4*x*(*AAaa*), obtain *A–aa* progeny, self, and distinguish the *Aaaa* types by their segregation ratios.

   e. Plate haploid cells on the herbicide, obtain resistant colonies, regenerate plants from them, and double their chromosomes with colchicine.

2. Solve this by putting *AA BB, AA bb, aa BB,* or *aa bb* as the female contributions, and fertilize each with one of four different male nuclei, *AB, Ab, aB,* or *ab*. (Use a Punnet square.)

4. 1/3 of the time, *B* pairs with *B*, and *b* with *b*. This produces asci of "type I." The other 2/3 of the time, *B* will pair with *b* at both homozygous pairs. Two equally frequent segregations will produce asci of "type I" and "type II." Hence, the answer is 2/3 asci type I and 1/3 type II.

	Bb	BB	
(type I)	Bb	BB	(type II)
	Bb	bb	
	Bb	bb	

6.

thurberi	$= \times 13$
herbaceum	$== \times 13$
thurb $\times$ herb sterile hybrid	$- \times 13 \; --- \times 13$
amphidiploid = hirsutum	$= \times 13 == \times 13$
hirs $\times$ thurb hybrid	$= \times 13 \; --- \times 13$
hirs $\times$ herb hybrid	$- \times 13 == \times 13$

Test by reconstructing amphidiploid with colchicine.

7. a. $1/36\ FFGG$, $4/36\ FFGg$, $1/36\ FFgg$, $4/36\ FfGG$, $16/36\ FfGg$, $4/36\ Ffgg$, $1/36\ ffGG$, $4/36\ ffGg$, $1/36\ ffgg$.

   b. $FFFf$ produced by $FF + Ff$ or $Ff + FF$
$$= 4/6 \times 1/6 \times 2 = 8/36$$

   $GGgg$ produced by $GG + gg$, $gg + GG$, or $Gg + Gg$
$$= 1/36 + 1/36 + 16/36 = 18/36$$

   Hence $FFFfGGgg = 8/36 \times 18/36 = 1/9$

   $ffffgggg$ only produced by $ffgg + ffgg$
$$= 1/36 \times 1/36 = 1/1296$$

11. We might expect half of the gametes to be 2×21 ($n + 1$) and half to be normal 1×21 (n). Thus, various pairings could give anywhere from 4×21 ($2n + 2$, probably lethal) to normal, 2×21 ($2n$).

16. a. Female zygote

   b. Klinefelter zygote

   c. Female zygote

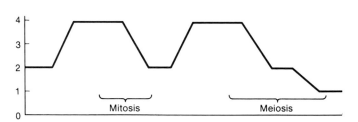

   d. i. Two zygotes fused?
      ii. Fertilization of egg by one sperm (say X) and fertilization of polar body by another (Y), and fusion.

   e. Same as in part c but at later mitosis so XX cells present.

18.
$$AAA \times aa$$
$$\downarrow$$
$$AAa \times aa$$
$$123$$

Segregation possibilities are

$$1(A)\ 2(A)/\ 3(a)$$
$$1(A)\ 3(a)/\ 2(A)$$
$$2(A)\ 3(a)/\ 1(A)$$

which gives a haploid gametic ratio of $2A : 1a$. Such a ratio in the diploid progeny is observed for y (chromosome 1), h (chromosome 10), and cot (chromosome 7).

20. Origin by meiotic nondisjunction, forming an $n + 1$ (disomic) P.O.M. of genotype

$$\frac{a + c + e}{+ b + d +}$$

The disomic was unstable and haploidized during cell growth to give haploid nuclei containing component chromosome types. One possibility:

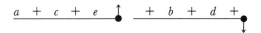

24. a. Mutation; **b.** crossover; **c.** nondisjunction.

Chapter 10

  1. 35%

  2. Assume a diploid cell.

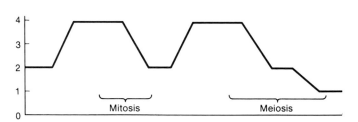

  7. Because A does not equal T, nor does G equal C, the DNA must be single-stranded. It replicates by synthesizing a complementary strand and uses that as a template.

  12. The virus DNA has probably inserted itself into the mouse DNA like a prophage. This may be the manner in which the viruses cause cancer in mice (and possibly in humans).

  14. From each harlequin pair of sister chromatids, another round of replication produces another harlequin pair of chromatids, plus an all-light pair.

Chapter 11

  2. Withhold lactose from the diet. Recessive.

  4. a. Main use is in diagnosing carriers. Parents of diseased individuals must be carriers, and these show intermediate enzyme levels. Also, using amniocentesis, the genotype of an unborn progeny may be determined (see next question).

b. One source of ambiguity is the range overlap shown in the galactosemia example; that is, an activity of 25 to 30 units could mean carrier or normal.

c. At the molecular level these genes show incomplete dominance, but at the phenotypic level they are dominant. Presumably a certain minimal level of activity (a threshold) is necessary for normal function and phenotype.

6. a

8. Development of wild-type eye color in v or cn disks transplanted to wild-type hosts suggests a factor made by the wild cells can diffuse into the transplants that lack it. Failure of a v host to provide a factor to a cn implant, while a cn host does provide a factor to a v implant, can be explained by a sequential reaction controlled by the two genes.

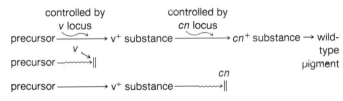

Thus, cn mutants have v^+ substance, which can diffuse into v cells, which can convert it to pigment. A simple test would be to grind up wild-type cells and inject into v and cn hosts and look for wild-type eye color. The substance (s) could be identified using such an assay system.

10. a. $E \rightarrow A \rightarrow C \rightarrow B \rightarrow D \rightarrow G$

b. 5 4 2 1 3

c. Yes, no, yes.

12. a. m_2; b. purple; c. 9 purple : 3 blue : 3 red : 1 white. d. because they lack functional enzyme.

14. A cistron V, W; B cistron U, X, Y, Z.

15. a. 2 black : 4 pale : 2 colorless.

b. 4 black : 4 colorless. (Another segregation is possible, but this would give 8 pale spores, the usual ascus in such crosses.)

19. a.

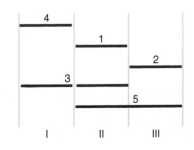

b.

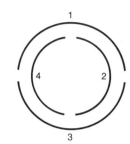

20. a.

$$\underset{2}{\overset{1}{|}} \quad \underset{12}{\overset{3}{|}} \quad \underset{6}{\overset{2}{|}} \quad \overset{4}{|}$$

b. No; homozygous crosses give no prototrophs.

23. S^n dominant. No. Mutations in other parts of genome could modify threshold to 40, perhaps by more efficient transport of the factor, or more efficient packaging into cell walls, etc., and hence S^f would become the dominant allele at generation t.

Chapter 12

2. a. Both $A + U/G + C$ ratios are compatible with the RNAs being transcribed off their primer DNA, but do *not* tell us if copied off one or both DNA strands since same $A + U/G + C$ ratio would result in either case.

b. The purine/pyrimidine ratio of 0.8 proves the *E. coli* RNA is not double-stranded. The 1.02 ratio could indicate double-strandedness of *B. subtilis* RNA, or alternatively that one strand of primer DNA has equal numbers of purines and pyrimidines.

3. One nucleotide change should give rise to three adjacent amino-acid substitutions in protein.

6. a. In 8 cases; b. 3 cases, Arg, Ser, and Leu.

8. a. 1/8; b. 1/4; c. 1/8; d. 1/8.

11. The codon changes in the RNA are as follows:

Mutant 1: missense mutation

(Ser) AGU $\longrightarrow$ (Arg) AGA/G

Mutant 2: nonsense mutation

(Trp) UGG $\longrightarrow$ (stop) UGA or UAG

Mutant 3: two frame-shift mutations

$$\overset{\ominus}{\downarrow} \qquad\qquad \overset{\oplus}{\downarrow}$$

Ala—Pro—Gly—Val—Lys—Asn—Cys—His

GCU CCU GGA GUG AAA AA$\overset{U}{\underset{C}{}}$ UG$\overset{U}{\underset{C}{}}$ CA$\overset{U}{\underset{C}{}}$

with C C above and A A, G G below the first two codons.

Mutant 4: inversion

Ala—Pro—Trp—Phe—Phe—Thr—Cys—His

UUU UUC ACU

The wild-type DNA sequence is

CGTGGT ACC TCA CTT TTT AC$\overset{A}{\underset{G}{}}$ GT$\overset{A}{\underset{G}{}}$

with A A above and G G, C C below.

13. e

15.

```
C G T A C C A C T G C A
G C A T G G T G A C G T
G C A U G G U G A C G U
C G U A C C A C U G C A
```

Ala   Trp   noth- noth-
              ing   ing
                    (stop)

17. a. 120 nucleotides

b.

		I	II	
1	Gln	C	A	A/G
2	Ser	A	G	U/C

Exchange in

I	II	I + II
AA A/G = Lys	AG A/G = Arg	CG A/G = Arg
CG U/C = Arg	CA U/C = His	AA U/C = Asn

Since Arg results from both singles, its frequency is twice that of His or Lys. Doubles are rare so Asn is least common. If markers are at adjacent nucleotides in DNA, the RF should be 4×10^{-7}.

Chapter 13

2. a. F$^+$; b. F$^-$; c. F$^-$; d. Hfr; e. Hfr; f. Hfr; g. F$^-$; h. F$^+$.

3. QWDMTPXACNBQ

6. a. To select for *met*$^+$ to ensure a merozygote.

b. *met* — *pur* — *thi*

c. *met* — *pur* RF = 52/338 = 15.4%
   met — *thi* RF = 58/338 = 17.2%
   thi — *pur* RF = 17.2 − 15.4 = 1.8%

8. The order is *ad*-Z_2-Z_1. In the first cross, Z_2^+ is sometimes included in the double that inserts *ad*$^+$:

$$ad^+ Z_2^+ Z_1^-$$

$$ad^- Z_2^- Z_1^+$$

In the second cross, a separate insertion is needed; hence the combined frequency is very low.

$$ad^+ Z_2^- Z_1^+$$

$$ad^- Z_2^+ Z_1^-$$

11. The *pro*$^+$ gene had been sexduced by an F′ episome which was transmitted infectiously for two generations.

15. a. Multiple transformants are most rare whenever B is selected, so B is the distant gene.

b. ADC

17. a. The distances are

$$m - r = \frac{162 + 520 + 474 + 172}{10,342} \times 100 = 12.8 \text{ map units}$$

$$r - tu = \frac{853 + 162 + 172 + 965}{10,342} \times 100 = 20.8 \text{ map units}$$

$$m - tu = \frac{853 + 520 + 474 + 965}{10,342} \times 100 = 27.2 \text{ map units}$$

(looking only at *m* and *tu*)

b. The linkage data suggest that *m* and *tu* are farthest apart, so the order must be *m* − *r* − *tu*. Now we can include the double crossovers, so that distance *m* − *tu* =

$$\frac{853 + (2 \times 162) + 520 + 474 + (2 \times 172) + 965}{10,342}$$

$$\times 100 = 33.7$$

c. The coefficient of coincidence = observed doubles/expected doubles =

$$\frac{162 + 172}{275.1} = \frac{334}{275.1} = 1.2$$

There is an excess of doubles over the expected, so interference is negative.

20. a. Specialized transduction; b. in the *cys-leu* region.

23. There is a group of genes in the order *cead*. Gene *b* is more distant as it is never cotransduced.

Chapter 14

2. a.

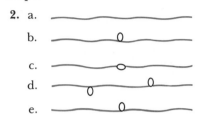

b.

c.

d.

e.

5. Palindrome DNA:

A	B	C	D	====	D¹	C¹	B¹	A¹
A¹	B¹	C¹	D¹		D	C	B	A

7.

	Eco	Hind	Hind	Eco	Hind	Eco	
4	2-3	2-2	2-1	3-2	3-1	1	

9. From the top (the ^{32}P end), the sequence of sites is

Hae-Hind-Hae-Hind-Hind-Hae-Hae-Hae-
                    Hind-Hae-Hae-Hind-Eco

Chapter 15

9. The enzyme or protein damaged by the mutation still has some residual activity; for example, it might still be able to bind substrate in its newly shaped active site on rare occasions.

10. The wild-type contained a gene that increases spontaneous mutation rate. Call it a mutator gene *m*; *m* appears to be unlinked to *ad-3*.

                A   ×   Wild-type
          ad-3, +   │   +, *m*
                          ↓
                    1. 1/4 *ad-3, m*
                    2. 1/4 *ad-3, +*
                    3. 1/4 +, *m*
                    4. 1/4 +, +

Prediction: Cross individual of type 2 to several *ad-3*⁺ progeny; half the crosses should show a repeat of the above results. Also test *m* on other reverting mutants.

11. a. UAA does not contain G or C so cannot be obtained this way. UAG and UGA could be derived by such transitions, but only from UAA, which is itself a nonsense codon.

b. Yes; for example, UGG → UAG.
                                (Trp)

c. No, since G is only site acted on and UAA is always produced. E.g., UAG → UAA.

13. Allele 1: a deletion or other chromosomal rearrangement

Allele 2: a base-pair substitution

Prototroph A: a true revertant. *nic* → +

Prototroph B: mutation at an unlinked suppressor locus. + → *su*(tRNA?)

Prototroph C: mutation at a very closely linked site (0.8 m.u. away). Possibly intragenic suppressor altering mutant protein conformation.

Chapter 16

3.

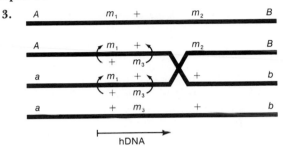

Order is $A/a - m_1 m_3 m_2 - B/b$ (or $m_3 m_1 m_2$)
    Hybrid DNA entered *m* gene from left and ended between m_3 and m_2, and hence spanned m_1 and m_3.
    One single excision-repair event corrected +m_3 to m_1 + on both hybrid DNA molecules.

5. a. Distortion in hybrid DNA is greater for addition/deletion and is corrected more efficiently by excision-repair system.

b. Excision-repair system recognizes buckle but excises the *other* strand; e.g., for hybrid DNA between addition *m* and +.

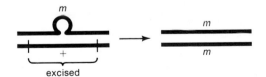

c. When excision-repair system recognizes frame-shift site, the excision and repair spans *both* the frame-shift site and the substitution site; e.g., for addition,

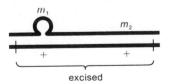

8. The second back-cross is obviously a testcross since it shows the segregation of some genetic factor that affects recombinant frequency. Call it *rec*; *rec*⁺, borne by *A, his-1*ₓ parent, is a dominant inhibitor of recombination. *rec*⁻, borne by *a, his-1*ᵧ parent, is a recessive allele which permits high recombinant frequency. The *rec* locus assorts independently of *his-1*, so half of the A, *his-1*$_x$ progeny are *rec*$^+$ and half are *rec*$^-$. The same applies to the a, *his-1*$_y$ progeny, but since the backcross is to *rec*$^+$ the segregation is not observed.

Test: 1/4 of the crosses between A, *his-1*$_x$ and a, *his-1*$_y$ progeny should be *rec*$^-$ × *rec*$^-$ and show high prototroph frequency. *rec* is a meiotic function occurring at meiosis in the diploid stage of the cycle.

Chapter 17

2. There is no correlation between loss of the element from the chromosome (precise excision) and transposition to a new locus. Also, experiments with phage *mu* have shown that when *mu* transposes, segments of *mu* phage remain at the original location in the chromosome. Intermediate cointegrate structures have been found during transposition of certain elements from one circular plasmid to another. These large fused circles have one copy of the element at opposite ends of the cointegrate.

6. Possibly caused by a transposable element.

Chapter 18

1. a. From line 1, $a^- = I^-$ or O^c. From line 2, $c^- = I^-$ or O^c. Therefore *b* must be the *Z* gene. From line 7, since I^- is recessive and we have a constitutive synthesis, the regulatory mutant producing the constitutive synthesis must be an O^c mutant. We know O^c mutants work only in cis, and a^- is the only candidate in cis conformation with a functional Z^+ gene. Therefore *a* is the *O* gene and *c* is the *I* gene.

b. Line 3, $c^- = I^-$ or I^s.
Line 4, $a^- = O^c$, $c^- = I^-$ or I^s.
Line 5, $a^- = o^c$, $c^- = I^-$.
Line 6, $a^- = o^c$, $c^- = I^-$.
Line 7, $a^- = o^c$, $c^- = I^-$ or I^s.

3. Type 1: Mutation probably in structural gene for E_1.

Type 2: Mutation probably in structural gene for E_2.

Type 3: Mutation in regulatory gene that controls function of both structural genes.

Points

i. Normal product of regulatory gene is needed for E_1 and E_2 production.

ii. Regulatory gene is on different chromosome.

iii. Genes for sequential enzymatic steps are not adjacent.

iv. Since regulatory gene must interact with structural loci there must be adjacent recognition sites, comparable to operators, for both. These might be found in an expanded mutant hunt, or even among types 1 and 2.

Chapter 19

1. c

6. The recognition point for the migration mechanism is in the vicinity of the heterochromatic knob.

9. a. The extent of denaturation of the DNA and the accessibility of the DNA to the RNA.

The type of radioactive emission determines the size of the "spot" on the film.

The length of time the emulsion is exposed to the chromosomes.

The number of DNA copies in the chromosome.

The specific activity of the RNA (i.e., the amount of radioactivity per set amount of RNA).

b. Add excess of cold RNA from a wide range of organisms and see if it will compete out the radioactive RNA.

c. You infer that you've located the gene(s) responsible for the production of that RNA.

10. Perhaps they act as pairing regions to keep chromosomes together in the nucleus, or initiate rough chromosome alignments prior to meiosis, or play some unknown role in directing spindle fibers to the centromere. Any reasonable speculation will do.

14. Assume the entire sequence of ADH is known. Isolate *adh*$^-$ mutants by selecting survivors on pentenol. Look for immunologically cross-reacting protein with anti-ADH serum. Sequence all mutant proteins and determine the amino acid affected. This will allow you to select mutants at each end of the *adh* cistron. Select for mutants affecting the amount of ADH (for example, overproduction of ADH might give flies that can tolerate very high levels of ethanol). Select for mutants that alter the time or tissue of ADH production.

Chapter 20

1. Both crosses show predominantly maternal inheritance of the alternative phenotypes. The genes concerned are presumably carried on the cpDNA since a chlorophyll character is affected. (The minority classes are possibly due to a small male contribution of cytoplasm to the zygote. This is often encountered in cytoplasmic inheritance—for example, in poky *Neurospora*.)

3. The results are explained by the influence of the maternal genotype on the phenotype of the zygote. Dwarfness is caused by a recessive nuclear gene *d*.

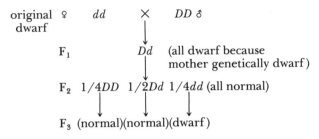

original ♀ dwarf *dd*   ✕   *DD* ♂

F₁   *Dd*   (all dwarf because mother genetically dwarf)

F₂   1/4*DD* 1/2*Dd* 1/4*dd* (all normal)

F₃ (normal)(normal)(dwarf)

4. Continually back-cross using pollen from plant B. In this way, the egg cytoplasm of plant A is maintained while the nucleus is "filled up" with genes from plant B. See accompanying figure.

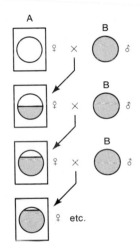

8. The higher the cosegregation frequency, the closer the loci must be. Therefore, a rough map would be

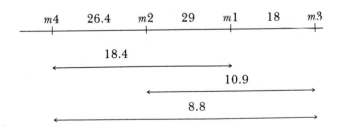

9. The positive heterokaryon test shows that the red phenotype must be caused by a cytoplasmic organelle mutation.

12. Define the *poky* gene as *p* and place it in brackets to show it is cytoplasmic, (*p*). A nuclear suppressor of *poky* will be called *f*. The ♀ parent is shown first.

   a. (+)+ ✕ (*p*)+ → all (+)+

   b. (+)*f* ✕ (*p*)+ → 1/2 (+)*f*, 1/2 (+)+

   c. (*p*)+ ✕ (+)+ → all (*p*)+

   d. (*p*)+ ✕ (+)*f* → 1/2 (*p*) + (=D), 1/2 (*p*)*f*(=E)

   e. (*p*)*f* ✕ (+)*f* → all (*p*)*f*

   f. (*p*)*f* ✕ (+)+ → 1/2 (*p*) +, 1/2 (*p*)*f*

13. a., b. Each meiosis shows uniparental inheritance. This suggests cytoplasmic (mitochondrial) inheritance.

   c. Since *ant*ᴿ is probably on mtDNA, and petites represent loss of mtDNA, *ant*ᴿ should be lost in some cases, making *ant*ˢ petites.

15. Single-gene losses were rarest for the *apt-cob* pair (45 total), most common for *apt-bar* (207), and intermediate for *bar-cob* (117). Rough map:

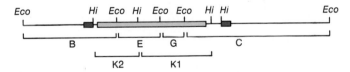

ratio of sizes

17. Some tetrads will show only strain-1 type DNA, other tetrads will show only strain-2 type DNA, and still others will show a recombinant DNA. (As an example of the latter, all the ascospores in one ascus might show recombinant DNA with 4 restriction sites, another ascus no restriction sites.)

21. Senescent cytoplasms are a mixture of normal and renegade mitochondria. These are parceled in different ratios into the ascospores. Eventually the renegades take over, possibly by replicative advantage, and death occurs. Some ascospores get no renegades.

   The renegades appear to have a transposable element inserted into their mt rRNA intron, as shown in the accompanying map.

Chapter 21

1. Somatic mutation, mitotic chromosome loss, mitotic chromosome nondisjunction, mitotic crossing-over, position-effect variegation, cytoplasmic mutation (and subsequent segregation), fusion of different zygotes.

6. a. Regeneration must be controlled by the nucleus.

   b. Hat-forming substance is localized near the top. If enucleate, new substance cannot be synthesized.

   c. No turnover of materials forming the hat.

10. For example, in the presence of excess S_1, P_1 is produced, so operon 2 would shut down and operon 1 would stay active. When some of the S_1 is used up, and S_2 is in excess, reversal of the situation occurs.

12. The woman was heterozygous (Gd^+Gd^-), and dosage compensation has occurred randomly, inactivating either the malarial resistance or the sensitivity-determining X chromosome.

15. Femaleness.

17. Petersen's studies suggest that muscular dystrophy results from defects in the nerves. The parabiosis studies show that the mutant effect is no longer operative in adults. Consequently, the nerve effects on muscles must be induced during development.

18. a. B is before A. (B product builds up and is later used when A functions.)

    b. A is before B.

    c. Both reactions have to be working simultaneously.

    d. The reactions of A and B are alternatives.

21. Inject two populations of blood-forming cells (distinguished by chromosome or restriction-fragment differences). Analyze individual foci and see whether all are homogeneous (single-cell origin) or some are heterogeneous (multiple-cell origin).

22. Culture 1 gives asci in which two ascospores are homothallic and 2 are *a*. Culture 2 gives asci in which all ascospores are homothallic.

23. The rat GH gene inserted at some unknown mouse chromosomal locus in 1 percent of cases, and there it responded to heavy metals and produced larger mice. In the single pedigree, the inserted fragment is inherited as a dominant gene, and the original male must have been heterozygous, that is, bears the insert on one homolog and no insert on the other homolog.

    Although obviously of great potential use in human gene therapy, there are still many problems, including (1) low efficiency, (2) the insertion site cannot be controlled, (3) the mutant allele is not eliminated, just compensated, and (4) the insertion could inactivate another gene, causing a new mutation.

25. The flies could have a structural defect in legs preventing normal movement. A simple example would be a muscle defect. The flies could have an alteration in their nerve wiring so that the wrong legs are signaled to move. If you could do physiological tests, action potentials of nerves and muscles could be tested and compared with wild type. Embryonic focus mapping using mosaics could indicate what cells and tissues are defective.

26. a. Wild-type flies are attracted to light and turn in the direction of moving vertical stripes. Select flies that do not move toward light at the end of a tube or that fail to move down a tube in direction of moving stripes.

    b. Prevent flies from walking out of a cylinder (with an electric grid). Suck off those that fly out. Some of those remaining in the cylinder should be anatomically normal but incapable of flying.

    c. Add a tasteless toxic compound to a sugar solution placed on filter paper at bottom of container. Wild-type flies will drink and die, leaving those that do not respond to sugar.

30. a. Different tissues produce different sets of mRNAs.

    b. Do a similar competition study with "hot" liver mRNA and increasing amounts of "cold" mRNA from either whole body or whole body minus liver. The difference between the experiments at maximum competition (that is, minimum amount of label binding) should reflect the liver-specific mRNA.

Chapter 22

1. a. Homozygous at 1 locus $3(1/2)^3 = 3/8$
       Homozygous at 2 loci $\ \ 3(1/2)^3 = 3/8$
       Homozygous at 3 loci $\ \ \ (1/2)^3 = 1/8$

    b. Carrying 0 capital-letter alleles $= (1/2)^6 = 1/64$
       Carrying 1 capital-letter alleles $= 6/64$
       Carrying 2 capital-letter alleles $= 15/64$
       Carrying 3 capital-letter alleles $= 20/64$
       Carrying 4 capital-letter alleles $= 15/64$
       Carrying 5 capital-letter alleles $= 6/64$
       Carrying 6 capital-letter alleles $= 1/64$

2. Since the loci are on different chromosomes, it is simple to calculate the proportion of any genotype. For example, *AABbcc* will be in proportion $(1/4)(1/2)(1/4) = 2/64$. Its phenotypic score will be $4 + 3 + 1 = 8$. There are 27 possible genotypes. The frequency and score for each one can be calculated in this manner and the distribution of scores constructed. The distribution of scores is

Score	Proportion
3	1/64
5	6/64
6	3/64
7	12/64
8	12/64
9	11/64
10	12/64
11	6/64
12	1/64

Note that the 3-bristle class, which represents 19/64 of all flies, includes 7 genotypes ranging from *AaBbCC* to *AABBCC*, while the 1-bristle class includes only *aabbcc* individuals. All the rest of the genotypes, 19 of them, ranging from *aabbcc* to *AABBcc*, fall into the 2-bristle class.

5. Mean = 4.783;   variance = 0.323;   standard deviation = 0.568.

6. a. 1.0; b. 0.83; c. 0.66; d. −0.20.

10. By looking across the rows, we can find the effect of substituting a "low" for a "high" chromosome I. In the first row the differences are $25.1 - 22.2 = 2.9$ and $22.2 - 19.0 = 3.2$. In the second row these differences are 3.1 and 5.2; in the third row they are 2.7 and 6.8. Averaging over all three rows, we see that the average difference between an *h/h* and *h/l* is $(2.9 + 3.2 + 2.7)/3 = 2.9$, while the average difference between an *h/l* and an *l/l* is $(3.2 + 5.2 + 6.8)/3 = 5.1$. Thus there is some dominance of the *h* genes, since the heterozygotes *h/l* are closer to *h/h* than to *l/l*.

A similar calculation for the columns gives the average effect of a difference between *h/h* and *h/l* and between *h/l* and *l/l* for chromosome II. These are 2.9 and 11.5, respectively, so there is even more dominance on chromosome II. Finally, there is distinct epistasis. For example, the average effect of changing from *h/l* to *l/l* for chromosome I is 5.1, and the same change in chromosome II causes a difference of 11.5. We then expect the difference between *h/l h/l* and *l/l l/l* to be $5.1 + 11.5 = 16.6$, but we see that it is 17.6. Another way to see this is that the effect of a change from *h/l* to *h/h* on the first row is only 3.2 bristles, while in the third row it is 6.8 bristles.

11.

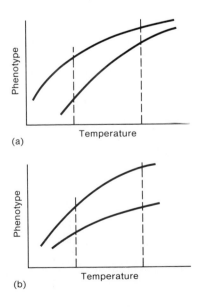

(a)

(b)

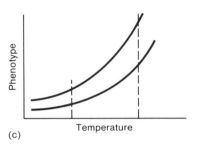

(c)

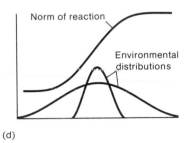

(d)

12. $H^2 = 4$ [correlation of full sibs − correlation of half-sibs]

$$= 4 \left[\frac{2.7}{14.8} - \frac{0.8}{14.8} \right] = 0.51$$

$H^2 = 4$ [correlation of full sibs] − 2 [parent-offspring correlation]

$$= 4 \left(\frac{2.7}{14.8} \right) - 2 \left(\frac{1.7}{14.8} \right) = 0.50$$

$$h^2 = 2 \text{ [parent-offspring correlation]} - 2 \left(\frac{1.7}{14.8} \right) = 0.23$$

Chapter 23

2. a. $p = \dfrac{406 + 372}{1482} = .525$. Therefore the expected members of the three genotypes are

$$L^M L^M = (0.525)^2 (1482) = 408.5$$
$$L^M L^N = 2(0.525)(0.475)(1482) = 739.1$$
$$L^N L^N = (0.475)^2 (1482) = 334.4$$

so the agreement with HWE is excellent.

b.

Mating	Expected frequency
$L^M L^M \times L^M L^M$	$(p^2)(p^2)(1482) = 56.3$
$L^M L^M \times L^M L^N$	$2(p^2)(2pq)(1482) = 203.7$
$L^M L^N \times L^M L^N$	$(2pq)(2pq)(1482) = 184.3$
$L^M L^M \times L^N L^N$	$2(p^2)(q^2)(1482) = 92.2$
$L^M L^N \times L^N L^N$	$2(2pq)(q^2)(1482) = 166.8$
$L^N L^N \times L^N L^N$	$(q^2)(q^2)(1482) = 37.7$

Again, the agreement is quite close.

3.

a.

Generation	$p\male$	$P\female$
0	0.8	0.2
1	0.2	0.5
2	0.5	0.35
3	0.35	0.425
$\cdot$	$\cdot$	$\cdot$
$\cdot$	$\cdot$	$\cdot$
$\cdot$	$\cdot$	$\cdot$
n	$P_{(n-1)}$	$\dfrac{P_{(n-1)} + p_{(n-1)}}{2}$

b. Let $d = P - p$. Then $d_{(n)} = (-1/2)\, d_{(n-1)}$, so $d_{(n)} = (-1/2)^n d_0$.

4. a. 1, 3, 6, 8, 9, 10

c. 0.102

d. $p = 0.5625$; $q = 0.4375$

5. a. 0.01

b. 10 times

c. A mating of a heterozygous female to a color-blind male. Proportion is $(2pq)(q) = (0.18)(0.1) = 0.018$.

d. All matings in which the female was homozygous normal. Proportion is $(0.9)^2 = 0.81$.

e. Female progeny proportion color-blind = 0.12
Male progeny proportion color-blind = 0.20

f. Female allele frequency = 0.40
Male allele frequency = 0.20

9. Color-blind male offspring = 0.2
Color-blind female offspring = 0.04

10. (a)

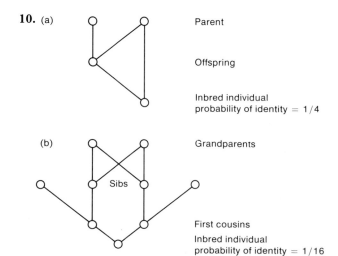

Parent

Offspring

Inbred individual
probability of identity = 1/4

(b)

Grandparents

Sibs

First cousins

Inbred individual
probability of identity = 1/16

(c)

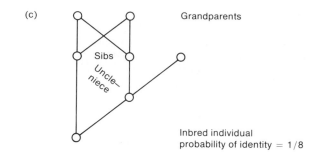

Grandparents

Sibs

Uncle-niece

Inbred individual
probability of identity = 1/8

12. Allele frequencies are $p(A) = q(a) = 0.50$. Assuming dominance of A over a, 80 percent of matings involve AA and Aa individuals, and 20 percent are $aa \times aa$. Among the 80 percent the frequencies are

$$AA \times AA = \left(\frac{0.2}{0.8}\right)^2 = 0.0625$$

$$AA \times Aa = 2\left(\frac{0.2}{0.8}\right)\left(\frac{0.6}{0.8}\right) = 0.3750$$

$$Aa \times Aa = \left(\frac{0.6}{0.8}\right)^2 = 0.5625$$

Each of these frequencies is then multiplied by 0.80 to get the frequencies in the total population of matings. The genotype frequencies in the next generation are as follows:

AA: from $AA \times AA = (0.0625)(0.8)$ $= 0.05$
from $AA \times Aa = (1/2)(0.3750)(0.8) = 0.15$
from $Aa \times Aa = (1/4)(0.5625)(0.8) = \underline{0.1125}$

Total 0.3125

Aa: from $AA \times Aa = (1/2)(0.3750)(0.8) = 0.15$
from $Aa \times AA = (1/2)(0.5625)(0.8) = \underline{0.225}$

Total 0.3750

aa: from $Aa \times Aa = (1/4)(0.5625)(0.8) = 0.1125$
from $aa \times aa =$ $\underline{0.20}$

Total 0.3125

For negative assortative mating, using a similar form of analysis, after a generation the frequencies will be (in the next generation): $AA = 0$, $Aa = 2/3$, $aa = 1/3$. In the second generation the frequencies will be $Aa = 0.5$ and $aa = 0.5$ and will remain so in the future.

14. a. $p^1 = 0.528$; b. $p = 0.75$.

15. Equilibrium frequency of $a = \sqrt{\mu/s}$, where μ is the mutation rate and s the selection coefficient. Therefore aa frequency is $\mu/s = 0.001$, and $s = 10^{-5}/10^{-3} = 10^{-2} = 0.01$.

16. Affected individuals occur at a frequency of $2pq$, and since p is nearly unity,

$$q = \frac{4.0 \times 10^{-6}}{2} = 2 \times 10^{-6}$$

For a partially dominant gene at equilibrium, $q = \mu/hs$, where hs is the loss of fitness of heterozygotes. Therefore, $\mu = hsq = (0.7)(2 \times 10^{-6}) = 1.4 \times 10^{-6}$.

17. For each recessive lethal the chance of having a normal child is $7/8 = 0.875$. If there are n recessive lethals, the chance of escaping homozygosity for any of them is $(0.875)^n$. Therefore $(0.875)^n = 13/31$. Using logarithms we find that $n = 6.5$, so the number of recessive lethals is between 6 and 7.

18.

a. $q = \sqrt{\frac{\mu}{s}} = \sqrt{\frac{10^{-5}}{0.5}} = 4.47 \times 10^{-3}$

genetic cost $= (0.5)(2 \times 10^{-5}) = 10^{-5}$

b. $q = \sqrt{\frac{2 \times 10^{-5}}{0.5}} = 6.32 \times 10^{-3}$

genetic cost $= (0.5)(4 \times 10^{-5}) = 2 \times 10^{-5}$

c. $q = \sqrt{\frac{10^{-5}}{0.3}} = 5.77 \times 10^{-3}$

genetic cost $= (0.3)(3.33 \times 10^{-5}) = 10^{-5}$, the same as in part a.

Index